Combinations   Order of selection is not important. The number of combinations of n elements taken r at a time $(0 \leq r \leq n)$ is given by

$$C(n, r) = \binom{n}{r} = \frac{n!}{r!(n-r)!}$$

● **ADDITION RULE**

If A and B are events, then

$$P(A \cup B) = P(A) + P(B) - P(A \cap B)$$

Note:

1. $P(A \cup B)$ is the same as $P(A$ or $B)$.
2. $P(A \cap B)$ is the same as $P(A$ and $B)$.

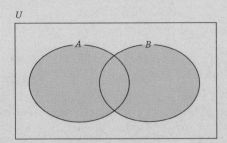

$A \cup B$ = shaded region

● **ADDITION RULE (SPECIAL CASE)**

If A and B are mutually exclusive events, then

$$P(A \cup B) = P(A) + P(B)$$

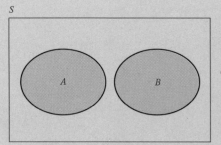

Mutually exclusive events
$A \cap B = \varnothing$

$A \cup B$ = shaded area

● **COMPLEMENT RULE**

$$P(E') = 1 - P(E)$$

where E' means "not E."

● **CONDITIONAL PROBABILITY**

If A and B are events in a sample space, S, then

$$P(A|B) = \frac{P(A \cap B)}{P(B)}$$

restricted sample space

provided $P(A \cap B)$ and $P(B)$ are known and $P(B) \neq 0$. This is illustrated in terms of the Venn diagram below.

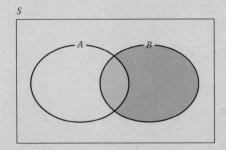

● **PRODUCT RULES**

If A and B are events with nonzero probabilities, then

$$P(A \cap B) = P(A)P(B|A)$$

or

$$P(A \cap B) = P(B)P(A|B)$$

where $A \cap B$ means the same as A *and* B.

● **PRODUCT RULE (SPECIAL CASE)**

If A and B are independent events, then

$$P(A \cap B) = P(A)P(B)$$

where $A \cap B$ means the same as A *and* B.

continues

Continued

● BAYES' FORMULA

Let $B_1, B_2, \ldots, B_k$ be mutually exclusive events such that

$$P(B_1) + P(B_2) + \ldots + P(B_k) = 1$$

Let A be an event such that $P(A) \neq 0$; then

$$P(B_i|A) = \frac{P(B_i)P(A|B_i)}{P(B_1 \cap A) + P(B_2 \cap A) + \ldots + P(B_k \cap A)}$$

$$= \frac{P(B_i)P(A|B_i)}{P(B_1)P(A|B_1) + P(B_2)P(A|B_2) + \ldots + P(B_k)P(A|B_k)}$$

for $i = 1, 2, \ldots, k$.

● DERIVATIVE

The derivative of a function $f(x)$ is defined by

$$f'(x) = \lim_{\Delta x \to 0} \frac{f(x + \Delta x) - f(x)}{\Delta x}$$

● RULES FOR FINDING DERIVATIVES

Constant Function Rule If $f(x) = k$. where k is a constant, then

$$f'(x) = 0$$

Power Rule If $f(x) = x^n$, where n is a real number, then

$$f'(x) = nx^{n-1}$$

Constant Multiplier Rule If $y = kf(x)$, where k is a constant and $f'(x)$ exists, then

$$\frac{dy}{dx} = kf'(x)$$

Sum or Difference Rule If $y = f(x) \pm g(x)$, where $f(x)$ and $g(x)$ are differentiable functions at x, then

$$\frac{dv}{dx} = f'(x) \pm g'(x)$$

Product Rule If $y = f(x)s(x)$, where $f(x)$ and $s(x)$ are differentiable functions at x, then

$$\frac{dy}{dx} = f(x)s'(x) + s(x)f'(x)$$

$$\frac{dy}{dx} = (\text{first})\binom{\text{derivative}}{\text{of second}} + (\text{second})\binom{\text{derivative}}{\text{of first}}$$

Quotient Rule $y = n(x)/d(x)$, where $n(x)$ and $d(x)$ are differentiable functions at x and $d(x) \neq 0$, then

$$\frac{dy}{dx} = \frac{d(x)n'(x) - n(x)d'(x)}{[d(x)]^2}$$

Chain Rule If $y = f(u)$ is a differentiable function of u and $u = g(x)$ is a differentiable function of x, then

$$\frac{dy}{dx} = \frac{dy}{du}\frac{du}{dx}$$

General Power Rule If $y = u^n$, where u is a differentiable function of x, then

$$\frac{dy}{dx} = nu^{n-1}\frac{du}{dx}$$

● FIRST-DERIVATIVE TEST FOR RELATIVE EXTREMA

If x_0 is a critical value of $f(x)$ (in other words, $f'(x_0) = 0$ or $f'(x_0)$ is undefined) where $f(x_0)$ is defined, then

1. $f(x_0)$ is a **relative maximum** of $f(x)$ if $f'(x)$ is positive for all nearby values of x to the left of x_0 and $f(x)$ is negative for all nearby values of x to the right of x_0.
2. $f(x_0)$ is a **relative minimum** of $f(x)$ if $f'(x)$ is negative for all nearby values of x to the left of x_0 and $f'(x)$ is positive for all nearby values of x to the right of x_0.

● TO GRAPH A FUNCTION $f(x)$ USING $f'(x)$ AND $f''(x)$

1. *First-derivative analysis.* Find $f'(x)$.

   ● Search for the critical values.

Set $f'(x) = 0$ and solve for x.	Determine values of x where $f'(x)$ does not exist, but $f(x)$ does.

continues

APPLIED MATHEMATICS
FOR BUSINESS AND THE
SOCIAL AND NATURAL SCIENCES

APPLIED MATHEMATICS

FOR BUSINESS AND THE SOCIAL AND NATURAL SCIENCES

Chester Piascik
Bryant College

WEST PUBLISHING COMPANY
St. Paul   New York   Los Angeles   San Francisco

Text design:	*Geri Davis, Quadrata, Inc.*
Copyedit:	*Sherry Goldbecker*
Composition:	*The Clarinda Company*
Art:	*Edward Rose, VGS*
Index:	*E. Virginia Hobbs*
Answers:	*Gloria Langer*
Cover image:	*"Boarderline" by David Graves, copyright © 1991*
Cover design:	*Geri Davis and Dick Hannus, Quadrata, Inc.*

Lotus® 1-2-3® is a registered trademark of Lotus Development Corporation. Lotus 1-2-3 tables and graphs in this text are copyright © 1986 Lotus Development Corporation. Used with permission.

Some graphs in this text were plotted using MINITAB statistical software. Also, MINITAB was used to obtain solutions to some examples and exercises. Such results and graphs are reprinted or adapted with permission. MINITAB is a registered trademark.

Minitab, Inc.
3081 Enterprise Drive
State College, PA 16801 USA
Telephone: (814) 238-3280
Telex: 881612   Fax: (814) 238-4383

Material from Uniform CPA Examination, Questions and Unofficial Answers, Copyright © 1970–1990 by American Institute of Certified Public Accountants, Inc., is reprinted or adapted with permission.

COPYRIGHT © 1992   By WEST PUBLISHING COMPANY
610 Opperman Drive
P.O. Box 64526
St. Paul, MN 55164-0526

Library of Congress Cataloging-in-Publication Data

Piascik, Chester.
    Applied mathematics for business and the social and natural
sciences / Chester Piascik.
        p.   cm.
    Includes index.
    ISBN 0-314-83981-X
    1. Business mathematics.   2. Mathematics.   3. Social sciences-
-Mathematics.   I. Title.
HF5691.P553   1992
650.01'51—dc20   90-26701
                                                                  CIP ∞

To My Parents

Contents

Preface

This text is designed to provide the mathematical concepts needed by students in business, economics, and the social and natural sciences. From past experience, I have found the algebra backgrounds of these students to be varied. Thus, one of my goals has been to make this text as readable as possible without sacrificing its mathematical content. Clear, direct, and concise explanations enhance this text's readability and provide the student with insightful and meaningful interpretations of an abundant supply of examples and applications. Also, an algebra review chapter is included at the beginning of the text. This chapter can be covered at the beginning of the course, skipped, or used as a reference throughout the text. In addition to preliminary material, this chapter contains a thorough introduction to the distributive law, multiplying binomials, and factoring. These sections have been written so that they can be assigned to students for self-study or review.

• *Graphics*

Another goal of this text is to train the student to think graphically. Wherever appropriate, graphics and graphical analyses are used to illustrate and reinforce the presentation of mathematical concepts. An abundance of graphs in two-color format complement the text's presentation. This emphasis weaves through Chapter 1 on linear functions, Chapter 2 on graphing polynomial and rational functions, and Chapter 3 on exponential and logarithmic functions. These chapters are also designed to prepare students for calculus. Since calculus students must often graph and work with higher-degree polynomial functions, rational functions, and exponential and logarithmic functions, prior study of these topics will help to reduce their "shock effect" when encountered in calculus.

• *Flexibility*

Topics are organized to allow the instructor maximum flexibility. For example, Chapter 2 on polynomial and rational functions can be used later in the course so that it is closer to the calculus chapters. Chapter 3 on exponential and logarithmic functions can be combined with Chapter 12 in the calculus portion of the text. This would necessitate either the elimination of or a different coverage of doubling, tripling, and quadrupling time in the mathematics of finance chapter. If this topic is omitted during the mathematics of finance coverage, it can be used as an application of logarithmic functions in the calculus portion.

Chapter 5 on linear systems and matrices is written so that matrices can be either skipped or included depending on instructor preferences. Specifically, the chapter begins with linear systems, introduces the concept of a tableau, and then develops students' problem-formulation skills prior to discussing the Gauss-Jordan method of row operations. Thus, before the students learn the Gauss-Jordan method, they know why they are learning to solve linear systems. The chapter then follows with matrices and their applications.

Linear programming is presented so that the simplex method can be either omitted or covered with varying degrees of depth. Sensitivity analysis can be covered if desired.

Chapter 8 on probability offers a flexible treatment of this topic. Many sections in Chapter 11 on applications of the derivative and Chapter 14 on further topics of integration can be omitted if desired.

• *Critical Thinking/Problem Solving*

Throughout this text, there is continuing emphasis on student interpretation of results—on understanding what the answer means. This feature is one of many that distinguish this text from its competitors. Wherever appropriate, this text fosters the comparison of problem results under changing conditions. For example, in the mathematic of finance chapter, a comparison of monthly mortgage payments for both 15-year and 30-year mortgages is presented. As alluded to earlier, problem-solving skills are developed early in the linear systems chapter. These continue into later chapters on linear programming and the simplex method where material on sensitivity analysis again offers an opportunity for critical thinking and problem-solving approaches.

• *Mathematics of Finance*

This text contains a more thorough coverage of mathematics of finance in response to management's express needs. Feedback from management professionals indicates that this is the mathematical topic requiring more extensive coverage. This text includes, in addition to the usual mathematics of finance topics, material on equations of value, deferred annuities, and complex annuities. These supplemental topics, which can be omitted if desired, are presented in a manner that does not require the learning of additional formulas.

Although the mathematics of finance chapter follows the exponential and logarithmic functions chapter, it can be covered at the beginning of the course or at other points during the course. For such cases, material on continuous compounding and doubling, tripling, and quadrupling time could be postponed and included as applications in the exponential and logarithmic functions chapter.

• *Careful Attention to Pedagogy*

Coherent explanations throughout this text enhance its readability. Concepts are developed from specific examples to general theory to provide insight into the method of mathematical discovery.

An introductory application opens each chapter to pique student interest and enhance motivation. The application is solved later in the chapter.

In-section and in-chapter summaries, problem-solving procedures, and highlighted formulas appear throughout the text. These are used to summarize ideas and procedures and to synthesize related ideas into conceptual entities.

Chapter highlights, being for the most part verbal in nature, appear at the end of each chapter to consolidate the information in the chapter and let the student know what is really happening. These are referenced by section, and, therefore, their study takes a student through the main concepts of each section within a chapter.

End-of-section exercises and end-of-chapter exercises provide plentiful problem-solving opportunities for students.

• *Applications*

Relevant and timely applications permeate this text. These range from Uniform CPA Examination problems to examples illustrating market dynamics, economics, managerial concepts, finance and investment, quality and productivity problems in industry, and social and natural science problems.

• *Examples*

This text contains an abundance of examples to reinforce explanations and discussions. Wherever appropriate, color screens and annotations are used to provide step-by-step details of problem-solving procedures.

• *Extra Dividends*

Many chapters are followed by sections dealing with topics and applications that are extensions of chapter concepts. Such sections are entitled "Extra Dividends." Specifically, Chapters 1 and 2 are followed by material on goodness of fit. In addition to setting the stage for the method of least squares, these sections show students how linear and quadratic models are fit to real-world data. These sections and Section 3-3 form a thread that culminates in a discussion of the method of least squares in the calculus portion of the text.

The exponential and logarithmic functions chapter is followed by a discussion of stock market forecasting that utilizes properties of logarithms. Other chapters are followed by discussions of such topics as net present value, and response surfaces.

• Calculator Exercises

Although calculators are appropriate for many exercises, some exercises are specifically designated for solution with a calculator. These calculator exercises are marked with the symbol ▦.

• Computer Exercises

Where appropriate, some exercises are intended for solution by computer. These exercises are labeled "Computer Exercises." Also, some exercises not labeled as computer exercises lend themselves to computer solution. This is true for exercises on the mathematics of finance, matrices, linear systems, and the simplex method.

• Answers

Answers to all odd-numbered end-of-section exercises, all odd-numbered end-of-chapter exercises, and all chapter highlight questions appear at the end of the text.

• Supplements

An **Instructor's Manual** containing step-by-step solutions to all exercises is available.

A **Student's Solutions Manual** containing step-by-step solutions to all odd-numbered exercises is available.

A **computer software package** entitled WESTWARE created by Mark Harris is available to adopters. The package has a spreadsheet format for data entry, generation and manipulation, and viewing tabular results. Among the topics included in the package are the simplex method, Gauss-Jordan row reduction, matrix operations, mathematics of finance, graphing (including multiple graphs on the same screen and the option to print the graph), exponentials and logarithmic functions, least squares lines, polynomials, and multiple linear regression. Also included is a means for iterating formulas so that data can be generated for graphs, limits, numerical integration, etc. This software package comes with complete documentation.

A set of **overhead transparencies** containing summaries, procedures, and figures useful for class lectures is available to adopters.

A **computerized test bank** is available to adopters.

• *Acknowledgements*

I wish to thank the many reviewers of this manuscript for their valuable suggestions. These include

Rohan Attele
University of North Carolina—Charlotte

Ronald Barnes
University of Houston, Downtown

Christie Bishop
Rochester Institute of Technology

Patricia Blitch
Lander College

Michael Bradley
Merrimack College

Gail A. Broome
Providence College

Richard Byrne
Portland State University

Eleanor Canter
Wentworth Institute of Technology

Raymond Coughlin
Temple University

James Crenshaw
Southern Illinois University at Carbondale

Duane Deal
Ball State University

Joseph Evans
Middle Tennessee State University

Sally Fischbeck
Rochester Institute of Technology

Nancy Fisher
University of Alabama

Patricia Hirschy
Delaware Technical and Community College

Richard Marshall
East Michigan University

Donald Mason
Elmhurst College

Robert Moreland
Texas Tech University

William Perry
Texas A & M University

Wes Sanders
Sam Houston State University

Neil Schwertman
California State University—Chico

Thomas Shilgalis
Illinois State University

William Soule
University of Maine

John Spellman
Southwest Texas State University

David Weinstein
California State University—Northridge

Wiley Williams
University of Louisville

I thank my colleagues at Bryant College for their comments and suggestions regarding this manuscript. In particular, I thank Helen Baron, Kristen Kennedy, Robert Muksian, Patricia Odell, Frederick Reinhardt, Martin Rosenzweig, Phyllis Schumacher, Richard Smith, and Robert Wall. A very special thanks goes to Alan Olinsky for suggestions and ideas regarding computer applications and pedagogy.

I thank Robert Girasole of Salve Regina College for theory and data on stock market activity. A special thanks goes to Gloria Langer for an excellent job in preparing the *Instructor's Manual,* the *Student's Solutions Manual,* and answers to homework exercises. Another special thanks goes to Michael Bradley of Merrimack College for an excellent job in preparing the test bank. Also, I thank Mark Harris for a dedicated and conscientious effort in developing the computer software package for this text.

I thank Robyn Langlais for her patient and persistent effort in typing many portions of this manuscript.

I thank the staff of West Educational Publishing for their dedicated efforts in the production of this text. In particular, I wish to extend my thanks and gratitude to Christine Hurney, my production editor. Her excellent organizational skills, and careful attention to all the many details of the project kept it moving along throughout the production phase. I thank Kathryn Grimes for her initiative and resourcefulness in developing materials for the marketing of this text. Special thanks go to my editors Ron Pullins and Denise Bayko. I thank Ron for providing this author with excellent editorial support and inspiration to strive for excellence. I thank Denise for excellent editorial support and conscientious persistent effort towards the goal of producing an excellent text. Last, but not least, a special thank you to Greg Pond, who first brought my project to the attention of the appropriate people at West.

R

ALGEBRA
REVIEW

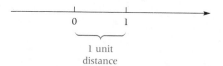

FIGURE R-1

FIGURE R-2

FIGURE R-3

R-1

• THE REAL NUMBERS AND INTERVAL NOTATION

All the numbers we will use in this text can be represented as points on a straight line. Such a representation can be constructed as follows. Begin with a straight line. Choose an arbitrary point, called the **origin,** on the line and label it 0. Then choose another point to the right of 0 and label it 1. Let the distance between 0 and 1 represent 1 unit of measure (see Figure R-1). The point on the straight line 1 unit to the right of 1 is labeled 2, the point 1 unit to the right of 2 is labeled 3, etc. (see Figure R-2). Also, the point on the straight line 1 unit to the left of 0 is labeled −1, the point 1 unit to the left of −1 is labeled −2, the point 1 unit to the left of −2 is labeled −3, etc. (see Figure R-2). The straight line in Figure R-2 is called the **real number line.** There is a one-to-one correspondence between the points on the real number line and the set of real numbers. In other words, each real number is associated with a particular point on this number line. Also, each point on this number line is associated with a particular real number. For example, the fraction 1/2 is associated with the point midway between 0 and 1, the number 1 3/4 is associated with the point three-quarters of the distance between 1 and 2, and the number −1/3 is associated with the point one-third of the distance between 0 and −1 (see Figure R-3).

There are several types of real numbers:

1. *Counting numbers.* These numbers are also called **natural numbers**.

$$1, 2, 3, 4, 5, \ldots *$$

2. *Whole numbers.*

$$0, 1, 2, 3, 4, \ldots$$

3. *Integers.*

$$\ldots, -4, -3, -2, -1, 0, 1, 2, 3, 4, \ldots$$

4. *Rational numbers.* All numbers that can be expressed as a quotient of two integers, where the denominator is not equal to 0. Examples are numbers such as 1/2, 3/4, 4/1, 3, and 1.23. Some rational numbers have decimal expansions that repeat but do not terminate. Some examples are

$$\frac{1}{3} = 0.333. \ldots \text{ which is written as } 0.\overline{3}$$

$$\frac{83}{99} = 0.838383. \ldots \text{ which is written as } 0.\overline{83}$$

5. *Irrational numbers.* These are all real numbers that are not rational. Ir-

---

*Here, the three dots indicate that the numbers continue indefinitely in the same manner.

rational numbers have decimal representations that are nonterminating and nonrepeating. Some examples are

$$\sqrt{2} = 1.4142135. \ . \ .^*$$
$$\pi = 3.1415926. \ . \ .$$
$$e = 2.718281. \ . \ .$$
$$-\sqrt{5} = -2.2360679. \ . \ .$$

Thus, a real number is either rational or irrational but cannot be both. The rational numbers include the integers, the integers include the whole numbers, and the whole numbers include the counting or natural numbers.

Inequality

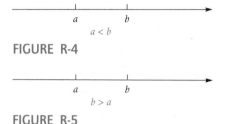

FIGURE R-4

FIGURE R-5

If a number a lies to the left of a number b on the real number line, then "a is less than b." This is written $a < b$ (see Figure R-4). Also, if a number b lies to the right of a number a on the real number line, then "b is greater than a." This is written $b > a$ (see Figure R-5). Thus, the statement "5 is less than 6" is written $5 < 6$, and the statement "8 is greater than 3" is written $8 > 3$.

The complete set of inequality phrases and their respective symbols are summarized as follows.

SUMMARY

Inequality Phrases and Symbols

"Is less than"	$<$
"Is greater than"	$>$
"Is less than or equal to"	$\leq$
"Is greater than or equal to"	$\geq$
"Is not equal to"	$\neq$

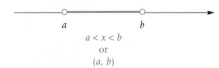

FIGURE R-6

Intervals

Sometimes it is necessary to refer to all real numbers located between two numbers a and b on the real number line (see Figure R-6). Such a set of numbers is called an **interval** and is expressed as all real numbers x such that

$$a < x < b$$

This interval is also denoted as (a, b). This way of expressing an interval is called **interval notation.** Observe that the endpoints, a and b, are not included in this interval. This situation is graphically expressed by using an open circle at each endpoint (see Figure R-6). An interval that does not

---

*These dots indicate that the decimal representations are nonterminating.

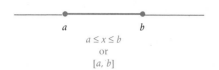

FIGURE R-7

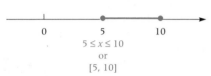

FIGURE R-8

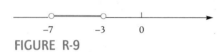

FIGURE R-9

FIGURE R-10

contain its endpoints is called an *open interval*. If the endpoints are to be included, then the set must be written as

$$a \leq x \leq b$$

or, in terms of interval notation, $[a, b]$. This interval is graphically expressed by using a solid circle at each endpoint (see Figure R-7). An interval that contains its endpoints is called a *closed interval*.

● **EXAMPLE R-1**

Graph all real numbers x such that $5 \leq x \leq 10$.

Solution

This interval includes all real numbers between 5 and 10. The endpoints are included. The graph appears in Figure R-8.

● **EXAMPLE R-2**

Express the interval in Figure R-9 by using the variable x and also by using interval notation.

Solution

This interval includes all real numbers between -7 and -3. The endpoints are not included. Hence, the interval is written as all real numbers x such that $-7 < x < -3$. Using interval notation, this interval is also denoted as $(-7, -3)$.

● **EXAMPLE R-3**

Graph all real numbers x such that $x \leq 9$.

Solution

This interval includes all real numbers less than or equal to 9. The endpoint, 9, is included. The graph appears in Figure R-10. This interval is also denoted as $(-\infty, 9]$.

●

The symbol $-\infty$ means minus infinity; the symbol ∞ means infinity. We note that ∞ is not a number; it enables us to indicate an interval that is unbounded to the right. $-\infty$ enables us to indicate an interval that is unbounded to the left. Also note that we always use open interval symbols with ∞ or $-\infty$ to indicate that ∞ and $-\infty$ are not actually real numbers that can be achieved by our intervals.

We now give further examples of interval notation.

Interval	Interval notation	Graph
$3 < x \leq 6$	$(3, 6]$	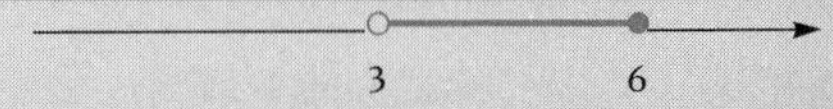
$-2 \leq x < 4$	$[-2, 4)$	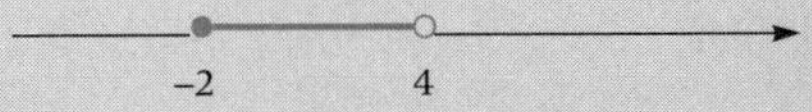
$1 \leq x \leq 7$	$[1, 7]$	

Interval	Interval notation	Graph
$8 \le x < \infty$	$[8, \infty)$	 8
$-\infty < x < 2$	$(-\infty, 2)$	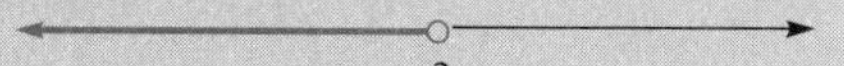 2
$4 < x < 9$	$(4, 9)$	 4 9

Absolute Value

The absolute value of a number x, written $|x|$, is defined by

$$|x| = \begin{cases} x & \text{if } x \text{ is positive or zero} \\ -x & \text{if } x \text{ is negative} \end{cases}$$

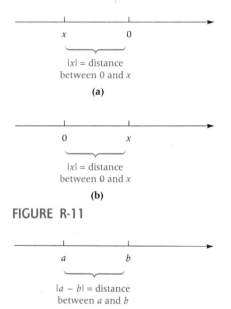

$|x|$ = distance
between 0 and x

(a)

$|x|$ = distance
between 0 and x

(b)

FIGURE R-11

$|a - b|$ = distance
between a and b

FIGURE R-12

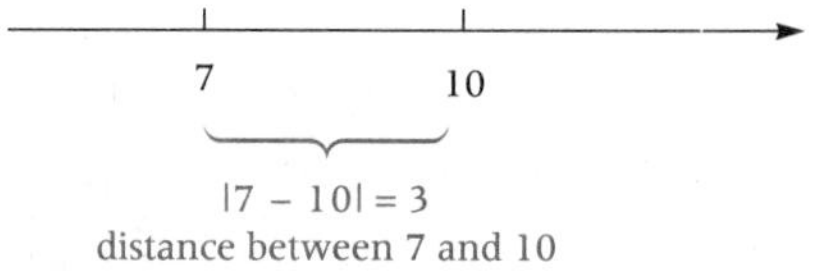

$|7 - 10| = 3$
distance between 7 and 10

FIGURE R-13

• **EXAMPLE R-4** ⎯⎯⎯⎯⎯⎯⎯⎯⎯⎯⎯

Evaluate $|-7|$.

Solution

Since -7 is negative, then by the definition of absolute value, $|-7| = -(-7) = 7$.

• **EXAMPLE R-5** ⎯⎯⎯⎯⎯⎯⎯⎯⎯⎯⎯

Evaluate $|8|$.

Solution

Since 8 is positive, then by the definition of absolute value, $|8| = 8$.

• **EXAMPLE R-6** ⎯⎯⎯⎯⎯⎯⎯⎯⎯⎯⎯

Evaluate $|9 - 14|$.

Solution

Since $9 - 14 = -5$, a negative number, then by the definition of absolute value, $|9 - 14| = -(-5) = 5$.

The absolute value of a number is always non-negative. In addition, $|x|$ gives the distance on the real number line between 0 and x, as indicated in Figures R-11 (a) and (b). This is why a number and its negative both have the same absolute value.

The distance between points a and b on the real number line in Figure R-12 is given by either $|a - b|$ or $|b - a|$. Thus, the distance between 7 and 10 on the real number line in Figure R-13 is given by $|7 - 10| = |-3| = 3$. This distance is also given by $|10 - 7| = |3| = 3$.

Exercises R-1

State whether each of the following is true or false.

1. $3 < 7$	**2.** $-3 < -7$	**3.** $-2 < -5$
4. $2 < 5$	**5.** $-6 < -2$	**6.** $-3 > -7$
7. $-2 > -5$	**8.** $0 < 5$	**9.** $0 > -3$
10. $9 > 6$	**11.** $8 > 10$	**12.** $-6 < -1$

13. Every counting number is a whole number.
14. Every whole number is an integer.
15. Every counting number is an integer.
16. Every integer is a rational number.
17. Every rational number is a real number.
18. Every integer is a whole number.
19. Every whole number is a counting number.
20. Every irrational number is a real number.
21. 7 is a rational number.
22. 3/5 is a rational number.
23. $-2/3$ is a rational number.
24. $\sqrt{11}$ is a rational number.
25. $\sqrt{11}$ is an irrational number.
26. 3.56345. . . is an irrational number.
27. 4.7065 is an irrational number.
28. 2.767676. . . is a rational number.

Graph each of the following on the real number line.

29. $-5 \leq x \leq -1$	30. $7 \leq x \leq 11$	31. $-4 < x < -2$
32. $9 < x < 15$	33. $-3 < x \leq 2$	34. $2 \leq x < 9$
35. $5 \leq x$	36. $x \geq 5$	37. $x \leq -3$
38. $x < 10$	39. $x > -2$	40. $x > 4$
41. $2 < x$	42. $x \geq -1$	43. $x \neq 2$
44. $x \neq -3, x \neq 5$		

State whether each of the following is an open interval or a closed interval.

45. $3 \leq x \leq 8$	46. $3 < x < 8$
47. $-4 < x < -1$	48. $-6 \leq x \leq -2$
49. $8 \leq x \leq 10$	50. $6 < x \leq 9$

Graph each of the following on the real number line:

51. $[3, 9]$	52. $(-1, 5)$	53. $(-\infty, -4]$	54. $[6, \infty)$
55. $(-\infty, 6)$	56. $(9, \infty)$	57. $(4, 9]$	58. $[2, 9)$

Evaluate each of the following:

59. $\|0\|$	60. $\|-1\|$	61. $\|1\|$
62. $\|-21\|$	63. $\|-2\|$	64. $\|15\|$
65. $\|-15\|$	66. $\|-20\|$	67. $\|20\|$
68. $\|5 - 9\|$	69. $\|9 - 5\|$	70. $\|16 - 7\|$
71. $\|7 - 16\|$	72. $\|14 - 8\|$	73. $\|9 - 15\|$
74. $\|-5 - 3\|$	75. $\|-4 - 9\|$	76. $\|-6 - 4\|$

77. Find the distance between 5 and 11 on the real number line.
78. Find the distance between -3 and 10 on the real number line.
79. Find the distance between -9 and -4 on the real number line.

R-2   • LINEAR EQUATIONS AND INEQUALITIES

Linear Equations in One Variable

A statement such as

$$3x + 5 = 17$$

is a linear equation (equality) in one variable. To find its solution, we first subtract 5 from both sides to obtain

$$3x = 12$$

Then we divide both sides by 3 to obtain the solution

$$x = 4$$

The solution is sketched on the real number line in Figure R-14.

When solving linear equations such as $3x + 5 = 17$, we use the following rules of equalities.

Solution: $x = 4$

FIGURE R-14

 SUMMARY

Rules of Equalities

Rule 1   If the same number is either added to or subtracted from both sides of an equality, the resulting equality remains true.

Rule 2   If both sides of an equality are either multiplied by or divided by the same nonzero number, the resulting equality remains true.

Linear Inequalities

We now consider linear inequalities. In general, if the equal sign (=) of a linear equality such as

$$3x + 5 = 7$$

is replaced by an inequality sign ($<$, $>$, $\leq$, $\geq$), the resulting statement is a linear inequality. Thus, the statements

$$3x + 5 < 7$$
$$3x + 5 > 7$$
$$3x + 5 \leq 7$$
$$3x + 5 \geq 7$$

are examples of linear inequalities. To solve linear inequalities, we may use the following rules of inequalities.

 SUMMARY

Rules of Inequalities

Rule 1   If the same number is either added to or subtracted from both sides of an inequality, the resulting inequality remains true.

Rule 2
a)   If both sides of an inequality are either multiplied by or divided by the same *positive* number, the resulting inequality remains true.
b)   If both sides of an inequality are either multiplied by or divided by the same *negative* number, the original inequality sign must be *reversed* in order for the resulting inequality to remain true.

Note that the rules of equalities also hold for inequalities with the exception involving either multiplication by or division by a negative number. Thus, if

$$2 < 5$$

then

$$-4(2) > -4(5)$$
$$-8 > -20$$

• EXAMPLE R-7

Solve the inequality $-5x + 3 \leq 13$ for x, sketch the solution on a real number line, and give the answer in interval notation.

Solution

We first subtract 3 from both sides (rule 1) to obtain

$$-5x \leq 10$$

Then we divide both sides by -5 [rule 2(b)] to get

$$x \geq -2$$

The solution is sketched in Figure R-15.

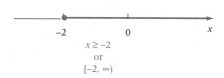

$x \geq -2$
or
$[-2, \infty)$

FIGURE R-15

• EXAMPLE R-8

Solve the inequality $3x + 5 < 17$ for x, sketch the solution on a real number line, and give the answer in interval notation.

Solution

Subtracting 5 from both sides (rule 1), we obtain

$$3x < 12$$

Dividing both sides by 3 [rule 2(a)] yields

$$x < 4$$

The solution is sketched in Figure R-16.

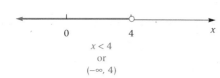

$x < 4$
or
$(-\infty, 4)$

FIGURE R-16

• EXAMPLE R-9

Solve the inequality $(-1/2)x + 3 \geq -1$ for x, sketch the solution on a real number line, and give the answer in interval notation.

Solution

Subtracting 3 from both sides (rule 1) gives us

$$-\frac{1}{2}x \geq -4$$

Multiplying both sides by -2 [rule 2(b)] yields

$$x \leq 8$$

The solution is sketched in Figure R-17.

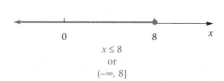

$x \leq 8$
or
$(-\infty, 8]$

FIGURE R-17

Exercises R-2

Solve each of the following.

1. $4x + 8 = 32$
2. $5x + 30 = 80$
3. $-2x + 6 = -12$
4. $-5x + 8 = -52$

5. $4x - 3 = 21 + 2x$ 6. $6x - 7 = 47 - 3x$
7. $(1/2)x + 6 = 10$ 8. $(3/4)x - 2 = 10$
9. $5y + 2 = 7y - 18$ 10. $6z + 4 = 10z - 28$

Solve each of the following inequalities, graph its solution on a real number line, and give the answer in interval notation.

11. $2x + 4 \leq 15$ 12. $-3x + 5 \leq 32$
13. $4x - 5 < 25$ 14. $5x + 3 > 17$
15. $-3x + 17 \geq -14$ 16. $-6x + 5 > 23$
17. $-6x - 5 \geq -23$ 18. $-3x - 2 \leq -14$
19. $3(x - 5) \geq 18$ 20. $-4(x + 7) < 32$

R-3 • EXPONENTS AND RADICALS

Exponents

If x is a number, the product of n x's is denoted by x^n. That is,

$$x^n = \underbrace{x \cdot x \cdot \ldots \cdot x}_{n \ x's}$$

The positive integer n, which indicates the number of times x appears as a factor, is an **exponent.** The number x is called the **base.**

We define a negative exponent as follows:

$$x^{-n} = \frac{1}{x^n} = \frac{1}{\underbrace{x \cdot x \cdot \ldots \cdot x}_{n \ x's}} \qquad (x \neq 0)$$

We define

$$x^0 = 1 \qquad (x \neq 0)$$

Note that 0^0 is undefined.

Laws of Exponents

In this section, we will discuss exponents and the laws governing their algebraic manipulation.

First Law of Exponents

If x is any nonzero real number, then

$$x^m \cdot x^n = x^{m+n}$$

for any non-negative integers m and n.

To verify this law, we observe that

$$x^m \cdot x^n = \underbrace{(x \cdot x \cdot \ldots \cdot x)}_{m \; x's}\underbrace{(x \cdot x \cdot \ldots \cdot x)}_{n \; x's}$$

$$= \underbrace{x \cdot x \cdot \ldots \cdot x}_{(m+n) \; x's}$$

$$= x^{m+n}$$

For example,

$$2^3 \cdot 2^4 = 2^{3+4} = 2^7$$
$$5^3 \cdot 5^6 = 5^{3+6} = 5^9$$

Second Law of Exponents

If x is any nonzero real number, then

$$\frac{x^m}{x^n} = x^{m-n}$$

for any non-negative integers m and n.

To verify this law, we note that if $m = 5$ and $n = 2$, then

$$\frac{x^m}{x^n} = \frac{x^5}{x^2} = \frac{\not{x} \cdot \not{x} \cdot x \cdot x \cdot x}{\not{x} \cdot \not{x}}$$
$$= x^{5-2} = x^3$$

And, similarly, we have

$$\frac{5^7}{5^3} = 5^{7-3} = 5^4 = 625$$

$$\frac{4^3}{4^5} = 4^{3-5} = 4^{-2} = \frac{1}{4^2} = \frac{1}{16}$$

It should be noted that the first two laws of exponents also hold true for negative integers m and n.

Third Law of Exponents

If x is any real number, then

$$(x^m)^n = x^{m \cdot n}$$

for all integers m and n.

To verify this law, we see that

$$(x^m)^n = \underbrace{x^m \cdot x^m \cdot \ldots \cdot x^m}_{n\ x^m{}'s}$$

$$= x^{\overbrace{m+m+\ldots+m}^{n\ m's}}$$

$$= x^{m \cdot n}$$

As examples, we have

$$(x^3)^2 = x^{3 \cdot 2} = x^6$$
$$(7^4)^5 = 7^{4 \cdot 5} = 7^{20}$$

Roots and Radicals

We now give meaning to the symbol $\sqrt[n]{x}$, where n is a positive integer. The symbol $\sqrt[n]{x}$ is called a **radical** and is read "the nth root of x." The nth root of x, $\sqrt[n]{x}$, represents a number that when multiplied by itself n times (i.e., raised to the nth power) yields x. Thus, if y is an nth root of x, then

$$y^n = x$$

If $n = 2$, then $\sqrt[2]{x}$ is called the **square root** of x and is usually written $\sqrt{x}$. Thus, $\sqrt{16} = 4$ since $4^2 = 16$. However, the equation $y^2 = 16$ has another solution, -4, since $(-4)^2 = 16$. In such a case, we take the **positive square root,** often called the **principal square root.** Thus, 4 is the principal square root of 16, and we write $\sqrt{16} = 4$. If we want to refer to the **negative square root** of 16, we indicate it by writing $-\sqrt{16} = -4$. Note that $\sqrt{-16}$ is undefined since there is no real number with a square of -16.

If $n = 3$, then $\sqrt[3]{x}$ is called the **cube root** of x. Note that $\sqrt[3]{8} = 2$ since $2^3 = 8$, and that $\sqrt[3]{-8} = -2$ since $(-2)^3 = -8$. Because $n = 3$ and 3 is an odd number, there is no need to define a principal cube root since the cube of a negative number is a negative number and the cube of a positive number is a positive number.

Observe that $\sqrt[4]{16} = 2$ since $2^4 = 16$. However, since $(-2)^4 = 16$, then $-\sqrt[4]{16} = -2$. Again, for even values of n, we call the positive nth root the **principal nth root.**

The preceding comments about $\sqrt[n]{x}$ are summarized as follows:

1. If $x > 0$ and n is even, then there are two solutions to the equation $y^n = x$. One is positive and the other is negative. To avoid ambiguity, we take the positive nth root, often called the principal nth root.
2. If $x < 0$ and n is even, then there are no real nth roots of x.
3. If n is odd, then there is one real nth root of x. Its sign is the same as that of x.
4. If $x = 0$, then the nth root of x is 0.

Rational Exponents

Up to this point, we have discussed only integer exponents. Thus, the first three laws of exponents were restricted to integral exponents. We now take a look at rational exponents. Consider the expression

$$x^{1/n}$$

where n is a nonzero integer. Hence, $1/n$ is a rational exponent. If $x^{1/n}$ is to be well defined, it must obey the laws of exponents. Specifically, the third law of exponents states that

$$(x^m)^n = x^{m \cdot n}$$

If this law is to hold true for $x^{1/n}$, then

$$(x^{1/n})^n = x^{(1/n)n} = x$$

This implies that the product of $x^{1/n}$ multiplied by itself n times equals x. **Hence, $x^{1/n}$ must equal the nth root of x,** or

$$x^{1/n} = \sqrt[n]{x}$$

Thus, $x^{1/n}$ is now defined. Specifically,

$$x^{1/2} = \sqrt{x}$$
$$x^{1/3} = \sqrt[3]{x}$$
$$4^{1/2} = \sqrt{4} = 2$$

Note that $(-4)^{1/2} = \sqrt{-4}$, which is undefined.

Since we have defined the expression $x^{1/n}$ for integral values of n, we now discuss expressions of the form

$$x^{m/n}$$

for integral values of m and n. If the expression $x^{m/n}$ is to be well defined, it must obey the laws of exponents. Specifically, if the third law of exponents is to hold true, then

$$(x^{1/n})^m = x^{(1/n)m} = x^{m/n}$$

Thus, $x^{m/n}$ may be defined as the **mth power of the nth root of x,** or

$$x^{m/n} = (\sqrt[n]{x})^m$$

As examples, we have

$$x^{5/2} = (\sqrt{x})^5$$
$$5^{2/3} = (\sqrt[3]{5})^2$$

Since the third law of exponents also indicates that

$$x^{m/n} = (x^m)^{1/n}$$

then $x^{m/n}$ may also be defined as the **nth root of x^m,** or

$$x^{m/n} = \sqrt[n]{x^m}$$

In summary, if m/n is reduced to lowest terms, we have

$$x^{m/n} = (\sqrt[n]{x})^m = \sqrt[n]{x^m}$$

Thus,

$$x^{5/2} = (\sqrt{x})^5 = \sqrt{x^5}$$
$$5^{2/3} = (\sqrt[3]{5})^2 = \sqrt[3]{5^2}$$

Since we have now defined rational exponents, it is appropriate to state that the first three laws of exponents hold true for all rational exponents m and n for which x^m and x^n are defined.

Fourth Law of Exponents

If x and y are real numbers, then

$$(x \cdot y)^n = x^n \cdot y^n$$

for any integral exponent n.

To verify this law, observe that

$$(xy)^n = \underbrace{xy \cdot xy \cdot \ldots \cdot xy}_{n \ xy's}$$

$$= \underbrace{(x \cdot x \cdot \ldots \cdot x)}_{n \ x's}\underbrace{(y \cdot y \cdot \ldots \cdot y)}_{n \ y's}$$

$$= x^n \cdot y^n$$

And, specifically,

$$(4 \cdot 3)^5 = 4^5 \cdot 3^5$$
$$(5x)^3 = 5^3 \cdot x^3 = 125x^3$$
$$(-2xy)^5 = (-2)^5 x^5 y^5 = -32x^5 y^5$$

It should be noted that the fourth law of exponents also holds true for any rational exponent n for which x^n and y^n are defined.

Fifth Law of Exponents

If x and y are real numbers, with $y \neq 0$, then

$$\left(\frac{x}{y}\right)^n = \frac{x^n}{y^n}$$

for any integral exponent n.

To verify this law, note that

$$\left(\frac{x}{y}\right)^n = \underbrace{\frac{x}{y} \cdot \frac{x}{y} \cdot \ldots \cdot \frac{x}{y}}_{n \frac{x}{y}\text{'s}}$$

$$= \frac{\overbrace{x \cdot x \cdot \ldots \cdot x}^{n\,x\text{'s}}}{\underbrace{y \cdot y \cdot \ldots \cdot y}_{n\,y\text{'s}}}$$

$$= \frac{x^n}{y^n}$$

Thus,

$$\left(\frac{5}{2}\right)^3 = \frac{5^3}{2^3}$$

$$\left(\frac{-3}{y}\right)^4 = \frac{(-3)^4}{y^4} = \frac{81}{y^4}$$

Again, we note that the fifth law of exponents also holds true for any rational exponent n for which x^n and y^n are defined.

Scientific Notation

Any positive number can be expressed in the form

$$c \times 10^n$$

where $1 \le c < 10$ and n is an integral exponent. When a number is expressed in this form, it is said to be in **scientific notation.** Specifically,

$$543 = 5.43 \times 10^2$$
$$84{,}000{,}000 = 8.4 \times 10^7$$
$$0.0003 = 3.0 \times 10^{-4}$$

Exercises R-3

Simplify each of the following. No exponents should appear in the final answer.

1. 3^2
2. $\left(\frac{2}{3}\right)^4$
3. $(-5)^2$

4. $(-5)^3$
5. $(4^2)^3$
6. 5^{-3}

7. 2^{-4}
8. $(-3)^{-2}$
9. $\frac{2^7}{2}$

10. $\frac{(-3)^9}{(-3)^7}$
11. $5^3 \cdot 5^4$
12. $4^2 \cdot 4^3$

13. $\left(\frac{3}{5}\right)^2$
14. $\left(\frac{4}{3}\right)^0$
15. $(2^{-3})^2$

16. $64^{1/2}$
17. $64^{-1/2}$
18. $216^{1/3}$

19. $16^{1/2}$	**20.** $16^{-1/2}$	**21.** $49^{1/2}$
22. $49^{-1/2}$	**23.** $64^{5/2}$	**24.** $64^{-5/2}$
25. $49^{3/2}$	**26.** $49^{-3/2}$	**27.** $216^{2/3}$
28. $216^{-2/3}$	**29.** 867^0	**30.** $(-3)^0$
31. $49^{5/2}$		

Rewrite each of the following using negative exponents.

32. $\dfrac{1}{3^2}$	**33.** $\dfrac{1}{5^6}$	**34.** $\dfrac{1}{x^7}$
35. $\dfrac{1}{(-5)^3}$	**36.** $\dfrac{1}{x^n}$	**37.** $\dfrac{1}{x^8}$

Rewrite each of the following using rational exponents.

38. $\sqrt[3]{5}$	**39.** $(\sqrt{4})^9$	**40.** $\sqrt[3]{x^5}$
41. $\sqrt[5]{2}$	**42.** $\sqrt{8^7}$	**43.** $\sqrt[7]{9^4}$
44. $(\sqrt{5})^3$	**45.** $(\sqrt[3]{5})^7$	**46.** $\sqrt[4]{x}$
47. $\dfrac{1}{\sqrt{5^3}}$	**48.** $\dfrac{1}{(\sqrt[3]{5})^8}$	**49.** $\dfrac{1}{\sqrt{x^5}}$
50. $\dfrac{1}{\sqrt{x^3}}$	**51.** $\dfrac{1}{\sqrt[3]{x^2}}$	**52.** $\dfrac{1}{(\sqrt[3]{x})^7}$

Using the fourth law of exponents, $(x \cdot y)^n = x^n \cdot y^n$, simplify each of the following.

53. $(-3x)^2$	**54.** $(2y)^4$	**55.** $(5xy)^3$
56. $(xyz)^9$	**57.** $(4 \cdot 81)^{1/2}$	**58.** $\sqrt{9 \cdot 64}$

Using the fifth law of exponents, $(x/y)^n = x^n/y^n$, simplify each of the following.

59. $\left(\dfrac{5}{6}\right)^3$	**60.** $\left(\dfrac{x}{y}\right)^4$	**61.** $\left(\dfrac{x}{3}\right)^5$	**62.** $\sqrt[3]{\dfrac{8}{27}}$
63. $\left(\dfrac{x}{5}\right)^2$	**64.** $\left(\dfrac{4}{x}\right)^3$	**65.** $\left(\dfrac{-2}{x}\right)^3$	**66.** $\sqrt{\dfrac{16}{25}}$

Simplify each of the following.

67. $\left(\dfrac{2^{-3} \cdot 2^5}{2^{-2}}\right)^3$ **68.** $3^{1/2} \cdot 3^{5/2}$

69. $\dfrac{3^{-7/2} \cdot 3^{3/2}}{3^{1/2} \cdot 3^{-3/2}}$ **70.** $\left(\dfrac{27^{5/3} \cdot 27^{-1/3}}{27^{1/3}}\right)^2$

Express each of the following in scientific notation.

71. 496	**72.** 5,870,000	**73.** 8,000,000,000
74. 0.00045	**75.** 0.0000008	**76.** 59.5
77. 0.56	**78.** 8730	**79.** 0.00357

R-4   • THE DISTRIBUTIVE LAW AND FACTORING

The Distributive Law

Consider the product of 3 times the sum of $2 + 8$ or

$$3(2 + 8)$$

Such a product can be determined by either of the following two methods:

1. Calculate the sum

$$2 + 8 = 10$$

and multiply the result by 3 to obtain

$$3(2 + 8) = 3(10)$$
$$= 30$$

2. Multiply both 2 and 8 by 3, and add the products to obtain

$$3(2 + 8) = (3 \cdot 2) + (3 \cdot 8)$$
$$= 6 + 24$$
$$= 30$$

Observe that, in the second method, the 3 is *distributed* throughout the sum of 2 + 8. This is a specific illustration of the *distributive law of multiplication over addition.*

> **Distributive Law**
>
> If a, b, and c are numbers, then
>
> $$a(b + c) = ab + ac$$

• **EXAMPLE R-10** _____

Using the distributive law, multiply $4(x + 2)$.

Solution

Distributing the 4 throughout the sum of $x + 2$, we have

$$\boxed{4}\,(x + 2) = \boxed{4}\,x + \boxed{4}\,\cdot 2$$
$$= 4x + 8$$

• **EXAMPLE R-11** _____

Using the distributive law, multiply $3[x + (-5)]$.

Solution

$$\boxed{3}\,(x + (-5)) = \boxed{3}\,x + \boxed{3}\,(-5)$$
$$= 3x - 15$$

Since the sum of $x + (-5)$ is equivalent to the *difference* of $x - 5$, we should realize that the distributive law also holds true for *multiplication over subtraction.* Hence,

$$\boxed{3}\,(x - 5) = \boxed{3}\,x - \boxed{3}\,\cdot 5$$
$$= 3x - 15$$

• **EXAMPLE R-12** _____

Using the distributive law, multiply $6(2x - 5)$.

Solution

$$\boxed{6}\,(2x - 5) = \boxed{6}\,\cdot 2x - \boxed{6}\,\cdot 5$$
$$= 12x - 30$$

The distributive law may be applied to products involving a sum or difference of more than two numbers, as illustrated in Example R-13.

• **EXAMPLE R-13** _____

Using the distributive law, multiply $-5(x^2 + 3x - 7)$.

Solution

$$-5\ (x^2 + 3x - 7) = \boxed{-5}\ x^2 + \boxed{-5}\ \cdot 3x - \boxed{(-5)}\ (7)$$
$$= -5x^2 - 15x + 35$$

• **EXAMPLE R-14** _____

Using the distributive law, multiply $-5xy^2(x^3 - 4x^2y)$.

Solution

$$-5xy^2\ (x^3 - 4x^2y) = \boxed{-5xy^2}\ \cdot x^3 - \boxed{(-5xy^2)}\ \cdot 4x^2y$$
$$= -5x^4y^2 + 20x^3y^3$$

Factoring

Many times the distributive law is used in *reverse*. This process is called **factoring.** Specifically, if we start with the expression

$$ab + ac$$

and rewrite it as the product

$$a(b + c)$$

then we have factored a from $ab + ac$.

• **EXAMPLE R-15** _____

Factor $3x + 6$.

Solution

$$3x + 6 = \boxed{3}\ x + \boxed{3}\ \cdot 2$$
$$= \boxed{3}\ (x + 2)$$

• **EXAMPLE R-16** _____

Factor $5x - 10y + 20$.

Solution

$$5x - 10y + 20 = \boxed{5}\ x - \boxed{5}\ \cdot 2y + \boxed{5}\ \cdot 4$$
$$= \boxed{5}\ (x - 2y + 4)$$

• **EXAMPLE R-17** _____

Factor $3x^5y^3 - 6x^2y^9$.

Solution

$$3x^5y^3 - 6x^2y^9 = \boxed{3x^2y^3}\ \cdot x^3 - \boxed{3x^2y^3}\ \cdot 2y^6$$
$$= \boxed{3x^2y^3}\ (x^3 - 2y^6)$$

FIGURE R-18

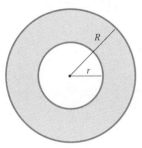

FIGURE R-19

• **EXAMPLE R-18** _____

Given that the area of a circle of radius r (see Figure R-18) is πr^2 where $\pi \approx$ 3.1415927 to seven decimal places, show that the area of the ring of Figure R-19 is $\pi(R^2 - r^2)$.

Solution

$$\text{area of ring} = \text{area of outer circle} - \text{area of inner circle}$$
$$= \pi R^2 - \pi r^2$$
$$= \pi(R^2 - r^2)$$

• **EXAMPLE R-19** _____

Using the distributive law, show that $P(1 + i) + P(1 + i)i = P(1 + i)^2$.

Solution

$$P(1 + i) + P(1 + i)i = \boxed{P(1 + i)} \cdot 1 + \boxed{P(1 + i)} \cdot i$$
$$= \boxed{P(1 + i)}\,(1 + i)$$
$$= P(1 + i)^2$$

• **EXAMPLE R-20** _____

Factor $7x(x - 5) + 3x(x - 5)$.

Solution

$$7x\,\boxed{(x - 5)} + 3x\,\boxed{(x - 5)} = \boxed{(x - 5)}\,(7x + 3x)$$
$$= (x - 5)10x$$
$$= 10x(x - 5)$$

_____•

Exercises R-4

Use the distributive law to multiply each of the following.

1. $3(x + 4)$	**2.** $5(x - 3)$	**3.** $-2(x + 6)$
4. $-5(x - 8)$	**5.** $9(x + 3)$	**6.** $9(2x + 3)$

7. $-4(x^2 - 3x + 7)$ **8.** $6x(x^2 + 2x - 5)$
9. $5x(x^3 - 4x^2 + 4x + 5)$ **10.** $-2x(x^2 + 6x + 7)$
11. $3x^2y^3(x^4 - 5y^2 + 6xy)$ **12.** $-2x^4y^3(x^3 - 6y^2 + 7xy)$

Factor each of the following.

13. $5x + 20$	**14.** $-2x - 8$	**15.** $3x - 27$
16. $8x - 16$	**17.** $6x - 30$	**18.** $4x + 32$
19. $3x^2 - 27x$	**20.** $5x^2 + 60x$	**21.** $-6x^2 + 48x$
22. $-4x^2 - 36x$	**23.** $7x^2 + 28x$	**24.** $9x^2 - 18x$

25. $3x^2y^4 + 6xy^2$ **26.** $4x^3y^5 - 8x^2y^6$
27. $-5x^4y^6 + 20x^3y^7$ **28.** $-2x^5y^3 + 6x^4y^3$
29. $3x^2y^6 + 9x^5y^3 + 6x^3y^4$ **30.** $5x^4y^6 - 10x^3y^7 + 30x^2y^3$
31. $P + Prt$ **32.** $S - Sdt$
33. $P + Pi$ **34.** $ax^2 + bx$

35. $ax^2 - bx$ **36.** $ax^3 + bx^2 + cx$
37. $P(1 + i)^2 + P(1 + i)^2 i$ **38.** $P(1 + i)^3 + P(1 + i)^3 i$
39. $3x(x - 7) + 3x(x + 4)$ **40.** $5x(x + 2) - 2x(x + 2)$
41. $2x(x + 3) - y(x + 3)$ **42.** $3xy(x + 2) - 6x^2(x + 2)$
43. $5xy(x - 2) + 8x^2(x - 2)$ **44.** $4xy^2(x - 1) + 5x^2y(x - 1)$

R-5 • MULTIPLYING BINOMIALS

An algebraic expression containing exactly two terms is called a **binomial.** For example, the expression

$$x + 7$$

is a binomial because it contains two terms, x and 7. The expression

$$4x - 5$$

is a binomial because it contains two terms, $4x$ and -5. The expression

$$x^2 + 6$$

is a binomial because it contains two terms, x^2 and 6. The product of two binomials can be determined by using the distributive law

$$a(b + c) = ab + ac$$

Specifically, the product

$$(x - 3)(x + 5)$$

can be determined by treating the binomial $x - 3$ as a and employing the distributive law as follows:

$$a(b + c) = ab + ac$$
$$(x - 3)(x + 5) = (x - 3)x + (x - 3) \cdot 5$$
$$= x^2 - 3x + 5x - 15$$
$$= x^2 + 2x - 15$$

Observe that the above product can also be determined by the following mechanical procedure, called the **FOIL** method:

Step 1   Multiply the first terms of the binomial factors   F
Step 2   Multiply the outer terms of the binomial factors   0
Step 3   Multiply the inner terms of the binomial factors   I
Step 4   Multiply the last terms of the binomial factors   L
Step 5   Add the above products and simplify if possible.

Using the FOIL method, we again determine the product

$$(x - 3)(x + 5)$$

as follows:

$$(x - 3)(x + 5) = x^2 + 5x - 3x - 15$$
$$= x^2 + 2x - 15$$

• EXAMPLE R-21

Determine the product $(3x - 5)(x + 2)$.

Solution

$$(3x - 5)(x + 2) = 3x^2 + 6x - 5x - 10$$
$$= 3x^2 + x - 10$$

• EXAMPLE R-22

Multiply $(4x + 3)(x - 7)$.

Solution

$$(4x + 3)(x - 7) = 4x^2 - \underline{\quad} + 3x - \underline{\quad}$$
$$= 4x^2 - 25x - 21$$

Answer

$$4x^2 - \underline{28x} + 3x - \underline{21} = 4x^2 - 25x - 21$$

• EXAMPLE R-23

Multiply $(x - 5)(x + 5)$.

Solution

$$(x - 5)(x + 5) = x^2 + 5x - \underline{\quad} - \underline{\quad}$$
$$= x^2 - 25$$

Answer

$$x^2 + 5x - \underline{5x} - \underline{25} = x^2 - 25$$

Notice that the product, $x^2 - 25$, does not contain an x term. That is because the sum of $+5x$ and $-5x$ is 0.

Difference of Two Squares

In general,

$$(x - a)(x + a) = x^2 - a^2$$

where the right-hand expression is called a difference of two squares.

• **EXAMPLE R-24** _____

Determine $(x + 3)^2$.

Solution

$$(x + 3)^2 = (x + 3)(x + 3) = x^2 + \underline{\quad} + 3x + 9$$
$$= x^2 + 6x + 9$$

Answer

$$x^2 + \underline{3x} + 3x + 9 = x^2 + 6x + 9$$

Since the product $x^2 + 6x + 9$ in Example R-24 is equivalent to the square of a binomial, namely $x + 3$, then $x^2 + 6x + 9$ is called a **perfect square**. Notice that when determining the square of a binomial, the products of the inner terms and outer terms are equal. In Example R-24, each is $3x$. Thus, to square a binomial, we can use the following modified procedure.

To Square a Binomial

Step 1 Square the first term.
Step 2 Multiply both terms of the binomial, and double this product.
Step 3 Square the last term.
Step 4 Add the above products.

For example,

$$(x + 5)^2 = x^2 + 2(5x) + 5^2$$
$$= x^2 + 10x + 25$$
$$(x - 7)^2 = x^2 + 2(-7x) + (-7)^2$$
$$= x^2 - 14x + 49$$
$$(2x - 5)^2 = (2x)^2 + 2[(2x)(-5)] + (-5)^2$$
$$= 4x^2 - 20x + 25$$

Exercises R-5

Determine each of the following products by using the FOIL method.

1. $(x - 2)(x + 3)$ **2.** $(x - 8)(x + 7)$
3. $(x + 1)(x + 5)$ **4.** $(x - 2)(x - 3)$
5. $(x - 8)(x - 7)$ **6.** $(x - 6)(x + 10)$
7. $(3x + 5)(x - 1)$ **8.** $(2x + 1)(3x + 4)$
9. $(4x - 7)(2x + 3)$ **10.** $(5x + 3)(x - 2)$
11. $(7x - 2)(3x + 1)$ **12.** $(9x + 1)(3x - 5)$

Determine each of the following products by using the difference of two squares formula.

13. $(x - 3)(x + 3)$ **14.** $(x - 7)(x + 7)$
15. $(x - 9)(x + 9)$ **16.** $(2x - 1)(2x + 1)$
17. $(3x - 2)(3x + 2)$ **18.** $(4x - 7)(4x + 7)$

Determine each of the following.

19. $(x - 2)^2$ **20.** $(x + 2)^2$
21. $(x + 5)^2$ **22.** $(x - 5)^2$
23. $(2x - 3)^2$ **24.** $(2x + 3)^2$

R-6

• FACTORING

In the previous section, we learned to multiply binomials. For example, we learned that the product $(x - 2)(x + 7)$ can be determined by the FOIL method as follows:

$$(x - 2)(x + 7) = x^2 + 7x - 2x - 14$$
$$= x^2 + 5x - 14$$

If we begin with $x^2 + 5x - 14$ and express it as the product $(x - 2)(x + 7)$, then we have *factored* $x^2 + 5x - 14$. The binomials $x - 2$ and $x + 7$ are called **factors.** Thus, factoring is the reverse of multiplication.

We will demonstrate the factoring process by factoring expressions of the form

$$ax^2 + bx + c$$

where a, b, and c are constants and $a \neq 0$. Also, we will begin with the special case where $a = 1$. Thus, for this special case, the above expression is written as

$$x^2 + bx + c$$

If factored, such an expression is written as the product of two binomials

$$(x + A)(x + B)$$

where A and B are constants. Thus, when we factor the expression $x^2 + bx + c$, we seek two constants, A and B, such that

$$(x + A)(x + B) = x^2 + bx + c \tag{1}$$

If we apply the FOIL method to the left-hand side of equation (1), we obtain

$$(x + A)(x + B) = x^2 + Bx + Ax + AB$$
$$= x^2 + (B + A)x + AB \tag{2}$$

Comparing the right-hand sides of equations (1) and (2), note that

$$B + A = b \text{ and } AB = c$$

This result is expressed as follows.

Factoring

When factoring the expression $x^2 + bx + c$ so that
$$(x + A)(x + B) = x^2 + bx + c$$
we seek two constants, A and B, whose sum equals b and whose product equals c.

As an example, let us factor $x^2 + 6x - 27$. This means that we wish to write $x^2 + 6x - 27$ as a product of two factors:

$$(x + A)(x + B)$$

Thus, we seek two numbers, A and B, whose sum is 6 and whose product is -27. The numbers of the pair -3, 9 satisfy the above requirements since $-3 + 9 = 6$ and $-3 \cdot 9 = -27$. Hence,

$$(x - 3)(x + 9) = x^2 + 6x - 27$$

and our two factors are $x - 3$ and $x + 9$.

• **EXAMPLE R-25** ─────────────────────────────

Factor $x^2 + 7x - 30$.

Solution

We wish to determine two factors such that

$$(x + \underline{\quad})(x + \underline{\quad}) = x^2 + 7x - 30$$

Thus, we seek two numbers whose sum is 7 and whose product is -30. The following are possible pairs of numbers whose product is -30:

$$-5, 6 \qquad 5, -6 \qquad -3, 10 \qquad 3, -10$$
$$-30, 1 \qquad 30, -1 \qquad 15, -2 \qquad -15, 2$$

Since the numbers of the pair -3, 10 have a sum of 7, then the factors are $x - 3$ and $x + 10$. Hence,

$$(x - 3)(x + 10) = x^2 + 7x - 30$$

Of course, we can always check our factoring by multiplying the factors to determine if their product is the original expression that was factored.

• EXAMPLE R-26

Factor $x^2 + 8x + 15$.

Solution

We wish to determine two factors such that

$$(x + \underline{\quad})(x + \underline{\quad}) = x^2 + 8x + 15$$

Thus, we seek two numbers whose sum is 8 and whose product is 15. The following are possible pairs of numbers whose product is 15:

$$3, 5 \qquad -3, -5 \qquad 1, 15 \qquad -1, -15$$

Since the numbers of the pair 3, 5 have a sum of 8, then the factors are $x + 3$ and $x + 5$. Hence,

$$(x + 3)(x + 5) = x^2 + 8x + 15$$

Of course, we can always check our factoring by multiplying the factors to determine if their product is the original expression that was factored.

• EXAMPLE R-27

Factor $x^2 - 36$.

Solution

Since $x^2 - 36$ does not contain an x term, we seek two numbers whose sum is 0 and whose product is -36. The numbers are -6 and $+6$. Hence,

$$(x - 6)(x + 6) = x^2 - 36$$

As discussed in the previous section, the expression $x^2 - 36$ in Example R-27 is called a **difference of two squares.** In general, a difference of two squares

$$x^2 - h^2$$

is factored as follows:

$$x^2 - h^2 = (x - h)(x + h)$$

• EXAMPLE R-28

Factor $x^2 + 12x + 36$.

Solution

We seek two numbers whose product is 36 and whose sum is 12. The numbers are 6 and 6, and the factors are $x + 6$ and $x + 6$. Hence,

$$(x + 6)(x + 6) = x^2 + 12x + 36$$

or

$$(x + 6)^2 = x^2 + 12x + 36$$

Since the expression $x^2 + 12x + 36$ (in Example R-28), when factored, is written as $(x + 6)^2$, the square of a binomial, then the expression $x^2 + 12x + 36$ is called a **perfect square.** In general, an expression of the form $x^2 + bx + c$ is a perfect square if, when factored, it is written as

$$(x + A)^2 = x^2 + bx + c \qquad (3)$$

where A is a constant.

We now discuss how to recognize a perfect square. Applying the FOIL method to the left-hand side of equation (3), we obtain

$$(x + A)(x + A) = x^2 + Ax + Ax + A^2$$
$$= x^2 + 2Ax + A^2 \qquad (4)$$

Comparing the right-hand sides of equations (3) and (4), note that *the coefficient of x is twice the square root of the constant* c. Thus, we state the following.

Perfect Square

An expression of the form

$$x^2 + bx + c$$

with $c \geq 0$ is a perfect square if

$$b = \pm 2\sqrt{c}$$

1. If $b = +2\sqrt{c}$, then the expression is written in factored form as

$$(x + \sqrt{c})^2$$

2. If $b = -2\sqrt{c}$, then the expression is written in factored form as

$$(x - \sqrt{c})^2$$

As another example, note that $x^2 - 12x + 36$ is a perfect square since $-12 = -2\sqrt{36}$. Hence,

$$x^2 - 12x + 36 = (x - 6)^2$$

We summarize the following.

$$x^2 - h^2 = (x - h)(x + h) \qquad \text{Difference of two squares}$$
$$x^2 + 2Ax + A^2 = (x + A)^2 \qquad \text{Perfect square}$$
$$x^2 - 2Ax + A^2 = (x - A)^2 \qquad \text{Perfect square}$$

Exercises R-6

Factor each of the following:

1. $x^2 + 7x - 18$ **2.** $x^2 - 7x - 18$

3. $x^2 + 2x - 15$ **4.** $x^2 + 10x + 21$

5. $x^2 - 3x + 2$ **6.** $x^2 + 13x + 40$

7. $x^2 - 13x + 40$ **8.** $x^2 - x + 42$

9. $x^2 - 81$ **10.** $x^2 - 64$

11. $x^2 - 49$ **12.** $x^2 - 25$

13. $x^2 + 6x + 9$ **14.** $x^2 - 6x + 9$

15. $x^2 - 10x + 25$ **16.** $x^2 + 10x + 25$

17. $x^2 + 18x + 81$ **18.** $x^2 - 18x + 81$

19. $x^2 - 6x - 27$ **20.** $x^2 - 100$

21. $x^2 - 4x - 45$ **22.** $x^2 - 20x + 100$

23. $x^2 + 7x + 6$ **24.** $x^2 + 2x + 1$

R-7   • MORE FACTORING

In the previous section, we demonstrated the factoring process by factoring expressions of the form

$$ax^2 + bx + c$$

where a, b, and c are constants and $a = 1$. In this section, we remove the restriction that $a = 1$. In other words, we will now discuss the factoring of expressions of the form

$$ax^2 + bx + c$$

where a, b, and c are constants, $a \neq 0$, and $a \neq 1$. As an example, we will factor

$$5x^2 + 33x - 14$$

Since the coefficient of x^2 is 5, then by the FOIL method, the product of the x terms of both factors must be $5x^2$. Hence, the x terms of the factors are $5x$ and x, and

$$(5x + \underline{\quad})(x + \underline{\quad}) = 5x^2 + 33x - 14$$

We now seek two numbers whose product is -14. We shall discover that the sum of these two numbers will not be 33, as would be the case if the coefficient of the x^2 term were 1 (i.e., if $a = 1$). The following are pairs of numbers whose product is -14:

$$7, -2 \qquad -7, 2 \qquad -1, 14 \qquad 1, -14$$

Now we must use a trial-and-error approach to determine which pair yields the correct middle term when the factors are multiplied by the FOIL method. We will begin with the pair 7, -2. Hence,

$$
\begin{array}{ll}
\overset{\text{F}}{5x^2} \quad \overset{\text{L}}{-14} & \\
(5x + 7)(x - 2) \overset{2}{=} 5x^2 + 33x - 14 & \qquad (1) \\
7x \qquad = 5x^2 - 10x + 7x - 14 & \qquad (2) \\
-10x \qquad = 5x^2 - 3x - 14 & \qquad (3) \\
\end{array}
$$

Note that we have placed a question mark above the equal sign of equation (1). Equations (2) and (3) give the results of multiplying the two factors. Note that since the x term of the product is $-3x$ and not $33x$, then the above factorization is not correct, and we must try another combination of numbers. However, before trying a different pair of numbers, we might interchange the positions of $+7$ and -2. Hence,

$$
\begin{array}{ll}
\overset{\text{F}}{5x^2} \quad \overset{\text{L}}{-14} & \\
(5x - 2)(x + 7) \overset{2}{=} 5x^2 + 33x - 14 & \qquad (4) \\
-2x \qquad = 5x^2 + 35x - 2x - 14 & \qquad (5) \\
35x \qquad = 5x^2 + 33x - 14 & \qquad (6) \\
\end{array}
$$

Notice that multiplication by the FOIL method in equations (5) and (6) has resulted in the correct middle term, $33x$. Thus, the above factorization in equation (4) is correct, and

$$5x^2 + 33x - 14 = (5x - 2)(x + 7)$$

• EXAMPLE R-29

Factor $6x^2 - 11x - 35$.

Solution

We wish to determine two factors such that

$$(\underline{}x + \underline{})(\underline{}x + \underline{}) = 6x^2 - 11x - 35$$

Since the coefficient of x^2 is 6, we first seek two numbers whose product is 6. From a number of possibilities, we choose 3 and 2. Hence,

$$(3x + \underline{})(2x + \underline{}) \overset{2}{=} 6x^2 - 11x - 35$$

We hasten to mention that this may not be the correct choice of numbers. This is why we have placed a question mark above the equal sign. However, we have no way of determining this until we choose the numbers for the remaining blanks in our factors and multiply by the FOIL method to determine whether the product equals $6x^2 - 11x - 35$.

Thus, we seek two numbers whose product is -35. From a number of possibilities, we choose 5 and -7. Hence,

$$(3x + 5)(2x - 7) \stackrel{?}{=} 6x^2 - 11x - 35 \tag{7}$$

$$= 6x^2 - 21x + 10x - 35 \tag{8}$$

$$= 6x^2 - 11x - 35 \tag{9}$$

Note that multiplication by the FOIL method in equations (8) and (9) has resulted in the correct middle term, $-11x$. Thus, the factorization in equation (7) is correct, and

$$6x^2 - 11x - 35 = (3x + 5)(2x - 7)$$

Exercises R-7

Factor each of the following.

1. $2x^2 - x - 28$
2. $6x^2 - 7x - 5$
3. $5x^2 + 18x - 8$
4. $21x^2 - 2x - 8$
5. $6x^2 - 13x - 5$
6. $4x^2 - 13x - 35$
7. $9x^2 - 36$
8. $64x^2 - 49$
9. $4x^2 + 20x + 25$
10. $9x^2 - 12x + 4$
11. $25x^2 - 70x + 49$
12. $81x^2 + 18x + 1$

R-8   • RATIONAL EXPRESSIONS

Expressions involving quotients such as

$$\frac{3x + 15}{2x} \qquad \frac{x^2 - 4x}{x - 7} \qquad \frac{x^2 - 36}{x + 9}$$

are called **rational expressions.** Sometimes we have to simplify or reduce such expressions to their lowest terms. Such simplifications are performed by using the following rules.

Rules Involving Rational Expressions

Assume that N, D, R, and S are expressions such that D and $S \neq 0$.

$$\frac{N \cdot S}{D \cdot S} = \frac{N}{D} \qquad \text{Fundamental rule}$$

$$\frac{N}{D} \cdot \frac{R}{S} = \frac{N \cdot R}{D \cdot S} \qquad \text{Multiplication rule}$$

$$\frac{N}{D} \div \frac{R}{S} = \frac{N}{D} \cdot \frac{S}{R} \qquad (R \neq 0) \qquad \text{Division rule}$$

$$\frac{N}{D} + \frac{R}{D} = \frac{N + R}{D} \qquad \text{Addition rule}$$

$$\frac{N}{D} - \frac{R}{D} = \frac{N - R}{D} \qquad \text{Subtraction rule}$$

The following examples illustrate applications of these rules.

• EXAMPLE R-30

Simplify each of the following.

a) $\dfrac{3x + 15}{3} = \dfrac{3(x + 5)}{3} = x + 5$ Factoring, fundamental rule

b) $\dfrac{x^2 + x - 20}{x^2 - 16} = \dfrac{(x - 4)(x + 5)}{(x - 4)(x + 4)} = \dfrac{x + 5}{x + 4}$ Factoring, fundamental rule

• EXAMPLE R-31

Perform the indicated operation.

a) $\dfrac{x^2 - 25}{x + 3} \cdot \dfrac{x^2 - 2x - 15}{x^2 - 10x + 25} = \dfrac{(x - 5)(x + 5)}{(x + 3)} \cdot \dfrac{(x - 5)(x + 3)}{(x - 5)(x - 5)}$

$= x + 5$ Factoring, mulitplication rule, fundamental rule

b) $\dfrac{x^2 + 2x - 8}{x + 6} \div \dfrac{x^2 + 3x - 4}{2x + 12} = \dfrac{x^2 + 2x - 8}{x + 6} \cdot \dfrac{2x + 12}{x^2 + 3x - 8}$ Division rule

$= \dfrac{(x - 2)(x + 4)}{x + 6} \cdot \dfrac{2(x + 6)}{(x + 4)(x - 1)}$ Factoring; fundamental rule

$= \dfrac{2(x - 2)}{x - 1}$ or $\dfrac{2x - 4}{x - 1}$ Division rule, factoring, fundamental rule

c) $\dfrac{6}{7x} + \dfrac{8}{7x} = \dfrac{6 + 8}{7x} = \dfrac{14}{7x} = \dfrac{7 \cdot 2}{7x} = \dfrac{2}{x}$ Addition rule, fundamental rule

d) $\dfrac{8}{x} - \dfrac{5}{2x} + \dfrac{4}{3x} = \dfrac{6 \cdot 8}{6 \cdot x} - \dfrac{3 \cdot 5}{3 \cdot 2x} + \dfrac{2 \cdot 4}{2 \cdot 3x} = \dfrac{48}{6x} - \dfrac{15}{6x} + \dfrac{8}{6x}$

$= \dfrac{48 - 15 + 8}{6x} = \dfrac{41}{6x}$ Addition and subtraction rules; fundamental rule

• EXAMPLE R-32

Divide by x.

$$\frac{3x + 5}{x} = \frac{3\cancel{x}}{\cancel{x}} + \frac{5}{x} = 3 + \frac{5}{x}$$ Addition rule; fundamental rule

• EXAMPLE R-33

Divide.

$$\frac{(1 + i)^{30} - 1}{i} \div (1 + i)^{30} = \frac{(1 + i)^{30} - 1}{i} \div \frac{(1 + i)^{30}}{1}$$

$$= \frac{(1 + i)^{30} - 1}{i} \cdot \frac{1}{(1 + i)^{30}}$$ Division rule

$$= \frac{(1 + i)^{30} - 1}{(1 + i)^{30} \; i}$$ Multiplication rule

$$= \frac{\dfrac{(1 + i)^{30}}{(1 + i)^{30}} - \dfrac{1}{(1 + i)^{30}}}{i}$$ Subtraction rule

$$= \frac{1 - (1 + i)^{-30}}{i}$$ Negative exponent

• EXAMPLE R-34

Multiply.

$$5x^3 \left(1 + \frac{2}{x} - \frac{3}{x^2} + \frac{6}{x^3}\right) = 1 \cdot 5x^3 + \frac{2 \cdot 5x^3}{x} - \frac{3 \cdot 5x^3}{x^2} + \frac{6 \cdot 5x^3}{x^3}$$

$$= 5x^3 + 10x^2 - 15x + 30$$

• EXAMPLE R-35

Factor out the highest-powered term: $2x^3 + 4x^2 - 2x + 8$.

Solution

$$\frac{2x^3}{2x^3}(2x^3 + 4x^2 - 2x + 8) = 2x^3\left(\frac{2x^3 + 4x^2 - 2x + 8}{2x^3}\right)$$

$$= 2x^3\left(\frac{2x^3}{2x^3} + \frac{4x^2}{2x^3} - \frac{2x}{2x^3} + \frac{8}{2x^3}\right)$$

$$= 2x^3\left(1 + \frac{2}{x} - \frac{1}{x^2} + \frac{4}{x^3}\right)$$

Exercises R-8

Simplify each of the following.

1. $\dfrac{4x - 28}{2}$ **2.** $\dfrac{-3x + 18}{3}$ **3.** $\dfrac{-(2x + 14)}{2}$ **4.** $\dfrac{5x - 30}{5}$

5. $\dfrac{x^2 - 6x}{x - 6}$ **6.** $\dfrac{4x^2 - 32x}{x - 8}$ **7.** $\dfrac{x^2 + 2x - 15}{x^2 - 25}$ **8.** $\dfrac{x + 8}{x^2 - 64}$

9. $\dfrac{x^2 + 3x - 4}{x^2 - 1}$ **10.** $\dfrac{x^2 + 2x - 8}{x^2 + 5x + 4}$ **11.** $\dfrac{x^2 + 8x + 15}{x^2 + 7x + 10}$

Perform the indicated operations.

12. $\dfrac{x^2 - 49}{x + 2} \cdot \dfrac{x^2 + 3x + 2}{x^2 - 6x - 7}$ **13.** $\dfrac{9}{6x^2} \cdot \dfrac{2x}{3}$

14. $\dfrac{20x^3}{7x} \div \dfrac{10}{21x}$ **15.** $\dfrac{x^2 - 4x - 5}{x^2 + 3x + 2} \cdot \dfrac{x^2 + 5x + 6}{x^2 - 7x + 10}$

16. $\dfrac{x^2 - x - 30}{x^2 - 36} \cdot \dfrac{x^2 + 7x + 6}{x^2 + 7x + 10}$ **17.** $\dfrac{x^2 - 81}{x^2 + 10x + 9} \div \dfrac{x^2 - 7x - 18}{x^2 + 4x + 3}$

18. $\dfrac{x^2 + 2x - 8}{x^2 + x - 2} \div \dfrac{x^2 + x - 12}{x^2 - 1}$

19. $\dfrac{x + 5}{4} + \dfrac{x + 7}{4}$ **20.** $\dfrac{2x + 3}{5} - \dfrac{5x - 7}{10}$ **21.** $\dfrac{5}{x} + \dfrac{8}{2x}$

22. $\dfrac{x}{x - 2} + \dfrac{3}{x + 2}$ **23.** $\dfrac{5}{x + 6} - \dfrac{8}{x}$ **24.** $\dfrac{8}{x - 5} + \dfrac{4}{x + 5}$

25. $\dfrac{5}{x^2 - 36} + \dfrac{9}{x + 6}$ **26.** $\dfrac{4}{x + 8} + \dfrac{3}{x^2 - 64}$ **27.** $\dfrac{7}{x - 9} - \dfrac{5}{x(x - 9)}$

Divide by x.

28. $\dfrac{4x - 9}{x}$ **29.** $\dfrac{2x + 7}{x}$ **30.** $\dfrac{8x - 9}{x}$ **31.** $\dfrac{3x^2 - 36x}{x}$

32. $\dfrac{5x^2 + 30x}{x}$ **33.** $\dfrac{4x^3 - 8x^2 + 6x}{x}$ **34.** $\dfrac{5x^2 - 6x + 8}{x}$

Multiply.

35. $4x^2\left(1 + \dfrac{2}{x} - \dfrac{3}{x^2}\right)$ **36.** $6x^3\left(1 + \dfrac{1}{x} + \dfrac{2}{x^2} - \dfrac{4}{x^3}\right)$

37. $5x^3\left(1 - \dfrac{1}{x} + \dfrac{6}{x^2} - \dfrac{2}{x^3}\right)$ **38.** $x^3\left(2 + \dfrac{3}{x} + \dfrac{8}{x^2} - \dfrac{4}{x^3}\right)$

Factor out the highest-powered term.

39. $x^3 - 4x^2 + 7x + 5$ **40.** $x^4 - 6x^3 + x^2 - x + 9$
41. $x^2 + 7x + 9$ **42.** $x^3 + 6x^2 + 8x + 4$

Divide.

43. $\dfrac{(1 + i)^{20} - 1}{i} \div (1 + i)^{20}$ **44.** $\dfrac{(1 + i)^{36} - 1}{i} \div (1 + i)^{26}$

45. $\dfrac{(1 + i)^{39} - (1 + i)}{i} \div (1 + i)^{38}$ **46.** $\dfrac{(1 + i)^{50} - 1}{i} \div (1 + i)$

EXTRA DIVIDENDS

FIGURE R-20

• *Percent Change*

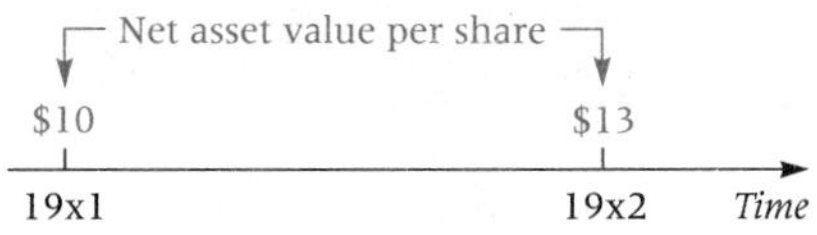

In the business world, assets usually change in value over periods of time. The amount of change is often put into perspective by expressing it as a percentage. For example, if the net asset value per share of mutual fund changes from $10 to $13 during a 1-year time period (see Figure R-20), this constitutes a change (in this case, an increase) of $13 − $10 = $3 per share during the indicated 1-year time period. If we divide the amount of change by the original value (i.e., the net asset value per share at the beginning of the year), the result

$$3/10 = 0.30$$
$$= 30\%$$

gives us the *percent change* (in this case, percent increase) in the net asset value per share of the fund during the indicated time period. We generalize as follows:

• Percent Change

If some quantity changes in value during a time interval, as indicated in Figure R-21, then the percent change is given by the following formula:

$$\text{percent change} = \frac{\text{new value} - \text{old value}}{\text{old value}} \times 100$$

If new value > old value, then the percent change is positive and thus is a percent increase. If new value < old value, then the percent change is negative and thus is a percent decrease.

Thus, if a stock's price changes from $40 to $10 during a 3-month time period, the percent change is determined as follows:

$$\text{percent change} = \frac{\text{new value} - \text{old value}}{\text{old value}} \times 100$$
$$= \frac{10 - 40}{40} \times 100$$
$$= \frac{-30}{40} \times 100$$
$$= -0.75 \times 100$$
$$= -75\%$$

Thus, the stock's price has decreased by 75%.

A percent change indicates a relationship between the new value and the old value of an asset. The equation expressing this relationship is determined by beginning with the formula for percent change and solving for the new value. Thus, if p denotes the percent change in decimal form (i.e., before we multiply by 100), OV denotes the old value, and NV denotes the new value, then

$$p = \frac{NV - OV}{OV}$$

Multiplying both sides of this equation by OV, we have

$$OV \cdot p = NV - OV$$

FIGURE R-21

Solving for NV, we have

$$OV + (OV \cdot p) = NV$$

or

$$NV = OV + (OV \cdot p)$$

Applying the distributive law to the right-hand side, we have

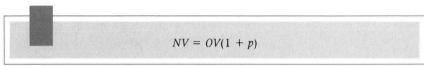

$$NV = OV(1 + p)$$

The boxed equation gives the relationship between the new value and the old value of some asset.

Thus, if an assset's value increases by 40% from $80 during a 6-month time interval, then its new value is given by the formula

$$NV = OV(1 + p)$$

where $p = 0.40$ and $OV = 80$. Hence,

$$
\begin{aligned}
NV &= 80(1 + 0.40) \\
&= 80(1.40) \\
&= 112
\end{aligned}
$$

Thus, the asset's new value at the end of the indicated 6-month time interval is $112.

Also, if an asset's value decreases by 30% from $80 during a specified time interval, then its new value is determined by the formula

$$NV = OV(1 + p)$$

where $p = -0.30$ and $OV = 80$. Hence,

$$
\begin{aligned}
NV &= 80(1 - 0.30) \\
&= 80(0.70) \\
&= 56
\end{aligned}
$$

Thus, the asset's new value at the end of the time period is $56.

Exercises

1. A mutual fund's net asset value per share changes from $40 to $50 during a 1-year time period. Find its percent change.
2. A stock's price changes from $60 to $20 during a 9-month time period. Find its percent change.
3. A stock's price increases by 20% from $60 during a 3-month time period. Find its new price.
4. A stock's price decreases by 30% from $80 during a given month. Find its new price.
5. The price of 1 ounce of gold increased by 40% to $600 during a given month. Find its old price at the beginning of the month.

TABLE R-1

Twentieth Century Growth	43.9%
Fidelity Magellan	48.0
Vanguard Windsor	56.1
Mutual Shares	60.5
Fidelity Puritan	41.9

Investment

Table R-1 gives percent changes of various mutual funds during a selected 3-year time period. If $10,000 were invested at the beginning the selected 3-year period, determine its value at the end of the 3-year period (assuming no withdrawals of either principal or income) for

6. Twentieth Century Growth **7.** Fidelity Magellan
8. Vanguard Windsor **9.** Mutual Shares
10. Fidelity Puritan

International: Trade

Table R-2 gives total trade (imports and exports in millions of U.S. dollars) in competitive world markets for three countries during various years. Determine the percent change from 1975 to 1980 for

11. United States **12.** Soviet Union **13.** Japan

Determine the percent change from 1980 to 1985 for

14. United States **15.** Soviet Union **16.** Japan

TABLE R-2

	1975	1980	1985
United States	$213,992	$477,771	$574,771
Soviet Union	30,791	67,059	65,967
Japan	113,569	271,737	307,652

Stocks

TABLE R-3

General Electric	451%
Exxon	365
AT&T	348
General Motors	182

Table R-3 gives the total return (change in value plus income) for the selected stocks during the decade of the 1980s. If, at the end of the decade, an investor had shares worth $100,000, what was the value of such shares at the beginning of the decade, assuming the shares were purchased at the beginning of the decade and no withdrawals of either principal or income were made? Answer this question if the shares purchased were

17. General Electric **18.** Exxon
19. AT&T **20.** General Motors

EXTRA DIVIDENDS

TABLE R-4 **Price per quart of milk**

1990	79¢
1980	56¢

• Using Index Numbers to Measure Change

An **index number** measures the change in some quantity (i.e., price, productivity, inventory, etc.) from one time period to another. The time periods are usually years, although this does not necessarily have to be the case. The time period used as the basis of comparison is called the **base period.** As an example, we consider the price of milk for the years 1990 and 1980, as given in Table R-4.

A simple index number is computed by dividing the 1990 price by the 1980 price. Thus, the ratio

$$\frac{1990 \text{ price}}{1980 \text{ price}} \times 100 = \frac{79\text{¢}}{56\text{¢}} \times 100$$

$$= 1.41 \times 100$$

$$= 141\%$$

gives an index comparing 1990 milk prices to those of 1980.

Since 1980 prices are the basis of the comparison, then 1980 is the *base year* of this index. Note that we multiply by 100 to express the index as a percentage. We will use the symbol

$$I_{80,90}$$

to denote an index number comparing the 1990 price with that of base year 1980. We summarize as follows.

Index Number

$$I_{b,t} = \frac{\text{value of some quantity at time } t}{\text{value of quantity at base period } b} \times 100$$

This index number compares prices at time period t to those at time period b.

Usually, the base period is the earlier time period, although this is not always the case. Thus, for our example comparing milk prices, the index

$$I_{80,90} = 141\%$$

indicates that 1990 milk prices are 141% of those of the base year 1980.

Since the above index compared prices for only one commodity, it is called a **simple index.** Index numbers are usually computed to include prices of a group of commodities. Such index numbers are called **composite index numbers.** The computation of composite index numbers is beyond the scope of this discussion. Here we will stress the use and interpretation of index numbers.

The Bureau of Labor Statistics computes a very important index called the **consumer price index,** abbreviated **CPI.** The CPI is a composite index that measures the change in cost of a fixed market basket of goods and services purchased by a specified group of consumers.

• *Using Index Numbers to Deflate*

Index numbers are often used as price deflators. For example, suppose that in 1988 a construction worker earns $800 per week. A union negotiator wishes to determine the purchasing power of this weekly wage in 1967 dollars. In other words, the union negotiator wants to deflate the 1988 weekly wage to 1967 dollars. To deflate a 1988 price to 1967 dollars, we need an index number (often, the CPI), $I_{67,88}$, that measures the change between 1967 and 1988 prices. Since, from a simplified perspective, the index $I_{67,88}$ is interpreted as a ratio of 1988 prices to 1967 prices, this relationship can be expressed in equation form as

$$I_{67,88} = \frac{1988 \text{ prices}}{1967 \text{ prices}} \times 100$$

Multiplying both sides by the right-hand denominator gives

$$1967 \text{ price} \times I_{67,88} = 1988 \text{ prices} \times 100$$

Solving for 1967 prices, we have

$$1967 \text{ price} = \frac{1988 \text{ price}}{I_{67,88}} \times 100$$

The above boxed formula indicates that a 1988 price is deflated to 1967 dollars by dividing the 1988 price by $I_{67,88}$ and then multiplying by 100. If $I_{67,88} = 250$, then

$$1967 \text{ price} = \frac{1988 \text{ price}}{I_{67,88}} \times 100$$
$$= \frac{800}{250} \times 100$$
$$= 320$$

Thus, the 1988 wage of $800 is the equivalent of $320 in 1967 dollars. Figure R-22 illustrates this relationship from a time diagram point of view.

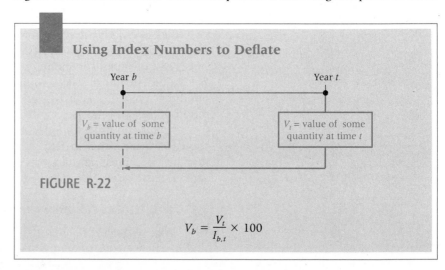

FIGURE R-22

$$V_b = \frac{V_t}{I_{b,t}} \times 100$$

To further illustrate the usefulness of deflating prices, we consider the following example. Suppose the construction worker of the previous example earned $300 per week in 1967. During the time period between 1967 and 1988, his percent increase in weekly wages is given by

$$\frac{800 - 300}{300} \times 100 = \frac{500}{300} \times 100$$
$$= 1.667 \times 100$$
$$= 166.7\%$$

This result is termed a 166.7% increase in nominal wages. However, if we deflate his 1988 wage of $800 to its equivalent in 1967 dollars, $320, then the percent increase in real wages (i.e., wages in 1967 dollars) is given by

$$\frac{320 - 300}{300} \times 100 = \frac{20}{300} \times 100$$
$$= .0667 \times 100$$
$$= 6.67\%$$

Thus, the construction worker's real wages have increased by only 6.67% during the 21-year period. The union negotiator, mentioned earlier, would certainly use this result as an argument for higher future wages.

Exercises

1. In 1970, a commodity sold for $80. Its 1988 price is $140. Compute $I_{70,88}$.
2. In 1980, a 94-pound bag of concrete cost $4.80. Its 1988 price is $6.90. Compute $I_{80,88}$.
3. B-MART's 1988 sales are $23,000,000. If $I_{70,88} = 280$, then deflate the 1988 sales to 1970 dollars.
4. A worker earns $600 per week during 1988. If $I_{79,88} = 240$, then deflate the 1988 wages to 1979 dollars.
5. A wage earner's 1975 income was $15,000, while her 1988 income is $30,000. If $I_{75,88} = 170$, then
   a) Compute the percent increase in nominal income.
   b) Compute the percent increase in real income.
6. A-TECH's 1980 sales were $15,000,000, while its 1988 sales are $40,000,000. If the industry's index is $I_{80,88} = 190$, then
   a) Compute the percent increase in nominal sales.
   b) Compute the percent increase in real sales.

Trade: Value of the Dollar

Figure R-23 gives a graph of index numbers indicating the dollar's value relative to base year 1980 against currencies of its major trading partners.

7. The dollar's value at the end of 1982 was what multiple of its 1980 value?
8. The dollar's value at the end of 1984 was what multiple of its 1980 value?
9. The dollar's value at the end of 1985 was what multiple of its 1980 value?
10. The dollar's value at the end of 1988 was what multiple of its 1980 value?

A weaker greenback

The dollar's value against the currencies of its major trading partners

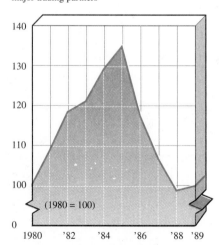

Note: Figure for 1989 reflects the average through November.
USN&WR—Basic data: Atlanta Federal Reserve Board

Copyright ©, Dec. 25, 1989—Jan. 1, 1990,
U.S. News & World Report. Reprinted by permission.

FIGURE R-23

Despite productivity gains...

U.S. manufacturing productivity compared with major industial competitors

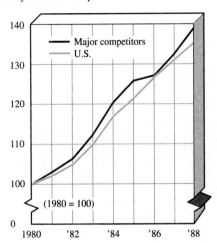

Note: Competitors include 11 industrialized countries. Productivity is worker output per hour.
USN&WR—Basic data: U.S. Dept. of Labor

Copyright ©, Dec. 25, 1989—Jan. 1, 1990, *U.S. News & World Report*. Reprinted by permission.

FIGURE R-24

TABLE R-5 **Consumer Price Index (1967 = 100)**

	1980	1982	1984
CPI	246.8	289.1	311.1

Productivity

Figure R-24 gives a graph of index numbers indicating productivity relative to base year 1980.

11. U.S. productivity for 1983 was what multiple of its 1980 value?
12. U.S. productivity for 1986 was what multiple of its 1980 value?
13. U.S. productivity for 1987 was what multiple of its 1980 value?
14. U.S. productivity for 1988 was what multiple of its 1980 value?

Consumer Price Index (CPI)

The Table R-5 gives the CPI for various years relative to base year 1967. Give the value in 1967 dollars of goods worth $1000 in

15. 1984 dollars   **16.** 1982 dollars   **17.** 1980 dollars

1

FUNCTIONS AND LINEAR MODELS

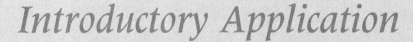

Introductory Application

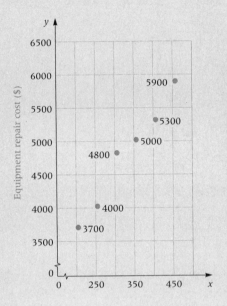

FIGURE 1-A

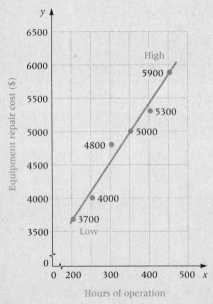

FIGURE 1-B

Cost Accounting: Cost Segregation

Businesses usually collect data giving total costs associated with various levels of a given quantity. Such data are often used to segregate the fixed and the variable portions of a total cost value. Table 1-A gives equipment repair costs for various hours of operation of a particular machine used to make precision tools. The data span a time interval of 6 months. Note that we have indicated the highest and lowest monthly repair costs.

The data are plotted to give a graph of cost versus hours of operation, as illustrated in Figure 1-A. Observe that the data points are not collinear. In other words, they do not lie in the path of a straight line.

The firm's cost accountant is faced with the following problem.

PROBLEM

Determine the fixed monthly repair cost and the variable equipment repair cost per hour of operation.

SOLUTION

Although the data points are not collinear, they seem to have a linear trend. The solution to this problem involves fitting a straight line (in other words, a linear model) to the set of data points, as illustrated in Figure 1-B. In this chapter, we will discuss linear models and how to fit such models to this type of problem.

TABLE 1-A

	Hours of operation	Equipment repair cost ($)	
January	250	4000	
February	300	4800	
March	200	3700	Low
April	400	5300	
May	350	5000	
June	450	5900	High

1-1 • FUNCTIONS

A **function** is a rule that associates a unique **output value** with each element in a set of possible **input values.** Consider, for example, the conversion of temperature from degees Fahrenheit to degrees Celsius. Given a temperature in degrees Fahrenheit (input value), we can find the corresponding value in degrees Celsius (output value) by the following rule:

$$\underbrace{\text{Celsius temperature}}_{\substack{\text{output} \\ \text{value}}} = \frac{5}{9} \underbrace{(\text{Fahrenheit temperature} - 32)}_{\substack{\text{input} \\ \text{value}}}$$

If C is temperature in degrees Celsius and F is temperature in degrees Fahrenheit, then this rule may be expressed by the equation

$$C = \frac{5}{9}(F - 32)$$

To determine the Celsius temperature (output value) associated with 50 degrees Fahrenheit, we substitute $F = 50$ (input value) into the equation and obtain

$$C = \frac{5}{9}(50 - 32)$$

$$= \frac{5}{9}(18)$$

$$= 10 \text{ degrees Celsius}$$

Thus, 10 degrees Celsius is associated with 50 degrees Fahrenheit. Since only one value of C is associated with a value of F, then this equation defines C as a function of F.

Observing the equation

$$C = \frac{5}{9}(F - 32)$$

$$\underset{\substack{\text{output} \\ \text{value}}}{\uparrow} \qquad \underset{\substack{\text{input} \\ \text{value}}}{\uparrow}$$

note that the output value, C, is dependent on the input value, F. Thus, C is called the **dependent variable,** and F is called the **independent variable.** This relationship is usually indicated by saying that C is a *function* of F.

Functional Notation

Often a letter is used to represent a function. Specifically, if the letter f is used to name the function defined by the equation

$$y = 5x^2 + 2x + 7$$

then the dependent variable, y, is represented by the symbol $f(x)$, read "f of x." Thus, the preceding equation is written

$$f(x) = 5x^2 + 2x + 7$$

To find the output value associated with $x = 3$, we replace x with 3 to obtain

$$f(3) = 5(3)^2 + 2(3) + 7$$
$$= 45 + 6 + 7$$
$$= 58$$

Rectangular Coordinate System

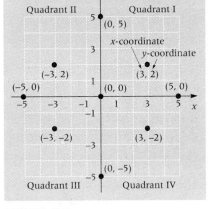

FIGURE 1-1

It is often useful to graph functions on a plane called the **rectangular coordinate system.** Such a system consists of two perpendicular real number lines in the plane, as shown in Figure 1-1. The horizontal number line is called the **x-axis,** and the vertical number line is called the **y-axis.** The point where the lines intersect is the zero point of both lines and is called the **origin.**

The plane consists of infinitely many **points.** Each point is assigned an **ordered pair** of numbers which locates its position relative to both axes. For example, looking at Figure 1-1, the ordered pair (3, 2) is associated with the point that may be plotted by starting at the origin and moving 3 units to the right horizontally and then 2 units upward vertically. The numbers 3 and 2 of the ordered pair (3, 2) are called the **x-coordinate** and **y-coordinate,** respectively.

Similarly, the ordered pair (−3, 2) in Figure 1-1 is associated with the point that may be plotted by starting at the origin and moving 3 units to the left horizontally and then 2 units upward vertically. The ordered pair (−3, −2) is associated with the point that may be plotted by starting at the origin and moving 3 units to the left horizontally and then 2 units downward and vertically. The ordered pair (3, −2) is associated with the point that may be plotted by starting at the origin and moving 3 units to the right horizontally and then 2 units downward vertically. The ordered pair (0, 0) is associated with the origin.

Further studying Figure 1-1, we note the following:

1. The x- and y-axes partition the plane into four quadrants, as numbered in the figure.
2. For any point in Quadrant I, the x- and y-coordinates are both positive, i.e., (+, +).
3. For any point in Quadrant II, the x-coordinate is negative and the y-coordinate is positive, i.e., (−, +).
4. For any point in Quadrant III, the x- and y-coordinates are both negative, i.e., (−, −).
5. For any point in Quadrant IV, the x-coordinate is positive and the y-coordinate is negative, i.e., (+, −).
6. Points on the axes belong to no quadrant. Points on the x-axis have y-coordinates of 0, and points on the y-axis have x-coordinates of 0.

Functions As Sets of Ordered Pairs

A function can be expressed as a set of ordered pairs (x, y) such that each value of y is the number associated with its corresponding value of x in ac-

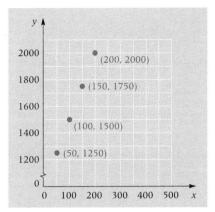

FIGURE 1-2

cordance with the rule defined by the equation. For example, consider the situation of a young entrepreneur manufacturing sneakers. She initially invests $1000 to pay for overhead items such as heat, electricity, etc. Additionally, each pair of sneakers costs $5 to manufacture. Thus, the total cost of producing x pairs of sneakers is given by the equation.

$$y = C(x) = 5x + 1000$$

During the first week of operation, the entrepreneur plans to manufacture either 50, 100, 150, or 200 pairs of sneakers. Table 1-1 shows the output value associated with each input value. The set of input values is called the **domain** of the function, and the set of output values is called the **range** of the function. Observing Table 1-1, note that the domain consists of the set of x-values (in the left column) and that the range consists of the set of y- or $C(x)$-values (in the right column). The function C consists of the set of ordered pairs (x, y) graphed in Figure 1-2.

TABLE 1-1

x	y	$y = C(x) = 5x + 1000$
50	1250	$C(50) = 5(50) + 1000 = 1250$
100	1500	$C(100) = 5(100) + 1000 = 1500$
150	1750	$C(150) = 5(150) + 1000 = 1750$
200	2000	$C(200) = 5(200) + 1000 = 2000$

We are now ready for a more formal definition of a function.

> **Function**
>
> A **function** is a set of ordered pairs (x, y) such that no two ordered pairs have the same first element, x, and different second elements, y. The set of first elements, x, is the **domain** of the function, and the set of second elements, y, is the **range** of the function.

Consider the equation

$$y^2 = x$$

The ordered pairs defined by this equation include $(4, 2)$, $(4, -2)$, $(9, 3)$, and $(9, -3)$. Note that the two numbers $+2$ and -2 are associated with $x = 4$. Since this equation associates more than one y-value for at least one x-value, it is not a function.

To graph the equation $y^2 = x$, we plot the points corresponding to its ordered pairs, some of which are $(4, 2)$, $(4, -2)$, $(9, 3)$, and $(9, -3)$. Figure 1-3 illustrates the graph of this equation. Referring to this illustration, note that since two y-values, $+2$ and -2, are associated with $x = 4$, a vertical line intersects the graph at two points. Generalizing, we have the following **vertical line test** for a function.

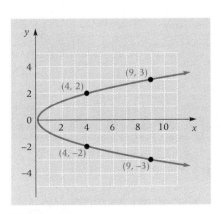

FIGURE 1-3

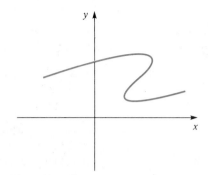

FIGURE 1-4

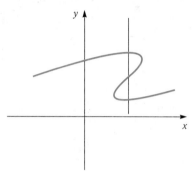

FIGURE 1-5

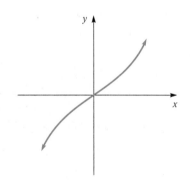

FIGURE 1-6

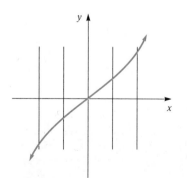

FIGURE 1-7

> ### Vertical Line Test
>
> If a vertical line intersects a graph at more than one point, then that graph does not represent a function.

• **EXAMPLE 1-1**

Use the vertical line test to determine if the graph of Figure 1-4 represents a function.

Solution

Since a vertical line can be drawn that intersects the graph at more than one point (see Figure 1-5), the graph does not represent a function.

• **EXAMPLE 1-2**

Use the vertical line test to determine if the graph of Figure 1-6 represents a function.

Solution

Since it is not possible to draw a vertical line that intersects the graph at more than one point (see Figure 1-7), the graph does represent a function.

Often the domain of a function is not specified. If this is the case, it is assumed that the domain is the set of all real numbers for which the function is defined. Consider the function defined by the equation

$$g(x) = \frac{1}{x - 2}$$

Since the domain of g is not specified, it is the set of all real numbers x for which $g(x)$ is defined. Note that $g(x)$ is defined for all real numbers x except $x = 2$, since

$$g(2) = \frac{1}{2 - 2} = \frac{1}{0} \quad \text{which is undefined.}$$

Thus, the domain of g is all real numbers x such that $x \neq 2$.

• **EXAMPLE 1-3**

Specify the domain of h where

$$h(x) = \frac{1}{(x - 3)(x + 5)}$$

Solution

Since the domain of h is not specified, it is the set of all real numbers x for which $h(x)$ is defined. Note that $h(x)$ is defined for all real numbers x except $x = 3$ and $x = -5$, since

$$h(3) = \frac{1}{(3 - 3)(3 + 5)} = \frac{1}{0} \quad \text{which is undefined,}$$

$$h(-5) = \frac{1}{(-5 - 3)(-5 + 5)} = \frac{1}{0} \quad \text{which is undefined.}$$

Thus, the domain of h is all real numbers x such that $x \neq 3$ and $x \neq -5$.

• **EXAMPLE 1-4** _____

If $f(x) = \sqrt{x - 7}$, specify the domain of f.

Solution

Since $\sqrt{x - 7}$ is defined as long as $x - 7 \geq 0$ or, equivalently, $x \geq 7$, then the domain of f is all real numbers x such that $x \geq 7$.

_____ •

We now give an example showing further calculations with functional notation.

• **EXAMPLE 1-5** _____

Given that $f(x) = 3x^2 - 2x + 5$, calculate each of the following:

a) $f(4)$ **b)** $f(x + h)$

c) $f(x + h) - f(x)$ **d)** $\dfrac{f(x + h) - f(x)}{h}$

Solutions

a) Since $f(x) = 3x^2 - 2x + 5$, then $f(4)$ is calculated by replacing x with 4. This gives us

$$f(4) = 3(4)^2 - 2(4) + 5$$
$$= 45$$

b) Since $f(x) = 3x^2 - 2x + 5$, then $f(x + h)$ is calculated by replacing x with $x + h$. Therefore, we have

$$f(x + h) = 3(x + h)^2 - 2(x + h) + 5$$
$$= 3(x^2 + 2hx + h^2) - 2x - 2h + 5$$
$$= 3x^2 + 6hx + 3h^2 - 2x - 2h + 5$$

c) Subtracting $f(x) = 3x^2 - 2x + 5$ from the result of part b yields

$$f(x + h) - f(x) = 3x^2 + 6hx + 3h^2 - 2x - 2h + 5 - (3x^2 - 2x + 5)$$
$$= 6hx + 3h^2 - 2h$$

d) Dividing the result of part c by h, we obtain

$$\frac{f(x + h) - f(x)}{h} = \frac{6hx + 3h^2 - 2h}{h}$$
$$= 6x + 3h - 2$$

This result is called a **difference quotient** and will be discussed further in Chapter 9.

_____ •

We now illustrate more functions and their graphs.

• **EXAMPLE 1-6**   **Parcel Cost.** _____

A private parcel service charges the following rates for delivering small packages:

- $1.00 for a package weighing less than 4 ounces
- $1.50 for a package weighing at least 4 ounces but less than 20 ounces
- $2.00 for a package weighing at least 20 ounces but less than 32 ounces

The service does not deliver packages weighing 32 ounces or more. Express delivery cost as a function of weight and graph the function.

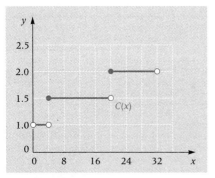

FIGURE 1-8

Solution

If x is the weight of a package, its delivery cost, $C(x)$, is given by

$$C(x) = \begin{cases} 1.00 & \text{if } 0 < x < 4 \\ 1.50 & \text{if } 4 \le x < 20 \\ 2.00 & \text{if } 20 \le x < 32 \end{cases}$$

Note that the domain of $C(x)$ is the interval $0 < x < 32$. The graph of $C(x)$ appears in Figure 1-8.

• **EXAMPLE 1-7   Call Options.** _____

A stock investor, believing that the price of a share of stock of Amtech, Inc., will rise to approximately $80 per share during the next 6 months, buys a contract entitling her to buy a specified number of shares of Amtech for $50 per share during the next 6-month time interval. The investor paid $10 per share for this contract. Determine the investor's profit function per share of stock.

Solution

This type of contract, which entitles an investor to buy a specified number of shares of a given stock at a given price (called the **striking price**) during a given time interval, is termed a **call option.** The investor's profit is dependent on the stock's market price per share. Thus, we let $P(x)$ denote the investor's profit per share at the stock's market price of x dollars per share. If the stock's market price per share is less than or equal to the striking price ($50), then the option is worthless to the investor, and, thus, the investor suffers a loss (i.e., a negative profit) of $10 per ʰare, the price paid for the option. This is written as

$$P(x) = -10 \quad \text{if} \quad 0 \le x \le 50$$

If the stock's market price per share exceeds the striking price of $50 during the given 6-month time interval, then the investor could exercise the option and buy the stock for $50 per share and obtain a profit per share of

$$x - 50 - 10$$

stock's market price ⤴   ⤴   ⌐ price of the call option

striking price ⌐

This assumes that the investor sells the stock for x dollars per share and is written as

$$P(x) = x - 50 - 10 \quad \text{if } x > 50$$

Thus, the profit function is defined as

$$P(x) = \begin{cases} -10 & \text{if } 0 \le x \le 50 \\ x - 60 & \text{if } x > 50 \end{cases}$$

and its graph appears in Figure 1-9.

If a stock's market price rises rapidly during a given time interval, a call option allows an investor to enjoy a substantial percentage gain with a small investment. For example, if Amtech's market price per share were to reach $80 within the given 6-month time interval, the investor would earn a profit of $80 - 50 - 10 = $20 per share on an investment of $10 per share, the price paid for the call option. This constitutes a 200% (i.e., $\frac{20}{10} \times 100$) rate of return during the 6-month time interval. One can understand why investors buy call options.

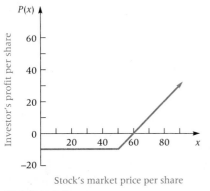

FIGURE 1-9

Note that each function in Examples 1-6 and 1-7 is defined by more than one formula. Functions that are defined by more than one formula are said to be **piecewise defined.** We now discuss another piecewise-defined function.

Absolute Value Function

In Section R-1, we defined the absolute value of a number x. We now define the **absolute value function,** $a(x)$, as

$$a(x) = |x| = \begin{cases} x & \text{if } x \text{ is positive or zero} \\ -x & \text{if } x \text{ is negative} \end{cases}$$

Note that this function associates a non-negative number with itself. Associated with each negative number is its additive inverse. Thus, $(-3, 3)$, $(-1, 1)$, $(-1/2, 1/2)$, $(0, 0)$, $(1, 1)$, $(2, 2)$, and $(5/2, 5/2)$ are some of the ordered pairs belonging to the absolute value function. The graph of $a(x)$ appears in Figure 1-10.

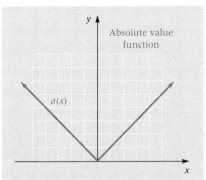

FIGURE 1-10

Exercises 1-1

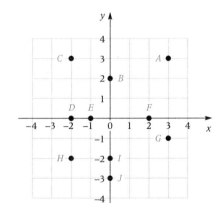

FIGURE 1-11

TABLE 1-2

x	$f(x)$
0	
1	
2	
3	

1. A function is defined by the equation

   $$y = 3x - 2$$

   a) Which number does this equation associate with $x = 0$?
   b) Which number does this equation associate with $x = 4$?

2. A function is defined by the equation

   $$y = 3x^2 - 4x + 5$$

   a) Which number does this equation associate with $x = 0$?
   b) Which number does this equation associate with $x = 2$?

3. If $f(x) = -2x + 7$, calculate each of the following:
   a) $f(0)$ b) $f(1)$
   c) $f(5)$ d) $f(-3)$

4. If $w(r) = r^3 - 7r^2 + 8r - 5$, calculate each of the following:
   a) $w(0)$ b) $w(2)$
   c) $w(-2)$ d) $w(4)$

5. If $z(t) = \dfrac{5}{t + 7}$, calculate each of the following:
   a) $z(0)$ b) $z(1)$
   c) $z(-6)$ d) $z(8)$

6. For each of the points A through J of Figure 1-11, find the associated ordered pair.

7. Plot each of the following points on the rectangular coordinate system: $(0, 0)$, $(2, 0)$, $(-5, 0)$, $(0, 2)$, $(0, 5)$, $(3, 1)$, $(5, 2)$, $(-7, 3)$, $(-8, -2)$, $(9, -3)$.

8. Plot the following points on the rectangular coordinate system, and state the quadrant in which each is located: $(4, 2)$, $(5, 8)$, $(-9, 3)$, $(-2, 1)$, $(-3, -5)$, $(-2, -7)$, $(8, -3)$, $(9, 2)$.

9. Graph the function defined by

   $$f(x) = 3x + 2$$

   with domain equal to the set of x-values in Table 1-2.

TABLE 1-3

x	S(x)
1/4	
1/2	
1	
2	

10. Graph the function defined by

$$S(x) = \frac{1}{x}$$

with domain equal to the set of x-values in Table 1-3.

11. If $f(x) = \dfrac{5}{(x - 2)(x + 7)}$, specify the domain of f.

12. If $g(x) = \dfrac{8}{(x - 5)}$, specify the domain of g.

13. If $f(x) = \sqrt{x - 2}$, specify the domain of f.

14. If $g(x) = \sqrt{2x + 5}$, specify the domain of g.

15. If $h(x) = \dfrac{8}{(x - 3)^2}$, specify the domain of h.

16. If $f(x) = \dfrac{6}{x^2 + x}$, specify the domain of f.

17. Which of the graphs in Figure 1-12 are graphs of functions?
18. Which of the graphs in Figure 1-13 are graphs of functions?
19. Does the equation $y^2 = x + 5$ define a function? Why or why not?
20. Does the equation $y^2 = 4x + 1$ define a function? Why or why not?
21. Given that $f(x) = x^2 - 4x + 5$, calculate each of the following:
    a) $f(x + h)$
    b) $f(x + h) - f(x)$
    c) $\dfrac{f(x + h) - f(x)}{h}$

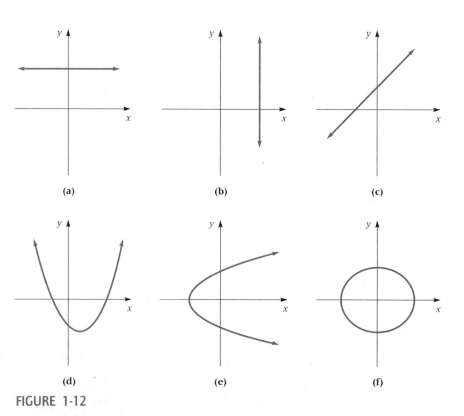

(a)　　　　(b)　　　　(c)

(d)　　　　(e)　　　　(f)

FIGURE 1-12

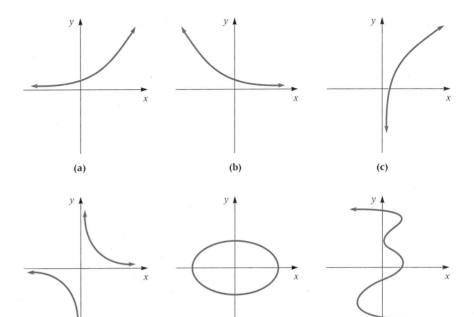

FIGURE 1-13

22. Given that $f(x) = -3x^2 + 5x - 2$, calculate each of the following:
   a) $f(x + h)$
   b) $f(x + h) - f(x)$
   c) $\dfrac{f(x + h) - f(x)}{h}$

23. Given that $f(x) = 5x^2 - 2x + 4$, calculate the difference quotient
   $$\frac{f(x + h) - f(x)}{h}$$

24. Given that $f(x) = -2x^2 + 3x - 9$, calculate the difference quotient
   $$\frac{f(x + h) - f(x)}{h}.$$

25. Given that $g(x) = x^3 - 4x^2 + 5x - 9$, calculate the difference quotient
   $$\frac{g(x + h) - g(x)}{h}$$

26. Given that $g(x) = 2x^3 - 3x + 5$, calculate the difference quotient
   $$\frac{g(x + h) - g(x)}{h}$$

27. Graph the function defined by
   $$h(x) = \begin{cases} 2 & \text{if } x < 1 \\ 4 & \text{if } 1 \le x < 6 \\ x & \text{if } x \ge 6 \end{cases}$$

28. Graph the function defined by

$$k(x) = \begin{cases} 3 & \text{if } x \le 4 \\ x & \text{if } 4 < x \le 9 \\ 9 & \text{if } x > 9 \end{cases}$$

29. A parcel service charges the following rates for delivering small packages:
   - $1.25 for a package weighing less than 8 ounces
   - $2.00 for a package weighing at least 8 ounces and at most 16 ounces
   - $5.00 for a package weighing more than 16 ounces and at most 40 ounces

   The service delivers no packages weighing more than 40 ounces.

   a) Express delivery cost as a function of weight.
   b) Graph the function of part a.

30. *Call options.* An investor bought a call option entitling him to buy a specified number of shares of Biotech, Inc., for $30 per share during the next 3-month time interval. The investor paid $5 per share for the call option. Determine the investor's profit function per share of stock. Also, graph the profit function.

31. *Put options.* An investor, believing that the price of a share of stock of Amex, Inc., will drop to approximately $10 per share during the next 6 months, buys a contract entitling him to sell a specified number of shares of Amex for $35 per share during the next 6-month time interval. The investor is actually selling shares of stock that he does not own. However, the investor will replace these sold shares by buying the same number of shares at a lower market price. The investor paid $7 per share for this contract. This type of contract, which entitles an investor to sell a specified number of shares of a given stock at a given price (called the **striking price**) during a given time interval, is called a *put option*. Determine the investor's profit function per share of stock for this put option. Also, graph the profit function. Remember that the investor's profit is dependent on the stock's market price per share.

32. *Wind power.* In designing a windmill, an engineer must use the fact that power y available in wind varies with the cube of wind speed. Thus, if x represents wind speed (in miles per hour), we have

$$y = kx^3$$

where k is a constant real number.

   a) If a 25-mile-an-hour wind produces 5000 watts, find k.
   b) How many watts of power will a 35-mile-per-hour wind produce?

1-2 • SLOPE AND EQUATIONS OF STRAIGHT LINES

Consider the straight line drawn through the two points (2, 8) and (4, 11) in Figure 1-14. Suppose we place the point of a pencil at (2, 8) and move along the line toward (4, 11). As the pencil moves along the line, its x- and y-coordinates change. When the pencil reaches (4, 11), its total vertical change (i.e., change in y) is $11 - 8 = 3$ units, and its total horizontal change (i.e., change in x) is $4 - 2 = 2$ (see Figure 1-15). The ratio 3/2 rep-

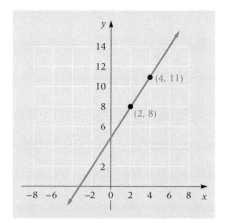

FIGURE 1-14

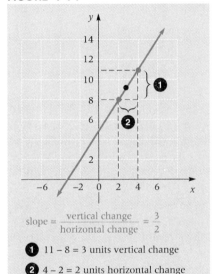

$$\text{slope} = \frac{\text{vertical change}}{\text{horizontal change}} = \frac{3}{2}$$

❶ $11 - 8 = 3$ units vertical change

❷ $4 - 2 = 2$ units horizontal change

FIGURE 1-15

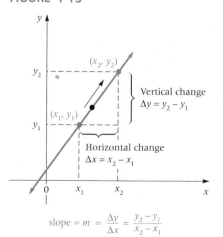

$$\text{slope} = m = \frac{\Delta y}{\Delta x} = \frac{y_2 - y_1}{x_2 - x_1}$$

FIGURE 1-16

resents the rate of change of vertical position (*y*) with respect to horizontal position (*x*) and is called the **slope** of the straight line. The slope 3/2 implies that as the pencil moves along the straight line, for every 2 units of horizontal change to the right the pencil experiences 3 units of vertical change upward.

In general, if (x_1, y_1) and (x_2, y_2) represent two points through which a straight line passes (see Figure 1-16) and we move along the straight line from (x_1, y_1) to (x_2, y_2) then the vertical change is denoted by Δy (read "delta *y*"), and our horizontal change is denoted by Δx (read "delta *x*"). Furthermore, $\Delta y = y_2 - y_1$ and $\Delta x = x_2 - x_1$ and the slope *m* of the straight line is determined by the following formula.

$$\text{Slope} = m = \frac{\Delta y}{\Delta x} = \frac{y_2 - y_1}{x_2 - x_1}$$

A property of a straight line is that its slope is the same no matter where it is measured. In other words, we can find the slope of a line by calculating the ratio $\Delta y / \Delta x$ from any two points on the line.

• **EXAMPLE 1-8** _____

A particle moves along the straight line from (3, 11) to (5, 7).

a) Find its vertical change, Δy.
b) Find its horizontal change, Δx.
c) Find the slope of the straight line.
d) Interpret the result of part c.

Solutions

a) We let $(x_1, y_1) = (3, 11)$, the point at which the particle starts, and $(x_2, y_2) = (5, 7)$. Then the vertical change is $\Delta y = y_2 - y_1 = 7 - 11 = -4$ (see Figure 1-17).

b) The horizontal change is $\Delta x = x_2 - x_1 = 5 - 3 = 2$ (see Figure 1-17).

c) The slope is given by

$$m = \frac{\Delta y}{\Delta x} = \frac{-4}{2} = -2$$

d) Referring to Figure 1-17, as the particle moves along the straight line from (3, 11) to (5, 7), the fact that the slope $\Delta y / \Delta x = -4/2 = -2/1$ means that for each unit of horizontal change to the right, the particle experiences 2 units of vertical change downward. If the particle were moving along the straight line from (5, 7) to (3, 11), as shown in Figure 1-18, then $\Delta y = 11 - 7 = 4$ and $\Delta x = 3 - 5 = -2$ so that $\Delta y / \Delta x = 4/(-2) = 2/(-1)$. Here, as the particle moves from (5, 7) to (3, 11), for each unit of horizontal change to the left, it experiences 2 units of vertical change upward.

•

Compare the straight line of Figure 1-15 with those of Figures 1-17 and 1-18. Note that a straight line with *positive slope* slants *upward to the right* whereas a straight line with *negative slope* slants *downward to the right*. This is illustrated in the following box.

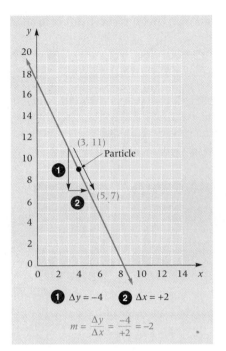

$$1 \;\; \Delta y = -4 \quad 2 \;\; \Delta x = +2$$

$$m = \frac{\Delta y}{\Delta x} = \frac{-4}{+2} = -2$$

FIGURE 1-17

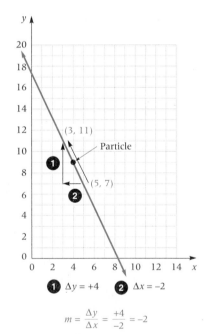

$$1 \;\; \Delta y = +4 \quad 2 \;\; \Delta x = -2$$

$$m = \frac{\Delta y}{\Delta x} = \frac{+4}{-2} = -2$$

FIGURE 1-18

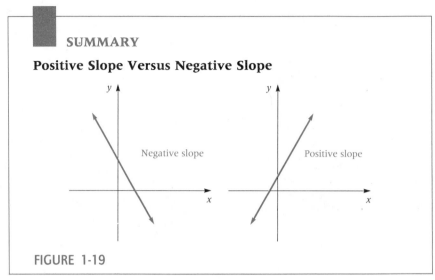

SUMMARY

Positive Slope Versus Negative Slope

FIGURE 1-19

Constant Rate of Change

Figure 1-20 again illustrates the straight line in Figure 1-14. Referring to Figure 1-20, suppose we move up along the line away from (4, 11) so that we experience 2 units of horizontal change to the right. Since the slope of the straight line is 3/2, then for each 2 units of horizontal change to the right, we experience 3 units of vertical change upward. Hence, we will be located at point (4 + 2, 11 + 3) = (6, 14).

Again referring to Figure 1-20, suppose we begin at point (2, 8) and move down along the straight line until we experience 2 units of horizontal change to the left. Since the slope of the straight line is 3/2 or $-3/(-2)$, then for each 2 units of horizontal change to the left, we experience 3 units of vertical change downward. Hence, we will now be located at point (2 − 2, 8 − 3) = (0, 5). Note that movement along this straight line results in the constant rate of change 3/2 of vertical position with respect to horizontal position.

Again refer to Figure 1-20. Note that the straight line crosses the y-axis at (0, 5). This point is called the **y-intercept** of the straight line. The point where the straight line crosses the x-axis is called the **x-intercept** of the straight line. We will learn a more formal method for determining the x- and y-intercepts of a straight line in Section 1-3.

Slope and Equations of Straight Lines

Study the straight line of Figure 1-20. Recall that this straight line was illustrated at the beginning of this section with the two points (2, 8) and (4, 11). After determining the slope to be 3/2, the rate of change concept was used to find other points on the line, specifically (6, 14) and (0, 5). The concept of slope can be used to determine other points on the line.

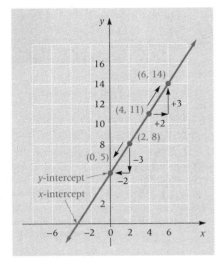

FIGURE 1-20

However, there is a better way. We must realize that the x- and y-coordinates of any point (x, y) on a straight line are related by an equation. Such an equation is called an **equation of the straight line.** An equation of a straight line exhibits the relationship between the x- and y-coordinates of any point (x, y) on the line.

 SUMMARY

Slope and Rate of Change

In general, movement along a straight line of slope m results in m vertical units gained for each horizontal unit gained. Thus, the slope, m, is the rate of change of vertical position (y) with respect to horizontal position (x), as is illustrated below.

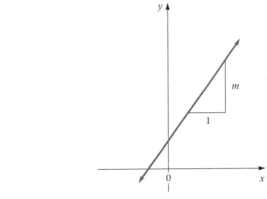

FIGURE 1-21

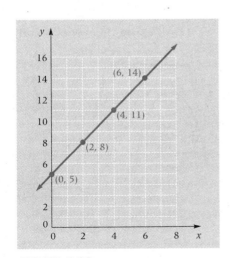

FIGURE 1-22

We will now determine the equation of the straight line of Figure 1-22. Choose one of the known points on the line, say, $(2, 8)$. Let (x, y) represent any point on the line. Since the slope of the straight line is 3/2, the slope between (x, y) and $(2, 8)$ must equal 3/2. Hence,

$$\frac{y - 8}{x - 2} = \frac{3}{2}$$

Multiplying both sides by $x - 2$, we obtain

$$y - 8 = \frac{3}{2}(x - 2)$$

This equation is called the **point-slope form** of the equation of the straight line. Observe that the coordinates of the point, $(2, 8)$, and the slope, 3/2, appear conspicuously in the equation—hence, the term *point-slope form.*

Solving the point-slope form for y, we obtain

$$y = \frac{3}{2}(x - 2) + 8$$

or

$$y = \frac{3}{2}x + 5$$

This equation is called the **slope-intercept form** of the equation of the straight line. Note that the slope, 3/2, and the y-intercept, 5, appear conspicuously in the equation—hence, the term *slope-interept form*.

Thus, the equation

$$y = \frac{3}{2}x + 5$$

exhibits the relationship between the x and y coordinates of any point (x, y) on the straight line. Observe that the points of the straight line satisfy its equation.

$$(0, 5) \qquad 5 = \frac{3}{2}(0) + 5$$

$$(2, 8) \qquad 8 = \frac{3}{2}(2) + 5$$

$$(4, 11) \qquad 11 = \frac{3}{2}(4) + 5$$

$$(6, 14) \qquad 14 = \frac{3}{2}(6) + 5$$

As previously mentioned, an equation of a straight line may be used to find other points on the line. Specifically, if $x = -4$, then

$$y = \frac{3}{2}(-4) + 5 = -1$$

Thus, $(-4, -1)$ is a point on this straight line. And if $x = 8$, then

$$y = \frac{3}{2}(8) + 5 = 17$$

Therefore, $(8, 17)$ is also a point on the line.

We now state the following generalizations

Equation

An equation of a straight line reveals the relationship between the x- and y-coordinates of any point (x, y) on the line.

Point-Slope Form

Given a point (x_1, y_1) on a straight line of slope m (see Figure 1-23), the **point-slope form** of the equation of that straight line is

$$y - y_1 = m(x - x_1)$$

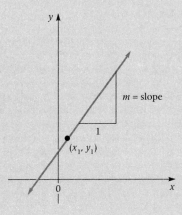

FIGURE 1-23

Slope-Intercept Form

If the point-slope form is solved for y (see Figure 1-24), the resulting equation is the **slope-intercept form**

$$y = mx + b$$

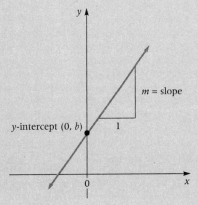

FIGURE 1-24

• EXAMPLE 1-9 _____

A straight line passes through $(4, 7)$ and $(9, 17)$.

a) Find its equation in point-slope form.
b) Convert the point-slope form into the slope-intercept form.
c) Find the point on this straight line corresponding to $x = 5$.
d) Sketch this straight line.

Solutions

a) If $(x_1, y_1) = (4, 7)$ and $(x_2, y_2) = (9, 17)$,* then

$$m = \frac{y_2 - y_1}{x_2 - x_1} = \frac{17 - 7}{9 - 4} = \frac{10}{5} = 2$$

Substituting $(x_1, y_1) = (4, 7)$ and $m = 2$ into the point-slope form

$$y - y_1 = m(x - x_1)$$

we obtain

$$y - 7 = 2(x - 4)$$

b) Solving for y gives us

$$y = 2(x - 4) + 7$$

or

$$y = 2x - 1$$

$$\underset{\text{slope \quad y-intercept}}{\uparrow \quad \uparrow}$$

c) If $x = 5$, then $y = 2(5) - 1 = 9$. Thus, $(5, 9)$ is a point on this line.
d) Observing the slope-intercept form, note that $(0, -1)$ is the y-intercept of this straight line. Using a straightedge, we connect the y-intercept with another point on the straight line, say, $(5, 9)$. The resulting graph is illustrated in Figure 1-25. Note that the points $(4, 7)$ and $(9, 17)$ also appear on the line.

• EXAMPLE 1-10 _____

A straight line has a slope of 6 and a y-intercept of -3. Find the equation of this line.

Solution

Substituting $m = 6$ and $b = -3$ into the slope-intercept form

$$y = mx + b$$

yields

$$y = 6x - 3$$

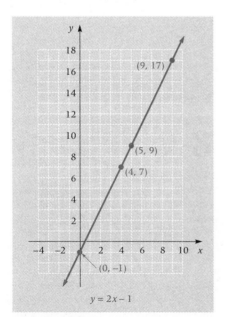

FIGURE 1-25

*Either point may be chosen as (x_1, y_1) or (x_2, y_2).

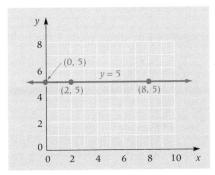

FIGURE 1-26

Horizontal Lines

Consider the straight line passing through the points $(2, 5)$ and $(8, 5)$. Since the y-coordinates are equal, the line passing through these points is horizontal (see Figure 1-26), and its slope is 0, as is determined below.

$$m = \frac{\Delta y}{\Delta x} = \frac{5 - 5}{8 - 2} = \frac{0}{6} = 0$$

Observing Figure 1-26, note that the y-intercept is 5. Substituting $m = 0$ and $b = 5$ into the slope-intercept form

$$y = mx + b$$

we obtain

$$y = 0x + 5$$

or

$$y = 5$$

The equation $y = 5$ expresses the fact that the y-coordinate of any point on this horizontal straight line is 5.

Horizontal Line

In general, the equation

$$y = b$$

represents a horizontal straight line with a y-intercept of b. Every horizontal line has a slope of 0.

Vertical Lines

Consider the straight line passing through the points $(3, 2)$ and $(3, 7)$. Since the x-coordinates are equal, the straight line is vertical (see Figure 1-27). Its x-intercept is 3. Because any point on this vertical line has an x-coordinate of 3, the equation of the line is appropriately $x = 3$.

The slope of this vertical line is

$$m = \frac{\Delta y}{\Delta x} = \frac{7 - 2}{3 - 3} = \frac{5}{0} \qquad \text{which is undefined.}$$

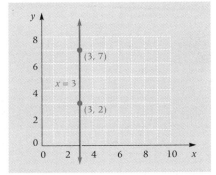

FIGURE 1-27

Vertical Line

In general, the equation

$$x = k$$

represents a vertical straight line with an x-intercept of k. Every vertical line has an undefined slope.

Linear Equations

Up to this point, we have encountered equations of straight lines in either the *point-slope form*

$$y - y_1 = m(x - x_1)$$

or the *slope-intercept form*

$$y = mx + b$$

These equations, which represent straight lines, are called **linear equations.** Linear equations occur in forms other than the preceding. For example,

$$3x + 5y = 16$$

is a linear equation. This is verified by converting it into slope-intercept form. Solving for y yields

$$5y = -3x + 16$$
$$y = -\frac{3}{5}x + \frac{16}{5}$$

General Form

In general, equations of the form

$$ax + by = c$$

where a, b, and c are constant real numbers, with a and b not both 0, are linear equations. This form is called the **general form** of a linear equation.

• **EXAMPLE 1-11** _____

Convert $4x - 7y = 18$ into slope-intercept form.

Solution

Solving for y yields

$$-7y = -4x + 18$$
$$y = \frac{-4}{-7}x + \frac{18}{-7}$$

or

$$y = \frac{4}{7}x - \frac{18}{7}$$

slope   *y*-intercept

_____ •

Parallel Lines

Slope, the ratio of vertical change to horizontal change resulting from movement along a straight line, is an indication of the steepness of a straight line. Straight lines that are equally steep are said to be parallel, and therefore, have the same slope.

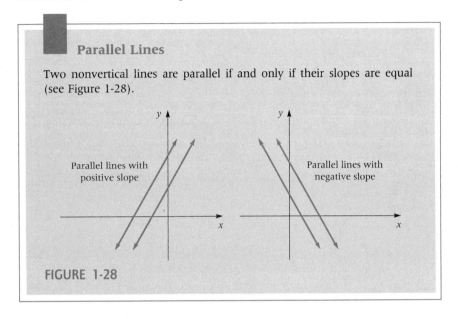

Parallel Lines

Two nonvertical lines are parallel if and only if their slopes are equal (see Figure 1-28).

Parallel lines with positive slope

Parallel lines with negative slope

FIGURE 1-28

• **EXAMPLE 1-12** _____

A straight line is parallel to the line $2x + 3y = 12$ and passes through the point $(3, 9)$.

a)   Find its equation   **b)**   Graph both lines

Solutions

a)   We first find the slope of the line $2x + 3y = 12$ by converting it into slope intercept form $y = mx + b$. Hence,

$$2x + 3y = 12 \quad \text{Given line}$$
$$3y = -2x + 12$$
$$y = -\frac{2}{3}x + 4 \quad \text{Slope-intercept form}$$
$$\underbrace{\phantom{-\frac{2}{3}}}_{\text{slope}}$$

From the slope-intercept form, the slope of the given line is $-2/3$, and, of course, the slope of the parallel line is also $-2/3$. Using the point-slope form, we find the equation of the parallel line.

$$y - y_1 = m(x - x_1) \quad \text{Point-slope form}$$

Letting $(x_1, y_1) = (3, 9)$ and $m = -2/3$ gives

$$y - 9 = -\frac{2}{3}(x - 3)$$
$$y - 9 = -\frac{2}{3}x + 2$$
$$y = -\frac{2}{3}x + 11 \quad \text{Equation of parallel line}$$

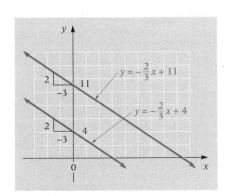

FIGURE 1-29

b)   Each line is graphed by placing our straightedge at its y-intercept and setting its pitch so that there are 2 units of vertical change for every -3 units of horizontal change. This is illustrated in Figure 1-29.

Application

Tax Function

The tax rate schedule Table 1-4 gives the amount of 1989 federal income tax due for people filing singly with an income of at most $93,130.

PROBLEM

Write the equations for the amount of federal income tax due at the various income levels, and graph the result.

SOLUTION

Let x denote the amount of taxable income and $T(x)$ the respective federal income tax.

From the *first line* of the schedule, if $0 < x \leq 18,550$, $T(x) = 0.15x$.

From the *second line* of the schedule, if $18,550 < x \leq 44,900$, $T(x) = 2782.50 + 0.28(x - 18,550)$.

From the *third line of the schedule*, if $44,900 < x \leq 93,130$, $T(x) = 10,160.50 + 0.33(x - 44,900)$.

This is written as

$$T(x) = \begin{cases} 0.15x & \text{if} \quad 0 < x \leq 18,550 \\ 2782.50 + 0.28(x - 18,550) & \text{if } 18,550 < x \leq 44,900 \\ 10,160.50 + 0.33(x - 44,900) & \text{if } 44,900 < x \leq 93,130 \end{cases}$$

The graph of $T(x)$ is given in Figure 1-30. Notice that the different slopes indicate the tax rates.

Specifically, for a person filing singly with taxable income of $60,000, the first $18,550 of taxable income is taxed at a rate of 15%; taxable income over $18,550, but not over $44,900, is taxed at a rate of 28%; taxable income over $44,900, but not over $93,130, is taxed at a rate of 33%. Thus, the federal income tax due on taxable income of $60,000 is given by

$$T(60,000) = 10,160.50 + 0.33(60,000 - 44,900)$$

$$= \$15,143.50 \quad \text{Federal income tax due on taxable income of \$60,000}$$

TABLE 1-4   Tax rate schedule

Taxable income		Federal income tax	
over	but not over		of the amount over
$ 0	$18,550	15%	$ 0
$18,550	44,900	$2782.50 + 28%	18,550
$44,900	93,130	$10,160.50 + 33%	44,900

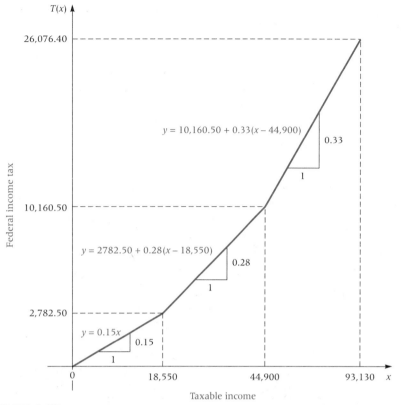

FIGURE 1-30

We close this section by providing a summary of the most common forms of linear equations.

SUMMARY

Linear Equations

1. Point-Slope Form

   $$y - y_1 = m(x - x_1)$$ Slope m, line passes through (x_1, y_1)

2. Slope-Intercept Form

   $$y = mx + b$$ Slope m, y-intercept $= b$

3. General Form

   $$ax + by = c$$ a, b, and c are constant real numbers, with a and b not both 0

4. Horizontal Line

   $$y = b$$ y-intercept $= b$, slope $= 0$, no x-intercept

5. Vertical Line

   $$x = k$$ x-intercept $= k$, no y-intercept, slope undefined

---

Note that a linear equation does not contain a variable with a nonzero exponent other than 1.

Exercises 1-2

1. A particle traveled along the straight line from (2, 5) to (6, 8).
   a) Find Δy, the change in y.   b) Find Δx, the change in x.
   c) Find the slope.   d) Interpret the slope.
2. A particle traveled along the straight line from (4, 12) to (7, 16).
   a) Find Δy, the change in y.   b) Find Δx, the change in x.
   c) Find the slope.   d) Interpret the slope.

Find the slope of the straight line passing through each of the following pairs of points.

3. (4, 5), (7, 16)   4. (1, 4), (6, 13)
5. (−1, 3), (7, 5)   6. (0, 6), (9, 4)
7. (−4, 3), (−5, −7)   8. (5, 9), (8, 7)
9. (−8, −2), (−3, −9)   10. (2, 11), (5, −3)

11. Graphically interpret each of the slopes found in Exercises 3, 8, and 10.

For each of the following, graph the straight line, given slope m through the indicated point:

12. $m = 1/3$, (0, 0)   13. $m = -1/3$, (0, 0)
14. $m = 5$, (1, 8)   15. $m = -2$, (2, 1)
16. $m = 6/5$, (0, 1)   17. $m = -3/4$, (4, −5)
18. $m = 6/5$, (10, 13)   19. $m = -5/3$, (0, 2)

Find the slope of the straight line passing through each of the following pairs of points, and graph the line.

20. (4, 6), (−7, 6)   21. (−9, −3), (−8, −3)
22. (8, 1), (11, 1)   23. (4, −2), (−6, −2)
24. (5, 3), (5, −1)   25. (6, 4), (6, −4)
26. (−2, 16), (−2, 4)   27. (4, −6), (4, 9)

For each of the following, find the equation, in point-slope form, of the straight line passing through the given pair of points. Then convert the equation into slope-intercept form, and sketch the straight line.

28. (1, 4), (3, 8)   29. (4, −1), (9, −8)
30. (5, −10), (7, −14)   31. (3, 2), (7, 10)
32. (−2, −3), (−5, 9)   33. (5, 5), (7, 7)
34. (4, 12), (6, 18)   35. (5, −3), (4, 2)

For each of the following, find the equation, in point-slope form, of the straight line passing through the given point and having slope m. Then convert the equation into slope-intercept form, and sketch the straight line.

36. (4, 3), $m = 2$ 37. (5, −1), $m = -3$
38. (0, −2), $m = -4$ 39. (−4, −9), $m = 6$
40. (−7, 2), $m = -1/2$ 41. (0, 6), $m = 5$
42. (3, 1), $m = -1/4$ 43. (−4, 7), $m = 1$

For each of the following linear equations, determine which of the given points lie on its corresponding straight line:

44. $3x - 5y = 30$; (0, −6), (5, 2), (10, 0), (15, 3)
45. $2x + 7y = 21$; (7, 1), (3, 0), (4, −3), (14, −1)
46. $8x + 6y = 0$; (0, 0), (1, 5), (−2, 8/3), (7, 13/7)
47. $y = 6x + 3$; (0, 6), (1, 9), (−1/2, 0), (−1, −3)

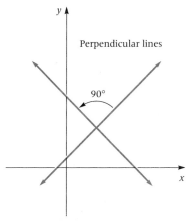

Perpendicular lines

90°

FIGURE 1-31

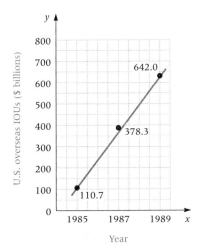

U.S. overseas IOUs ($ billions)

642.0

378.3

110.7

1985   1987   1989   *x*

Year

U.S. Department of Commerce

FIGURE 1-32

48. $f(x) = 2x + 4$; $(0, 4)$, $(1, 5)$, $(-1, 2)$, $(-2, 0)$
49. $g(x) = -3x$; $(0, 0)$, $(1, -3)$, $(2, -6)$, $(5, 14)$

For each of the following, find the equation of the straight line passing through the given pair of points. Also, sketch the straight line.

50. $(4, 2)$, $(4, 7)$ **51.** $(-3, 1)$, $(-3, 9)$
52. $(5, -9)$, $(8, -9)$ **53.** $(4, 1)$, $(6, 1)$

For each of the following, find the equation of the straight line passing through the given point and having slope *m*. Also, sketch the straight line.

54. $(4, 3)$, $m = 0$ **55.** $(-8, 1)$, $m = 0$
56. $(9, -1)$, m is undefined   **57.** $(7, 2)$, m is undefined

58. Find the equation of the straight line passing through $(9, -5)$ and parallel to $6x + 2y = 18$. Sketch both lines.
59. Straight lines intersecting each other at right angles (90°) are said to be perpendicular Figure 1-31 illustrates two perpendicular straight lines. Slopes of perpendicular straight lines are negative reciprocals of each other. In other words, if a straight line has slope *m*, then a straight line perpendicular to it has slope $-1/m$. This relationship between slopes of perpendicular lines does not hold for vertical or horizontal lines
    Find the equation of the straight line passing through $(5, 6)$ and perpendicular to $y = 3x - 2$. Sketch both lines.
60. Find the equation of the straight line passing through $(8, -2)$ and perpendicular to $4x - 3y = 24$. Sketch both lines.

Which of the following pairs of straight lines are parallel?

61. $y = 6x - 14$, $y = 6x + 13$ **62.** $3x - 2y = 15$, $6x - 4y = 60$
63. $y = -4x + 8$, $y = 4x + 16$ **64.** $5x - 8y = 11$, $6x + y = 13$

Which of the following pairs of straight lines are perpendicular?

65. $y = 3x + 5$, $y = -(1/3)x + 16$ **66.** $y = 6x + 5$, $y = -6x + 5$
67. $y = 2x - 3$, $2y + x = 10$ **68.** $3x + 6y = 11$, $5x + 2y = 13$

Convert each of the following linear equations into slope-intercept form.

69. $3x - 5y = 11$ **70.** $x = -2y + 15$
71. $3x - 2y = 0$ **72.** $2x + 5y + 16 = 0$

Which of the following equations are linear?

73. $y = 6x - 54$ **74.** $y = x^2 - 4x$
75. $y = 3x^2 - 4$ **76.** $y^2 = 5x + 7$
77. $3x - 4y = 5$ **78.** $y = xy + 7$
79. $y = x^3 - 5$ **80.** $y^3 = x + 4$

Applications

81. *U.S. overseas IOUs.* U.S. net foreign debt (overseas IOUs) for each of the three years is given in Figure 1-32.
    a) Find the slope of the straight line of the figure.
    b) Interpret the slope.
    c) Find the equation of the straight line. Express the final result in slope-intercept form.
    d) If U.S. net foreign debt follows the trend of this straight line, predict U.S. net foreign debt for the year 1992.

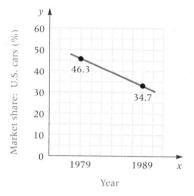

Fortune, April 9, 1990

FIGURE 1-33

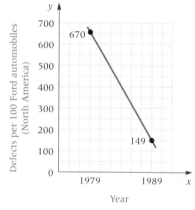

Fortune, April 9, 1990

FIGURE 1-34

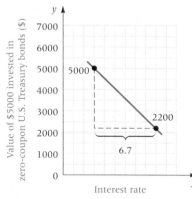

FIGURE 1-35

82. *Market share: U.S. automobiles.* General Motors' share of the U.S. automobile market slipped from 46.3% to 34.7% during the years from 1979 to 1989 as indicated in Figure 1-33.
   a) Find the slope of the straight line of the figure.
   b) Interpret the slope.
   c) Find the equation of the straight line. Express the final result in slope-intercept form.
   d) If General Motors' market share continues to decline at the same rate, predict its market share for the year 1993.

83. *Defects: U.S. automobiles.* The number of defects per 100 vehicles for Ford's North American operations declined from 670 to 149 during the years from 1979 to 1989, as indicated in Figure 1-34
   a) Find the slope of the straight line of the figure.
   b) Interpret the slope.
   c) Find the equation of the straight line. Express the final answer in slope-intercept form.
   d) If Ford's defects continue to decline at the same rate, predict its defects per 100 vehicles (North America) for the year 1991.

84. *Investment.* A money manager noted that $5000 invested in zero-coupon U.S. Treasury bonds would have declined in value to $2200 over a 4-year time interval beginning January 1, 1977, during which time interest rates rose 6.7 percentage points. This is illustrated in Figure 1-35.
   a) Find the slope of the straight line of the figure.
   b) Interpret the slope.

85. *Investment.* A $5000 investment in gold would have increased in value to $22,000 over a 4-year time interval beginning January 1, 1977, during which time inflation rose from 6.5% to 13.3%. This is illustrated in Figure 1-36.
   a) Find the slope of the straight line of the figure.
   b) Interpret the slope.

86. *Tax function.* The tax rate schedule in Table 1-5 gives the amount of 1989 federal income tax due for married people filing jointly with an income of at most $155,320.
   a) Write the equations for the amount of federal income tax due at the various income levels.
   b) Graph the result of part a.

87. *Tax function.* The tax rate schedule in Table 1-6 gives the amount of 1989 federal income tax due for married people filing separately with an income of at most $117,895.
   a) Write the equations for the amount of federal income tax due at the various income levels.
   b) Graph the result of part a.

TABLE 1-5 Tax rate schedule

| Taxable income | | Federal income tax | |
over	but not over		of the amount over
$ 0	$ 30,950	15%	$ 0
30,950	74,850	$4642.50 + 28%	30,950
74,850	155,320	$16,934.50 + 33%	74,850

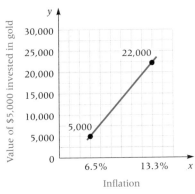

FIGURE 1-36

TABLE 1-6 **Tax rate schedule**

Taxable income		Federal income tax	
over	**but not over**		**of the amount over**
$ 0	$ 15,475	15%	$ 0
15,475	37,425	$2321.25 + 28%	15,475
37,425	117,895	$8467.25 + 33%	37,425

1-3 • GRAPHING LINEAR EQUATIONS

Since all straight lines, except vertical straight lines, are graphs of functions, their equations define **linear functions.** In this section, we will discuss the graphing of linear functions given their equations. In Section 1-2, we graphed a linear function by determining two points on the straight line and connecting them with a straightedge. In this section, instead of determining any two points on the straight line, we will determine the x-intercept and the y-intercept. Recall from Section 1-2 that the y-intercept is the point at which the straight line crosses the y-axis. Thus, the x-intercept is the point at which the straight line crosses the x-axis.

We now graph the linear function defined by

$$2x - 3y = 12$$

by finding its x-intercept and y-intercept.

x-Intercept

As previously mentioned, the x-intercept of a straight line is the point where the straight line crosses the x-axis. Thus, the x-intercept is located on the x-axis, and, therefore, its y-coordinate is 0. Since the x-intercept is also located on the straight line, its coordinates must satisfy the equation of the straight line. Thus, to determine the x-intercept of a straight line, we set $y = 0$ in its equation and solve for x. Using the straight line

$$2x - 3y = 12$$

as an example, we set $y = 0$ and solve for x to determine its x-intercept. Hence,

$$2x - 3(0) = 12$$
$$2x = 12$$
$$x = 6$$

The x-intercept (6, 0) is illustrated in Figure 1-37.

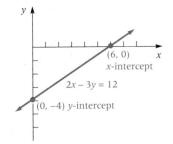

FIGURE 1-37

y-Intercept

As mentioned earlier, the *y*-intercept of a straight line is the point where the straight line crosses the *y*-axis. Thus, the *y*-intercept is located on the *y*-axis, and, therefore, its *x*-coordinate is 0. Since the *y*-intercept is also located on the straight line, its coordinates must satisfy the equation of the straight line. Thus, to determine the *y*-intercept of a straight line, we set $x = 0$ in its equation and solve for *y*. Hence, for the straight line

$$2x - 3y = 12$$

we obtain

$$2(0) - 3y = 12$$
$$-3y = 12$$
$$y = -4$$

The *y*-intercept $(0, -4)$ is illustrated in Figure 1-37.

The straight line defined by $2x - 3y = 12$ is graphed in Figure 1-37.

• **EXAMPLE 1-13** _____

Graph $-7x + 2y = 28$.

Solution

First, we find the *x*-intercept. We set $y = 0$ and solve for *x*. Hence,

$$-7x + 2(0) = 28$$
$$-7x = 28$$
$$x = -4$$

Thus, the *x*-intercept is $(-4, 0)$. Next, we determine the *y*-intercept. We set $x = 0$ and solve for *y*. Hence,

$$-7(0) + 2y = 28$$
$$2y = 28$$
$$y = 14$$

Therefore, the *y*-intercept is $(0, 14)$. The straight line is graphed in Figure 1-38.

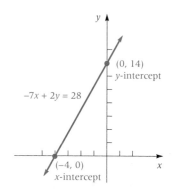

FIGURE 1-38

• **EXAMPLE 1-14** _____

Sketch the graph of $y = f(x) = -3x - 2$.

Solution

First, find the *x*-intercept. Set $y = 0$ and solve for *x*. Therefore,

$$0 = -3x - 2$$
$$3x = -2$$
$$x = -\frac{2}{3}$$

Thus, the *x*-intercept is $(-2/3, 0)$. Then find the *y*-intercept. Since the equation $y = -3x - 2$ is in the slope-intercept form, by inspection we determine the *y*-intercept to be $(0, -2)$. The straight line is graphed in Figure 1-39.

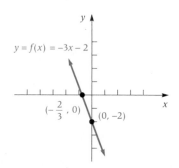

FIGURE 1-39

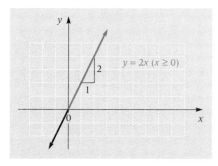

FIGURE 1-40

• **EXAMPLE 1-15** _____

Graph $y = 2x$, $x \geq 0$.

Solution

The equation $y = 2x$ is in the slope-intercept form $y = mx + b$, with $m = 2$ and $b = 0$. Thus, the y-intercept is the origin, $(0, 0)$. Since the origin is also the x-intercept, we do not have two distinct intercepts to connect with a straightedge. However, if we place our straightedge at the origin and set it so that the slope is 2, we have the straight line of Figure 1-40. The restriction $x \geq 0$ implies that we are to consider only that portion of the line above the interval $x \geq 0$. Accordingly, we have sketched this portion of the line in color.

Before proceeding to the next example, we should study the graphing summary following Example 1-16.

• **EXAMPLE 1-16** _____

Graph $2x + 5y = 0$.

Solution

Setting $x = 0$ to find the y-intercept yields $y = 0$, and setting $y = 0$ to find the x-intercept yields $x = 0$. Thus, both intercepts are at the origin, $(0, 0)$. This is so because the equation $2x + 5y = 0$, when solved for y, becomes $y = (-2/5)x$. Since $y = (-2/5)x$ is of the form $y = mx$, with $m \neq 0$, then, as is discussed in the graphing summary following this example, its graph goes through the origin and has a negative slope. The graph appears in Figure 1-41.

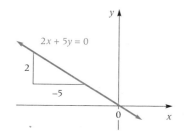

FIGURE 1-41

■ **To Graph a Linear Equation**

To graph a linear equation of the form $ax + by = c$,

1. Find the y-intercept. Set $x = 0$ and solve for y. Mark the y-intercept on the y-axis.
2. Find the x-intercept. Set $y = 0$ and solve for x. Mark the x-intercept on the x-axis.
3. Connect the intercepts with a straightedge.

To graph a linear equation in slope-intercept form, $y = mx + b$,

1. Find the y-intercept. The y-intercept is given by b. Mark the y-intercept on the y-axis.
2. Find the x-intercept. Set $y = 0$ and solve for x. Mark the x-intercept on the x-axis.
3. Connect the intercepts with a straightedge.

To graph a linear equation of the form $y = mx$, with $m \neq 0$, note the following:

1. Such an equation is in slope-intercept form, with $b = 0$. Thus, its y-intercept is the origin, $(0, 0)$.
2. Since the origin is also the x-intercept of the straight line, we do not have two distinct intercepts to connect with a straightedge.

continues

> **To Graph a Linear Equation—***Continued*
>
> **3.** To graph such a linear equation, we place our straightedge at the origin and set it so that the slope is *m*. The resulting straight line will resemble one of those shown in Figure 1-42.
>
>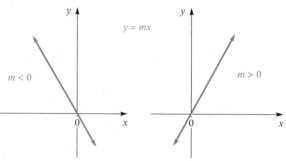
>
> **FIGURE 1-42**

Exercises 1-3

Graph each of the following linear equations by finding the *x* and *y* intercepts:

1. $4x - 6y = 24$ **2.** $5x + 3y = 45$

3. $-3x + 2y = 8$ **4.** $5x - 6y = 10$

5. $2x + 7y = 11$ **6.** $-3x - 5y = 9$

7. $y = -4x + 13$ **8.** $f(x) = -2x + 15$

9. $f(x) = 6x + 4$ **10.** $g(x) = (5/2)x + 13$

Graph each of the following linear equations:

11. $y = 2x$ **12.** $f(x) = -3x$

13. $3x + 2y = 0$ **14.** $2x - 5y = 0$

15. $g(x) = 7x$ **16.** $f(x) = (-1/2)x$

17. $f(x) = x$ **18.** $y = -x$

Graph each of the following:

19. $f(x) = 3x + 5, x \geq 0$

20. $g(x) = 4x, x \geq 0$

21. $f(x) = 2x + 3, x \geq 1$

22. $h(x) = 3x - 15, x \geq 5$

1-4 • LINEAR MODELS

In this section, we present some applications of linear functions. The functions presented will serve as models for later applications in this text.

Cost Function

A manufacturer of chairs can produce 10 chairs at a total cost of $1100, while 50 such chairs cost $3500. The **total cost** in each case consists of two components:

1. **Fixed costs,** which include costs that must be paid no matter how few or how many units of product are produced (fixed costs usually include rent, insurance, taxes, etc.).
2. **Variable costs,** which include costs that vary in direct proportion to the number of units of product produced (variable costs usually include material costs, labor costs, and other costs directly attributed to the cost of the product).

Thus,

$$\text{total cost} = \text{variable cost} + \text{fixed cost}$$

If x = number of chairs produced and y = total cost, then we will determine

a) The variable cost per chair.
b) The equation relating x and y.

a) Since 10 chairs cost $1100 and 50 chairs cost $3500, we let $(x_1, y_1) = (10, 1100)$ and $(x_2, y_2) = (50, 3500)$. The variable cost per chair is given by the slope of the straight line passing through the two points. Hence,

$$m = \frac{\Delta y}{\Delta x} = \frac{y_2 - y_1}{x_2 - x_1} = \frac{3500 - 1100}{50 - 10} = \frac{2400}{40} = 60$$

Note that the production of 40 additional chairs costs an additional $2400. Thus, the variable cost per chair is the slope, i.e., $60 (see Figure 1-43.)

b) We assume that x and y are linearly related and, therefore, use the point-slope form to find the equation of the straight line passing through the two points, $(10, 1100)$ and $(50, 3500)$. Substituting $(x_1, y_1) = (10, 1100)$ and $m = 60$ into the point-slope form

$$y - y_1 = m(x - x_1)$$

we obtain

$$y - 1100 = 60(x - 10)$$

Solving for y, we have

$$y = 60(x - 10) + 1100$$

or

$$y = \underbrace{60x}_{\text{variable cost}} + \underset{\uparrow}{500}\ \text{fixed cost}$$

Since the equation $y = 60x + 500$ relates total cost to number of units produced, it is called a **cost equation.** The function that it defines is called a

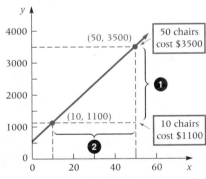

$$① \quad \Delta y = 3500 - 1100 = 2400$$

$$② \quad \Delta x = 50 - 10 = 40$$

$$m = \frac{\Delta y}{\Delta x} = \frac{3500 - 1100}{50 - 10} = \frac{2400}{40} = 60$$

variable cost per chair = $60

FIGURE 1-43

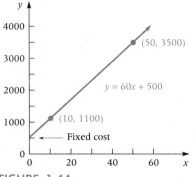

FIGURE 1-44

cost function (see Figure 1-44). Note that only the first quadrant portion of the graph of the cost function is shown since the function has meaning only for non-negative values of x.

Since fixed cost is not directly attributed to the cost of the product, it can be defined as the cost of producing 0 units. It is determined by substituting $x = 0$ into the cost equation and solving for y to obtain $y = 60(0) + 500 = 500$. Note that the fixed cost equals the y-intercept (see Figure 1-44).

The variable cost is the product of the variable cost per unit (i.e., the slope, $m = 60$) and the number of units produced (x).

SUMMARY

Linear Cost Function

In general, if total cost (C) and number of units produced (x) are linearly related, then the cost function is defined by

$$C(x) = vx + F \qquad (x \geq 0)$$

where $C(x)$ = cost of producing x units, v = variable cost per unit, and F = fixed cost. The graph of such a cost function appears in Figure 1-45.

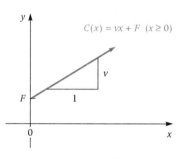

FIGURE 1-45

Revenue Function

Suppose the chair manufacturer of the above illustrative example sells the chairs that he produces for $110. If $R(x)$ = total sales revenue gained from selling x chairs, then

$$\text{sales revenue} = (\text{unit selling price})(\text{number of units sold})$$

or

$$R(x) = 110x$$

The function, R, which relates total sales revenue to number of units sold, is called a **sales revenue function.** Its graph appears in Figure 1-46. Note

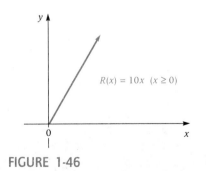

FIGURE 1-46

that only the first quadrant portion of the graph of the revenue function is shown since the function has meaning only for non-negative values of x.

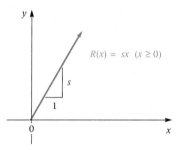

SUMMARY

Sales Revenue Function

In general, if total sales revenue (R) and number of units sold (x) are linearly related, then the sales revenue function is given by

$$R(x) = sx \qquad (x \geq 0)$$

where $R(x)$ = total sales revenue gained from selling x units and s = unit selling price. Its graph is given in Figure 1-47.

FIGURE 1-47

Profit Function

Suppose the chair manufacturer of the above illustrative examples wishes to determine the equation that relates total profit (P) to number of units sold (x). The function that defines this relationship is called a **profit function** and is found by the formula

$$\text{profit} = \text{revenue} - \text{cost}$$

Thus, if $P(x)$ = profit gained from selling x chairs, then

$$P(x) = R(x) - C(x)$$

Since, as determined in the previous illustrative examples, $R(x) = 110x$ and $C(x) = 60x + 500$, then substituting these results into the above equation gives

$$P(x) = 110x - (60x + 500)$$
$$= 110x - 60x - 500$$
$$= 50x - 500$$

This result is graphed in Figure 1-48. Note that only the first and fourth quadrant portion of the graph of the profit function is shown since the function has meaning only for non-negative values of x.

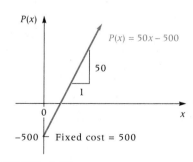

FIGURE 1-48

SUMMARY

Profit Function

In general, given a linear cost function $C(x) = vx + F$ and a sales revenue function $R(x) = sx$ where x = number of units produced and sold, v = variable cost per unit, F = fixed cost, and s = unit selling price, the profit function is determined as follows:

$$P(x) = R(x) - C(x)$$
$$= sx - (vx + F)$$
$$P(x) = (s - v)x - F \qquad (x \geq 0)$$

The slope, $s - v$, of the profit function is called the *unit contribution margin*.

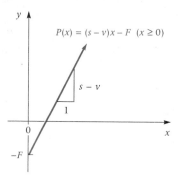

FIGURE 1-49

Demand Function

Demand (q) for a product is sometimes linearly related to the product's unit price (p). The equation describing such a relationship between demand and unit price is called a **demand equation,** and its associated function is called a **demand function.**

Consider a case where 20 units of some commodity are demanded by the marketplace when the unit price of that commodity is $45, whereas 40 units are demanded at a unit price of $30. We must determine the linear equation relating demand (q) to unit price (p).

Typically, demand (q) is a function of unit price (p), or, in other words, $q = f(p)$. However, since most economists graph the relationship between demand (q) and unit price (p) by writing (p) on the vertical axis and (q) on the horizontal axis, we will also follow this convention. Thus, we summarize the information of the previous paragraph in Table 1-7 by listing first q and then p.

To determine the linear equation relating q and p, we first find the slope

$$m = \frac{\Delta p}{\Delta q} = \frac{30 - 45}{40 - 20} = \frac{-15}{20} = -\frac{3}{4}$$

Rewriting the point-slope form

$$y - y_1 = m(x - x_1)$$

TABLE 1-7

q	p	Ordered pairs (q, p)
20	$45	(20, 45)
40	$30	(40, 30)

with p replacing y and q replacing x, we have

$$p - p_1 = m(q - q_1)$$

Arbitrarily selecting $(q_1, p_1) = (40, 30)$, we substitute this result into the above equation along with $m = -3/4$ to obtain

$$p - 30 = -\frac{3}{4}(q - 40)$$

Solving for p, we first multiply $q - 40$ by $-3/4$ (using the distributive law) to obtain

$$p - 30 = -\frac{3}{4}q - \left(-\frac{3}{4}\right)(40)$$

$$= -\frac{3}{4}q + 30$$

and then we add 30 to both sides to obtain the demand equation

$$p = -\frac{3}{4}q + 60$$

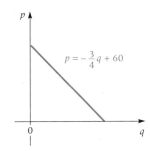

$$p = -\frac{3}{4}q + 60$$

FIGURE 1-50

which is graphed in Figure 1-50. Observing the graph of the demand function in Figure 1-50, note that its slope is negative. This is typically the case for demand functions since an increase in unit price usually results in a decrease in demand. Note that only the first quadrant portion of the graph of the demand function is shown since the function has meaning only for non-negative values of q and p.

We also note that a demand equation can be written in the form $q = f(p)$. Specifically, if we were to solve the above demand equation for q, we would obtain

$$q = -\frac{4}{3}p + 80$$

SUMMARY

Linear Demand Functions

A demand function expresses a relationship between demand (q) for some product and the product's unit price (p). The graph of a linear demand function has a *negative slope* and resembles that of Figure 1-51.

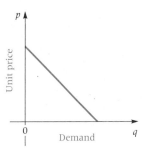

FIGURE 1-51

Supply Function

If a given commodity is selling at a unit price of \$18, suppliers are willing to produce 30 units of this commodity. However, if the commodity is selling at a unit price of \$28, then suppliers are willing to produce 60 units of this commodity. Note that suppliers are willing to produce more of this commodity if it is selling at a higher price than if it is selling at a lower price. This is typical of what usually occurs in the marketplace for most commodities.

An equation that expresses the relationship between the supply for some product and the product's unit price is called a **supply equation,** and its associated function is called a **supply function.** Assuming that supply and demand are linearly related, we now determine the supply equation for the above commodity.

We let p denote unit price and q denote the number of units supplied. As with demand functions, we will consider p the dependent variable and q the independent variable. Thus, we summarize the information of the first paragraph in Table 1-8.

Finding the slope, we obtain

$$m = \frac{\Delta p}{\Delta q} = \frac{28 - 18}{60 - 30} = \frac{10}{30} = \frac{1}{3}$$

As with our previous demand problem, we rewrite the point-slope form

$$y - y_1 = m(x - x_1)$$

by replacing y with p and x with q to obtain

$$p - p_1 = m(q - q_1)$$

Arbitrarily selecting $(q_1, p_1) = (30, 18)$, we substitute this result into the above equation along with $m = 1/3$ to obtain

$$p - 18 = \frac{1}{3}(q - 30)$$

Solving for p, we first multiply $q - 30$ by $1/3$ to obtain

$$p - 18 = \frac{1}{3}q - 10$$

and then we add 18 to both sides to obtain the supply equation

$$p = \frac{1}{3}q + 8$$

which is graphed in Figure 1-52. Observing the graph of the supply function in Figure 1-52, note that its slope is positive. This is typically the case for supply functions since an increase in unit price usually results is an increase in supply. Note that only the first quadrant portion of the graph of the supply function is shown since the function has meaning only for nonnegative values of q and p.

TABLE 1-8

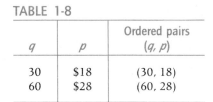

q	p	Ordered pairs (q, p)
30	\$18	(30, 18)
60	\$28	(60, 28)

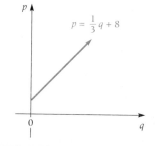

FIGURE 1-52

We also note that a supply equation can be written in the form $q = f(p)$. Specifically, if we were to solve the above supply equation for q, we would obtain

$$q = 3p - 24$$

SUMMARY

Linear Supply Functions

A supply function expresses a relationship between supply (q) for some product and the product's unit price (p). The graph of a linear supply function has a *positive slope* and resembles that of Figure 1-53.

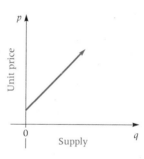

FIGURE 1-53

Consumption Function

TABLE 1-9

x	y
56	50
76	67.2

Table 1-9 exhibits a relationship between a nation's disposable income, x (in billions of dollars), and personal consumption expenditures, y (in billions of dollars). The equation that expresses the relationship between these two quantities defines a **consumption function.** If x and y are linearly related, the slope between the two points in Table 1-9 is

$$m = \frac{\Delta y}{\Delta x} = \frac{y_2 - y_1}{x_2 - x_1} = \frac{67.2 - 50}{76 - 56} = \frac{17.2}{20} = 0.86$$

Economists call this result the **marginal propensity to consume,** abbreviated **MPC.** Since MPC = 0.86, then for each dollar increase in disposable income, consumption increases by \$0.86. In other words, 86% of each additional dollar earned is spent, and 14% is saved.

The linear equation relating x and y is determined below. We arbitrarily choose $(x_1, y_1) = (56, 50)$ and substitute this result along with $m = 0.86$ into the point-slope form

$$y - y_1 = m(x - x_1)$$

to obtain

$$y - 50 = 0.86(x - 56)$$

Solving for y, we obtain

$$y = 0.86x + 1.84$$

SUMMARY

Linear Consumption Function

A consumption function expresses a relationship between consumption (y) and income (x). For a linear consumption function, the *slope* is called the *marginal propensity to consume*, abbreviated MPC. The MPC indicates the portion spent of an additional dollar earned. The graph of a typical linear consumption function is given in Figure 1-54.

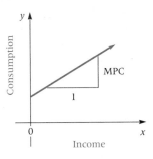

FIGURE 1-54

Linear Depreciation

Most assets decrease in value over a period of time. This decrease in value is called **depreciation.** Suppose a company spends $11,000 (total cost) for a truck expected to last 5 years **(economic life),** at which time it will probably be worth $1000 **(salvage value).** For tax purposes, such an asset may be considered to depreciate each year by a fixed amount determined as follows:

$$\frac{\text{depreciable amount}}{\text{economic life}} = \frac{\text{total cost} - \text{salvage value}}{\text{economic life}} = \frac{11{,}000 - 1000}{5}$$
$$= \$2000 \uparrow \text{annual depreciation}$$

Therefore, after 1 year, the value of the truck, y, is

$$y = 11{,}000 - 2000 = \$9000$$

After 2 years, the value of the truck, y, is

$$y = 11{,}000 - 2000(2) = \$7000$$

After 3 years, the value of the truck, y, is

$$y = 11{,}000 - 2000(3) = \$5000$$

After x years, the value of the truck, y, is

$$y = 11{,}000 - 2000x$$

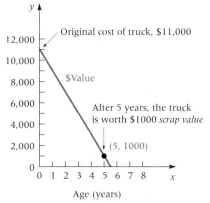

FIGURE 1-55

Thus, the linear equation $y = 11,000 - 2000x$ relates the value of the truck, y, to its age, x, in years. This method of depreciation is called the **straight-line method.** The equation is graphed in Figure 1-55.

We will now determine formulas for the y-intercept and slope of the linear equation relating the value of an asset with its age in years. Referring to the linear equation

$$y = 11,000 - 2000x$$

y-intercept   slope (annual
(total cost)   depreciation)

note that the y-intercept, 11,000, is the total cost of the asset and that the slope, -2000, indicates that the value of the truck decreases by $2000 per year.

We generalize as follows.

SUMMARY

Linear Depreciation

If

C = total cost of an asset

n = number of years of economic life of the asset

S = salvage value of the asset

then the linear equation relating the value, y, of the asset with its age, x, in years is given by

$$y = C - \left(\frac{C - S}{n}\right)x$$

Note that the y-intercept is C and the *slope* is

$$-\left(\frac{C - S}{n}\right)$$

• **EXAMPLE 1-17** _____

The Beefup Company buys a refrigerator for $20,000. The refrigerator has an economic life of 10 years, after which time it will probably have a salvage value of $2000. Find the linear equation relating the value, y, of the refrigerator to its age, x. Use the straight-line method of depreciation.

Solution

We know that $C = \$20,000$, $n = 10$, and $S = \$2000$. Substituting these values into the linear equation

$$y = C - \left(\frac{C - S}{n}\right)x$$

gives us

$$y = 20{,}000 - \left(\frac{20{,}000 - 2000}{10}\right)x$$
$$= 20{,}000 - 1800x$$

Exercises 1-4

Cost Functions

1. If 60 units of some product cost $1400 and 40 units cost $1200 to manufacture, then
   a) Determine the variable cost per unit.
   b) Determine the linear cost equation.
   c) Determine the fixed cost.
   d) Graph the cost function.

2. If 20 units of some product cost $2500 and 50 units cost $3400 to produce, then
   a) Determine the variable cost per unit.
   b) Determine the linear cost equation.
   c) Determine the fixed cost.
   d) Graph the cost function.

3. If 30 units of some commodity cost $2200 and 70 units cost $4200 to produce, then
   a) Determine the variable cost per unit.
   b) Determine the linear cost equation.
   c) Determine the fixed cost.
   d) Determine the total cost of producing 50 units.

4. If 30 units of some commodity cost $3100 and 50 units cost $3500 to manufacture, then
   a) Determine the variable cost per unit.
   b) Determine the linear cost equation.
   c) Determine the fixed cost.
   d) Determine the total cost of producing 70 units.

For each of the following, determine the equation of the linear cost function and also the total cost of producing 100 units.

5. Variable cost per unit = $20 and fixed cost = $1000
6. Variable cost per unit = $70 and fixed cost = $900
7. $F = \$8700$ and $v = \$15$
8. $F = \$5000$ and $v = \$90$

Cost, Sales Revenue, and Profit Functions

For each of the following, determine the linear cost, sales revenue, and profit equations. Graph each equation.

9. Variable cost per unit = $40, fixed cost = $900, and unit selling price = $70
10. Variable cost per unit = $90, fixed cost = $2000, and unit selling price = $100
11. $F = \$8000$, $v = \$100$, and $s = \$140$
12. $F = \$9000$, $v = \$50$, and $s = \$80$
13. $F = \$7500$, $v = \$25$, and $s = \$40$
14. $F = \$6000$, $v = \$90$, and $s = \$110$

Demand Functions

For each of the following, determine the equation defining the linear demand function. Graph the result.

15. If clocks are priced at $5 each, there will be a demand for 75 clocks; if clocks are priced at $10 each, the demand will decrease to 50 clocks.

16. At a unit price of $10, 500 units of some product will be demanded; at a unit price of $30, only 300 units will be demanded.

17.

q	p
50	$120
80	$60

18.

q	p
90	$40
30	$80

19.

q	p
300	$200
100	$600

Solve each of the following demand equations for q.

20. $4p + 3q = 12$ **21.** $6p + 5q = 30$
22. $p + 2q = 8$ **23.** $2p + q = 6$

Solve each of the following demand equations for p.

24. $6p + 4q = 24$ **25.** $p + 3q = 6$
26. $p + 5q = 20$ **27.** $8p + 5q = 40$

Supply Functions

For each of the following, determine the supply equation and graph the result.

28. If gadgets are priced at $9 each, suppliers are willing to produce 86 gadgets. If a gadget's price drops to $5, suppliers are willing to produce only 46 gadgets.

29. At a unit price of $20, suppliers are willing to produce 10 units of some product; at a unit price of $120, suppliers are willing to produce 30 units.

30.

q	p
50	$65
80	$80

31.

q	p
30	$100
90	$120

32.

q	p
20	$ 50
50	$110

Solve each of the following supply equations for q.

33. $4p - 3q = 12$ **34.** $5p - 4q = 20$

Solve each of the following supply equations for p.

35. $3p - 5q = 30$ **36.** $4p - 5q = 40$

Consumption Functions

For Exercises 37-39, if x denotes income and y denotes consumption, then
a) Calculate and interpret the MPC.
b) Determine the equation defining the linear consumption function.
c) Graph the result of part b.

37.

x	y
80	58
90	65

38.

x	y
50	44
80	68

39.

x	y
100	97
200	187

TABLE 1-10

x	y
48	44
68	60

TABLE 1-11

x	y
60	55
90	79

40. Table 1-10 presents the relationship between a nation's disposable income, x (in billions of dollars), and personal consumption expenditures, y (in billions of dollars).
   a) Calculate the MPC.
   b) According to the MPC of part a, for each dollar increase in disposable income, consumption increases by how much?
   c) Another rate of change is the *marginal propensity to save*, abbreviated MPS. It is defined as

$$MPS = 1 - MPC$$

   Calculate the MPS for the nation of this example.
   d) According to the MPS calculated in part c, for each dollar increase in disposable income, how many additional dollars are saved?
   e) Determine the equation defining the linear consumption function.
   f) Graph the result of part e.

41. Table 1-11 presents the relationship between a nation's disposable income, x (in billions of dollars), and personal consumption expenditures, y (in billions of dollars).
   a) Calculate and interpret the MPC.
   b) Calculate and interpret the MPS.
   c) Determine the equation defining the linear consumption function.
   d) Calculate the personal consumption expenditures corresponding to disposable income to $85 billion.

Linear Depreciation

In each of the following cases, determine the equation relating the value, y, of an asset to its age, x (in years).

42. $C = \$500,000$, $n = 5$, $s = \$50,000$
43. $C = \$90,000$, $n = 4$, $s = \$10,000$
44. $C = \$60,000$, $n = 6$, $s = 0$
45. $C = \$45,000$, $n = 3$, $s = 0$

46. A corporation buys an automobile for $10,500. The automobile's useful life is 5 years, after which time it will have a scrap value of $500.
   a) Find the linear equation relating the value of the automobile, y, to its age, x. Use the linear depreciation method.
   b) Sketch this linear equation.
   c) What is the value of the automobile after 3 years?

47. Made-Fresh Bakery buys an oven for $30,000. The useful life of the oven is 10 years, after which time it will have a scrap value of $1000.
   a) Find the linear equation relating the value of the oven, y, to its age, x.
   b) Graph the linear function defined by the equation of part a.
   c) What is the value of the oven after 6 years?

1-5 • BREAK-EVEN ANALYSIS; MARKET EQUILIBRIUM

Break-Even Analysis

Sally Adams, a recent college graduate, plans to start her own business manufacturing bicycle tires. After careful research, she concludes the following:

1. She will need $3000 for overhead (fixed cost).
2. Additionally, each tire will cost her $2 to produce (variable cost per unit).
3. To remain competitive, she must sell her tires for no more than $5 apiece.

Having compiled this information, Sally asks this crucial question:

How many tires must be produced and sold in order to break even?

This type of question is answered in the following manner. First, we must find the cost equation. If x represents the number of tires produced and sold, and $C(x)$ represents the total cost of producing x tires, then

$$C(x) = 2x + 3000 \qquad \text{Cost equation}$$

variable cost   fixed cost
per tire

Second, we must find the sales revenue equation. The sales revenue is simply the unit selling price times the number of units sold. If $R(x)$ represents the total sales revenue gained from selling x tires at $5 each, then

$$R(x) = 5x \qquad \text{Sales revenue equation}$$

Third, we sketch both cost and sales revenue functions on the same set of axes (see Figure 1-56). Observing Figure 1-56, note that the intersection of the graphs of a revenue function and a cost function is the **break-even point, (x_B, y_B)**. Here,

$$\text{total sales revenue} = \text{total cost}$$

or

$$\text{profit} = 0$$

If $x < x_B$, then total cost is greater than total sales revenue, and the result is a loss. If $x > x_B$, then total sales revenue is greater than total cost, and the result is a profit. Thus, Sally's business will be profitable as long as x, the number of tires produced and sold, is greater than x_B, the x-coordinate of the break-even point.

To find the break-even point, (x_B, y_B), we equate $R(x)$ with $C(x)$. Thus,

$$R(x) = C(x)$$
$$5x = 2x + 3000$$

Solving for x, we obtain

$$3x = 3000$$
$$x = 1000 \qquad \text{Break-even}$$

Thus, x_B, the x-coordinate of the break-even point, is 1000. The corresponding y-coordinate, y_B, is determined by calculating either $C(1000)$ or $R(1000)$. Hence,

$$C(x) = 2x + 3000 \qquad \text{or} \qquad R(x) = 5x$$
$$C(1000) = 2(1000) + 3000 \qquad\qquad R(1000) = 5(1000)$$
$$= 5000 \qquad\qquad\qquad\qquad\qquad = 5000$$

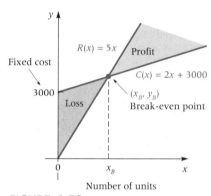

FIGURE 1-56

Therefore, the break-even point is (1000, 5000), and Sally must produce and sell 1000 tires to break even. If Sally produces and sells more than 1000 tires, she will make a profit.

Having determined the break-even point, Sally conducts a marketing research study which indicates that she can sell at least 10,000 tires at $5 apiece. Also, there is a strong possibility that she can sell as many as 20,000 tires at this price. Since both of these demand levels are greater than $x_B = 1000$, Sally knows she will make a profit. However, she wishes to determine the amount of profit corresponding to each of the demand levels of 10,000 and 20,000 tires.

One way of calculating profits is to find the profit equation. As discussed in the previous section, if

$$P(x) = \text{total profit from selling } x \text{ tires}$$
$$R(x) = \text{total sales revenue from selling } x \text{ tires}$$
$$C(x) = \text{total cost of producing } x \text{ tires}$$

then

$$P(x) = R(x) - C(x)$$
$$= 5x - (2x + 3000)$$
$$= 3x - 3000$$

Thus, the profit function is defined by

$$P(x) = 3x - 3000$$

Hence, if 10,000 tires are sold, the corresponding profit is

$$P(10,000) = 3(10,000) - 3000 = \$27,000$$

And if 20,000 tires are sold, the corresponding profit is

$$P(20,000) = 3(20,000) - 3000 = \$57,000$$

Since Sally is satisfied with either of these amount, she decides to start her tire-manufacturing business.

We note that the break-even point can also be determined by setting the profit equation equal to 0 and solving for x. This works because $P(x) = R(x) - C(x)$, and, therefore, setting $P(x) = 0$ gives $0 = R(x) - C(x)$ or $R(x) = C(x)$. Hence, for the above example, setting $P(x) = 0$ and solving for x gives

$$0 = 3x - 3000$$
$$x = 1000 \qquad \text{Break-even}$$

The break-even analysis process is summarized on page 45. It should be studied before proceeding to the next example.

Break-Even Analysis

Linear Functions

In general, if s = unit selling price, v = variable cost per unit, F = fixed cost, and x = number of units produced and sold, then, as discussed in Section 1-4, the **cost function** is given by

$$C(x) = vx + F \qquad (x \geq 0)$$

the **sales revenue function** is given by

$$R(x) = sx \qquad (x \geq 0)$$

and the **profit function** is given by

$$P(x) = (s - v)x - F \qquad (x \geq 0)$$

The x-coordinate of the **break-even point,** the point where total sales revenue = total cost, can be determined by two methods.

Method 1 Set $R(x) = C(x)$ and solve for x. This gives

$$sx = vx + F$$
$$(s - v)x = F$$
$$x = \frac{F}{s - v}$$

Method 2 Set $P(x) = 0$ and solve for x. This gives

$$0 = (s - v)x - F$$
$$x = \frac{F}{s - v}$$

We now consider Example 1-18, which illustrates a format often used to present information on fixed and variable costs and sales revenue.

• EXAMPLE 1-18

This problem appeared on a past Uniform CPA Examination. In a recent period, the Zero Company had the following experience:

Sales (10,000 units @ $200 per unit)			$2,000,000
	Fixed	Variable	
Costs			
Direct material	$ —	$ 200,000	
Direct labor	—	400,000	
Factory overhead	160,000	600,000	
Administrative expenses	180,000	80,000	
Other expenses	200,000	120,000	
Total costs	$540,000	$1,400,000	1,940,000
			$ 60,000

a) Find the sales revenue equation.
b) Find the cost equation.
c) Find the break-even point.
d) How many units must be sold in order to generate a profit of $96,000?
e) What is the break-even point if management makes a decision that increases fixed costs by $18,000?

Solutions

a) If $R(x)$ is the sales revenue from selling x units at $200 each, then
$$R(x) = 200x$$

b) We have
$$\text{fixed cost} = \$540,000$$
The variable cost per unit is determined by dividing the total variable cost by the number of units. Hence,
$$\text{variable cost per unit} = \frac{\text{total variable cost}}{\text{number of units}}$$
$$= \frac{1,400,000}{10,000} = \$140$$

Thus, if $C(x)$ is the total cost of producing x units, then
$$C(x) = 140x + 540,000$$

c) At the break-even point,
$$R(x) = C(x)$$
$$200x = 140x + 540,000$$

Solving for x yields
$$60x = 540,000$$
$$x = 9000 \text{ units}$$

Thus, the Zero Company must produce and sell 9000 units in order to break even. Note that $R(9000) = C(9000) = \$1,800,000$.

d) If $P(x)$ is the profit from selling x units, then
$$P(x) = R(x) - C(x)$$
$$= 200x - (140x + 540,000)$$
$$= 60x - 540,000$$

If $P(x) = 96,000$, then
$$96,000 = 60x - 540,000$$

Solving for x yields
$$-60x = -636,000$$
$$x = 10,600 \text{ units}$$

Thus, the Zero Company must sell 10,600 units in order to generate a profit of $96,000.

e) The cost equation becomes
$$C(x) = 140x + \underbrace{540,000 + 18,000}_{\text{fixed cost}}$$

$$= 140x + 558,000$$

At the break-even point,
$$R(x) = C(x)$$

Thus,

$$200x = 140x + 558,000$$

Solving for x yields

$$60x = 558,000$$

$$x = 9300 \text{ units} \qquad \text{Break-even}$$

Therefore, the Zero Company must produce 9300 units to break even. Note that $R(9300) = C(9300) = \$1,860,000$.

• EXAMPLE 1-19

Amtron, Inc., produces two products, AM50 and AM60, that are used in the computer industry. Projections for next year are given in Table 1-12.

a) Determine the profit function for AM50.
b) Determine the break-even point for AM50.
c) Because 3 AM50s are inserted into a part that also requires 2 AM60s, customers purchase composite units of 3 AM50s and 2 AM60s. Determine the composite profit function and break-even point.

Solutions

a) The unit selling price for AM50 is determined as follows:

$$s = \frac{\text{total sales revenue}}{\text{number of units}}$$

$$= \frac{\$100,000}{20,000} = \$5$$

The variable cost per unit for AM50 is determined as follows:

$$v = \frac{\text{total variable cost}}{\text{number of units}}$$

$$= \frac{\$30,000}{20,000} = \$1.50$$

The fixed cost for AM50 is $F = \$5100$.
The profit function is given by

$$P(x) = (s - v)x - F$$
$$= (5 - 1.5)x - 5100$$
$$= 3.5x - 5100$$

where x = number of units sold.

b) We determine the break-even point by setting $P(x) = 0$ and solving for x. Hence,

$$0 = 3.5x - 5100$$
$$-3.5x = -5100$$
$$x = 1457.14, \text{ which we round to } 1457$$

TABLE 1-12

	AM50		AM60	
	units	amount	units	amount
Sales	20,000	$100,000	12,000	$72,000
Costs				
Fixed		$ 5,100		$ 6,000
Variable		30,000		24,000
		$ 35,100		$30,000

c) We must determine the unit contribution margin for the composite: 3 AM50s and 2 AM60s. In part a, we determined the unit selling price and the variable cost per unit for AM50. Now we must determine the same for AM60. Hence, for AM60

$$\text{unit selling price} = \frac{\$72,000}{12,000} = \$6$$

$$\text{variable cost per unit} = \frac{\$24,000}{12,000} = \$2$$

Thus, for the composite units of 3 AM50s and 2 AM60s, the unit selling price (denoted by s_c) is determined below:

$$s_c = 3(\text{AM50 unit selling price}) + 2(\text{AM60 unit selling price})$$
$$= 3(\$5) + 2(\$6)$$
$$= \$27$$

Also, the variable cost per unit (denoted by v_c) for the composite is determined below:

$$v_c = 3\left(\frac{\text{AM50 variable cost}}{\text{per unit}}\right) + 2\left(\frac{\text{AM60 variable cost}}{\text{per unit}}\right)$$
$$= 3(\$1.50) + 2(\$2)$$
$$= \$8.50$$

The fixed cost (denoted by F_c) for the composite is the sum of the fixed costs of the two products. Hence,

$$F_c = \$5100 + \$6000 = \$11,100$$

Thus, the composite profit function is given by

$$P(x) = (s_c - v_c)x - F_c$$
$$= (27.00 - 8.50)x - 11,100$$
$$= 18.5x - 11,100$$

where x = number of composite units of 3 AM50s and 2 AM60s. To determine the break-even point, we set $P(x) = 0$ and solve for x. Hence,

$$0 = 18.5x - 11,100$$
$$-18.5x = -11,100$$
$$x = 600 \text{ composite units of 3 AM50s and 2 AM60s}$$

Note that the break-even point, $x = 600$ composite units, means that

$$3(600) \text{ or } 1800 \text{ AM50s}$$
$$\text{and}$$
$$2(600) \text{ or } 1200 \text{ AM60s}$$

must be sold in order to break even.

Market Equilibrium

In the previous section, we noted that the graph of a linear demand function has a negative slope, whereas the graph of a linear supply function has a positive slope. This implies that as the price of some product increases, its demand decreases and its supply increases. Conversely, as the price of the product decreases, its demand increases and its supply decreases. Figure 1-57 illustrates the graphs of typical linear supply and demand functions.

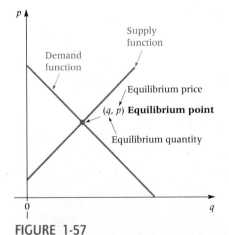

FIGURE 1-57

Economists often must determine the point where supply equals demand. Such a point is called the **equilibrium point.** Graphically, this is the intersection point of the graphs of the supply and demand functions, as illustrated in Figure 1-57. The first coordinate of the equilibrium point is called the **equilibrium quantity;** the second coordinate is called the **equilibrium price.** The equilibrium price is the unit price at which supply = demand for a given product.

We now consider the example below.

• **EXAMPLE 1-20** ————————————————————————

The demand and supply equations for some commodity are given below.

$$\text{Demand equation:}\quad p = -2q + 100$$
$$\text{Supply equation:}\quad p = 3q$$

Determine the equilibrium point.

Solution

Since the equilibrium point is the intersection of the graphs of the demand and supply functions, it is found by equating the values of p given by the demand and supply equations. This gives

$$3q = -2q + 100$$

Solving for q gives

$$5q = 100$$
$$q = 20 \qquad \text{Equilibrium quantity}$$

The *equilibrium price* is determined by substituting the equilibrium quantity into either the supply or the demand equation. Arbitrarily selecting the supply equation, we get

$$p = 3q$$
$$p = 3(20) = \$60 \qquad \text{Equilibrium price}$$

If we had selected the demand equation, we would have gotten the same result, as is shown below.

$$p = -2q + 100$$
$$= -2(20) + 100$$
$$= \$60$$

The graphical illustration is given in Figure 1-58. Note that only the first quadrant portion of the graph of each function is shown since each function has meaning only for non-negative values of q and p.

• ——

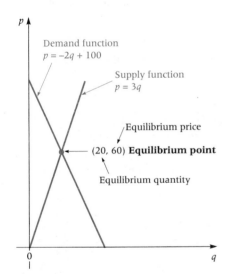

FIGURE 1-58

Exercises 1-5

Break-Even Point

For each of the following, determine the cost, sales revenue, and profit equations. Also, determine the *x*-coordinate of the break-even point by two methods.

1. $F = \$1000$, $v = \$5$, $s = \$9$
2. $F = \$8000$, $v = \$6$, $s = \$14$
3. $F = \$100{,}000$, $v = \$20$, $s = \$120$

4. $F = \$150,000$, $v = \$30$, $s = \$180$
5. $F = \$80,000$, $v = \$25$, $s = \$65$
6. $F = \$90,000$, $v = \$30$, $s = \$75$

7. A manufacturer has fixed costs of $2000 and a variable cost of $5 per unit. She sells her product for $15 apiece.
   a) Find the cost equation that relates cost to the number of units produced.
   b) Find the sales revenue equation that relates sales revenue to the number of units produced.
   c) Sketch both the cost and sales revenue equations on the same set of axes.
   d) Find the break-even point.
   e) Find the profit equation that relates profit to the number of units produced.
   f) Sketch the profit equation.
   g) Find the profit that results from producing and selling 300 units of this product.
   h) Find the profit that results from producing and selling 100 units of this product.
   i) How many units must be produced and sold in order to obtain a profit of $40,000?

8. The WVW Corporation has fixed costs of $5000. Its variable cost for producing 400 units is $16,000. The corporation sells its product for $60 apiece.
   a) Find the cost equation.
   b) Find the sales revenue equation.
   c) Sketch both the cost and sales revenue equations on the same set of axes.
   d) Find the break-even point.
   e) Find the profit equation.
   f) Sketch the profit equation.
   g) Find the profit that results from producing and selling 450 units.
   h) How many units must be produced and sold in order to yield a profit of $25,000?

TABLE 1-13

Fixed costs	
Administrative	$200,000
Building and land	50,000
Other fixed overhead	10,000
Variable cost for 100 units of production	
Materials	$ 50,000
Labor	70,000
Selling expense	10,000
Selling price per unit	$ 1,800

9. The VUV Corporation has presented the information in Table 1-13 to its accountant.
   a) Find the variable cost per unit.
   b) Find the cost equation.
   c) Find the sales revenue equation.
   d) Sketch both the cost and sales revenue functions on the same graph.
   e) Find the break-even point.
   f) Find the profit equation.
   g) Sketch the profit equation.
   h) Find the profit that results from producing and selling of 1000 units.
   i) How many units must be produced and sold in order to obtain a profit of $104,000?

10. Envelex, Inc., produces two types of envelopes, EZ101 and EZ102. Projections for the next year are given in Table 1-14.
    a) Determine the profit equation for EZ101.
    b) Determine the break-even point for EZ101.
    c) How many units of EZ101 should be sold in order to yield a profit of $4000?
    d) Determine the profit equation for EZ102.
    e) Determine the break-even point for EZ102.
    f) How many units of EZ102 should be sold in order to yield a profit of $5000?

TABLE 1-14

	EZ101		EZ102	
	units	amount	units	amount
Sales	10,000	$15,000	8,000	$16,800
Costs				
Fixed		$ 1,600		$ 5,100
Variable		7,000		3,200
		$ 8,600		$ 8,300

g) If customers purchase composite units of 4 EZ101s and 3 EZ102s, determine the composite profit equation and break-even point.

h) If customers purchase composite units of 1 EZ101 and 1 EZ102, determine the composite profit equation and break-even point.

11. *This problem appeared on a past Uniform CPA Examination.* Use the information in Table 1-15 to answer the following questions. Let x = number of units produced and sold.
   a) Find the sales revenue equation.
   b) Find the cost equation.
   c) Find the break-even point.
   d) Find the profit equation.
   e) How many units should be sold in order to yield a profit of 4000?
   f) What would be the operating income if sales increased by 25%?
   g) What would be the break-even point if fixed factory overhead increased by $1700?

12. *This problem appeared on a past Uniform CPA Examination.* The Jarvis Company has fixed costs of $200,000. It has two products that it can sell: Tetra and Min. Jarvis sells these products at a rate of 2 units of Tetra to 1 unit of Min. The unit profit is $1 per unit for Tetra and $2 per unit for Min. How many units of Min would be sold at the break-even point?

13. The Algor Company markets two statistical software packages, Stat I and Stat

TABLE 1-15 **Full Ton Company financial projection for product USA for the year ended December 31, 19x7**

Sales (100 units @ $100 a unit)		$10,000
Manufacturing cost of goods sold		
Direct labor	$1,500	
Direct materials used	1,400	
Variable factory overhead	1,000	
Fixed factory overhead	500	
Total manufacturing cost of goods sold		4,400
Gross profit		5,600
Selling expenses		
Variable	600	
Fixed	1,000	
Administrative expenses		
Variable	500	
Fixed	1,000	
Total selling and administrative expenses		3,100
Operating income		$ 2,500

II, which account for 60% and 40%, respectively, of the total sales revenue of Algor. Stat I's variable cost is 60% of its sales revenue, and Stat II's is 85% of its sales revenue. Total fixed costs are $180,000.

a) Determine Algor's break-even point in sales dollars.

b) If Algor's total fixed costs increase by 40%, determine the sales revenue necessary to yield a profit of $105,000.

14. A company's projected sales volume for one of its products is 300,000 units. The fixed cost is $500,000, and the variable cost is 60% of the selling price. Determine the unit selling price necessary to yield a profit of $340,000.

Equilibrium Point

For each of the following, determine the equilibrium point. State the equilibrium price and the equilibrium quantity.

15. Demand equation: $p = \dfrac{-7}{3}q + 31$

Supply equation: $p = \dfrac{5}{3}q + 15$

16. Demand equation: $p = -5q + 68$
Supply equation: $p = 9q + 40$

17. Demand equation: $p = \dfrac{-1}{3}q + 13$

Supply equation: $p = \dfrac{1}{4}q + 6$

18. Demand equation: $p = -3q + 90$
Supply equation: $p = 5q + 42$

19. Susan Time can sell 150 watches at a price of $35 each. If the price drops to $20 apiece, Susan can sell 300 watches.

a) Find the linear demand equation.
Susan's suppliers are willing to supply only 125 watches if the price per watch is $25. However, if the price per watch increases to $40 per watch, the suppliers are willing to provide Susan with 350 watches.

b) Find the linear supply equation.

c) Sketch both the supply and demand equations on the same set of axes.

d) Find the equilibrium point.

e) For supply to equal demand, Susan's watches must be priced at how much apiece?

EXTRA DIVIDENDS

• *Cost Accounting: Cost Segregation*

Businesses usually collect data giving total costs associated with various levels of a given quantity. Such data are often used to segregate the fixed and variable portions of a total cost value. Table 1-16 gives equipment repair costs for various hours of operation of a particular machine used to make precision tools. The data span a time interval of 6 months. Note that we have indicated the highest and lowest monthly repair costs.

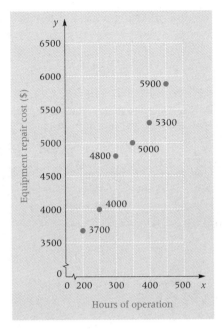

FIGURE 1-59

TABLE 1-16

	Hours of operation	Equipment repair cost ($)	
January	250	4000	
February	300	4800	
March	200	3700	Low
April	400	5300	
May	350	5000	
June	450	5900	High

The data are plotted to give a graph of cost versus hours of operation as illustrated in Figure 1-59. Observe that the data points are not collinear. In other words, they do not lie in the path of a straight line.

The firm's cost accountant is faced with the following problem.

PROBLEM

Determine the fixed monthly equipment repair cost and the variable equipment repair cost per hour of operation.

SOLUTION

Although the data points are not collinear, they seem to have a linear trend. If we can find the equation of a straight line that captures the trend of the data, then

1. Its y-intercept estimates the monthly fixed repair cost.
2. Its slope estimates the variable repair cost per hour of operation

One such straight line passes through the points of highest and lowest costs. Thus, the cost accountant determines the equation of the straight line passing through the points labeled High and Low in Table 1-16 and Figure 1-60. Accordingly, this method of segregating the fixed and variable portions of cost is called the **high-low point method.**

Using the points of highest and lowest costs, the cost accountant finds the slope (and also the estimated variable cost per hour) to be

$$\text{Slope} \qquad m = \frac{5900 - 3700}{450 - 200} = 8.80 \qquad \text{Variable cost per hour}$$

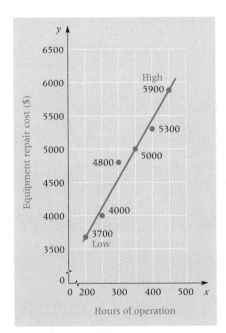

FIGURE 1-60

Using the point-slope form and choosing either the point of lowest cost or the point of highest cost gives

$$y - y_1 = m(x - x_1) \qquad \text{Point-slope form}$$
$$y - 3700 = 8.80(x - 200)$$

Solving for y gives the slope-intercept form

$$y = 8.80x + 1940$$

variable cost ↑   ↑ fixed monthly
per hour of ┘   └ repair cost
operation

We summarize the high-low point method of fitting a straight line to a set of data points.

High-Low Point Method

Given a set of data points relating total costs associated with various levels of some quantity, an equation defining a linear cost function can be determined from the data as follows:

1. Choose the points of *highest* and *lowest* costs.
2. Find the equation of the straight line passing through these points.
3. The y-*intercept* of the straight line estimates the *fixed cost;* the *slope* estimates the *variable cost per unit.*

This is graphically illustrated in Figure 1-61.

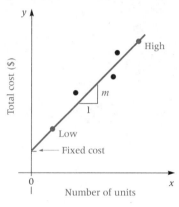

slope = variable cost per unit

FIGURE 1-61

Note: This method works best when a plot of the data points reveals a linear trend.

The advantage of the high-low point method is that it is quick and easy to apply. A more accurate method of fitting a straight line to a set of data points will be presented in a later chapter.

Exercises

1. *Electric power costs.* Table 1-17 lists electric power costs associated with various hours of operation for some firm.
   a) Use the high-low point method to find the equation of the linear cost function that fits this set of data points.
   b) State the fixed cost.
   c) State the variable cost per hour.

2. *Office expense.* Table 1-18 lists office expenses associated with hours of operation for some firm.
   a) Use the high-low point method to find the equation of the linear cost function that fits this set of data points.

TABLE 1-17

Hours	Cost ($)
5800	7000
5000	6500
5600	6700
5900	7400

TABLE 1-18

Hours	Cost ($)
4000	41,000
5000	48,000
6000	59,000

TABLE 1-19

	Highest	Lowest
Cost per month	$39,200	$32,000
Machine hours	24,000	15,000

b) State the fixed cost.
c) State the variable cost per hour.

The following problems have appeared on past Uniform CPA Examinations. The questions have been adapted to conform to the format of these exercises.

3. *Maintenance expenses.* The maintenance expenses of a company are to be analyzed for purposes of constructing a flexible budget. Examination of past records disclosed the costs and volume measures listed in Table 1-19. Using the high-low point method of analysis,
   a) Determine the estimated variable cost per machine hour.
   b) Determine the estimated monthly fixed cost for maintenance expenditures.
   c) Use the result of part b to determine the estimated annual fixed cost for maintenance expenditures.

4. Paine Corporation wishes to determine the fixed portion of its electricity expense (a semivariable expense), as measured against direct labor hours, for the first 3 months of a given year. Information for the first 3 months is listed in Table 1-20. What is the fixed portion of Paine's electricity expense rounded to the nearest dollar?

TABLE 1-20

	Direct labor hours	Electricity expense ($)
January	34,000	610
February	31,000	585
March	34,000	610

EXTRA DIVIDENDS

• Model Fitting: Goodness of Fit

Table 1-21 gives a set of data that relates grades obtained on a mathematics exam by a very small class to the number of hours studied for the exam. Specifically, for each student, x denotes the number of hours that the student studied for the mathematics exam and y denotes the exam grade for that student.

Figure 1-62 gives a plot of the data points (x, y). Figure 1-63 gives a plot of the data and the graph of the straight line

$$y = 20x + 40$$

TABLE 1-21

x	Study time (in hours)	0.5	1.0	1.5	2.0	2.5	3.0
y	Exam grade	43	64	68	88	97	99

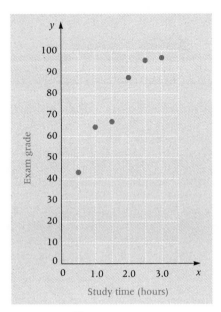

FIGURE 1-62

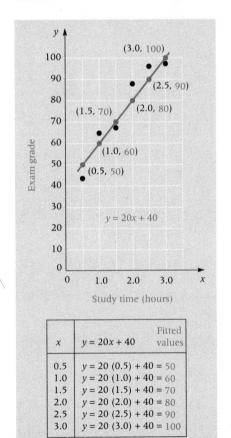

x	$y = 20x + 40$	Fitted values
0.5	$y = 20(0.5) + 40 = 50$	
1.0	$y = 20(1.0) + 40 = 60$	
1.5	$y = 20(1.5) + 40 = 70$	
2.0	$y = 20(2.0) + 40 = 80$	
2.5	$y = 20(2.5) + 40 = 90$	
3.0	$y = 20(3.0) + 40 = 100$	

FIGURE 1-63

that appears to capture the relationship between x and y. Observe, in Figure 1-63, that the fitted values are determined by substituting the x-values into the equation of the fitted linear model. Hence, the fitted values are simply the y-coordinates of points on the fitted line.

We will not be concerned with how the equation (or, in other words, the linear model) $y = 20x + 40$ was obtained. Such discussion is the topic of Section 15-4 in the calculus portion of this text. In this section, we address the issue of assessing the goodness of fit of a straight line fit to a set of data points.

● *Goodness of Fit*

To assess the goodness of fit of a model fit to a set of data, we determine, for each data point, the vertical distance between the given data point and the fitted line, as illustrated in Figure 1-64. Such vertical distances are called **residuals** and indicate the extent to which the fitted model does not fit the data points. An overall measure of the extent to which the fitted model (in this case, the straight line) does not fit the data is given by the sum of the squares of the residuals. This result is called the sum of squares error and is denoted by S, as is shown below.

Sum of Squares Error

$$S = (43 - 50)^2 + (64 - 60)^2 + (68 - 70)^2 + (88 - 80)^2 + (97 - 90)^2 + (99 - 100)^2$$

$$= (-7)^2 + (4)^2 + (-2)^2 + (8)^2 + (7)^2 + (-1)^2$$

$$= 183 \quad \text{Sum of squares error}$$

If another straight line, say

$$y = 10x + 60$$

is fitted to the set of data points, it can be determined whether or not this line is a better fit to the data by computing the sum of squares error for this line and comparing the result with that of the previous line, $y = 20x + 40$. The better-fitting line is the one that has a smaller sum of squares error. The residuals for the new line, $y = 10x + 60$, are illustrated in Figure 1-65, and the sum of squares error is computed below.

Sum of Squares Error

$$S = (43 - 65)^2 + (64 - 70)^2 + (68 - 75)^2 + (88 - 80)^2 + (97 - 85)^2 + (99 - 90)^2$$

$$= (-22)^2 + (-6)^2 + (-7)^2 + (8)^2 + (12)^2 + (9)^2$$

$$= 858 \quad \text{Sum of squares error}$$

Since the sum of squares error for the first line is less than that for the second line, the first line, $y = 20x + 40$, better-fits this set of data than does the second line, $y = 10x + 60$.

We summarize as follows.

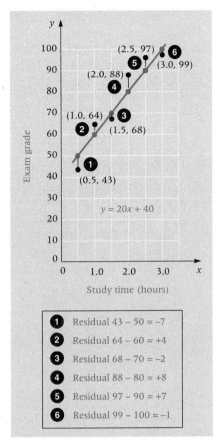

FIGURE 1-64

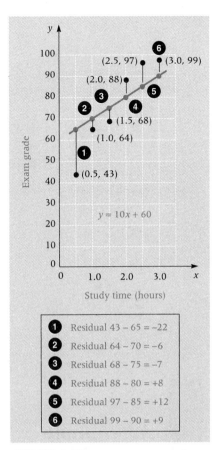

FIGURE 1-65

To Determine Goodness of Fit

The **goodness of fit** of a model fitted to a given set of data points is determined as follows:

1. Compute the **fitted values** by substituting the x-values of the data points into the equation of the fitted model.
2. Compute the **residual** for each data point in accordance with the formula.

$$\text{residual} = \text{data value} - \text{fitted value}$$

3. Compute the **sum of squares error, S,** as given below.

$$S = \text{sum of the squares of the residuals}$$

Note: The sum of squares error is an overall measure of the extent to which the fitted model does not fit the data.

Note: If more than one model is fit to the same set of data points, then the model resulting in the **smallest** sum of squares error is the better-fitting model for the set of data point.

If different types of models are fit to a given set of data points, the sum of squares error can be used to determine which type of model better fits the data according to this criterion. The model resulting in the smaller sum of squares error is the better-fitting model.

Lastly, we mention that in Section 15-4, we will learn how to find the equation of a straight line that best fits a set of data points. This entails the use of calculus, which we will study in later chapters of this text.

Exercises

For each of the following sets of data, the equations of two fitted linear models are given.
a) Determine the sum of squares error for each fitted linear model.
b) Write the equation of the better-fitting linear model.

1.

x	2	4	6	8	9
y	7	9	13	16	25

$y = 2x + 1$
$y = 3x - 2$

2.

x	1	3	4	7	9
y	9	13	16	24	35

$y = 3x + 5$
$y = 4x + 1$

3.

x	2	3	7	8	9
y	6	9	19	28	35

$y = 4x - 3$
$y = 3x + 2$

4.

x	2	4	5	8	9
y	9	19	27	38	47

$y = 5x - 1$
$y = 4x + 5$

Applications

Time Series

A set of data that relates some quantity to time is called a **time series.** The data in Exercises 5, 6, and 7 constitute time series. For these exercises, the variable, x, denotes successive time periods, such as weeks, months, quarters, or years, and the variable, y, denotes the quantity related to time.

5. *Stock prices: S&P 500.* The following data give quarterly values of Standard & Poors 500 Composite Index (denoted S&P 500), which measures stock market movement. The S&P 500 values given here begin with the second quarter of 1985 and end with the third quarter of 1988. The successive quarters are denoted by $x = 1, x = 2, \dots , x = 14$.

x	1	2	3	4	5	6	7
y S&P 500	153.18	166.10	167.24	180.66	191.85	182.08	211.28
x	8	9	10	11	12	13	14
y S&P 500	238.90	250.84	231.32	242.17	291.70	304.00	337.00

The following two linear models are fit to this set of data:

$$y = 13x + 130 \qquad y = 20x + 70$$

a) Determine the sum of squares error for each fitted linear model.
b) Write the equation of the better-fitting linear model.

6. *Stock prices: S&P 500.* The following data give quarterly values of Standard & Poors 500 Composite Index (denoted S&P 500), which measures stock market movement. The S&P 500 values given here begin with the fourth quarter of

1972 and end with the third quarter of 1974. The successive quarters are denoted by $x = 1, x = 2, \ldots, x = 8$.

x	1	2	3	4	5	6	7	8
y S&P 500	118.05	111.52	104.26	108.43	97.55	93.98	86.00	63.54

The following two linear models are fit to this set of data:

$$y = -7x + 130 \qquad y = -10x + 140$$

a) Determine the sum of squares error for each fitted linear model.
b) Write the equation of the better-fitting linear model.

7. *Systolic Blood Pressure (SBP).* A person's systolic blood pressure (SBP) is recorded weekly with the following results:

x Week	1	2	3	4	5	6	7	8	9
y SBP	125	128	130	129	135	138	140	146	145

The following two linear models are fit to this set of data:

$$y = 3x + 120 \qquad y = 4x + 115$$

a) Determine the sum of squares error for each fitted linear model.
b) Write the equation of the better-fitting linear model.

8. *Education.* The data below relate undergraduate grade point average (GPA) to starting salary (in thousands of dollars) for a sample of recent graduates at a small liberal arts college.

x GPA	2.5	3.0	2.4	3.5	2.1	2.6
y Starting salary	15.5	19.7	15.2	22.8	14.6	15.8

The following two linear models are fit to this set of data:

$$y = 6x + 1 \qquad y = 7x - 1$$

a) Determine the sum of squares error for each fitted linear model.
b) Write the equation of the better-fitting linear model.

9. *Medical science.* The data below relate serum cholesterol level (in milligrams/100 milliliters) with age for a sample of adult males.

x Age	20	35	27	40	49	55
y Cholesterol	210	279	230	190	252	287

The following two linear models are fit to the set of data:

$$y = 2x + 170 \qquad y = 3x + 100$$

a) Determine the sum of squares error for each fitted linear model.
b) Write the equation of the better-fitting linear model.

CHAPTER 1 HIGHLIGHTS

• *Concepts*

Your ability to answer the following questions is one indicator of the depth of your mastery of this chapter's important concepts. Note that the questions are grouped under various topic headings. For any question that you cannot answer, refer to the section of the chapter indicated by the topic heading. Pay particular attention to the summary boxes within a section.

1-1 FUNCTIONS

1. Explain the following terms: function, domain, range, dependent variable, independent variable, ordered pair, x-coordinate, y-coordinate, x-axis, y-axis, origin, quadrant.
2. A function is usually defined by a (an) _____ that expresses a (an) _____ between two quantities.
3. How can we determine whether or not a given graph represents a function?
4. Draw a graph of the absolute value function.
5. If a function is defined by more than one formula, the function is said to be _____ defined.

1-2 SLOPE AND EQUATIONS OF STRAIGHT LINES

6. Which of the following do not represent slope?
   a) Steepness of a straight line.
   b) Rate of change of the dependent variable with respect to the independent variable.
   c) Vertical change/horizontal change.
   d) Horizontal change/vertical change.
7. A straight line, $y = mx + b$, has slope $= -5/3$. State the effect on y if x increases by 3 units.
8. Draw a graph that typifies a straight line with

   a) Positive slope.   b) Negative slope.
   c) Zero slope.   d) Undefined slope.
9. A straight line with an equation of the form $y = mx$ passes through the _____.
10. A horizontal straight line has an equation of the form _____.
11. A vertical straight line has an equation of the form _____.
12. A linear equation in slope-intercept form is easily graphed by first plotting the _____ and then drawing the straight line upward to the right if its slope is _____ or upward to the left if its slope is _____.
13. A tax function is an example of a piecewise-defined function. The different slopes of a tax function represent _____ _____.

1-3 GRAPHING LINEAR EQUATIONS

14. Explain the following terms: x-intercept, y-intercept.
15. An x-intercept has a y-coordinate that equals _____.
16. A y-intercept has an x-coordinate that equals _____.
17. State the procedure for graphing a linear equation of the form $ax + by = c$.
18. State the procedure for graphing a linear equation of the form $y = mx$.

1-4 LINEAR MODELS

Cost, Sales Revenue, and Profit Functions

19. A cost function expresses a relationship between what two quantities?
20. A sales revenue function expresses a relationship between what two quantities?
21. A profit function expresses a relationship between what two quantities?
22. Give an interpretation of the slope of a linear cost function.
23. The y-intercept of a cost function is the _____ _____ ; explain this term.

Supply and Demand Functions

24. A demand equation relates the quantities _____ and _____.

25. A supply equation relates the quantities _____ and _____.

Consumption Function and MPC

26. A consumption function relates the quantities _____ and _____.

27. Give an interpretation of the MPC.

Linear Depreciation

28. Give the linear equation that relates the value of an asset to its age. Interpret its y-intercept and slope.

1-5 **BREAK-EVEN ANALYSIS; MARKET EQUILIBRIUM**

Break-Even Point

29. Give an interpretation of a break-even point.
30. Given cost and sales revenue functions, state the procedure for finding the break-even point.
31. The x-intercept of a profit function equals the x-coordinate of the _____-_____ _____.
32. Given a profit function, state the procedure for finding the break-even point.

Market Equilibrium

33. Graphically, an equilibrium point is the _____ of a supply function and a (an) _____ function.
34. Give an interpretation of the coordinates of an equilibrium point.

REVIEW EXERCISES

• Functions and Functional Notation

For each of the following, calculate $f(0)$, $f(1)$, and $f(3)$.

1. $f(x = 4x - 2$ **2.** $f(x) = 5x + 3$

3. $f(x) = x^2 + 2x - 1$ **4.** $f(x) = \dfrac{3x + 5}{x + 1}$

For each of the following, calculate the difference quotient

$$\frac{f(x + h) - f(x)}{h}$$

5. $f(x) = 4x + 8$ **6.** $f(x) = x^2 + 6x - 5$
7. $f(x) = x^2 - 4x + 3$ **8.** $f(x) = x^3 - x^2 + 7$

Specify the domain of each of the following functions.

9. $f(x) = \sqrt{x - 4}$ **10.** $f(x) = \sqrt{x + 8}$

11. $f(x) = \dfrac{x + 6}{(x - 7)(x + 5)}$ **12.** $f(x) = \dfrac{4x + 10}{x - 2}$

● *Functions and Graphs*

State whether each of the following is the graph of a function.

13.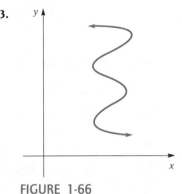

FIGURE 1-66

14.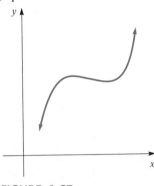

FIGURE 1-67

Graph each of the following.

15. $f(x) = \begin{cases} 2 & \text{if } x \le 3 \\ 5 & \text{if } 3 < x \le 8 \\ x & \text{if } x > 8 \end{cases}$

16. $g(x) = \begin{cases} -1 & \text{if } x \le 2 \\ x & \text{if } 2 < x \le 5 \\ 7 & \text{if } x > 5 \end{cases}$

17. *Call options.* An investor bought a call option entitling her to buy a specified number of shares of a stock for $20 per share during the next 3 months. The investor paid $4 per share for the call option. Determine the investor's profit function per share of stock. Graph the profit function.

● *Slope and Equations of Straight Lines*

Find the slope of the straight line passing through each of the following pairs of points.

18. $(3, -7)$ and $(-8, 26)$ **19.** $(6, 5)$ and $(4, -3)$

Find the equation of the straight line passing through each of the following pairs of points. Express the answer in slope-intercept form.

20. $(-1, 6)$ and $(4, 16)$ **21.** $(3, -2)$ and $(5, 8)$

For each of the following, determine which of the given points lie on the straight line.

22. $2x + 5y = 20$: $(0, 4), (10, 0), (2, 4), (5, 2), (3, 4)$
23. $4x - 2y = 10$: $(1, -3), (2, 5), (0, -5), (3, 0), (-1, -2)$

Draw the graph of a straight line that passes through the origin and has

24. Positive slope.   **25.** Negative slope.

Draw the graph of a straight line that passes through $(3, 4)$ and

26. Has slope $= 0$.   **27.** Has an undefined slope.

Write the equation of the straight line of

28. Exercise 26.   **29.** Exercise 27.

Which of the following pairs of straight lines are parallel?

30. $y = 5x + 7$, $y = 4x - 9$ **31.** $2x + 6y = 30$, $-4x - 12y = 24$

32. *Defects: U.S. automobiles.* The number of defects per 100 vehicles for Chrysler's North American operations declined from 810 to 175 during the years from 1979 to 1989.
   a) Find the slope of the straight line that indicates this trend.
   b) Interpret the slope.
   c) Find the equation of the straight line. Express the final answer in slope-intercept form.
   d) If Chrysler's defects continue to decline at the same rate, predict its defects per 100 vehicles (North America) for the year 1991.

• Graphing Linear Equations

Graph each of the following by finding the *x*- and *y*-intercepts.

33. $5x - 2y = 20$ **34.** $y = 7x - 14$
35. $f(x) = 6x$ **36.** $3x - 6y = 0$

• Cost, Sales Revenue, and Profit Functions

For Exercises 37 and 38, determine the linear cost, sales revenue, and profit equations. Graph each on the same set of axes. Determine the break-even point.

37. Variable cost per unit = $30, fixed cost = $1200, and unit selling price = $50
38. Variable cost per unit = $80, fixed cost = $1600, and unit selling price = $120

This problem is adapted from a past Uniform CPA Examination. The Dooley Company manufactures two products, baubles and trinkets. The Table 1-22 lists projections for the coming year:

39. Determine the profit equation for baubles.
40. Determine the break-even point for baubles.
41. Determine the profit equation for trinkets.
42. Determine the break-even point for trinkets.
43. If customers purchase composite units of 4 baubles and 3 trinkets, determine the composite profit equation and break-even point.

44. *Population.* The suburban population of a state is currrently 6,500,000 and is decreasing at the rate of 200,000 per year. The urban population is currently 3,700,000 and is increasing at the rate of 150,000 per year. How many years from now will both populations be equal?
45. *Market share.* The U.S. market share of Ford Motor Company was 20.8% for 1979 and 22.0% for 1989. The U.S. market share of Japanese automobiles was 15.2% for 1979 and 25.6% for 1989. Determine the break-even year.

TABLE 1-22

	Baubles		Trinkets	
	units	amount	units	amount
Sales	10,000	$10,000	7500	$10,000
Costs				
Fixed		$ 2000		$ 5600
Variable		6000		3000
		$ 8000		$ 8600
Income Before Taxes		$ 2000		$ 1400

• Supply, Demand, and Equilibrium Point

Determine the supply and demand equations and the equilibrium point. Graph the results.

46. *Demand:* If a given product is priced at $7 per unit, there is a demand for 4 units; if the product is priced at $6 per unit, there is a demand for 8 units.
Supply: If the product is priced at $9 per unit, suppliers are willing to produce 4 units; if the product is priced at $23 per unit, suppliers are willing to produce 12 units.

• Consumption Function, MPC, and MPS

For Exercises 47 and 48, if x denotes income and y denotes consumption, then
a) Calculate and interpret the MPC.
b) Calculate and interpret the MPS.
c) Determine the equation defining the linear consumption function.
d) Graph the result of part C.

47.

x	y
50	85
60	94

48.

x	y
40	62
70	86

• Linear Depreciation

49. A construction company buys a truck for $80,000. The useful life of the truck is 5 years, after which time it will have a scrap value of $5000.
a) Find the linear equation relating the value of the truck, y, to its age, x.
b) Graph the result of part a.
c) What is the value of the truck after 3 years?

2

GRAPHING POLYNOMIAL AND RATIONAL FUNCTIONS

Introductory Application

Revenue and Cost Functions and Break-Even Points

Revenue Function

In Chapter 1, we learned that if the unit selling price of a particular product is constant, the resulting revenue function is linear. However, for some businesses, the unit selling prices of their products depend on the demand levels of the products. Such a relationship between unit selling price and demand is given by a demand equation

$$p = f(x)$$

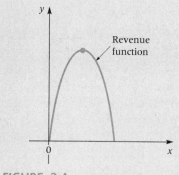

FIGURE 2-A

where p denotes the unit price and x denotes the number of units demanded of the product. The sales revenue function is defined as follows:

$$\text{sales revenue} = (\text{number of units sold})(\text{unit price})$$
$$R(x) = xp$$
$$= xf(x)$$

If the demand equation is linear, the sales revenue function usually resembles the curve of Figure 2-A. Studying the graph of the revenue function of Figure 2-A, notice that sales revenue increases up to a certain point and then decreases as the number of units sold increases. In Section 2-3, we will explain in greater detail why this occurs.

Break-Even Analysis

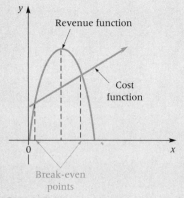

FIGURE 2-B

If a business's cost function is linear, then a graph of both the cost and sales revenue functions is typified by that of Figure 2-B[o]. Note, in Figure 2-B, that the intersection points of the graphs of the cost and revenue functions are the points where sales revenue = cost. As in Chapter 1, these points are called break-even points. We will discuss such cases more fully in Section 2-3.

2-1   • GRAPHING CONCEPTS

In this section, we discuss graphing concepts that enable us to quickly sketch the graphs of functions whose equations are derived from equations of functions with known graphs. Also, we will use these graphing concepts to explain the graphs of functions, where appropriate, in this chapter.

Vertical Shifts

We begin with the graph of the absolute value function

$$f(x) = |x|$$

that was discussed in Chapter 1. Recall that to each non-negative number, the absolute value function associates the non-negative number; to each negative number, the absolute value function associates the negative number's additive inverse.

We now consider the graph of the function

$$y = |x| + 4$$

The y-values of this new function are 4 greater than those of the absolute value function. Thus, the graph of $y = |x| + 4$ is obtained from the graph of $y = |x|$ by *lifting the graph* of $y = |x|$ *vertically by 4 units*. This is called a **vertical shift** and is illustrated in Figure 2-1.

Also, the graph of

$$y = |x| - 4$$

is obtained from the graph of $y = |x|$ by *lowering the graph* of $y = |x|$ *vertically by 4 units* as the y-values of $y = |x| - 4$ are 4 less than those of $y = |x|$. This *vertical shift* is also illustrated in Figure 2-1.

We generalize as follows.

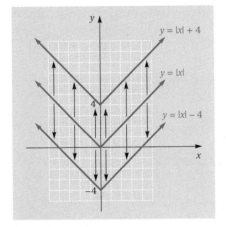

FIGURE 2-1

SUMMARY

Vertical Shifts

Assume the graph of $y = f(x)$ is known.

1. The graph of $y = f(x) + c$, where $c > 0$, is obtained by *lifting the graph* of $y = f(x)$ *vertically by c units,* as illustrated in Figure 2-2.

2. The graph of $y = f(x) - c$, where $c > 0$, is obtained by *lowering the graph* of $y = f(x)$ *vertically by c units,* as illustrated in Figure 2-2.

continues

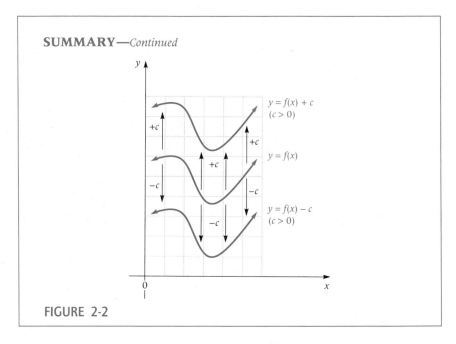

FIGURE 2-2

Horizontal Shifts

Consider the graph of

$$y = |x - 5|$$

as illustrated in Figure 2-3. Note that for any given value of y, the x-coordinates of points on $y = |x - 5|$ are 5 greater than those of $y = |x|$. Thus, the graph of $y = |x - 5|$ is obtained by *shifting the graph* of $y = |x|$ *horizontally to the right by 5 units,* as illustrated in Figure 2-3. This is an example of a **horizontal shift.**

Observe also in Figure 2-3 that the graph of the function

$$y = |x + 5|$$

is obtained by *shifting the graph* of $y = |x|$ *horizontally to the left by 5 units.* This is because for any given value of y, the x-coordinates of points on $y = |x + 5|$ are 5 less than those of $y = |x|$.

We generalize as follows.

SUMMARY

Horizontal Shifts

Assume that the graph of $y = f(x)$ is known.

1. The graph of $y = f(x - c)$, where $c > 0$, is obtained by *shifting the graph* of $y = f(x)$ *horizontally to the right by* c *units,* as illustrated in Figure 2-4.
2. The graph of $y = f(x + c)$, where $c > 0$, is obtained by *shifting the graph* of $y = f(x)$ *horizontally to the left by* c *units,* as illustrated in Figure 2-4.

continues

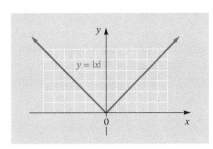

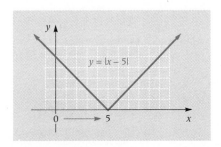

FIGURE 2-3

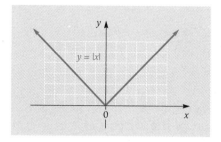

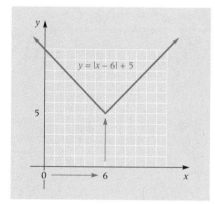

FIGURE 2-5

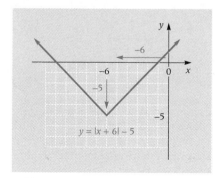

FIGURE 2-7

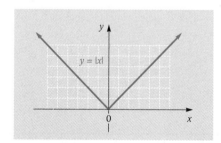

SUMMARY—*Continued*

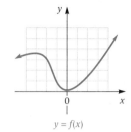 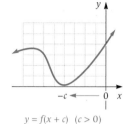 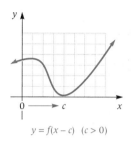

FIGURE 2-4

• **EXAMPLE 2-1** _____

Graph $y = |x - 6| + 5$.

Solution

This graph involves a horizontal shift followed by a vertical shift. First, the graph of $y = |x - 6|$ is obtained by shifting the graph of $y = |x|$ horizontally to the right by 6 units. Then the graph of $y = |x - 6| + 5$ is obtained by lifting the graph of $y = |x - 6|$ vertically by 5 units. This is illustrated in Figure 2-5. •

Horizontal and Vertical Shifts

A combination of horizontal and vertical shifts is illustrated, in general, in Figure 2-6.

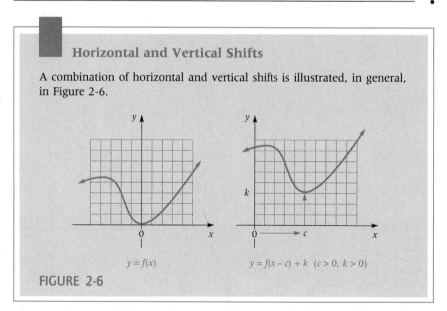

FIGURE 2-6

• **EXAMPLE 2-2** _____

Graph $y = |x + 6| - 5$.

Solution

The graph of $y = |x + 6|$ is obtained by shifting the graph of $y = |x|$ horizontally to the left by 6 units. Then the graph of $y = |x + 6| - 5$ is obtained by lowering the graph of $y = |x + 6|$ vertically by 5 units. This is illustrated in Figure 2-7. •

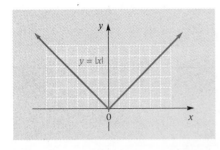

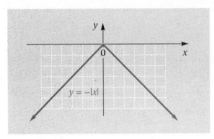

FIGURE 2-8

Reflections in the *x*-Axis

Consider the function

$$y = -|x|$$

Since the *y*-values of the function $y = -|x|$ are the negatives of those of $y = |x|$, then the graph of $y = -|x|$ is obtained by *drawing the graph* of $y = |x|$ *upside down*. This is called a **reflection in the *x*-axis** and is illustrated in Figure 2-8.

We generalize as follows.

SUMMARY

Reflections in the *x*-Axis

Assume the graph of $y = f(x)$ is known. The graph of $y = -f(x)$ is obtained by *drawing the graph* of $y = f(x)$ *upside down*, as illustrated in Figure 2-9.

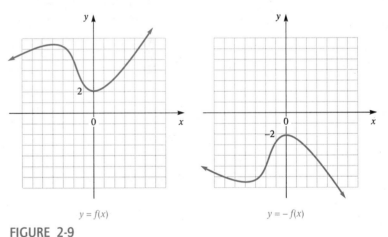

$y = f(x)$ $y = -f(x)$

FIGURE 2-9

• **EXAMPLE 2-3** _____

Graph $y = -|x - 3| + 5$.

Solution

We begin with the graph of $y = |x|$ and shift it horizontally to the right 3 units to obtain the graph of $y = |x - 3|$. Then we draw the graph of $y = |x - 3|$ upside down (reflection in the *x*-axis) to obtain the graph of $y = -|x - 3|$. Finally, we lift the graph of $y = -|x - 3|$ vertically 5 units (vertical shift) to obtain the graph of $y = -|x - 3| + 5$. This is illustrated in Figure 2-10.

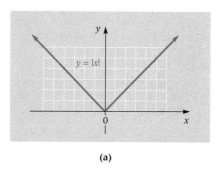

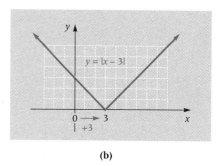

Horizontal shift

(a)

(b)

Reflection in the *x*-axis

Vertical shift

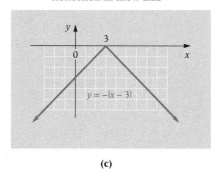

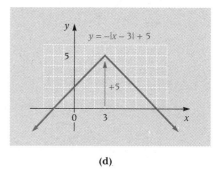

(c)

(d)

FIGURE 2-10

Symmetry with respect to the
vertical axis (even functions)

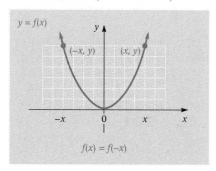

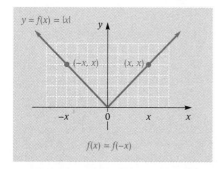

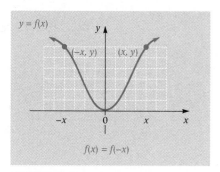

FIGURE 2-11

Symmetry

Observe the graphs of Figure 2-11. Note that for any of these graphs, if (x, y) is on the graph, then $(-x, y)$ is also on the graph. In other words, $f(-x) = f(x)$ for such functions. If a function f satisfies the above condition, it is called an **even function,** and its graph is **symmetrical with respect to the vertical axis.**

Observe the graphs of Figure 2-12 on page 72. Note that for any of these graphs, if (x, y) is on the graph, then $(-x, -y)$ is on the graph. In other words, $f(-x) = -f(x)$ for such functions. If a function satisfies this condition, it is called an **odd function,** and its graph is **symmetrical with respect to the origin.**

We generalize as follows.

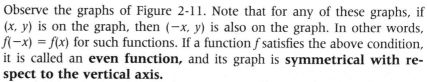

SUMMARY

Symmetry

1. *Symmetry with respect to the vertical axis.* If $f(-x) = f(x)$, then f is an **even function,** and its graph is symmetrical with respect to the vertical axis, as illustrated in Figure 2-13.

continues

**Symmetry with respect to the orgin
(odd functions)**

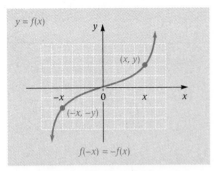

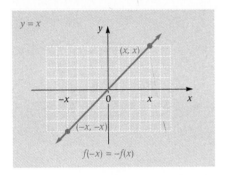

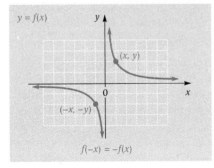

FIGURE 2-12

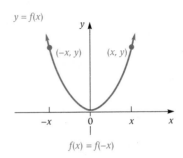

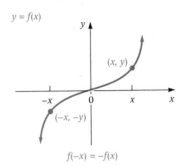

SUMMARY—*Continued*

FIGURE 2-13

2. *Symmetry with respect to the origin.* If $f(-x) = -f(x)$, then f is an **odd function,** and its graph is symmetrical with respect to the origin, as illustrated in Figure 2-14.

FIGURE 2-14

• **EXAMPLE 2-4** _____

Note that

$$f(x) = x^{2/3}$$

is an even function, as indicated by its table of x- and y-values below. Specifically, $f(-x) = f(x)$, and the graph of f is symmetrical with respect to the y-axis, as illustrated in Figure 2-15.

x	-3	-2	-1	0	1	2	3
$f(x)$	2.08	1.59	1	0	1	1.59	2.08

• **EXAMPLE 2-5** _____

Note that

$$f(x) = x^{1/3}$$

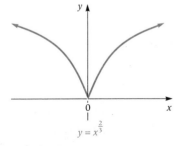

FIGURE 2-15

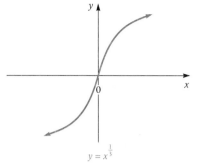

FIGURE 2-16

is an odd function, as indicated by its table of *x*- and *y*-values below. Specifically, $f(-x) = -f(x)$, and the graph of f is symmetrical with respect to the origin, as illustrated in Figure 2-16.

x	-3	-2	-1	0	1	2	3
$f(x)$	-1.44	-1.26	-1	0	1	1.26	1.44

Exercises 2-1

Graph each of the following.

1. $y = -|x - 2|$ **2.** $y = -|x + 6|$ **3.** $y = |x - 8| + 2$
4. $y = -|x - 6| + 4$ **5.** $y = -|x + 3| - 8$ **6.** $y = -|x + 7| - 9$

Observe the graph of $f(x) = x^{2/3}$ of Figure 2-15, Example 2-4. Then graph each of the following.

7. $f(x) = (x - 3)^{2/3}$ **8.** $f(x) = (x + 4)^{2/3}$
9. $f(x) = (x + 7)^{2/3} + 5$ **10.** $f(x) = (x - 6)^{2/3} - 2$
11. $f(x) = -(x - 5)^{2/3}$ **12.** $f(x) = -(x + 2)^{2/3}$
13. $f(x) = -(x - 3)^{2/3} - 1$ **14.** $f(x) = -(x + 2)^{2/3} + 4$

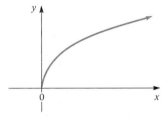

$f(x) = \sqrt{x}$

FIGURE 2-17

Observe the graph of $f(x) = x^{1/3}$ of Figure 2-16, Example 2-5. Then graph each of the following.

15. $f(x) = (x + 2)^{1/3}$ **16.** $f(x) = (x - 5)^{1/3}$
17. $f(x) = (x - 2)^{1/3} + 9$ **18.** $f(x) = (x + 1)^{1/3} - 2$
19. $f(x) = -(x - 1)^{1/3}$ **20.** $f(x) = -(x + 2)^{1/3}$
21. $f(x) = -(x - 5)^{1/3} + 2$ **22.** $f(x) = -(x - 4)^{1/3} + 7$

The graph of $f(x) = \sqrt{x}$ is given in Figure 2-17. Graph each of the following.

23. $f(x) = \sqrt{x - 5}$ **24.** $f(x) = \sqrt{x + 2}$
25. $f(x) = \sqrt{x + 9} + 2$ **26.** $f(x) = \sqrt{x - 4} - 6$
27. $f(x) = -\sqrt{x}$ **28.** $f(x) = -\sqrt{x} + 1$
29. $f(x) = -\sqrt{x} - 3$ **30.** $f(x) = -\sqrt{x + 1} - 2$

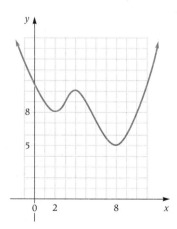

FIGURE 2-18

The graph of some function f is given in Figure 2-18. Graph each of the following.

31. $y = f(x - 2)$ **32.** $y = f(x + 4)$ **33.** $y = -f(x)$
34. $y = -f(x - 6)$ **35.** $y = f(x - 1) + 4$ **36.** $y = -f(x) + 5$
37. $y = -f(x - 2) + 1$ **38.** $y = -f(x + 1) - 2$ **39.** $y = -f(x) - 6$

For each of the graphs below, state whether the function is odd, even, or neither.

40.

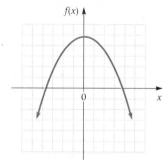

41.

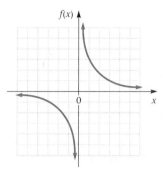

42.

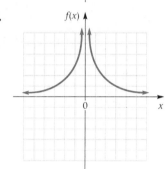

43.

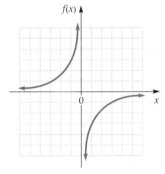

For each of the following:

a) Determine whether the function is odd, even, or neither by filling in the indicated table of x- and $f(x)$-values. Use a calculator if necessary.

b) Sketch a graph by plotting the points from part a.

44. $f(x) = x^2$

x	-3	-2	-1	0	1	2	3
$f(x)$							

45. $f(x) = x^3$

x	-3	-2	-1	0	1	2	3
$f(x)$							

46. $f(x) = 1/(1 + x^2)$

x	-3	-2	-1	$-1/2$	0	1/2	1	2	3
$f(x)$									

47. $f(x) = 1/x$

x	-3	-2	-1	$-1/2$	0	1/2	1	2	3
$f(x)$									

48. $f(x) = (x - 2)^2$

x	−3	−2	−1	0	1	2	3
$f(x)$							

Applications

Cost, Revenue, and Profit Functions

The graphs of cost, revenue, and profit functions for some product are given in Figure 2-19.

49. Indicate the effect on the graph of the cost function of a $100 increase in the fixed cost.

50. Indicate the effect on the graph of the profit function of a $100 increase in the fixed cost.

Market Dynamics: Supply, Demand, Equilibrium

In Chapter 1, we learned that a demand function relates the unit price of some product to the demand for that product. Also, a supply function relates the unit price of some product to the number of units supplied of the product. In Chapter 1, we worked with linear supply and demand functions. Thus, their corresponding graphs were straight lines. If the graph of a demand function is nonlinear, its graph is usually referred to as a **demand curve.** Analogously, if the graph of a supply function is nonlinear, its graph is called a **supply curve.**

51. The graphs of the supply and demand functions for some product are given in Figure 2-20. If the demand for this product increases by 5 units, then the graph of the demand function will shift horizontally to the right by 5 units, as illustrated. State the new equilibrium price.

52. Consider the supply and demand curves of Figure 2-21. If the supply of this product increases by 4 units, then the graph of the supply function will shift horizontally to the right by 4 units. State the new equilibrium price.

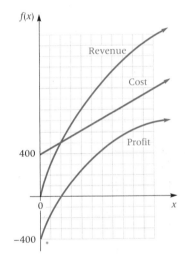

FIGURE 2-19

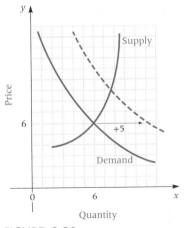

FIGURE 2-20

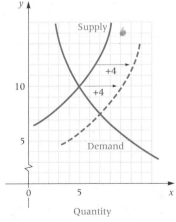

FIGURE 2-21

2-2 • QUADRATIC FUNCTIONS AND THEIR GRAPHS

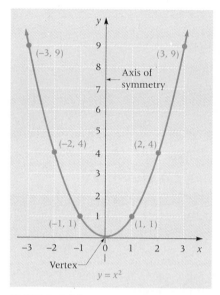

In this and the next section, we will learn to graph equations like

$$y = 3x^2 - 4x + 7$$

Such an equation defines a **quadratic function.** Note that the highest-powered term of a quadratic equation is of the **second degree.**

$$y = f(x) = 3x^2 - 4x + 7$$

second-degree   first-degree   constant
term   term   term

In general, any equation of the form

$$y = ax^2 + bx + c$$

where a, b, and c are constant real numbers and $a \neq 0$, is called a **quadratic equation.** Without the restriction $a \neq 0$, the equation becomes the linear equation $y = bx + c$.

If the quadratic equation

$$y = 3x^2 - 4x + 7$$

is compared with the general form

$$y = ax^2 + bx + c$$

then $a = 3$, $b = -4$, and $c = 7$.

As a start in learning to graph quadratic functions, we consider the simplest of all quadratic equations, which is

$$y = x^2$$

Comparing this equation with the general quadratic form, $y = ax^2 + bx + c$, we have $a = 1$, $b = 0$, and $c = 0$.

A sketch of $y = x^2$ may be obtained by finding some ordered pairs (x, y) satisfying the equation and plotting their corresponding points on the rectangular coordinate system. Arbitrarily choosing values of x and finding their corresponding y-values, we have the following:

x-*Value*	*Equation* $(y = x^2)$	*Ordered Pair* (x, y)
If $x = -3$, then	$y = (-3)^2 = 9$	$(-3, 9)$
If $x = -2$, then	$y = (-2)^2 = 4$	$(-2, 4)$
If $x = -1$, then	$y = (-1)^2 = 1$	$(-1, 1)$
If $x = 0$, then	$y = 0^2 = 0$	$(0, 0)$
If $x = 1$, then	$y = 1^2 = 1$	$(1, 1)$
If $x = 2$, then	$y = 2^2 = 4$	$(2, 4)$
If $x = 3$, then	$y = 3^2 = 9$	$(3, 9)$

Plotting the ordered pairs (x, y) and sketching the curve through them, we obtain the graph of Figure 2-22. This graph form is called a **parabola.** In

FIGURE 2-22

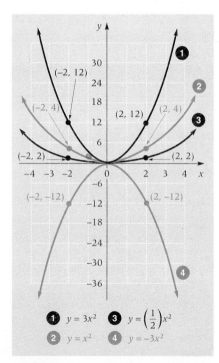

FIGURE 2-23

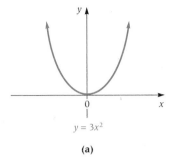

$y = 3x^2$

(a)

Horizontal shift

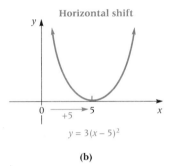

$y = 3(x - 5)^2$

(b)

Vertical shift

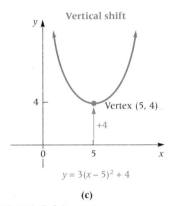

Vertex (5, 4)

$y = 3(x - 5)^2 + 4$

(c)

FIGURE 2-24

fact, the graph of any quadratic function is a parabola. Note that the origin, $(0, 0)$, is the lowest point on the parabola $y = x^2$ of Figure 2-22. The lowest point on the parabola is called the **vertex.** Thus, $(0, 0)$ is the vertex of $y = x^2$.

Still referring to the parabola $y = x^2$ of Figure 2-22 note that the y-axis separates the parabola into two symmetrical parts, each the mirror image of the other. Such a vertical line passing through the vertex is called the **axis of symmetry.**

We now consider quadratic equations of the form

$$y = ax^2$$

with a $\neq$ 1. If a > 0, then the parabola has the same general shape as $y = x^2$ of Figure 2-22, but it is narrowed if a > 1 and widened if $a < 1$. If $a < 0$, then the y-coordinates are negative, and the parabola appears below the x-axis. To illustrate these comments, see the graphs of $y = x^2$ $y = 3x^2$, $y = (1/2)x^2$, and $y = -3x^2$ in Figure 2-23.

The graphs of quadratic functions with a > 0 are said to *open up,* whereas those with $a < 0$ are said to *open down.* Thus, the graphs of $y = x^2$, $y = 3x^2$, and $y = (1/2)x^2$ of Figure 2-23 are described as opening up, while the graph of $y = -3x^2$ is said to open down. Note that for a parabola that *opens down,* its **vertex** is the *highest point* on the parabola.

We now consider the graph of the quadratic function defined by

$$y = 3(x - 5)^2 + 4$$

The graph of this function can be sketched by drawing the graph of $y = 3x^2$, shifting it horizontally to the right by 5 units, and then shifting the result vertically by 4 units. This is illustrated in Figure 2-24.

In general, the graph of the quadratic function defined by
$$y = a(x - h)^2 + k$$
1. Opens up if $a > 0$ and opens down if $a < 0$.
2. Has its vertex at (h, k).
3. Has the line $x = h$ as its axis of symmetry.

We now consider quadratic equations of the form

$$y = f(x) = ax^2 + bx + c$$

We will derive a formula for the x = coordinate of the vertex, (h, k), in terms of a, b, and c by expressing the equation $y = a(x - h)^2 + k$ in the form $y = ax^2 + bx + c$. We begin with $y = a(x - h)^2 + k$ and replace $(x - h)^2$ with its equivalent expression, $x^2 - 2hx + h^2$, to obtain

$$y = a(x^2 - 2hx + h^2) + k$$

Simplifying this expression, we get

$$y = ax^2 - 2ahx + ah^2 + k$$

Comparing this result with the general quadratic form, $y = ax^2 + bx + c$, we have

$$b = -2ah \quad \text{and} \quad c = ah^2 + k$$

Solving the equation $b = -2ah$ for h, we obtain

$$h = \frac{-b}{2a} \qquad \textit{x-coordinate of vertex}$$

Of course, the corresponding y-coordinate of the vertex is obtained by substituting the above result into the quadratic equation. Thus, the y-coordinate of the vertex is given by

$$f(-b/2a) \qquad \textit{y-coordinate of vertex}$$

We now consider the following example.

• **EXAMPLE 2-6** _____

Graph $y = f(x) = 3x^2 + 5x + 2$.

Solution

Comparing this equation with the form $y = f(x) = ax^2 + bx + c$, we have $a = 3$, $b = 5$, and $c = 2$. Since a is positive, the parabola opens up. The $x =$ coordinate of the vertex, (h, k), is

$$h = -\frac{b}{2a} = -\frac{5}{2(3)} = -\frac{5}{6} \qquad \textit{x-coordinate of vertex}$$

The y-coordinate of the vertex is

$$f\left(-\frac{b}{2a}\right) = f\left(-\frac{5}{6}\right) = 3\left(-\frac{5}{6}\right)^2 + 5\left(-\frac{5}{6}\right) + 2 = -\frac{1}{12} \qquad \textit{y-coordinate of vertex}$$

Thus, the vertex is $(-5/6, -1/12)$.

The y-intercept is

$$y = f(0) = 3(0^2) + 5(0) + 2 = 2$$

The x-intercepts are found by setting $y = 0$ and solving for x. Hence,

$$0 = 3x^2 + 5x + 2$$
$$0 = (3x + 2)(x + 1)$$
$$3x + 2 = 0 \qquad\qquad x + 1 = 0$$
$$x = -\frac{2}{3} \qquad\qquad x = -1$$

Therefore, the x-intercepts are $(-2/3, 0)$ and $(-1, 0)$. The graph appears in Figure 2-25.

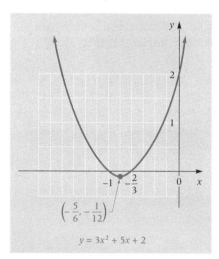

$$\left(-\frac{5}{6}, -\frac{1}{12}\right)$$

$$y = 3x^2 + 5x + 2$$

FIGURE 2-25

Quadratic Formula

When finding the x-intercepts of a parabola, we must often solve a quadratic equation of the form

$$ax^2 + bx + c = 0$$

where a, b, and c are constant real numbers and $a \neq 0$. Sometimes such an equation may be solved by factoring, as was the case in Example 2-6. A more general method is given by the **quadratic formula.***

Quadratic Formula

$$x = \frac{-b \pm \sqrt{b^2 - 4ac}}{2a}$$

We will review the use of the quadratic formula by calculating the x-intercepts of the parabola of Example 2-6. Substituting $a = 3$, $b = 5$, and $c = 2$ into the quadratic formula

$$x = \frac{-b \pm \sqrt{b^2 - 4ac}}{2a}$$

gives us

$$x = \frac{-5 \pm \sqrt{5^2 - 4(3)(2)}}{2(3)}$$

$$= \frac{-5 \pm \sqrt{25 - 24}}{6} = \frac{-5 \pm \sqrt{1}}{6}$$

$$= \frac{-5 \pm 1}{6} = \begin{cases} \dfrac{-5 + 1}{6} = -\dfrac{2}{3} \\ \dfrac{-5 - 1}{6} = -1 \end{cases}$$

Thus, the x-intercepts are $(-2/3, 0)$ and $(-1, 0)$.

The expression $b^2 - 4ac$, which appears under the square root sign in the quadratic formula, determines the character of the solutions. Hence, it is called the **discriminant.** Specifically,

1. If $b^2 - 4ac > 0$, there are two real solutions (two x-intercepts).
2. If $b^2 - 4ac = 0$, there is one real solution (one x-intercept).
3. If $b^2 - 4ac < 0$, there are no real solutions (no x-intercepts).

Each of the above situations is illustrated in Figure 2-26.

We now give a procedure for graphing a quadratic function.

Two x-intercepts: $b^2 - 4ac > 0$

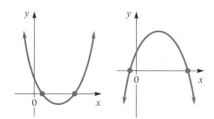

One x-intercept: $b^2 - 4ac = 0$

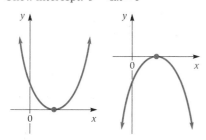

No x-intercepts: $b^2 - 4ac < 0$

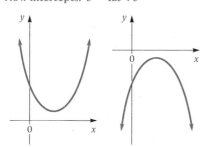

FIGURE 2-26

---

*A derivation of the quadratic formula is given in Appendix B.

To Graph a Quadratic Function

To graph a quadratic function whose equation is in the form

$$y = f(x) = ax^2 + bx + c$$

1. Determine whether the parabola *opens up* or *down*.
   Rule: If $a > 0$, parabola opens up $\smile$.
   If $a < 0$, parabola opens down $\frown$.
2. Find the y-*intercept*.
$$y = f(0) = a(0)^2 + b(0) + c = c$$
   Hence, the y-intercept is always $(0, c)$.
3. Find the coordinates of the *vertex* (____, ____).
   $$-b/2a \quad\quad f(-b/2a)$$
4. Find any x-*intercepts*. Set $y = 0$ and solve the resulting equation for x.
   Note:
   • You might have to factor.
   • You might have to use the quadratic formula.
   • There will be two, one, or no x-intercept.

• **EXAMPLE 2-7** _____

Graph $f(x) = x^2 - 2x - 8$.

Solution

Note that $a = 1$, $b = -2$, and $c = -8$.

1. The parabola opens up since $a > 0$ $(a = 1)$.
2. The y-intercept is $(0, c) = (0, -8)$.
3. Vertex (____, ____)

   x-coordinate
   $$\frac{-b}{2a} = \frac{-(-2)}{2(1)}$$
   $$= 1$$

   y-coordinate
   $$f(1) = 1^2 - 2(1) - 8 = -9$$

4. x-intercepts
$$0 = x^2 - 2x - 8$$
$$0 = (x + 2)(x - 4)$$
$$x + 2 = 0 \quad\quad \text{or} \quad\quad x - 4 = 0$$
$$\boxed{x = -2} \quad\quad\quad \boxed{x = 4}$$

x-intercepts

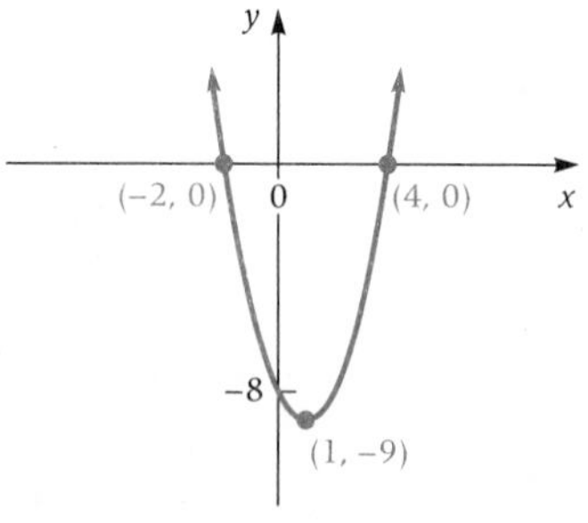

The graph is drawn in Figure 2-27.

• **EXAMPLE 2-8** _____

Graph $f(x) = -x^2 + 6x$.

Solution

Note that $a = -1$, $b = 6$, and $c = 0$.

FIGURE 2-27

$(-2, 0)$ 0 $(4, 0)$

-8

$(1, -9)$

$y = x^2 - 2x - 8$

1. The parabola opens down since $a < 0$ ($a = -1$).
2. The y-intercept is $(0, c) = (0, 0)$.
3. Vertex (____, ____)

   x-coordinate: $-b/2a = -6/2(-1) = 3$

   y-coordinate: $f(3) = -(3)^2 + 6(3) = 9$

4. x-intercepts

$$0 = -x^2 + 6x$$
$$0 = x(-x + 6)$$
$$x = 0 \quad \text{or} \quad -x + 6 = 0$$
$$\boxed{x = 0} \qquad\qquad \boxed{x = 6}$$

$\uparrow$_____ x-intercepts _____$\uparrow$

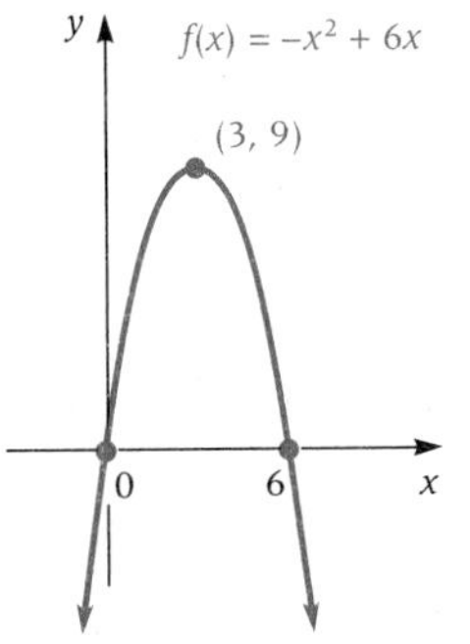

The parabola is drawn in Figure 2-28.

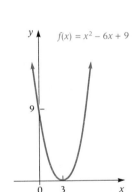

$f(x) = -x^2 + 6x$

(3, 9)

FIGURE 2-28

• **EXAMPLE 2-9** _____

Graph $f(x) = x^2 - 6x + 9$.

Solution

Note that $a = 1$, $b = -6$, and $c = 9$.

1. The parabola opens up since $a > 0$ ($a = 1$).
2. The y-intercept is $(0, c) = (0, 9)$.
3. Vertex (____, ____)

   x-coordinate: $-b/2a = -(-6)/2(1) = 3$

   y-coordinate: $f(3) = 3^2 - 6(3) + 9 = 0$

4. x-intercepts

$$0 = x^2 - 6x + 9$$
$$0 = (x - 3)^2 \quad \text{Perfect square}$$
$$0 = x - 3$$
$$x = 3 \quad \text{Only one } x\text{-intercept}$$

The parabola is drawn in Figure 2-29.

$f(x) = x^2 - 6x + 9$

FIGURE 2-29

Exercises 2-2

1. Graph each of the following:
   a) $y = 5x^2$
   b) $y = -5x^2$
   c) $y = (1/2)x^2$
   d) $y = -(1/2)x^2$

2. Graph the following on the same set of axes: $y = x^2$, $y = 6x^2$, $y = (1/4)x^2$.
3. Graph the following on the same set of axes: $y = -x^2$, $y = -4x^2$, $y = -(1/3)x^2$.
4. Graph the following on the same set of axes: $f(x) = x^2$, $f(x) = 3x^2$, $f(x) = 7x^2$.

Graph each of the following by using a vertical shift.

5. $y = x^2 + 7$
6. $f(x) = 3x^2 + 5$
7. $y = x^2 - 9$
8. $y = -x^2 + 9$
9. $f(x) = 2x^2 - 8$
10. $y = -4x^2 + 36$

Graph each of the following by using a horizontal shift.

11. $y = (x - 3)^2$ **12.** $y = (x + 3)^2$
13. $y = 4(x - 1)^2$ **14.** $y = 4(x + 1)^2$
15. $f(x) = -2(x + 5)^2$ **16.** $f(x) = -2(x - 3)^2$

Graph each of the following by shifting.

17. $y = 2(x - 1)^2 + 3$ **18.** $y = -(x - 4)^2 - 1$
19. $f(x) = 3(x - 2)^2 - 1$ **20.** $f(x) = -3(x - 2)^2 + 4$
21. $y = -3(x + 2)^2 - 5$ **22.** $y = 4(x + 3)^2 - 2$
23. $f(x) = (x + 3)^2 - 1$ **24.** $f(x) = (x - 2)^2 + 4$
25. $f(x) = -(x + 2)^2 + 1$ **26.** $f(x) = -(x - 3)^2 + 2$

Graph each of the following.

27. $y = 2x^2 + 8x$ **28.** $f(x) = -3x^2 + 7x$
29. $f(x) = x^2 - 5x$ **30.** $y = -x^2 + 8x$
31. $y = -2x^2 + 6x$ **32.** $y = 3x^2 - 2x$
33. $y = x^2 - 6x + 5$ **34.** $y = x^2 - 2x - 3$
35. $f(x) = x^2 - 6x - 16$ **36.** $f(x) = x^2 - 8x + 7$
37. $y = x^2 - 2x - 15$ **38.** $y = x^2 - 8x + 15$
39. $y = x^2 - 4x - 5$ **40.** $y = x^2 + 7x + 6$
41. $f(x) = -5x^2 + 6x + 4$ **42.** $y = x^2 - 8x + 16$
43. $y = -x^2 + 8x - 16$ **44.** $f(x) = x^2 + x + 1$
45. $f(x) = x^2 - 10x + 26$ **46.** $y = 2x^2 - 3x + 6$
47. $f(x) = 2x^2 + 4x + 1$ **48.** $f(x) = x^2 - 6x + 7$
49. $f(x) = x^2 - 10x + 25$ **50.** $f(x) = x^2 + 10x + 25$
51. $y = x^2 - 6x + 9$ **52.** $f(x) = x^2 + 6x + 9$

Equations in Factored Form

If the equation of a quadratic function is given in factored form, such as

$$f(x) = a(x - x_1)(x - x_2)$$

where a, x_1, and x_2 are constants, then the x-intercepts are easily determined as shown below.

$$0 = a(x - x_1)(x - x_2)$$
$$x - x_1 = 0 \quad \text{or} \quad x - x_2 = 0$$
$$x = x_1 \qquad\qquad x = x_2$$
$$\underline{\quad\quad \text{x-intercepts} \quad\quad}$$

Then, since the x-coordinate of the vertex lies midway between the x-intercepts (due to symmetry), it is determined as shown below.

$$\text{x-coordinate of vertex} = \frac{x_1 + x_2}{2}$$

The y-coordinate of the vertex is determined as indicated below.

$$\text{y-coordinate of vertex} = f\left(\frac{x_1 + x_2}{2}\right)$$

The sign of coefficient a indicates whether the parabola opens up or down. Specifically, if a is positive, the parabola opens up, and if a is negative, the parabola opens down. The y-intercept is determined by setting $x = 0$ and solving for y.

Using the above comments, graph each of the following.

53. $y = (x - 2)(x + 3)$ **54.** $f(x) = (x + 1)(x - 5)$
55. $y = 4(x - 2)(x + 3)$ **56.** $y = -2(x + 1)(x - 5)$

57. $f(x) = (x - 6)^2$ **58.** $y = -(x - 6)^2$
59. $y = -5(x + 1)^2$ **60.** $f(x) = (x + 6)(x - 6)$
61. $y = (x - 2)(x + 2)$ **62.** $f(x) = (x + 6)(x + 6)$
63. $y = -3(x - 2)(x + 2)$ **64.** $f(x) = 4(x + 1)(x - 1)$

2-3 • APPLICATIONS OF QUADRATIC FUNCTIONS

Revenue, Cost, and Profit Functions

Revenue Function. We begin this section by discussing, in greater detail, the introductory application to this chapter. Recall that sometimes the unit selling price of a firm's product depends on the demand level of the product. Such a relationship is given by a demand equation

$$p = f(x)$$

where p denotes the unit price and x denotes the number of units demanded of the product. The sales revenue function is determined as follows.

$$\text{sales revenue} = (\text{number of units sold})(\text{unit price})$$
$$R(x) = xp$$
$$= xf(x)$$

As an example, suppose we are given the demand equation

$$p = -20x + 14,100$$

and asked to find the sales revenue function $R(x)$. We proceed as follows.

$$R(x) = xp$$
$$= x(-20x + 14,100)$$
$$= -20x^2 + 14,100x$$

This revenue function is graphed in Figure 2-30(a). Observe that the vertex point gives the maximum sales revenue. Thus, the maximum sales revenue of $2,485,125 is realized when 352.5 units of the product are sold. Later in this text, we will use calculus concepts to maximize or minimize quantities.

Studying the graph of the revenue function of Figure 2-30(a), observe that after the vertex point, sales revenue decreases as the number of units sold increases. This is because of the nature of the relationship between unit price and demand as given by the demand equation. Note that as demand increases, unit price decreases. Thus, as more and more units of this product are sold, they are sold at lower and lower unit prices. This ultimately results in decreases in sales revenue as the number of units sold increases.

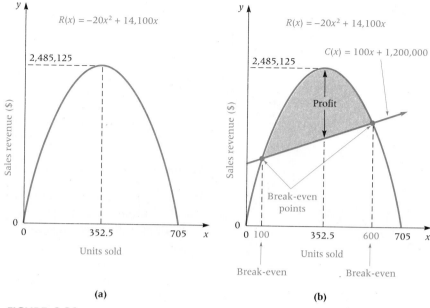

(a)

(b)

FIGURE 2-30

Cost Function.   If this product has a fixed cost of $1,200,000 and a unit variable cost of $100, then the cost function is given by

$$C(x) = 100x + 1,200,000$$

Figure 2-30(b) gives a graph of both the cost and sales revenue functions on the same set of axes.

Break-Even Analysis.   Note that the intersection points of the graphs of the cost and revenue functions of Figure 2-30(b) are the points where sales revenue = cost. As in Chapter 1, these points are called the **break-even points.** Also note that a positive profit results if the number of units sold lies between the x-coordinates of the break-even points. We will use the profit function to determine the break-even points.

Profit Function: Break-Even Analysis.   Using the revenue and cost functions discussed above, we find the equation of the profit function as follows.

$$\text{profit} = \text{revenue} - \text{cost}$$
$$P(x) = R(x) - C(x)$$

$$= -20x^2 + 14,100x - (100x + 1,200,000)$$
$$= -20x^2 + 14,000x - 1,200,000$$

The graph of the profit function is given in Figure 2-31.

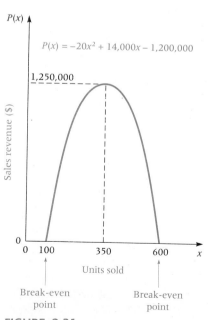

FIGURE 2-31

Since the break-even points are the points where sales revenue = cost, or, in other words, profit = 0, we find the break-even points by finding the

x-intercepts of the profit function. Thus, we set $P(x) = 0$ and solve for x to obtain

$$0 = -20x^2 + 14{,}000x - 1{,}200{,}000$$
$$0 = -20(x^2 - 700x + 60{,}000)$$
$$0 = -20(x - 100)(x - 600)$$
$$x - 100 = 0 \quad \text{or} \quad x - 600 = 0$$
$$\boxed{x = 100} \qquad \boxed{x = 600} \qquad x\text{-intercepts}$$

↑————— break-even points —————↑

Thus, a positive profit is realized as long as the number of units sold, x, lies within the interval $100 < x < 600$.

Studying the graph of the profit function of Figure 2-31 note also that the vertex point gives the maximum profit. Thus, the maximum profit of $1,250,000 occurs when 350 units of this product are sold. We will, in later chapters, use calculus concepts to find maximum or minimum quantities.

Optimal Unit Price. If $x = 350$ units of this product are sold, then profit is maximized at $1,250,000. Substituting $x = 350$ into the demand equation

$$p = -20x + 14{,}100$$

gives the unit price that yields the maximum profit for this product. Hence,

$$p = -20(350) + 14{,}100$$
$$= \$7100 \qquad \text{optimal unit price}$$

Supply, Demand, and Market Equilibrium

In Chapter 1, we learned that a demand function relates the unit price of some product to the corresponding demand; a supply function relates the unit price to the corresponding supply. Given the *supply function*

$$p = x^2 + 1 \qquad (x > 0)$$

and the *demand function*

$$p = (x - 5)^2 \qquad (0 < x \leq 5)$$

where p denotes the unit price in dollars and x denotes the number of units of the product supplied or demanded in millions of units, find the equilibrium point.

Remember, from Chapter 1, that the equilibrium point is the intersection of the graphs of the supply and demand functions. In other words, the equilibrium point is the point at which supply equals demand. Thus, to find the equilibrium point, we set the supply equation equal to the demand equation. Hence,

$$\text{supply} = \text{demand}$$
$$(x - 5)^2 = x^2 + 1$$
$$x^2 - 10x + 25 = x^2 + 1$$
$$-10x = -24$$
$$x = 2.4 \quad \text{equilibrium quantity}$$

We find the equilibrium price by substituting $x = 2.4$ into either the supply or the demand equation.

Supply Function

$$p = (2.4 - 5)^2 = \$6.76 \quad \longleftarrow$$

Demand Function — equilibrium price

$$p = (2.4)^2 + 1 = \$6.76 \quad \longleftarrow$$

Equilibrium Point. Thus, when supply = demand = 2.4 million units, the equilibrium price is $6.76 per unit. The graphs of the supply and demand functions are given in Figure 2-32.

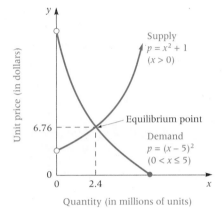

FIGURE 2-32

• **EXAMPLE 2-10** **Quality Control and Profits.** _____

This problem is adapted from one that appeared on a past Uniform CPA Examination. MacKenzie Park sells its trivets for $0.25 per unit. The variable cost is $0.10 per trivet. Production capacity is limited to 15,000 trivets per day.

The company does not maintain an inspection system, but has an agreement to reimburse the wholesaler $0.50 for each defective unit the wholesaler finds. The wholesaler uses a method of inspection that detects all defective units. The number of defective units in each lot of 300 units is equal to the daily unit production rate divided by 200. Let x = daily production in units.

a) Determine the algebraic expression that represents the number of defective units per day.

b) Determine the function that expresses the total daily contribution to profit, including the reimbursement to the wholesaler for defective units.

c) What is the maximum daily profit? How many units are produced daily in order to yield the maximum daily profit?

Solutions

a) If x = daily production in units and a lot contains 300 units, then $x/300$ lots are produced in a day. Each of the $x/300$ lots contains $x/200$ defective units. Thus, the number of defective units per day is

$$\frac{x}{200} \cdot \frac{x}{300} = \frac{x^2}{60,000}$$

b) First, we have

$$\text{profit} = \text{sales revenue} - \text{cost} - \text{reimbursement}$$

$$P(x) = 0.25x - 0.10x - 0.50\left(\frac{x^2}{60,000}\right)$$

$$= 0.15x - \frac{x^2}{120,000}$$

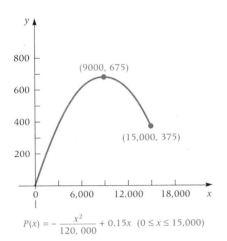

$$P(x) = -\frac{x^2}{120,000} + 0.15x \quad (0 \le x \le 15,000)$$

FIGURE 2-33

Thus, the profit function is defined by

$$P(x) = -\frac{x^2}{120,000} + 0.15x \quad (0 \le x \le 15,000)$$

Its graph appears in Figure 2-33. Since $0 \le x \le 15,000$, the parabola is drawn as a solid line over this interval.

c) As seen in Figure 2-33, the vertex, (9000, 675), is the maximum point on the parabola. Thus, when 9000 units are produced daily, the daily profit will be maximized at $675.

• **EXAMPLE 2-11   Time Series.** _____

A company's annual profits, P (in millions of dollars), are related to the time, t (in years), since its incorporation by the function

$$P(t) = 0.4t^2 + 30 \quad (t > 0)$$

Graph the function P and find the company's annual profit for the third year.

Solution

The graph of P is drawn by beginning with the graph of $0.4t^2$ and shifting it vertically by 30 units, as is illustrated in Figure 2-34
   The company's annual profit for the third year is given by

$$P(3) = 0.4(3)^2 + 30$$
$$= \$33.6 \text{ million}$$

This corresponding point is illustrated in Figure 2-34.   •

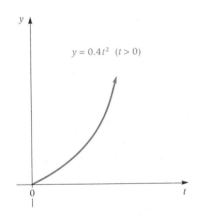

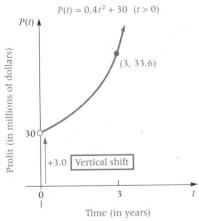

FIGURE 2-34

Light: Parabolic Reflectors

Parabolas possess the following properties when used as reflectors of light.

SUMMARY

Properties of Parabolic Reflectors

Property 1   If light rays (from some light source such as the sun or some other object) parallel to the axis of symmetry are directed toward a parabola, then such light rays will focus at a single point called the **focus,** as illustrated in Figure 2-35. The vertical distance along the axis of symmetry from the vertex of the parabola to the focus is given by

$$p = \frac{1}{4a}$$

where a is the coefficient of the x^2-term in the equation of the parabola.
                                                               continues

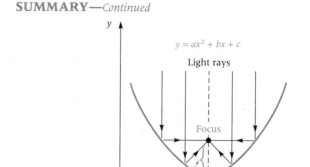

FIGURE 2-35

Property 2   If the source of light is located at the focus of a parabola, then light rays will reflect parallel to the axis of symmetry. This is graphically illustrated by reversing the direction of the arrows in Figure 2-35.

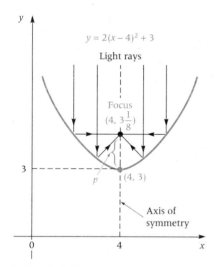

FIGURE 2-36

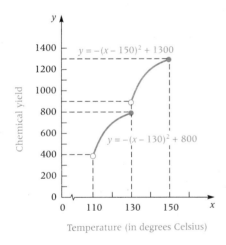

$$y = f(x) = \begin{cases} -(x-130)^2 + 800 & \text{if } 110 < x \le 130 \\ -(x-150)^2 + 1300 & \text{if } 130 < x \le 150 \end{cases}$$

FIGURE 2-37

Because they possess the above properties, parabolic reflectors are used for TV dishes, solar collectors, satellite communications, flashlights, automobile headlights, and more.

As an example, if the light rays are directed toward the parabola

$$y = 2(x - 4)^2 + 3$$

as illustrated in Figure 2-36, then the distance, p, from the vertex to the focus is

$$p = \frac{1}{4a} = \frac{1}{4(2)} = \frac{1}{8}$$

Thus, the focus is given by the point $(4, 3\frac{1}{8})$, as illustrated in Figure 2-36

Productivity: Chemical Process Yield

The productivity of a chemical process is measured in terms of its yield. After running a chemical process many times, a chemical company discovered that the yield, y, of the process is dependent on the temperature, x (in degrees Celsius), as given by the function

$$y = f(x) = \begin{cases} -(x - 130)^2 + 800 & \text{if } 110 < x \le 130 \\ -(x - 150)^2 + 1300 & \text{if } 130 < x \le 150 \end{cases}$$

Since this function is defined by more than one formula, then, as was discussed in Section 1-1, it is said to be **piecewise defined.** The parabola

$y = -(x - 130)^2 + 800$ over the interval $110 < x \le 130$ constitutes the first piece; the parabola $y = -(x - 150)^2 + 1300$ over the interval $130 < x \le 150$ constitutes the second piece. The graph of f is given in Figure 2-37.

Exercises 2-3

Revenue Functions

For each of the following demand dequations, p denotes the unit price in dollars, and x denotes the number of units demanded of some product.
a) Determine the equation of the revenue function, $R(x)$.
b) Graph the revenue function.
c) State the maximum sales revenue.
d) How many units must be sold in order to achieve the maximum sales revenue?
e) Substitute the result of part d into the demand equation to determine the unit price that maximizes sales revenue.

1. Demand function: $p = -2x + 100$
2. Demand function: $p = -3x + 180$
3. Demand function: $p = -4x + 320$
4. Demand function: $p = -5x + 1000$
5. Demand function: $p = -6x + 1800$
6. Demand function: $p = -3x + 240$

Revenue, Cost, and Profit Functions; Break-Even Analysis

For each of the following, p denotes the unit price in dollars, and x denotes the number of units produced and sold of some product.
a) Determine the equation of the revenue function, $R(x)$.
b) Graph both the revenue and cost functions on the same set of axes.
c) How many units of the product should be produced and sold in order to break even?
d) State the interval over which profit is positive.
e) Determine the equation of the profit function.
f) Graph the profit function.
g) Using the profit function, determine the break-even points. Verify that they agree with the answer to part c.
h) Using the profit function, state the interval over which profit is positive. Verify that this answer agrees with that of part d.
i) State the maximum profit.
j) How many units of the product should be produced and sold in order to maximize profit?
k) Find the unit price that yields the maximum profit.

7. Demand function: $p = -x + 1200$
   Cost function: $C(x) = 200x + 160{,}000$
8. Demand function: $p = -2x + 2400$
   Cost function: $C(x) = 400x + 180{,}000$
9. Demand function: $p = -2x + 2700$
   Cost function: $C(x) = 300x + 540{,}000$
10. Demand function: $p = -x + 2200$
    Cost function: $C(x) = 800x + 240{,}000$

Supply, Demand, and Market Equilibrium

For each of the following supply and demand functions, p denotes the unit price in dollars, and x denotes the number of units supplied or demanded of some product in millions of units.
a) Determine the equilibrium quantity.
b) Determine the equilibrium price.
c) Graph both the supply and demand functions on the same set of axes.

11. Supply function: $p = x^2 + 12$ $(x > 0)$
     Demand function: $p = (x - 6)^2$ $(0 < x \le 6)$
12. Supply function: $p = x^2 + 3$ $(x > 0)$
     Demand function: $p = (x - 3)^2$ $(0 < x \le 3)$
13. Supply function: $p = x^2 + 16$ $(x > 0)$
     Demand function: $p = (x - 8)^2$ $(0 < x \le 8)$
14. Supply function: $p = x^2 + 20$ $(x > 0)$
     Demand function: $p = (x - 10)^2$ $(0 < x \le 10)$

15. *Quality control and profits.* The Container Corporation manufactures wooden barrels. Each barrel costs $200 to produce and sells for $270. The barrels are manufactured in production lots. Each production lot contains 500 barrels. Quality control procedures have revealed that there are $x/20$ defective barrels per lot where x = the number of barrels produced per month. Each defective barrel costs the company an additional $50 to repair.
 a) Find the equation that relates profit, P, with monthly production volume.
 b) Graph the equation of part a.
 c) Determine the maximum profit.
 d) Determine the monthly production volume, x, that maximizes profit.

Time Series

16. A company's annual profits, P (in millions of dollars), are related to the time, t (in years), since its incorporation by the function

$$P(t) = 0.6t^2 + 20 \qquad (t > 0)$$

 a) Graph the function P.
 b) Find the company's annual profit for the second year.
 c) Find the company's annual profit for the fourth year.
 d) Find the company's annual profit for the fifth year.

17. A company's annual profits, P (in millions of dollars), are related to the time, t (in years), since its incorporation by the function

$$P(t) = 0.8(t - 2)^2 + 40 \qquad (t > 0)$$

 a) Graph the function P.
 b) Find the company's annual profit for the second year.
 c) Find the company's annual profit for the fourth year.
 d) Find the company's annual profit for the fifth year.

18. *Earnings per share.* The annual earnings per share (abbreviated EPS and expressed in dollars) of a corporation is calculated by dividing the corporation's annual earnings by the number of shares of its stock outstanding. That is,

$$\text{EPS} = \frac{\text{annual earnings}}{\text{number of shares of stock outstanding}}$$

The EPS is helpful in evaluating the performance of a corporation.

 Assume that the EPS, denoted by y, for a corporation is related to the time, t (in years), since its incorporation by the function

$$y = 0.9(t - 3)^2 + 35 \qquad (t > 0)$$

a) Graph the function defined by the above equation.
b) Find the EPS for the second year.
c) Find the EPS for the third year.
d) Find the EPS for the fifth year.
e) Find the EPS for the sixth year.

19. *Production possibility curve.* A textile company produces amounts x and y of two different jeans using the same production process. The amounts x and y are related by the equation

$$y = -0.10x^2 + 30 \qquad (0 \le x \le 17)$$

Since the amounts x and y give the production possibilities for the two different jeans, the graph of the above equation is called a **production possibility curve.**

a) Graph the production possibility curve defined by the above equation.
b) Determine the production possibility for $x = 5$.
c) Determine the production possibility for $x = 10$.
d) If the company wants to produce an amount x such that it is twice as much as amount y (i.e., $x = 2y$), what amounts x and y should be produced?

20. *Cost.* The Haskins Company produces ornamental bells. The equation

$$C(x) = x^2 - 100x + 2900 \qquad (x \ge 0)$$

relates total daily production cost, C, to daily production, x, of bells.

a) Graph the cost function C.
b) Find the total daily production cost for a daily production level of $x = 650$ bells.
c) How many bells should the company produce daily in order to minimize daily production cost?
d) State the minimum daily production cost.

21. *Projectile.* A ball is projected vertically into the air. The function defined by

$$s(t) = -16t^2 + 192t \qquad (0 \le t \le 12)$$

gives the height of the ball (in feet) above the ground t seconds after it is projected into the air.

a) Graph the function S.
b) When does the ball reach maximum height? What maximum height does it reach?
c) When is the ball at zero height?

Parabolic Reflectors

Assume that for each of the following parabolas, rays of light parallel to the axis of symmetry are directed toward the parabola, as illustrated in Figure 2-38. Find the coordinates of the focus for each parabola.

22. $y = x^2$
23. $y = 0.5(x - 7)^2$
24. $y = (x - 2)^2 + 6$
25. $y = 2(x - 1)^2 + 3$
26. $y = 0.5(x - 3)^2 + 1$
27. $y = 0.1(x - 4)^2 + 5$

28. *Satellite dish.* Satellite dishes are used to transmit and receive radio signals. The cross-sectional center of a parabolic satellite dish is given by the equation

$$y = 0.5x^2$$

Give the x- and y-coordinates of the location of the transmitter and receiver.

29. *Solar collector.* A parabolic solar collector focuses sunlight into a container

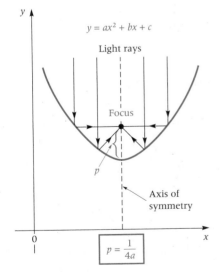

FIGURE 2-38

called a furnace. If the cross-sectional center of the solar collector is given by the equation

$$y = 0.25x^2$$

find the x- and y-coordinates of the location of the furnace.

30. *Flashlight.* The cross-sectional center of a parabolic reflector used in a flashlight is given by the equation

$$y = 0.125x^2$$

Determine the x- and y-coordinates of the location of the bulb.

31. *Productivity: Chemical process yield.* A chemical company has discovered that the yield, y, of a chemical process depends on its reaction time, t (in hours), as given by the function

$$y = f(t) = \begin{cases} (t - 5)^2 + 40 & \text{if } 1 < t \le 5 \\ (t - 10)^2 + 12 & \text{if } 5 < t \le 10 \end{cases}$$

a) Graph $f(t)$.
Compute the process yield for
b) $t = 3$ c) $t = 4$ d) $t = 6$ e) $t = 8$

32. *Delivery time.* The delivery time, y (in hours), for a manufacturer's product depends on the distance to be shipped, x (in thousands of miles), and the mode of transportation as given by the function

$$y = f(x) = \begin{cases} -(x - 2)^2 + 50 & \text{if } 0 < x \le 2 \text{ (by truck)} \\ -(x - 4)^2 + 60 & \text{if } 2 < x \le 4 \text{ (by rail)} \end{cases}$$

a) Graph $f(x)$.
According to the above function
b) For what shipping distances does the manufacturer ship by rail?
c) For what shipping distances does the manufacturer ship by truck?
Determine the delivery time for each of the following shipping distances
d) $x = 0.5$ e) $x = 1$ f) $x = 2.5$ g) $x = 3$

2-4 • SOME SPECIAL POLYNOMIAL AND RATIONAL FUNCTIONS

Polynomial Functions

In Chapter 1, we discussed linear functions. Recall that a linear function is defined by an equation of the form

$$f(x) = mx + b$$

Since the highest-powered term, mx, is of the first degree, linear functions are sometimes called **first-degree polynomial functions.** The graphs of first-degree polynomial functions are straight lines, as we learned in Chapter 1.

In Sections 2-2 and 2-3, we discussed quadratic functions. Recall that a quadratic function is defined by an equation of the form

$$f(x) = ax^2 + bx + c \qquad (a \ne 0)$$

Since the highest-powered term, ax^2, is of the second degree, quadratic functions are sometimes called **second-degree polynomial functions.**

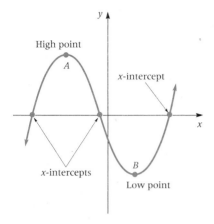

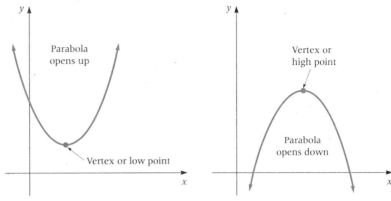

FIGURE 2-39

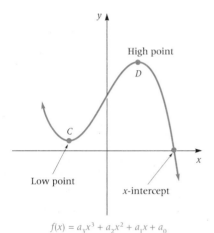

$$f(x) = a_3x^3 + a_2x^2 + a_1x + a_0$$

FIGURE 2-40

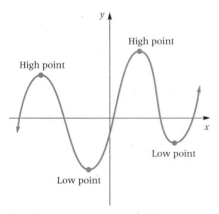

$$y = f(x) = a_nx^n + a_{n-1}x^{n-1} + \ldots + a_1x + a_0$$

FIGURE 2-41

The graphs of second-degree polynomial functions are parabolas (see Figure 2-39), as we learned in Sections 2-2 and 2-3. Note that a second-degree quadratic function (a parabola) has one point, the vertex, where its graph changes direction (see Figure 2-39). Also, a second-degree polynomial function has at most two x-intercepts.

An equation such as

$$f(x) = x^3 - 5x^2 + 3x + 9$$

defines a **third-degree polynomial function** since the highest-powered term, x^3, is of the third degree. The general form of the equation of a third-degree polynomial function is

$$f(x) = a_3x^3 + a_2x^2 + a_1x + a_0$$

where a_3, a_2, a_1, and a_0 are constant real numbers and $a_3 \neq 0$. Figure 2-40 illustrates possible shapes of graphs of third-degree polynomial functions. The points labeled A, B, C, and D, called high/low points, in Figure 2-40 are places where the graph of $f(x)$ changes direction. A third-degree polynomial function has at most two high/low points and at most three x-intercepts.

In general, an equation of the form

$$f(x) = a_nx^n + a_{n-1}x^{n-1} + \ldots + a_2x^2 + a_1x + a_0$$

where n is a positive integer, and a_n, a_{n-1}, . . ., a_2, a_1, and a_0 are constant real numbers, and $a_n \neq 0$, defines the **nth-degree polynomial function.** *An nth-degree polynomial function has at most n − 1 high/low points and at most n x-intercepts.*

• **EXAMPLE 2-12**

The graph of a polynomial function appears in Figure 2-41. Its degree must be at least what number?

Solution

The graph has 4 high/low points. Since the graph of a polynomial function of degree n has at most $n - 1$ such points, then the degree of the polynomial function in Figure 2-39 is at least 5. Also, the graph has 5 x-intercepts, which implies that the degree of the polynomial function is at least 5.

We now turn our attention to the graphs of some special case polynomial functions.

Special Case Polynomial Functions

We first consider the graphs of polynomial functions defined by equations of the form

$$f(x) = ax^n$$

where a is a constant coefficient and n is a positive integer. We consider the following two cases and their graphs in the following summary box.

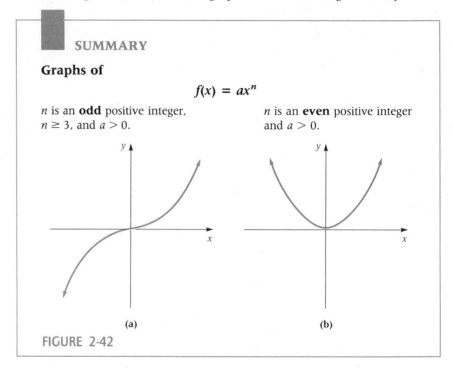

SUMMARY

Graphs of

$$f(x) = ax^n$$

n is an **odd** positive integer, $n \geq 3$, and $a > 0$.

n is an **even** positive integer and $a > 0$.

(a)

(b)

FIGURE 2-42

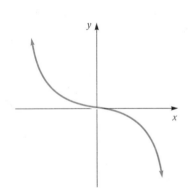

FIGURE 2-43

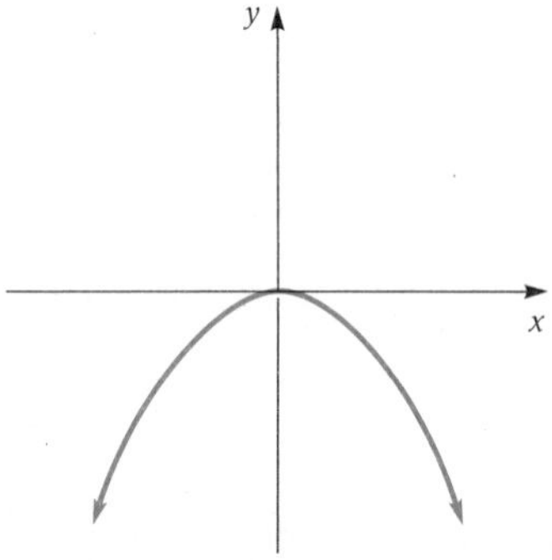

$f(x) = ax^n$
($a < 0$, n is an even positive integer)

FIGURE 2-44

Thus, the graphs of $y = 2x^3$, $y = 3x^7$, and $y = 10x^9$ resemble those of Figure 2-42(a), whereas the graphs of $y = 3x^2$, $y = 7x^4$, and $y = 8x^{10}$ resemble those of Figure 2-42(b).

Also, the graphs of $y = -3x^5$, $y = -2x^7$, and $y = -8x^9$ are reflections in the x-axis of those resembling Figure 2-42(a). These resemble the graph of Figure 2-43.

The graphs of $y = -3x^4$, $y = -5x^8$, and $y = -6x^{10}$ are reflections in the x-axis of those resembling Figure 2-42(b). These resemble the graph of Figure 2-44.

Graphs of Some Rational Functions

If a function $f(x)$ is defined as the quotient of two polynomials, it is called a **rational function.** Thus, a rational function $f(x)$ is defined by

$$f(x) = \frac{g(x)}{h(x)}$$

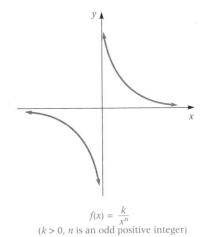

$f(x) = \dfrac{k}{x^n}$
($k > 0$, n is an odd positive integer)

FIGURE 2-45

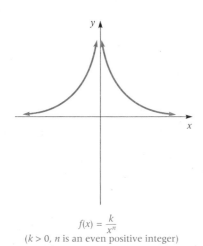

$f(x) = \dfrac{k}{x^n}$
($k > 0$, n is an even positive integer)

FIGURE 2-46

where $g(x)$ and $h(x)$ are polynomials and $h(x) \neq 0$. In this section, we will discuss the graphs of a special category of rational functions defined by equations of the form

$$y = f(x) = \frac{k}{x^n}$$

where k is a constant real number, n is a positive integer, and $x \neq 0$. We begin with rational functions defined by equations of the form

$$y = f(x) = \frac{k}{x^n}$$

where $k > 0$ and n is an *odd positive integer*. The graphs of such functions are typified by the graph in Figure 2-45. Observing Figure 2-45, note that as x takes on values closer and closer to 0, the graph of $f(x)$ gets closer and closer to the vertical line $x = 0$ (i.e., the y-axis). Such a vertical line is called a **vertical asymptote.** *Vertical asymptotes occur at values of* x *for which the denominator of a rational function = 0 and the numerator $\neq$ 0.* Note that the graph of $f(x)$ approaches different ends of the vertical asymptote from different sides. Further study of the graph in Figure 2-45 reveals that as x takes on values of larger and larger magnitude, the graph of $f(x)$ gets closer and closer to the horizontal line $y = 0$ (i.e., the x-axis). Such a horizontal line is called a **horizontal asymptote.**

For example, the graphs of $y = 2/x^5$, $y = 3/x^7$, and $y = 6/x^3$ resemble that in Figure 2-45.

Now we consider rational functions defined by equations of the form

$$y = f(x) = \frac{k}{x^n}$$

where $k > 0$ and n is an *even positive integer*. The graphs of such functions are typified by the graph in Figure 2-46. Studying this graph, note that the y-axis is a vertical asymptote and that the graph of $f(x)$ approaches the same end of this vertical asymptote from different sides. Also, the x-axis is a horizontal asymptote. For example, the graphs of $y = 5/x^4$, $y = 8/x^6$, and $y = 3x^8$ resemble that in Figure 2-46.

We summarize as follows.

 SUMMARY

Graphs of

$$f(x) = \frac{k}{x^n} \quad (k > 0)$$

n is an **odd** positive integer. n is an **even** positive integer.

continues

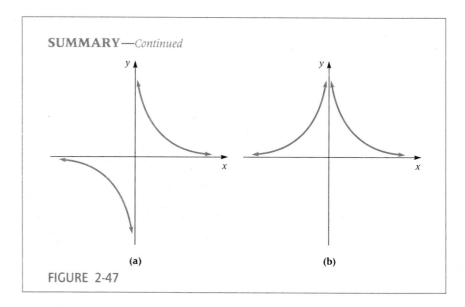

SUMMARY—*Continued*

(a)   (b)

FIGURE 2-47

Of course, if $k < 0$, then the resulting graphs are reflections about the x-axis of those in Figure 2-47.

Applications

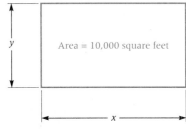

Area = 10,000 square feet

FIGURE 2-48

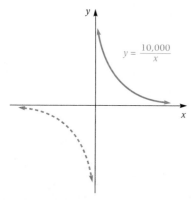

$y = \dfrac{10,000}{x}$

FIGURE 2-49

• **EXAMPLE 2-13   Area.**

A rectangular pasture must be enclosed so that the enclosed area equals 10,000 square feet, as illustrated in Figure 2-48. Draw a graph showing the possible x and y dimensions.

Solution

Since the enclosed area must be 10,000 square feet, then

$$xy = 10,000$$

Solving for y gives

$$y = \frac{10,000}{x}$$

Note that this equation is of the form $f(x) = k/x^n$, where n is an odd positive integer and $k > 0$. Thus, its graph resembles that of Figure 2-47(a). The graph of y versus x is drawn in Figure 2-49. Since x and y must be positive, we have drawn the portion of the graph in the first quadrant as a solid curve.

• **EXAMPLE 2-14   Production Possibility Curve.** _____

A firm produces x units of Product A and y units of Product B. The equation

$$y = \frac{2,000,000}{x^2} \qquad (00 \le x \le 500)$$

relates x and y and thus gives the production possibilities between these two products. The graph of y versus x is therefore called a **production possibility curve.**

a)   Graph the production possibility curve.

b)   State the production possibility for $x = 200$.

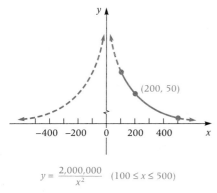

$$y = \frac{2,000,000}{x^2} \quad (100 \le x \le 500)$$

FIGURE 2-50

Solutions

a) The equation

$$y = \frac{2,000,000}{x^2}$$

is of the form $y = k/x^n$, where n is even and $k > 0$. Its graph is drawn in Figure 2-50.

b) When $x = 200$,

$$y = \frac{2,000,000}{(200)^2} = 50$$

Thus, when $x = 200$ units of Product A are produced, $y = 50$ units of Product B are produced. This is illustrated in Figure 2-50.

———————————————————————————————— •

Average Cost Per Unit. If $C(x)$ denotes the total cost of producing x units of some product, then the *average cost per unit* is given by

$$\overline{C}(x) = \frac{\text{total production cost}}{\text{number of units produced}}$$

or, in other words,

$$\overline{C}(x) = \frac{C(x)}{x} \qquad (x > 0)$$

The function $\overline{C}$ is called an **average cost function.**

As an example, if

$$C(x) = 80x + 120,000$$

then the *average cost per unit* is given by

$$\overline{C}(x) = \frac{80x + 120,000}{x} \qquad (x > 0)$$

Dividing each term of the numerator by x, we obtain the equivalent expression for $\overline{C}(x)$ given below.

$$\overline{C}(x) = 80 + \frac{120,000}{x} \qquad (x > 0)$$

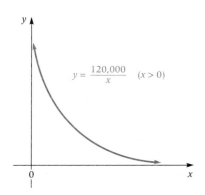

$$y = \frac{120,000}{x} \quad (x > 0)$$

We graph the function $\overline{C}$ by noting that the term $120,000/x$ is of the form $f(x) = k/x^n$, where n is an odd positive integer and $k > 0$. Thus, we draw the graph of $\overline{C}$ by beginning with the graph of $y = 120,000/x$ and shifting it vertically by 80 units, as illustrated in Figure 2-51. Since $x > 0$, only that corresponding portion of the graph is drawn as a solid curve.

Studying the graph of Figure 2-51, note that the average cost per unit approaches the variable cost per unit, 80 (the horizontal asymptote), as the number of units, x, gets larger and larger. This is because the fixed cost is averaged out over the x units and becomes rather insignificant when x is

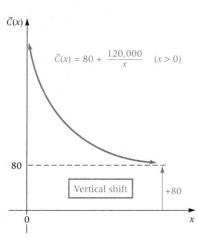

$$\overline{C}(x) = 80 + \frac{120,000}{x} \quad (x > 0)$$

Vertical shift   +80

FIGURE 2-51

very large. We illustrate this numerically by computing the average cost per unit for each of the following production levels. Hence,

$$\overline{C}(10{,}000) = 80 + \frac{120{,}000}{10{,}000}$$

$$= 80 + 12 = \$92 \text{ per unit}$$

$$\overline{C}(100{,}000) = 80 + \frac{120{,}000}{100{,}000}$$

$$= 80 + 1.2 = \$81.20 \text{ per unit}$$

Exercises 2-4

State the degree of each polynomial function.

1. $y = -6x + 7$ **2.** $f(x) = 6x^4 - 8x + 9$
3. $f(x) = 9x^8 + 4x^6 - 8x^3 + 6$ **4.** $y = -x^2 + 3x + 4$
5. $y = 4x^3 - 8x^2 + 7x + 3$ **6.** $f(x) = x^5 - 8x^4 + x^3$

7. The graph of a polynomial function appears in Figure 2-52. Its degree must be at least what number?

8. The graph of a polynomial function appears in Figure 2-53. Its degree must be at least what number?

9. Show why graphs of equations of the form $f(x) = ax^n$, where $n \geq 3$ is an odd positive integer and $a > 0$, resemble that of Figure 2-42(a). Use $f(x) = x^3$ as an example and fill in the following table:

x	-4	-3	-2	-1	0	1	2	3	4
$f(x)$									

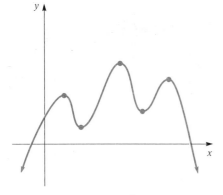

$y = f(x) = a_n x^n + a_{n-1} x^{n-1} + \dots + a_1 x + a_0$

FIGURE 2-52

10. Show why graphs of equations of the form $f(x) = ax^n$, where n is an even positive integer and $a > 0$, resemble that of Figure 2-42(b). Use $f(x) = x^4$ as an example and fill in the following table:

x	-4	-3	-2	-1	0	1	2	3	4
$f(x)$									

Graph each of the following.

11. $f(x) = x^2$ **12.** $f(x) = 5x^2$
13. $f(x) = x^4$ **14.** $y = x^6$
15. $y = -4x^2$ **16.** $y = -x^6$
17. $y = x^3$ **18.** $f(x) = -2x^3$
19. $f(x) = x^5$ **20.** $f(x) = 4x^7$
21. $f(x) = -2x^5$ **22.** $y = -4x^7$

23. Show why graphs of equations of the form $f(x) = k/x^n$, where n is an odd positive integer and $k > 0$, resemble that of Figure 2-47(a). Use $f(x) = 1/x^3$ as an example and fill in the following table:

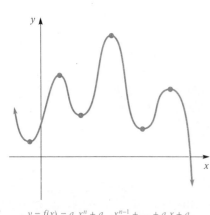

$y = f(x) = a_n x^n + a_{n-1} x^{n-1} + \dots + a_1 x + a_0$

FIGURE 2-53

x	-4	-3	-2	-1	0	1	2	3	4
$f(x)$									

24. Show why graphs of equations of the form $f(x) = k/x^n$, where n is an even positive integer and $k > 0$, resemble that of Figure 2-47(b). Use $f(x) = 1/x^4$ as an example and fill in the following table:

x	-4	-3	-2	-1	0	1	2	3	4
$f(x)$									

Graph each of the following:

25. $y = 3/x^2$ **26.** $f(x) = 4/x^3$

27. $f(x) = 5/x^7$ **28.** $y = 6/x^4$

29. $f(x) = 2/x^5$ **30.** $y = 7/x^2$

31. $y = 5/x^3$ **32.** $f(x) = 8/x^7$

33. $y = 6/x^8$ **34.** $y = 10/x^{12}$

35. $f(x) = 4/x^5$ **36.** $f(x) = 3/x$

37. $y = -6/x^8$ **38.** $y = -3/x^4$

39. $y = -5/x^3$ **40.** $y = -3/x$

41. $y = -7/x^6$ **42.** $y = -4/x^5$

Use horizontal and vertical shifts to graph the following.

43. $y = 2(x - 5)^4$ **44.** $y = 2(x - 4)^5$

45. $y = 5(x + 2)^3$ **46.** $y = 3(x - 1)^6$

47. $y = (x - 2)^4 + 5$ **48.** $y = (x - 3)^6 + 7$

49. $y = (x + 5)^3 - 2$ **50.** $y = (x + 7)^5 - 1$

51. $y = 3/(x - 5)$ **52.** $y = 4/(x - 2)^2$

53. $y = 2/(x + 5)^6$ **54.** $y = 1/(x + 7)^3$

55. $y = \dfrac{7}{(x - 2)^4} + 3$ **56.** $y = \dfrac{3}{(x - 5)^2} - 4$

57. $y = \dfrac{2}{(x - 3)^5} - 1$ **58.** $y = \dfrac{1}{(x + 1)^5} + 2$

Applications

59. *Area.* A rectangular pasture of dimensions x feet by y feet must be enclosed so that the enclosed area equals 30,000 square feet. Draw a graph of y versus x.

60. *Production possibility curve.* A company produces x units of Product A and y units of Product B. The equation

$$y = \frac{4,000,000}{x^2} \qquad (100 \le x \le 400)$$

relates x and y and thus gives the production possibilities for these two products.

a) Graph the production possibility curve.

b) State the production possibility for $x = 100$.

c) State the production possibility for $x = 200$.

d) State the production possibility for $x = 400$.

61. *Production possibility curve.* A company produces x units of Product A and y units of Product B. The equation

$$y = \frac{200,000}{x} \qquad (1000 \le x \le 5000)$$

relates x and y and thus gives the production possibilities for these two products.

a) Graph the production possibility curve.

b) State the production possibility for $x = 1000$.

c) State the production possibility for $x = 2000$.
d) State the production possibility for $x = 4000$.
e) State the production possibility for $x = 5000$.

62. *Demand curve.* The equation

$$p = \frac{10,000}{x - 3} \qquad (3 < x \le 4003)$$

gives the relationship between the unit price, p, and the number of units demanded, x, for some product.
a) Graph the demand curve.
b) Find the unit price when the demand is 1003 units.
c) Find the unit price when the demand is 2003 units.
d) Find the unit price when the demand is 4003 units.

63. *Demand curve.* The equation

$$p = \frac{20,000}{x - 10} \qquad (10 < x \le 5010)$$

gives the relationship between the unit price, p, and the number of units demanded, x, for some product.
a) Graph the demand curve.
b) Find the unit price when the demand is 1010 units.
c) Find the unit price when the demand is 2010 units.
d) Find the unit price when the demand is 4010 units.
e) Find the unit price when the demand is 5010 units.

Average Cost Functions

For each of the following, $C(x)$ denotes the total cost (in dollars) of producing x units of some product.
a) Determine the equation of the average cost function.
b) Graph the result of part a.
c) Evaluate $\overline{C}(1000)$, $\overline{C}(10,000)$, and $\overline{C}(100,000)$, and interpret the results.
d) As the production level increases, the average cost per unit is approaching what value?

64. $\overline{C}(x) = 40x + 80,000$ **65.** $\overline{C}(x) = 50x + 40,000$
66. $\overline{C}(x) = 100x + 90,000$ **67.** $\overline{C}(x) = 20x + 60,000$

68. *Quality/productivity: Loss functions.* The graphs of Figures 2-54 and 2-55 give the loss in dollars to a producer of some product. The notations LSL and USL denote lower specification limit and upper specification limit, respectively. As an example, if a product, say, a disk, must be made to diameter specification limits of

$$3.50 \text{ inches} \pm 0.10 \text{ inches}$$

then the LSL = $3.50 - 0.10 = 3.40$ inches, and the USL = $3.50 + 0.10 = 3.60$ inches. Thus, such a disk is considered to be within specification if

$$3.40 \text{ inches} < \text{disk diameter} < 3.60 \text{ inches}$$

a) According to the loss function of Figure 2-54, does the company incur a loss if its product remains within the specification limits?
b) According to the loss function of Figure 2-54, if the product deviates from the average, but remains within the specification limits, does the company incur a loss?
Note: Experts in the field of quality/productivity refer to this type of loss function as "the old thinking."

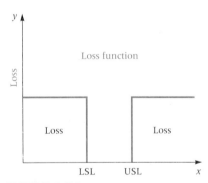

FIGURE 2-54

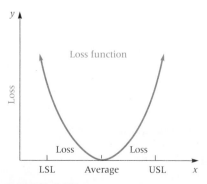

FIGURE 2-55

c) According to the loss function of Figure 2-55, does the company incur a loss as soon as its product deviates from the average?

d) According to the loss function of Figure 2-55, if the product deviates from the average, but remains within the specification limits, does the company incur a loss?

Note: Experts in the field of quality/productivity refer to this type of loss function as "the new thinking."

2-5

• GRAPHING POLYNOMIAL FUNCTIONS (OPTIONAL)

As was discussed in Section 2-4, an equation of the form

$$f(x) = a_n x^n + a_{n-1} x^{n-1} + \ldots + a_2 x^2 + a_1 x + a_0$$

where n is a positive integer, and $a_n, a_{n-1}, \ldots, a_2, a_1,$ and a_0 are constant real numbers, and $a_n \neq 0$, defines the **nth degree polynomial function.** In this section, we will develop and illustrate a procedure for sketching the graphs of factorable polynomial equations of at least the third degree.

We now consider the function defined by

$$f(x) = 2x^3 + 2x^2 - 10x + 6$$

This equation can be written in factored form as

$$f(x) = 2(x + 3)(x - 1)^2$$

Note that the y-intercept is $f(0) = 6$. To determine the x-intercepts, we set $f(x) = 0$. Hence,

$$0 = 2(x + 3)(x - 1)^2$$

Setting each factor equal to 0 and solving for x yields

$$x + 3 = 0 \qquad (x - 1)^2 = 0$$
$$x = -3 \qquad\qquad x = 1$$

Thus, the x-intercepts are $(-3, 0)$ and $(1, 0)$.

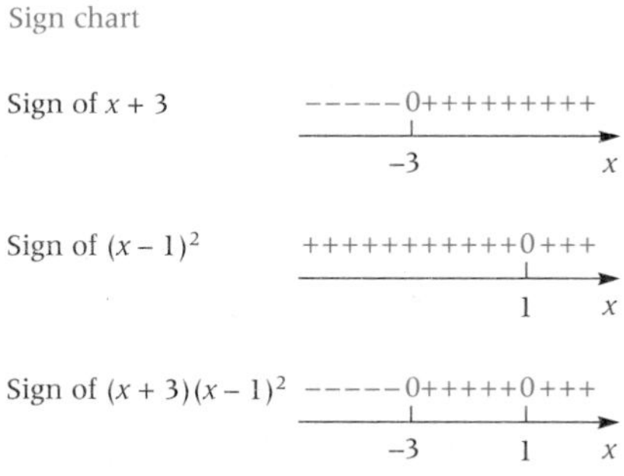

The x-intercepts divide the x-axis into the subintervals $x < -3$, $-3 < x < 1$, and $x > 1$. Important information about the graph of $f(x)$ is obtained by analyzing the sign of $f(x)$ on these subintervals. Figure 2-56 gives a sign chart that shows the sign of each factor of $f(x)$ and the sign of $f(x)$ for values of x. Studying this figure, note that the sign of $x + 3$ is negative for $x < -3$ and positive for $x > -3$. Of course, $x + 3 = 0$ at $x = -3$. Observe that the sign of $(x - 1)^2$ is positive at all values of x except $x = 1$, where it is 0. Multiplying the sign of $x + 3$ by the sign of $(x - 1)^2$, we obtain the sign of $(x + 3)(x - 1)^2$. The sign of $(x + 3)(x - 1)^2$ is the same as the sign of $f(x) = 2(x + 3)(x - 1)^2$ since the positive constant multiplier 2 does not change the sign of the original product, $(x + 3)(x - 1)^2$. Thus, $f(x)$ is non-negative for $x > -3$ and negative for $x < -3$.

Notice that $f(x)$ changes sign at the x-intercept of $x = -3$. Thus, the graph of $f(x)$ *crosses* the x-axis at $x = -3$. However, since $f(x)$ does not change sign at the x-intercept of $x = 1$, the graph of $f(x)$ *is tangent to,* and does not cross, the x-axis at $x = 1$ (see Figure 2-57). Note that $f(x)$ does not

Sign chart

Sign of $x + 3$ $-----0+++++++++$
                        -3 x

Sign of $(x - 1)^2$ $++++++++++++0+++$
                              1 x

Sign of $(x + 3)(x - 1)^2$ $-----0+++++0+++$
                           -3 1 x

FIGURE 2-56

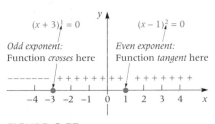

$(x + 3)^1 = 0$ $(x - 1)^2 = 0$

Odd exponent: *Even exponent:*
Function *crosses* here   Function *tangent* here

FIGURE 2-57

change sign at $x = 1$ because the corresponding factor $(x - 1)^2$ has an *even exponent*. Similarly, $f(x)$ does change sign at $x = -3$ because the factor $x + 3$ has an *odd exponent*. In general, we state the following rule to determine whether the graph of a function either crosses or is tangent to the x-axis at an x-intercept.

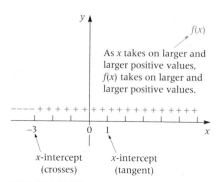

FIGURE 2-58

x-Intercept Rule

If the factor yielding the x-intercept has an *odd exponent*, then the graph of the function *crosses* the x-axis at that x-intercept. If the factor yielding the x-intercept has an *even exponent*, then the graph of the function *is tangent to*, and does not cross, the x-axis at that x-intercept.

Lastly, we determine the behavior of $f(x)$ as x increases without limit and as x becomes more and more negative without limit. We will show that the highest-powered term determines the behavior of a polynomial function at such values of x. We begin by factoring out $2x^3$, the highest-powered term of

$$f(x) = 2x^3 + 2x^2 - 10x + 6$$

and obtain

$$f(x) = 2x^3\left(1 + \frac{1}{x} - \frac{5}{x^2} + \frac{3}{x^3}\right)$$

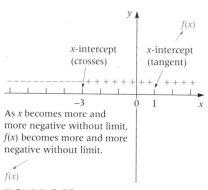

FIGURE 2-59

As x takes on larger and larger positive values, the terms $1/x$, $-5/x^2$, and $3/x^3$ all approach 0. Thus, the highest-powered term, $2x^3$, determines the behavior of $f(x)$ as x increases without limit. Since the highest-powered term, $2x^3$, takes on larger and larger positive values as x takes on larger and larger positive values, $f(x)$ gets larger and larger as x gets larger and larger. This implies that for positive values of x far away from the origin, the graph of $f(x)$ is located in the upper right-hand corner of the first quadrant, as illustrated in Figure 2-58.

As x takes on negative values of larger and larger magnitude, the highest-powered term, $2x^3$, takes on negative values of larger and larger magnitude. Thus, $f(x)$ becomes more and more negative without limit as x becomes more and more negative without limit. This implies that for negative values of x far away from the origin, the graph of $f(x)$ is located in the lower left-hand corner of the third quadrant, as is shown in Figure 2-59.

Using the information gained in the previous paragraphs, we sketch the graph of $f(x)$ in Figure 2-60. In Figure 2-60, we have labeled as A and B the high and low points. In subsequent chapters, we will use calculus to determine the locations of such points.

We summarize the following.

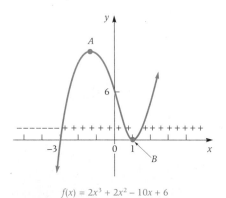

$$f(x) = 2x^3 + 2x^2 - 10x + 6$$

FIGURE 2-60

> ### To Graph a Polynomial Function
> To graph a polynomial function whose equation is in factored form:
> 1. Find the y-intercept.
>   - Set $x = 0$ and solve for y.
> 2. Find the x-intercept(s).
>   - Set $y = 0$ and solve for x.
>   - Apply the x-intercept rule to determine tangency or crossing.
>   - Draw a sign chart (optional).
> 3. Determine the behavior of the function
>   As x gets more and more positive.
>   As x gets more and more negative.
>   - Use the highest-powered term for this analysis.

Sign chart

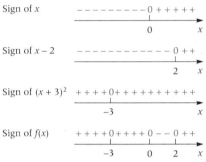

FIGURE 2-61

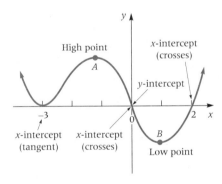

$$y = f(x) = x^4 + 4x^3 - 3x^2 - 18x$$

FIGURE 2-62

• **EXAMPLE 2-15** _____

Graph $f(x) = x^4 + 4x^3 - 3x^2 - 18x = x(\text{x} - 2)(x + 3)^2$.

Solution

The y-intercept is $f(0) = 0$. To determine the x-intercepts, we set $f(x) = 0$. Hence,

$$0 = x(x - 2)(x + 3)^2$$

Thus, the x-intercepts are $(0, 0)$, $(2, 0)$, and $(-3, 0)$. Since the factors yielding the x-intercepts $(0, 0)$ and $(2, 0)$ have odd exponents, the graph of $f(x)$ crosses the x-axis at these x-intercepts. Since the factor yielding the x-intercept $(-3, 0)$ has an even exponent, the graph of $f(x)$ is tangent to the x-axis at $(-3, 0)$. The sign chart of Figure 2-61 shows the sign of each factor of $f(x)$ and the sign of $f(x)$ for values of x.

Then, we determine the behavior of $f(x)$ as x increases without limit. Note that the highest-powered term, x^4, takes on larger and larger positive values as x takes on larger and larger positive values. This implies that for positive values of x far away from the origin, the graph of $f(x)$ is located in the upper right-hand corner of the first quadrant.

Also, as x takes on negative values of larger and larger magnitude, the highest-powered term, x^4, takes on larger and larger positive values. This implies that for negative values of x far away from the origin, the graph of $f(x)$ is located in the upper left-hand corner of the second quadrant.

Combining all of the preceding information, we sketch the graph of $f(x)$ in Figure 2-62. Observe that we have labeled as A and B the high and low points whose coordinates are unknown. In forthcoming chapters, we will use calculus to determine the locations of such points.

Application

• **EXAMPLE 2-16   Volume.**

A company manufactures open boxes by beginning with a square piece of tin 16 inches on each side, cutting equal squares from the corners of this piece of tin, and folding up the flaps to form sides (see Figure 2-63).

a) Express the volume, V, of the box as a function of x, the length of each side of the cut-out square.

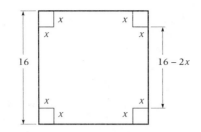

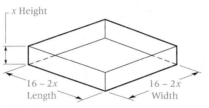

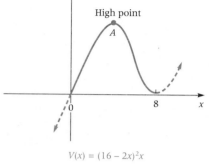

FIGURE 2-63   FIGURE 2-64

b) Referring to Figure 2-64, for what values of x is $V(x)$ non-negative? Does this make sense in terms of Figure 2-63?

Solutions

a) The volume of a box is the product of its length, width, and height (see Figure 2-63). Thus

$$V(x) = (\text{length})(\text{width})(\text{height})$$
$$= (16 - 2x)(16 - 2x)(x)$$
$$= (16 - 2x)^2 x$$

The graph of this function appears in Figure 2-64.

b) If $x \geq 0$, then $V(x) \geq 0$. However, referring to Figure 2-63, note that if $x = 8$, then all the tin would be cut away. And if $x > 8$, then more tin would be cut away than exists—an impossibility. Hence, the function "makes sense" only for $0 \leq x \leq 8$. Thus, that portion of the graph is drawn with a solid curve in Figure 2-64.

c) We note that volume is maximal at the x-coordinate of point A. As mentioned earlier, we will use calculus in forthcoming chapters to determine the locations of such points.

Exercises 2-5

Graph each of the following.

1. $f(x) = x^3 - 7x + 6 = (x - 1)(x + 3)(x - 2)$
2. $y = x^4 + x^3 - 21x^2 - x + 20 = (x - 1)(x - 4)(x + 1)(x + 5)$
3. $f(x) = x^3 - 7x^2 + 11x - 5 = (x - 1)^2(x - 5)$
4. $f(x) = x^3 - 4x^2 - 3x + 18 = (x - 3)^2(x + 2)$
5. $y = 3x^4 - 3x^3 - 9x^2 + 15x - 6 = 3(x - 1)^3(x + 2)$
6. $y = 5x^6 + 10x^5 - 15x^4$
7. $f(x) = x^3 + 3x^2 - 9x + 5 = (x - 1)^2(x + 5)$
8. $y = x^4 + 2x^3 - 15x^2$
9. $f(x) = -x^3 + 36x$
10. $f(x) = x^4 - 2x^3 + 15x^2$
11. $f(x) = x^3 - 19x - 30 = (x + 2)(x - 5)(x + 3)$

12. $f(x) = x^3 - 4x^2 - 3x + 18 = (x + 2)(x - 3)^2$
13. $f(x) = x^3 + x^2 - 5x + 3 = (x - 1)^2(x + 3)$
14. $f(x) = x^5 + x^4 - 5x^3 + 3x^2$
15. $y = x^3 + 3x^2 - 16x + 12 = (x - 1)(x + 6)(x - 2)$
16. $f(x) = x^4 + 6x^3 - 7x^2 - 60x = x(x - 3)(x + 4)(x + 5)$

Each of the following is a polynomial equation $f(x) = a_n x^n + a_{n-1}x^{n-1} + \ldots + a_2 x^2 + a_1 x + a_0$ expressed in factored form. Graph each one.

17. $f(x) = (1/2)(x - 2)^3(x + 5)$ **18.** $y = -(1/4)(x - 3)^2(x + 1)$
19. $f(x) = -3x^5(x - 2)^3(x + 4)$ **20.** $f(x) = x^2(x - 2)(x + 5)$
21. $f(x) = 2x^3(x - 5)(x + 6)^2$ **22.** $f(x) = x^2(x - 5)^4(x - 2)$
23. $y = (x - 2)(x + 3)^4(x - 1)$ **24.** $y = (x - 1)^2(x + 3)(x + 1)^2$

Applications

25. *Batch process and unit profits.* The Super Oar Company manufactures plastic paddles using the batch process (i.e., no production takes place until enough orders are received to produce a batch). The size of a batch is variable and may range from 0 to 30 paddles. The company statistician has found unit profit, p, and batch size, x, to be related by the polynomial equation

$$p(x) = -0.0001x^4 + 0.005x^3 - 0.07x^2 + 0.3x \qquad (0 \le x \le 30)$$

When factored, this becomes

$$p(x) = -0.0001x(x - 10)^2(x - 30)$$

  a) Graph the function.
  b) For which batch sizes will the company make zero unit profit?
  c) Will Super Oar Company make a positive unit profit if batch size, x, falls within the interval $0 < x < 10$?
  d) Will Super Oar Company make a positive unit profit if batch size, x, falls within the interval $10 < x < 30$?
  e) Calculate the profit per paddle at a batch size of $x = 20$.

26. *Batch process and unit profits.* The factored polynomial equation

$$p(x) = \left(\frac{1}{10,000}x^2\right)(x - 20)(x - 30)^2 \qquad (0 \le x \le 40)$$

relates unit profit, p, with batch size, x, for Supergo Corporation.
  a) Sketch the graph of this function.
  b) For which batch sizes will Supergo Corporation make zero unit profit?
  c) Will Supergo make a unit profit if batch size, x, falls within the interval $0 \le x \le 20$?
  d) Will Supergo make a unit profit if batch size, x, falls within the interval $20 < x < 30$?
  e) Will Supergo make a unit profit if batch size, x, falls within the interval $30 < x \le 40$?
  f) Calculate the unit profit at each of the following batch sizes: $x = 25$, $x = 35$, $x = 40$.

27. *Volume.* A company manufactures open boxes from rectangular pieces of tin of dimensions 10 inches by 20 inches. The process involves cutting equal squares from the corners of each piece of tin and folding up the flaps to form sides.
  a) Express the volume, V, of the box as a function of x, the length of each side of the cut-out square.
  b) Graph the function $V(x)$ of part a.
  c) For which values of x is volume, V, non-negative? Does this make sense?

d) Graphically indicate the location of the value of x at which volume will be maximal.

28. *Sales revenue.* A company manufactures electric switches. The equation

$$p(x) = -\frac{1}{400}x^2 + 90 \qquad (0 \le x \le 185)$$

represents the selling price per case, p, as a function of the number of cases sold, x.

a) Determine the sales revenue, R, as a function of x.
b) Graph the revenue function, $R(x)$.
c) For which values of x is sales revenue non-negative?
d) Graphically indicate the location of the value of x at which sales revenue is maximal.

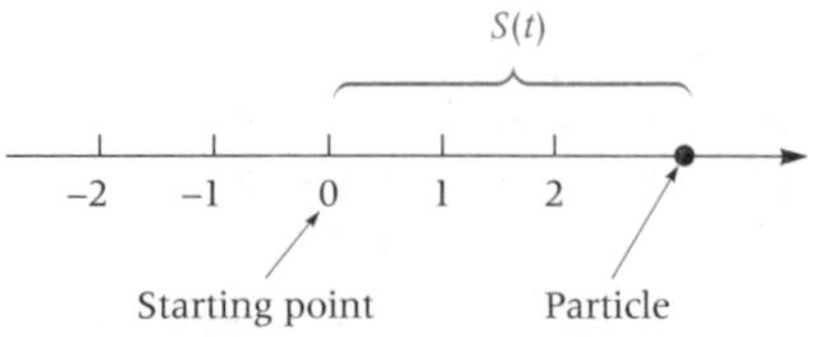

29. *Particle movement.* A particle starts at point 0 and moves along a horizontal line as illustrated in Figure 2-65. The equation $S(t) = t^3 - 16t^2$ expresses the distance, $S(t)$, between the particle and its starting point, 0, after t seconds have elapsed.

a) Graph $S(t)$.
b) Where is the particle in relation to its starting point after 5 seconds have elapsed?
c) Where is the particle after 20 seconds have elapsed?
d) At what points in time is the particle at the starting point?

FIGURE 2-65

2-6 • GRAPHING RATIONAL FUNCTIONS (OPTIONAL)

In this section, we will learn to graph equations like

$$y = f(x) = \frac{6x + 12}{2x - 1}$$

Such an equation defines a **rational function** since it is a quotient of two polynomial functions.

A graph of $y = f(x) = (6x + 12)/(2x - 1)$ may be obtained by finding some ordered pairs (x, y) that satisfy the equation $y = (6x + 12)/(2x - 1)$ and plotting their corresponding points on the rectangular coordinate system. Table 2-1 shows values of y, or $f(x)$, for various values of x. The corresponding ordered pairs (x, y) are plotted in Figure 2-66. Studying the graph of Figure 2-66, note that this rational function is undefined at $x = 1/2$. As x takes on values closer and closer to $1/2$, $f(x)$ gets larger and larger in magnitude. The graph of $f(x)$ gets closer and closer to the vertical line $x = 1/2$. Such a vertical line is called a **vertical asymptote.** Note that vertical asymptotes occur at values of x for which the denominator of a rational function $= 0$ and the numerator $\ne 0$.

Further study of the graph of Figure 2-66 shows us that as x takes on larger and larger positive values, $f(x)$ gets closer and closer to 3. Thus, for positive values of x far away from the origin, the graph of $f(x)$ approaches the horizontal line $y = 3$. As x takes on negative values of larger and larger magnitude, $f(x)$ again gets closer and closer to 3. Thus, for negative values of x far away from the origin, the graph of $f(x)$ also approaches the hori

TABLE 2-1

x	$f(x)$
-50	2.85
-10	2.29
-3	0.86
-2	0
0	-12
1/3	-42
1	18
3	6
50	3.15

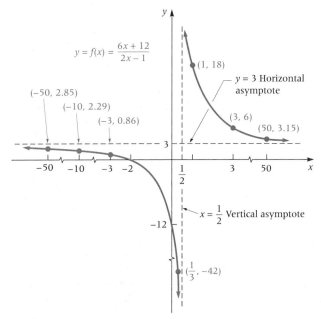

FIGURE 2-66

zontal line $y = 3$. Such a horizontal line is called a **horizontal asymptote.** Given the equation of a rational function, the horizontal asymptote (if it exists) is found by determining the behavior of the rational function at values of x far away from the origin. We will see that the behavior of a rational function at values of x far away from the origin is determined by the quotient

$$\frac{\text{highest-powered term of numerator}}{\text{highest-powered term of denominator}}$$

We begin by factoring out the highest-powered term of the numerator and also the highest-powered term of the denominator of our rational function

$$y = f(x) = \frac{6x + 12}{2x - 1}$$

This operation gives us

$$y = f(x) = \frac{6x\left(1 + \dfrac{2}{x}\right)}{2x\left(1 - \dfrac{1}{2x}\right)}$$

As x takes on larger and larger positive values, the terms $2/x$ and $1/2x$ approach 0. Thus, the quotient

$$\frac{\text{highest-powered term of numerator}}{\text{highest-powered term of denominator}} = \frac{6x}{2x} = 3$$

determines the behavior of $f(x)$ as x takes on larger and larger positive values. Also, as x takes on negative values of larger and larger magnitude, the quotient of the highest-powered terms of both the numerator and denominator determines the behavior of the graph of $f(x)$ at negative values of x far away from the origin. For this example, the quotient is the constant 3, indicating that the horizontal asymptote is $y = 3$.

Although we sketched the rational function $y = f(x) = (6x + 12)/(2x - 1)$ by choosing arbitrary x-values and plotting their corresponding points, there is a more methodical procedure, outlined by the following steps:

Step 1 Find the y-intercept.

Step 2 Find the x-intercept(s).

Step 3 Find the vertical asymptote(s).

Step 4 Determine the behavior of the function as x takes on values farther and farther away from the origin.

We now illustrate this procedure by sketching the graph of the rational function defined by

$$y = f(x) = \frac{2(x - 1)^3(x + 4)}{(x - 3)^2(x + 1)}$$

Step 1 Find the y-intercept. Here, we use

$$y = f(0) = \frac{2(0 - 1)^3(0 + 4)}{(0 - 3)^2(0 + 1)} = \frac{2(-1)^3(4)}{(-3)^2(1)} = \frac{-8}{9}$$

Thus, the y-intercept is $(0, -8/9)$.

Step 2 Find the x-intercept(s). Set $y = 0$. Hence,

$$0 = \frac{2(x - 1)^3(x + 4)}{(x - 3)^2(x + 1)}$$

$$0 = 2(x - 1)^3(x + 4)$$

$$(x - 1)^3 = 0 \qquad\qquad (x + 4)^1 = 0$$

$$x = 1 \qquad\qquad\qquad x = -4$$

odd exponent: ↑   *odd exponent:* ↑
graph crosses   graph crosses
x-axis here ⌐ x-axis here ⌐

Step 3 Find the vertical asymptote(s). Vertical asymptotes exist at those values of x for which the denominator of a rational function equals 0. Thus, we set the denominator equal to 0. This gives us

$$0 = (x - 3)^2(x + 1)$$

$$(x - 3)^2 = 0 \qquad x + 1 = 0$$

$$x = 3 \qquad\qquad x = -1$$

↑   ↗

vertical asymptotes

Note that the numerator $2(x - 1)^3(x + 4)$, does not equal 0 at $x = 3$ and $x = -1$.

Before leaving step 3, we must determine whether the function approaches the *same end* of the vertical asymptote from both sides, or whether it approaches *different ends* of the vertical asymptote from both sides (see Figures 2-67 and 2-68). The behavior of a rational function at a vertical asymptote is determined by noting whether the exponent of the factor from which the vertical asymptote was calculated is odd or even. The following rule is applied.

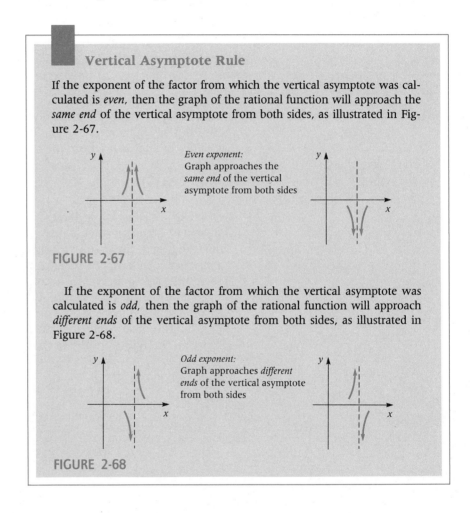

Vertical Asymptote Rule

If the exponent of the factor from which the vertical asymptote was calculated is *even*, then the graph of the rational function will approach the *same end* of the vertical asymptote from both sides, as illustrated in Figure 2-67.

Even exponent:
Graph approaches the
same end of the vertical
asymptote from both sides

FIGURE 2-67

If the exponent of the factor from which the vertical asymptote was calculated is *odd*, then the graph of the rational function will approach *different ends* of the vertical asymptote from both sides, as illustrated in Figure 2-68.

Odd exponent:
Graph approaches *different ends* of the vertical asymptote from both sides

FIGURE 2-68

Returning to our example, note that the vertical asymptotes were calculated as follows:

$$(x - 3)^2 = 0$$
$$x = 3$$

even exponent:
graph approaches the *same end*
of the vertical asymptote $x = 3$
from both sides

$$(x + 1)^1 = 0$$
$$x = -1$$

odd exponent:
graph approaches *differents ends*
of the vertical asymptote $x = -1$
from both sides

One can see why this rule works by noting that for the rational function defined by

$$f(x) = \frac{2(x-1)^3(x+4)}{(x-3)^2(x+1)}$$

the values of $f(x)$ do not change sign as x takes on values from either side of 3 since the exponent of the factor $(x-3)^2$ is 2, an even number. Hence, $f(x)$ approaches the vertical asymptote $x = 3$ from the same end. However, for values of x smaller than -1, the factor $x + 1$ is negative, whereas for values of x larger than -1, the factor $x + 1$ is positive, thereby causing a sign change in $f(x)$. Hence, $f(x)$ approaches the vertical asymptote $x = -1$ from different ends.

Step 4 Determine the behavior of the function as x takes on values farther and farther away from the origin. The quotient of the highest-powered terms of both numerator and denominator determines the behavior of $f(x)$ at values of x far away from the origin. In our example, this quotient is

$$\frac{2x^4}{x^3} = 2x$$

As x takes on larger and larger positive values, the quotient $2x$ takes on larger and larger positive values. Thus, for positive values of x far away from the origin, the graph of $f(x)$ is located in the upper right-hand corner of the first quadrant. As x takes on negative values of larger and larger magnitude, the quotient $2x$ becomes more and more negative. Thus, for negative values of x, the graph of $f(x)$ is located in the lower left-hand corner of the third quadrant.

The information obtained in the preceding four steps is illustrated in Figure 2-69. The graph of $f(x)$ appears in Figure 2-70.

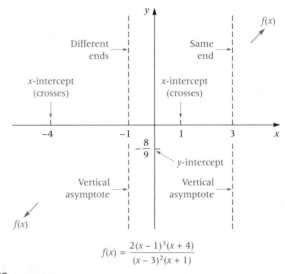

$$f(x) = \frac{2(x-1)^3(x+4)}{(x-3)^2(x+1)}$$

FIGURE 2-69

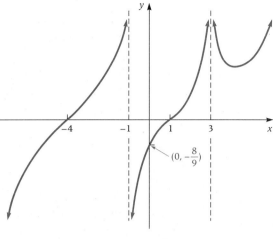

$$y = f(x) = \frac{2(x-1)^3(x+4)}{(x-3)^2(x+1)}$$

FIGURE 2-70

We now give a codified procedure for graphing rational functions.

 To Graph a Rational Function

Step 1 Find the y-intercept.
- Set $x = 0$ and solve for y.

Step 2 Find the x-intercept(s).
- Set $y = 0$ and solve for x. This results in setting the numerator = 0 and solving for x.
- Apply the x-intercept rule to determine tangency or crossing.

Step 3 Find the vertical asymptote(s).
- Set the denominator = 0 and solve for x.
- Verify that the numerator $\neq 0$ at the solution values of x.
- Apply the vertical asymptote rule.

Step 4 Determine the behavior of the function
- As x gets more and more positive.
- As x gets more and more negative.
- Use the quotient

$$\frac{\text{highest-powered term of numerator}}{\text{highest-powered term of denominator}}$$

for this analysis.

 Application

• **EXAMPLE 2-17   Cost-Benefit Curve.**

The equation

$$y = f(x) = \frac{20x}{104 - x} \qquad (0 \leq x \leq 100)$$

expresses the cost, y (in thousands of dollars), of removing $x\%$ of a certain pollutant from the atmosphere of a large city. The graph of such a function is called a **cost-benefit curve.**

a) Sketch the cost-benefit curve.
b) Find the cost of removing 90% of the pollutant.
c) Find the cost of removing 95% of the pollutant.
d) Find the cost of removing 100% of the pollutant.

Solutions

a) **Step 1** *Find the y-intercept.* If $x = 0$, then

$$y = \frac{20(0)}{104 - 0} = \frac{0}{104} = 0$$

Thus, the y-intercept is $(0, 0)$

Step 2 *Find the x-intercept(s).* Set $y = 0$ and solve for x. This leads to

$$0 = \frac{20x}{104 - x}$$
$$0 = 20x^1 \quad \longleftarrow$$
$$x = 0 \qquad \text{—— } \textit{odd exponent:}$$
$$\uparrow \qquad\qquad \text{graph } \textit{crosses } x\text{-axis}$$
$$x\text{-intercept} \qquad \text{here}$$

Step 3 *Find the vertical asymptote(s).* Set the denominator equal to 0. Hence,

$$104 - x = 0$$
$$x = 104$$

and the line $x = 104$ is a vertical asymptote. Since the exponent of the factor $104 - x$ is odd, the graph of $f(x)$ approaches different ends of the vertical asymptote from both sides.

Step 4 *Determine the behavior of* f(x) *as* x *takes on values farther and farther away from the origin.* The quotient of the highest-powered terms of both the numerator and denominator is

$$\frac{20x}{-x} = -20$$

Since this quotient is the constant -20, then $y = -20$ is a horizontal asymptote.

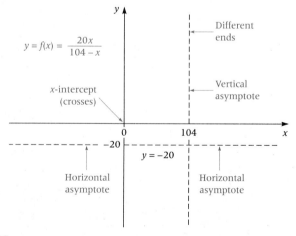

FIGURE 2-71

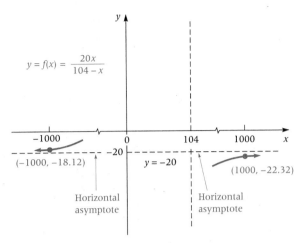

$$y = f(x) = \frac{20x}{104 - x}$$

FIGURE 2-72

The information in steps 1 through 4 is summarized in Figure 2-71.

Since this function has a horizontal asymptote, we must determine whether the graph of $f(x)$ approaches the horizontal asymptote from *above* or *below* as x takes on larger and larger positive values, and also as x takes on negative values of larger magnitude. This is accomplished by evaluating the function at relatively large values of x.

Specifically, to get some idea of whether the function approaches the horizontal asymptote from above or below as x takes on larger and larger positive values, we will evaluate $f(x)$ at $x = 1000$. Here,

$$y = f(1000) = \frac{20(1000)}{104 - 1000} = \frac{20{,}000}{-896} = -22.32$$

Since $-22.32 < -20$, then, for large positive values of x, the graph of $f(x)$ appears to approach the horizontal asymptote, $y = -20$, from below (see Figure 2-72).

Similarly, to get some idea of whether the graph approaches the horizontal

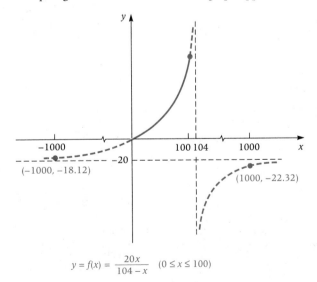

$$y = f(x) = \frac{20x}{104 - x} \quad (0 \le x \le 100)$$

FIGURE 2-73

asymptote from above or below as x takes on negative values of larger and larger magnitude, we evaluate $f(x)$ at $x = -1000$. In this case,

$$y = f(-1000) = \frac{20(-1000)}{104 - (-1000)} = \frac{-20,000}{1104} = -18.12$$

Since $-18.12 > -20$, then, as x takes on negative values far away from the origin, the graph of $f(x)$ appears to approach the horizontal asymptote, $y = -20$, from above (see Figure 2-72).

The completed graph is sketched in Figure 2-73. Note that the graph of the function is drawn as a solid curve for values of x within the interval $0 \le x \le 100$.

b) The cost of removing 90% of the pollutant is

$$y = f(90) = \frac{20(90)}{104 - 90} = \frac{1800}{14} \approx \$129 \text{ thousand*}$$

c) The cost of removing 95% of the pollutant is

$$y = f(95) = \frac{20(95)}{104 - 95} = \frac{1900}{9} \approx \$211 \text{ thousand}$$

d) The cost of removing 100% of the pollutant is

$$y = f(100) = \frac{20(100)}{104 - 100} = \frac{2000}{4} = \$500 \text{ thousand}$$

Note that it gets increasingly expensive to remove the last small portion of the pollutant.

Exercises 2-6

Graph each of the following.

1. $y = \dfrac{(x-3)^2(x+8)}{(x-1)^2}$

2. $f(x) = \dfrac{(x+5)(x-1)^4}{x(x-2)}$

3. $f(x) = \dfrac{(x-1)(x+3)^2}{(x+1)^3(x+4)}$

4. $y = \dfrac{(x-1)(x+3)^2}{x^4(x+4)}$

5. $y = \dfrac{1}{x-4}$

6. $f(x) = \dfrac{5}{(x+3)^2}$

7. $y = \dfrac{3x+12}{x-2}$

8. $f(x) = \dfrac{2x-10}{x+3}$

9. $f(x) = \dfrac{2x-16}{x+1}$

10. $f(x) = \dfrac{5x-30}{x^2-81}$

11. $y = \dfrac{x^2-9x}{3x-15}$

12. $f(x) = \dfrac{x^3-8x^2}{x^2-36}$

13. Graph the function defined by

$$f(x) = \frac{(x-3)(x+3)}{x^2+1}$$

This rational function does not have any vertical asymptotes. Why not? Also, use a calculator to fill in the table below by computing the indicated $f(x)$-

---

*The symbol $\approx$ means "approximately equal to."

values. Plot the corresponding points on the graph to determine the behavior of the graph of f over the interval $-3 < x < 3$.

x	-2	-1	$-1/2$	0	$1/2$	1	2
$f(x)$							

14. Graph the function defined by

$$f(x) = \frac{x^2 - 16}{x^2 + 2}$$

This rational function does not have any vertical asymptotes. Why not? Also, use a calculator to fill in the table below by computing the indicated $f(x)$-values. Plot the corresponding points on the graph to determine the behavior of the graph of f over the interval $-4 < x < 4$.

x	-3	-2	-1	$-1/2$	0	$1/2$	1	2	3
$f(x)$									

Applications

15. *Production possibility curve.* The Strong Steel Company produces two types of steel beams: I shaped and T shaped. The rational function defined by

$$y = \frac{420(x - 200)}{x - 210} \qquad (0 \le x \le 200)$$

relates the number, x, of I-shaped beams and the number, y, of T-shaped beams produced during a month. Such a function's graph is called a **production possibility curve.**
a) Sketch this production possibility curve.
b) If no I-shaped beams are produced, how many T-shaped are produced?
c) If no T-shaped beams are produced, how many I-shaped beams are produced?
d) If 70 I-shaped beams are produced, how many T-shaped beams are produced?

16. *Production possibility curve.* Keep-Cool Corporation manufactures two types of air conditioners: Model SM401 and Model LG535. The production possibility curve with equation

$$y = \frac{500(x - 300)}{x - 320} \qquad (0 \le x \le 300)$$

expresses the relationship between the number, x, of Model SM401 and the number, y, of Model LG535 produced during a month.
a) Sketch this production possibility curve.
b) If Keep-Cool Corporation produces no Model SM401s, how many Model LG535s can it produce?
c) If Keep-Cool Corporation produces no Model LG535s, how many Model SM401s can it produce?
d) If Keep-Cool Corporation produces 220 Model SM401s, how many Model LG535s can it produce?

17. *Cost-benefit curve.* The rational function defined by

$$y = \frac{40x}{110 - x} \qquad (0 \le x \le 100)$$

expresses the relationship between the cost, y (in millions of dollars), of removing x% of a pollutant from the atmosphere. This is an example of a cost-benefit curve.

a) Sketch the graph of this function.
b) Find the cost of removing the following amounts of pollution: 10%, 20%, 50%, 80%, 100%.

18. *Cost-benefit curve.* The rational function defined by

$$y = \frac{20x}{100 - x} \qquad (0 \le x < 100)$$

expresses the relationship between the cost, y (in thousands of dollars), of removing x% of a pollutant.

a) Sketch this cost-benefit curve.
b) Find the cost of removing the following amounts of pollution: 10%, 20%, 50%, 80%, 90%.
c) According to this function, is it possible to remove 100% of the pollutant?

EXTRA DIVIDENDS

• Model Fitting: Goodness of Fit

In the Extra Dividends section entitled "Model Fitting: Goodness of fit" following Chapter 1, we discussed how to determine the goodness of fit of linear models fit to given sets of data. This section applies the same concepts to nonlinear models. Specifically, if we are given a nonlinear model fit to a set of data, its goodness of fit is determined as it was in the previously mentioned section—by computing the sum of squares error. Although these concepts were summarized in the previous Extra Dividends, we repeat the summary here for completeness. We also note, as in the earlier section, that we are not concerned with how the fitted model is obtained. Such discussion is the topic of Section 15-4 in the calculus portion of this text.

To Determine Goodness of Fit

The **goodness of fit** of a model fitted to a given set of data points is determined as follows:

1. Compute the **fitted values** by substituting the x-values of the data points into the equation of the fitted model. These are simply the y-coordinates of points on the graph of the fitted model.
2. Compute the **residual** for each data point in accordance with the formula

$$\text{residual} = \text{data value} - \text{fitted value}$$

3. Compute the **sum of squares error, S,** as given below.

$$S = \text{sum of the squares of the residuals}$$

Note: The sum of squares error is an overall measure of the extent to which the fitted model does not fit the data.
Note: If more than one model is fit to the same set of data points, then the model resulting in the **smallest** sum of squares error is the better-fitting model for the set of data points.

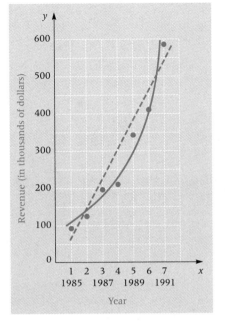

FIGURE 2-74

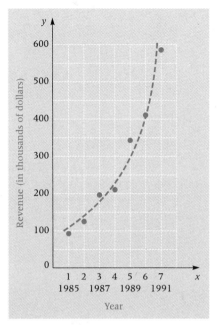

FIGURE 2-75

We now consider Table 2-2, a set of data relating annual sales revenues (in thousands of dollars) with time (in years). We learned in a previous Extra Dividends section that a set of data that relates some quantity to time is called a **time series.** For time series data, the successive time periods are denoted by $x = 1$, $x = 2$, . . . , etc. Although we use the variable x to denote the successive time periods, the letter t is also often used.

TABLE 2-2

Years	1985	1986	1987	1988	1989	1990	1991
x	1	2	3	4	5	6	7
y revenues	90	120	190	220	340	420	580

The data of Table 2-2 are plotted in Figure 2-74. Observe that the data appear to exhibit a nonlinear trend. This is made more explicit in Figure 2-75, where it is observed that a nonlinear model might be a better fit to the data.

Figure 2-76 gives a plot of the data and the fitted quadratic model (i.e., a parabola)

$$y = 10x^2 + 70$$

that appears to capture the relationship between x and y. Observe, in Figure 2-76, that the fitted values are determined by substituting the x-values into the equation of the fitted model. As mentioned earlier, we will not be concerned with how the quadratic model, $y = 10x^2 + 70$, was obtained as

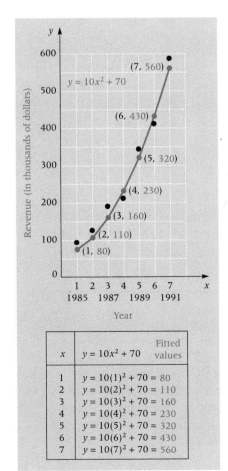

FIGURE 2-76

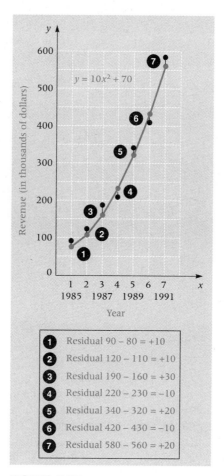

FIGURE 2-77

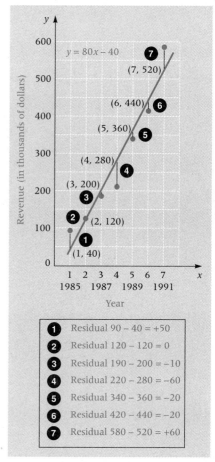

FIGURE 2-78

this will be discussed in Section 15-4 in the calculus portion of this text. Here we address the issue of assessing the goodness of fit of a nonlinear model fit to a set of data points.

Goodness of Fit

As discussed in the previous Extra Dividends section at the end of Chapter 1, to assess the goodness of fit of a model fit to a set of data points, we determine, for each data point, the vertical distance between the given data point and the graph of the fitted model, as illustrated in Figure 2-77. Recall that these vertical distances are called **residuals** and indicate the extent to which the fitted model does not fit the data points. Also, as discussed earlier, an overall measure of the extent to which the fitted model (in this case, the parabola $y = 10x^2 + 70$) does not fit the data is given by the sum of squares error and is denoted by S, as is shown below.

Sum of Squares Error

$$S = (90 - 80)^2 + (120 - 110)^2 + (190 - 160)^2 + (220 - 230)^2$$
$$+ (340 - 320)^2 + (420 - 430)^2 + (580 - 560)^2$$
$$= (10)^2 + (10)^2 + (30)^2 + (-10)^2 + (20)^2 + (-10)^2 + (20)^2$$
$$= 2100 \quad \text{Sum of squares error}$$

Figure 2-78 illustrates the goodness of fit of the linear model.

$$y = 80x - 40$$

to the set of data points in Table 2-2. The sum of squares error is computed below.

Sum of Squares Error

$$S = (90 - 40)^2 + (120 - 120)^2 + (190 - 200)^2 + (220 - 280)^2$$
$$+ (340 - 360)^2 + (420 - 440)^2 + (580 - 520)^2$$
$$= (50)^2 + (0)^2 + (-10)^2 + (-60)^2 + (-20)^2 + (-20)^2 + (60)^2$$
$$= 10,600 \quad \text{Sum of squares error}$$

Comparing the sum of squares error of the linear model, 10,600, with that of the quadratic model, 2100, it is apparent that the quadratic model, having a smaller sum of squares error, is the better-fitting model for this set of data.

• *Best-Fitting Models*

We have stated that in Section 15-4 of this text, we will learn how to fit models to data. Actually, we will learn more than that. We will learn how to determine the best-fitting linear model for a set of data, how to determine the best-fitting quadratic model for a set of data, etc. We caution that the linear model fit to the data of Table 2-2 is not necessarily the best-fitting linear model for the data. The quadratic model $y = 10x^2 + 70$ is not necessarily the best-fitting quadratic model for this set of data. Thus, when our comparison of the goodness of fit of both models indicated the quadratic model to be the better-fitting model, that does not necessarily imply that the best-fitting quadratic model fits this set of data better than the best-fitting linear model does. This determination can be made by comparing the sum of squares error for both best-fitting models.

Exercises

For each of the following sets of data, the equations of two fitted models are given.
a) Determine the sum of squares error for each fitted model.
b) Select the better-fitting model.

1.

x	1	2	3	4	5
y	40	80	200	300	530

$y = 20x^2 + 10$
$y = 100x - 90$

2.

x	2	3	5	7	10
y	35	60	150	240	530

$y = 5x^2 + 20$
$y = 45x - 40$

Application

3. *Time series: GNP.* Figure 2-79 gives a MINITAB plot of quarterly U.S. gross national product (GNP) from 1970 through 1980. Also given are the equations of two fitted models and their associated sum of squares errors. Select the better-fitting model.

Fitted Model	*Sum of Squares Error*
$y = 48.4x + 768$	1,568,435
$y = 1.2x^2 + 1111$	1,596,801

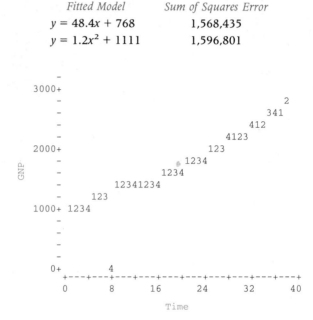

Each digit 1, 2, 3, and 4 indicates which quarter of a particular year's GNP is plotted at that location.

* This graph was drawn using the MINITAB statisitical software package. The annotations have been added.

FIGURE 2-79

CHAPTER 2 HIGHLIGHTS

• *Concepts*

Your ability to answer the following questions is one indicator of the depth of your mastery of this chapter's important concepts. Note that the questions are grouped under various topic headings. For any question that you cannot answer, refer to the section of the chapter indicated by the topic heading. Pay particular attention to the summary boxes within a section.

2-1   GRAPHING CONCEPTS

Explain each of the following terms, and indicate how it is related to the equation of a graph.

1. Vertical shift
2. Horizontal shift
3. Reflection in the x-axis
4. Symmetry with respect to the vertical axis
5. Symmetry with respect to the origin

2-2   QUADRATIC FUNCTIONS AND THEIR GRAPHS

6. Write the general form of a quadratic equation; write the formula for the x-coordinate of the vertex; the y-intercept is given by (0, ____).
7. Give the rule for determining whether a parabola opens up or down.
8. Give the procedure for finding the x-intercept(s) of a parabola.
9. A parabola may have as many as ____ x-intercepts.
10. If a parabola has exactly one x-intercept, then the x-intercept is also the

    _____.

2-3   APPLICATIONS OF QUADRATIC FUNCTIONS

11. Sales revenue is determined by beginning with the formula

    sales revenue = (_____)(_____)

12. A profit equation is determined by beginning with the formula

    profit = (_____) − (_____)

13. Given a profit equation, state the procedure for determining the break-even points.
14. Given the supply and demand equations, state the procedure for determining the equilibrium point.
15. If an equation relates some quantity to time, its graph is called a(an)

    _____.

2-4   SOME SPECIAL POLYNOMIAL AND RATIONAL FUNCTIONS

16. Write the general form for the equation of an nth-degree polynomial function.
17. An nth-degree polynomial function has at most ____ high/low points and at most ____ x-intercepts.
18. Draw the graph that typifies equations of the form $f(x) = ax^n$, where n is an odd positive integer, $n > 3$, and $a > 0$.
19. Draw the graph that typifies equations of the form $f(x) = ax^n$, where n is an even positive integer and $a > 0$.
20. Draw the graph that typifies equations of the form $f(x) = k/x^n$, where n is an odd positive integer and $k > 0$.
21. Draw the graph that typifies equations of the form $f(x) = k/x^n$, where n is an even positive integer and $k > 0$.
22. Give the procedure for determining vertical asymptotes of rational functions.
23. If $C(x)$ denotes the total cost of producing x units of some product, write the equation that gives the average cost per unit.

2-5   GRAPHING POLYNOMIAL FUNCTIONS (OPTIONAL)

24. Given a polynomial equation in factored form, state the rule for determining whether its graph crosses or is tangent to the x-axis at a particular x-intercept.

25. Give the procedure for graphing a polynomial function whose equation is given in factored form.

2-6   GRAPHING RATIONAL FUNCTIONS (OPTIONAL)

26. Give the procedure for graphing a rational function.

27. Give the vertical asymptote rule for rational functions.

REVIEW EXERCISES

• Graphing Concepts

Graph each of the following.

1. $y = |x - 7|$ **2.** $y = |x + 5| - 3$ **3.** $y = -|x + 2| + 1$

For Exercises 4-6, determine whether the function is odd, even, or neither by filling in the indicated table of x- and $f(x)$-values.

4. $f(x) = x^4$

x	-3	-2	-1	0	1	2	3
$f(x)$							

5. $f(x) = 1/x^3$

x	-3	-2	-1	0	1	2	3
$f(x)$							

6. $f(x) = 3x - 4$

x	-3	-2	-1	0	1	2	3
$f(x)$							

• Quadratic Functions

Graph Exercises 7-18.

7. $f(x) = x^2 - 25$ **8.** $f(x) = -x^2 + 36$

9. $f(x) = -3(x + 2)^2 + 4$ **10.** $f(x) = (x - 5)^2 - 3$

11. $y = -4x^2 + 24x$ **12.** $y = 5x^2 - 30x$

13. $f(x) = x^2 + 2x - 15$ **14.** $f(x) = x^2 - 9x + 8$

15. $f(x) = x^2 - 8x + 16$ **16.** $f(x) = x^2 + 10x + 25$

17. $y = (x + 4)(x - 6)$ **18.** $y = (x - 7)(x - 9)$

19. *Revenue function.* Given the demand equation $p = -2x + 140$, where p denotes the unit price in dollars and x denotes the number of units demanded of some product,

a) Determine the equation of the revenue function, $R(x)$.

b) Graph the revenue function.

c) State the maximum sales revenue.

d) How many units must be sold in order to achieve the maximum sales revenue?

e) Substitute the result of part d into the demand equation to determine the unit price that maximizes sales revenue.

20. *Revenue, cost, and profit functions; Break-even analysis.* Given the following:

$$\text{Demand function: } p = -2x + 2700$$
$$\text{Cost function: } C(x) = 300x + 400,000$$

where p denotes the unit price in dollars and x denotes the number of units produced and sold of some product,

a) Determine the equation of the revenue function, $R(x)$.
b) Graph both the revenue and cost functions on the same set of axes.
c) How many units of the product should be produced and sold in order to break even?
d) State the interval over which profit is positive.
e) Determine the equation of the profit function.
f) Graph the profit function.
g) Using the profit function, determine the break-even points. Verify that they agree with the answer to part c.
h) Using the profit function, state the interval over which profit is positive. Verify that this answer agrees with that of part d.
i) State the maximum profit.
j) How many units of the product should be produced and sold in order to maximize profit?

21. *Supply, demand, and market equilibrium.* For the following supply and demand functions, p denotes the unit price in dollars and x denotes the number of units supplied or demanded of some product in millions of units.

$$\text{Supply function: } p = x^2 + 8 \qquad (x > 0)$$
$$\text{Demand function: } p = (x - 4)^2 \qquad (0 < x \le 4)$$

a) Determine the equilibrium quantity.
b) Determine the equilibrium price.
c) Graph both the supply and demand functions on the same set of axes.

22. *Time series.* A company's annual profits, P (in millions of dollars), are related to the time, t (in years), since its incorporation by the function

$$P(t) = 0.8t^2 + 40 \qquad (t > 0)$$

a) Graph the function $P(t)$.
b) Find the company's annual profit for the third year.
c) Find the company's annual profit for the sixth year.

• *Some Special Polynomial and Rational Functions*

Graph Exercises 23-32.

23. $y = x^6$ **24.** $y = x^5$ **25.** $y = 5x^8$ **26.** $y = -7x^4$
27. $y = 3/x^4$ **28.** $y = 6/x^7$ **29.** $y = -8/x^3$ **30.** $y = -2/x^2$
31. $y = -4(x - 2)^4 + 3$ **32.** $y = 2/(x - 5)^5$

33. *Production possibility curve.* A company produces x units of Product A and y units of Product B. The equation

$$y = 8,000,000/x^2 \qquad (200 \le x \le 800)$$

relates x and y and thus gives the production possibilities for the two products.

a) Graph the production possibility curve.
b) State the production possibility for $x = 200$.
c) State the production possibility for $x = 600$.
d) State the production possibility for $x = 800$.

34. *Demand curve.* The equation

$$p = 40,000/(x - 20) \qquad (20 < x < 8020)$$

gives the relationship between the unit price, p, and the number of units demanded, x, of some product.
a) Graph the demand curve.
b) Find the unit price when the demand is 1020 units.
c) Find the unit price when the demand is 6020 units.

35. *Average cost function.* The total cost in dollars of producing x units of some product is given by

$$C(x) = 800x + 480,000 \qquad (x > 0)$$

a) Determine the equation of the average cost function.
b) Graph the result of part a.
c) Evaluate $\overline{C}(2000)$, $\overline{C}(10,000)$, and $\overline{C}(100,000)$, and interpret the results.
d) As the production level increases, the average cost per unit is approaching what value?

• Polynomial Functions

Graph Exercises 36-39.

36. $f(x) = (x + 3)(x - 1)^2(x - 8)$ **37.** $f(x) = (x + 2)^3(x - 6)^2$
38. $f(x) = x^4 - 4x^2$ **39.** $f(x) = x^3 - 4x^2 + 4x$

40. *Volume.* A company makes open boxes from square pieces of tin of dimensions 20 inches by 20 inches. Equal squares are cut from the corners of each piece of tin, and the remaining flaps are folded up to form the sides.
a) Express the volume, V, of the box as a function of x, the length of each side of the cut-out square.
b) Graph the function $V(x)$ of part a.
c) For which values of x is volume, V, non-negative? Does this make sense?

• Rational Functions

Graph the following.

41. $f(x) = \dfrac{(x + 2)(x - 5)^2}{(x - 1)}$ **42.** $f(x) = \dfrac{(x + 4)(x - 7)}{(x - 3)^3}$

43. $f(x) = \dfrac{5x - 40}{x - 2}$ **44.** $f(x) = \dfrac{x^2 - 25}{x^2 - 4}$

45. $f(x) = \dfrac{x^2 - 36}{x - 8}$ **46.** $f(x) = \dfrac{x^3 - 4x^2 + 4x}{(x - 1)^2}$

3

EXPONENTIAL AND LOGARITHMIC FUNCTIONS

Introductory Application

Market Penetration: Long-Range Forecasting

The exponential function defined by

$$y = A - Be^{-mx}$$

where A, B, and m are positive constants, is used to model market penetration of a product that exhibits rapid sales growth upon introduction into the marketplace. The above function is called the **modified exponential model.** Its graph appears in Figure 3-A. Note that x denotes time (in years), y denotes the percentage of the market penetrated by the product, and the constant, A, denotes the market saturation level—not to exceed 100% ($A = 100$). Observe that the graph of Figure 3-A indicates rapid sales growth upon introduction of the product (at $x = 0$). This sales growth continues for some time until it eventually slows as the market reaches saturation level.

- **EXAMPLE**

The market penetration for television sets has followed the modified exponential model.

In this chapter, we discuss exponential and logarithmic functions, including the modified exponential model and the logistic growth model, along with other applications.

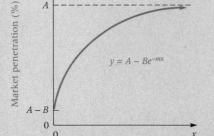

FIGURE 3-A

In this chapter, we will discuss functions used to describe growth and decay of various quantities. Such functions are called **exponential functions.** We will also consider **logarithms** and **logarithmic functions.** The derivatives of exponential and logarithmic functions will be discussed along with various applications.

3-1 • EXPONENTIAL FUNCTIONS AND THEIR GRAPHS

Consider two quantities, y and x, related by the equation

$$y = 2^x$$

Since the variable x is an exponent, such an equation defines an exponential function. The constant 2, is called the **base.** A graph and a table of x- and y-values are illustrated in Figure 3-1 and Table 3-1, respectively. Observing the graph of Figure 3-1, note that $(0, 1)$ is the y-intercept. Since 2^x approaches 0 as x takes on negative values of larger and larger magnitude, the graph of $y = 2^x$ approaches the x-axis as x takes on negative values far away from the origin. Thus, the x-axis is a horizontal asymptote.

Note that Table 3-1 shows values of 2^x for rational values of x. It is possible to evaluate 2^x for irrational values of x by approximating each irrational value of x by rational values. For example, $2^{\sqrt{3}}$ may be approximated to varying degrees of accuracy by considering the sequence of rational powers

$$2^1, 2^{1.7}, 2^{1.73}, 2^{1.732}, \ldots$$

Recall that $\sqrt{3} \approx 1.732$. Thus, as the exponents get closer and closer to $\sqrt{3}$, the corresponding powers of 2 get closer and closer to $2^{\sqrt{3}}$. Therefore, the exponential function defined by $y = 2^x$ has all of the real numbers as its domain, and its graph is the continuous curve illustrated in Figure 3-1.

We now consider the function defined by the equation

$$y = 2^{-x}$$

Again, since the variable x appears as an exponent, this equation defines an exponential function. Note that the exponent, $-x$, has a negative sign. The graph of $y = 2^{-x}$ and a table of $x-$ and $y-$ values are given on page 128 in Figure 3-2 and Table 3-2, respectively.

Studying the graph of Figure 3-2, we see that $(0, 1)$ is the y-intercept. Note that 2^{-x} approaches 0 as x takes on larger and larger positive values. Thus, the x-axis is a horizontal asymptote. The graphs of $y = 2^x$ and $y = 2^{-x}$ are reflections of one another through the y-axis.

We now consider the function defined by

$$y = 5 \cdot 2^x$$

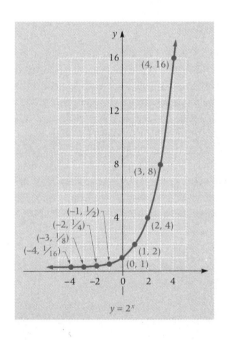

TABLE 3-1

x	$y = 2^x$
-4	$y = 2^{-4} = (1/2)^4 = 1/$
-3	$y = 2^{-3} = (1/2)^3 = 1/$
-2	$y = 2^{-2} = (1/2)^2 = 1/$
-1	$y = 2^{-1} = (1/2)^1 = 1/$
0	$y = 2^0 = 1$
1	$y = 2^1 = 2$
2	$y = 2^2 = 4$
3	$y = 2^3 = 8$
4	$y = 2^4 = 16$

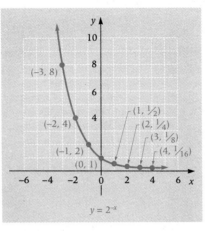

FIGURE 3-2

TABLE 3-2

x	$y = 2^{-x}$
-4	$y = 2^{-(-4)} = 2^4 = 16$
-3	$y = 2^{-(-3)} = 2^3 = 8$
-2	$y = 2^{-(-2)} = 2^2 = 4$
-1	$y = 2^{-(-1)} = 2^1 = 2$
0	$y = 2^{-(0)} = 2^0 = 1$
1	$y = 2^{-1} = \dfrac{1}{2}$
2	$y = 2^{-2} = \dfrac{1}{2^2} = \dfrac{1}{4}$
3	$y = 2^{-3} = \dfrac{1}{2^3} = \dfrac{1}{8}$
4	$y = 2^{-4} = \dfrac{1}{2^4} = \dfrac{1}{16}$

Since the variable x appears as an exponent, this equation also defines an exponential function. Its graph and a table of x- and y-values are illustrated in Figure 3-3 and Table 3-3, respectively. Looking at Figure 3-3, note that $(0, 5)$ is the y-intercept and that the x-axis is a horizontal asymptote.

If we compare the graphs of $y = 2^x$ and $y = 5 \cdot 2^x$ by sketching both functions on the same axis system, we obtain Figure 3-4. Note that the x-axis is the horizontal asymptote for both functions. Also, $(0, 1)$ is the y-intercept of $y = 2^x$, whereas $(0, 5)$ is the y-intercept of $y = 5 \cdot 2^x$. Observe that the graph of $y = 5 \cdot 2^x$ is similar to the graph of $y = 2^x$. The only effects of the constant multiplier, 5, on the graph of $y = 2^x$ are changes in its y-intercept and curvature. This is because the y-values of $y = 5 \cdot 2^x$ are 5 times those of $y = 2^x$.

TABLE 3-3

x	$y = 5 \cdot 2^x$
-3	$y = 5 \cdot 2^{-3} = 5 \cdot (1/2)^3 = 5/8$
-2	$y = 5 \cdot 2^{-2} = 5 \cdot (1/2)^2 = 5/4$
-1	$y = 5 \cdot 2^{-1} = 5 \cdot (1/2)^1 = 5/2$
0	$y = 5 \cdot 2^0 = 5 \cdot 1 = 5$
1	$y = 5 \cdot 2^1 = 5 \cdot 2 = 10$
2	$y = 5 \cdot 2^2 = 5 \cdot 4 = 20$
3	$y = 5 \cdot 2^3 = 5 \cdot 8 = 40$
4	$y = 5 \cdot 2^4 = 5 \cdot 16 = 80$

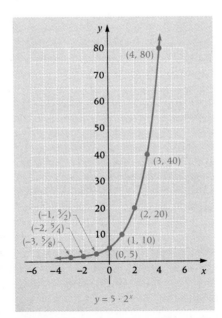

FIGURE 3-3

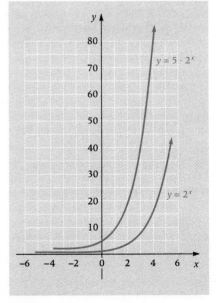

FIGURE 3-4

Step 1
Begin with the graph $y = 5 \cdot 2^x$.

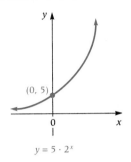

$y = 5 \cdot 2^x$

Step 2
Draw the graph of $y = 5 \cdot 2^x$ upside down to obtain the graph of $y = -5 \cdot 2^x$.

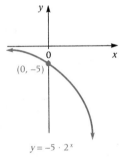

$y = -5 \cdot 2^x$

FIGURE 3-5

We note that if the constant multiplier is negative—say, -5,—then the y-values of the function $y = -5 \cdot 2^x$ are the negatives of those of $y = 5 \cdot 2^x$, and, therefore, the graph of $y = -5 \cdot 2^x$ is a reflection on the x-axis of the graph of $y = 5 \cdot 2^x$, as illustrated in Figure 3-5. In other words, the graph of $y = -5 \cdot 2^x$ can be obtained by drawing the graph of $y = 5 \cdot 2^x$ upside down.

Base e

The following discussion will involve values of the expression

$$\left(1 + \frac{1}{x}\right)^x$$

as x gets larger and larger. This expression occurs so often in mathematics that we use a calculator to evaluate it for larger and larger values of x as illustrated below.

$$\left(1 + \frac{1}{1000}\right)^{1000} = 2.716923924. . .$$

$$\left(1 + \frac{1}{10,000}\right)^{10,000} = 2.718145918. . .$$

$$\left(1 + \frac{1}{100,000}\right)^{100,000} = 2.718268237. . .$$

$$\left(1 + \frac{1}{1,000,000}\right)^{1,000,000} = 2.718281828. . .$$

$$\left(1 + \frac{1}{10,000,000}\right)^{10,000,000} = 2.718281828. . .$$

Note how $(1 + 1/x)^x$ is approaching a single value close to 2.718281828 to nine decimal places. Mathematicians have assigned the letter e to the limiting value of the expression $(1 + 1/x)$ as x gets larger and larger. In other words,

$$\left(1 + \frac{1}{x}\right)^x \boxed{\text{approaches}} \!\!\!> e$$

as x gets larger and larger, and e denotes the irrational number whose decimal expansion to nine decimal places is given as follows.

$$e = 2.718281828$$

We note that powers of e (i.e., e^2, e^3, $e^{1.5}$, $e^{-1.67}$, etc.) can be computed by using a calculator. Also, Appendix C gives values of e^x and e^{-x} for various values of x.

Up to this point, we have graphed exponential functions with base 2. However, we often encounter exponential functions with base e. Some examples include $y = e^x$, $y = e^{-x}$, $y = 5e^x$, and $y = -5e^x$. Since we have already graphed $y = 2^x$, $y = 2^{-x}$, $y = 5 \cdot 2^x$, and $y = -5 \cdot 2^x$, we note that the graphs of these equations resemble those of $y = e^x$, $y = e^{-x}$, $y = 5e^x$, and $y = -5e^x$, respectively.

We now summarize the concepts discussed up to this point in this section.

SUMMARY

Graphs of Exponential Functions

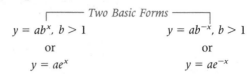

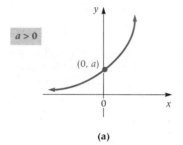

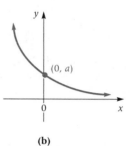

(a) (b)

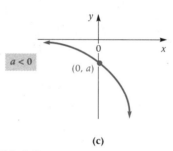

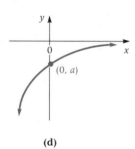

(c) (d)

FIGURE 3-6

Note: The graphs for $a < 0$ are reflections (in other words, drawn upside down) of those for $a > 0$.

• **EXAMPLE 3-1**

a) The graphs of $y = 5 \cdot 3^x$, $y = e^x$, and $y = 4e^x$ resemble that of Figure 3-6(a).

b) The graphs of $y = 5 \cdot 3^{-x}$, $y = e^{-x}$, and $y = 7e^{-x}$ resemble that of Figure 3-6(b).

c) The graphs of $y = -4 \cdot 2^x$, $y = -e^x$, and $y = -8e^x$ resemble that of Figure 3-6(c).

d) The graphs of $y = -5 \cdot 3^{-x}$, $y = -e^{-x}$, and $y = -6e^{-x}$ resemble that of Figure 3-6(d).

$y = ab^x + c$ and $y = ab^{-x} + c$ Where $b > 1$

Sometimes we encounter an exponential function defined by an equation such as

$$y = 3e^x + 2$$

Step 1
Begin with the graph of $y = 3e^x$.

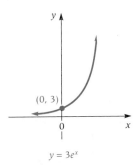

Step 2 *Vertical shift*
Lift the graph of $y = 3e^x$ vertically by 2 units to obtain the graph of $y = 3e^x + 2$.

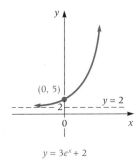

FIGURE 3-7

Since the constant 2 is added to $y = 3e^x$, the y-values of $y = 3e^x + 2$ are 2 *greater than* those of $y = 3e^x$. Hence, $y = 3e^x + 2$ may be sketched by beginning with the graph of $y = 3e^x$ and *lifting it vertically by 2 units* (see Figure 3-7). As discussed in Chapter 2, this is called a **vertical shift.** Note that the horizontal line $y = 2$ is the horizontal asymptote for $y = 3e^x + 2$.

Step 1
Begin with the graph of $y = -2e^x$.

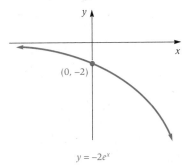

Step 2 *Vertical shift*
Lower the graph of $y = -2e^x$ vertically by 1 unit to obtain the graph of $y = -2e^x - 1$.

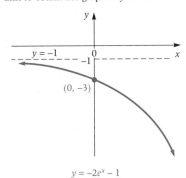

FIGURE 3-8

> ### To Graph Exponential Functions
>
> $$y = ab^x + c \quad \text{or} \quad y = ab^{-x} + c$$
> $$\text{where } b > 1$$
>
> **Step 1** Begin with the graph of $y = ab^x$ or $y = ab^{-x}$.
> **Step 2** Vertical Shift
>
> If $c > 0$, lift the graph of Step 1 vertically by c units.
> If $c < 0$, lower the graph of Step 1 vertically by $|c|$ units.

• **EXAMPLE 3-2** ─────────────

Sketch $f(x) = -2e^x - 1$.

Solution

Compare this equation with the general form $y = ab^x + c$, where $a = -2$ (a negative number), $b = e$, and $c = -1$. The graph is sketched in Figure 3-8.

• **EXAMPLE 3-3** ─────────────

Sketch $y = -4e^{-x} + 6$.

Solution

This function is of the form $y = ab^{-x} + c$, where $a = -4$ (a negative number), $b = e$, and $c = 6$. Its graph is sketched in Figure 3-9 on page 132.

─────────────────────────────── •

Step 1
Begin with the graph of $y = -4e^{-x}$.

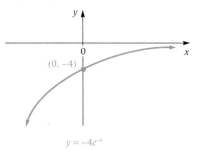

Step 2 *Vertical shift*
Lift the graph of $y = -4e^{-x}$ vertically by 6 units to obtain the graph of $y = -4e^{-x} + 6$.

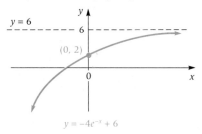

FIGURE 3-9

All of the equations defining exponential functions in this section have appeared in either of the following two forms:

$$y = ab^x + c \qquad (b > 1)$$

or

$$y = ab^{-x} + c \qquad (b > 1)$$

Note that for each form, $b > 1$. We now consider the cases for which $b \le 1$. If $b = 1$, then $b^x = 1^x = 1$ for all finite x-values. Thus, the equation $y = ab^x + c$ becomes the horizontal line $y = a + c$. The same happens to the form $y = ab^{-x} + c$. We have little interest in such exponential functions.

We now show that the case in which $0 < b < 1$ is not really a new case at all. If $0 < b < 1$, then b^x may be written as b_1^{-x}, with $b_1 = 1/b$ and $b_1 > 1$. For example, $(1/2)^x = 2^{-x}$, $(1/3)^x = 3^{-x}$, $(2/5)^x = (5/2)^{-x}$, etc. Also, b^{-x} becomes b_1^x, with $b_1 = 1/b$ and $b_1 > 1$. For example, $(1/2)^{-x} = 2^x$, $(1/3)^{-x} = 3^x$, $(2/5)^{-x} = (5/2)^x$, etc. Thus, the equation $y = ab^x + c$, with $0 < b < 1$, may be written as $y = ab_1^{-x} + c$, with $b_1 > 1$, since $b_1 = 1/b$. Also, the equation $y = ab^{-x} + c$, with $0 < b < 1$, may be rewritten as $y = ab_1^x + c$, with $b_1 > 1$, since $b_1 = 1/b$.

If $b \le 0$, we have little interest in equations of the form $y = ab^x + c$ or $y = ab^{-x} + c$ since the function is not defined at many x-values. Specifically, if $b = 0$ and $x = -1$, then $y = ab^x + c$ is undefined; if $b = -4$ and $x = 1/2$, then $y = ab^x + c$ is undefined.

We state the following property.

If $b > 0$, there is a value k such that

$$b = e^k$$

In other words, any positive number b can be expressed as e^k.*

Exponential Functions with Terms e^{kx} and e^{-kx}

Since

$$b^x = (e^k)^x = e^{kx}$$

equations of the forms

$$y = ab^x + c \qquad (b > 1)$$

and

$$y = ab^{-x} + c \qquad (b > 1)$$

*We will learn how to find k in Section 3-2.

Step 1
Begin with the graph of $y = -3e^{-0.05x}$.

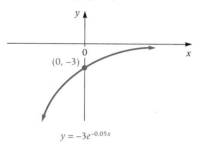

$y = -3e^{-0.05x}$

Step 2 *Vertical shift*
Lift the graph of $y = -3e^{-0.05x}$ vertically by 7 units to obtain the graph of $y = -3e^{-0.05x} + 7$.

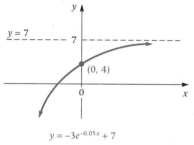

$y = -3e^{-0.05x} + 7$

FIGURE 3-10

may be restated as

$$y = ae^{kx} + c \qquad (k > 0)$$

and

$$y = ae^{-kx} + c \qquad (k > 0)$$

respectively. Therefore, the procedures of this section also apply to sketching exponential functions expressed in the latter forms that contain the terms e^{kx} and e^{-kx}.

• **EXAMPLE 3-4** _____

Sketch $y = -3e^{-0.05x} + 7$.

Solution

The graph is sketched in Figure 3-10.

_____ •

Before ending this section, we state the following property.

If $b > 0$ and $b \neq 1$, then $b^x = b^y$ if and only if $x = y$.

For example, if $3^{18} = 3^{2x}$, then $2x = 18$ and $x = 9$. If $5^{40} = 5^{4x}$, then $4x = 40$ and $x = 10$.

Applications

Radioactive Decay

A radioactive substance loses its mass (or, if you prefer, weight) as time passes. Specifically, its mass, y, is related to the time elapsed, t, by an equation of the form

$$y = ae^{-kt} \qquad (k > 0)$$

Note that at $t = 0$, the initial mass is

$$y = ae^{-k(0)}$$
$$= a \cdot 1$$
$$= a$$

The letter k represents a constant associated with the specific radioactive substance being considered. If, for a particular radioactive substance, the initial mass is $a = 1000$ grams and $k = 0.70$, then the equation

$$y = 1000e^{-0.70t}$$

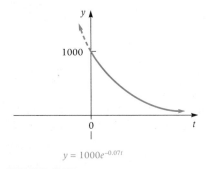

FIGURE 3-11

relates its mass, y (in grams), with the time elapsed, t (in minutes). Thus, at $t = 1$ (after 1 minute has elapsed), the mass is

$$y = 1000e^{-0.70(1)}$$
$$= 1000e^{-0.70}$$
$$\approx 1000(0.496585)$$
$$\approx 496.59 \text{ grams}$$

The graph of $y = 1000e^{-0.70t}$ is illustrated in Figure 3-11. Observe that the radioactive mass is decreasing as time is increasing.

Newton's Law of Cooling

Newton's law of cooling expresses the relationship between the temperature of a cooling object and the time elapsed since cooling first began. According to Newton's law of cooling, if

y = temperature of a cooling object after t units of time

c = temperature of the medium surrounding the cooling object

then the exponential function

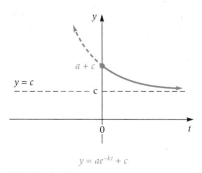

FIGURE 3-12

$$y = ae^{-kt} + c$$

relates temperature, y, with time, t. The letters a and k represent constants associated with the cooling object. A sketch of the general function $y = ae^{-kt} + c$ appears in Figure 3-12. The constants a and k are non-negative. Studying Figure 3-12, we note that the temperature y of the cooling object approaches the temperature c of the surrounding medium as t gets larger and larger. Thus, the temperature of a cooling object will not fall below the temperature of the surrounding medium.

As a specific example, consider a cup of tea heated to 210°F. The room temperature is 70°F. Here, the exponential function

$$y = 140e^{-0.01t} + 70 \qquad (t \geq 0)$$

relates the temperature, y, of the tea with the time elapsed, t (in minutes). Hence, after 10 minutes have elapsed ($t = 10$), we find that

$$y = 140e^{-0.01(10)} + 70$$
$$= 140e^{-0.1} + 70$$
$$\approx 140(0.904837) + 70$$
$$\approx 126.67718 + 70$$
$$\approx 196.7$$

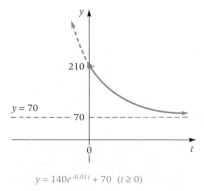

$y = 140e^{-0.01t} + 70 \quad (t \geq 0)$

FIGURE 3-13

Thus, the object at this point in time has cooled to a temperature of approximately 197°F. The graph of $y = 140e^{-0.01t} + 70$ is sketched in Figure 3-13.

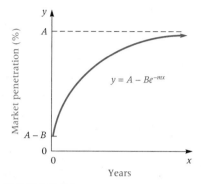

FIGURE 3-14

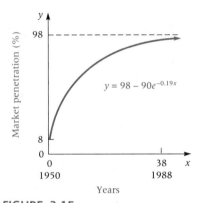

FIGURE 3-15

Market Penetration: Long-Range Forecasting

We discuss two exponential functions used to model and, thus, forecast the market penetration of products introduced into the marketplace. The first is called the modified exponential model, and the second is called the logistic growth model.

Modified Exponential Model.   As discussed in the introductory application to this chapter, the exponential function defined by

$$y = A - Be^{-mx}$$

where A, B, and m are positive constants, is used to model market penetration of a product that exhibits rapid sales growth upon introduction into the marketplace. The above function is called the **modified exponential model.** Its graph appears in Figure 3-14. Note that x denotes time (in years), y denotes the percentage of the market penetrated by the product, and the constant, A, denotes the market saturation level—not to exceed 100% ($A = 100$). Observe that the graph of Figure 3-14 indicates rapid sales growth upon introduction of the product (at $x = 0$). This sales growth continues for some time until it eventually slows as the market reaches saturation level.

The market penetration for television sets has followed the modified exponential model, as illustrated in Figure 3-15. The equation

$$y = 98 - 90e^{-0.19x}$$

approximates the relationship between market penetration and time exhibited by the curve of Figure 3-15. Here $x = 0$ corresponds to the year 1950, and $x = 38$ corresponds to the year 1988.

USING THE MODEL TO FORECAST   We forecast the percentage of the market penetrated by television sets for the year 1995 by substituting $x = 45$ into the equation of the model to obtain

$$y = 98 - 90e^{-0.19(45)} \qquad \text{Use a calculator}$$
$$\approx 97.98 \qquad \text{Forecast}$$

Thus, approximately 97.98% of all households are projected to have television sets in 1995.

Logistic Growth Model.   The exponential function defined by

$$y = \frac{A}{1 + Be^{-mx}}$$

where A, B, and m are positive constants, is used to model market penetration of a product that exhibits slow sales growth when first introduced into the marketplace, then a period of rapid growth followed by a gradual decline in growth, and, finally, no growth as the market reaches saturation level. This is illustrated in Figure 3-16, which gives the graph of the above function. This function is called the **logistic growth model;** the variable,

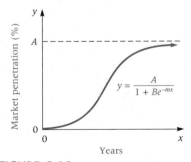

FIGURE 3-16

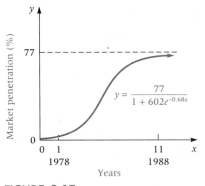

y↑
Market penetration (%)
77 - - - - - - - - - -

$y = \dfrac{77}{1 + 602e^{-0.68x}}$

0
0 1   11   x
1978   1988
Years

FIGURE 3-17

x, denotes time (in years), y denotes the percentage of the market penetrated by the product, and the constant, A, denotes the market saturation level—not to exceed 100% ($A = 100$).

The market penetration for videocassette recorders (VCRs) has followed the logistic growth model, as illustrated in Figure 3-17. The equation

$$y = \frac{77}{1 + 602e^{-0.68x}}$$

approximates the relationship between market penetration and time exhibited by the curve of Figure 3-17. Here $x = 1$ corresponds to the year 1978, and $x = 11$ corresponds to the year 1988.

USING THE MODEL TO FORECAST   We forecast the percentage of the market penetrated by videocassette recorders for the year 1995 by substituting $x = 18$ into the equation of the model to obtain

$$y = \frac{77}{1 + 602e^{-0.68(18)}} \qquad \text{Use a calculator}$$

$$\approx 76.77 \qquad \text{Forecast}$$

Thus, approximately 76.77% of all households are projected to have videocassette recorders in 1995.

Exercises 3-1

Sketch the following. Identify the y-intercept and the horizontal asymptote in each case.

1. $f(x) = 5^x$ **2.** $y = 3^x$ **3.** $y = 4^x$

4. $f(x) = 4 \cdot 5^x$ **5.** $y = 2 \cdot 3^x$ **6.** $y = 3 \cdot 4^x$

7. $f(x) = -4 \cdot 5^x$ **8.** $f(x) = -2 \cdot 3^x$ **9.** $y = -3 \cdot 4^x$

10. $y = 3e^x$ **11.** $f(x) = 7e^x$ **12.** $y = 10e^x$

13. $y = -3e^x$ **14.** $y = -7e^x$ **15.** $y = -10e^x$

16. $y = 2 \cdot 3^x + 5$ **17.** $f(x) = -3 \cdot 4^x + 8$

18. $f(x) = 4e^x + 1$ **19.** $y = 4e^x - 1$

20. $y = -2e^x + 8$ **21.** $f(x) = -2e^x - 5$

22. $y = 5^{-x}$ **23.** $f(x) = 3^{-x}$

24. $y = 4^{-x}$ **25.** $y = 4 \cdot 5^{-x}$

26. $f(x) = 2 \cdot 3^{-x}$ **27.** $y = 3 \cdot 4^{-x}$

28. $y = -4 \cdot 5^{-x}$ **29.** $f(x) = -2 \cdot 3^{-x}$

30. $y = -3 \cdot 4^{-x}$ **31.** $y = 3e^{-x}$

32. $y = 7e^{-x}$ **33.** $y = 10e^{-x}$

34. $y = -3e^{-x}$ **35.** $f(x) = -7e^{-x}$

36. $y = -10e^{-x}$ **37.** $y = 2 \cdot 3^{-x} + 5$

38. $f(x) = -3 \cdot 4^{-x} + 8$ **39.** $f(x) = 4e^{-x} + 1$

40. $y = 4e^{-x} - 1$ **41.** $y = -2e^{-x} + 30$

42. $f(x) = -2e^{-x} - 5$ **43.** $y = 30e^{-x} + 30$

44. $f(x) = 50 - 50e^{-x}$ **45.** $y = 10(1 - e^{-x})$

46. $f(x) = -5(1 - e^{-x})$ **47.** $y = (1/2)^x$

48. $y = (2/3)^x$ **49.** $y = (1/2)^{-x}$

50. $f(x) = (2/3)^{-x}$

51. $y = 5 \cdot (1/5)^x + 1$

52. $f(x) = -4 \cdot (1/6)^{-x} + 2$

53. $y = 3e^{2x} + 1$

54. $f(x) = 4e^{-3x} + 1$

55. $f(x) = -2e^{0.05x} + 1$

56. $y = 3e^{-0.02x} - 5$

57. $y = 10e^{0.07x}$

58. $y = -5e^{0.03x}$

59. $f(x) = 7e^{-0.10x}$

60. $y = -3e^{-0.06x}$

61. $y = 10(1 - e^{-0.20x})$

62. $y = -2e^{-0.3x} - 6$

63. $y = -8e^{-0.40x}$

64. $y = 70e^{-0.50x} + 10$

Applications

65. *Bacteria growth.* A certain type of bacteria triples its numbers each day. Initially, there were 500,000 such bacteria present. Let y represent the number of bacteria present and t represent the number of days elapsed.
a) Find the equation that relates y and t.
b) Sketch the graph of the equation of part a.
c) How many bacteria are present after 4 days?
d) How many bacteria are present after 6 days?

66. *Depreciation.* A certain car depreciates in such a way that it loses two-thirds of its value each year. The car initially cost $4000. Let y represent the car's value (in dollars) at the end of the xth year.
a) Find the equation that relates y and x.
b) Sketch the graph of the equation of part a.
c) Find the car's value at the end of the fourth year.
d) Find the car's value at the end of the fifth year.

67. *Time series.* The annual sales, y (in millions of dollars), of a particular company are related to time, t, by the equation

$$y = 3 \cdot 2^t$$

with $t = 0$ corresponding to the year 19x0, $t = 1$ corresponding to the year 19x1, etc.
a) Sketch $y = 3 \cdot 2^t$.
b) Find the annual sales for years 19x0, 19x1, and 19x2.

68. *Time series.* The annual earnings per share of AKD Corporation are related to time by the equation

$$y(t) = e^{0.1t}$$

where $y(t)$ represents the earnings per share for year t. Note that $t = 0$ corresponds to the year 19x0, $t = 1$ corresponds to the year 19x1, etc.
a) Sketch $y(t) = e^{0.1t}$.
b) Find the earnings per share for years 19x0, 19x1, 19x2, and 19x3.

69. *Maintenance cost.* The annual maintenance cost, y, of a machine is related to the number of years it is run, t, by the equation

$$y = 1000e^{0.05t} \qquad (t \geq 0)$$

a) Sketch $y = 1000e^{0.05t}$, $t \geq 0$.
b) Find the annual maintenance cost after the machine has run for 2 years.

70. *Population decline.* The population, $P(t)$, of a certain city is related to time, t (in years), by the exponential function

$$P(t) = 10{,}000e^{-0.03t}$$

Note that $t = 0$ corresponds to the year 19x0, $t = 1$ corresponds to the year 19x1, etc.

a) Sketch $P(t) = 10{,}000e^{-0.03t}$.
b) Find this city's population for 19x0, 19x1, 19x2, and 19x3.

71. *Radioactive decay.* A certain radioactive substance decays in accordance with the equation

$$y(t) = 2000e^{-0.60t} \qquad (t \geq 0)$$

where $y(t)$ represents the mass (in grams) related to time, t (in hours).

a) Sketch $y(t) = 2000e^{-0.60t}$.
b) Calculate the initial mass of the substance.
c) Calculate the mass of the substance after 1/2 hour has elapsed.
d) Calculate the mass of the substance after 3 hours have elapsed.

Learning Curve

Psychologists have found that when a person learns a new task, learning is rapid at first. Then, as time passes, learning tends to taper off. Once the task is mastered, the person's level of performance approaches an upper limit. The function that relates a learner's performance with the time elapsed is called a **learning curve.** Learning curves are often expressed by exponential functions.

72. *Learning curve.* Consider the learning curve expressed by the exponential function

$$y = 40 - 40e^{-0.2x} \qquad (x \geq 0)$$

Here, the performance, y, is the number of items produced by the worker during the xth day following the training period.

a) Sketch $y = 40 - 40e^{-0.2x}$.
b) How many items are produced during the third day following the training period?
c) This worker's daily production will never exceed how many units?

73. *Learning curve.* The graph of the exponential function defined by

$$N(x) = 50 - 50e^{-0.3x} \qquad (x \geq 0)$$

is a learning curve, where $N(x)$ represents the number of items produced by an assembly line worker during the xth day after the training period.

a) Sketch $N(x) = 50 - 50e^{-0.3x}$.
b) How many items are produced during the fifth day following the training period?
c) This worker's daily production will never exceed how many units?

74. *Newton's law of cooling.* The temperature, y, of a heated cup of coffee is related to the time elapsed, t (in minutes), by the equation

$$y = 150e^{-0.02t} + 65 \qquad (t \geq 0)$$

a) Sketch $y = 150e^{-0.02t} + 65$.
b) Calculate the temperature of the coffee before cooling began.
c) Calculate the temperature of the coffee after 5 minutes have elapsed.
d) What is the room temperature?
e) The temperature of the coffee will not decline below what value?

75. *Newton's law of cooling.* A coroner determines that the temperature, T, of a murder victim's body is related to the time elapsed, t (in hours), since death by the equation

$$T = 38.6e^{-0.05t} + 60 \qquad (t \geq 0)$$

a) Sketch $T = 38.6e^{-0.05t} + 60$.
b) What is the room temperature?
c) Calculate the dead body's temperature after 2 hours have elapsed.

76. *Sales.* The function defined by

$$y = 3.6e^{0.02x} \qquad (x \ge 0)$$

approximates the relationship between sales, y (in billions of dollars), and advertising expenditure, x (in millions of dollars).

a) Sketch $y = 3.6e^{0.02x}$.
b) Calculate the expected sales for an advertising expenditure of $5 million.

77. *Market penetration: Long-range forecasting.* The percentage of market penetration for a product x years after it has been introduced is given by

$$y = 80 - 60e^{-0.70x}$$

a) Graph $y = 80 - 60e^{-0.70x}$ for $x \ge 0$.
b) Determine the percentage of market penetration for the second year.
c) Determine the percentage of market penetration for the tenth year.
d) Determine the saturation level.

78. *Market penetration: Long-range forecasting.* The percentage of market penetration for a product x years after it has been introduced is given by

$$y = \frac{80}{1 + 200e^{-0.90x}}$$

a) Determine the percentage of market penetration for the second, sixth, and twelfth years.
b) Determine the saturation level.

3-2 • LOGARITHMIC FUNCTIONS

Logarithm

If three numbers, L, b, and N (and $b > 0$, $b \ne 1$, and $N > 0$), are related in such a way that

$$N = b^L$$

then the exponent, L, is defined as "the logarithm of N to the base b." This definition is written in shorthand notation as

$$L = \log_b N$$

Thus, the statement $N = b^L$ has the same meaning as the statement $L = \log_b N$. The statement $N = b^L$ is written in **exponential form.** The statement $L = \log_b N$ is written in **logarithmic form.** Specifically, the statement $9 = 3^2$ may be expressed in logarithmic form as $2 = \log_3 9$, read "2 equals the log of 9 to the base 3."

• EXAMPLE 3-5 _____

Rewrite the statement $5^3 = 125$ in logarithmic form.

Solution

$3 = \log_5 125$, read "3 equals the log of 125 to the base 5."

• EXAMPLE 3-6 _____

Rewrite the statement $10^4 = 10,000$ in logarithmic form.

Solution

$4 = \log_{10} 10,000$, read "4 equals the log of 10,000 to the base 10."

Studying the preceding examples, we note that a **logarithm** is an *exponent* of a number called the **base.** Thus, the statement

$$2 = \log_{10} 100$$

has the same meaning as the statement

$$10^2 = 100$$

Note that 2, the logarithm, is the exponent of 10, the base.

• EXAMPLE 3-7 _____

Find y if $y = \log_2 8$.

Solution

Since $y = \log_2 8$ means $2^y = 8$, then $y = 3$. Thus, 3 is the log of 8 to the base 2.

• EXAMPLE 3-8 _____

Find $\log_{10} 100$.

Solution

Let $y = \log_{10} 100$. Translated into exponential form, the statement becomes $10^y = 100$. Hence, $y = 2$. Thus, 2 is the log of 100 to the base 10.

Different Bases

We again emphasize that a logarithm is an exponent of a number called the base (study Examples 3-5 through 3-8). Two bases are most commonly used: **base 10** and **base e.** Base-10 logarithms are called **common logarithms.** Base-e logarithms are called **natural logarithms,** or **Napierian logarithms.** The following notation is used to distinguish between common logarithms and natural logarithms. Specifically, the common logarithm of x, $\log_{10} x$, is abbreviated $\log x$; the natural logarithm of x, $\log_e x$, is abbreviated $\ln x$. Thus, the statement $y = \log x$ means $10^y = x$; the statement $y = \ln x$ means $e^y = x$.

• EXAMPLE 3-9 _____

Find log 10.

Solution

Let $L = \log 10$. Rewriting the statement in exponential form, we have

$$10^L = 10$$

Hence, $L = 1$. Thus, the common logarithm of 10 is 1.

• **EXAMPLE 3-10** _____

Find $\ln e$.

Solution

Let $L = \ln e$. Rewriting this statement in exponential form gives us

$$e^L = e$$

Hence, $L = 1$. Thus, the natural logarithm of e is 1.

• **EXAMPLE 3-11** _____

In Section 3-1, we stated that for any positive number, b, there is a value k such that $b = e^k$. Find k.

Solution

Rewriting the statement $b = e^k$ in logarithmic form, we have

$$k = \ln b$$

Thus, $b = e^k = e^{\ln b}$
                                                                              •

Calculators and Logarithms

Appendix C contains common logarithm tables to find common logarithms of numbers and natural logarithm tables to find natural logarithms of numbers. However, if a student has a calculator with "log" and "ln" buttons, then the common log of a number may be easily found by using the "log" button, and the natural log of a number may be determined by using the "ln" button.

• **EXAMPLE 3-12** _____

Use a calculator to determine each of the following:

a) $\ln 5396$ b) $\ln 8.43$
c) $\ln 0.765$ d) $\log 0.492$

Solutions

Enter		Key	Result
a)	5396	ln	8.593413
b)	8.43	ln	2.131796
c)	0.765	ln	−0.267879
d)	0.492	log	−0.308035

We note that the answers are truncated to six decimal places.
                                                                              •

TABLE 3-4

$y = \log x,$ or $x = 10^y$	Ordered pairs (x, y)
If $y = -3$, then $x = 10^{-3} = 1/1000$	$(1/1000, -3)$
If $y = -2$, then $x = 10^{-2} = 1/100$	$(1/100, -2)$
If $y = -1$, then $x = 10^{-1} = 1/10$	$(1/10, -1)$
If $y = 0$, then $x = 10^0 = 1$	$(1, 0)$
If $y = 1$, then $x = 10^1 = 10$	$(10, 1)$
If $y = 2$, then $x = 10^2 = 100$	$(100, 2)$
If $y = 3$, then $x = 10^3 = 1000$	$(1000, 3)$

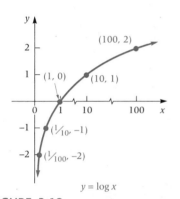

FIGURE 3-18

• **EXAMPLE 3-13** _____

Find x for each of the following:

a) $\ln x = 0.783$

b) $\log x = 2.863$

Solutions

a) $\ln x = 0.783$

Rewriting this statement in exponential form, we have

$$x = e^{0.783}$$

$$\approx 2.188 \quad \text{Use the } \boxed{e^x} \text{ button on a calculator.}$$

b) $\log x = 2.863$

Rewriting this statement in exponential form gives

$$x = 10^{2.863}$$

$$\approx 729.458 \quad \text{Use the } \boxed{y^x} \text{ or } \boxed{x^y} \text{ button on a calculator.}$$

•

Logarithmic Functions

Consider two variables, x and y, related by the equation

$$y = \log x \qquad (x > 0)$$

Since this is an equation with two variables, it may be graphed by computing a table of x- and y-values. Such a table is easily obtained by rewriting the equation $y = \log x$ in exponential form as $10^y = x$ and then choosing arbitrary y-values (see Table 3-4). The graph is sketched in Figure 3-18.

The equation $y = \log x$ defines a logarithmic function. The graph of $y = \log x$, illustrated in Figure 3-18, is typical of the graph of a logarithmic function with a *base greater than 1*. Studying Figure 3-18, we see that $(1, 0)$ is the x-intercept and that the y-axis is a vertical asymptote. Also, note that $y = \log x$ is undefined for $x \le 0$. A few trial values of x will indicate why. If $x = 0$, then $y = \log 0$ means $10^y = 0$. But no value of y exists such that $10^y = 0$. Thus, log 0 is undefined. However, as y takes on negative values of larger magnitude, 10^y approaches 0, and the y-axis is a vertical asymptote. If x is a negative number, such as $x = -3$, then $y = \log -3$ means $10^y = -3$. Again, no value of y exists such that $10^y = -3$.

• **EXAMPLE 3-14** _____

Sketch the graph of $y = \ln x$.

Solution

Since this logarithmic function has base e (a number greater than 1), its graph will resemble that of $y = \log x$. See Figure 3-19.

•

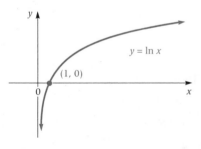

x-intercept
$y = \ln x$ means $x = e^y$.
If $y = 0$, then $x = e^0 = 1$.
Hence, $(1, 0)$ is the x-intercept.

FIGURE 3-19

Properties of Logarithms

Logarithms obey certain rules called **properties of logarithms.** These properties simplify much of our work with logarithms. They also enable us to perform certain arithmetic operations using logarithms. We now state the five properties of logarithms.

Properties of Logarithms

Let x, y, and b be any positive real numbers with $b \neq 1$. Also, let p be any real number.

Property 1 $\quad \log_b xy = \log_b x + \log_b y$

Property 2 $\quad \log_b \dfrac{x}{y} = \log_b x - \log_b y$

Property 3 $\quad \log_b x^p = p \log_b x$

Property 4 $\quad \log_b b = 1$

Property 5 $\quad \log_b 1 = 0$

Since it is important to understand the meaning of these properties of logarithms, we will consider each in turn.

Property 1 $\quad \log_b xy = \log_b x + \log_b y$

This property states that *the logarithm of a product of two numbers is equal to the sum of their logarithms.* The following are a few numerical illustrations of this property:

$$\log_2 (8 \cdot 32) = \log_2 8 + \log_2 32$$
$$\log (5.23 \times 100) = \log 5.23 + \log 100$$
$$\ln (3 \cdot 7) = \ln 3 + \ln 7$$

Property 2 $\quad \log_b \dfrac{x}{y} = \log_b x - \log_b y$

This property states that *the logarithm of a quotient of two numbers is equal to the difference of their logarithms.* The following are a few numerical illustrations of this property:

$$\log_2 \frac{64}{16} = \log_2 64 - \log_2 16$$

$$\log \frac{5.63}{100} = \log 5.63 - \log 100$$

$$\ln \frac{40}{3} = \ln 40 - \ln 3$$

Property 3 $\quad \log_b x^p = p \log_b x$

This property states that *the logarithm of the pth power of a number is equal to p times the logarithm of the number.* The following are a few numerical illustrations of this property:

$$\log_2 4^3 = 3 \log_2 4$$
$$\ln 8^2 = 2 \ln 8$$
$$\log 3^{1/2} = \frac{1}{2}(\log 3)$$

Property 4 $\log_b b = 1$

This property states that *the logarithm of its base is 1*. Thus,

$$\log_5 5 = 1 \quad \log_3 3 = 1 \quad \log 10 = 1 \quad \ln e = 1$$

Property 5 $\log_b 1 = 0$

This property states that *the logarithm of 1 is 0*. Thus,

$$\log_5 1 = 0 \quad \log_3 1 = 0 \quad \log 1 = 0 \quad \ln 1 = 0$$

We now give the proofs of the properties of logarithms.

Proofs of Properties of Logarithms

Note that the properties of logarithms are simply translations of laws of exponents.

Property 1   Let $L_1 = \log_b x$ and $L_2 = \log_b y$. Rewriting these statements in exponential form, we have

$$x = b^{L_1} \qquad y = b^{L_2}$$

Thus,

$$xy = b^{L_1} \cdot b^{L_2}$$
$$= b^{L_1 + L_2}$$

Rewriting the statement $xy = b^{L_1 + L_2}$ in logarithmic form, we obtain

$$\log_b xy = L_1 + L_2$$

Since $L_1 = \log_b x$ and $L_2 = \log_b y$, the preceding statement may be rewritten as

$$\log_b xy = \log_b x + \log_b y$$

Property 2   Let $L_1 = \log_b x$ and $L_2 = \log_b y$. Rewriting these statements in exponential form results in

$$x = b^{L_1} \qquad y = b^{L_2}$$

Thus,

$$\frac{x}{y} = \frac{b^{L_1}}{b^{L_2}}$$
$$= b^{L_1 - L_2}$$

Rewriting the statement $x/y = b^{L_1 - L_2}$ in logarithmic form, we have

$$\log_b \frac{x}{y} = L_1 - L_2$$

Since $L_1 = \log_b x$ and $L_2 = \log_b y$, the preceding statement may be rewritten as

$$\log_b \frac{x}{y} = \log_b x - \log_b y$$

Property 3 Let $L = \log_b x$. Rewriting this statement in exponential form, we have

$$x = b^L$$

Raising both sides to the pth power, we obtain

$$x^p = (b^L)^p$$
$$= b^{Lp}$$
$$= b^{pL}$$

Rewriting the statement $x^p = b^{pL}$ in logarithmic form gives us

$$\log_b x^p = pL$$

Since $L = \log_b x$, this statement may be rewritten as

$$\log_b x^p = p \log_b x$$

Property 4 Let $L = \log_b b$. This statement is rewritten in exponential form as

$$b^L = b$$

Hence, $L = 1$ and

$$\log_b b = 1$$

Property 5 Let $L = \log_b 1$. This statement is rewritten as

$$b^L = 1$$

Hence, $L = 0$ and

$$\log_b 1 = 0$$

• EXAMPLE 3-15

Given that $\log 3 = 0.4771$ and $\log 5 = 0.6990$, find each of the following using the properties of logarithms:

a) $\log 15$ **b)** $\log 625$
c) $\log \sqrt{5}$ **d)** $\log 0.6$

Solutions

a) $\log 15 = \log (5 \cdot 3)$
          $= \log 5 + \log 3$ Property 1
          $= 0.6990 + 0.4771$
          $= 1.1761$

b) $\log 625 = \log 5^4$
          $= 4 \log 5$ Property 3
          $= 4(0.6990)$
          $= 2.7960$

c) $\log \sqrt{5} = \log 5^{1/2}$
          $= \frac{1}{2}(\log 5)$ Property 3
          $= \frac{1}{2}(0.6990)$
          $= 0.3495$

d) $\log 0.6 = \log \dfrac{3}{5}$

$\qquad\qquad = \log 3 - \log 5$ Property 2

$\qquad\qquad = 0.4771 - 0.6990$

$\qquad\qquad = -0.2219$

• **EXAMPLE 3-16** _____

Express each of the following in simpler form:

a) $\log \left(\dfrac{A}{BC} \right)$ 　　　　　　　　　　　　　　**b)** $\log \left(\dfrac{A}{B} \right)^{.706}$

Solutions

a) $\log \left(\dfrac{A}{BC} \right) = \log A - \log (BC)$ Property 2

$\qquad\qquad = \log A - [\log B + \log C]$ Property 1

$\qquad\qquad = \log A - \log B - \log C$

b) $\log \left(\dfrac{A}{B} \right)^{.706} = .706 \log \dfrac{A}{B}$ Property 3

$\qquad\qquad = .706 \, [\log A - \log B]$ Property 2

$\qquad\qquad = .706 \log A - .706 \log B$

_____   •

We now state two more properties of logarithms that are useful in many applications. These properties are indicated by the graphs of logarithmic functions (Figures 3-18 and 3-19).

Property 6

$$\log_b x = \log_b y \text{ if and only if } x = y$$

where x, y, and b are positive real numbers with $b \neq 1$.

Property 7

$$\log_b x > \log_b y \text{ if and only if } x > y$$

where x, y, and b are positive real numbers with $b \neq 1$.

We now give an example where logarithms are used to solve for one quantity in terms of another.

• **EXAMPLE 3-17** _____

The demand, x (in millions), for a product is related to its unit price, p (in dollars), by the equation

$$p = e^{5 - 0.2x}$$

a) Express the demand, x, in terms of unit price, p.

b) Calculate the demand associated with a unit price of $6.

Solution

a) Taking the natural logarithm of each side, we have

$$\ln p = 5 - 0.2x$$

Solving for x yields

$$x = \frac{\ln p - 5}{-0.2}$$

b) Since $p = \$6$, then

$$x = \frac{\ln p - 5}{-0.2}$$

$$= \frac{\ln 6 - 5}{-0.2}$$

$$\approx \frac{1.791759 - 5}{-0.2}$$

$$\approx 16.04 \text{ million units}$$

Doubling Time: Exponential Growth

If a quantity, y, is related to time, t, by the exponential model

$$y = y_0 e^{kt}$$

where y_0 and k are positive constants, then the *initial value of y* (i.e., the value of y at $t = 0$) is

$$y = y_0 e^{k(0)}$$
$$= y_0 e^0$$
$$= y_0(1)$$
$$= y_0$$

The time it takes for the quantity y_0 to double itself is determined by setting $y = 2y_0$ and solving the resulting equation for t. Hence,

$$y = y_0 e^{kt}$$

$$2y_0 = y_0 e^{kt} \qquad \text{Set } y = 2y_0.$$

$$2 = e^{kt} \qquad \text{Multiply both sides by } 1/y_0.$$

$$kt = \ln 2 \qquad \text{Rewrite in logarithmic form.}$$

$$t = \frac{\ln 2}{k} \qquad \text{Doubling time}$$

For example, if

$$y = 1000e^{0.10t}$$

where t denotes time (in years), the initial value of y is 1000, and the doubling time is given by

$$t = \frac{\ln 2}{0.10}$$

$$= \frac{0.6931}{0.10}$$

$$= 6.931 \text{ years} \qquad \text{Doubling time}$$

Exercises 3-2

Rewrite each of the following statements in logarithmic notation:

1. $5^2 = 25$ **2.** $4^2 = 16$ **3.** $2^6 = 64$
4. $10^5 = 100,000$ **5.** $10^{-2} = 0.01$ **6.** $10^1 = 10$
7. $t^w = S$ **8.** $4^3 = 64$ **9.** $b^{x+y} = N$

Find y for each of the following:

10. $y = \log_3 9$ **11.** $y = \log_9 81$
12. $y = \log_2 8$ **13.** $y = \log_3 1$
14. $y = \log_2 16$ **15.** $y = \log_7 7$
16. $y = \log_{10} 1$ **17.** $y = \log_{10} 10$
18. $y = \log_{10} 100$ **19.** $y = \log_{10} 1000$
20. $y = \log_{10} 10,000$ **21.** $y = \log_{10} 100,000$
22. $y = \ln 1$ **23.** $y = \ln e^2$

Find each of the following logarithms:

24. $\log_3 81$ **25.** $\log_2 32$ **26.** $\log_4 16$
27. $\log_3 1$ **28.** $\log_5 1$ **29.** $\log_8 1$
30. $\log 1$ **31.** $\log 10$ **32.** $\log 100$
33. $\log 1000$ **34.** $\log 10,000$ **35.** $\log 100,000$

36. Sketch the graph of $y = \log_2 x$. What is the x-intercept?
37. Sketch the graph of $y = \log_3 x$. What is the x-intercept?

Given that $\log 2 = 0.3010$ and $\log 7 = 0.8451$, find each of the following using the properties of logarithms:

38. $\log 14$ **39.** $\log 3.5$ **40.** $\log \frac{2}{7}$
41. $\log 49$ **42.** $\log 98$ **43.** $\log 56$
44. $\log \sqrt{2}$ **45.** $\log \sqrt[3]{2}$ **46.** $\log \sqrt{7}$
47. $\log \sqrt{14}$ **48.** $\log \sqrt[5]{7}$ **49.** $\log \sqrt{98}$

Given that $\log 3.71 = 0.5694$, find each of the following using the properties of logarithms. (Remember that $\log 10 = 1$.)

50. $\log 37.1$ **51.** $\log 371$ **52.** $\log 3710$
53. $\log 37,100$ **54.** $\log 371,000$ **55.** $\log 0.371$
56. $\log 0.0371$ **57.** $\log 0.00371$ **58.** $\log 0.000371$

Given that ln 3 = 1.098612 and ln 2 = 0.693147, find each of the following using the properties of logarithms:

59. ln 6   **60.** ln 1.5   **61.** ln $\dfrac{2}{3}$

62. ln 81   **63.** ln 8   **64.** ln 12
65. ln $\sqrt{3}$ **66.** ln $\sqrt[3]{2}$ **67.** ln 0.75

Using a calculator with a "log" button, find each of the following:

68. log 4.76   **69.** log 8.73   **70.** log 92.1
71. log 4760   **72.** log 0.0673   **73.** log 0.80

Using a calculator with an "ln" button, find each of the following.

74. ln 2.8   **75.** ln 10   **76.** ln 25
77. ln 0.15   **78.** ln 0.60   **79.** ln 80

Find x for each of the following:

80. log x = 0.7738   **81.** log x = 0.9047
82. log x = 2.7738   **83.** log x = 3.9047
84. log x = 1.4698   **85.** log x = 5.4099
86. ln x = 0.6419   **87.** log x = 1.3610
88. ln x = 3.6889   **89.** ln x = 1.7047

Express each of the following numbers as e^k:

90. 7   **91.** 3.4   **92.** 14   **93.** 5.5   **94.** 750

Use properties of logarithms to express each of the following in simpler form.

95. $\log\left(\dfrac{xy}{z}\right)$ **96.** $\log\left(\dfrac{x}{y}\right)^{5.83}$

97. $\log (x^2 y)$ **98.** $\log (xy)^7$
99. $\log \sqrt{xy}$
                                                      100. $\log \sqrt{\dfrac{xy}{z}}$

Applications

101. *Sales.* A company's sales, $S(x)$ (in thousands of dollars), are related to advertising expenditure, x (in thousands of dollars), by the equation

$$S(x) = 100{,}000 + 8000 \ln (x + 2)$$

   a) Calculate the sales associated with each of the following advertising expenditures: $1000, $3000, $10,000, and $20,000.
   b) Calculate $S(21) - S(20)$ and interpret the answer.
   c) If the company increases its advertising expenditures from $30,000 to $31,000, find the corresponding increase in sales.

102. *Sales.* A company's sales, $S(x)$ (in thousands), are related to advertising expenditures, x, (in thousands of dollars), by the equation

$$S(x) = 200{,}000 + 10{,}000 \ln x$$

   a) Calculate the sales associated with each of the following advertising expenditures: $2000, $5000, $10,000, and $30,000.
   b) Calculate $S(13) = S(12)$ and interpret the answer.
   c) If the company increases its advertising expenditure from $19,000 to $20,000, find the corresponding increase in sales.

103. *Revenue.* A company's sales revenue, $R(x)$ (in thousands of dollars), is related to the number of units sold, x, by the equation

$$R(x) = 10 \log(20x + 1)$$

a) Calculate and interpret each of the following: $R(1)$, $R(2)$, $R(5)$, and $R(10)$.

b) Calculate $R(11) - R(10)$ and interpret the answer.

c) If the company increases its sales from 20 units to 21 units, calculate the increase in sales revenue.

104. *Cost.* A company's total production cost, $C(x)$ (in dollars), is related to the number of units produced, x, by the equation.

$$C(x) = 9000 + 10 \ln(x + 1)$$

a) Calculate and interpret each of the following: $C(0)$, $C(1)$, $C(5)$, and $C(10)$.

b) Calculate $C(19) - C(18)$ and interpret the answer.

c) If the company increases its production from 12 units to 13 units, calculate the increase in total production cost.

105. *Tripling time: Exponential growth.* If a quantity, y, is related to time, t, by the exponential model

$$y = y_0 e^{kt}$$

where y_0 and k are positive constants, verify that the tripling time is given by

$$t = \frac{\ln 3}{k}$$

If

$$y = 2000 e^{0.20t}$$

where t denotes time in days,

a) Determine the initial value of y.

b) Determine the tripling time.

c) Determine the quadrupling time.

106. *Doubling time.* If a quantity, y, is related to time, t, by the exponential model

$$y = y_0 b^{kt}$$

where y_0, k, and b are positive constants such that $b > 1$ and $b \neq e$, verify that the doubling time is given by

$$t = \frac{\ln 2}{k \ln b}$$

107. *Population growth.* The population, P, of a certain town is related to time, t (in years), by the exponential function

$$P = 1000 e^{0.05t}$$

a) How long will it take for the population to double itself?

b) How long will it take for the population to triple itself?

108. *Demand.* The demand, x (in billions), for a product is related to its unit price, p (in dollars), by the equation

$$p = e^{8 - 0.3x}$$

a) Express demand, x, in terms of unit price, p.

b) Find the demand associated with a unit price of $9.

109. *Supply.* The supply, y (in millions), for a product is related to its unit price, p (in dollars), by the supply equation

$$p = e^{1 + 0.3y}$$

a) Express supply, y, in terms of unit price, p.

b) Find the supply associated with a unit price of $10.

3-3   • FITTING EXPONENTIAL MODELS

In this section, we discuss fitting an exponential model of the form

$$y = ab^x$$

to a set of data points. First, we restate the above equation in logarithmic form by taking the natural logarithm of each side to obtain

$$
\begin{aligned}
\ln y &= \ln ab^x &&\text{Logarithm property 6}\\
&= \ln a + \ln b^x &&\text{Logarithm property 2}\\
&= \ln a + x \ln b &&\text{Logarithm property 3}\\
&= \ln a + (\ln b)x
\end{aligned}
$$

Thus, the exponential equation $y = ab^x$ is restated in logarithmic form as $\ln y = \ln a + (\ln b)x$. Observe that the logarithmic form expresses a linear relationship between the variables $\ln y$ and x. This means that for points (x, y) on the graph of the exponential function $y = ab^x$, the graph of the corresponding points $(x, \ln y)$ is a straight line. In other words, if a plot of y-values versus x-values has the graph of an exponential function $y = ab^x$, then a plot of $\ln y$-values versus x-values has the graph of a straight line. Thus, given points (x, y) of an exponential model $y = ab^x$, the coefficients a and b are determined by fitting the linear model $\ln y = \ln a + (\ln b)x$ (straight line) to the points $(x, \ln y)$ and then by determining a and b, given their logarithms. We note that common logarithms can be used in place of natural logarithms.

To Fit an Exponential Model

The **exponential model**

$$y = ab^x$$

is restated in **logarithmic form** as

$$\ln y = \ln a + (\ln b)x \qquad \text{Linear form}$$

$\ln y$-intercept   slope

This has the following implications:

1. If a plot of y-values versus x-values has the graph of an exponential function $y = ab^x$, then a plot of $\ln y$-values versus x-values has the graph of a straight line, as is illustrated in Figure 3-20.

continues

To Fit an Exponential Model—*Continued*

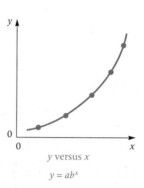 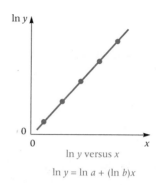

y versus *x*
$y = ab^x$

ln *y* versus *x*
$\ln y = \ln a + (\ln b)x$

FIGURE 3-20

2. Given points (x, y) of an exponential model $y = ab^x$, the coefficients a and b are determined by fitting a straight line to the points $(x, \ln y)$. The straight line has the equation

$$\ln y = \ln a + (\ln b)x$$

$\underset{\text{ln } y\text{-intercept}}{\uparrow} \quad \underset{\text{slope}}{\uparrow}$

The coefficients a and b are determined from their logarithms.
Note: Common logarithms can be used in place of natural logarithms.

As an example, we will determine the coefficients a and b of the exponential model $y = ab^x$ whose graph contains the points $(1, 3)$ and $(5, 30)$. Use the following procedure.

Step 1 *Replace the* y*-value of each given data point with its logarithm.* Use either common or natural logarithms. We will use natural logarithms.

Using a calculator, we find that $\ln 3 \approx 1.10$ and $\ln 30 \approx 3.40$. This gives the corresponding points $(1, 1.10)$ and $(5, 3.40)$, which are plotted in Figure 3-21.

Step 2 *Find the equation of the straight line passing through the new points* (x, *ln* y). Begin by finding the slope.

$$\text{slope} = \frac{3.40 - 1.10}{5 - 1}$$

$$= \frac{2.30}{4} \approx 0.58$$

Using the point-slope form

$$y - y_1 = m(x - x_1)$$

with y replaced by $\ln y$, we choose the point $(1, 1.10)$ to obtain

$$\ln y - 1.10 = 0.58(x - 1)$$

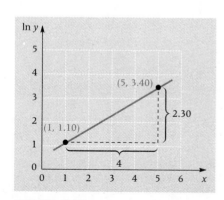

FIGURE 3-21

Simplifying, we get

$$\ln y - 1.10 = 0.58x - 0.58$$
$$= 0.58x - 0.58$$
$$\ln y = 0.58x - 0.58 + 1.10$$
$$\ln y = 0.58x + 0.52 \qquad \text{Logarithmic form}$$

This last equation is our answer in logarithmic form. However, it must be written in the exponential form $y = ab^x$.

Step 3 *Use the definition of a logarithm to determine the coefficients* a *and* b *of the exponential equation* $y = ab^x$. The above equation, when written as

$$\ln y = 0.52 + 0.58x$$

is of the form

$$\ln y = \ln a + (\ln b)x$$

where

$$\ln a = 0.52 \qquad \text{and} \qquad \ln b = 0.58$$

Rewriting the above in exponential form allows us to solve for a and b (with a calculator) as indicated below.

$$a = e^{0.52} \qquad\qquad b = e^{0.58}$$
$$\approx 1.68 \qquad\qquad\quad \approx 1.79$$

Thus, the exponential model

$$y = ab^x$$

containing the points $(1, 3)$ and $(5, 30)$ is given by

$$y = 1.68(1.79^x)$$

Application

Earnings Per Share

Annual earnings per share (EPS) in dollars of a corporation are determined by dividing the corporation's annual earnings by the number of shares of its stock outstanding. That is,

$$\text{EPS} = \frac{\text{annual earnings}}{\text{number of shares of stock outstanding}}$$

The EPS is used to evaluate the performance of a corporation.

The EPS for Lotus Development Corporation is given for the indicated years in Table 3-5 on page 154. Note that the years are coded, with $x = 1$ corresponding to 1986, $x = 2$ to 1987, . . ., $x = 5$ to 1990. Graphs of y-versus x-values and $\ln y$- versus x-values are given in Figure 3-22 on page 154. Observe that the graph of $\ln y$- versus x-values appears to have a linear trend. Thus, we fit the linear form

$$\ln y = \ln a + (\ln b)x$$

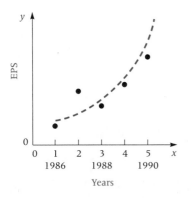

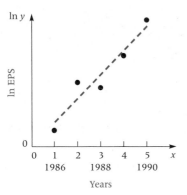

FIGURE 3-22

TABLE 3-5 Lotus Development Corporation: Earnings per share

Years	1986	1987	1988	1989	1990
x = coded years	1	2	3	4	5
y = EPS	1.03	1.58	1.29	1.61	2.30
ln y	0.0296	0.4574	0.2546	0.4762	0.8329

Step 1 We use the first and last data points with ln y-values, $(1, 0.0296)$ and $(5, 0.8329)$.

Step 2 The slope is given by

$$m = \frac{0.8329 - 0.0296}{5 - 1}$$

$$= \frac{0.8033}{4}$$

$$= 0.20 \quad \text{Slope}$$

Using the point-slope form

$$y - y_1 = m(x - x_1)$$

with y replaced by ln y, we choose the point $(5, 0.8329)$ to obtain

$$\ln y - 0.8329 = 0.20(x - 5)$$
$$= 0.20x - 1$$

Solving for ln y gives

$$\ln y = 0.20x - 0.17 \quad \text{Logarithmic form}$$

Step 3 The above result, when rewritten as

$$\ln y = -0.17 + 0.20x$$

is of the form

$$\ln y = \ln a + (\ln b)x$$

where

$$\ln a = -0.17 \quad \text{and} \quad \ln b = 0.20$$

Hence,

$$a = e^{-0.17} \qquad\qquad b = e^{0.20}$$
$$\approx 0.84 \qquad\qquad \approx 1.22 \quad \text{Use a calculator}$$

Thus, the fitted exponential model, $y = ab^x$, is given by

$$y = 0.84(1.22^x)$$

Using the Model to Forecast. If the EPS for Lotus Development Corporation continue to grow in accordance with the above model, then the 1991 EPS are forecast by substituting $x = 6$ into the equation as given below.

$$y = 0.84(1.22^6)$$
$$\approx 0.84(3.2973)$$
$$\approx 2.77 \quad \text{1991 EPS}$$

Caution: Although we used the first and last data points to fit the linear model $\ln y = \ln a + (\ln b)x$, this does not necessarily give the best-fitting linear model. For this example, it does provide a reasonably good fit to the set of data points. Recall the goodness of fit of a model was discussed in the "Extra Dividends" following Chapters 1 and 2. Those concepts also apply to exponential models. Although we do not pursue the goodness of fit of exponential models here, we will learn how to determine the equation of a best-fitting model to a set of data points in Section 15-4.

Exercises 3-3

Determine the coefficients a and b of the exponential model $y = ab^x$ whose graph passes through the following given points.

1. (2, 6) and (8, 40)   **2.** (1, 8) and (5, 50)

3. (3, 20) and (6, 70)   **4.** (4, 10) and (7, 80)

5. (1, 15) and (5, 85)   **6.** (3, 27) and (8, 92)

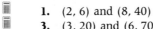

Applications

Earnings Per Share

In exercises 7-9 the EPS of a company is given for a period. For each exercise
a) Fit the exponential model $y = ab^x$ by using the points appearing in color screen.
b) Assuming that the EPS continue to grow in accordance with the model determined in part a, forecast the next year's EPS.

7. Kellogg Company

Year	1981	1982	1983	1984	1985	1986	1987	1988	1989
x	1	3	4	5	6	7	8	9	10
EPS	1.35	1.49	1.59	1.68	2.28	2.58	3.20	3.90	3.46

8. Bristol-Myers Squibb Company

Year	1980	1981	1982	1983	1984	1985	1986	1987	1988	1989
x	1	2	3	4	5	6	7	8	9	10
EPS	1.02	1.15	1.30	1.50	1.73	1.93	2.07	2.47	2.88	1.43

9. Ford Motor Company

Year	1983	1984	1985	1986	1987	1988	1989
x	1	2	3	4	5	6	7
EPS	3.43	5.27	4.55	6.16	9.05	10.96	8.22

10. *Population growth.* The population of a particular town has grown exponentially from 20,000 in 1985 to 50,000 in 1990.
a) Determine the equation of the exponential model $y = ab^x$ whose curve passes through the two data points.
b) If the town's population continues to grow in accordance with the model derived in part a, forecast the town's population for 1991.

EXTRA DIVIDENDS

• *Stock Market Forecasting*

The *Value Line Investment Survey,* a reputable investment advisory newsletter, gave the following equation for predicting the Dow Jones Industrial Average (DJIA) for a given future year.

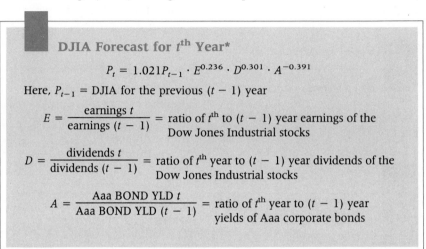

DJIA Forecast for t^{th} Year*

$$P_t = 1.021 P_{t-1} \cdot E^{0.236} \cdot D^{0.301} \cdot A^{-0.391}$$

Here, P_{t-1} = DJIA for the previous $(t-1)$ year

$$E = \frac{\text{earnings } t}{\text{earnings } (t-1)} = \text{ratio of } t^{\text{th}} \text{ to } (t-1) \text{ year earnings of the Dow Jones Industrial stocks}$$

$$D = \frac{\text{dividends } t}{\text{dividends } (t-1)} = \text{ratio of } t^{\text{th}} \text{ year to } (t-1) \text{ year dividends of the Dow Jones Industrial stocks}$$

$$A = \frac{\text{Aaa BOND YLD } t}{\text{Aaa BOND YLD } (t-1)} = \text{ratio of } t^{\text{th}} \text{ year to } (t-1) \text{ year yields of Aaa corporate bonds}$$

For example, if earnings are expected to increase by 8% next year, then

$$E = \frac{\text{earnings } t}{\text{earnings } (t-1)} = 1.08$$

If dividends are expected to increase by 5% next year, then

$$D = \frac{\text{dividends } t}{\text{dividends } (t-1)} = 1.05$$

If aaa corporate bond yields are expected to decrease by 3% next year, then

$$A = \frac{\text{Aaa BOND YLD } t}{\text{Aaa BOND YLD } (t-1)} = 1 - 0.03 = 0.97$$

PROBLEM

We will use the properties of logarithms to determine the effect on the DJIA forecast of

1. An increase in earnings
2. A decrease in earnings
3. An increase in dividends
4. A decrease in dividends
5. An increase in Aaa Bond yields
6. A decrease in Aaa Bond Yields

---

*Copyright © 1989 by Value Line, Inc.; used by permission.

SOLUTION

First, we must rewrite the equation in a form that is easier to analyze. We take the natural logarithm (or, if one prefers, the common logarithm) of each side to obtain

$$\ln P_t = \ln 1.021 + \ln P_{t-1} + \ln E^{0.236} + \ln D^{0.301} + \ln A^{-0.391} \;\reflectbox{$\urcorner$}$$
property 1

$$\ln P_t = \ln 1.021 + \ln P_{t-1} + 0.236 \ln E + 0.301 \ln D + (-0.391) \ln A \;\reflectbox{$\urcorner$}$$
property 3

At this point, we restate the following logarithmic property, which is determined by studying the graph of the logarithmic function illustrated in Figure 3-23.

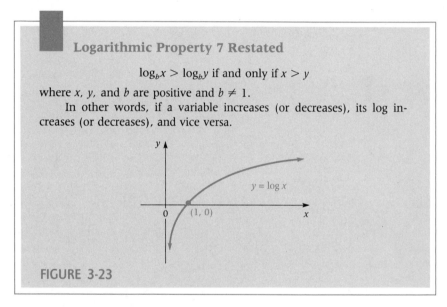

Logarithmic Property 7 Restated

$$\log_b x > \log_b y \text{ if and only if } x > y$$

where x, y, and b are positive and $b \neq 1$.

    In other words, if a variable increases (or decreases), its log increases (or decreases), and vice versa.

$y = \log x$

$(1, 0)$

FIGURE 3-23

We now address our previously stated concerns.

1. If earnings are projected to increase for the next year, then the earnings ratio will be greater than 1, and, therefore, its natural logarithm (look at the graph of the logarithm function of Figure 3-23) will be positive. This result, when multiplied by 0.236, gives an increase in $\ln P_t$ which, by logarithmic property 7, implies an increase in P_t (the DJIA for the future year). This assumes that dividends and bond yields remain constant.

2. If earnings are projected to decrease for the next year, then the earnings ratio will be greater than 0, but smaller than 1, and, therefore, its natural logarithm (look at the graph of the logarithm function of Figure 3-23) will be negative. This result, when multiplied by 0.236, gives a decrease in $\ln P_t$ which, by logarithmic property 7, implies a decrease in P_t (the DJIA for the future year). This assumes that dividends and bond yields remain constant.

3. P_t will increase. The reasoning is the same as that for part 1.

4. P_t will decrease. The reasoning is the same as that for part 2.

5. If Aaa bond yields are projected to increase for the next year. Then the Aaa ratio will be greater than 1, and, therefore, its natural logarithm (look at the graph of the logarithm function of Figure 3-23) will be positive. This result, when multiplied by -0.391, gives a decrease in $\ln P_t$ which, by logarithmic property 7, implies a decrease in P_t (the DJIA for the future year). This assumes that earnings and dividends remain constant.

6. If Aaa bond yields are projected to decrease for the next year, then the Aaa ratio will be greater than 0, but smaller than 1, and, therefore, its natural logarithm (look at the graph of the logarithm function of Figure 3-23) will be negative. This result, when multiplied by -0.391, gives an increase in $\ln P_t$ which, by logarithmic property 7, implies an increase in P_t (the DJIA for the future year). This assumes that earnings and dividends remain constant.

FORECAST

We now forecast next year's DJIA under the following assumptions:

1. Previous year DJIA closing price: 2166
2. 7.5% increase in earnings
3. 10.2% increase in dividends
4. 1.5% increase in Aaa bond yields

Thus,

$$\ln P_t = \ln 1.021 + \ln 2166 + 0.236 \ln 1.075 \\ + 0.301 \ln 1.102 - 0.391 \ln 1.015$$

$$\ln P_t = 0.0208 + 7.6806 + 0.236(0.0723) \\ + 0.301(0.0971) - 0.391(0.0149)$$

$$\ln P_t = 7.7419$$

Rewriting this result in exponential form gives

$$P_t = e^{7.7419}$$
$$= 2302.84 \qquad \text{Use } e^x \text{ key on calculator.}$$

Thus, the DJIA forecast for the next year is 2302.84.

We note that, using statistical analysis techniques beyond the scope of this text, this forecast can be expanded into an interval within which the DJIA can be expected to fall with a predictable probability.

CHAPTER 3 HIGHLIGHTS

● *Concepts*

Your ability to answer the following questions is one indicator of the depth of your mastery of this chapter's important concepts. Note that the questions are grouped under various topic headings. For any question that you cannot answer, refer to the appropriate section of the chapter indicated by the topic heading. Pay particular attention to the summary boxes within a section.

3-1 EXPONENTIAL FUNCTIONS AND THEIR GRAPHS

For Exercises 1-4, draw the graph that typifies each function.

1. $y = ae^x$, $a > 0$ **2.** $y = ae^{-x}$, $a > 0$
3. $y = ae^x$, $a < 0$ **4.** $y = ae^{-x}$, $a < 0$
5. Give the procedure for graphing exponential functions of the form $y = ab^x + c$ or $y = ab^{-x} + c$, where $b > 1$.
6. Write the equation for Newton's law of cooling. Explain the dependent and independent variables.
7. Write the equations for the two market penetration models. Explain the dependent and independent variables.

3-2 LOGARITHMIC FUNCTIONS

8. A logarithm is a(an) _____ of a number that is called a base.
9. Base e logarithms are called _____ logarithms.
10. Base 10 logarithms are called _____ logarithms.
11. For any positive number b, there is a value k such that $b = e^k$, where $k =$ _____ .
12. Draw the graph of the logarithmic function $y = \ln x$. The x-intercept is (____, 0). Is there a y-intercept? Is the function defined for $x < 0$?
13. State the seven properties of logarithms. Explain each property using examples.

3-3 FITTING EXPONENTIAL MODELS

14. Write the linear form that corresponds to the exponential model $y = ab^x$.
15. For points (x, y) of the exponential function $y = ab^x$, the graph of the corresponding points $(x, \ln y)$ is a(an) _____ .

REVIEW EXERCISES

• Exponential Functions

Graph the following.

1. $y = 7^x$ **2.** $y = 7^{-x}$ **3.** $y = e^x$ **4.** $y = e^{-x}$
5. $y = 8e^x$ **6.** $y = -3e^x$ **7.** $y = -5e^{-x}$ **8.** $y = -e^x$
9. $f(x) = 4 + 2e^x$ **10.** $f(x) = -2 + 5e^{-x}$
11. $f(x) = 9 - 2e^{-x}$ **12.** $f(x) = 6 - 4e^x$
13. $f(x) = -1 + 5e^{-x}$ **14.** $f(x) = 2 + e^{3x}$
15. $f(x) = 5 + e^{-2x}$ **16.** $f(x) = 3 - e^{-x}$

17. *Time series.* The annual income, y (in millions of dollars), of a firm is related to time, t (in years), by the equation

$$y = 5e^t$$

where $t = 0$ denotes the year 19x0, $t = 1$ denotes the year 19x1, and so on.
a) Graph $y = 5e^t$ for $t \geq 0$.
b) Determine the annual earnings for the years 19x2, 19x3, and 19x5.

18. *Time series: Sales decay.* The annual sales, y (in millions of dollars), of a company are given by

$$y = 10e^{-t}$$

where $t = 0$ denotes the year 19x0, $t = 1$ denotes the year 19x1, and so on.

a) Graph $y = 10e^{-t}$ for $t \geq 0$.
b) Determine the annual sales for the years 19x0, 19x2, and 19x5.

19. *Market penetration: Long-range forecasting.* The percentage of market penetration for a product x years after it has been introduced is given by

$$y = 80 - 74e^{-0.27x}$$

a) Graph $y = 80 - 74e^{-0.27x}$ for $x \geq 0$.
b) Determine the percentage of market penetration for the third year.
c) Determine the percentage of market penetration for the tenth year.
d) Determine the saturation level.

20. *Market penetration: Long-range forecasting.* The percentage of market penetration for a product x years after it has been introduced is given by

$$y = \frac{90}{1 + 400e^{-0.80x}}$$

a) Determine the percentage of market penetration for the second, seventh, and twelfth years.
b) Determine the saturation level.

• Logarithmic Functions

Rewrite the following in logarithmic notation.

21. $10^4 = 10{,}000$ **22.** $5^3 = 125$
23. $y = e^x$

Find the logarithm for each of the following.

24. $\log_2 8$ **25.** $\log_3 9$ **26.** $\ln e^2$
27. $\log 1$ **28.** $\ln 1$ **29.** $\log 10$

Using a calculator with an "ln" button, find each the following.

30. $\ln 23$ **31.** $\ln 0.987$ **32.** $\ln 356$

Find x for the following.

33. $\log x = 0.8875$ **34.** $\ln x = 2.1576$
35. $\log x = 4.56$

Express each of the following as e^k.

36. 5 **37.** 4.6 **38.** 0.45

Use properties of logarithms to express the following in simpler form:

39. $\log (st/r)$ **40.** $\log (x^3 y)$ **41.** $\log (uv)^5$
42. $\log (x/y)^4$ **43.** $\log uv$ **44.** $\log uv/w$

45. Graph $y = \ln x$
46. *Demand.* The demand, x (in millions), for a product is related to its unit price, p (in dollars), by the equation

$$p = e^{4 - 0.2x}$$

a) Express demand, x, in terms of unit price, p.
b) Find the demand associated with a unit price of \$4.

• Fitting Exponential Models

47. Determine the coefficients a and b of the exponential model $y = ab^x$, whose graph passes through the points $(2, 8)$ and $(5, 60)$.

48. *Health care's share of GNP.* The U.S. health care industry's share of the gross national product (% of GNP) for the years 1965 to 2010 is given below: (Estimates are given for years beyond 1990.)

x = Coded Years	1	2	3	4	5	6	7
y = % of GNP	6	8	11	12	15.5	20	28

a) Fit the exponential model $y = ab^x$ by using the points appearing in color screens.

b) Assuming that each x-value denotes a time interval of approximately $7\frac{1}{2}$ years, forecast health care's share of GNP for the next $7\frac{1}{2}$ year time interval beyond the year 2010.

4

MATHEMATICS
OF FINANCE

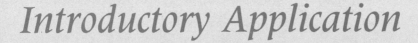

Introductory Application

Amortization: Comparing Mortgage Terms

A couple plans to purchase a home for $200,000. They have put $50,000 down and will obtain a mortgage for $150,000 at an interest rate of 10.5% compounded monthly. They must decide whether to apply for either a 30-year or a 15-year mortgage. Find the monthly payment and the total interest for both a 30-year and a 15-year mortgage at an interest rate of 10.5% compounded monthly. Compare the total interest paid for each mortgage.

In this chapter, we will learn mathematics of finance concepts that enable us to solve problems such as the above and others. The above problem is solved in Example 4-33.

4-1 • SIMPLE INTEREST AND DISCOUNT

Interest is the price paid for the use of money. The amount of money lent (or borrowed or invested) is called the **principal.** After a given time period, the borrower must repay the principal plus interest. The interest is computed as a percentage of the principal. This percentage is called the **interest rate.** An interest rate is stated as a specified percentage per unit of time. In this section, the unit of time will be a year. Thus, an interest rate of 5% means 5% per year. Specifically, if Henry Orwell borrows $1000 for 2 years at an interest rate of 5%, then the principal is $1000, the interest rate is 5% per year, and the time period is 2 years. The following notation will be used:

P = principal (original amount lent, borrowed, or invested)

r = interest rate per year (annual rate)

t = time (duration of loan or investment in years)

I = amount of simple interest in dollars

S = total amount (principal + interest) due at the end of the time period

Simple interest is computed by the following formula.

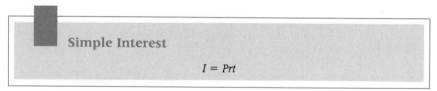

Simple Interest

$$I = Prt$$

Thus, the interest on Henry Orwell's 2-year, $1000 loan (at 5% per year) is

$$I = 1000(0.05)(2) = \$100$$

The total amount, S, that Henry must repay is calculated by the following formula.

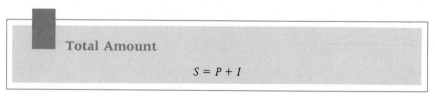

Total Amount

$$S = P + I$$

Hence, at the end of 2 years, Henry must repay

$$S = \$1000 + \$100 = \$1100$$

The bank views this loan as an investment. Its principal of $1000 is worth $1100 at the end of 2 years. Thus, the total amount (in this case, $1100) is often called the **future value,** whereas the principal (in this case, $1000) is called the **present value** (see the time diagram of Figure 4-1).

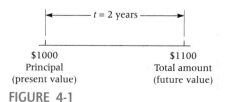

$t = 2$ years

$1000
Principal
(present value)

$1100
Total amount
(future value)

FIGURE 4-1

The formulas for I and S on page 165 can be combined to give one formula for S in terms of P, r, and t. If we begin with

$$S = P + I$$

and replace I with Prt, we get

$$S = P + Prt$$
$$= P(1 + rt)$$

We summarize below.

Total Amount

$$S = P + Prt \quad \text{or} \quad S = P(1 + rt)$$

• **EXAMPLE 4-1** ————————————————————

An investor lent $10,000 to a business associate for 6 months at an interest rate of 8% per year.

a) Calculate the simple interest.
b) Calculate the total amount (future value) by two methods.

Solutions

Here $P = \$10,000$, $r = 0.08$, and $t = 1/2$ year.

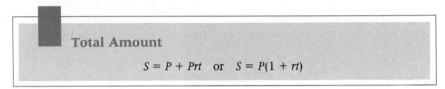

a) $I = Prt$

$$= 10{,}000(0.08)\left(\frac{1}{2}\right)$$

$$= \$400$$

— Convert 6 months to years $\left(\text{i.e., } \frac{6}{12} = \frac{1}{2}\right)$.
— Convert 8% to a decimal (i.e., 8% = 0.08).

b) *Method 1.*

$$S = P + I$$
$$= \$10{,}000 + \$400$$
$$= \$10{,}400$$

Method 2.

$$S = P(1 + rt)$$
$$= 10{,}000[1 + (0.08)(1/2)]$$
$$= 10{,}000(1.04) = \$10{,}400$$

Thus, the investor's $10,000 is worth $10,400 at the end of 6 months (see the time diagram of Figure 4-2).

•

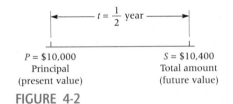

$P = \$10,000$
Principal
(present value)

$S = \$10,400$
Total amount
(future value)

FIGURE 4-2

Value of Money at Simple Interest

If a sum of money, P, is invested at simple interest, its value increases by the same amount each year. This can be shown by beginning with the formula for total amount

$$S = P + I$$

and replacing I with the equivalent expression Prt. The result is

$$S = P + Prt$$

Given values for P and r, this formula expresses a linear relationship between total amount, S, and time, t. The slope is Pr. Specifically, if a person invests \$1000 at 8% per year, after 1 year,

$$S = 1000 + 1000(0.08)(1)$$
$$= \$1080$$

after 2 years,

$$S = 1000 + 1000(0.08)(2)$$
$$= \$1160$$

after 3 years,

$$S = 1000 + 1000(0.08)(3)$$
$$= \$1240$$

and after t years,

$$S = 1000 + 1000(0.08)t$$
$$= 1000 + 80t$$

Note that the slope, 80, is the yearly increase in S. The linear function defined by $S = 1000 + 80t$ is sketched in Figure 4-3.

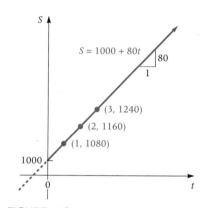

FIGURE 4-3

Calculating the Present Value

Sometimes it is necessary to calculate the present value (principal), given the future value (total amount). Thus, we now derive a formula for present value, P. We begin with

$$S = P(1 + rt)$$

and solve for P to get the equation in the box below.

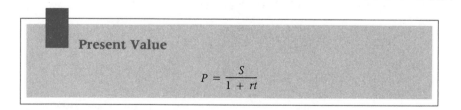

Present Value

$$P = \frac{S}{1 + rt}$$

• **EXAMPLE 4-2** _____

What amount of money should be invested now at 6% per year to yield a future value of \$8000 7 months from now?

Solution

Since $S = \$8000$, $r = 0.06$, and $t = 7/12$ year, then

7 months $= \dfrac{7}{12}$ year

6% = 0.06

$$P = \frac{S}{1 + rt}$$

$$= \frac{8000}{1 + (0.06)(7/12)}$$

$$= \frac{8000}{1 + 0.035}$$

$$= \$7729.47 \qquad \text{(See Figure 4-4.)}$$

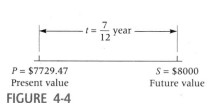

$t = \dfrac{7}{12}$ year

$P = \$7729.47$ $S = \$8000$
Present value   Future value

FIGURE 4-4

Sometimes a loan is transacted by the borrower giving the lender a signed paper promising to pay a specified amount by a given date. Such an instrument is called a **note.** The future value of the loan is called the **future value,** or the **maturity value,** of the note. To illustrate, suppose Henry Orwell transacted his 2-year, $1000 loan by giving the bank a note. Then, $1100, the future value of the loan, is also the future or maturity value of the note. The bank is called the **holder** of the note.

The holder of a note may sell the note prior to maturity. The buyer usually pays an amount less than the maturity value. When the borrower repays the loan (with the interest), the money (maturity value of the note) is automatically transferred to the buyer (now the present holder) of the note.

• **EXAMPLE 4-3** _____

Willis Harcase wishes to buy a note that has a maturity value of $3000. The note is due 9 months from today. If Willis wants to earn 8% per year on his invested money, how much should he pay for the note?

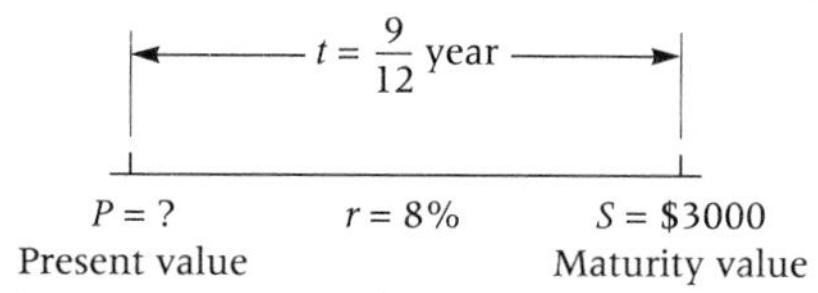

$t = \dfrac{9}{12}$ year

$P = ?$ $r = 8\%$ $S = \$3000$
Present value   Maturity value

FIGURE 4-5

Solution

The time diagram of Figure 4-5 illustrates this problem. Willis must calculate the present value of the note. Hence,

$$P = \frac{S}{1 + rt}$$

$$= \frac{3000}{1 + (0.08)(3/4)}$$

9 months $= \dfrac{9}{12}$

$= \dfrac{3}{4}$ year

8% = 0.08

$$= \frac{3000}{1 + 0.06}$$

$$\approx \$2830.19$$

Thus, if Willis pays 2830.19 for the note today, he will earn 8% per year on his money when the note is repaid in 9 months.

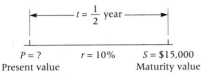

$t = \frac{1}{2}$ year

$P = ?$ $r = 10\%$ $S = \$15,000$
Present value   Maturity value

FIGURE 4-6

EXAMPLE 4-4

Melanie borrows a sum of money from Harry at 10% per year. She gives Harry a 6-month note with a maturity value of $15,000. How much did Melanie borrow from Harry?

Solution

See the time diagram of Figure 4-6. Calculating the present value, we have

$$P = \frac{S}{1 + rt}$$

$$= \frac{15,000}{1 + (0.10)(1/2)}$$

$$= \frac{15,000}{1.05}$$

$$\approx \$14,285.71$$

Therefore, Melanie borrowed $14,285.71 from Harry.

• EXAMPLE 4-5

Referring to Example 4-4, suppose Harry sold the note to Jacob 2 months before maturity. What amount did Jacob pay for the note if his invested money is earning 12% per year?

Solution

The time diagram of Figure 4-7 illustrates this problem. We must calculate the present value of $15,000 2 months before maturity. The simple interest rate is 12%. Hence,

$$P = \frac{S}{1 + rt}$$

$$= \frac{15,000}{1 + (0.12)(1/6)}$$

$$\approx \$14,705.88$$

Thus, Jacob paid $14,705.88 for the note. His profit is $15,000.00 − $14,705.88 = $294.12. Harry's profit is $14,705.88 − $14,285.71 = 420.17.

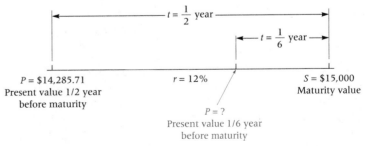

$t = \frac{1}{2}$ year

$t = \frac{1}{6}$ year

$P = \$14,285.71$ $r = 12\%$ $S = \$15,000$
Present value 1/2 year   Maturity value
before maturity

$P = ?$
Present value 1/6 year
before maturity

FIGURE 4-7

Simple Discount Note

In simple interest problems, the simple interest rate, r, is applied to the principal, P. Sometimes a loan is transacted by a **discount note.** In such a case, the cost of borrowing is called the **discount D.** The discount is computed as a percentage of the maturity value, S. This percentage is called the **discount rate, d.** Thus, if t is the length of time (in years) that the money is borrowed, then

discount = (maturity value)(discount rate)(length of time)

or

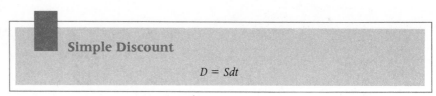

Simple Discount

$$D = Sdt$$

Specifically, consider the following example. Sam Schultz borrows a sum of money for 9 months by giving his bank a discount note for $1000. The discount rate is 8%. Thus, we have $S = \$1000$, $d = 0.08$, and $t = 9/12 = 3/4$ year. Hence, the discount is

$$D = Sdt$$
$$= 1000(0.08)(3/4)$$
$$= \$60$$

Although the note is written in terms of the maturity value of $1000, Sam only receives

$$\$1000 - \$60 = \$940$$

This amount is called the **proceeds, B,** of the note. In general, the proceeds of a discount note are calculated by the equation

proceeds = maturity value − discount

or

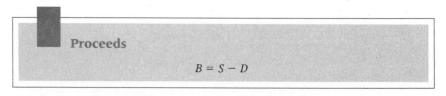

Proceeds

$$B = S - D$$

Of course, Sam will have to pay the bank $1000 (the maturity value) at the end of the 9-month time period to cancel the debt. This situation is illustrated by the time diagram of Figure 4-8.

When using a discount note, although the maturity value is referred to as the amount borrowed, the borrower actually receives only the proceeds after the discount is deducted from the maturity value.

If we use the above formula to determine the proceeds, we must first compute the discount by using the formula $D = Sdt$ and then compute the

$$t = \frac{3}{4} \text{ year}$$

$B = S - D$	$D = Sdt$	$S = \$1000$
$= 1000 - 60$	$= 1000(0.08)\left(\dfrac{3}{4}\right) = 60$	Maturity value
$= \$940$		
Proceeds		

FIGURE 4-8

proceeds with the formula $B = S - D$. This is a two-step procedure. Since it is often easier to use a one-step procedure, we now derive such a formula for the proceeds. We begin with the formula for proceeds

$$B = S - D$$

and replace D with Sdt to get

$$B = S - Sdt$$
$$= S(1 - dt)$$

Thus, we now have an alternate formula for the proceeds. We summarize below.

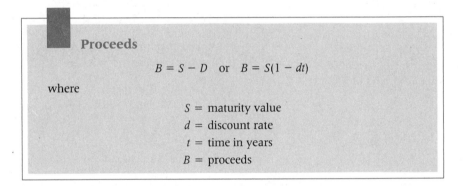

> **Proceeds**
>
> $$B = S - D \quad \text{or} \quad B = S(1 - dt)$$
>
> where
>
> $$S = \text{maturity value}$$
> $$d = \text{discount rate}$$
> $$t = \text{time in years}$$
> $$B = \text{proceeds}$$

• **EXAMPLE 4-6** _____

You give your bank a 4-month discount note for $12,000. The discount rate is 9%.

a) How much money do you receive from the bank?
b) How much money do you pay the bank at the end of 4 months to cancel your debt?
c) How much money does the bank earn on this transaction?

Solutions

a) We seek the proceeds, B. Since $S = \$12,000$, $d = 0.09$, and $t = 4/12 = 1/3$ year, then

$$B = S(1 - dt)$$
$$= 12,000[1 - (0.09)(1/3)]$$
$$= 12,000(1 - 0.03)$$
$$= 12,000(0.97)$$
$$= \$11,640 \quad \text{Proceeds}$$

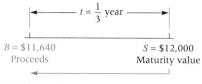

FIGURE 4-9

This situation is illustrated by the time diagram of Figure 4-9.

b) You must pay the bank the maturity value of the note, $12,000.

c) The bank earns the discount, D, which can be determined by either of the following methods:

Method 1.

$$D = Sdt$$
$$= 12,000(0.09)(1/3)$$
$$= \$360 \quad \text{Discount}$$

Method 2. The discount is also the difference between the maturity value and the proceeds, or, in other words,

$$D = S - B$$
$$= 12,000 - 11,640$$
$$= \$360 \quad \text{Discount}$$

Determining Maturity Value

Since a discount note is written in terms of its maturity value, but the borrower receives the lesser amount, called the **proceeds,** then the following problem arises when a discount note is written:

What should the maturity value, S, of a discount note be in order to yield a given amount of proceeds, B, at a specified discount rate, d?

To answer this question, we determine a formula for S in the following manner. We start with the formula

$$B = S(1 - dt)$$

and solve for S to obtain

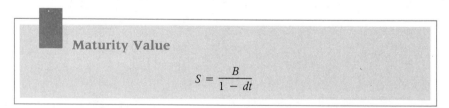

Maturity Value

$$S = \frac{B}{1 - dt}$$

We now return to our introductory example with Sam Schultz who gave his bank an 8%, 9-month discount note. If Sam wants to receive proceeds of $950 (instead of the original $940), the note must be written with the following maturity value:

$$S = \frac{950}{1 - (0.08)(3/4)}$$
$$= \frac{950}{1 - 0.06}$$
$$= \$1010.64$$

• **EXAMPLE 4-7** _____

You want to receive $8,000 for 6 months. Your bank offers you a 12% discount note.

a) Determine the maturity value of the discount note that you will sign.
b) How much does it cost you to use $8,000 for 6 months with this discount note?

Solutions

a) We seek S where $B = \$8,000$, $d = 0.12$, and $t = 6/12 = 1/2$ year. Hence,

$$S = \frac{B}{1 - dt}$$

$$= \frac{8000}{1 - (0.12)(1/2)}$$

$$= \frac{8000}{1 - 0.06}$$

$$= \frac{8000}{0.94} = \$8510.64 \quad \text{Maturity value}$$

b) Since you must, at the end of 6 months, pay the bank the maturity value, $8,510.64, the cost of using $8,000 for 6 months is the discount, D. In this case, the easiest way of computing the discount is to subtract the proceeds from the maturity value. Hence,

$$D = S - B$$

$$= 8510.64 - 8000$$

$$= \$510.64 \quad \text{Discount}$$

Of course, the discount is the amount earned by the bank. This situation is illustrated in the time diagram of Figure 4-10.

•

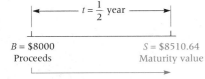

$t = \frac{1}{2}$ year

$B = \$8000$ $S = \$8510.64$
Proceeds   Maturity value

FIGURE 4-10

Interest-Bearing Notes

Often, in the world of financial transactions, we encounter interest-bearing notes that are sold (or discounted) prior to their maturity dates. An interest-bearing note is written in terms of its face value, which is actually the principal, P, of a loan. The maturity value of such a note must first be determined by using the formula for total amount:

$$S = P(1 + rt)$$

Then the formulas for finding the proceeds, B, can be applied when discounting such a note. We illustrate the above comments in the next example.

• **EXAMPLE 4-8** _____

A 1¼-year, 7% simple-interest-bearing note has a face value of $6,000. The bank holding this note needs cash and, thus, sells (or discounts) this note at 8% to another bank 3 months prior to its maturity date. How much does the second bank pay for the note?

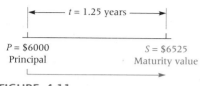

FIGURE 4-11

Solution

First, we find the maturity value, S, of the note. Since $P = \$6,000$, $r = 0.07$, and $t = 1.25$ years (we change $1\frac{1}{4}$ years to 1.25 years), then

$$S = P(1 + rt)$$
$$= 6000[1 + (0.07)(1.25)]$$
$$= 6000(1 + 0.0875)$$
$$= \$6525 \quad \text{Maturity value}$$

This is illustrated in the time diagram of Figure 4-11.

Next, we find the proceeds of the note 3 months prior to maturity. In other words, we discount the note at its discount rate, 8%, 3 months prior to maturity. This is illustrated in the time diagram of Figure 4-12. Thus, we use the formula

$$B = S(1 - dt)$$

where $S = 6525$, $d = 0.08$, and $t = 3/12 = 1/4$ year. Hence,

$$B = 6525[1 - (0.08)(1/4)]$$
$$= 6525 (1 - 0.02)$$
$$= 6525(.98)$$
$$= \$6394.50 \quad \text{Proceeds}$$

Thus, the second bank buys the note for $6,394.50 in order to receive $6,525 at the end of 3 months from the original borrower (or signer of the note).

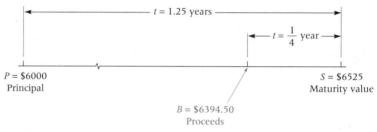

FIGURE 4-12

Simple Interest Rate

If a discount note is analyzed from a simple interest point of view, the simple interest rate is usually larger than the discount rate. For example, if we consider Sam Schultz's first discount rate for $1000 with proceeds of $940, we realize that Sam paid $60 interest to borrow $940 for 3/4 year. If we begin with the formula for simple interest

$$I = Prt$$

and solve for the simple interest rate, r, we have

$$r = \frac{I}{Pt}$$
$$= \frac{60}{940(3/4)}$$
$$= \frac{60}{705}$$
$$= 0.0851 = 8.51\% \quad \text{Simple interest rate}$$

Thus, a discount rate of 8% for 3/4 year is equivalent to a simple interest rate of 8.51% for the same time period.

Exercises 4-1

Find the simple interest and total amount of each of the following loans.

1. $1000 for 3 years at 7%
2. $10,000 for 2 years at 6%
3. $5000 for 6 months at 8%
4. $8000 for 3 months at 12%
5. $2000 for 4 months at 9%
6. $9000 for 1 year at 10%

7. A person invests $10,000 at 9% per year.
   a) Determine the equation that expresses total amount, S, as a function of time, t (in years).
   b) Graph the equation of part a.
   c) By how much does the total amount, S, increase each year? Relate this answer to the graph of part b.

8. A person invests $30,000 at 8% per year.
   a) Determine the equation that expresses total amount, S, as a function of time, t (in years).
   b) Graph the equation of part a.
   c) By how much does the total amount, S, increase each year? Relate this answer to the graph of part b.

Determine the present value (or principal), P, for each of the following.

9. $S = \$8,000$, $r = 0.09$, $t = 2$ years
10. $S = \$12,000$, $r = 0.10$, $t = 3$ years
11. $S = \$15,000$, $r = 0.08$, $t = 2.5$ years
12. $S = \$10,000$, $r = 0.07$, $t = 3.4$ years
13. Maturity value = $20,000, annual interest rate = 8%, time = 3 months
14. Maturity value = $30,000, annual interest rate = 9%, time = 8 months.

Determine the proceeds for each of the following discount notes.

15. Maturity value = $10,000, discount rate = 9%, time = 4 months
16. Maturity value = $90,000, discount rate = 8%, time = 9 months
17. Maturity value = $5,000, discount rate = 6%, time = 6 months
18. Maturity value = $20,000, discount rate = 8%, time = 3 months
19. $S = \$30,000$, $d = 0.09$, $t = 2/3$ year
20. $S = \$18,000$, $d = 0.10$, $t = 1/2$ year

21-26. For Exercises 9-14, determine the simple interest rate equivalent to the discount note.

For Exercises 27-32, determine the maturity value for each discount note.

27. Proceeds = $8,000, discount rate = 8%, time = 9 months
28. Proceeds = $5,000, discount rate = 6%, time = 8 months
29. Proceeds = $12,000, discount rate = 12%, time = 10 months
30. Proceeds = $10,000, discount rate = 9%, time = 8 months
31. $B = \$9,000$, $d = 0.10$, $t = 1/2$ year
32. $B = \$20,000$, $d = 0.06$, $t = 2/3$ year

Exercises 33-38 entail simple-interest-bearing notes discounted prior to maturity. Determine the proceeds of each note at the time of discount.

33. Face value = $10,000; 9-month note; annual interest rate = 8%; discounted at 6% 2 months prior to maturity

34. Face value = $9,000; 6-month note; annual interest rate = 7%; discounted at 8% 3 months prior to maturity

35. Face value = $14,000; 3-month note; annual interest rate = 8%; discounted at 6% 1 month prior to maturity

36. Face value = $20,000; 15-month note; annual interest rate = 8%; discounted at 9% 6 months prior to maturity

37. Face value = $30,000; 18-month note; annual interest rate = 9%; discounted at 8% 9 months prior to maturity

38. Face value = $15,000; 1.5-year note; annual interest rate = 7%; discounted at 6% 6 months prior to maturity

39. What amount of money should be invested now at 8% per year to yield a future value of $10,000 9 months from now?

40. A note with a maturity value of $1000 matures in 5 months. If one wishes to earn 9% per year, how much should be paid for the note now?

41. Sam Smith plans to buy a note with a maturity value of $10,000. The note is due 5 years from now. If Sam wishes to earn 10% per year on his invested money, how much should he pay for the note?

42. Helen borrows a sum of money from Tom at 9% per year by giving Tom a 6-month note with a maturity value of $9000.
    a) How much money did Helen borrow from Tom?
    b) Two years before maturity, Tom sells the note to Susan. What amount does Susan pay for the note if she is earning 10% per year?

43. Ellen Rydell borrows a sum of money for 5 years by giving her bank a discount note for $6000. The discount rate is 9%.
    a) Find the discount.
    b) Find the proceeds.
    c) Find the equivalent simple interest rate.

44. A woman borrows a sum of money for 6 months by giving her bank a discount note for $8000. The discount rate is 10%.
    a) Find the discount.
    b) Find the proceeds.
    c) How much money did the woman receive?
    d) Find the equivalent simple interest rate.

45. Glenn Nash receives $5000 for 4 months by giving his bank a discount note. The discount rate is 7%.
    a) Find the maturity value of the note.
    b) Find the equivalent simple interest rate.

46. A man receives $5000 from his bank for 9 months by using a discount note. The discount rate is 12%.
    a) Find the maturity value of the note.
    b) Find the equivalent simple interest rate.

47. Find the maturity value of an interest note for $600 issued for 4 months at an interest rate of 6% per year.

48. Find the present value of a 3-month interest note with a maturity value of $6000. Assume that the interest rate is 8% per year.

49. A 1½-year, 10% simple-interest-bearing note with a face value of $20,000 is sold to an investment firm 6 months prior to maturity at a discount rate of 9%.
    a) How much does the investment firm pay for the note?
    b) How much does the investment firm earn on the note?

50. A 21-month, 8% simple-interest-bearing note with a face value of $30,000 is sold to an investor 6 months prior to maturity at a discount rate of 7%.
   a) How much does the investor pay for the note?
   b) How much does the investor earn on the note?

The following problems have appeared on past Uniform CPA Examinations

51. Fay, Inc., received a $30,000, 6-month, 12% interest-bearing note from a customer. The note was discounted the same day by Carr National Bank at 15%. The amount of cash received by Fay from the bank was
   a) $30,000   b) $29,550
   c) $29,415   d) $27,750

52. Tallent Company received a $30,000, 6-month, 10% interest-bearing note from a customer. After holding the note for 2 months, Tallent was in need of cash and discounted the note at the United National Bank at a 12% discount rate. The amount of cash received by Tallent from the bank was
   a) $31,260   b) $30,870
   c) $30,300   d) $30,240

4-2 • COMPOUND INTEREST

In Section 4-1, we learned that the value of a sum of money, P, invested at simple interest increases by the same amount each year. This is due to the fact that the interest rate, r, is applied to the original principal, P. In this section, we will discuss a method of computing interest in which the value of a sum of money, P, increases by a larger amount each year. Here, the interest rate, r, will be applied to the original principal plus interest, rather than to just the original principal. Such a method of computing interest is called **compounding.** The result is **compound interest.**

Compound interest is usually computed periodically throughout the year. If compound interest is computed every month (12 times a year), it is said to be **compounded monthly.** Each month is called a **conversion period,** or **interest period.** If compound interest is computed every 3 months (4 times a year), it is said to be **compounded quarterly.** Thus, each 3-month time interval between successive compoundings is a conversion or interest period. If compound interest is computed every 6 months (2 times a year), it is said to be **compounded semiannually.** Hence, each 6-month time interval

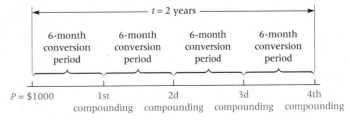

FIGURE 4-13

FIGURE 4-14

between successive compoundings is a conversion or interest period. Interest may also be compounded annually, weekly, daily, and continuously.

We now compute the total amount of $1000 invested for 2 years at 8% compounded semiannually. Note that $P = \$1000$ and $r = 0.08$. Since the interest is compounded semiannually, there will be two compoundings per year (see Figure 4-13 on page 177).

Thus, there will be four compoundings and four conversion periods during the 2-year time interval. We now show each compounding.

1. **First Compounding** (at End of First Conversion Period)—The interest is calculated and added to the original principal. Hence,

$$I = Prt$$
$$= 1000(0.08)(1/2)$$
$$= 1000(0.04)$$
$$= \$40$$
$$S = P + I$$
$$= \$1000 + \$40$$
$$= \$1040$$

Thus, the original investment is now worth $1040 (see Figure 4-14).

2. **Second Compounding** (at End of Second Conversion Period)—The total amount from the previous compounding becomes the *new principal.* Interest is calculated on the new principal. The total amount is calculated by adding the interest to the new principal. Hence, we have

$$I = \text{new principal} \cdot r \cdot t$$
$$= 1040(0.08)(1/2)$$
$$= 1040(0.04)$$
$$= \$41.60$$
$$S = \text{new principal} + I$$
$$= \$1040.00 + \$41.60$$
$$= \$1081.60$$

Thus, the original investment is now worth $1081.60 (see Figure 4-15).

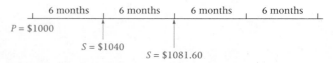

FIGURE 4-15

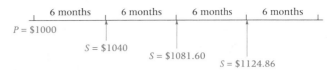

FIGURE 4-16

3. Third Compounding (at End of Third Conversion Period)—The process is repeated, and we obtain

$$I = \text{new principal} \cdot r \cdot t$$
$$= 1081.60(0.08)(1/2)$$
$$= 1081.60(0.04)$$
$$= \$43.26$$
$$S = \text{new principal} + I$$
$$= \$1081.60 + \$43.26$$
$$= \$1124.86$$

Hence, the original investment is now worth $1124.86 (see Figure 4-16).

4. Fourth Compounding (at End of Fourth Conversion Period)—The process is repeated, giving us

$$I = \text{new principal} \cdot r \cdot t$$
$$= 1124.86(0.08)(1/2)$$
$$= 1124.86(0.04)$$
$$= \$44.99$$
$$S = \text{new principal} + I$$
$$= \$1124.86 + \$44.99$$
$$= \$1169.85$$

Thus, the original investment is now worth $1169.85 (see Figure 4-17). This total is often called the **compound amount.**

Observe that, for each compounding in our example, the new principal is always multiplied by $(0.08)(1/2) = 0.04$. This value is called the **interest rate per conversion period.** In general, the interest rate per conversion period will be indicated by the symbol i. Hence, for the previous example, we write

$$i = 0.08(1/2) = 0.04$$

Thus, 8% compounded semiannually is equivalent to 4% per conversion period. Note that the interest rate per conversion period may be calculated

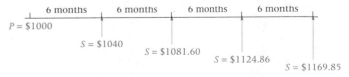

FIGURE 4-17

by dividing the quoted interest rate by the number of conversion periods per year. Thus, if

r = annual (or quoted) interest rate (or **nominal rate**)

m = number of conversion periods per year

then

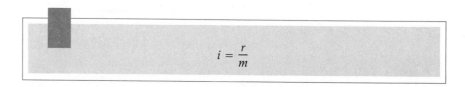

$$i = \frac{r}{m}$$

Observe, also, that the number of conversion periods, n, may be calculated by multiplying the number of conversion periods per year, m, by the number of years, t. Hence,

$$n = mt$$

Thus, for the illustrated example,

m = 2 conversion periods per year

t = 2 years

$n = 2(2)$ = 4 conversion periods

• **EXAMPLE 4-9**

A sum of money is invested for 4 years at 6% compounded monthly. Calculate i and n.

Solution

Since $r = 6\%$, $m = 12$ conversion periods per year, and $t = 4$ years, then

$$i = \frac{r}{m}$$

$$= \frac{6\%}{12} = \frac{1}{2}\% \text{ per month}$$

$$n = mt$$

$$= 12(4) = 48 \text{ conversion periods}$$

We will now derive a general formula for the compound amount, S. If

P = original principal

i = interest rate per conversion period

n = total number of conversion periods

S = compound amount (or total amount or maturity value or accumulated value)

then, at the end of the first conversion period,

$$I = Pi$$
$$S = P + I$$
$$= P + Pi$$
$$= P(1 + i)$$

At the end of the second conversion period,

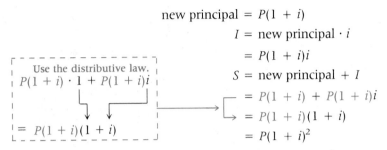

$$\text{new principal} = P(1 + i)$$
$$I = \text{new principal} \cdot i$$
$$= P(1 + i)i$$
$$S = \text{new principal} + I$$
$$= P(1 + i) + P(1 + i)i$$
$$= P(1 + i)(1 + i)$$
$$= P(1 + i)^2$$

At the end of the third conversion period,

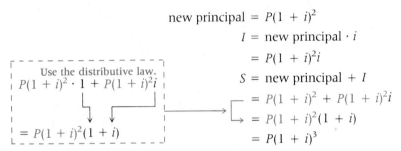

$$\text{new principal} = P(1 + i)^2$$
$$I = \text{new principal} \cdot i$$
$$= P(1 + i)^2 i$$
$$S = \text{new principal} + I$$
$$= P(1 + i)^2 + P(1 + i)^2 i$$
$$= P(1 + i)^2(1 + i)$$
$$= P(1 + i)^3$$

And at the end of the nth conversion period,

$$S = P(1 + i)^n$$

The time diagram of Figure 4-18 summarizes the preceding calculations.

Thus, if we invest P dollars for n periods at an interest rate per conversion period of i, the compound amount, S, is given by

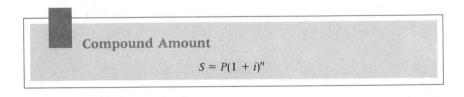

Compound Amount

$$S = P(1 + i)^n$$

FIGURE 4-18

Returning to the introductory problem of this section where $P = 1000$, $n = 4$, and $i = 0.04$, we use the above formula to compute the compound amount. Hence,

$$S = P(1 + i)^n$$
$$= 1000(1 + 0.04)^4$$

Using a calculator, we evaluate $(1 + 0.04)^4 = (1.04)^4 \approx 1.169859$ to six decimal places. Thus,

$$S \approx 1000(1.169859)$$
$$\approx \$1169.86$$

We note that Table 4 in Appendix C gives values of $(1 + i)^n$ for various rates, i, and numbers of periods, n. Using Table 4 to determine the value of $(1.04)^4$, we locate the "$i = 4\%$" column and then move four periods down in that column to find $(1.04)^4 = 1.169859$.

• **EXAMPLE 4-10**

Find the compound amount of $10,000 invested for 5 years at 8% compounded quarterly.

Solution

Here $P = \$10,000$, $r = 8\%$, $m = 4$, and $t = 5$ years. Thus,

$$i = \frac{r}{m} = \frac{8\%}{4} = 2\% \text{ per conversion period}$$
$$n = mt = 4(5) = 20 \text{ conversion periods}$$
$$S = P(1 + i)^n$$
$$= 10,000(1 + 0.02)^{20} \quad \text{Using Appendix C, Table 4, or a}$$
$$\approx 10,000(1.485947) \quad \text{calculator } (1 + 0.02)^{20} \approx 1.485947.$$
$$\approx \$14,859.47 \quad \text{(See Figure 4-19.)}$$

$P = \$10,000$ $S = \$14,859.47$

FIGURE 4-19

Sometimes we must use the formula $S = P(1 + i)^n$ repeatedly for more complex situations. Example 4-11 illustrates such a case.

• **EXAMPLE 4-11**

A person deposits $10,000 in a savings account that pays 6% compounded semiannually. Three years later, this person deposits an additional $8,000 in the savings account. Also, at this time, the interest rate changes to 8% compounded quarterly. How much is in the account 5 years after the original $10,000 deposit?

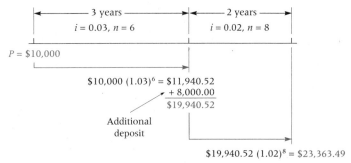

FIGURE 4-20

Solution

First, we find the compound amount of $10,000 after 3 years at 6% compounded semiannually (see Figure 4-20). This is given by

$$S = P(1 + i)^n$$
$$= 10,000(1 + 0.03)^6$$

$n = 3(2) = 6$
$i = \frac{6\%}{2} = 0.03$

$$\approx 10,000(1.194052)$$
$$= \$11,940.52$$

Second, since $8,000 is deposited in the account after 3 years, we add this amount to the compound amount of $11,940.52 to obtain 11,940.52 + 8,000.00 = $19,940.52. Now we find the compound amount of $19,940.52 after 2 years at 8% compounded quarterly to obtain

$$S = P(1 + i)^n$$
$$= 19,940.52(1 + 0.02)^8$$

$n = 2(4) = 8$
$i = \frac{8\%}{4} = 0.02$

$$\approx 19,940.52(1.171659)$$
$$= \$23,363.49 \qquad \text{Answer}$$

This situation is also illustrated in Figure 4-20.

Present Value at Compound Interest

The formula

$$S = P(1 + i)^n$$

accumulates or brings forward a principal (or present value), *P, for n* periods at an interest rate of *i* per period, as illustrated in the time diagram of Figure 4-21. Sometimes it is necessary to calculate the present value, *P,*

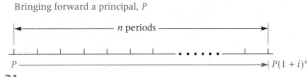

FIGURE 4-21

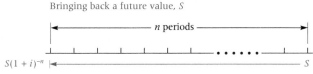

Bringing back a future value, S

FIGURE 4-22

given the compound amount. A formula for P may be derived by beginning with the equation for compound amount

$$S = P(1 + i)^n$$

and solving for P. The result is

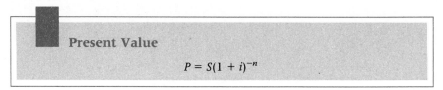

Present Value

$$P = S(1 + i)^{-n}$$

This formula is used to find the present value of a given compound amount. Table 5 in Appendix C gives values of $(1 + i)^{-n}$ for various values of i and n. A calculator can also be used to compute these values. We note that this formula brings back a future value of S for n periods at an interest rate of i per period, as shown in the time diagram of Figure 4-22.

• **EXAMPLE 4-12** _____

What sum of money should be invested for 4 years at 9% compounded monthly in order to provide a compound amount of $8000?

Solution

Here, $S = \$8000$, $r = 9\%$, $m = 12$, and $t = 4$ years. Thus,

$$i = \frac{r}{m} = \frac{9\%}{12} = \frac{3}{4}\% \text{ per month}$$

$$n = mt = 12(4) = 48 \text{ conversion periods}$$

$$P = S(1 + i)^{-n}$$
$$= 8000(1 + 0.0075)^{-48} \quad \text{Using a calculator or Appendix C,}$$
$$\approx 8000(0.698614) \quad \text{Table 5, } (1 + 0.0075)^{-48} \approx 0.698614.$$
$$\approx \$5588.91 \quad \text{(See Figure 4-23.)}$$

•

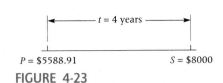

$P = \$5588.91$ $S = \$8000$

FIGURE 4-23

Equivalent Rates

Sometimes it is helpful to convert interest rates from, for example, a compounded quarterly basis to a compounded monthly basis, from a compounded monthly basis to a compounded annually basis, etc. This is easily accomplished as long as we understand the concept of *equivalent interest rates,* which we define as follows.

Equivalent Rates

If, at the beginning of a specified time period, the same amount of money is invested at various interest rates so that the resulting compound amounts are equal at the end of the time period, then the interest rates are **equivalent rates.**

Although we can use any length time period, we usually use a 1-year time interval. Thus, if P dollars are invested at annual rate r compounded m times a year, and another P dollars are invested at annual rate s compounded k times a year, then the rates are equivalent as long as

$$\underbrace{P(1 + r/m)^m}_{} = \underbrace{P(1 + s/k)^k}_{}$$

Compound amount of P dollars invested for 1 year at annual rate r compounded m times a year

Compound amount of P dollars invested for 1 year at annual rate s compounded k times a year

Dividing both sides of the above equation by P gives the equivalent rates equation which can be solved for either r or s, depending on which is the unknown.

Equivalent Rates

Use this equation to find equivalent rates.

$$(1 + r/m)^m = (1 + s/k)^k \tag{1}$$

• **EXAMPLE 4-13**

What rate compounded monthly is equivalent to 8% compounded quarterly?

Solution

Let r be the equivalent rate compounded monthly. Then, using equation (1),

$$(1 + r/12)^{12} = (1 + 0.08/4)^4$$
$$= (1.02)^4$$

Solving for r, we take the 12th root of each side to obtain

$$1 + r/12 = ((1.02)^4)^{1/12}$$
$$= (1.02)^{1/3}$$
$$r/12 = (1.02)^{1/3} - 1 \qquad \text{Using a calculator,}$$
$$\approx 1.006622 - 1 \qquad (1.02)^{1/3} \approx (1.02)^{0.3333} \approx 1.006622.$$
$$= 0.006622$$
$$r = 12(0.006622)$$
$$\approx 0.079476$$
$$\approx 7.95\%$$

Thus, 7.95% compounded monthly is equivalent to 8% compounded quarterly.

Effective Rate

If we convert from an interest rate compounded m times a year (where $m > 1$) to an interest rate compounded annually (i.e., once a year), the resulting equivalent rate is called the *effective annual interest rate* or, simply, **effective rate.** Thus, to determine the effective rate, s, corresponding to the annual rate, r, compounded m times a year, we use equation (1) to obtain the equation

$$(1 + r/m)^m = 1 + s$$

which, when solved for s, gives the following formula for the effective rate.

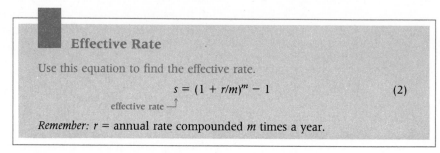

Effective Rate

Use this equation to find the effective rate.

$$s = (1 + r/m)^m - 1 \qquad (2)$$

effective rate ⤴

Remember: r = annual rate compounded m times a year.

As an example, the effective rate corresponding to 8% compounded quarterly is given by

$$s = (1 + r/m)^m - 1$$
$$= (1 + 0.08/4)^4 - 1$$
$$= (1.02)^4 - 1 \qquad \text{Using a calculator,}$$
$$\approx 1.082432 - 1 \qquad (1.02)^4 \approx 1.082432.$$
$$= 0.082432 \approx 8.24\% \qquad \text{Effective rate}$$

Thus, 8% compounded quarterly is equivalent to 8.24% compounded annually.

• **EXAMPLE 4-14** _____

Find the effective rate corresponding to 6% compounded monthly.

Solution

Using equation (2), we have

$$s = (1 + r/m)^m - 1$$
$$= (1 + 0.06/12)^{12} - 1$$
$$= (1.005)^{12} - 1 \qquad \text{Using a calculator,}$$
$$\approx 1.061678 - 1 \qquad (1.005)^{12} \approx 1.061678.$$
$$= 0.061678 \approx 6.17\% \qquad \text{Effective rate}$$

Thus, 6% compounded monthly is equivalent to 6.17% compounded annually.

•

Effective rates are used to compare competing interest rates offered by banks and other financial institutions. The next example illustrates such a case.

• **EXAMPLE 4-15** _____

One bank pays interest on its savings accounts at the rate of 8.65% compounded quarterly; another bank pays 8.70% compounded semiannually. Which pays its savers more interest?

Solution

We find the effective rate for each bank's rate by using a calculator as follows.

8.65% compounded quarterly: The *effective rate* is given by

$$(1 + 0.0865/4)^4 - 1 \approx 1.089347 - 1 = 0.089347 \approx 8.93\%$$

8.70% compounded semiannually: The *effective rate* is given by

$$(1 + 0.0870/2)^2 - 1 \approx 1.088892 - 1 = 0.088892 \approx 8.89\%$$

The bank that has the greater effective rate pays its savers more interest. Thus, the bank that pays 8.65% compounded quarterly has the greater effective rate and, therefore, pays more interest to its savers.

_____ •

"Double, Triple, Quadruple . . . Your Money"

Consider the following question:

How long does it take a principal to double itself at 8% compounded quarterly?

The answer is found by beginning with the formula for compound amount

$$S = P(1 + i)^n$$

and substituting $2P$ for S. Hence,

$$2P = P(1 + i)^n$$

Dividing by P, we obtain

$$2 = (1 + i)^n$$

We must now solve the equation for n. Taking the natural logarithm of each side, we get

$$\ln 2 = \ln (1 + i)^n$$
$$= n \ln (1 + i)$$

Solving for n yields

$$n = \frac{\ln 2}{\ln (1 + i)}$$

Since $i = 8\%/4 = 2\% = 0.02$, then

$$n = \frac{\ln 2}{\ln 1.02}$$

$$\approx \frac{0.6931}{0.0198}$$

$$\approx 35 \text{ conversion periods}$$

Thus, the principal, P, will double itself after $n = 35$ conversion periods or $35/4 = 8\frac{3}{4}$ years (since there are 4 conversion periods per year). We note that the above procedure could also be employed by using common logarithms.

Daily Compounding

So far in this chapter we have worked examples where interest has been compounded annually, semiannually, quarterly, and monthly. Interest may also be compounded weekly, daily, and hourly. When interest is compounded daily, most financial institutions have used a 360-day year. However, with the increasing use of computers and calculators, many are using a 365-day year. In this text, we will employ a 365-day year. Hence, if interest is compounded daily, then $i = r/365$.

• EXAMPLE 4-16

A man invests $18,000 for 3 years at 10% compounded daily. Find the compound amount

Solution

Here, we use

$$S = P(1 + i)^n$$

where $P = \$18,000$, $i = 0.10/365$, and $n = 365(3) = 1095$. Hence,

$$S = 18,000\left(1 + \frac{0.10}{365}\right)^{1095}$$

Let us first evaluate $(1 + 0.10/365)^{1095}$. Using a calculator, we determine that $(1 + 0.10/365)^{1095} \approx 1.349803332$. Thus, the compound amount is

$$S \approx 18,000(1.349803332)$$
$$\approx \$24,296.46$$

• EXAMPLE 4-17

Find the effective annual interest rate corresponding to 12% compounded daily.

Solution

We must evaluate

$$\left(1 + \frac{0.12}{365}\right)^{365} - 1$$

Using a calculator, we determine that $(1 + 0.12/365)^{365} \approx 1.127475$. Hence, the effective annual interest rate is

$$\left(1 + \frac{0.12}{365}\right)^{365} - 1 \approx 1.127475 - 1$$
$$= 0.127475$$

Thus, 12% compounded daily is equivalent to 12.75% compounded annually.

Continuous Compounding

In Section 3-1, we learned that the expression

$$\left(1 + \frac{1}{x}\right)^x \;\boxed{\text{approaches}}\!\!> \; e$$

as x gets larger and larger. Also we used a calculator to compute $(1 + 1/x)^x$ for larger and larger values of x and determined that

$$e = 2.718281828. \; . \; .$$

We now show how this result is used in the continuous compounding of interest.

The previous two examples have involved daily compounding of interest. We may go further and compound every minute, every second, every half-second, etc. As the number of compoundings per year, m, increases without bound, the interest is said to be **compounded continuously.**

To determine the formula for the future value of an amount P that is compounded continuously, we begin with

$$S = P\left(1 + \frac{r}{m}\right)^{mt}$$

where r = nominal interest rate, m = number of conversion periods per year, and t = number of years. As m increases without bound, the preceding formula for S is rewritten as

$$S = P\left[\left(1 + \frac{1}{m/r}\right)^{m/r}\right]^{rt}$$

Hence, as m increases, m/r increases. Eventually, the factor

$$\left(1 + \frac{1}{m/r}\right)^{m/r}$$

approaches $e = 2.718281828 \; . \; . \; . \; .$ Thus, when interest is compounded continuously at a nominal rate, r, the future value, S, is given by

Future Value

$$S = Pe^{rt}$$

• **EXAMPLE 4-18** _____

A financial analyst invests \$10,000 at 7% compounded continuously for 10 years. Find the compound amount.

Solution

Here $P = \$10,000$, $r = 0.07$, and $t = 10$ years.
Thus,

$$
\begin{aligned}
S &= Pe^{rt} \\
&= 10,000e^{0.07(10)} \\
&\approx 10,000(2.013753) \\
&= \$20,137.53
\end{aligned}
$$

Using a calculator or Appendix C, Table 3, $e^{0.70} \approx 2.013753$.

Effective Rate: Continuous Compounding

To determine a formula for the effective rate when compounding continuously at an annual rate, r, we find its equivalent rate, s, compounded annually by using the equation below.

$$e^{r(1)} = 1 + s$$

Compound amount of \$1 invested ___↑   ↑___ Compound amount of \$1 invested
for 1 year at annual rate r for 1 year at annual rate s
compounded continuously   compounded annually

Solving the above equation for s gives the following formula for the effective rate when compounding continuously.

Effective Rate

Use this formula to find the effective rate when compounding continuously.

$$\underset{\text{effective rate}}{s} = e^r - 1$$

• **EXAMPLE 4-19** _____

Find the effective annual interest rate corresponding to 10% compounded continuously.

Solution

We seek the interest earned by investing \$1 at 10% compounded continuously for 1 year. This is given by

$$e^{0.10} - 1 \approx 1.105171 - 1$$
$$= 0.105171 \approx 10.52\%$$

Thus, 10% compounded continuously is equivalent to approximately 10.52% compounded annually.

                                                                            •

Present Value at Continuous Compounding

The formula for present value at continuous compounding is found by beginning with the formula for compound amount

$$S = Pe^{rt}$$

and solving for P. Thus,

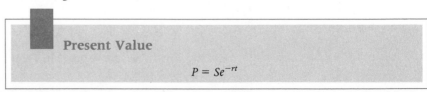

Present Value

$$P = Se^{-rt}$$

• **EXAMPLE 4-20** _____

What sum of money should be invested for 5 years at 6% compounded continuously in order to provide a compound amount of $9000?

Solution

In this case, we have S = $9000, r = 0.06, and t = 5 years. Therefore,

$$P = Se^{-rt}$$
$$= 9000e^{-0.06(5)}$$
$$\approx 9000(0.740818)$$
$$\approx \$6667.36$$

Using a calculator,
$e^{-0.30} \approx 0.740818$.

_____   •

Exercises 4-2

Using a calculator or Appendix C, Table 4 (or both), find the compound amount and interest for each of the following situations:

1. P = $1000, r = 0.08, m = 4, n = 40
2. P = $5000, r = 0.08, m = 2, n = 30
3. P = $8000, r = 0.06, m = 1, n = 10
4. P = $3000, r = 0.12, m = 3, n = 36
5. $5000 invested at 4% compounded quarterly for 6 years
6. $10,000 invested at 8% compounded semiannually for 15 years
7. $3000 invested at 12% compounded monthly for 4 years
8. $20,000 invested at 6% compounded semiannually for 11 years

Determine the present value in each of the following situations.

9. S = $8,000, interest rate is 8% compounded semiannually, time is 5 years
10. S = $10,000, interest rate is 10% compounded semiannually, time is 6 years
11. S = $6,000, interest rate is 8% compounded quarterly, time is 9 years
12. S = $15,000, interest rate is 7% compounded quarterly, time is 3 years
13. S = $9,000, interest rate is 8% compounded annually, time is 20 years
14. S = $12,000, interest rate is 6% compounded annually, time is 15 years.

Find the present value of each of the following.

15. $8000 due in 4 years with money worth 8% compounded quarterly
16. $4000 due in 10 years with money worth 5% compounded annually
17. $20,000 due in 20 years with money worth 8% compounded semiannually
18. $10,000 due in 3 years with money worth 12% compounded monthly
19. A man borrows $10,000 from a bank. The bank charges interest at the rate of 8% compounded quarterly. Ten years later, the man repays the loan in a lump-sum payment.
    a) Find the lump-sum payment.
    b) Find the interest.
20. During a 10-year period, the population of a city increased at a rate of 4% a year (i.e., 4% compounded annually). If the initial population was 500,000, what was the population 10 years later? What was the increase?
21. The day a girl was born, her parents deposited $500 into a bank account paying 5% compounded annually. How much will be in this account on the girl's 20th birthday?
22. A woman deposits $10,000 into a bank account. During the first 4 years, the account earns interest at 5% compounded annually. During the last 6 years,

the account earns interest at 6% compounded semiannually. Find the total amount.

23. Jean Scott deposits $5000 into a bank account earning interest at the rate of 8% compounded semiannually. Three years later, Jean deposits an additional $6000. Also, at this time, the bank's interest rate is increased to 10% compounded semiannually. How much is in the account 10 years after the initial $5000 deposit was made? Assume that no withdrawals have been made.

24. Harry Mazzuri deposited $900 in a savings account that paid 6% compounded semiannually. Seven years later, the bank changed its interest rate to 10% compounded quarterly. How much will Harry's account be worth 10 years after the original deposit of $900?

25. Lucy Maceratta deposited $600 in a savings account. Six years later, she deposited an additional $300. How much will be in Lucy's account 11 years after the original deposit of $600 if the interest rate is 8% compounded quarterly?

26. How much money should be invested for 6 years at 8% compounded semiannually in order to provide a compound amount of $10,000?

27. An investment contract with a maturity value of $1000 matures in 5 years. If one wishes to earn interest at 6% compounded semiannually, how much should be paid for the investment contract now?

28. Hank Jackson plans to buy a note with a maturity value of $9000. The note is due 6 years from now. If Hank wishes to earn interest at 12% compounded monthly, how much should he pay for the note?

29. A 3-year note has a maturity value of $10,000. The interest rate is 12% compounded quarterly.
    a) How much money is needed to pay the debt now?
    b) How much money is needed to pay the debt 2 years from now?

30. How much money should be deposited now in order to accumulate into $8000 in 10 years at an interest rate of 12% compounded quarterly?

Find the effective annual interest rate corresponding to each of the following.

31. 6% compounded semiannually
32. 4% compounded quarterly
33. 12% compounded monthly
34. 8% compounded semiannually

How long will it take money to double itself at each of the following rates?

35. 6% compounded semiannually
36. 8% compounded semiannually
37. 8% compounded annually
38. 12% compounded monthly

How long will it take money to triple itself at each of the following rates?

39. 8% compounded quarterly
40. 6% compounded semiannually

How long will it take money to quadruple itself at each of the following rates?

41. 8% compounded quarterly
42. 6% compounded semiannually

Use a calculator to solve each of the following problems. Find the value of $(1 + i)^n$ for each of the following.

43. 7% compounded monthly for 3 years
44. 5% compounded monthly for 5 years
45. 10% compounded monthly for 4 years
46. 8% compounded monthly for 6 years

47. 9% compounded weekly for 2 years
48. 6% compounded weekly for 3 years
49. 9% compounded daily for 3 years
50. 5% compounded daily for 2 years
51. 8% compounded daily for 4 years
52. 6% compounded daily for 3 years
53. A person deposits $10,000 into a bank account that pays interest at 8% compounded daily. How much is in the account at the end of 5 years?
54. Determine the compound amount of $80,000 that earns interest at 10% compounded daily for 2 years.
55. How much should be invested now at 7% compounded daily in order to accumulate $50,000 at the end of 3 years?
56. How much should be invested now at 9% compounded daily in order to accumulate $10,000 at the end of 2 years?
57. What rate compounded semiannually is equivalent to 8% compounded quarterly?
58. What rate compounded quarterly is equivalent to 10% compounded semiannually?
59. What rate compounded monthly is equivalent to 6% compounded semiannually?
60. What rate compounded quarterly is equivalent to 10% compounded monthly?

Which would you rather earn?

61. 8.8% compounded annually or 8.5% compounded daily
62. 10% compounded annually or 9.75% compounded daily
63. 9% compounded annually or 8.75% compounded monthly

Find the compound amount of each of the following.

64. $1000 invested for 3 years at 6% compounded continuously
65. $5000 invested for 8 years at 5% compounded continuously
66. $10,000 invested for 10 years at 8% compounded continuously
67. $6000 invested for 5 years at 6% compounded continuously

Find the present value of each of the following.

68. $6000 due in 3 years at 6% compounded continuously
69. $10,000 due in 7 years at 10% compounded continuously
70. $8000 due in 10 years at 8% compounded continuously
71. $4000 due in 2 years at 7% compounded continuously

Find the effective annual interest rate corresponding to each of the following.

72. 6% compounded continuously
73. 7% compounded continuously
74. 8% compounded continuously
75. 9% compounded continuously

4-3 • GEOMETRIC SERIES AND ANNUITIES

Geometric Series

A **geometric series** is an expression of the form

$$a + ar + ar^2 + \ldots + ar^{n-1}$$

Each term is a constant multiple, r, of the preceding term. If S_n denotes the sum of the first n terms of a geometric series, then

$$S_n = a + ar + ar^2 + \ldots + ar^{n+1}$$

$$\begin{array}{cccc} \uparrow & \uparrow & \uparrow & \uparrow \\ \text{1st} & \text{2d} & \text{3d} & n\text{th} \\ \text{term} & \text{term} & \text{term} & \text{term} \end{array}$$

An alternate formula for evaluating S_n is derived as follows. Take the equation

$$S_n = a + ar + ar^2 + \ldots + ar^{n-1}$$

and multiply both sides by r to obtain

$$rS_n = ar + ar^2 + \ldots + ar^{n-1} + ar^n$$

Now consider both equations:

$$S_n = a + ar + ar^2 + \ldots + ar^{n-1}$$
$$rS_n = \phantom{a + {}} ar + ar^2 + \ldots + ar^{n-1} + ar^n$$

Note that

$$S_n - rS_n = a - ar^n$$

Factoring both sides of this last equation gives us

$$S_n(1 - r) = a(1 - r^n)$$

Hence,

$$S_n = \frac{a(1 - r^n)}{1 - r}$$

Thus, for the geometric series

$$9 + 9 \cdot 2 + 9 \cdot 2^2 + 9 \cdot 2^3 + 9 \cdot 2^4 + 9 \cdot 2^5$$

$$\begin{array}{cccccc} \uparrow & \uparrow & \uparrow & \uparrow & \uparrow & \uparrow \\ \text{1st} & \text{2d} & \text{3d} & \text{4th} & \text{5th} & \text{6th} \\ \text{term} & \text{term} & \text{term} & \text{term} & \text{term} & \text{term} \end{array}$$

$a = 9$, $r = 2$, and $n = 6$. Then

$$\begin{aligned} S_6 &= \frac{a(1 - r^n)}{1 - r} \\ &= \frac{9(1 - 2^6)}{1 - 2} \\ &= \frac{9(1 - 64)}{1 - 2} \\ &= \frac{9(-63)}{-1} \\ &= 567 \end{aligned}$$

Note that if the series is added term by term, we will obtain the same result.

• **EXAMPLE 4-21** _____

Find the sum of the seven terms of the geometric series

$$5 + 5 \cdot 3 + 5 \cdot 3^2 + 5 \cdot 3^3 + 5 \cdot 3^4 + 5 \cdot 3^5 + 5 \cdot 3^6$$

Solution

Comparing this geometric series with the general form

$$a + ar + ar^2 + \ldots + ar^{n-1}$$

we have $a = 5$, $r = 3$, and $n = 7$. Hence,

$$S_7 = \frac{a(1 - r^n)}{1 - r}$$
$$= \frac{5(1 - 3^7)}{1 - 3}$$
$$= \frac{5(1 - 2187)}{1 - 3}$$
$$= \frac{5(-2186)}{-2}$$
$$= 5465$$

Annuities

An **annuity** is a series of equal payments made at equal intervals of time. Many everyday business transactions are annuities. Mortgage payments, premium payments on insurance plans, rental payments on a lease, and installment purchases are a few examples. In general, any series of equal payments made at equal intervals of time is an annuity. Each payment is called the **periodic payment,** or **period rent.** Periodic payment will be denoted by R. The total time during which these payments are made is called the **term** of the annuity.

Specifically, if a person deposits $100 at the end of each 6-month period for 2 years, then the periodic payment, R, is $100, the payment period is 6 months, and the term is 2 years (see Figure 4-24). Note that each payment is made *at the end* of the payment period. Such an annuity is called an **ordinary annuity.** If each payment were made *at the beginning* of the payment period, the annuity would be called an **annuity due.** In this section, we will begin with ordinary annuities. Annuities due will be covered later in the section.

Each payment, R, of an annuity earns compound interest. Here, and in Sections 4-4 through 4-5, we will discuss only those annuities for which

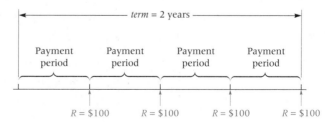

FIGURE 4-24

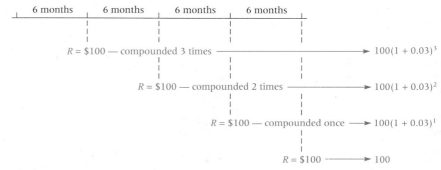

FIGURE 4-25

the payment period and conversion period coincide. Returning to our example, since each $100 payment is deposited semiannually, the interest will be compounded semiannually. We will use an interest rate of 6% compounded semiannually. Hence, $i = 3\%$ per conversion period.

The sum of all periodic payments, R, plus their interest is called the **total amount,** or **future value,** of the annuity. It will be denoted by S. To calculate the total amount, S, of an annuity, we must realize that each periodic payment, R, is made at a different point in time. Hence, each payment, R, earns compound interest for the duration of its term in the annuity. This is illustrated in Figure 4-25 for our previous annuity of $100 deposited semiannually for 2 years at an interest rate of 6% compounded semiannually. Studying Figure 4-25, note that the total amount, S, of the annuity is equal to the sum of the compound amounts of the payments of $100. Hence,

$$S = 100 + 100(1 + 0.03)^1 + 100(1 + 0.03)^2 + 100(1 + 0.03)^3$$

Observe that the expression for S is a geometric series with $a = 100$, $r = 1 + 0.03 = 1.03$, and $n = 4$. Using either Table 4 in Appendix C or a calculator, we evaluate the above.

$$S = 100 + 100(1.03) + 100(1.0609) + 100(1.09273)$$
$$= 100 + 103 + 106.09 + 109.27$$
$$= \$418.36$$

Now we will derive a general formula for the total amount (or future value), S, of an ordinary annuity. The time diagram of Figure 4-26 illustrates an ordinary annuity of n payments of R dollars each.

Thus, there are n payment periods (or conversion periods). As usual, $i =$ interest rate per conversion period. Studying Figure 4-26, we note that the total amount, S, of the annuity is equal to the sum of the compound amounts of the payments, R. Therefore,

$$S = R + R(1 + i) + R(1 + i)^2 + \ldots + R(1 + i)^{n-2} + R(1 + i)^{n-1}$$

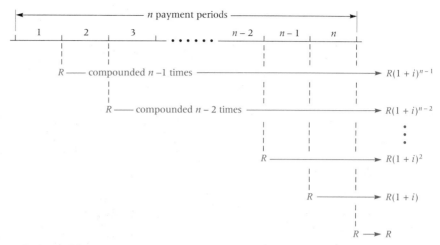

FIGURE 4-26

Observe that this expression is a geometric series of this form

$$a + ar + ar^2 . . . + ar^{n-1}$$

with $a = R$ and $r = 1 + i$. Recall that the sum of the n terms of this latter geometric series is given by the formula

$$\frac{a(1 - r^n)}{1 - r}$$

Substituting R for a and $1 + i$ for r yields

$$\frac{R[1 - (1 + i)^n]}{1 - (1 + i)}$$

which simplifies to

$$R\left[\frac{(1 + i)^n - 1}{i}\right]$$

Thus, the formula for the total amount, S, of an ordinary annuity of n payments of R dollars each is

$$S = R\left[\frac{(1 + i)^n - 1}{i}\right]$$

where i = interest rate per conversion period.

Appendix C, Table 6 lists the tabulations of the quantity $[(1 + i)^n - 1]/i$ for various values of i and n. For brevity, this quantity is usually denoted by the symbol $s_{\overline{n}|i}$, read "s angle n at i." This quantity can also be evaluated with a calculator. Thus, the preceding formula for the total amount, S, of an ordinary annuity is usually written

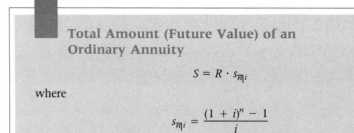

Total Amount (Future Value) of an Ordinary Annuity

$$S = R \cdot s_{\overline{n}|i}$$

where

$$s_{\overline{n}|i} = \frac{(1 + i)^n - 1}{i}$$

Returning to the previous example, where $R = \$100$, $i = 0.03$, and $n = 4$, the total amount is calculated as

$$S = R \cdot s_{\overline{4}|0.03}$$
$$\approx 100(4.183627)$$
$$\approx \$418.36$$

Using Appendix C, Table 6,
$s_{\overline{4}|0.03} \approx 4.183627$.
Using a calculator,
$s_{\overline{4}|0.03} = [(1.03)^4 - 1]/0.03 = 4.183627$.

• **EXAMPLE 4-22** _____

Mr. Haskins deposits $200 at the end of each quarter into a pension fund earning interest at 8% compounded quarterly.

a) Find the total amount at the end of 10 years.

b) How much interest was earned?

Solutions

Here we have $R = \$200$, $i = 8\%/4 = 2\% = 0.02$, and $n = 4(10) = 40$.

a) The calculation is

$$S = R \cdot s_{\overline{n}|i}$$
$$= 200 \cdot s_{\overline{40}|0.02}$$
$$\approx 200(60.401983)$$
$$\approx \$12,080.40$$

Using a calculator,
$s_{\overline{40}|0.02} = [(1.02)^{40} - 1]/0.02 \approx 60.401983$.

b) Mr. Haskins actually deposited 40 payments of $200 each, or 40($200) = $8000. Thus, the interest earned is

$$\$12,080.40 - \$8000.00 = \$4080.40$$

_____ •

Note that, for the annuities discussed up to this point, the payment intervals are coincident with the interest (or conversion) periods. Such an annuity where the payment intervals coincide with the interest (or conversion) periods is called a **simple annuity.** All of the annuities of this chapter are simple annuities until Section 4-6.

Annuity Due

As was stated earlier, if each payment, R, of an annuity is made *at the beginning* of the payment period, the annuity is called an **annuity due.** The

Ordinary annuity

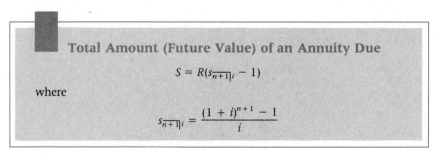

Annuity due

FIGURE 4-27

time diagram of Figure 4-27 compares an ordinary annuity and an annuity due.

Note that both annuities have n payments of R dollars each. However, since each payment of an annuity due is made at the beginning of the period, then each payment earns interest for one additional period. We now derive the formula for the total amount of an annuity due (see Figure 4-28).

Studying Figure 4-28, note that

$$S = R(1 + i) + R(1 + i)^2 + \cdots + R(1 + i)^{n-1} + R(1 + i)^n$$
$$= \underbrace{[R + R(1 + i) + R(1 + i)^2 + \cdots + R(1 + i)^n]}_{\text{geometric series}} - R$$

Applying the formula for the sum of a geometric series, we have

$$S = R\left[\frac{1 - (1 + i)^{n+1}}{1 - (1 + i)}\right] - R$$
$$= R\left[\frac{(1 + i)^{n+1} - 1}{i}\right] - R$$
$$= R \cdot s_{\overline{n+1}|i} - R$$
$$= R(s_{\overline{n+1}|i} - 1)$$

Thus, the formula for the total amount (or future value), S, of an annuity due is as follows.

Total Amount (Future Value) of an Annuity Due

$$S = R(s_{\overline{n+1}|i} - 1)$$

where

$$s_{\overline{n+1}|i} = \frac{(1 + i)^{n+1} - 1}{i}$$

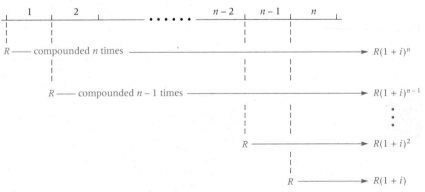

FIGURE 4-28

• **EXAMPLE 4-23** _____

Ms. Jones deposits $100 at the beginning of each quarter into a bank account earning interest at 8% compounded quarterly. Find the total amount at the end of 9 years.

Solution

Here, $R = \$100$, $i = 8\%/4 = 2\% = 0.02$, and $n = 4(9) = 36$. Therefore,

$$S = R(s_{\overline{n+1}|i} - 1)$$
$$= 100(s_{\overline{37}|0.02} - 1)$$
$$\approx 100(54.034255 - 1)$$
$$= 100(53.034255)$$
$$\approx \$5303.43$$

Using a calculator,
$s_{\overline{37}|0.02} = [(1.02)^{37} - 1]/0.02 \approx 54.034255$.

• **EXAMPLE 4-24**   **Ordinary Annuity Versus Annuity Due.**

A person deposits $300 per month into a bank account earning interest at 6% compounded monthly. Find the total amount at the end of 4 years if each payment is made:

a)   At the end of the month   **b)**   At the beginning of the month

Solutions

a)   If each payment is made at the end of the month, the annuity is an ordinary annuity, with $n = (12)(4) = 48$ and $i = 0.06/12 = 0.005$. The total amount of the annuity is determined as follows:

$$S = R \cdot s_{\overline{n}|i}$$
$$= 300\, s_{\overline{48}|0.005}$$
$$\approx 300(54.097832)$$
$$\approx \$16,229.35$$

Using a calculator,
$s_{\overline{48}|0.005} = [(1.005)^{48} - 1]/0.005 \approx 54.097832$.

b)   If each payment is made at the beginning of the month, the annuity is an annuity due, with $n = 48$, $n + 1 = 49$, and $i = 0.005$. The total amount is determined as follows:

$$S = R(s_{\overline{n+1}|i} - 1)$$
$$= 300(s_{\overline{49}|0.005} - 1)$$
$$\approx 300(55.368321 - 1)$$
$$= 300(54.368321)$$
$$\approx \$16,310.50$$

Using a calculator,
$s_{\overline{49}|0.005} = [(1.005)^{49} - 1]/0.005 \approx 55.368321$.

Note that, for the same interest rate and time period, the future value of the annuity due is greater than that of the corresponding ordinary annuity. This is because each deposit of the annuity due earns interest for an additional conversion period.

•

Exercises 4-3

For each of the following geometric series, find the sum of the indicated terms in two ways.

1. $2 + 2 \cdot 5 + 2 \cdot 5^2 + 2 \cdot 5^3$
2. $3 + 3 \cdot 2 + 3 \cdot 2^2 + 3 \cdot 2^3 + 3 \cdot 2^4 + 3 \cdot 2^5$
3. $7 + 7 \cdot 4 + 7 \cdot 4^2 + 7 \cdot 4^3 + 7 \cdot 4^4 + 7 \cdot 4^5 + 7 \cdot 4^6$

Find the total amount of each of the following ordinary annuities:

4. $100 each quarter for 5 years at 7% compounded quarterly
5. $1000 semiannually for 20 years at 6% compounded semiannually
6. $500 monthly for 4 years at 12% compounded monthly
7. $5000 annually for 20 years at 5% compounded annually
8. $900 monthly for 5 years at 6% compounded monthly
9. $1,500 quarterly for 6 years at 8% compounded quarterly

10-15. Repeat Exercises 4-9 under the assumption that each annuity is an annuity due.

16. A woman deposits $100 at the end of each quarter into a fund earning interest at 4% compounded quarterly.

    a) Find the total amount at the end of 12 years.
    b) How much interest was earned?

17. A man deposits $1500 at the end of each year into a pension fund earning interest at 5% compounded annually.

    a) Find the total amount at the end of 20 years.
    b) How much interest was earned?

18. Sally Smith deposits $1000 at the end of each 6-month period for 15 years into a fund earning interest at 6% compounded semiannually.

    a) Find the total amount at the end of 15 years.
    b) If Sally leaves the total amount in the fund for 5 more years without making any additional deposits, how much is her fund worth if it earns interest at 6% compounded semiannually?

19. For 4 years, a man deposits $100 into a retirement account at the beginning of each month. If the interest rate is 12% compounded monthly, how much is in the account after 4 years?

20. A woman deposits $1000 at the beginning of each quarter for 5 years. Each deposit earns interest at 12% compounded quarterly.

    a) Find the total amount at the end of 5 years.
    b) If the woman leaves the total amount in the fund for 4 more years without making any additional deposits, how much is her fund worth if the interest rate is 12% compounded quarterly?

21. Jane deposits $100 at the end of each month into a bank account earning interest at 12% compounded monthly. How much is in the account at the end of 4 years? Assume that no withdrawals have been made.

22. Referring to Exercise 21, suppose that Jane, after 4 years, deposits $200 at the end of each month for the next 3 years. If the $200 deposits earn interest at 12% compounded monthly and the accumulated amount of the $100 deposits also earns interest at 12% compounded monthly, how much does Jane have in her account at the end of 7 years (i.e., 7 years after she first opened the account)?

23. A man deposits $500 at the end of each 6-month period into a bank account for 4 years. At that time, his deposits are changed to $600 semiannually for the next 5 years. If all deposits earn interest at 12% compounded semiannually, how much is in the account at maturity?

24. Repeat Exercise 23 under the assumption that each payment is made at the beginning of the 6-month period.

Use a calculator and the following formula to solve problems 25-28.

$$s_{\overline{n}|i} = \frac{(1 + i)^n - 1}{i}$$

25. $s_{\overline{100}|0.015}$

26. $s_{\overline{360}|0.024}$

27. $s_{\overline{n}|i}$ for an interest rate of 20% compounded monthly for 10 years

28. $s_{\overline{n}|i}$ for an interest rate of 11% compounded monthly for 5 years

29. A person deposits $400 at the end of each month into a bank account that pays interest at the rate of 10% compounded monthly. How much is in the account after 7 years?

30. A person deposits $200 at the end of each month into a bank account that pays interest at 7% compounded monthly. How much is in the account after 5 years?

31. Repeat Exercise 29 under the assumption that the deposits are made at the beginning of each month.

32. Repeat Exercise 30 under the assumption that the deposits are made at the beginning of each month.

4-4 • PRESENT VALUE OF AN ANNUITY

The **present value of an annuity** is the sum of the present values of all the periodic payments R (see Figure 4-29).

Observing Figure 4-29, the present value, A, of an annuity is

$$A = R(1 + i)^{-n} + R(1 + i)^{-(n-1)} + R(1 + i)^{-(n-2)} + \ldots$$
$$+ R(1 + i)^{-2} + R(1 + i)^{-1}$$

Thus, an annuity of R dollars per period for n periods is worth A dollars now. In other words, a lump-sum investment of A dollars now will provide payments of R dollars per period for the next n periods.

The preceding formula for A may be simplified. Multiplying the right-hand side by $(1 + i)^n/(1 + i)^n$ yields

$$A = \frac{R + R(1 + i) + R(1 + i)^2 + \cdots + R(1 + i)^{n-2} + R(1 + i)^{n-1}}{(1 + i)^n}$$

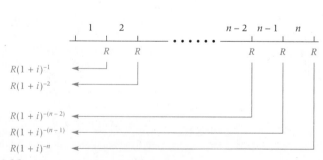

FIGURE 4-29

Note that the numerator is a geometric series. Applying the formula for its sum, we obtain

$$A = \frac{R\left[\dfrac{(1 + i)^n - 1}{i}\right]}{(1 + i)^n}$$

$$= R\left[\frac{1 - (1 + i)^{-n}}{i}\right]$$

Thus, the formula for the present value, A, of an ordinary annuity of n payments of R dollars each is

$$A = R\left[\frac{1 - (1 + i)^{-n}}{i}\right]$$

where i = interest rate per conversion period.

Appendix C, Table 7 lists the tabulations of the quantity $[1 - (1 + i)^{-n}]/i$ for various values of i and n. For brevity, this quantity will be denoted by the symbol $a_{\overline{n}|i}$, read "a angle n at i." This quantity can also be evaluated with a calculator. Thus, the preceding formula for the present value, A, of an ordinary annuity may be written as follows.

Present Value of an Ordinary Annuity

$$A = R \cdot a_{\overline{n}|i}$$

where

$$a_{\overline{n}|i} = \frac{1 - (1 + i)^{-n}}{i}$$

• **EXAMPLE 4-25**

A parent wishes to provide for quarterly payments of $400 each for the next 4 years. The payments will be made at the end of each quarter to a daughter who will be attending college. How much should the parent invest at 8% compounded quarterly?

Solution

The answer is the present value, A, of the annuity. Note that $R = \$400$, $i = 8\%/4 = 2\% = 0.02$, and $n = 4(4) = 16$. Thus,

$$A = R \cdot a_{\overline{n}|i}$$
$$= 400 \cdot a_{\overline{16}|0.02}$$
$$\approx 400(13.577709)$$
$$\approx \$5431.08$$

Using Appendix C, Table 7, $a_{\overline{16}|0.02} \approx 13.577709$. Using a calculator, $a_{\overline{16}|0.02} = [1 - (1.02)^{-16}]/0.02 \approx 13.577709$

Thus, the parent's investment of $5431.08 will provide for 16 payments of $400, or 16($400) = $6400, over the next 4 years.

• **EXAMPLE 4-26**

This problem is adapted from one that appeared on a past Uniform CPA Examination. Cause Company is planning to invest in a machine with a useful life of 5 years and no salvage value. The machine is expected to produce cash flow from operations, net of income taxes, of $20,000 in each of the 5 years. Cause's expected rate of return is 10% compounded annually. How much will the machine cost?

Solution

We seek the present value of this annuity. Here $i = 0.10$, $n = 5$, and $R = 20,000$. Thus,

$$A = R \cdot a_{\overline{n}|i}$$
$$= 20,000 \cdot a_{\overline{5}|0.10}$$
$$\approx 20,000(3.790787)$$
$$\approx \$75,815.74$$

Using a calculator,
$a_{\overline{5}|0.10} = (1 - (1.10)^{-5})/0.10 \approx 3.790787$

Thus, the machine cost $75,815.74.

We should also understand that the present value of an annuity, A, if invested for the duration of the annuity, will yield the same total amount, S, as the annuity. In other words, if Mr. Johnson deposits n payments of R dollars each and Mr. Thomas deposits a lump sum of A dollars now, then after n conversion periods, both will have the same total amount (assuming that the interest rate, i, is the same for both). The time diagrams of Figure 4-30 illustrate this example.

Observe that if we equate the formulas for the total amount, S, we have

$$A(1 + i)^n = R\left[\frac{(1 + i)^n - 1}{i}\right]$$

Solving for A yields

$$A = R\left[\frac{1 - (1 + i)^{-n}}{i}\right]$$

Note that this is the formula for the present value of an annuity.

• **EXAMPLE 4-27** _____

Henry deposits $100 at the end of each month for 3 years into a savings account. If Cindy wishes to have the same amount in her account at the end of 3 years, what single sum of money should she deposit now? Assume that both accounts earn interest at 6% compounded monthly.

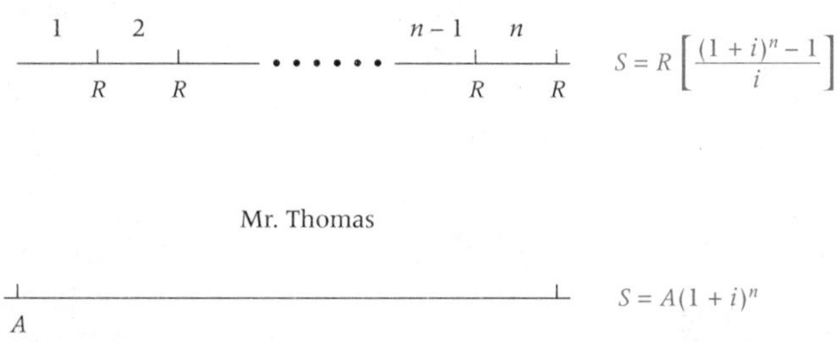

Mr. Johnson

$$S = R\left[\frac{(1 + i)^n - 1}{i}\right]$$

Mr. Thomas

$$S = A(1 + i)^n$$

FIGURE 4-30

Solution

The answer is the present value, A, of the annuity. Note that $R = \$100$, $i = 6\%/12 = (1/2)\% = 0.005$, and $n = 12(3) = 36$. Thus,

$$A = R \cdot a_{\overline{n}|i}$$
$$= 100 \cdot a_{\overline{36}|0.005}$$
$$\approx 100(32.871016)$$
$$\approx \$3287.10$$

• **EXAMPLE 4-28   Leases.** _____

A corporation can either lease a machine with a 5-year useful life for $2000 per year or buy it for a lump sum of $8000.

a) If money is worth 7% compounded annually, which alternative is preferable?
b) If money is worth 8% compounded annually, which alternative is preferable?

Solutions

a) The leasing alternative involves an annuity with $R = \$2000$, $n = 5$, and $i = 0.07$. The present value of this annuity is

$$A = R \cdot a_{\overline{n}|i}$$
$$= 2000 \cdot a_{\overline{5}|0.07}$$
$$\approx 2000(4.100197)$$
$$\approx \$8200.39$$

Since this amount exceeds the purchase price, purchasing the machine is cheaper.

b) In this case,

$$A = R \cdot a_{\overline{n}|i}$$
$$= 2000 \cdot a_{\overline{5}|0.08}$$
$$\approx 2000(3.992710)$$
$$\approx \$7985.42$$

Since this amount is less than the purchase price, leasing the machine is cheaper.

• **EXAMPLE 4-29   Capital Expenditure Analysis.** _____

A corporation wants to modernize its equipment in order to reduce labor costs. It has a chance of purchasing two machines for a certain assembly operation. Machine A costs $7000, will save $1600 annually, and has a useful life of 6 years. Machine B costs $9000, will save $1900 annually, and has a useful life of 7 years. If money is worth 8% compounded annually, which machine should the company buy?

Solution

Machine A saves $1600 annually for 6 years. The present value of this annuity at 8% compounded annually is

$$A = R \cdot a_{\overline{n}|i}$$
$$= 1600 \cdot a_{\overline{6}|0.08}$$
$$\approx 1600(4.622880)$$
$$\approx \$7396.61$$

Thus, the annual savings of \$1600 for 6 years are equivalent to a lump-sum savings of \$7396.61 now. Since Machine A costs \$7000, the net saving is

$$\$7396.61 - \$7000 = \$396.61$$

Machine B saves \$1900 annually for 7 years. The present value of this annuity at 8% compounded annually is

$$
\begin{aligned}
A &= R \cdot a_{\overline{n}|i} \\
&= 1900 \cdot a_{\overline{7}|0.08} \\
&\approx 1900(5.206370) \\
&\approx \$9892.10
\end{aligned}
$$

Thus, the annual savings of \$1900 for 7 years are equivalent to a lump-sum savings of \$9892.10 now. Since Machine B costs \$9000, the net saving is

$$\$9892.10 - \$9000 = \$892.10$$

Since Machine B has the larger net saving, this is the one the corporation should buy.

Present Value of an Annuity Due

The formula for the present value of an annuity due is derived by observing the time diagram of Figure 4-31 and equating the total amounts. Thus, we have

$$
\begin{aligned}
A(1 + i)^n &= R\left[\frac{(1 + i)^{n+1} - 1}{i} - 1\right] \quad \text{Replace 1 with } \frac{i}{i}, \text{ and} \\
&\text{then add the numerators} \\
&= R\left[\frac{(1 + i)^{n+1} - 1 - i}{i}\right] \quad \text{to obtain} \\
&= R\left[\frac{(1 + i)^{n+1} - (1 + i)}{i}\right]
\end{aligned}
$$

Dividing both sides by $(1 + i)^n$ yields

$$
\begin{aligned}
A &= R\left[\frac{(1 + i) - (1 + i)^{-(n-1)}}{i}\right] \\
&= R\left[1 + \frac{1 - (1 + i)^{-(n-1)}}{i}\right]
\end{aligned}
$$

$$
\begin{aligned}
&\frac{1}{i} + \frac{i}{i} - \frac{(1 + i)^{-(n-1)}}{i} \\
&= 1 + \frac{1}{i} - \frac{(1 + i)^{-(n-1)}}{i} \\
&= 1 + \frac{1 - (1 + i)^{-(n-1)}}{i}
\end{aligned}
$$

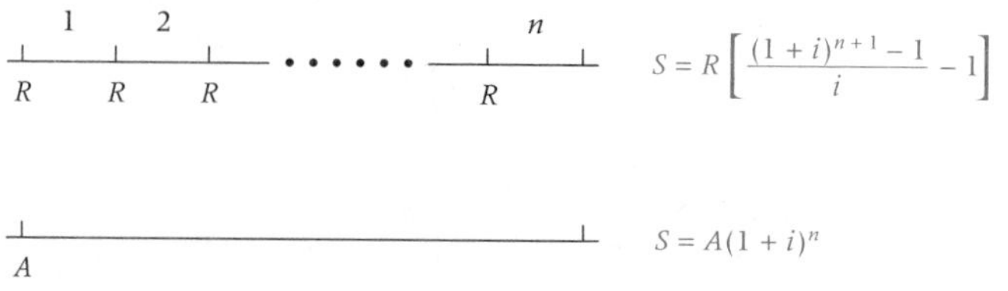

$$S = R\left[\frac{(1 + i)^{n+1} - 1}{i} - 1\right]$$

$$S = A(1 + i)^n$$

FIGURE 4-31

Since

$$\frac{1 - (1 + i)^{-(n-1)}}{i} = a_{\overline{n-1}|i}$$

then the present value of an annuity due is found by the following formula.

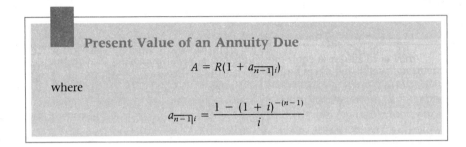

Present Value of an Annuity Due

$$A = R(1 + a_{\overline{n-1}|i})$$

where

$$a_{\overline{n-1}|i} = \frac{1 - (1 + i)^{-(n-1)}}{i}$$

• **EXAMPLE 4-30** _____

Find the present value of an annuity due of $1000 quarterly for 5 years at 8% compounded quarterly.

Solution

Here we have $R = \$1000$, $i = 8\%/4 = 2\% = 0.02$, and $n = 4(5) = 20$. Thus,

$$\begin{aligned}
A &= R(1 + a_{\overline{n-1}|i}) \\
&= 1000(1 + a_{\overline{19}|0.02}) \\
&\approx 1000(1 + 15.678462) \\
&= 1000(16.678462) \\
&\approx \$16{,}678.46
\end{aligned}$$

Using a calculator,
$a_{\overline{19}|0.02} = [1 - (1.02)^{-19}]/0.02 \approx 15.678462.$

• **EXAMPLE 4-31   Ordinary Annuity Versus Annuity Due.**

Determine the present value of an annuity of $300 per month for 4 years at an interest rate of 6% compounded monthly if each payment is made

a)   At the end of the month   **b)**   At the beginning of the month

Recall that we determined the future values of this annuity in Example 4-24.

Solutions

a)   If each payment is made at the end of the month, the annuity is an ordinary annuity, with $n = (12)(4) = 48$ and $i = 0.06/12 = 0.005$. The present value is determined as follows:

$$\begin{aligned}
A &= Ra_{\overline{n}|i} \\
&= 300\, a_{\overline{48}|0.005} \\
&\approx 300(42.580318) \\
&\approx \$12{,}774.10
\end{aligned}$$

Using a calculator,
$a_{\overline{48}|0.005} = [1 - (1.005)^{-48}]/0.005 \approx 42.580318.$

b)   If each payment is made at the beginning of the month, the annuity is an annuity due, with $n = 48$, $n - 1 = 47$, and $i = 0.005$. The present value is determined as follows:

$$A = R(a_{\overline{n-1}|}\,i + 1)$$
$$= R(a_{\overline{47}|0.005} + 1)$$
$$\approx 300(41.793219 + 1)$$
$$= 300(42.793219)$$
$$\approx \$12{,}837.97$$

Using a calculator,
$a_{\overline{47}|0.005} = [1 - (1.005)^{-47}]/0.005 \approx 41.793219.$

Note that for the same interest rate and time period, the present value of an annuity due is greater than that of the corresponding ordinary annuity. This is because, in terms of a time diagram, each payment of an annuity due is brought back one less conversion period than that of an ordinary annuity.

We now provide a summary of the formulas used in the application of compound interest. Since it is most helpful to relate each formula to a time diagram, we have provided such in the following summary box. Thus, we urge you to visualize and relate the associated time diagram to each formula.

The summary box is followed by a box providing a problem-solving procedure for approaching mathematics of finance problems. As we have proceeded through this chapter, we have been given more and more formulas for various financial problems. Thus, at this point, when we begin to solve a problem, we need a procedure to guide our thinking in selecting an appropriate formula (or formulas) to solve the problem. Since it is difficult to provide a step-by-step procedure for solving all mathematics of finance problems, the boxed procedure is applicable to the types of problems that occur most often.

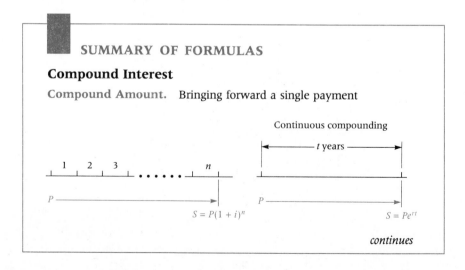

SUMMARY OF FORMULAS

Compound Interest

Compound Amount.   Bringing forward a single payment

Continuous compounding

t years

1   2   3 . . . . . n

P

$S = P(1 + i)^n$

P

$S = Pe^{rt}$

continues

SUMMARY OF FORMULAS—*Continued*

Present Value.   Bringing back a single payment

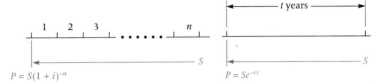

$$P = S(1 + i)^{-n}$$

$$P = Se^{-rt}$$

Future Value of Annuity.   Bringing forward a series of equal payments

Ordinary Annuity

   Each payment occurs at the end of the payment period.

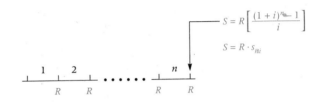

$$S = R\left[\frac{(1 + i)^{n} - 1}{i}\right]$$

$$S = R \cdot s_{\overline{n}|i}$$

Annuity Due

   Each payment occurs at the beginning of the payment period.

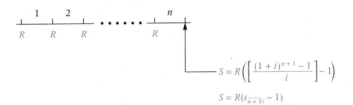

$$S = R\left(\left[\frac{(1 + i)^{n + 1} - 1}{i}\right] - 1\right)$$

$$S = R(s_{\overline{n + 1}|i} - 1)$$

Present Value of an Annuity.   Bringing back a series of equal payments

Ordinary Annuity

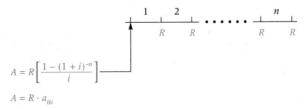

$$A = R\left[\frac{1 - (1 + i)^{-n}}{i}\right]$$

$$A = R \cdot a_{\overline{n}|i}$$

continues

210 • CHAPTER 4 MATHEMATICS OF FINANCE

SUMMARY OF FORMULAS—*Continued*

Annuity Due

$$A = R\left(\left[\frac{1-(1+i)^{-(n-1)}}{i}\right]+1\right)$$

$$A = R(a_{\overline{n-1}|i}+1)$$

To Solve Problems Involving Compound Interest

1. Draw a time diagram of the problem. Determine the values of i and n.
2. Determine whether the problem involves a single payment or a series of equal payments.

Single Payment. If only a single payment is involved, you should be thinking of using the following formulas:

		Continuous Compounding
Future value	$S = P(1 + i)^n$	$S = Pe^{rt}$
Present value	$P = S(1 + i)^{-n}$	$P = Se^{-rt}$

Series of Equal Payments. If a series of equal payments is involved, you should be thinking of using the following annuity formulas:

	Ordinary Annuity	*Annuity Due*
Future value	$S = R \cdot s_{\overline{n}|i}$	$S = R(s_{\overline{n+1}|i} - 1)$
Present value	$A = R \cdot a_{\overline{n}|i}$	$A = R(a_{\overline{n-1}|i} + 1)$

3. Determine whether the solution to the problem involves a future value or a present value and then focus on the appropriate formulas. Occasionally, more than one formula may have to be used to solve the problem.

Exercises 4-4

Find the present value of each of the following ordinary annuities.

1. $3000 quarterly for 6 years at 8% compounded quarterly
2. $10,000 annually for 4 years at 5% compounded annually
3. $2000 semiannually for 10 years at 6% compounded semiannually
4. $6000 monthly for 3 years at 12% compounded monthly
5. $5,000 quarterly for 9 years at 12% compounded quarterly
6. $2,000 monthly for 3 years at 6% compounded monthly

7-12. Repeat Exercises 1-6 under the assumption that each annuity is an annuity due.

13. Maria Lopez wishes to provide for a semiannual payment of $2000 at the end of each 6-month period for the next 10 years. The payments will be made to her daughter who will be attending college and medical school. How much money should Maria invest now at 10% compounded semiannually?

14. Mr. Wang buys a car by agreeing to pay $500 at the end of each quarter for the next 5 years. This includes interest at 12% compounded quarterly. If instead of financing the car Mr. Johnson decides to pay cash now, how much should he pay?

15. Holly deposits $400 at the end of each quarter into a savings account. If Sara wishes to have the same amount in her account at the end of 5 years, what single sum of money should she deposit now? Assume that both accounts earn interest at 8% compounded quarterly.

16. A company is planning a project that will generate a cash inflow of $10,000 a year for 8 years. If the company wants a rate of return on its invested capital of at least 10% compounded annually, what should be the maximum amount invested in this project now?

17. An investment contract promises to pay its holder $500 at the beginning of each month for 3 years. If one wishes to earn 12% compounded monthly, how much should be paid for this contract now?

18. A certain investment contract promises to pay $1000 at the end of each quarter for the next 7 years. If we wish to buy this investment contract and earn 12% compounded quarterly, how much should we pay for it now?

19. Repeat Exercise 18 under the assumption that the payments are made at the beginning of each quarter.

20. Mr. Cambra wishes to provide for payments of $400 at the end of each quarter to his son for the next 5 years. What sum should be deposited now at 8% compounded quarterly to attain Mr. Cambra's objective?

21. Repeat Exercise 20 under the assumption that the payments are made at the beginning of each quarter.

Use a calculator and the following formula to solve problems 22-25.

$$a_{\overline{n}|i} = \frac{1 - \dfrac{1}{(1 + i)^n}}{i}$$

22. $a_{\overline{100}|0.016}$

23. $a_{\overline{365}|0.024}$

24. $a_{\overline{n}|i}$ for an interest rate of 15% compounded monthly for 10 years

25. $a_{\overline{n}|i}$ for an interest rate of 10% compounded monthly for 20 years

26. Parents of a college freshman wish to set up a fund that will pay $400 per month (at the end of the month) to their daughter for 4 years. How much should the parents deposit now if the fund earns interest at 5% compounded monthly?

27. Parents of a college freshman wish to set up a fund that will pay $600 per month (at the end of the month) to their son for 4 years. How much should the parents deposit now if the fund earns interest at 7% compounded monthly?

28. Repeat Exercise 26 assuming an annuity due.

29. Repeat Exercise 27 assuming an annuity due.

30. Repeat Exercise 26 assuming that the payments are to continue for 6 years.

31. Repeat Exercise 27 assuming that the payments are to continue for 6 years.

32. *This problem is adapted from one that appeared on a past Uniform CPA Examination.* On January 1, 19xx, Liberty Company sold a machine to Bell Corporation in an "arms length" transaction. Bell signed a noninterest-bearing note requiring payment of $20,000 annually for 10 years. The first payment was made on January 1, 19xx. The prevailing rate of interest for this type of note at the date of issuance was 12% (compounded annually). Liberty should record the above sale in January 19xx at what value?

4-5 • SINKING FUNDS AND AMORTIZATION

Often a person decides to accumulate a sum of money by making periodic deposits into a fund. At the end of a specified time period, the deposits plus the interest earned equal the desired accumulated amount. Such a fund is called a **sinking fund.**

Sinking Funds

As an example, consider a contractor foreseeing the need for a new truck 4 years from now. The price of the truck is forecasted to be $20,000. The contractor wishes to accumulate this amount by setting aside semiannual payments of R dollars each for 4 years. Each payment of this sinking fund earns interest at 10% compounded semiannually. The contractor must determine the semiannual payment, R. This situation is illustrated by the time diagram of Figure 4-32.

Since the semiannual payments constitute an annuity with a total amount of $20,000, then

$$S = R \cdot s_{\overline{n}|i}$$
$$20,000 = R \cdot s_{\overline{8}|0.05}$$

Solving for R yields

$$R = \frac{20,000}{s_{\overline{8}|0.05}}$$
$$\approx \frac{20,000}{9.549109}$$
$$\approx \$2094.44$$

Thus, the series of semiannual payments, $R = \$2094.44$, plus interest will accumulate to $S = \$20,000$. Note that the contractor will make eight payments of $2094.44 each, or 8($2094.44) = $16,755.52. Therefore, the interest earned is

$$\$20,000 - \$16,755.52 = \$3244.48$$

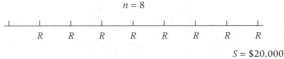

FIGURE 4-32

Sinking Fund Schedule

The accumulation of value in a sinking fund is illustrated by a sinking fund schedule. Such a schedule for the above problem is given in Table 4-1. The *interest* for a given period is the product of i and the total value of the fund at the beginning of the period, as is illustrated in Table 4-1. The *total* value of the fund for a given period is the sum of its payment, interest, and the previous period's total.

Studying the sinking fund schedule of Table 4-1, note that the interest for each period is determined by multiplying $i = 0.05$ times the previous period's total. Observe that the total interest is $3244.53. The $0.05 discrepancy from the previous calculation is due to round-off error.

TABLE 4-1 **Sinking fund schedule**

Payment number	Payment	Interest	Total
1	$2,094.44	$ 0	$2,094.44
2	2,094.44	104.72	4,293.60
3	2,094.44	214.68	6,602.72
4	2,094.44	330.14	9,027.30
5	2,094.44	451.37	11,573.11
6	2,094.44	578.66	14,246.21
7	2,094.44	712.31	17,052.96
8	2,094.44	852.65	20,000.05
		$3,244.53	

2094.44(0.05) = $104.72

4293.60(0.05) = $214.68

• **EXAMPLE 4-32**

A business executive wishes to set aside semiannual payments to purchase machinery 2 years from now. The machinery's estimated cost is $5000. Each payment earns interest at 12% compounded semiannually.

a) Find the semiannual payment.
b) Find the total interest earned.
c) Prepare a sinking fund schedule similar to that of Table 4-1.

Solutions

a) Here, $S = \$5000$, $i = 12\%/2 = 6\% = 0.06$, and $n = 2(2) = 4$. We must determine R. Since

$$S = R \cdot s_{\overline{n}|i}$$

then

$$5000 = R \cdot s_{\overline{4}|0.06}$$

Solving for R yields

$$R = \frac{5000}{s_{\overline{4}|0.06}}$$

$$\approx \frac{5000}{4.374616}$$

$$\approx \$1142.96$$

b) The business executive will make four payments of $1142.96 each, or 4($1142.96) = $4571.84. Thus, the interest earned is

$$\$5000.00 - \$4571.84 = \$428.16$$

c) The sinking fund schedule is shown in Table 4-2. Observing this sinking fund schedule, note that the interest for each period is determined by multiplying $i = 0.06$ times the previous period's total. Here, the total interest is $428.17. The $0.01 discrepancy from the previous calculation is due to round-off error.

TABLE 4-2

Payment number	Payment	Interest	Total
1	$1142.96	$ 0	$1142.96
2	1142.96	68.58	2354.50
3	1142.96	141.27	3638.73
4	1142.96	218.32	5000.01
		$428.17	

Amortization

Often a loan is repaid by a series of equal payments made at equal intervals of time—an annuity. The *amount of the loan* is the *present value of the annuity*. A portion of each payment is applied against the principal, and the remainder is applied against the interest. When a loan is repaid by an annuity, it is said to be **amortized.**

Consider a person borrowing $7000. The loan plus interest is to be repaid in equal quarterly installments made at the end of each quarter during a 2-year interval. The interest rate is 16% compounded quarterly. We must determine the quarterly payment, R. This situation is illustrated by the time diagram of Figure 4-33.

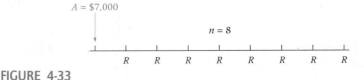

FIGURE 4-33

Since the quarterly payments constitute an annuity with a present value of $7000, then

$$A = R \cdot a_{\overline{n}|i}$$
$$7000 = R \cdot a_{\overline{8}|0.04}$$

Solving for R yields

$$R = \frac{7000}{a_{\overline{8}|0.04}}$$
$$\approx \frac{7000}{6.732745}$$
$$\approx \$1039.69$$

Thus, the borrower will make eight payments of $1039.69 each, or 8($1039.69) = $8317.52, to repay the $7000 loan. Thus, the interest is

$$\$8317.52 - \$7000.00 = \$1317.52$$

Amortization Schedule

The amortization of a loan on a payment-by-payment basis is illustrated in an amortization schedule. Such a schedule for the above problem is given in Table 4-3.

Studying the amortization schedule of Table 4-3, note that the interest for each period is determined by multiplying $i = 0.04$ times the previous period's balance. The amount of **principal reduction** for a period is the difference between the payment, R, and the interest for that period. Each entry in the *balance* column is the difference between the previous period's balance and the principal reduction for the given period. Note, in Table 4-3, that the last payment is increased by $0.04 in order to reduce the final balance to zero.

We also note that the balance of the loan after a given payment has been made can be determined by finding the present value of the remain-

TABLE 4-3   Amortization schedule

Payment number	Payment R	interest	principal reduction	Balance
0				$7000.00
1	$1039.69	$280.00	$759.69	$6240.31
2	1039.69	249.61	790.08	5450.23
3	1039.69	218.01	821.68	4628.55
4	1039.69	185.14	854.55	3774.00
5	1039.69	150.96	888.73	2885.27
6	1039.69	115.41	924.28	1960.99
7	1039.69	78.44	961.25	999.74
8	1039.73	39.99	999.74	0.00
		$1317.56		

7000(0.04)
6240.31(0.04)

ing annuity. To illustrate, the balance of the loan of Table 4-3 after the fifth payment is determined by computing the present value of the remaining three payments. Hence,

$$\text{balance} = 1039.69 a_{\overline{3}|0.04}$$
$$\approx 1039.69(2.775091)$$
$$\approx \$2,885.23$$

Notice that this agrees with the balance after the fifth payment given in Table 4-3 except for a \$0.04 roundoff error.

• **EXAMPLE 4-33**   **Mortgage: Comparing Terms.** _____

A couple plans to purchase a home for \$200,000. They have put \$50,000 down and will obtain a mortgage for \$150,000 at an interest rate of 10.5% compounded monthly. They must decide whether to apply for either a 30-year or a 15-year mortgage. Find the monthly payment and the total interest for both a 30-year and a 15-year mortgage at an interest rate of 10.5% compounded monthly. Compare the total interest paid for each mortgage.

Solution

For either mortgage, $i = 0.105/12 = 0.00875$.

30-year mortgage

$$n = (12)(30) = 360 \qquad \text{and} \qquad a_{\overline{360}|0.00875} = 109.3207656$$

Since the amount of the mortgage is the present value of the annuity, then the monthly payment is determined as follows:

$$A = R \cdot a_{\overline{n}|i}$$
$$150{,}000 = R \cdot a_{\overline{360}|0.00875}$$

Solving for R, we obtain

$$R \approx \frac{150{,}000}{109.3207656} \approx \$1372.11 \qquad \text{Monthly payment}$$

With this mortgage, the couple would make 360 payments of \$1372.11 each, or 360(\$1372.11) = \$493,959.60. Thus, the total interest is

$$\$493{,}959.60 - \$150{,}000.00 = \$343{,}959.60 \qquad \text{Total interest}$$

15-year mortgage

$$n = (12)(15) = 180 \qquad \text{and} \qquad a_{\overline{180}|0.00875} = 90.4650781$$

Again, since the amount of the mortgage is the present value of the annuity, then the monthly payment is determined as follows:

$$A = R \cdot a_{\overline{n}|i}$$
$$150{,}000 = R \cdot a_{\overline{180}|0.00875}$$

Solving for R, we obtain

$$R \approx \frac{150{,}000}{90.4650781} \approx \$1658.10 \qquad \text{Monthly payment}$$

With this mortgage, the couple would make 180 payments of \$1658.10 each, or 180(\$1658.10) = \$298,458.00. Thus, the total interest is

$$\$298{,}458 - \$150{,}000 = \$148{,}458 \qquad \text{Total interest}$$

Comparison

1. Note that the monthly payment for the 15-year mortgage is only $1658.10 − $1372.11 = $285.99 more than that for the 30-year mortgage. Thus, reducing the term of a mortgage by one-half does not double the monthly payment. Note that the monthly payment for the 15-year mortgage is much less than twice the monthly payment for the 30-year mortgage.

2. Note that the total interest for the 15-year mortgage is $148,458 versus $343,959.60 for the 30-year mortgage for a savings of $343,959.60 − $148,458.00 = $195,501.60.

SUMMARY

Sinking Fund Versus Amortization

1. *Sinking fund.* The future value of an annuity is usually given. The problem usually involves determining the periodic payment, R, by using the formula

$$S = R \cdot s_{\overline{n}|i}$$

and then solving for R to obtain

$$R = \frac{S}{s_{\overline{n}|i}}$$

2. *Amortization.* The present value of an annuity is usually given. The problem usually involves determining the periodic payment, R, by using the formula

$$A = R \cdot a_{\overline{n}|i}$$

and then solving for R to obtain

$$R = \frac{A}{a_{\overline{n}|i}}$$

Add-On Interest

Some lending institutions compute the periodic payment necessary to amortize a loan by the **add-on-interest method.** When using this method, the lender determines the periodic payment necessary to amortize the loan by the following procedure:

1. Compute the simple interest on the original loan amount (the principal) for the term of the loan.
2. Add the interest to the original loan amount.
3. Divide the resulting sum by the number of payments to obtain the periodic payment.

As an example, we consider the $7000 2-year loan with its amortization schedule appearing in Table 4-3. Recall, from Table 4-3 that, at 16% compounded quarterly, the periodic payment necessary to amortize this loan was $1039.69. We now compute the periodic payment by the add-on-interest method. We will use the same interest rate of 16%. However, we will use simple interest since the add-on-interest method uses simple interest. Thus, we compute the periodic payment as follows:

Step 1 Compute the simple interest.

$$I = Prt = 7000(0.16)(2) = \$2240$$

Step 2 Add the interest to the principal.

$$S = P + I = 7000 + 2240 = \$9240$$

Step 3 Divide the result of step 2 by the number of payments.

$$\text{Periodic payment} = 9240/8 = \$1155$$

Note that the periodic payment, $1155, is larger than $1039.69, the payment computed by using the annuity formula at 16% compounded quarterly. Thus, the interest rate on this loan, using the add-on-interest method, is greater than 16% compounded quarterly.

This is because the add-on-interest method entails computation of interest on the original loan amount for the entire term of the loan despite the fact that payments will begin, in this example, 3 months after the loan was granted. In contrast, the method using the annuity formula, $A = R \cdot a_{\overline{n}|i}$, computes interest only on the unpaid balance of the loan. In other words, the lender pays interest on the full loan amount only for the first payment period, and then the balance of the loan is reduced by the principal reduction portion of the periodic payment, so that interest for the second payment period is computed on a smaller balance. This process continues, with a smaller portion of each successive payment allocated to interest.

Exercises 4-5

Determine the periodic payment for each of the following sinking funds. Assume an ordinary annuity.

1. $S = \$35,000$; quarterly payments for 5 years; interest rate is 8% compounded quarterly

2. $S = \$18,000$; monthly payments for 4 years; interest rate is 12% compounded monthly.

3. $S = \$10,000$; semiannual payments for 6 years; interest rate is 6% compounded semiannually

4. $S = \$20,000$; annual payments for 9 years; interest rate is 7% compounded annually

5. $S = \$28,000$; annual payments for 6 years; interest rate is 9% compounded annually

6. $S = \$50,000$; quarterly payments for 5 years; interest rate is 6% compounded quarterly

 7. $S = \$145,000$; monthly payments for 10 years; interest rate is 10.2% compounded monthly

8. $S = \$270,000$; monthly payments for 20 years; interest rate is 9.42% compounded monthly

Determine the periodic payment necessary to amortize each of the following loans. Assume an ordinary annuity.

9. $30,000 loan; annual payments for 5 years; interest rate is 9% compounded annually

10. $25,000 loan; quarterly payments for 7 years; interest rate is 7% compounded quarterly

11. $95,000 loan; monthly payments for 5 years; interest rate is 6% compounded monthly

12. $130,000 loan; monthly payments for 6 years; interest rate is 12% compounded monthly

13. $80,000 loan; semiannual payments for 10 years; interest rate is 8% compounded semiannually

14. $150,000 loan; annual payments for 20 years; interest rate is 9% compounded annually

15. $230,000 mortgage; monthly payments for 25 years; interest rate is 10.68% compounded monthly

16. $130,000 mortgage; monthly payments for 30 years; interest rate is 9.12% compounded monthly

17. A grocer anticipates a need for a new freezer 5 years from now. The price is expected to be $10,000. If the grocer wishes to accumulate this amount by setting aside quarterly payments earning interest at 8% compounded quarterly for the next 5 years, how much should be set aside at the end of each quarter?

18. A person wishes to accumulate $20,000 in 20 years by setting aside annual payments earning interest at 5% compounded annually. How much should be set aside at the end of each year?

19. Six years from now, Gerry Grumble must pay Brian Broker $5000. Gerry wishes to set aside into a bank account, at the end of each 6-month period, a payment earning interest at 6% compounded semiannually. How much should each payment be in order to retire the debt in 6 years?

20. Wan Li borrows $10,000. This loan will be repaid by a monthly installment at the end of each month over the next 4 years. If the interest rate is 12% compounded monthly, what is Wan's monthly payment?

21. Tom Thrift buys a house with a purchase price of $80,000. He makes a down payment of $20,000 and finances the remainder with a mortgage requiring a quarterly payment at the end of each quarter for the next 12 years. If the interest rate is 8% compounded quarterly, what is Tom's quarterly payment?

22. A debt of $20,000 is to be amortized over 10 years by a payment at the end of each 6-month period. If the interest rate is 6% compounded semiannually, how much is each payment?

23. A payment is made at the end of each year for 4 years into a sinking fund with a future value of $60,000. Each payment earns interest at 10% compounded annually.

    a) Determine the annual payment.
    b) Determine the total interest earned.
    c) Prepare a sinking fund schedule similar to that of Table 4-1.

24. A company sets aside a payment at the end of each 6-month period to provide for the replacement of equipment 3 years from now. Each payment earns interest at 10% compounded semiannually, and the equipment's projected cost is $20,000.

    a) Find the semiannual payment.
    b) Find the total interest earned.
    c) Prepare a sinking fund schedule similar to that of Table 4-1.

25. A 5-year mortgage for $90,000 is amortized with annual payments (at the end of the year). The interest rate is 9% compounded annually.
   a)   Determine the annual payment.
   b)   Determine the total interest.
   c)   Prepare an amortization schedule similar to that of Table 4-3.
   d)   What is the balance after 2 years?

26. Maria Diaz has purchased a car for $10,000. She has made a down payment of $4000 and will finance the balance by making a payment at the end of each quarter for 2 years. The interest rate is 12% compounded quarterly.
   a)   Find the quarterly payment.
   b)   How much will Maria pay out for the loan after 2 years, and what will the total interest be?
   c)   What is the balance after 1¼ years?
   d)   Prepare an amortization schedule similar to that of Table 4-3.

27. A 30-year mortgage for $100,000 is amortized with monthly payments (at the end of the month). The interest rate is 9% compounded monthly.
   a)   Find the monthly payment.
   b)   Find the balance after 4 years.

28. A 30-year mortgage for $150,000 is amortized with monthly payments (at the end of the month). The interest rate is 9.2% compounded monthly. Find the monthly payment.

29. Mr. and Mrs. Barrera have purchased a home for $120,000. They have put $30,000 down and will obtain a 15-year mortgage for $90,000 at an interest rate of 12% compounded monthly.
   a)   Find the payment due at the end of each month.
   b)   How much will the Barreras pay out for the loan after 15 years, and what will be the total interest?
   c)   What is the balance after 10 years?

30. Verify that the quarterly payment necessary to amortize a $20,000 loan is twice that for a $10,000 loan. Assume an ordinary annuity, a 5-year time interval, and an interest rate of 8% compounded quarterly.

31. Show that for given values of i and n, the periodic payment necessary to amortize a loan of $2L$ dollars is twice that for a loan of L dollars. Also, show that, in general, the periodic payment necessary to amortize a loan of kL dollars is k times that of a loan of L dollars.

32. *Mortgage: Comparing terms.* Compare the monthly payments and total interest for 30-year and 15-year mortgages of $100,000 at an interest rate of 9.75% compounded monthly.

33. *Mortgage: Comparing interest rates.* Compare monthly payments and total interest for 30-year mortgages of $100,000 at interest rates of 9.75% and 10.75% compounded monthly.

34. *Mortgage: Comparing interest rates.* Compare monthly payments and total interest for 15-year mortgages of $100,000 at interest rates of 9.75% and 10.75% compounded monthly.

35. *This problem is adapted from one that appeared on a past Uniform CPA Examination.* On January 15, 1988, Carr Corporation adopted a plan to accumulate funds for environmental improvements beginning July 1, 1992, at an estimated cost of $2,000,000. Carr plans to make four equal annual deposits in a fund that will earn interest at 10% compounded annually. The first deposit was made on July 1, 1988. Find the annual deposit.

36-39. *Add-on interest.* Determine the periodic payments necessary to amortize the loans of Exercises 9-12 by the add-on-interest method.

4-6

• EQUATIONS OF VALUE; DEFERRED ANNUITIES; COMPLEX ANNUITIES

Equations of Value

Before going on, let us summarize some basic concepts from previous sections of this chapter. For any financial transaction, the value of an amount of money changes with time as a result of the application of interest. Thus, to *accumulate* or *bring forward* a single payment, R, for n periods at an interest rate of i per period, we multiply R by $(1 + i)^n$, as illustrated in Figure 4-34. To *bring back* a single payment, R, for n periods at an interest rate of i per period, we multiply R by $(1 + i)^{-n}$, as shown in Figure 4-35. To accumulate or bring forward an annuity of n payments of R dollars each, we multiply R by $s_{\overline{n}|i}$, where $s_{\overline{n}|i} = [1 + i)^n - 1]/i$, as pictured in Figure 4-36 on page 222. To bring back an annuity of n payments of R dollars each, we multiply R by $a_{\overline{n}|i}$, where $a_{\overline{n}|i} = [1 - (1 + i)^{-n}]/i$, as illustrated in Figure 4-37 on page 222.

We now consider the following problem.

PROBLEM

A business person has a debt of $4000 due in 3 years. He wants to repay this debt by making a $3000 payment 2 years from now and a last payment 5 years from now. If the interest rate is 12% compounded annually, what must be the amount of the last payment?

SOLUTION

This situation is illustrated in the time diagram of Figure 4-38 on page 222. Note that the last payment is denoted by x. Thus, we want to determine x so that the value of the two payments on the lower time line is equivalent to the value of the single payment on the upper time line if the interest rate is 12% compounded annually.

Since the value of any amount of money changes with time as a result of the application of interest, we must choose a point on both time lines at

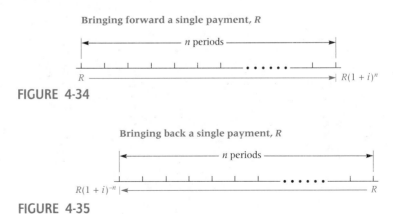

Bringing forward a single payment, R

FIGURE 4-34

Bringing back a single payment, R

FIGURE 4-35

Bringing forward an annuity of n equal payments

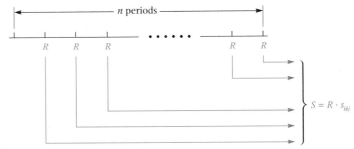

FIGURE 4-36

Bringing back an annuity of n equal payments

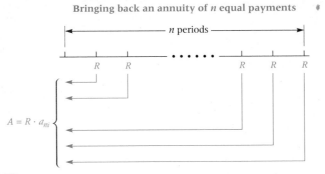

FIGURE 4-37

FIGURE 4-38

which we will equate the values of the payments of both time lines. Such a point is called a **comparison point** and may be chosen arbitrarily.

If, for the situation of Figure 4-38, we choose the comparison point to be "Now," we must

1. Bring back the $4000 payment on the upper time line three periods
2. Bring back the $3000 payment on the lower time line two periods and the unknown payment five periods (see Figure 4-39)

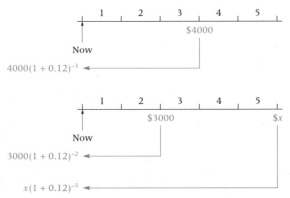

FIGURE 4-39

Equating the values of both time lines at the comparison point, "Now," we obtain the equation

$$4000(1 + 0.12)^{-3} = 3000(1 + 0.12)^{-2} + x(1 + 0.12)^{-5}$$

This equation is called an **equation of value.** Solving for x, we multiply both sides by $(1 + 0.12)^5$ to obtain

$$4000(1 + 0.12)^2 = 3000(1 + 0.12)^3 + x$$

Hence,

$$x = 4000(1 + 0.12)^2 - 3000(1 + 0.12)^3$$

Using Table 4 in Appendix C to obtain the needed powers of $(1 + 0.12)$, we have

$$x = 4000(1.254400) - 3000(1.404928)$$
$$= \$802.82$$

Thus, the last payment is $802.82.

As mentioned before, the comparison point may be chosen arbitrarily. If the comparison point for the preceding problem is chosen to be the end of the fifth year, then each payment must be brought forward to the end of the fifth year. The resulting equation of value is

$$4000(1 + 0.12)^2 = 3000(1 + 0.12)^3 + x$$

Note that this equation of value is equivalent to the first one. If we multiply both sides of the first equation of value by $(1 + 0.12)^5$ (which we did in order to solve it), we obtain the latter one. Again, the last payment, x, is $802.82.

• EXAMPLE 4-34

A business person wishes to borrow $10,000 today and $6000 3 years from today. She wishes to repay both loans with equal annual payments at the end of each year for the next 4 years. If the interest rate is 15% compounded annually, what is the annual payment?

Solution

This problem is illustrated by the time lines of Figure 4-40. The annual payment is denoted by x. If the beginning of the first year is chosen as the comparison point, then the annuity of four payments of x dollars each must be brought back to the comparison point. We do this by multiplying x by $a_{\overline{4}|0.15}$. Also, $6000 must be brought back to the comparison point. We do this by multiplying $6000 by $(1 + 0.15)^{-3}$. Hence, the equation of value is

$$10,000 + 6000(1 + 0.15)^{-3} = x \cdot a_{\overline{4}|0.15}$$

Solving for x, we have

$$x = \frac{10,000 + 6000(1 + 0.15)^{-3}}{a_{\overline{4}|0.15}}$$
$$= \$4884.48$$

Thus, the annual payment is $4884.48.

Comparison point

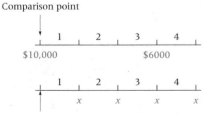

Comparison point

FIGURE 4-40

Variable Annuities

Some financial institutions offer graduated payment loans. The repayment of such a loan involves an annuity whose later payments are larger than its earlier ones. Such an annuity is called a **variable annuity.**

• EXAMPLE 4-35 _____

Mrs. Logan finances the purchase of a new car with a cash price of $10,000 by a variable annuity. During the first 3 years, she will make payments of a certain amount at the end of each year. During the last 4 years, her annual payment will be twice as large. If the interest rate is 12% compounded annually, what are the annual payments?

Solution

The time lines of Figure 4-41 illustrate this problem.

Observe that x denotes the first three annual payments and $2x$ denotes the remaining payments. If the comparison point is chosen to be the end of the third year, then the annuity consisting of three payments of x dollars each must be brought forward to the comparison point. This is done by multiplying x by $s_{\overline{3}|0.12}$. Also, the annuity consisting of four payments of $2x$ dollars each must be brought back to the comparison point. This is done by multiplying $2x$ by $a_{\overline{4}|0.12}$. Finally, $10,000 must be brought forward to the comparison point. This is done by multiplying $10,000 by $(1 + 0.12)^3$. Hence, the equation of value is

$$x \cdot s_{\overline{3}|0.12} + 2x \cdot a_{\overline{4}|0.12} = 10,000(1 + 0.12)^3$$

Using either tables or a calculator to determine $s_{\overline{3}|0.12}$, $a_{\overline{4}|0.12}$, and $(1 + 0.12)^3$, this equation becomes

$$x(3.374400) + 2x(3.037349) = 10,000(1.404928)$$

Solving for x, we have

$$3.3744x + 6.074698x = 14049.28$$
$$x = \$1486.84$$

Thus, the first three annual payments are $1486.84, and the remaining annual payments are $2(\$1486.84) = \$2973.68$.

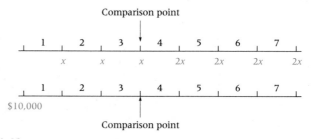

FIGURE 4-41

Deferred Annuities

A **deferred annuity** is an annuity whose payments begin later than at the end of the first period. For example, if a person finances the purchase of

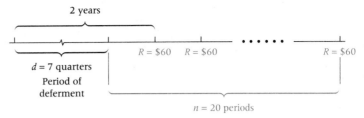

FIGURE 4-42

some item by agreeing to pay 20 quarterly payments of $60 each, *with the first payment due 2 years from now,* then this series of payments constitutes a deferred annuity. The length of time from the present to the beginning of the first payment time interval is called the **period of deferment.** If d = number of periods of deferment, then, as illustrated in Figure 4-42, $d = 7$, and the annuity consists of $n = 20$ payments, each payment made at the end of a quarter. Note that although eight payment periods precede the first payment, the period of deferment consists of one less period ($d = 8 - 1 = 7$) since the period of deferment is defined as the length of time from the present to the beginning of the first payment time interval. Thus, the period preceding the first payment is counted along with those of the annuity and not with the period of deferment.

The total amount of a deferred annuity is its future value at the end of n periods and is determined by the usual formula for the total amount of an annuity:

$$S = R \cdot s_{\overline{n}|i}$$

For the annuity of Figure 4-42, if the interest rate is 12% compounded quarterly, then $i = 0.03$ and

$$S = 60 \cdot s_{\overline{20}|0.03}$$
$$\approx 60(26.870374)$$
$$\approx \$1612.22$$

Present Value of a Deferred Annuity

In general, the present value, A, of a deferred annuity of n payments with d periods of deferment (see Figure 4-43) at an interest rate of i per conversion period may be determined by the following formula.

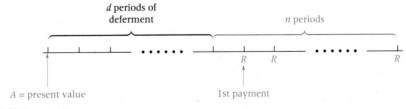

FIGURE 4-43

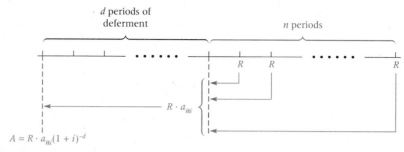

FIGURE 4-44

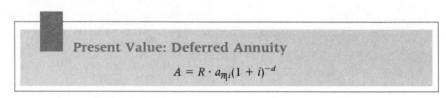

Observing Figure 4-44, note that the term $R \cdot a_{\overline{n}|i}$ gives the present value of the annuity at the beginning of the first payment period. Multiplying $R \cdot a_{\overline{n}|i}$ by $(1 + i)^{-d}$ brings this result back d periods to yield the present value of the deferred annuity. Thus, for the deferred annuity of Figure 4-42, the present value is

$$A = R \cdot a_{\overline{n}|i}(1 + i)^{-d}$$
$$= 60 \cdot a_{\overline{20}|0.03}(1 + 0.03)^{-7}$$
$$\approx 60(14.877475)(0.813092)$$
$$\approx \$725.81$$

• EXAMPLE 4-36 _____

Sara Smith agrees to repay a loan by making $200 payments at the end of each month for 3 years. The first payment is due at the end of 6 months. If the interest rate is 12% compounded monthly, then find the amount of the loan.

Solution

The amount of the loan is the present value of this deferred annuity. Observing Figure 4-45, note that $d = 5$, $n = 12(3) = 36$, and $R = \$200$. Also, $i = 0.12/12 = 0.01$. Hence, the present value is

$$A = R \cdot a_{\overline{n}|i}(1 + i)^{-d}$$
$$= 200 \cdot a_{\overline{36}|0.01}(1 + 0.01)^{-5}$$
$$\approx 200(30.107505)(0.951466)$$
$$\approx \$5729.25$$

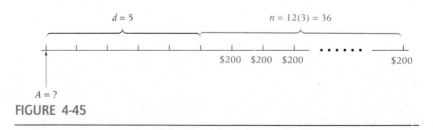

FIGURE 4-45

Complex Annuities

Up to this point, we have been considering annuities in which the payment periods coincide with the conversion (interest) periods. As stated earlier, such annuities are called simple annuities. If we have an annuity where the payment period does not coincide with the conversion (interest) period, we have a **complex annuity,** or **general annuity.** Here we will present a method for determining present and future values of complex annuities. Although there is more than one method for determining the present and future values of complex annuities, we will change the original interest rate to an equivalent interest rate such that its conversion (interest) period coincides with the payment period of the annuity. Thus, the annuity with an equivalent interest rate where the interest period coincides with the payment period becomes a simple annuity.

PROBLEM

As an example, we find the future and present values of an annuity of seven payments of $1000 each made at the end of each quarter with an interest rate of 12% compounded monthly.

SOLUTION

Since we have quarterly payment periods and monthly interest periods, we must change the interest rate to coincide with the quarterly payment periods. Specifically, we must find the equivalent interest rate compounded quarterly corresponding to 12% compounded monthly. Using equation (1) on page 185, we have

$$(1 + r/4)^4 = (1 + 0.12/12)^{12}$$

where r is the equivalent annual rate compounded quarterly. Since we need the interest rate per conversion period, $r/4$, for our computations, we solve for $r/4$ by taking the fourth root of each side of the above equation to obtain

$$
\begin{aligned}
1 + r/4 &= [(1 + 0.01)^{12}]^{1/4} \\
&= (1 + 0.01)^3 \\
r/4 &= (1 + 0.01)^3 - 1 \\
&\approx 0.030301 \quad \text{Equivalent interest rate per quarter}
\end{aligned}
$$

Now we use the formulas for the future and present values of simple annuities that we learned in the previous sections of this chapter. Thus, for this annuity, $n = 7$, $i = 0.030301$, and $R = 1000$.

Future Value

$$
\begin{aligned}
S &= R \cdot s_{\overline{n}|i} \\
&= 1000 s_{\overline{7}|0.030301} \\
&\approx 1000(7.66944789) \\
&\approx \$7669.45
\end{aligned}
$$

Using a calculator,
$s_{\overline{7}|0.030301} = [(1.030301)^7 - 1]/0.030301$
$\approx 7.66944789.$

Present Value

$A = R \cdot a_{\overline{n}|i}$

$= 1000 a_{\overline{7}|0.030301}$ Using a calculator,

$\approx 1000(6.223221394)$ $a_{\overline{7}|0.030301} = [(1 - (1.030301)^{-7}]/0.030301$
$\approx 6.223221394.$

$\approx \$6223.22$

This method is also used for complex annuities due by applying the respective formulas that we have learned in previous sections for annuities due.

• **EXAMPLE 4-37   Complex Annuity Due.** _____

A person deposits \$800 at the beginning of each month for 3 years into a bank account that pays interest at 8% compounded semiannually. Find the total amount and present value of this annuity.

Solution

Since we have monthly payments and semiannual interest periods, we must change the interest rate to coincide with the monthly payment periods. Thus, we must find the equivalent interest rate compounded monthly corresponding to 8% compounded semiannually. If r denotes the annual rate compounded monthly, then, using equation (1) on page 185, we have

$$(1 + r/12)^{12} = (1 + 0.08/2)^2$$

Solving for $r/12$, the interest rate per conversion period, we take the 12th root of each side to obtain

$1 + r/12 = [(1.04)^2]^{1/12}$

$= (1.04)^{1/6}$

≈ 1.006558

$r/12 \approx 1.006558 - 1$

≈ 0.006558 Equivalent interest rate per month

Now we use formulas for the future and present values of annuities due that we learned in Sections 4-3 and 4-4. For this annuity, $n = (12)(3) = 36$, $i = 0.006558$, and $R = 800$.

Future Value

$S = R(s_{\overline{n+1}|i} - 1)$ $n + 1 = 36 + 1 = 37$

$= 800(s_{\overline{37}|0.006558} - 1)$ Using a calculator,

$\approx 800(41.721258 - 1)$ $s_{\overline{37}|0.006558} = [(1.006558)^{37} - 1]/0.006558$
$\approx 41.721258.$

$= 800(40.721258)$

$\approx \$32,577.01$

Present Value

$A = R(a_{\overline{n-1}|i} + 1)$ $n - 1 = 36 - 1 = 35$

$= 800(a_{\overline{35}|0.006558} + 1)$ Using a calculator,

$\approx 800(31.182828 + 1)$ $a_{\overline{35}|0.006558} = [1 - (1.006558)^{-35}]/0.006558$
$\approx 31.182828.$

$= 800(32.182828)$

$\approx \$25,746.26$

Exercises 4-6

Equations of Value

1. Mr. Evans has a debt of $8000 due in 4 years. He wants to repay this debt by making a $2000 payment 1 year from now, a $1000 payment 3 years from now, and a last payment 6 years from now. If the interest rate is 10% compounded annually, what must be the amount of the last payment?

2. A business person's debt is payable as follows: $2000 1 year from now and $5000 5 years from now. The business person wants to repay the debt as follows: a $1000 payment now, a $2000 payment 2 years from now, a $1000 payment 3 years from now, and the last payment 4 years from now. If the interest rate is 12% compounded annually, find the amount of the last payment.

3. A woman wishes to borrow $5000 now and $4000 2 years from now. She wishes to repay both loans with equal annual payments at the end of each year for the next 5 years. If the interest rate is 10% compounded annually, find the annual payment.

4. If money is worth 12% compounded annually, what single payment made 2 years from now can replace the following two payments: $3000 due 1 year from now and $5000 due 4 years from now.

5. A person wishes to borrow $6000 now and $5000 3 years from now. Both loans are to be repaid by equal annual payments at the end of each year for the next 7 years. If the interest rate is 8% compounded annually, determine the annual payment.

6. Mary Smith signed a mortgage for $10,000. The mortgage is to be repaid with equal monthly payments for the first 2 years and equal monthly payments twice as large for the next 3 years. If the interest rate is 12% compounded monthly, find the monthly payments. Assume each payment is made at the end of the month.

7. Find the present value of a variable annuity consisting of $500 at the end of each year for the first 4 years and $800 at the end of each year for the next 5 years. The interest rate is 10% compounded annually.

8. A man buys a car with a cash price of $12,000 by financing it over a 5-year period. At the end of each of the first 2 years, he will make equal payments. At the end of each of the next 3 years, his equal payments will be $1\frac{1}{2}$ times as large. If the interest rate is 12% compounded annually, find his annual payments.

Use a calculator to solve each of the following problems.

9. A person plans to borrow $8,000 now and $5,000 3 years from now. Both loans will be repaid with equal monthly payments at the end of each month for the next 6 years. If the interest rate is 7% compounded monthly, determine the monthly payment.

10. A $20,000 loan is to be repaid with monthly payments (at the end of the month) over the next 5 years. If the monthly payments during the last 3 years are twice those of the first 2 years, determine the monthly payments, assuming an interest rate of 8% compounded monthly.

11. A $150,000 loan is to be amortized with equal monthly payments (at the end of the month) for the first 10 years and payments $1\frac{1}{2}$ times as large for the last 15 years. If the interest rate is 10.08% compounded monthly, determine the monthly payments.

12. A $300,000 loan is to be amortized with equal monthly payments (at the end of the month) for the first 10 years, payments 1½ times as large for the next 10 years, and payments twice as large for the last 10 years. If the interest rate is 8.64% compounded monthly, find the monthly payments.

Deferred Annuities

For each of the following deferred annuities, determine d, the number of periods of deferment.

13. Quarterly payments with the first payment at the end of 2 years
14. Semiannual payments with the first payment at the end of 4 years
15. Monthly payments with the first payment at the end of 1½ years
16. Annual payments with the first payment at the end of 3 years
17. Quarterly payments with the first payment at the end of 5½ years
18. Semiannual payments with the first payment at the end of 7½ years

19. A loan is repaid by paying $500 at the end of each quarter for 10 years. The first payment is due 1 year from now. If the interest rate is 16% compounded quarterly, what is the amount of the loan?

20. If a person repays a loan with monthly payments of $400 at the end of each month for 3 years, what is the amount of the loan if the first payment is due in 6 months and the interest rate is 24% compounded monthly?

21. Ms. James is considering buying an investment contract that promises to pay $1000 at the end of each 6 months for 10 years. The first payment is due in 18 months. If Ms. James wishes to earn 16% compounded semiannually on her investment, how much should she pay for this investment contract?

22. Harry Morgan wishes to set up a fund to provide for $2000 payments at the end of each quarter for 4 years. The payments will be made to Harry's college-age daughter who will enter college 1 year from now. Thus, the first payment will be made 1 year from now. If Harry earns 16% compounded quarterly on his money, how much should be deposited into this fund now?

23. A loan of $50,000 will be repaid by quarterly payments made at the end of each quarter for 5 years. If the interest rate is 20% compounded quarterly and the first payment is due 1½ years from now, what is the quarterly payment?

24. A mortgage of $70,000 will be repaid by monthly payments made at the end of each month for 8 years. If the interest rate is 18% compounded monthly and the first payment is due in 1 year, find the monthly payment.

Complex Annuities

Use a calculator to solve each of the following problems.

25. Find the total amount and present value of an annuity of $1000 payable at the end of each quarter for 5 years at an interest rate of 12% compounded monthly.

26. Find the total amount and present value of an annuity of $3500 payable at the end of each 6 months for 10 years. The interest rate is 8% compounded quarterly.

27. Find the total amount and present value of an annuity of $5600 payable at the end of each month for 6 years. The interest rate is 12% compounded quarterly.

28. Find the total amount and present value of an annuity of $1300 payable at the end of each quarter for 10 years. The interest rate is 15% compounded annually.

29. A loan is to be repaid with quarterly payments of $650 at the end of each quarter for 6 years. If the interest rate is 12% compounded monthly, find the amount of the loan.

30. A loan is repaid by monthly payments of $250 at the end of each month for 5 years. If the interest rate is 6% compounded semiannually, find the amount of the loan.

31. A borrower will repay a loan with 21 monthly payments of $1000 each. The first payment is due 10 months from now. If the interest rate is 12% compounded quarterly, find the amount of the loan.

32. A loan will be repaid by six annual payments of $4500 each. The first payment is due 2 years from now. If the interest rate is 6% compounded quarterly, find the amount of the loan.

33. A loan of $12,500 is to be repaid by semiannual payments at the end of each 6 months for 7 years. If the interest rate is 6% compounded monthly, find the semiannual payment.

Complex Annuities Due

Use a calculator to solve each of the following problems.

34. Find the total amount and present value of an annuity of $1200 payable at the beginning of each half-year if the interest rate is 6% compounded monthly. The payments continue for 8 years.

35. Find the total amount and present value of an annuity due of $150 monthly for 4 years if the interest rate is 6% compounded semiannually.

36. Find the total amount and present value of an annuity due of $890 quarterly for 5 years if the interest rate is 12% compounded monthly.

37. Find the total amount and present value of an annuity due of $500 semiannually for 10 years if the interest rate is 9% compounded annually.

38. A loan of $8500 is to be repaid by semiannual payments at the beginning of each 6-month time period over a period of 8 years. If the interest rate is 9% compounded monthly, find the semiannual payment.

39. A loan of $4600 is to be repaid by monthly payments at the beginning of each month for 5 years. If the interest rate is 8% compounded quarterly, find the monthly payment.

40. A person wishes to accumulate $10,000 during a 5-year period by making monthly deposits into a fund earning interest at 16% compounded quarterly. Find the monthly deposit if payments are made at the beginning of each month.

41. A person wishes to accumulate $8000 over a 4-year period by making annual deposits into a fund earning interest at 6% compounded quarterly. Find the annual deposit if payments are made at the beginning of each year.

EXTRA DIVIDENDS

• Net Present Value (Capital Investment Decision)

Write Graphics, Inc., is planning to invest $350,000 in new computer equipment, which is expected to reduce labor costs by $100,000 per year (after taxes) for the next 5 years. The management of Write Graphics, Inc., wishes to determine if the investment is cost effective (assuming money is currently worth 10% compounded annually).

The time diagram of Figure 4-46 illustrates the cash flows involved in

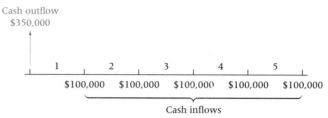

FIGURE 4-46

this investment decision. To determine whether the investment of $350,000 is cost effective at 10% compounded annually, management must determine the **net present value** (denoted by **NPV**) of the cash flows. The net present value is defined by

$$\text{NPV} = \begin{array}{c}\text{present value of}\\\text{cash inflows}\end{array} - \begin{array}{c}\text{present value of}\\\text{cash outflows}\end{array}$$

The present value of the cash outflow is the initial investment of $350,000. The present value of cash inflows at 10% compounded annually is determined by the formula for the present value of an annuity:

$$A \doteq R \cdot a_{\overline{5}|0.10}$$
$$\approx 100{,}000(3.790787)$$
$$\approx \$379{,}078.70$$

Thus, the net present value of this investment is

$$\text{NPV} = \begin{array}{c}\text{present value of}\\\text{cash inflows}\end{array} - \begin{array}{c}\text{present value of}\\\text{cash outflows}\end{array}$$
$$= \$379{,}078.70 - \$350{,}000.00$$
$$= \$29{,}078.70$$

The net present value is positive because the present value of the cash inflows exceeds the present value of the cash outflow. Thus, the investment is cost effective at an interest rate of 10% compounded annually. This means that the investment of $350,000 is earning a rate of return greater than the quoted interest rate of 10% compounded annually.

If the present value of the cash inflows had been less than the present value of the cash outflow, the net present value would have been negative and the investment would not have been cost effective at the quoted interest rate of 10% compounded annually. In other words, the investment of $350,000 would be earning a rate of return less than the quoted interest rate of 10% compounded annually.

If the present value of the cash inflows had equaled the present value of the cash outflow, the net present value would have been 0, and the investment would have been cost effective at the quoted interest rate of 10% compounded annually. In other words, the investment of $350,000 would be earning a rate of return of 10% compounded annually.

The net present value concept is used in making decisions regarding capital investments, as summarized in the box below.

SUMMARY

Net Present Value and Rate of Return

For a net present value (NPV) for some capital investment computed at a given interest rate,

1. If NPV > 0, the rate of return on the invested capital is *greater than* the interest rate at which the NPV was computed.
2. If NPV = 0, the rate of return on the invested capital *equals* the interest rate at which the NPV was computed.
3. If NPV < 0, the rate of return on the invested capital is *less than* the interest rate at which the NPV was computed.

Exercises

1. If the preceding investment resulted in cash inflows of $70,000, $80,000, $100,000, $110,000, and $130,000 at the end of the first, second, third, fourth, and fifth years, respectively, calculate the net present value if money is worth 10% compounded annually. Is the investment earning a rate of return of at least 10% compounded annually?

2. Assume that the initial investment is changed to an amount different from $350,000 and that the resulting cash inflows are $80,000, $100,000, $110,000, $120,000, and $140,000 at the end of the first, second, third, fourth, and fifth years, respectively. If the net present value is −$1000, find the amount invested, assuming money is worth 12% compounded annually.

The following problems are adapted from some that have appeared on past Uniform CPA Examinations. For each of the following problems, assume interest rates are compounded annually.

3. On January 1, 19xx, Jenkins, Inc., purchased for $520,000 a new machine with a useful life of 8 years and no salvage value. The machine is expected to produce an annual cash flow from operations, net of income taxes, of $120,000. Assuming that Jenkins uses a rate of return of 14%, what is the net present value?

4. Hillsdale Company purchased a machine for $480,000. The machine has a useful life of 6 years and no salvage value. The machine is expected to generate cash flows from operations, net of income taxes, of $140,000 in each of the 6 years. Hillsdale's desired rate of return is 14%. Find the net present value.

5. Hamilton Company invested in a 2-year project having a rate of return of 12%. The project is expected to produce cash flows from operations, net of income taxes, of $60,000 in the first year and $70,000 in the second year. How much will the project cost?

6. Scott, Inc., is planning to invest $120,000 in a 10-year project. Scott estimates that the annual cash inflow from this project, net of income taxes, will be

$20,000. Scott's desired rate of return on an investment of this type is 10%. Information on present value factors is as follows:

	At 10%	At 12%
Present value of $1 for ten periods	0.386	0.322
Present value of an annuity of $1 for ten periods	6.145	5.650

Scott's expected rate of return on this investment is

a) Less than 10%, but more than 0%
b) 10%
c) Less than 12%, but more than 10%
d) 12%

7. Sant Company is planning to invest $40,000 in a machine with a useful life of 5 years and no salvage value. Sant estimates that the annual cash inflow from operations from using this machine, net of income taxes, will be $10,000. Sant's desired rate of return on investments of this type is 10%. The present value of an ordinary annuity of $1 for 5 years at 10% is 3.791. The present value of $1 for five periods at 10% is 0.621. Using the net present value method, Sant's true rate of return on this investment is

a) 0%
b) Less than 10%, but more than 0%
c) 10%
d) More than 10%

8. Virginia Company invested in a 4-year project. Virginia's expected rate of return is 10%. The cash inflows from operations resulting from this project are $4000 for the first year, $4400 for the second year, $4800 for the third year, and $5200 for the fourth year. Assuming a positive net present value of $1000, what was the amount of the original investment?

9. Hilltop Company invested $100,000 in a 2-year project. Hilltop's expected rate of return was 12%. The cash flow, net of income taxes, was $40,000 for the first year. Assuming that the rate of return was exactly 12%, what was the cash flow, net of income taxes, for the second year of the project?

10. Tracy Corporation is planning to invest $80,000 in a 3-year project. Tracy's expected rate of return is 10%. The cash flow, net of income taxes, will be $30,000 for the first year and $36,000 for the second year. Assuming that the rate of return is exactly 10%, what will the cash flow, net of income taxes, be for the third year?

CHAPTER 4 HIGHLIGHTS

• Concepts

Your ability to answer the following questions is one indicator of the depth of your mastery of this chapter's important concepts. Note that the questions are grouped under various topic headings. For any question that you cannot answer, refer to the appropriate section of the chapter indicated by the topic heading. Pay particular attention to the summary boxes within a section.

4-1   **SIMPLE INTEREST AND DISCOUNT**

1. Write the formula for simple interest, and explain each component.
2. Explain the term *total amount*, and write its formula.

3. Explain the term *present value,* and write its formula.
4. Explain the difference between simple interest and simple discount.
5. Write the formula for simple discount, and explain each component.
6. Explain the term *proceeds,* and write its formula.
7. When discounting an interest-bearing note, one must first compute its

  _____ _____.

4-2   COMPOUND INTEREST

8. Write the formula for compound amount, and explain its components. Use a time diagram.
9. Explain the term *interest rate per conversion period,* and write its formula.
10. Explain the term *total number of conversion periods,* and write its formula.
11. Write the formula for present value, and explain its components. Use a time diagram.
12. Explain the term *equivalent interest rates.* Write the equation used to find equivalent interest rates, and explain its components.
13. Explain the term *effective rate,* and give its formula.
14. Write the formula for future value when interest is compounded continuously, and explain its components. Use a time diagram.
15. Write the formula for present value when interest is compounded continuously, and explain its components. Use a time diagram.
16. Write the formula for the effective rate when interest is compounded continuously.

4-3   GEOMETRIC SERIES AND ANNUITIES

17. What is an annuity?
18. Explain the difference between an ordinary annuity and an annuity due.
19. Explain, using a time diagram, the term *total amount* (future value) of an ordinary annuity, and write its formula.
20. Write the formula for the total amount of an annuity due, and explain its components. Use a time diagram.

4-4   PRESENT VALUE OF AN ANNUITY

21. Explain, using a time diagram, the term *present value of an ordinary annuity,* and write its formula.
22. Write the formula for the present value of an annuity due, and explain its components. Use a time diagram.

4-5   SINKING FUNDS AND AMORTIZATION

23. What is a sinking fund? Write the formula to determine the periodic payment for a sinking fund, and explain its components.
24. In a sinking fund schedule, explain how the interest for a particular period is determined.
25. Explain the term *amortization.* Write the formula to determine the periodic payment for an amortization problem, and explain its components.
26. In an amortization schedule, explain how, for a particular period,
  a) The interest is determined   b) The balance is determined
27. Explain how to determine the balance of a loan after a particular payment has been made.
28. Explain the add-on-interest method of amortizing a loan. Contrast this method with the method that involves the annuity formula.

4-6   EQUATIONS OF VALUE; DEFERRED ANNUITIES;
COMPLEX ANNUITIES

29. To bring forward a single payment on a time diagram, multiply by the expression _____. Explain the components of this expression.

30. To bring back a single payment on a time diagram, multiply by the expression _____. Explain the components of this expression.

31. To bring forward an annuity of *n* equal payments on a time diagram, multiply an individual payment by the expression _____. Explain the components of this expression.

32. To bring back an annuity of *n* equal payments on a time diagram, multiply an individual payment by the expression _____. Explain the components of this expression.

33. What is a variable annuity?

34. What is a deferred annuity? Write the formula for the present value of a deferred annuity, and explain its components.

35. What is a complex annuity? What is the difference between a complex annuity and a simple annuity?

36. To find the present and future values of complex annuities, we change the _____ and use the formulas for simple annuities.

REVIEW EXERCISES

● *Simple Interest and Discount*

1. A person invests $1000 at 9% per year for 6 years.
   a) Find the simple interest earned.
   b) Find the future value.

2. A person earns $20 on a principal of $500 during a 3-month time interval. Find the rate of interest.

3. A person invests $10,000 at 8% per year for 10 years.
   a) Find the simple interest earned.
   b) Find the future value.

4. The maturity value of a 9-month discount note is $10,000. The note is discounted at 8% by a bank.
   a) Find the discount.
   b) Find the proceeds.

5. Mary Jones wishes to receive $8000 for 6 months by using a discount note with a discount rate of 8%.
   a) Find the maturity value of the discount note.
   b) Mary's note is sold to a third party 2 months before maturity at a discount rate of 6%. How much does the third party pay for the note? How much did the original holder earn on the note?

6. A 9-month, 8% simple-interest-bearing note with a face value of $10,000 is sold to an investor 3 months prior to maturity at a discount rate of 7%.
   a) How much does the investor pay for the note?
   b) How much does the investor earn on the note?

● *Compound Amount and Present Value*

7. Carl Johnson deposits $10,000 into a bank that pays 8% compounded semiannually. What amount will he have at the end of 11 years?

8. How much money does R. T. White need now if he can invest the money at

6% compounded quarterly for 7 years and receive $6000 at the end of the period?

9. A 5-year note has a maturity value of $10,000. If we wish to purchase this note now and earn 12% compounded quarterly on our investent, how much should we pay for the note now (5 years before maturity)?

10. A person invests $9000 at 8% compounded quarterly for 9 years. Find the maturity value.

11. How much money should be deposited now at 12% compounded monthly in order to accumulate $80,000 in 8 years?

12. Determine the compound amount of $15,000 invested for 2 years at 7% compounded daily.

13. Determine the compound amount of $8000 invested for 3 years at 6% compounded continuously.

14. What amount should be invested now at 8% compounded continuously in order to accumulate $20,000 at the end of 4 years?

Find the effective rate for Exercises 15-18.

15. 9% compounded monthly   16. 8.75% compounded continuously
17. 7.9% compounded daily   18. 8.4% compounded quarterly

19. A person deposits $10,000 into a bank account that earns interest at 6% compounded semiannually for 3 years. At the end of the 3-year time interval, the person reinvests the original $10,000 plus its interest and deposits an additional $5000. At this time the interest rate changes to 7% compounded continuously. How much is in the account 5 years after the original $10,000 deposit?

• *Simple Annuities; Amortization; Sinking Funds*

20. Miss Smith deposits $600 at the end of each quarter for 11 years. Each deposit earns interest at 12% compounded quarterly. Find the total amount in this account at the end of 11 years.

21. Mr. Jones wants to accumulate the same total amount as Miss Smith in Exercise 20. However, he wants to deposit one lump-sum payment now. Assuming that the interest rate and time period are the same as in Miss Smith's case, how much should Mr. Jones deposit now?

22. A man deposits $100 in a bank at the end of each month for 3 years and 4 months. If the money earns interest at 12% compounded monthly, how much money does he have in his account at the end of the period?

23. A woman wishes to withdraw $400 at the end of every 6 months for 10 years. If the money earns interest at 6% compounded semiannually, how much must she deposit now?

24. A certain investment contract promises to pay $1000 at the end of each quarter for the next 7 years. If we wish to buy this investment contract and earn 12% compounded quarterly on our money, how much should we pay for it now?

25. A grocer anticipates an expenditure of $10,000 for a new freezer 5 years from now. How much should he deposit at the end of each month into a sinking fund earning interest at 6% compounded monthly?

26. A woman buys a piece of real estate selling for $60,000 by putting $40,000 down and financing the balance with a 20-year mortgage having an interest rate of 16% compounded quarterly. Find the payment due at the end of each quarter.

27. A certain investment contract promises to pay $500 at the end of each quarter

for the next 2 years and a lump sum of $6000 3 years thereafter. How much is this investment contract worth now at 12% compounded quarterly?

28. Joan Hill deposits $100 at the end of each quarter for 12 years into a savings account paying interest at 8% compounded quarterly. How much money will be in her account at the end of 12 years? How much interest is earned?

29. John owes Harry $20,000 10 years from now. Instead of waiting 10 years, John wishes to pay an equal sum at the end of each quarter for the next 10 years. If the interest is compounded quarterly at 8%, find the quarterly payment.

30. A man has a 12-year mortgage of $20,000 at an interest rate of 8% compounded quarterly. If a payment is made at the end of each quarter, find the payment.

31. A company is considering purchasing new equipment that will result in an increased cash flow of $10,000 per year for the next 5 years. If the goal is a rate of return of 8% compounded annually on the investment, how much should be spent now on the new equipment?

32. A person borrows $7000 to buy a car. The loan is to be paid off by a payment at the end of each month over a 4-year period. The interest rate is 24% compounded monthly.
    a) Find the borrower's monthly payment.
    b) At the end of 4 years, how much did the borrower actually pay for the car?
    c) Find the amount of interest paid.

33. Mrs. Elipe purchased equipment that required a $1000 down payment, and she agreed to pay $100 at the end of each month for the next 5 years. If money is worth 12% compounded semiannually, what would have been the price had Mrs. Elipe decided to pay cash for the entire purchase?

34. In anticipation of an expenditure of $30,000 6 years from now, the H. J. Ellis Co. establishes a sinking fund into which a payment is made at the end of each month. Assuming that the interest rate is 12% compounded monthly, find the monthly payment.

35. A woman purchased a house for $70,000. She made a down payment of $20,000 and financed the balance with a 20-year mortgage calling for equal semiannual payments. If the interest rate is 8% compounded semiannually and the first payment is due in six months, find the semiannual payment.

36. A man desires to have a $12,000 fund at the end of 10 years. If his savings can be invested at 8% compounded quarterly, how much must he invest at the end of each quarter for 10 years?

37. A grocer anticipates an expenditure of $10,000 for a new freezer 5 years from now. How much should she deposit at the end of each month into a sinking fund earning interest at 12% compounded monthly?

38. A man deposits $100 in a bank at the end of each month for 3 years and 9 months. If the money earns interest at 12% compounded monthly, how much money does he have in his account at the end of the period?

39. A woman wishes to withdraw $600 at the end of every 6 months for 10 years. If the money earns interest at 6% compounded semiannually, how much must she deposit now?

40. A businessperson wants to accumulate $1 million in 10 years from now by depositing a payment at the end of each year into an account earning interest at the rate of 8% compounded annually. Find the annual payment.

41. Mr. Johnson deposits $100 at the beginning of each month into an account earning interest at 24% compounded monthly. How much is in the account at the end of 4 years?

42. Susan Sullivan wants to accumulate $40,000 10 years from now by depositing a payment at the end of each year into an account earning interest at the rate of 10% compounded annually. Find the annual payment.

• *Equations of Value; Deferred Annuities*

43. A person wishes to borrow $4000 now and $5000 1 year from now. Both loans are to be repaid by a $3000 payment 2 years from now and a final payment 3 years from now. If the interest rate is 8% compounded annually, determine the final payment.

44. A person wishes to borrow $5000 now and $6000 1 year from now. Both loans are to be repaid by equal annual payments at the end of each year for the next 5 years. If the interest rate is 9% compounded annually, determine the annual payment.

45. Find the present value of an annuity consisting of 12 semiannual payments of $1000, with the first payment due 3 years from now. The interest rate is 8% compounded quarterly.

46. A loan is to be repaid by making $400 payments at the end of each quarter for 5 years. The first payment is due 1 year from now. If the interest rate is 12% compounded quarterly, find the amount of the loan.

• *Complex Annuities*

47. Find the total amount and present value of an annuity of $600 payable at the end of each year for 5 years if the interest rate is 8% compounded quarterly.

48. Find the total amount and present value of an annuity of $800 payable at the beginning of each year for 3 years if the interest rate is 12% compounded monthly.

49. Find the total amount and present value of an annuity of $1000 payable at the end of each month for 4 years if the interest rate is 12% compounded semiannually.

50. Find the total amount and present value of an annuity of $1000 payable at the beginning of each month for 3 years if the interest rate if 10% compounded annually.

51. A loan of $35,000 is to be repaid by quarterly payments at the beginning of each quarter for 5 years. The first payment is due 1 year from now. If the interest rate is 6% compounded monthly, find the quarterly payment.

5

LINEAR
SYSTEMS AND
MATRICES

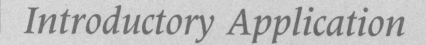
Introductory Application

Production Costs

The following problem appeared on a past Uniform CPA Examination.

PROBLEM

Total production costs for Gallop, Inc., are budgeted at $230,000 for 50,000 units of budgeted output and at $280,000 for 60,000 units of budgeted output. Because of the need for additional facilities, budgeted fixed costs for 60,000 units are 25% more than budgeted fixed costs for 50,000 units. How much is Gallop's budgeted variable cost per unit of output?

SOLUTION

In this chapter, we present a procedure for translating such word problems into an algebraic formulation. Then the chapter provides methods for solving such algebraic formulations.

5-1

• LINEAR SYSTEMS

We begin this section with a problem whose solution will lead us through the main concepts of this section. Additionally, we will develop a systematic procedure for translating word problems into an algebraic formulation and then methods for solving such a formulation.

PROBLEM

Nutrition: Diet

A dietician must determine how many ounces of each of two food types—food A and food B—to include in a diet to ensure that sufficient quantities of protein and calcium are derived from the diet. Specifically, each ounce of food A contains 3 milligrams of protein and 6 milligrams of calcium. Also, each ounce of food B contains 4 milligrams of protein and 5 milligrams of calcium. The nutritionist must ensure that the diet provides exactly 64 milligrams of protein and 98 milligrams of calcium. How many ounces of each food type should the diet include?

SOLUTION

Step 1 *Identify the unknowns. Use letters (or, in other words, variables) to denote these quantities.*
We must determine the number of ounces of food A and food B to include in a diet. Thus, we let

- x = number of ounces of food A to be included in the diet
- y = number of ounces of food B to be included in the diet

Step 2 *Organize the given information, and write the equations that express any relationships existing among the variables.*
The information is organized in the table below.

Milligrams per ounce of food type

	Food A	Food B		
Protein	3	4	64	nutritional requirements
Calcium	6	5	98	in milligrams

We now write the protein and calcium requirements as equations.

Protein Requirement

Since each ounce of food A contains 3 milligrams of protein and each ounce of food B contains 4 ounces of protein, then the expression

3(number of ounces of food A) + 4(number of ounces of food B)

<table>
<tr><td>milligrams of protein
derived from food A</td><td>milligrams of protein
derived from food B</td></tr>
</table>

represents the number of milligrams of protein derived from both food A and food B. Since the diet must provide exactly 64 milligrams of protein, we set the above expression equal to 64 to obtain the equation

3(number of ounces of food A) + 4(number of ounces of food B) = 64

Since x = number of ounces of food A and y = number of ounces of food B, the above becomes

$$3x + 4y = 64$$

Calcium Requirement

Since each ounce of food A contains 6 milligrams of calcium and each ounce of food B contains 5 ounces of calcium, then the expression

6(number of ounces of food A) + 5(number of ounces of food B)

milligrams of calcium derived from food A　　milligrams of calcium derived from food B

represents the number of milligrams of calcium derived from both food A and food B. Since the diet must provide exactly 98 milligrams of calcium, we set the above expression equal to 98 to obtain the equation

6(number of ounces of food A) + 5(number of ounces of food B) = 98

Since x = number of ounces of food A and y = number of ounces of food B, the above becomes

$$6x + 5y = 98$$

Thus, we seek values of x and y that simultaneously satisfy the two equations

$$3x + 4y = 64$$
$$6x + 5y = 98$$

Note that each of the above equations is of the form

$$ax + by = c$$

where a, b, and c real number constants. As we learned in Chapter 1, such equations are linear equations in two variables. The two equations constitute a **system** of two linear equations in two variables. A system of linear equations is often called a **linear system.**

Step 3　*Solve the linear system of step 2.*
A solution to a linear system of two equations is a sequence of numbers x and y that, when substituted into each equation, results in a true statement. In other words, the values of x and y must satisfy both equations. The solution may be written as the ordered pair (x, y).

Graphical Interpretation

Graphically, each equation of a linear system is a straight line. Figure 5-1 gives the graphs of both equations of the above linear system of our illus-

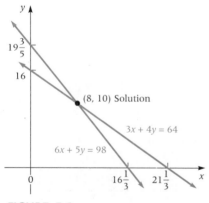

FIGURE 5-1

trative problem. Note that each point (x, y) on the straight line $3x + 4y = 64$, where x and y are non-negative, represents a possible diet that meets the protein requirement. Also, each point (x, y) on the straight line $6x + 5y = 98$, where x and y are non-negative, represents a possible diet that meets the calcium requirement.

Since both the protein and the calcium requirements must be met, then, graphically, the coordinates of any point that lies on both lines constitute a **solution** to the diet problem. In Figure 5-1, we see that a solution occurs at the intersection of both straight lines. The x- and y-coordinates of such a point satisfy both equations of the linear system. Thus, the x- and y-coordinates of the intersection point of the straight lines of our linear system constitute a solution to the linear system. As illustrated in Figure 5-1, the solution, determined by graphing both lines and noting the coordinates of the intersection point, is given by the ordered pair (8, 10). In other words,

$x = 8$ ounces of food A should be included in the diet

$y = 10$ ounces of food B should be included in the diet

Note that this solution was obtained by sketching both straight lines on graph paper and using the grid to determine the coordinates of the intersection point. We check our solution by substituting the results into both equations of the linear system. Hence,

$$3x + 4y = 64 \qquad\qquad 6x + 5y = 98$$
$$3(8) + 4(10) \overset{?}{=} 64 \qquad\qquad 6(8) + 5(10) \overset{?}{=} 98$$
$$64 \overset{\checkmark}{=} 64 \qquad\qquad 98 \overset{\checkmark}{=} 98$$

This concludes the introductory problem to this section. We now summarize the problem-solving procedure used throughout this example. We will use this procedure to solve further applied examples in this section and chapter.

Problem-Solving Procedure

Step 1   Identify the unknown quantities to be found. Use letters to denote these quantities. Since these unknowns usually constitute an integral part of some decision-making process, they are often called **decision variables.**

Step 2   Reread the problem, over and over if necessary, to organize the given information. Write equations for the relationships among the variables. To obtain such equations, think of similar or related problems encountered in the past. At the completion of this step, the problem is formulated algebraically.

Step 3   Solve the equations of step 2 and check your results. This usually entails algebraic methods that have been previously learned. In this chapter, we will discuss such methods useful for solving many algebraic formulations.

Since the algebraic formulations of many word problems result in linear systems, we further discuss linear systems. Returning to the diet problem, we note that the solution to the diet problem was determined graphically. This was to provide insight and intuition regarding linear systems. However, in this section, we will discuss algebraic methods for solving linear systems. Such methods provide more efficient methods for solving linear systems.

We summarize as follows.

SUMMARY

Solution to a Linear System

The **solution** to a linear system of two equations in two variables is given by the coordinates of any point where the corresponding straight lines *intersect*.

Since a pair of straight lines can be drawn so that they intersect, are parallel, or coincide (see Figure 5-2), then three possibilities exist for a solution to a linear system. These are described in the following box.

Linear System Possibilities

Two Equations in Two Variables

1. The linear system has a **unique solution.** The straight lines *intersect* at one point [see Figure 5-2(a)].
2. The linear system has **no solution.** The straight lines are *parallel* and do not intersect [see Figure 5-2(b)].
3. The linear system has **infinitely many solutions.** The straight lines *coincide* [see Figure 5-2(c)].

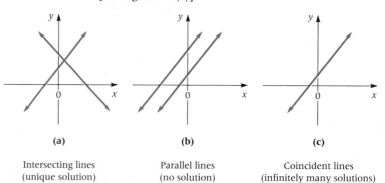

(a)

(b)

(c)

Intersecting lines
(unique solution)

Parallel lines
(no solution)

Coincident lines
(infinitely many solutions)

FIGURE 5-2

Solving Linear Systems

We now discuss two algebraic methods for solving linear systems of two equations in two variables. The first method, which involves adding equations to eliminate variables, is called the **method of elimination.** The second method involves solving either equation for one variable in terms of the other variable and then substituting the result into the other equation. Hence, this method is called the **method of substitution.** Although these methods can be generalized to larger size linear systems, they are most efficient for linear systems of two equations in two variables, and, therefore, we present them from that perspective. In Section 5-2, we will learn a method that is very efficient for any size linear system.

Method of Elimination

We return to the linear system associated with the diet problem of this section. We restate the linear system below.

$$3x + 4y = 64$$
$$6x + 5y = 98$$

To solve a linear system by the method of elimination, the linear system must be written so that the coefficients of one of the variables are additive inverses. Then the two equations can be added with the result that the variable whose coefficients are additive inverses is *eliminated.* Thus, for the above linear system, we multiply the first equation by -2 to obtain

$$-2(3x + 4y) = (-2)64 \qquad \longrightarrow \qquad -6x - 8y = -128$$
$$6x + 5y = 98 \qquad\qquad\qquad\qquad 6x + 5y = 98$$

The resulting linear system has the same solution as the original linear system and is thus said to be equivalent to the original system. Thus, we add the resulting equations as indicated below.

$$-6x - 8y = -128$$
$$\underline{6x + 5y = 98}$$
$$0x - 3y = -30$$
$$-3y = -30$$
$$y = 10$$

Note how the variable x is eliminated when we add the two equations.

We now substitute the value $y = 10$ into either of the two original equations and solve for the remaining variable. Choosing the first equation, we obtain

$$3x + 4y = 64$$
$$3x + 4(10) = 64$$
$$3x + 40 = 64 \qquad \text{Add } -40 \text{ to each side.}$$
$$3x = 24 \qquad \text{Multiply each side by 1/3.}$$
$$x = 8$$

Thus, the solution is $x = 8$ and $y = 10$, or $(8, 10)$. This corresponds to what we obtained graphically at the beginning of this section. We refrain from checking this solution as we have already done so earlier.

• EXAMPLE 5-1

Solve the linear system below by the elimination method.

$$5x + 2y = 22$$
$$4x - 3y = -10$$

Solution

Multiplying the first equation by 3 and the second by 2 gives an equivalent linear system with coefficients of y that are additive inverses. Thus,

$$3(5x + 2y) = 3(22) \qquad \longrightarrow \qquad 15x + 6y = 66$$
$$2(4x - 3y) = 2(-10) \qquad\qquad\qquad 8x - 6y = -20$$

Adding the two resulting equations gives

$$15x + 6y = 66$$
$$\underline{8x - 6y = -20}$$

Note how variable y is eliminated when we add the two equations.

$$23x + 0y = 46$$
$$23x = 46$$
$$x = 2$$

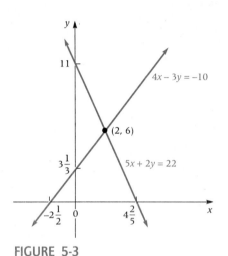

FIGURE 5-3

Now we substitute the value $x = 2$ into either equation of the original system and solve for y. Choosing the first equation, we obtain

$$5x + 2y = 22$$
$$5(2) + 2y = 22$$
$$10 + 2y = 22 \qquad \text{Add } -10 \text{ to both sides.}$$
$$2y = 12 \qquad \text{Multiply both sides by 1/2.}$$
$$y = 6$$

Thus, the solution to the linear system is $x = 2$ and $y = 6$. This is written as the ordered pair $(2, 6)$. The graph of this linear system is given in Figure 5-3. Also, we check our solution below.

$$5x + 2y = 22 \qquad\qquad 4x - 3y = -10$$
$$5(2) + 2(6) \overset{?}{=} 22 \qquad\qquad 4(2) - 3(6) \overset{?}{=} -10$$
$$22 \overset{\checkmark}{=} 22 \qquad\qquad -10 \overset{\checkmark}{=} -10$$

• EXAMPLE 5-2

Solve the linear system

$$3x - 2y = 8$$
$$-6x + 4y = 10$$

Solution

Multiplying the first equation by 2 gives an equivalent system with coefficients of y that are additive inverses. Hence,

$$6x - 4y = 16$$
$$-6x + 4y = 10$$

Adding the two equations of the equivalent system, we obtain

$$6x - 4y = 16$$
$$\underline{-6x + 4y = 10}$$
$$0 = 26$$

Inconsistent
(no solutions)

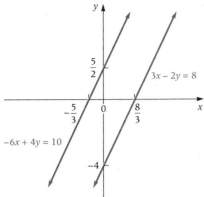

FIGURE 5-4

Infinitely many solutions

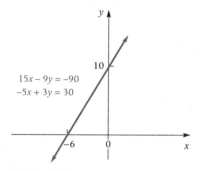

FIGURE 5-5

The statement $0 = 26$ is a false statement, indicating that the linear system has no solution. Such a linear system (having no solutions) is called **inconsistent.** The graph of this system appears in Figure 5-4. Note that the two straight lines are parallel and, therefore, do not intersect.

• **EXAMPLE 5-3** ─────────────────────────

Solve the linear system

$$-5x + 3y = 30$$
$$15x - 9y = -90$$

Solution

Multiplying the first equation by 3 yields the equivalent system

$$-15x + 9y = 90$$
$$15x - 9y = -90$$

Adding the two resulting equations, we obtain the true statement $0 = 0$. The statement $0 = 0$ indicates that both equations of the linear system are equivalent. Hence, they have the same graph. Thus, if we graph each equation on the same set of axes, we will draw one straight line on top of the other straight line. The intersection points consist of all points on either straight line, and, thus, there are infinitely many solutions (see Figure 5-5).

The following example provides an additional application of linear systems. Example 5-4, in particular, demonstrates the determination of an equilibrium point by solving a linear system.

• **EXAMPLE 5-4   Equilibrium Point.** ──────────────

The demand and supply equations for a given commodity are as follows:

$$\text{Demand equation} \to 5q + 2p = 50$$
$$\text{Supply equation} \to 4q - 3p = -52$$

where p is the unit price and q is the number of units in thousands. Find the equilibrium point.

Solution

Solving this system by the elimination method, we multiply the first equation by 3 and the second by 2 to obtain

$$15q + 6p = 150$$
$$8q - 6p = -104$$

Adding the resulting equations yields

$$23q = 46$$
$$q = 2$$

We may substitute $q = 2$ into either of the original equations. Choosing the first equation, we have

$$5q + 2p = 50$$
$$5(2) + 2p = 50$$
$$p = 20$$

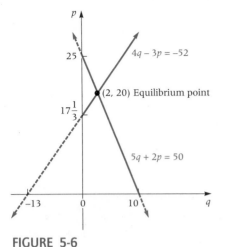

FIGURE 5-6

Thus, at a unit price of $20, supply = demand = 2 thousand units. The graphical interpretation appears in Figure 5-6.

Method of Substitution

Sometimes a linear system of two equations in two variables is most efficiently solved by the method of substitution. As mentioned earlier, this involves solving one of the equations for one variable in terms of the other variable and substituting the result into the other equation. For example, consider the linear system.

$$3x + 5y = 38$$
$$2x + y = 16$$

Since the second equation has a variable with a coefficient of 1, it is easy to solve for that variable and then substitute the result into the other equation. Thus, we solve the second equation for y to obtain

$$y = -2x + 16$$

and substitute this result into the first equation to get

$$3x + 5(-2x + 16) = 38$$

Solving for x gives

$3x - 10x + 80 = 38$	Combine the x-terms.
$-7x + 80 = 38$	Add -80 to both sides.
$-7x = -42$	Multiply both sides by $-1/7$.
$x = 6$	

Although we can substitute this result into either equation and solve for the other variable, the most efficient procedure is to substitute this result into the equation that gives one variable in terms of the other. Thus, we substitute $x = 6$ into the equation

$$y = -2x + 16$$

to obtain

$$y = -2(6) + 16$$
$$= 4$$

Thus, the solution to the linear system is $x = 6$ and $y = 4$. This can be written as the ordered pair $(6, 4)$. We check this solution below.

$$3x + 5y = 38 \qquad\qquad 2x + y = 16$$
$$3(6) + 5(4) \stackrel{?}{=} 38 \qquad\qquad 2(6) + 4 \stackrel{?}{=} 16$$
$$38 \stackrel{\checkmark}{=} 38 \qquad\qquad 16 \stackrel{\checkmark}{=} 16$$

We now consider an application.

• **EXAMPLE 5-5** _____

C.P. Realty, Inc., is planning to build a housing development consisting of two- and three-bedroom ranch-style houses. Public demand indicates a need for three times as many three-bedroom houses as two-bedroom houses. Each two-bedroom house provides a net profit of $15,000. Each three-bedroom house provides a new profit of $16,000. If C.P. Realty, Inc., must net a total profit of $6,300,000 from this development, how many of each type ranch house should be built?

Solution

Applying our problem-solving procedure yields the results below.

Step 1   *Identify the unknowns. Use letters to denote these quantities.*
We wish to determine the number of two-bedroom and three-bedroom houses to be built. Thus, we let

$$x = \text{number of two-bedroom houses}$$
$$y = \text{number of three-bedroom houses}$$

Step 2   *Organize the given information, and write the equations that express any relationships existing among the unknowns.*
The information is organized in the table below.

	Two-bedroom	Three-bedroom	
Profits	$15,000	$16,000	$6,300,000
Numbers	# of three-bedroom houses = 3(# of two-bedroom houses)		

Since each two-bedroom house provides a net profit of $15,000 and each three-bedroom a net profit of $16,000, then the expression

$$15,000x + 16,000y$$

represents the total net profit from building x two-bedroom and y three-bedroom houses. Since the desired total net profit must be $6,300,000, we set the above expression equal to 6,300,000 to obtain the equation

$$15,000x + 16,000y = 6,300,000$$

Also, since the number of three-bedroom houses must equal three times the number of two-bedroom houses, this relationship is expressed by the equation

$$y = 3x$$

Thus, we have the linear system

$$15,000x + 16,000y = 6,300,000$$
$$y = 3x$$

Step 3   *Solve the linear system of step 2.*
This system is most efficiently solved by the substitution method since the second equation expresses y in terms of x. *Substituting $3x$ for y in the first equation yields*

$$15,000x + 16,000(3x) = 6,300,000$$

Solving for x, we obtain

$$15,000x + 48,000x = 6,300,000$$
$$63,000x = 6,300,000$$
$$x = 100$$

We may substitute $x = 100$ into either of the two equations. Choosing the second equation, we obtain

$$y = 3(100)$$
$$= 300$$

Thus, C.P. Realty, Inc., should build $x = 100$ two-bedroom houses and $y = 300$ three-bedroom houses.

•

PROBLEM

We conclude this section by applying our problem-solving procedure to the Uniform CPA Examination problem encountered in the Introductory Application to this chapter.

SOLUTION

Step 1 *Identify the unknowns. Use letters to denote these quantities.*
For the above example, we must find the variable cost per unit. Thus, using notation developed in Chapter 1, we let

$$v = \text{variable cost per unit}$$

Step 2 *Organize the given information, and write the equations that express any relationships existing among the unknowns.*
In Chapter 1, we learned that a cost function is defined by the equation

$$C = vx + F$$

where C = total cost of producing x units, v = variable cost per unit, and F = fixed cost.

The first sentence of the problem indicates that if $x = 50,000$ units produced, then the total cost is $C = \$230,000$. Substituting these values for C and x into the cost equation

gives the equation

$$230,000 = v(50,000) + F$$

The first and second sentences of the problem indicate that if $x = 60,000$ units produced, then $C = \$280,000$, and the corresponding fixed costs are 25% more than those of the first equation. Substituting these values for C, x, and F into the cost equation gives

$$280,000 = v(60,000) + 1.25F$$

Thus, the two equations constitute a linear system such that

$$230,000 = v(50,000) + F$$
$$280,000 = v(60,000) + 1.25F$$

expresses the relationships among the various quantities of the problem.

Step 3 *Solve the linear system of step 2.*

The above linear system can be written as

$$50{,}000v + F = 230{,}000$$

$$60{,}000v + 1.25F = 280{,}000$$

To solve this system by the elimination method, we multiply the first equation by -6 and the second by 5 to obtain

$$-6(50{,}000v + F) = -6(230{,}000) \qquad -300{,}000v - 6F = -1{,}380{,}000$$

$$5(60{,}000v + 1.25F) = 5(280{,}000) \longrightarrow \quad 300{,}000v + 6.25F = 1{,}400{,}000$$

Adding the two equations gives

$$-300{,}000v - 6F = -1{,}380{,}000$$

$$\underline{300{,}000v + 6.25F = 1{,}400{,}000}$$

$$0v + 0.25F = 20{,}000$$

$$0.25F = 20{,}000$$

$$F = 80{,}000$$

Now we choose either of the original equations and substitute 80,000 for F. Choosing the first equation, we have

$$50{,}000v + F = 230{,}000$$

$$50{,}000v + 80{,}000 = 230{,}000 \qquad \text{Subtract 80,000 from each side.}$$

$$50{,}000v = 150{,}000 \qquad \text{Divide both sides by 50,000.}$$

$$v = 3 \qquad \text{Answer}$$

Thus, the answer to the problem is that the variable cost per unit is $3.

Exercises 5-1

Solve each of the following linear systems by the method of elimination.

1. $2x - 3y = 6$
$x - 7y = 25$

2. $4x - 5y = -2$
$3x + 2y = -13$

3. $4x + y = 8$
$6x - 2y = -9$

4. $2x + 3y = 3$
$12x - 15y = -4$

5. $-3x + 10y = 5$
$2x + 7y = 24$

6. $\dfrac{1}{2}x + 5y = 17$
$3x + 2y = 18$

7. $1.5x + 2y = 20$
$2.5x - 5y = -25$

8. $3.5x - y = 13$
$3x + 2y = 14$

Solve each of the following linear systems by the method of elimination. To eliminate the fractions, multiply each side of the equation by the common denominator of its fractions.

9. $\dfrac{1}{3}x - \dfrac{3}{2}y = -4$
$5x - 4y = 14$

10. $\dfrac{x}{5} + \dfrac{y}{4} = \dfrac{7}{10}$
$\dfrac{x}{3} - y = \dfrac{-5}{3}$

11. $\dfrac{x}{2} + \dfrac{y}{5} = \dfrac{8}{5}$

$\dfrac{x}{3} + \dfrac{y}{4} = \dfrac{17}{12}$

12. $\dfrac{x}{4} + \dfrac{3y}{5} = \dfrac{-7}{20}$

$5x - 3y = 8$

Solve each of the following by the method of substitution.

13. $2x + y = 21$
$\quad y = 5x$

14. $x + 2y = 24$
$\quad x = 4y$

15. $-5x + y = 13$
$\quad y = 7x - 1$

16. $2x + 3y = 36$
$\quad y = -4x + 2$

17. $\quad x = 2y - 5$
$3x + 4y = 5$

18. $\quad y = -2x + 1$
$5x + 3y = 7$

Solve each of the following linear systems and include its graphical interpretation.

19. $x + 2y = 1$
$\quad 3x - 5y = -8$

20. $2x - y = -7$
$\quad -x + 2y = 8$

21. $3x + 5y = 7$
$\quad 2x - 6y = 11$

22. $x + y = 11$
$\quad x - y = 1$

23. $2x + y = 11$
$\quad 3x + 2y = 18$

24. $-3x + 4y = 23$
$\quad 2x - 5y = -20$

Solve each of the following linear systems. Choose the method that you feel is the more efficient.

25. $-3x + 4y = 23$
$\quad 2x - 5y = -20$

26. $x + 2y = 2$
$\quad 3x + 5y = 9$

27. $2x + 3y = -13$
$\quad 4x - 5y = 29$

28. $3x - 2y = -14$
$\quad x + y = -3$

29. $\quad x + y = -2$
$-2x + 3y = -11$

30. $6x + y = -4$
$\quad 4x - 2y = -8$

31. $4x - 3y = 2$
$\quad x + 2y = -5$

32. $-2x + 5y = -9$
$\quad 3x - 2y = 8$

33. Try to solve the linear system

$$5x - 7y = 70$$
$$-10x + 14y = 120$$

Note that your result is the contradictory statement $0 = 260$. To explain this result, show that this linear system has no solution by expressing each linear equation in slope-intercept form. What do you observe? What are your conclusions? Include the graphical interpretation.

34. Try to solve the linear system

$$5x - 7y = 70$$
$$-10x + 14y = -140$$

Note that your result is the statement $0 = 0$. Show that this linear system has infinitely many solutions by expressing each linear equation in slope-intercept form. What do you observe? What are your conclusions? Include the graphical interpretation.

Determine which of the following have no solutions and which have infinitely many solutions.

35. $\quad 3x - 8y = 10$
$12x - 32y = 75$

36. $\quad 7x - 8y = -11$
$-35x + 40y = 55$

37. $2x - y = 1$
$-6x + 3y = 8$

38. $x - 2y = 1$
$-3x + 6y = -3$

39. $3x - y = 9$
$y = 3x$

40. $2x - y = 3$
$y = 2x + 3$

41. *Nutrition.* A diet must provide exactly 1200 milligrams of protein and 1000 milligrams of iron. These nutrients will be obtained by eating meat and spinach. Each pound of meat contains 500 milligrams of protein and 100 milligrams of iron. Each pound of spinach contains 200 milligrams of protein and 800 milligrams of iron. How many pounds of meat and spinach should be eaten in order to provide the proper amounts of nutrients?

42. *Agriculture.* A farmer wants to plant a combination of two crops, cabbage and corn, on 100 acres. Cabbage requires 60 person-hours of labor per acre, and corn requires 80 person-hours of labor per acre. If the farmer has 6600 person-hours available, how many acres of each crop should be planted?

43. *Product mix.* A toy company manufactures wagons and cars. The company usually sells four times as many wagons as cars. Each wagon provides a net profit of $6, and each car provides a net profit of $5. How many wagons and cars must be produced in order to give a total profit of $29,000?

44. *Equilibrium point.* The demand and supply equations for watches appear in the linear system

Demand equation	$5p + 4q = 650$
Supply equation	$3p - 7q = -1020$

where p is the unit price and q is the number of watches. Find the equilibrium point. Interpret the result.

45. *Break-even analysis.* A company's sales revenue and cost equations appear in the linear system

Revenue equation	$y = 25x$
Cost equation	$y = 10x + 6000$

where x is the number of units and y is the dollar amount. Find the break-even point. Interpret the result.

46. *Product mix.* A company manufactures bicycles and tricycles. Each bicycle and tricycle must pass through two departments: department I (Assembly) and department II (Finishing and Inspection). Each bicycle requires 3 hours in department I and 5 hours in department II. Each tricycle requires 4 hours in department I and 2 hours in department II. Each month, departments I and II have available 450 and 400 hours, respectively. All of the time in both departments must be used (i.e., there must be no idle time or slack time). How many bicycles and tricycles should the company produce each month?

47. *Investment.* A young executive has $100,000 earmarked for investment. A portion of the $100,000 will be invested in corporate bonds that yield 12%, and the remainder will be invested in U.S. Treasury bonds that yield 8%. If the executive wishes to earn a yield of 9% on the $100,000, how much should be invested in each type of bond?

48. *Production costs.* The total cost of producing 100,000 units of some product is $500,000. The total cost of producing 200,000 units of this product is $790,000. Because of the need for additional facilities, the fixed costs for 200,000 units are 30% more than those for 100,000 units. Determine the variable cost per unit for this product and the fixed costs for both 100,000 and 200,000 units of production.

49. *Mixture.* A 20-pound mixture of cashews and peanuts costs $60. If cashews cost $6 per pound and peanuts cost $2 per pound, then how many pounds of each kind are there in the mixture?

50. *Product mix.* A company produces gadgets and widgets. Each gadget requires 3 pounds of a particular raw material, and each widget requires 5 pounds of the same raw material. The company's inventory contains 22 pounds of this raw material. Also, each gadget and widget must pass through a production department that has 20 hours of time available for the manufacture of these two products. Each gadget requires 2 hours, and each widget requires 6 hours of time in the production department. How many gadgets and widgets should be produced if all available resources are to be used?

51. *Decision making: Equipment selection.* A company is considering purchasing one of two possible machines for its production facility. Machine 1 costs $300,000 and produces items at a unit cost of $5. Machine 2 costs $400,000 and produces items at a unit cost of $4. If the total cost of each machine is determined by the formula

total cost = (unit production cost)(production volume) + machine cost

a) What production volume yields the same total cost for each machine?
b) For production volume of 60,000 units, which machine results in a lower total cost? State the minimum cost.
c) For a production volume of 120,000 units, which machine results in a lower total cost? State the minimum cost.

5-2 • LINEAR SYSTEMS; TABLEAUS; PROBLEM FORMULATION

In Section 5-1, we discussed two methods of solving linear systems consisting of two equations in two variables. In this section, we set the stage for the application of a more structured method for solving linear systems of any size. This method, called the Gauss-Jordan method of solving linear systems, is discussed in the next section. This method consists of replacing an original linear system with a succession of equivalent linear systems (which have the same solution as the original linear system), the last of which is made up of equations that explicitly give the solution values of the variables. Additionally, we present applied problems whose algebraic formulations result in linear systems with more than two equations in two variables.

Notation

In Section 5-1, we encountered linear equations written in the form

$$ax + by = c$$

where a, b, and c are constant real numbers. In this and succeeding sections of this chapter, we will often use x_1 and x_2 in place of x and y, respectively. This allows for a smoother transition to linear systems with more than two variables.

Tableau Format

The Gauss-Jordan method for solving linear systems is most efficiently performed by writing the linear system in **tableau** form. We illustrate by considering the linear system

$$2x_1 + 3x_2 = 9$$
$$x_1 + 4x_2 = 17$$

After making certain that the x_1- and x_2-terms and the right-hand-side constants are arranged in their separate columns, we write a tableau consisting of the coefficients of x_1 and x_2 and the right-hand-side constants, as shown below.

$$
\begin{array}{cc}
 & x_1 \quad x_2 \\
\text{first equation} \longrightarrow \\
\text{second equation} \longrightarrow
\end{array}
\begin{bmatrix} 2 & 3 & \bigg| & 9 \\ 1 & 4 & \bigg| & 17 \end{bmatrix}
\begin{array}{l} \longleftarrow \text{right-hand-side} \\ \longleftarrow \text{constants} \end{array}
$$

coefficients

A tableau, such as the one above, consists of a rectangular array of numbers. Later in this chapter we will learn that a rectangular array of numbers is called a **matrix.** A tableau, such as the one above, that contains coefficients of variables as well as right-hand-side constants, is called an **augmented matrix.** Thus, we will use the terms *tableau* and *augmented matrix* interchangeably.

Studying the above tableau, note that the first column consists of the coefficients of x_1 of the linear system, the second column consists of the coefficients of x_2, the vertical line replaces the equal signs, and the column to the right of the vertical line consists of the right-hand-side constants of the linear system.

Since it is important to be able to write a tableau (or augmented matrix) corresponding to a linear system, we now consider the following examples.

• **EXAMPLE 5-6** _____

Write the tableau (or augmented matrix) for this linear system.

$$-2x + 7y = 80$$
$$x + 4y = 60$$

Solution

The tableau (or augmented matrix) is given below.

$$
\begin{array}{cc}
x & y
\end{array}
\begin{bmatrix} -2 & 7 & \bigg| & 80 \\ 1 & 4 & \bigg| & 60 \end{bmatrix}
$$

• **EXAMPLE 5-7** _____

Write the tableau (or augmented matrix) for this linear system.

$$6x_1 - 9x_2 = 45$$
$$x_2 = 50$$

Solution

The tableau (or augmented matrix) is given below.

$$\begin{array}{cc} x_1 & x_2 \\ \begin{bmatrix} 6 & -9 \\ 0 & 1 \end{bmatrix} & \left.\begin{array}{c} 45 \\ 50 \end{array}\right] \end{array}$$

Since it is as important to be able to write a linear system corresponding to a given tableau as it is to be able to write a tableau corresponding to a given linear system, we consider the next examples.

• **EXAMPLE 5-8**

Write the linear system corresponding to the tableau

$$\begin{bmatrix} -4 & 6 & | & 20 \\ 3 & 2 & | & 46 \end{bmatrix}$$

Solution

Using x_1 and x_2 for variables and remembering that each row of the tableau represents an equation of the linear system, the corresponding linear system is

$$-4x_1 + 6x_2 = 20$$
$$3x_1 + 2x_2 = 46$$

• **EXAMPLE 5-9**

Write the linear system corresponding to the tableau

$$\begin{bmatrix} 1 & 0 & | & 5 \\ 0 & 1 & | & 7 \end{bmatrix}$$

Solution

The corresponding linear system is

$$\begin{array}{llll} x_1 + 0x_2 = 5 & \text{or} & x_1 \quad\;\; = 5 \\ 0x_1 + \;\; x_2 = 7 & & \quad\;\; x_2 = 7 \end{array}$$

Study the form of the columns to the left of the vertical line in the tableau of Example 5-9. Note that the first entry in column 1 is 1, with the remaining column 1 entry being 0; the second entry in column 2 is 1, with the remaining column 2 entry being 0. When a tableau (or augmented matrix) has the above format, the resulting linear system constitutes its own solution. In other words, the right-hand-side constants of such a tableau constitute the solution to the linear system. Such a tableau is called a **final tableau.** We note that the Gauss-Jordan method for solving linear systems, which we will study in the next section, provides a systematic procedure for changing the tableau corresponding to a linear system to an equivalent final tableau. The concept of a final tableau is so important that we summarize it in the box below.

Final Tableau

Two Equations in Two Variables

$$\begin{bmatrix} \overset{x_1}{1} & \overset{x_2}{0} & \bigg| & c_1 \\ 0 & 1 & \bigg| & c_2 \end{bmatrix}$$

A tableau having the above form constitutes the solution to its associated linear system. The **solution** is given by the right-hand-side constants as follows:

$$x_1 = c_1$$
$$x_2 = c_2$$

We now consider an applied problem that results in a linear system of three equations in three variables.

PROBLEM

Production Planning

A company makes videocassette recorders (VCRs), stereos, and televisions. To do this requires amounts of labor and raw materials. Specifically, each VCR requires 2 person-hours of time in the assembly department, 1 person-hour in the finishing and inspection department, and 4 units of a part identified as XBH104. Each stereo requires 3 person-hours in assembly, 2 person-hours in finishing and inspection, and 1 unit of part XBH104. Each television requires 5 person-hours in assembly, 1 person-hour in finishing and inspection, and 3 units of part XBH104. For the coming day, the company will have available 780 person-hours in the assembly department, 320 person-hours in the finishing and inspection department, and 500 units of part XBH104. How many of each item should the company make during the coming day if it is to operate at full capacity?

SOLUTION

We apply our problem-solving procedure to solve this problem.

Step 1 *Identify the unknowns. Use letters to denote these quantities.*
We must determine the number of VCRs, stereos, and televisions to make during the coming day. Thus, we let

- x = the number of VCRs to be made
- y = the number of stereos to be made
- z = the number of televisions to be made

Step 2 *Organize the given information, and write the equations that express any relationships existing among the unknowns.*
The information is organized in the following table.

	VCRs	Stereos	Televisions	Limited resources
Assembly	2	3	5	780 person-hours
Finishing and Inspection	1	2	1	320 person-hours
Part XBH104	4	1	3	500 parts

We now write the labor and raw material requirements as equations. First, we consider the assembly department. Since each VCR requires 2 person-hours in assembly, each stereo requires 3 person-hours, and each television requires 5 person-hours, then the expression

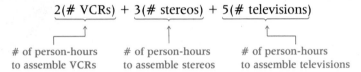

represents the number of person-hours of assembly department time used to make all three products. Since 780 person-hours of assembly time must be used, we set the above expression equal to 780 to give the equation

$$2(\# \text{ VCRs}) + 3(\# \text{ stereos}) + 5(\# \text{ televisions}) = 780$$

Since $x = \#$ VCRs, $y = \#$ stereos, and $z = \#$ televisions, the above becomes

$$2x + 3y + 5z = 780$$

Analogously, for the finishing and inspection department, the equation is

$$1(\# \text{ VCRs}) + 2(\# \text{ stereos}) + 1(\# \text{ televisions}) = \# \text{ person-hours}$$

or

$$x + 2y + z = 320$$

Note that this equation implies that the 320 person-hours available in the finishing and inspection department will be used. Finally, the requirement that 500 units of Part XBH104 be used is expressed by the equation

$$4(\# \text{ VCRs}) + 1(\# \text{ stereos}) + 3(\# \text{ televisions}) = \# \text{ parts}$$

or

$$4x + y + 3z = 500$$

Thus, we seek values of x, y, and z that simultaneously satisfy the three equations

$$2x + 3y + 5z = 780$$
$$x + 2y + z = 320$$
$$4x + y + 3z = 500$$

Note that each equation is of the form

$$a_1 x + a_2 y + a_3 z = b$$

where a_1, a_2, a_3, and b are real number constants. Such an equation is a **linear equation in three variables.** Later we will give a more formal definition of a linear equation in n variables. These three equations constitute a **system** of three linear equations in three variables.

Step 3   *Solve the linear system of step 2.*

A **solution** to a linear system of three equations in three variables is a sequence of numbers x, y, and z that, when substituted into each equation, results in a true statement. In other words, the values of x, y, and z must satisfy all three equations. The solution may be written as the ordered triple (x, y, z). In the homework exercises for Section 5-3, we will present this linear system for solution by the Gauss-Jordan method. Now we give a more formal definition of a linear equation in n variables.

An equation of the form

$$a_1 x_1 + a_2 x_2 + \ldots + a_n x_n = b$$

where a_1, a_2, $\ldots$, a_n, and b are real number constants, is a **linear equation in n variables.** The variables $x_1, x_2, \ldots, x_n$ are often written as letters, $x, y, z, t, w, \ldots$, etc.

• **EXAMPLE 5-10**

Write the tableau (or augmented matrix) corresponding to the linear system for the above production planning problem.

Solution

Using the same concepts as for linear systems of two equations in two variables, we obtain

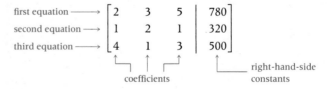

• **EXAMPLE 5-11**

Write the linear system corresponding to the tableau

$$\begin{bmatrix} 1 & 0 & 0 & | & -3 \\ 0 & 1 & 0 & | & 2 \\ 0 & 0 & 1 & | & 5 \end{bmatrix}$$

Solution

Remembering that each row of the tableau represents an equation of the linear system, the corresponding linear system is

$$
\begin{array}{rcl}
x_1 + 0x_2 + 0x_3 &=& -3 \\
0x_1 + x_2 + 0x_3 &=& 2 \\
0x_1 + 0x_2 + x_3 &=& 5
\end{array}
\quad \text{or} \quad
\begin{array}{rcl}
x_1 &=& -3 \\
x_2 &=& 2 \\
x_3 &=& 5
\end{array}
$$

•

Study the form of the columns to the left of the vertical line in the tableau of Example 5-11. Note that the first entry in column 1 is 1, with the remaining entries in column 1 being 0s, the second entry in column 2 is 1, with the remaining entries in column 2 being 0s, and the third entry in column 3 is 1, with the remaining entries in column 3 being 0s. When a tableau has the above format, the resulting linear system constitutes its own solution. In other words, the constants to the right of the vertical line of such a tableau constitute the solution to the linear system. Such a tableau is called a **final tableau.** This is such an important concept that we summarize it in the box below.

SUMMARY

Final Tableau

The final tableau for a linear system consisting of n equations in n variables is given below.

$$
\begin{array}{ccccc|c}
x_1 & x_2 & x_3 & & x_n & \\
1 & 0 & 0 & \dots & 0 & c_1 \\
0 & 1 & 0 & \dots & 0 & c_2 \\
0 & 0 & 1 & \dots & 0 & c_3 \\
\vdots & \vdots & \vdots & & \vdots & \vdots \\
0 & 0 & 0 & & 1 & c_n
\end{array}
$$

The **solution** to the linear system is given by the right-hand-side constants as follows:

$$
\begin{array}{rcl}
x_1 & & = c_1 \\
x_2 & & = c_2 \\
x_3 & & = c_3 \\
& \cdots & \vdots \\
x_n & & = c_n
\end{array}
$$

We conclude this section with more applications that result in linear systems.

Application

A Transportation Problem

A company makes lawn tractors at two plants. The tractors must be transported from the two plants to two retail outlets, as is illustrated in Table 5-1. The plants are called supply points, and the retail outlets are called demand points. Studying Table 5-1, note that plants 1 and 2 have production capacities of 900 and 500 lawn tractors, respectively. Retail outlets 1 and 2 have demand requirements of 600 and 800 lawn tractors, respectively.

PROBLEM

If each plant is to operate at full capacity, how many lawn tractors should be shipped from each plant to each retail outlet in order to ensure that the retail outlets' demand requirements are met?

SOLUTION

Looking at Table 5-1, we let

- x_1 = number of lawn tractors shipped from plant 1 to retail outlet 1
- x_2 = number of lawn tractors shipped from plant 1 to retail outlet 2
- x_3 = number of lawn tractors shipped from plant 2 to retail outlet 1
- x_4 = number of lawn tractors shipped from plant 2 to retail outlet 2

Since plant 1 is to operate at full capacity, then

$$\underbrace{x_1 + x_2}_{\text{number shipped from plant 1}} = 900$$

Since plant 2 is to operate at full capacity, then

$$\underbrace{x_3 + x_4}_{\text{number shipped from plant 2}} = 500$$

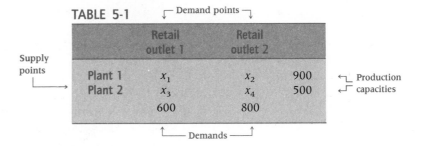

TABLE 5-1

Demand points

Supply points		Retail outlet 1	Retail outlet 2		Production capacities
	Plant 1	x_1	x_2	900	
	Plant 2	x_3	x_4	500	
		600	800		

Demands

The demand requirement of retail outlet 1 indicates that

$$\underbrace{x_1 + x_3}_{} = 600$$

number shipped to retail outlet 1

The demand requirement of retail outlet 2 indicates that

$$\underbrace{x_2 + x_4}_{} = 800$$

number shipped to retail outlet 2

Thus, our problem is formulated below.

$$
\begin{aligned}
x_1 + x_2 &&&= 900 \\
&& x_3 + x_4 &= 500 \\
x_1 && + x_3 &= 600 \\
x_2 && + x_4 &= 800
\end{aligned}
$$

where x_1, x_2, x_3, and $x_4 \geq 0$. Note that this linear system consists of four equations in four variables. We write its tableau below.

$$
\begin{bmatrix}
1 & 1 & 0 & 0 & 900 \\
0 & 0 & 1 & 1 & 500 \\
1 & 0 & 1 & 0 & 600 \\
0 & 1 & 0 & 1 & 800
\end{bmatrix}
$$

Investment: Portfolio Allocation

An investment company has $400,000 to be allocated for investment among three types of mutual funds: stock, bond, and money market. The projected annual rate of return and risk level for each of three types of funds are given below

Projected annual rate of return

Stock fund	Bond fund	Money market fund
20%	16%	8%

Risk level

Stock fund	Bond fund	Money market fund
9	3	1

PROBLEM

If the investor wants a projected average annual rate of return of at least 15.5% and a risk level of at most 5, how much should be invested in each type of fund in order to meet these requirements exactly?

SOLUTION

Let

- x_1 = number of dollars invested in the stock fund
- x_2 = number of dollars invested in the bond fund
- x_3 = number of dollars invested in the money market fund

Constraint 1. *Total amount invested.*
Since $400,000 is to be invested, then

$$x_1 + x_2 + x_3 = 400{,}000$$

Constraint 2. *Average annual rate of return.*

$$\text{average annual rate of return} = \frac{\text{dollars of interest earned in 1 year}}{\text{total number of dollars invested}}$$

Since x_1, x_2, and x_3 dollars are to be invested at 20%, 16%, and 8%, respectively, then

$$\text{average annual rate of return} = \frac{\overbrace{0.20x_1 + 0.16x_2 + 0.08x_3}^{\substack{\text{dollars of interest}\\\text{earned in 1 year}}}}{\underbrace{x_1 + x_2 + x_3}_{\substack{\text{total number of}\\\text{dollars invested}}}}$$

Since constraint 1 indicates that $x_1 + x_2 + x_3 = 400{,}000$, and since the average annual rate of return is to be 15.5%, we rewrite the above equation as

$$\frac{0.20x_1 + 0.16x_2 + 0.08x_3}{400{,}000} = 0.155$$

Multiplying both sides by 400,000 gives the constraint

$$0.20x_1 + 0.16x_2 + 0.08x_3 = 62{,}000$$

Constraint 3. *Average risk level.*
If x_1 dollars are invested at a risk level of 9, x_2 dollars are invested at a risk level of 3, and x_3 dollars are invested at a risk level of 1, then

$$\text{average risk level} = \frac{\overbrace{9x_1 + 3x_2 + 1x_3}^{\substack{\text{total risk weighted by number of}\\\text{dollars invested at each risk level}}}}{\underbrace{x_1 + x_2 + x_3}_{\text{total dollars invested}}}$$

Since $x_1 + x_2 + x_3 = 400{,}000$ from constraint 1, and since the average risk level is to be 5, then we rewrite the above as

$$\frac{9x_1 + 3x_2 + 1x_3}{400{,}000} = 5$$

Multiplying both sides by 400,000 gives the constraint

$$9x_1 + 3x_2 + x_3 = 2,000,000$$

Thus, our problem is formulated as the linear system

$$x_1 + x_2 + x_3 = 400,000$$
$$0.20x_1 + 0.16x_2 + 0.08x_3 = 62,000$$
$$9x_1 + 3x_2 + x_3 = 2,000,000$$

We write its tableau below.

$$\begin{bmatrix} 1 & 1 & 1 & 400,000 \\ 0.20 & 0.16 & 0.08 & 62,000 \\ 9 & 3 & 1 & 2,000,000 \end{bmatrix}$$

Exercises 5-2

Write the tableau corresponding to each of the following linear systems. Do not solve.

1. $2x + 7y = 9$
$-x + 4y = 15$

2. $-4x + 3y = 19$
$8x - 2y = 14$

3. $3x_1 = -1$
$4x_1 + 3x_2 = 7$

4. $x_1 + x_2 = 9$
$x_2 = 3$

5. $x_1 + 2x_2 + 5x_3 = 6$
$2x_1 - 3x_2 - 8x_3 = 4$
$-x_1 + 4x_2 + 5x_3 = 9$

6. $4x_1 + 8x_2 - x_3 = 10$
$x_1 + x_2 = 9$
$2x_1 + x_3 = 6$

7. $5x_1 - 7x_2 = 4$
$3x_2 = 9$
$x_1 + x_3 = 15$

8. $2x_1 = 10$
$3x_2 + x_3 = 6$
$x_3 = 5$

Write the linear system corresponding to each of the following tableaus.

9. $\begin{bmatrix} 4 & 8 & 5 \\ -2 & 6 & 0 \end{bmatrix}$

10. $\begin{bmatrix} 3 & -1 & 2 \\ 5 & -2 & 6 \end{bmatrix}$

11. $\begin{bmatrix} -1 & 1 & 2 & 3 \\ 4 & 0 & -1 & 5 \\ 2 & 1 & -1 & 6 \end{bmatrix}$

12. $\begin{bmatrix} 1 & 0 & -1 & 9 \\ 2 & 4 & 3 & 1 \\ 0 & 0 & 1 & 4 \end{bmatrix}$

13. $\begin{bmatrix} 1 & 0 & 1 & 2 \\ 0 & 1 & 0 & 3 \\ 0 & 0 & 1 & 5 \end{bmatrix}$

14. $\begin{bmatrix} 1 & 0 & 0 & 8 \\ 0 & 1 & 0 & 2 \\ 0 & 0 & 1 & 7 \end{bmatrix}$

Indicate which of the following is a final tableau. For those that are final tableaus, state the solution.

15. $\begin{bmatrix} 1 & 0 & 5 \\ 1 & -1 & 6 \end{bmatrix}$

16. $\begin{bmatrix} 1 & 0 & 4 \\ 0 & 1 & -6 \end{bmatrix}$

17. $\begin{bmatrix} 1 & 0 & 8 \\ 0 & 1 & 3 \end{bmatrix}$

18. $\begin{bmatrix} 0 & 1 & 4 \\ 1 & 0 & 3 \end{bmatrix}$

19. $\begin{bmatrix} 1 & 0 & 0 & 2 \\ 0 & 1 & 0 & -4 \\ 0 & 0 & 1 & 5 \end{bmatrix}$

20. $\begin{bmatrix} -1 & 0 & 0 & 3 \\ 0 & 0 & 1 & 2 \\ 0 & 1 & 0 & -1 \end{bmatrix}$

21. $\begin{bmatrix} 1 & 0 & 0 & 3 \\ 0 & -1 & 0 & 2 \\ 0 & 0 & 1 & 4 \end{bmatrix}$

22. $\begin{bmatrix} 1 & 0 & 0 & 4 \\ 0 & 1 & 0 & -2 \\ 0 & 0 & 1 & 2 \end{bmatrix}$

Applications

23. *Production planning.* A textile company manufactures three types of sweaters: conservative, sporty, and practical. The table below gives the time requirements in person-hours) for a dozen of each type of sweater in the various departments.

	Conservative	Sporty	Practical
Cutting department	5	2	3
Sewing department	3	2	4
Inspection department	1	2	1

If the cutting, sewing, and inspection departments have available 660, 480, and 220 hours, respectively, then how many dozen of each type of sweater should be manufactured? Write the linear system for this problem. Do not solve the linear system.

24. *Investment: Portfolio allocation.* An investor has $600,000 to be allocated among three types of mutual funds: stock, bond, and money market. The projected annual rates of return and risk levels for these three types of funds are given below.

Projected annual rate of return

Stock fund	Bond fund	Money market fund
16%	12%	8%

Risk level

Stock fund	Bond fund	Money market fund
6	3	1

If the investor wants a projected average annual rate of return of at least 13% and a risk level of at most 4, how much should be invested in each type of fund in order to meet these requirements exactly? Write the linear system for this problem. Do not solve.

25. *Transportation problem.* A company makes roll-top desks at two plants. The desks must be transported from the two plants to two retail outlets, as is illustrated in Table 5-2. The production capacities of the plants and demand requirements of the retail outlets are given in Table 5-2.

TABLE 5-2

	Retail outlet 1	Retail outlet 2		
Plant 1	x_1	x_2	300	⌐ Production
Plant 2	x_3	x_4	200	⌐ capacities
	150	350		

└──── Demand ────┘

If each plant is to operate at full capacity, how many desks should be shipped from each plant to each retail outlet in order to ensure that the retail outlets' demand requirements are met exactly? Write the linear system for this problem. Do not solve.

26. *Nutrition.* A diet is to consist of three types of foods: A, B, and C. The diet is to provide at least 3100 milligrams of protein, at least 2050 milligrams of iron, and at least 2800 milligrams of calcium. The following table gives the amounts of the above nutrients contained per unit of each type food.

Milligrams per unit of food type

	Food A	Food B	Food C
Protein	8	2	10
Iron	2	7	4
Calcium	6	4	8

If the nutritional requirements are to be met exactly, how many units of each type of food should be included in the diet? Write the linear system for this problem. Do not solve.

27. *Investment: Portfolio allocation.* An investor has $2,000,000 to be allocated among three types of investments: real estate, stocks, and bonds. The projected annual rate of return and risk level for each of the three investments are given below

Projected annual rate of return

Real Estate	Stocks	Bonds
12%	9%	8%

Risk level

Real Estate	Stocks	Bonds
4	6	3

If the investor wants a projected average annual rate of return of at least 11% and a risk level of at most 5, how much should be invested in each type of investment in order to meet these requirements exactly? Write the linear system for this problem. Do not solve.

5-3   • GAUSS-JORDAN METHOD OF SOLVING LINEAR SYSTEMS

In Section 5-2, we learned how to write a linear system in tableau form. We also encountered problems that, when formulated algebraically, resulted in linear systems of sizes larger than two equations in two variables. In this section, we present a method for efficiently solving linear systems of any size. This method is called the **Gauss-Jordan method.** Before proceeding, we restate three possibilities that exist for a solution to a linear system.

SUMMARY

Linear System Possibilities

1. The linear system has a **unique solution.**
2. The linear system has **no solution.**
3. The linear system has **infinitely many solutions.**

In Section 5-1, we provided graphical insight into each of the above possibilities for linear systems consisting of two equations in two variables. For linear systems of three equations in three variables, we note that each equation represents a plane in three-dimensional space. Figure 5-7 illustrates some of the possible relationships among three planes. Specifically, the three planes in Figure 5-7(a) intersect at a single point. This illustrates a linear system that has a unique solution. If the letters x, y, and z denote the

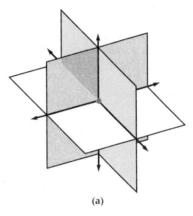

(a)

Unique solution
Planes intersect at a single point

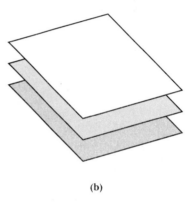

(b)

No solution
Parallel planes

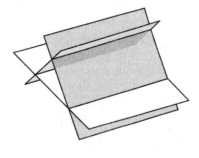

(c)

No solution
There is no point where all
three planes intersect

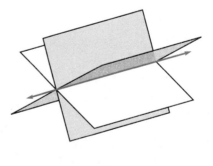

(d)

Infinitely many solutions
The three planes intersect in a straight line

FIGURE 5-7

variables of the linear system, then the intersection point of all three planes is denoted by the ordered triple (x, y, z) that satisfies all three equations. Observe that the planes of Figure 5-7(b) are parallel and, therefore, do not intersect. This illustrates a linear system that has no solution. Figure 5-7(c) illustrates three planes that do not intersect at a single point. This also illustrates a linear system that has no solution. Finally, Figure 5-7(d) illustrates three planes that intersect in a straight line. Each point on the straight line constitutes a solution to the linear system. Since there are infinitely many points on a straight line, there are infinitely many solutions to the respective linear system.

Row Operations

We now consider the Gauss-Jordan method for solving linear systems. As we mentioned in Section 5-2, this method consists of replacing an original linear system by a succession of equivalent linear systems (which have the same solution as the original linear system), the last of which is made up of equations that yield the solution values of the variables. An equivalent linear system is obtained by applying any of the following row operations to any equation (i.e., row) of a linear system. Note that we use the terms *row* and *equation* interchangeably.

SUMMARY

Three Fundamental Row Operations

1. Interchange two rows (equations).
2. Multiply a row (equation) by a nonzero constant.
3. Add a multiple of a row (equation) to another row (equation).

TABLE 5-3

1. Interchange two equations.

   $3x + 5y = 19 \longrightarrow x + 4y = 11$
   $x + 4y = 11 \longrightarrow 3x + 5y = 19$

2. Multiply an equation by a nonzero constant.

   $x + 4y = 11 \qquad\qquad\qquad x + 4y = 11$
   $4(3x + 5y) = 4(19) \longrightarrow 12x + 20y = 76$

3. Add a multiple of an equation to another equation.

   -3 times equation 1, add to equation 2

   $x + 4y = 11 \qquad -3(x + 4y) = -3(11) \longrightarrow -3x - 12y = -33$
   $3x + 5y = 19 \qquad\qquad\qquad\qquad\qquad\qquad\quad 3x + 5y = 19$

   Equation 2 becomes $\longrightarrow 0x - 7y = -14$

   or

   $-7y = -14$
   $y = 2$

Note that the above row operations are only formal restatements of some operations that were used to solve linear systems in Section 5-1. For example, if we interchange two equations—say, the first and second equations—of a linear system, we write the first equation second and the second equation first, as is illustrated in Table 5-3. The resulting linear system has the same solution as the original and is thus equivalent. Regarding the second row operation, if we multiply an equation by a nonzero constant (see Table 5-3), the resulting equation is equivalent to the original. We applied this property when using the elimination method of Section 5-1. Finally, we also used the third row operation in Section 5-1 when we multiplied an equation by a nonzero constant to get a variable whose coefficients were additive inverses and then added the two equations to eliminate the variable. This is also illustrated in Table 5-3.

Solving Linear Systems by the Gauss-Jordan Method

We now illustrate the use of row operations to solve linear systems by the Gauss-Jordan method. We begin by considering the linear system

$$2x_1 + 3x_2 = 9$$
$$x_1 + 4x_2 = 17$$

Notation

Note that we are using x_1 and x_2 in place of x and y. Since either choice is acceptable, we will sometimes use $x_1, x_2, x_3, \ldots$ as variables and sometimes $x, y, z, \ldots$.

After making certain that the x_1- and x_2-terms and the right-hand-side constants are arranged in their separate columns, then, as was discussed in Section 5-2, we write a tableau consisting of the coefficients of x_1 and x_2 and the right-hand-side constants, as shown below.

Initial Tableau

$$\begin{bmatrix} 2 & 3 & 9 \\ 1 & 4 & 17 \end{bmatrix}$$

Since the above tableau is associated with the original linear system to be solved, it is called the **initial tableau.**

Now we must use row operations to obtain an equivalent final tableau having the form below.

Final Tableau

$$\begin{bmatrix} 1 & 0 & c_1 \\ 0 & 1 & c_2 \end{bmatrix}$$

As was discussed in Section 5-2, the constants c_1 and c_2 represent the solution values to the linear system. We proceed as follows.

Step 1 We must change column 1 of the initial tableau to $\begin{bmatrix} 1 \\ 0 \end{bmatrix}$, the first column of the final tableau. We do this by changing the first coefficient of column 1 to 1 and then changing the remaining coefficient of column 1 to 0.

We change the first coefficient of column 1 to 1 by interchanging rows 1 and 2. This is written in shorthand form as R1 ↔ R2. The double arrow indicates that row 1 becomes row 2 and vice versa. This is illustrated below.

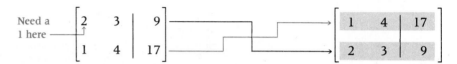

We note that the following row operation could have been used to accomplish the above goal.

Multiply Row 1 by 1/2

or, in other words, [(1/2)R1 → R1]

Note: The notation [(1/2)R1 → R1] means that row 1 is replaced with (1/2)R1.

Since this row operatifon would have given fractions for some row 1 entries, we use the previous row operation, R1 ↔ R2. We do not always have a choice of row operations to accomplish a desired goal.

Now we must change the remaining entry of column 1 to 0. We change the 2 of column 1 to 0 by the row operation

−2 times Row 1, add the result to Row 2

or, in other words, [(−2)R1 + R2 → R2]

Note: The notation [(−2)R1 + R2 → R2] means that row 2 is replaced with (−2)R1 + R2. This is illustrated below. The row operation computations are shown in the grey shaded area.

$$
\begin{array}{c}
\text{Need a} \\
\text{0 here}
\end{array}
\begin{bmatrix} 1 & 4 & | & 17 \\ 2 & 3 & | & 9 \end{bmatrix} \rightarrow
\begin{array}{l}
(-2)\text{R1:} \quad -2 \quad -8 \quad | -34 \\
\quad + \text{R2:} \quad\;\; 2 \quad\;\; 3 \quad | \;\;\; 9 \\
\hline
\quad\;\; \text{Sum} \rightarrow \quad 0 \quad -5 \; | -25
\end{array}
\rightarrow
\begin{bmatrix} 1 & 4 & | & 17 \\ 0 & -5 & | & -25 \end{bmatrix}
$$

Step 2 Now we must change column 2 to $\begin{bmatrix} 0 \\ 1 \end{bmatrix}$, the second column of the final tableau. We do this by changing the second coefficient of column 2 to 1 and then changing the remaining coefficient of column 2 to 0.

We first change the −5 of column 2 to 1 by the row operation

Multiply Row 2 by −1/5

or, in other words, [(−1/5)R2 → R2]

This is illustrated below. The row operation computations are shown in the grey shaded area.

Need a 1 here
$$\begin{bmatrix} 1 & 4 & | & 17 \\ 0 & -5 & | & -25 \end{bmatrix} \rightarrow \boxed{(-1/5)R2: \quad 0 \quad 1 \; | \; 5} \rightarrow \begin{bmatrix} 1 & 4 & | & 17 \\ 0 & 1 & | & 5 \end{bmatrix}$$

Now we must change the remaining entry, 4, of column 2 to 0. We do this by using the row operation

-4 times Row 2, add the result to Row 1

or, in other words, $[(-4)R2 + R1 \rightarrow R1]$

This is illustrated below. The row operation computations are shown in the grey shaded area.

Need a 0 here
$$\begin{bmatrix} 1 & 4 & | & 17 \\ 0 & 1 & | & 5 \end{bmatrix} \rightarrow \begin{array}{l} (-4)R2: \quad 0 \quad -4 \; | \; -20 \\ + R1: \quad 1 \quad 4 \; | \; 17 \\ \hline \text{Sum} \rightarrow \quad 1 \quad 0 \; | \; -3 \end{array} \rightarrow \begin{array}{c} \textit{Final Tableau} \\ \begin{bmatrix} 1 & 0 & | & -3 \\ 0 & 1 & | & 5 \end{bmatrix} \end{array}$$

The final tableau indicates the solution $x_1 = -3$ and $x_2 = 5$. We check this result below.

$$2x_1 + 3x_2 = 9 \qquad\qquad x_1 + 4x_2 = 17$$
$$2(-3) + 3(5) \overset{?}{=} 9 \qquad (-3) + 4(5) \overset{?}{=} 17$$
$$9 \overset{\checkmark}{=} 9 \qquad\qquad 17 \overset{\checkmark}{=} 17$$

We now present an overall summary, followed by a step-by-step summary, of the Gauss-Jordan method.

OVERALL SUMMARY

Gauss-Jordan Method

Consider the linear system

$$a_{11}x_1 + a_{12}x_2 + \ldots + a_{1n}x_n = b_1$$
$$a_{21}x_1 + a_{22}x_2 + \ldots + a_{2n}x_n = b_2$$
$$\vdots \qquad \vdots \qquad\qquad \vdots \qquad \vdots$$
$$a_{n1}x_1 + a_{n2}x_2 + \ldots + a_{nn}x_n = b_n$$

where the double subscript (i, j) of a_{ij} denotes the location of a_{ij} within the tableau. Specifically, the double subscript (i, j) of the coefficient a_{ij} indicates that a_{ij} is located in row i and column j of the tableau. Thus, a_{23} is located in row 2 and column 3, a_{31} is located in row 3 and column 1, etc.

continues

OVERALL SUMMARY—*Continued*

To solve such a linear system by the Gauss-Jordan method, we begin with the initial tableau (shown below)

Initial Tableau

$$\left[\begin{array}{ccccc|c} a_{11} & a_{12} & \cdots & a_{1n} & & b_1 \\ a_{21} & a_{22} & \cdots & a_{2n} & & b_2 \\ \cdot & \cdot & & \cdot & & \cdot \\ \cdot & \cdot & & \cdot & & \cdot \\ a_{n1} & a_{n2} & \cdots & a_{nn} & & b_n \end{array}\right]$$

and use row operations to obtain the final tableau (shown below)

Final Tableau

$$\left[\begin{array}{ccccc|c} 1 & 0 & \cdots & 0 & & c_1 \\ 0 & 1 & \cdots & 0 & & c_2 \\ \cdot & \cdot & & \cdot & & \cdot \\ \cdot & \cdot & & \cdot & & \cdot \\ 0 & 0 & \cdots & 1 & & c_n \end{array}\right]$$

where $x_1 = c_1, x_2 = c_2, \ldots, x_n = c_n$ is the solution to the linear system. If we cannot obtain the final tableau, then the linear system has either no solutions or infinitely many solutions.

STEP-BY-STEP SUMMARY

Gauss-Jordan Method

Step 1   Change column 1 of the initial tableau to $\begin{bmatrix} 1 \\ 0 \\ \cdot \\ \cdot \\ 0 \end{bmatrix}$ by changing the first coefficient of column 1 to 1 and then changing the remaining coefficients of column 1 to 0s. The 1 is usually obtained by using the row operation "Multiply a row by a nonzero constant." Sometimes the row operation "Interchange two rows" is helpful here, as we saw in the illustrative example of this section. The 0s are usually obtained by using the row operation "Add a multiple of a row to another row."

When this step is completed, the tableau will look like the one shown below.

continues

STEP-BY-STEP SUMMARY—*Continued*

Step 2   Change column 2 of the resulting tableau to $\begin{bmatrix} 0 \\ 1 \\ 0 \\ \cdot \\ \cdot \\ \cdot \\ 0 \end{bmatrix}$ by changing the second coefficient of column 2 to 1 and then changing the remaining coefficients of column 2 to 0s. Again, the 1 is usually obtained by using the row operation "Multiply a row by a nonzero constant," and the 0s are usually obtained by using the row operation "Add a multiple of a row to another row."

When this step is completed, the tableau will look like the following:

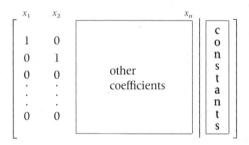

Step n   Change column n of the previous tableau to $\begin{bmatrix} 0 \\ \cdot \\ \cdot \\ \cdot \\ 0 \\ 1 \end{bmatrix}$ by changing the nth coefficient of column n to 1 and then changing the remaining coefficients to 0s. Again, the 1 is usually obtained by using the row operation "Multiply a row by a nonzero constant," and the 0s are usually obtained by using the row operation "Add a multiple of a row to another row."

When this step is completed, the tableau will look like the final tableau shown below.

Final Tableau

$$\begin{bmatrix} x_1 & x_2 & x_3 & & x_n & \\ 1 & 0 & 0 & \cdots \cdots 0 & & c_1 \\ 0 & 1 & 0 & \cdots \cdots 0 & & c_2 \\ 0 & 0 & 1 & \cdots \cdots 0 & & c_3 \\ \cdot & \cdot & \cdot & & \cdot & \cdot \\ \cdot & \cdot & \cdot & & \cdot & \cdot \\ 0 & 0 & 0 & \cdots \cdots 1 & & c_n \end{bmatrix}$$

The following examples further illustrate the Gauss-Jordan method.

• **EXAMPLE 5-12** _____

Solve the following linear system by the Gauss-Jordan method.

$$x_1 + 2x_2 - x_3 = 4$$
$$x_1 + x_2 - 2x_3 = 2$$
$$x_1 + 2x_2 + 3x_3 = 8$$

Solution

We first write the initial tableau

Initial Tableau

$$\begin{bmatrix} 1 & 2 & -1 & 4 \\ 1 & 1 & -2 & 2 \\ 1 & 2 & 3 & 8 \end{bmatrix}$$

and then we use row operations, as outlined in the step-by-step summary of the Gauss-Jordan method on pages 274-275.

Step 1 *Change column 1 of the initial tableau to* $\begin{bmatrix} 1 \\ 0 \\ 0 \end{bmatrix}$.

We already have a 1 for the first element of column 1. We need a 0 for the second element in column 1. This is obtained by the row operation

-1 times Row 1, add the result to Row 2

or, in other words, $[(-1)R1 + R2 \rightarrow R2]$

This is illustrated below. The row operation computations are shown in the grey shaded area.

We now need a 0 for the third element of column 1. This is obtained by the row operation

-1 times Row 1, add the result to Row 3

or, in other words, $[(-1)R1 + R3 \rightarrow R3]$

This is illustrated below.

Step 2 *Change column 2 of the above tableau to* $\begin{bmatrix} 0 \\ 1 \\ 0 \end{bmatrix}$.

First, we get the 1 by using the row operation

Multiply Row 2 by -1

or, in other words, $[(-1)R2 \rightarrow R2]$

This is illustrated below. The row operation computations are shown in the grey shaded area.

$$
\begin{bmatrix} 1 & 2 & -1 & 4 \\ 0 & -1 & -1 & -2 \\ 0 & 0 & 4 & 4 \end{bmatrix} \rightarrow \boxed{(-1)R2: \quad 0 \ 1 \ 1 \ | \ 2} \rightarrow \begin{bmatrix} 1 & 2 & -1 & 4 \\ 0 & 1 & 1 & 2 \\ 0 & 0 & 4 & 4 \end{bmatrix}
$$

Need a 1 here

Now we need a 0 for the first element of column 2. We use the row operation

$$-2 \text{ times Row 2, add the result to Row 1}$$

or, in other words, $[(-2)R2 + R1 \rightarrow R1]$

This is illustrated below. The row operation computations are shown in the grey shaded area.

$$
\begin{bmatrix} 1 & 2 & -1 & 4 \\ 0 & 1 & 1 & 2 \\ 0 & 0 & 4 & 4 \end{bmatrix} \rightarrow
\begin{array}{l} (-2)R2: \ 0 \ -2 \ -2 \ | -4 \\ + R1: \ \ 1 \ \ \ 2 \ -1 \ | \ \ 4 \\ \hline \text{Sum} \rightarrow \ 1 \ \ \ 0 \ -3 \ | \ \ 0 \end{array}
\rightarrow \begin{bmatrix} 1 & 0 & -3 & 0 \\ 0 & 1 & 1 & 2 \\ 0 & 0 & 4 & 4 \end{bmatrix}
$$

Need a 0 here

Step 3   *Change column 3 of the above tableau to* $\begin{bmatrix} 0 \\ 0 \\ 1 \end{bmatrix}$.
First we get the 1 by the row operation

$$\text{Multiply Row 3 by } 1/4$$

or, in other words, $[(1/4)R3 \rightarrow R3]$

This is illustrated below. The row operation computations are shown in the grey shaded area.

$$
\begin{bmatrix} 1 & 0 & -3 & 0 \\ 0 & 1 & 1 & 2 \\ 0 & 0 & 4 & 4 \end{bmatrix} \rightarrow \boxed{(1/4)R3: \quad 0 \ 0 \ 1 \ | \ 1} \rightarrow \begin{bmatrix} 1 & 0 & -3 & 0 \\ 0 & 1 & 1 & 2 \\ 0 & 0 & 1 & 1 \end{bmatrix}
$$

Need a 1 here

Now we need a 0 for the second entry in column 3. This is obtained by using the row operation

$$-1 \text{ times Row 3, add the result to Row 2}$$

or, in other words, $[(-1)R3 + R2 \rightarrow R2]$

This is illustrated below. The row operation computations are shown in the grey shaded area.

$$
\begin{bmatrix} 1 & 0 & -3 & 0 \\ 0 & 1 & 1 & 2 \\ 0 & 0 & 1 & 1 \end{bmatrix} \rightarrow
\begin{array}{l} (-1)R3: \ \ 0 \ 0 \ -1 \ | -1 \\ + R2: \ \ \ 0 \ 1 \ \ \ 1 \ | \ \ 2 \\ \hline \text{Sum} \ \ \ \ \ 0 \ 1 \ \ \ 0 \ | \ \ 1 \end{array}
\rightarrow \begin{bmatrix} 1 & 0 & -3 & 0 \\ 0 & 1 & 0 & 1 \\ 0 & 0 & 1 & 1 \end{bmatrix}
$$

Need a 0 here

Now we need a 0 for the first entry in column 3. We use the row operation

$$3 \text{ times Row 3, add the result to Row 1}$$

or, in other words, $[(3)R3 + R1 \rightarrow R1]$

This is illustrated below. The row operation computations are shown in the grey shaded area.

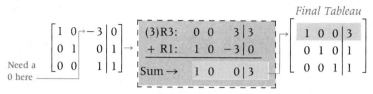

Final Tableau

$$\begin{bmatrix} 1 & 0 & -3 & | & 0 \\ 0 & 1 & 0 & | & 1 \\ 0 & 0 & 1 & | & 1 \end{bmatrix} \rightarrow \begin{array}{l} (3)\text{R3:} \quad 0 \;\; 0 \quad\;\; 3 \,|\, 3 \\ \underline{+ \text{ R1:} \quad 1 \;\; 0 \;\; -3 \,|\, 0} \\ \text{Sum} \rightarrow \;\; 1 \;\; 0 \quad\;\; 0 \,|\, 3 \end{array} \rightarrow \begin{bmatrix} 1 & 0 & 0 & | & 3 \\ 0 & 1 & 0 & | & 1 \\ 0 & 0 & 1 & | & 1 \end{bmatrix}$$

Need a 0 here

The final tableau indicates the solution $x_1 = 3$, $x_2 = 1$, $x_3 = 1$, or the ordered triple $(3, 1, 1)$. We leave it to the reader to check this solution.

• EXAMPLE 5-13 _____

Use the Gauss-Jordan method of row operation to solve the linear system

$$x_1 + 2x_2 = 3$$
$$2x_1 + 4x_2 = 8$$

Solution

We first write the initial tableau

Initial Tableau

$$\begin{bmatrix} 1 & 2 & | & 3 \\ 2 & 4 & | & 8 \end{bmatrix}$$

and then use row operations as outlined in the summary on pages 274-275.

Step 1 *Change column 1 to* $\begin{bmatrix} 1 \\ 0 \end{bmatrix}$.

Since we already have a 1 for the first element of column 1, we proceed to change the remaining entry of column 1 to 0 by using the row operation

−2 times Row 1, add the result to Row 2

or, in other words, [(−2)R1 + R2 → R2]

The resulting tableau is

$$\begin{bmatrix} 1 & 2 & | & 3 \\ 0 & 0 & | & 2 \end{bmatrix}$$

Notice that the second row of the above tableau gives the equation

$$0x_1 + 0x_2 = 2 \quad \text{or} \quad 0 = 2$$

This is an untrue statement (an *inconsistency*) and, hence, an indication that the system has *no solution.* Thus, we proceed no further.

• EXAMPLE 5-14 _____

Use the Gauss-Jordan method to solve

$$x_1 + 2x_2 + x_3 = 3$$
$$2x_1 - 3x_2 - 2x_3 = 5$$
$$2x_1 + 4x_2 + 2x_3 = 6$$

Solution

We first write the initial tableau

Initial Tableau

$$\begin{bmatrix} 1 & 2 & 1 & | & 3 \\ 2 & -3 & -2 & | & 5 \\ 2 & 4 & 2 & | & 6 \end{bmatrix}$$

and then use row operations as outlined in the summary on pages 274-275.

Step 1   *Change column 1 to* $\begin{bmatrix} 1 \\ 0 \\ 0 \end{bmatrix}$.

We already have a 1 for the first coefficient of column 1. We need 0s for the remaining coefficients of column 1. These are obtained by the following two row operations:

- $[(-2)R1 + R2 \rightarrow R2]$ gives us a 0 for the second entry in Column 1.
- $[(-2)R1 + R3 \rightarrow R3]$ gives us a 0 for the third element of Column 1.

The resulting tableau appears below.

$$\begin{bmatrix} 1 & 2 & 1 & 3 \\ 0 & -7 & -4 & -1 \\ 0 & 0 & 0 & 0 \end{bmatrix}$$

Note that since all the entries in row 3 are 0s, it will not be possible to get a 1 for the third element in row 3. If we write the linear system for the above tableau, we get

$$x_1 + 2x_2 + x_3 = 3$$
$$-7x_2 - 4x_3 = -1$$
$$0x_1 + 0x_2 + 0x_3 = 0$$

Observe that the third equation is $0 = 0$, which indicates that the original linear system is equivalent to a system with one less equation.

We continue our attempt to obtain the final tableau and, thus, proceed to step 2.

Step 2   *Change column 2 of the above tableau to* $\begin{bmatrix} 0 \\ 1 \\ 0 \end{bmatrix}$.

We get the 1 by the row operation $[(-1/7)R2 \rightarrow R2]$. The resulting tableau is

$$\begin{bmatrix} 1 & 2 & 1 & 3 \\ 0 & 1 & 4/7 & 1/7 \\ 0 & 0 & 0 & 0 \end{bmatrix}$$

Now, we need a 0 for the first entry in column 2. Using the row operation $[(-2)R2 + R1 \rightarrow R1]$ gets us the 0. The resulting tableau is

$$\begin{bmatrix} 1 & 0 & -1/7 & 19/7 \\ 0 & 1 & 4/7 & 1/7 \\ 0 & 0 & 0 & 0 \end{bmatrix}$$

Step 3   *Change column 3 to* $\begin{bmatrix} 0 \\ 0 \\ 1 \end{bmatrix}$.

However, since row 3 consists of all 0s, this is impossible. Thus, the preceding tableau is the final tableau. Writing the equations corresponding to this final tableau, we have

$$x_1 - \frac{1}{7}x_3 = \frac{19}{7}$$

$$x_2 + \frac{4}{7}x_3 = \frac{1}{7}$$

Note that the third equation, $0 = 0$, is deleted since it is satisfied by all ordered triples (x_1, x_2, x_3). Thus, the original linear system consisting of three equations in three variables is now reduced to two equations in three variables.

Infinitely Many Solutions

In general, when the final tableau of a linear system has more variables than equations, the linear system has infinitely many solutions. For such situations, we classify the variables into two groups:

1. The variables corresponding to the final tableau columns are called **basic variables.**
2. The remaining variables are called **nonbasic variables.**

These are illustrated below for the above problem.

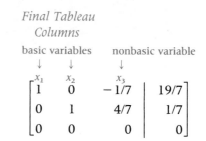

The infinitely many solutions to a linear system are expressed by solving for the basic variables in terms of the nonbasic variables.

Thus, for the above problem, we solve for x_1 and x_2 in terms of x_3, as is illustrated below.

$$x_1 = \frac{1}{7}x_3 + \frac{19}{7}$$

$$x_2 = -\frac{4}{7}x_3 + \frac{1}{7}$$

Now we let $x_3 = t$, where t denotes any real number; then the *infinitely many solutions* to the linear system are written as

$$x_1 = \frac{1}{7}t + \frac{19}{7}$$

$$x_2 = -\frac{4}{7}t + \frac{1}{7}$$

$$x_3 = t$$

If $t = 0$, then a solution to the linear system is given by

$$x_1 = \frac{1}{7}(0) + \frac{19}{7} = \frac{19}{7}$$

$$x_2 = -\frac{4}{7}(0) + \frac{1}{7} = \frac{1}{7}$$

$$x_3 = 0$$

If $t = 2$, then a solution is given by

$$x_1 = \frac{1}{7}(2) + \frac{19}{7} = 3$$

$$x_2 = -\frac{4}{7}(2) + \frac{1}{7} = -1$$

$$x_3 = 2$$

SUMMARY

Three Possibilities Exist for Linear Systems with n Equations in n Unknowns

1. *Unique solution.* A linear system has a unique solution if its final tableau has the form below.

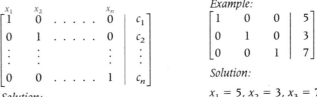

$$\begin{array}{ccccc} x_1 & x_2 & & x_n & \\ \begin{bmatrix} 1 & 0 & \ldots \ldots & 0 & c_1 \\ 0 & 1 & \ldots \ldots & 0 & c_2 \\ \vdots & \vdots & & \vdots & \vdots \\ 0 & 0 & \ldots \ldots & 1 & c_n \end{bmatrix} \end{array}$$

Solution:

$$x_1 = c_1,\ x_2 = c_2,\ \ldots,\ x_n = c_n$$

Example:

$$\begin{bmatrix} 1 & 0 & 0 & 5 \\ 0 & 1 & 0 & 3 \\ 0 & 0 & 1 & 7 \end{bmatrix}$$

Solution:

$$x_1 = 5,\ x_2 = 3,\ x_3 = 7$$

2. *No solution.* If a tableau contains an inconsistency, then there is no solution to the linear system. Recall that an inconsistency appears as a row with 0 entries to the left of the vertical line and a nonzero right-hand-side constant, as illustrated in the tableau below.

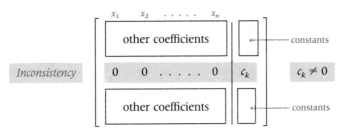

Example:

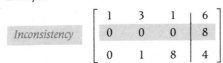

$$\text{Inconsistency} \quad \begin{bmatrix} 1 & 3 & 1 & 6 \\ 0 & 0 & 0 & 8 \\ 0 & 1 & 8 & 4 \end{bmatrix}$$

3. *Infinitely many solutions.* If the final tableau has more variables than equations, then there are infinitely many solutions. We then classify the variables as either **basic** or **nonbasic** variables, as illustrated below.

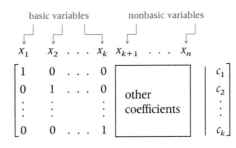

continues

SUMMARY—*Continued*

Then we **solve** for the basic variables in terms of the nonbasic variables.

Example:

basic variables   nonbasic variable

x_1 x_2 x_3

$$\begin{bmatrix} 1 & 0 & -2 & | & 5 \\ 0 & 1 & 3 & | & 4 \end{bmatrix} \quad \begin{array}{l} x_1 \quad -2x_3 = 5 \\ x_2 + 3x_3 = 4 \end{array} \quad \text{or} \quad \begin{array}{l} x_1 = \quad 2x_3 + 5 \\ x_2 = -3x_3 + 4 \end{array}$$

Example:

basic variables   nonbasic variables

x_1 x_2 x_3 x_4

$$\begin{bmatrix} 1 & 0 & -4 & 3 & | & 8 \\ 0 & 1 & 2 & -7 & | & 9 \end{bmatrix}$$

$$\begin{array}{l} x_1 \quad -4x_3 + 3x_4 = 8 \\ x_2 + 2x_3 - 7x_4 = 9 \end{array} \quad \text{or} \quad \begin{array}{l} x_1 = \quad 4x_3 - 3x_4 + 8 \\ x_2 = -2x_3 + 7x_4 + 9 \end{array}$$

• **EXAMPLE 5-15** _____

Using the Gauss-Jordan method, solve the linear system

$$\begin{array}{rrrrr} x_1 + 2x_2 & & + x_4 = & 5 \\ x_2 + & 2x_4 = & 6 \\ 2x_1 + 4x_2 + x_3 + & x_4 = & -5 \end{array}$$

Solution

We write the initial tableau.

$$\begin{bmatrix} 1 & 2 & 0 & 1 & | & 5 \\ 0 & 1 & 0 & 2 & | & 6 \\ 2 & 4 & 1 & 1 & | & -5 \end{bmatrix}$$

Since we have more variables than equations, we use row operations to try to obtain an equivalent tableau of the form

$$\begin{array}{cccc} x_1 & x_2 & x_3 & x_4 \\ \end{array}$$
$$\begin{bmatrix} 1 & 0 & 0 & t_1 & | & c_1 \\ 0 & 1 & 0 & t_2 & | & c_2 \\ 0 & 0 & 1 & t_3 & | & c_3 \end{bmatrix}$$

with x_4 as a nonbasic variable. This means that we should use row operations to try to change as many columns as possible to

$$\begin{bmatrix} 1 \\ 0 \\ 0 \end{bmatrix}, \begin{bmatrix} 0 \\ 1 \\ 0 \end{bmatrix}, \dots$$

Using the row operation $[(-2)R1 + R3 \rightarrow R3]$, followed by $[(-2)R2 + R1 \rightarrow R1]$, we transform the initial tableau into the final tableau below.

Final Tableau

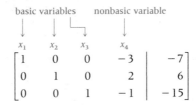

basic variables   nonbasic variable

$x_1 \quad x_2 \quad x_3 \quad x_4$

$$\begin{bmatrix} 1 & 0 & 0 & -3 & | & -7 \\ 0 & 1 & 0 & 2 & | & 6 \\ 0 & 0 & 1 & -1 & | & -15 \end{bmatrix}$$

Writing the equations corresponding to this tableau, we have

$$
\begin{aligned}
x_1 \qquad\qquad - 3x_4 &= -7 \\
x_2 \qquad + 2x_4 &= 6 \\
x_3 - x_4 &= -15
\end{aligned}
$$

Solving for the basic variables, x_1, x_2, x_3, in terms of the nonbasic variable, x_4, gives

$$
\begin{aligned}
x_1 &= 3x_4 - 7 \\
x_2 &= -2x_4 + 6 \\
x_3 &= x_4 - 15
\end{aligned}
$$

If we let $x_4 = t$, where t denotes any real number, then there are *infinitely many solutions* that are expressed as

$$
\begin{aligned}
x_1 &= 3t - 7 \\
x_2 &= -2t + 6 \\
x_3 &= t - 15 \\
x_4 &= t
\end{aligned}
$$

Thus, if $t = 0$, a solution is

$$
\begin{aligned}
x_1 &= 3(0) - 7 = -7 \\
x_2 &= -2(0) + 6 = 6 \\
x_3 &= 0 - 15 = -15 \\
x_4 &= 0
\end{aligned}
$$

If $t = 4$, a solution is

$$
\begin{aligned}
x_1 &= 3(4) - 7 = 5 \\
x_2 &= -2(4) + 6 = -2 \\
x_3 &= 4 - 15 = -11 \\
x_4 &= 4
\end{aligned}
$$

Application

A Transportation Problem

We now solve the transportation problem presented at the end of Section 5-2. Recall that we had to determine how many lawn tractors should be shipped from each plant (assuming each plant is operating at full capacity) to each retail outlet in order to ensure that the reail outlets' demand requirements are met exactly as indicated in Table 5-4 on page 284.

Recall that this problem yielded the linear system below.

Plant 1	$x_1 + x_2 \qquad\qquad = 900$
Plant 2	$x_3 + x_4 = 500$
Retail outlet 1	$x_1 \qquad + x_3 \qquad = 600$
Retail outlet 2	$x_2 \qquad + x_4 = 800$

TABLE 5-4

	Retail outlet 1	Retail outlet 2	
Plant 1	x_1	x_2	900 ⤶ Production
Plant 2	x_3	x_4	500 ⤶ capacities
	600	800	

↳———— Demands ————↱

We now proceed to solve the linear system by writing the initial tableau below.

Initial Tableau

$$\begin{array}{cccc} x_1 & x_2 & x_3 & x_4 \\ \left[\begin{array}{cccc|c} 1 & 1 & 0 & 0 & 900 \\ 0 & 0 & 1 & 1 & 500 \\ 1 & 0 & 1 & 0 & 600 \\ 0 & 1 & 0 & 1 & 800 \end{array}\right] \end{array}$$

Using the row operations $[(-1)R1 + R3 \rightarrow R3]$, $[R2 \leftrightarrow R4]$, $[(1)R2 + R3 \rightarrow R3]$, $[(-1)R2 + R1 \rightarrow R1]$, and $[(-1)R3 + R4 \rightarrow R4]$ in the order given, we obtain the final tableau.

Final Tableau

basic variables   nonbasic variable

↓   ↓   ↓   ↰

$$\begin{array}{cccc} x_1 & x_2 & x_3 & x_4 \\ \left[\begin{array}{cccc|c} 1 & 0 & 0 & -1 & 100 \\ 0 & 1 & 0 & 1 & 800 \\ 0 & 0 & 1 & 1 & 500 \\ 0 & 0 & 0 & 0 & 0 \end{array}\right] \end{array}$$

Solving for the basic variables in terms of the nonbasic variable, we express the *infinitely many solutions* as

$$\begin{aligned} x_1 &= x_4 + 100 \\ x_2 &= -x_4 + 800 \\ x_3 &= -x_4 + 500 \end{aligned}$$

or, letting $x_4 = t$,

$$\begin{aligned} x_1 &= t + 100 \\ x_2 &= -t + 800 \\ x_3 &= -t + 500 \\ x_4 &= t \end{aligned}$$

Since x_1, x_2, x_3, and $x_4 \geq 0$, then the following inequalities hold:

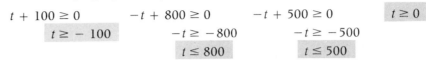

We have solved each of the above inequalities. The solutions appear in the color screens. Since t must satisfy all of the above results in the color screens, we graph these results in Figure 5-8 and shade the most restrictive range for t in color. Thus, t must satisfy the inequality $0 \leq t \leq 500$, as indicated in Figure 5-8.

Thus, if $t = 300$, then a solution to our problem is $x_1 = 300 + 100 = 400$, $x_2 = -300 + 800 = 500$, $x_3 = -300 + 500 = 200$, and $x_4 = 300$. Looking at Table 5-4, this means that $x_1 = 400$ lawn tractors should be shipped from plant 1 to retail outlet 1, $x_2 = 500$ lawn tractors should be shipped from plant 1 to retail outlet 2, $x_3 = 200$ lawn tractors should be shipped from plant 2 to retail outlet 1, and $x_4 = 300$ lawn tractors should be shipped from plant 2 to retail outlet 2. We should keep in mind that this is only one of infinitely many possible solutions; others can be obtained by choosing values of t such that $0 \leq t \leq 500$.

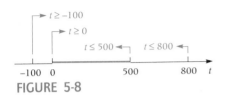

FIGURE 5-8

More Equations Than Variables

Sometimes we encounter a linear system with more equations than variables. The following linear system is such an example:

$$x_1 - x_2 = 1$$
$$4x_1 - x_2 = 7$$
$$3x_1 - x_2 = 5$$

Note that each equation has a straight line as its graph. Thus, the three lines might intersect at a common point, in which case there would be a unique solution; the three lines might be parallel, in which case there would be no solution; the three lines might intersect at different points, in which case there would be no solution; two of the three lines might be the same, so that the intersection with the third line would yield a unique solution; etc.

We will attempt to solve the preceding linear system by the Gauss-Jordan method of row operations. Writing the initial tableau, we have

$$\begin{bmatrix} 1 & -1 & | & 1 \\ 4 & -1 & | & 7 \\ 3 & -1 & | & 5 \end{bmatrix}$$

Since there are more equations than variables, we must use row operations to try to change as many columns as possible to

$$\begin{bmatrix} 1 \\ 0 \\ 0 \end{bmatrix}, \begin{bmatrix} 0 \\ 1 \\ 0 \end{bmatrix}, \ldots$$

Thus, we try to obtain a final tableau with the left-hand side as shown below.

$$\left[\begin{array}{cc|c} 1 & 0 & \Box \\ 0 & 1 & \\ 0 & 0 & \end{array}\right]$$

$\uparrow$ — constants

Using row operations, we transform the initial tableau into the final tableau.

$$\left[\begin{array}{cc|c} 1 & 0 & 2 \\ 0 & 1 & 1 \\ 0 & 0 & 0 \end{array}\right]$$

Converting this tableau into equation form, we have

$$x_1 = 2$$
$$x_2 = 1$$

Note that the third row is converted into the equation $(0x_1 + 0x_2 = 0$. Since this equation is satisfied by all ordered pairs (x_1, x_2), we delete it from the system. Thus, our linear system has the unique solution $x_1 = 2$ and $x_2 = 1$, or the ordered pair $(2, 1)$.

• **EXAMPLE 5-16** _____

Using the Gauss-Jordan method, solve

$$x_1 - x_2 = 4$$
$$2x_1 + 3x_2 = 8$$
$$5x_1 + x_2 = 7$$

Solution

We write the initial tableau.

$$\left[\begin{array}{cc|c} 1 & -1 & 4 \\ 2 & 3 & 8 \\ 5 & 1 & 7 \end{array}\right]$$

Using row operations, we transform the initial tableau into

$$\left[\begin{array}{cc|c} 1 & 0 & 4 \\ 0 & 1 & 0 \\ 0 & 0 & -13 \end{array}\right]$$

Note that the third row results in the equation $0x_1 + 0x_2 = -13$, or $0 = -13$, an *inconsistency*. Hence, the system has *no solution*.

• **EXAMPLE 5-17** _____

Using the Gauss-Jordan method, solve

$$x_1 + 2x_2 + x_3 = -3$$
$$2x_1 + 2x_2 + 4x_3 = 2$$
$$x_1 + x_2 + 2x_3 = 1$$
$$-4x_1 - 4x_2 - 8x_3 = -4$$

Solution

We write the initial tableau.

$$\begin{bmatrix} 1 & 2 & 1 & -3 \\ 2 & 2 & 4 & 2 \\ 1 & 1 & 2 & 1 \\ -4 & -4 & -8 & -4 \end{bmatrix}$$

Using row operations, we transform the initial tableau into

$$\begin{bmatrix} 1 & 0 & 3 & 5 \\ 0 & 1 & -1 & -4 \\ 0 & 0 & 0 & 0 \\ 0 & 0 & 0 & 0 \end{bmatrix}$$

Note that each of the last two rows consists of the identity $0 = 0$. Since this identity is satisfied by all ordered triples (x_1, x_2, x_3), we delete the last two rows. The corresponding linear system becomes

$$\begin{aligned} x_1 \quad + 3x_3 &= 5 \\ x_2 - x_3 &= -4 \end{aligned}$$

Solving for x_1 and x_2 in terms of x_3, we obtain

$$\begin{aligned} x_1 &= -3x_3 + 5 \\ x_2 &= x_3 - 4 \end{aligned}$$

Letting $x_3 = t$, the *infinitely many solutions* are expressed as

$$\begin{aligned} x_1 &= -3t + 5 \\ x_2 &= t - 4 \\ x_3 &= t \end{aligned}$$

If $t = 2$, a solution is

$$\begin{aligned} x_1 &= -3(2) + 5 = -1 \\ x_2 &= 2 - 4 = -2 \\ x_3 &= 2 \end{aligned}$$

Exercises 5-3

Perform the indicated row operation on each tableau below.

1. $\begin{bmatrix} 1 & 2 & 4 \\ -2 & 3 & -5 \end{bmatrix}$ $\xrightarrow{(2)R1 + R2 \to R2}$

2. $\begin{bmatrix} 4 & 6 & 8 \\ 3 & 2 & 1 \end{bmatrix}$ $\xrightarrow{(1/4)R1 \to R1}$

3. $\begin{bmatrix} 2 & 4 & 16 & 10 \\ 0 & 1 & 8 & 9 \\ 3 & 1 & 2 & 4 \end{bmatrix}$ $\xrightarrow{(1/2)R1 \to R1}$

4. $\begin{bmatrix} 1 & 0 & 8 & | & 9 \\ 0 & 1 & 2 & | & 1 \\ 0 & 5 & 3 & | & 8 \end{bmatrix}$ $\xrightarrow{(-5)R2 + R3 \rightarrow R3}$ $\begin{bmatrix} \square & \square & \square & | & \square \\ \square & \square & \square & | & \square \\ \square & \square & \square & | & \square \end{bmatrix}$

Perform the indicated row operations successively on the tableaus below.

5. $\begin{bmatrix} 1 & 0 & 3 & | & 2 \\ 2 & -1 & 2 & | & 4 \\ -3 & 1 & -1 & | & 5 \end{bmatrix}$ $\begin{matrix} \xrightarrow{(-2)R1 + R2 \rightarrow R2} \\ \xrightarrow{(3)R1 + R3 \rightarrow R3} \end{matrix}$ $\begin{bmatrix} \square & \square & \square & | & \square \\ \square & \square & \square & | & \square \\ \square & \square & \square & | & \square \end{bmatrix}$

6. $\begin{bmatrix} 1 & 3 & 1 & | & 2 \\ 0 & 1 & -2 & | & 4 \\ 0 & -4 & 6 & | & 5 \end{bmatrix}$ $\begin{matrix} \xrightarrow{(-3)R2 + R1 \rightarrow R1} \\ \xrightarrow{(4)R2 + R3 \rightarrow R3} \end{matrix}$ $\begin{bmatrix} \square & \square & \square & | & \square \\ \square & \square & \square & | & \square \\ \square & \square & \square & | & \square \end{bmatrix}$

7. $\begin{bmatrix} 1 & 0 & -3 & | & -1 \\ 0 & 1 & 4 & | & -2 \\ 0 & 0 & 1 & | & 3 \end{bmatrix}$ $\begin{matrix} \xrightarrow{(-4)R3 + R2 \rightarrow R2} \\ \xrightarrow{(3)R3 + R1 \rightarrow R1} \end{matrix}$ $\begin{bmatrix} \square & \square & \square & | & \square \\ \square & \square & \square & | & \square \\ \square & \square & \square & | & \square \end{bmatrix}$

8. $\begin{bmatrix} 1 & 0 & -2 & | & 3 \\ 0 & 1 & 5 & | & -1 \\ 0 & 0 & 1 & | & 4 \end{bmatrix}$ $\begin{matrix} \xrightarrow{(-5)R3 + R2 \rightarrow R2} \\ \xrightarrow{(2)R3 + R1 \rightarrow R1} \end{matrix}$ $\begin{bmatrix} \square & \square & \square & | & \square \\ \square & \square & \square & | & \square \\ \square & \square & \square & | & \square \end{bmatrix}$

Solve each of the following linear systems by using the Gauss-Jordan method of row operations.

9. $2x - 3y = 6$
$x - 7y = 25$

10. $2x_1 + 3x_2 = 3$
$12x_1 - 15x_2 = -4$

11. $2x + 3y - 5z = -13$
$-x + 2y + 3z = -7$
$3x - 4y - 7z = 15$

12. $x_1 + 3x_2 + x_3 = -3$
$2x_1 + 9x_2 + 2x_3 = -5$
$5x_1 + 48x_2 + 7x_3 = -16$

13. $2x + y + 3z = 11$
$4x + 3y - 2z = -1$
$6x + 5y - 4z = -4$

14. $x_1 + x_2 - 5x_3 = -3$
$2x_1 + x_2 + 10x_3 = 2$
$3x_1 + 2x_2 + 25x_3 = 3$

15. $x_1 + 10x_2 = 34$
$3x_1 + 2x_2 = 18$

16. $2x - y = -7$
$-x + 2y = 8$

17. $5x_1 + 7x_2 + x_3 = 1$
$3x_1 + 2x_2 + 3x_3 = 8$
$2x_1 + 3x_2 + 5x_3 = 19$

18. $3x + 7y + 2z = 2$
$4x + 3y + 3z = 8$
$x + 2y + 4z = -9$

19. $x_1 + 2x_2 + x_3 = 4$
$2x_1 + x_2 - x_3 = -4$
$3x_1 + x_2 + x_3 = 1$

20. $x_1 + x_2 - x_3 = -4$
$-x_1 + x_2 - 2x_3 = 3$
$2x_1 - x_2 - x_3 = 7$

21. $-x_1 + x_2 - x_3 = -6$
$x_1 + 3x_2 + x_3 = 10$
$-2x_1 + x_2 = 6$

22. $x_1 + x_2 + x_3 = -1$
$-x_1 + x_2 = -3$
$x_2 + x_3 = -3$

23. $\begin{aligned} x_1 - x_2 - x_3 &= -4 \\ x_1 - 4x_2 &= -14 \\ x_2 + 2x_3 &= 1 \end{aligned}$

24. $\begin{aligned} x_1 - x_2 - 2x_3 &= 3 \\ -x_1 + 2x_2 + x_3 &= -6 \\ -x_1 + x_2 + 3x_3 &= -2 \end{aligned}$

Solve the following linear systems by using the Gauss-Jordan method of row operations.

25. $\begin{aligned} x_1 + 2x_2 + x_3 - x_4 &= 9 \\ x_2 - x_3 + 2x_4 &= -3 \\ 4x_1 \qquad + 5x_3 + 3x_4 &= 16 \\ 2x_3 + 52x_4 &= -46 \end{aligned}$

26. $\begin{aligned} x_1 + 2x_2 - x_3 + x_4 &= -7 \\ 2x_1 + x_2 + x_3 + 2x_4 &= 1 \\ -3x_1 - x_2 + x_3 - x_4 &= 3 \\ x_1 \qquad\qquad + 2x_4 &= -1 \end{aligned}$

Some of the following linear systems have no solution, and some have infinitely many solutions. Try to solve each by the Gauss-Jordan method of row operations. If the system has no solution, then state so. If the system has infinitely many solutions, express them in terms of t.

27. $\begin{aligned} 3x - 5y &= 8 \\ -6x + 10y &= 30 \end{aligned}$

28. $\begin{aligned} 2x_1 + 3x_2 &= 7 \\ -x_1 - 1.5x_2 &= -4.5 \end{aligned}$

29. $\begin{aligned} 8x_1 - 2x_2 &= 10 \\ -4x_1 + x_2 &= -5 \end{aligned}$

30. $\begin{aligned} 4x_1 - x_2 &= 9 \\ -12x_1 + 3x_2 &= 36 \end{aligned}$

31. $\begin{aligned} x_1 - 2x_2 + x_3 &= 3 \\ 3x_1 - 7x_2 + 2x_3 &= 4 \\ -2x_1 + 4x_2 - 2x_3 &= 8 \end{aligned}$

32. $\begin{aligned} x_1 + 4x_2 + x_3 &= 6 \\ 2x_1 + 9x_2 + 2x_3 &= 8 \\ 3x_1 + 12x_2 + 3x_3 &= 18 \end{aligned}$

33. $\begin{aligned} x_1 + x_2 + x_3 &= 4 \\ x_1 + 2x_2 + 3x_3 &= 2 \\ 2x_1 + 4x_2 + 6x_3 &= 5 \end{aligned}$

34. $\begin{aligned} x_1 - 2x_2 - 2x_3 &= 4 \\ -2x_1 + 4x_2 + 4x_3 &= -8 \\ x_1 + 3x_2 + 2x_3 &= 4 \end{aligned}$

Using the Gauss-Jordan method, solve or attempt to solve each of the following linear systems. If the system has no solutions, then state so. If the system has infinitely many solutions, express them in terms of t.

35. $\begin{aligned} x_1 + 2x_2 + x_3 &= 4 \\ 2x_1 + x_2 + 5x_3 &= 6 \end{aligned}$

36. $\begin{aligned} x_1 - 3x_2 + x_3 &= 6 \\ -2x_1 + 6x_2 - 2x_3 &= 9 \end{aligned}$

37. $\begin{aligned} x_1 + 2x_2 + x_3 &= 4 \\ -x_1 - x_2 \qquad + x_4 &= 5 \\ 3x_1 + 6x_2 + x_3 + x_4 &= 6 \end{aligned}$

38. $\begin{aligned} x_1 + 2x_2 + x_3 + x_4 &= 5 \\ x_1 + 3x_2 + 2x_3 + x_4 &= 6 \\ 2x_1 + 5x_2 + 2x_3 + x_4 &= 8 \end{aligned}$

39. $\begin{aligned} 2x_1 + x_2 + x_3 - x_4 &= 6 \\ x_1 + x_2 + x_3 - x_4 &= 8 \\ -2x_1 - x_2 - x_3 + x_4 &= 9 \end{aligned}$

40. $\begin{aligned} x_1 + x_2 - x_3 + x_4 &= 8 \\ -x_1 + 2x_2 + 2x_3 + x_4 &= -4 \end{aligned}$

41. $\begin{aligned} x_1 + 2x_2 - x_3 - x_4 &= 5 \\ 2x_1 + 5x_2 + x_3 - 2x_4 &= 8 \end{aligned}$

42. $\begin{aligned} x_1 + 2x_2 - x_3 &= 5 \\ -x_1 + 4x_2 - 11x_3 &= 13 \end{aligned}$

Using the Gauss-Jordan method, solve or attempt to solve each of the following linear systems. If the system has a unique solution, then state the solution. If the system has no solutions, then state so. If the system has infinitely many solutions, express them in terms of t.

43. $\begin{aligned} x_1 + x_2 &= 1 \\ 2x_1 + x_2 &= 4 \\ 4x_1 + 2x_2 &= 8 \end{aligned}$

44. $\begin{aligned} x_1 + 2x_2 &= 3 \\ 2x_1 - x_2 &= 1 \\ 2x_1 + x_2 &= 4 \end{aligned}$

45. $\begin{aligned} x_1 + 3x_2 &= 4 \\ 2x_1 + 6x_2 &= 8 \\ -3x_1 - 9x_2 &= -12 \end{aligned}$

46. $\begin{aligned} x_1 + x_2 &= 4 \\ 2x_1 + 3x_2 &= 1 \\ x_1 - x_2 &= 8 \end{aligned}$

47.
$$2x_1 + x_2 + 3x_3 = 11$$
$$6x_1 + 5x_2 - 4x_3 = -4$$
$$4x_1 + 3x_2 - 2x_3 = -1$$
$$-6x_1 - 5x_2 + 4x_3 = 4$$

48.
$$x_1 + x_2 + 2x_3 = 4$$
$$2x_1 + 3x_2 + x_3 = 8$$
$$2x_1 + 2x_2 + 4x_3 = 8$$
$$-x_1 - x_2 - 2x_3 = -4$$

Applications

49. *Production planning.* Reread the production planning problem beginning on page 259 in Section 5-2. Recall that this problem, when formulated, yielded the linear system

$$2x + 3y + 5z = 780$$
$$x + 2y + z = 320$$
$$4x + y + 3z = 500$$

Solve this linear system and interpret the result.

50. *Investment: Portfolio allocation.* Reread the portfolio allocation problem beginning on page 264 in Section 5-2. Recall that this problem, when formulated, yielded the linear system

$$x_1 + x_2 + x_3 = 400{,}000$$
$$0.20x_1 + 0.16x_2 + 0.08x_3 = 62{,}000$$
$$9x_1 + 3x_2 + x_3 = 2{,}000{,}000$$

Solve this linear system and interpret the result.

51. *Production planning.* Solve the linear system in Exercise 23 on page 267 at the end of Section 5-2. Interpret the result.

52. *Investment: Portfolio allocation.* Solve the linear system in Exercise 24 on page 267 at the end of Section 5-2. Interpret the result.

53. *Transportation problem.* Solve the linear system in Exercise 25 on page 267 at the end of Section 5-2. Interpret the result.

54. *Production planning.* A company makes three products: A, B, and C. Each product must pass through departments 1 and 2. The time requirements (in person-hours) for a unit of each product in each department are given below.

	Products			Total time (person-hours) available per department
	A	B	C	
Department 1	2	1	1	80
Department 2	1	2	1	100

If each department is to operate at full capacity, how many units of each product should be produced? Write and solve the linear system for this problem. Interpret the result.

55. *Transportation problem.* A company makes industrial air compressors at two plants. The air compressors must be transported from the two plants to two distribution centers, as is illustrated below.

	Distribution center 1	Distribution center 2	Production capacities
Plant 1	x_1	x_2	500
Plant 2	x_3	x_4	300
	600	200	

Demands

The production capacity of each plant and the demand of each distribution center are given above. If each plant is to operate at full capacity, how many air compressors should be shipped from each plant to each distribution center to ensure that the distribution centers' demands are met exactly? Write and solve the linear system for this problem. Interpret the result.

56. *Marketing research: Survey planning.* A marketing research firm is planning a survey of households that are cross-classified with regard to whether or not the household has children versus whether the interview is to take place during the day or evening, as indicated in the table below.

Household	Day	Evening	
Children	x_1	x_2	300
No children	x_3	x_4	200
	100	400	

Total households

Note that

x_1 = number of households that have children and are to be interviewed during the day

x_2 = number of households that have children and are to be interviewed during the evening

x_3 = number of households that have no children and are to be interviewed during the day

x_4 = number of households that have no children and are to be interviewed during the evening

How many of each type of household should be interviewed in order to ensure that all the households are interviewed? Write and solve the linear system for this problem. Interpret the result.

57. *Blending problem.* A company has developed a new gasoline additive for automobiles. The additive is a blend of threé liquid ingredients: A, B, and C. The company's immediate production plans are to make 100,000 gallons of this additive. The cost per gallon for each ingredient is given in the table below.

Cost per gallon

Ingredient A	Ingredient B	Ingredient C
$2	$4	$8

The company wants to ensure that the total cost of 100,000 gallons of this additive does not exceed $600,000 (or, in other words, $6 per gallon). How many gallons of each ingredient should be blended to make 100,000 gallons of additive if the total cost requirement is to be met exactly and if the 100,000-gallon blend is to have an amount of ingredient C that is 5.5 times the amount of ingredient A? Write and solve the linear system for this problem. Interpret the result.

58. *Product mix.* A company uses three types of raw materials to make three products: A, B, and C. The table below indicates the amount of each raw material required for a unit of each product.

Raw material requirements

	Product A	Product B	Product C	Total amounts of raw materials available (pounds)
Raw Material 1	1	2	1	800
Raw Material 2	2	1	5	1300
Raw Material 3	1	2	0	700

How many units of each product should be produced if the raw material supplies are to be exhausted? Wrote and solve the linear system for this problem. Interpret the result.

59. *Nutrition.* A diet consisting of various amounts of three types of foods A, B, and C—must provide minimal amounts of each of three nutrients as indicated below. The table below gives the number of milligrams of each nutrient contained in one ounce of each type of food. Also given are the minimal nutritional requirements for the respective nutrients.

Milligrams of nutrient per ounce of food

Nutrient	Food A	Food B	Food C	Minimal nutritional requirements (milligrams)
Calcium	20	20	40	1800
Iron	10	20	10	800
Vitamin B	20	10	10	700

How many ounces of each type of food should be included in the diet if the minimal nutritional requirements are to be met exactly?

5-4 • MATRICES

In the previous section, we have used tableaus or rectangular arrays to express linear systems. We have learned that a rectangular array of numbers is called a **matrix.** In this section, we will see more uses of rectangular arrays of numbers, or matrices.

We begin with a furniture manufacturer that makes three models—A, B, and C—of dining room sets and kitchen sets. During a given week, the company makes 30 model A, 20 model B, and 45 model C dining room sets. Also, during the same week, the company makes 40 model A, 35 model B, and 60 model C kitchen sets.

We wish to organize this information so that it can be efficiently displayed. The table below is one such display.

	Model A	Model B	Model C
Dining Room Sets	30	20	45
Kitchen Sets	40	35	60

The rectangular array of numbers

$$\begin{bmatrix} 30 & 20 & 45 \\ 40 & 35 & 60 \end{bmatrix}$$

is called a matrix. We now formalize this concept.

A **matrix** is a rectangular array of numbers. Each number is called an **element** of the matrix. Specifically.

$$\begin{array}{c} \\ \text{row 1} \rightarrow \\ \text{row 2} \rightarrow \end{array} \begin{array}{ccc} \text{col 1} & \text{col 2} & \text{col 3} \\ \begin{bmatrix} 3 & 1 & 2 \\ 8 & 0 & -5 \end{bmatrix} \end{array}$$

is a matrix with two rows and three columns. Thus, it is of **dimension** 2×3, read "two by three." In general, a matrix with m rows and n columns is of dimension $m \times n$. The following are matrices of various dimensions:

$$\begin{bmatrix} 3 \\ 4 \\ 2 \end{bmatrix} \qquad [2 \quad 4 \quad -7] \qquad \begin{bmatrix} 4 & 5 \\ 6 & -1 \end{bmatrix}$$

$$\begin{array}{ccc} \text{dimension} & \text{dimension} & \text{dimension} \\ 3 \times 1 & 1 \times 3 & 2 \times 2 \end{array}$$

A matrix of only one column is called a **column matrix.** The matrix

$$\begin{bmatrix} 3 \\ -1 \end{bmatrix}$$

is an example of a column matrix. A matrix of only one row is called a **row matrix.** The matrix

$$[5 \quad 0 \quad -1 \quad 7]$$

is an example of a row matrix. A matrix with as many rows as columns is called a **square matrix.** The matrix

$$\begin{bmatrix} 3 & 4 \\ 6 & 0 \end{bmatrix}$$

is an example of a square matrix.

As we have already seen, matrices provide useful ways of presenting data. As a specific example, we consider the following product-mix problem.

• **EXAMPLE 5-18** _____

A company makes three types—A, B, and C—of table saws. The time requirement for each type of table saw in each of three departments is given in the 3×3 matrix.

$$\begin{array}{ccc} \text{Type A} & \text{Type B} & \text{Type C} \\ \begin{bmatrix} 2 & 3 & 4 \\ 3 & 5 & 2 \\ 6 & 3 & 5 \end{bmatrix} & \begin{array}{l} \text{Department I} \\ \text{Department II} \\ \text{Department III} \end{array} \end{array}$$

Assuming that the time requirements are given in hours, state how many hours each type of table saw requires in each department.

Solution

Studying this matrix, note that each type A table saw requires 2 hours in department 1, 3 hours in department II, and 6 hours in department III. Each type B table saw requires 3 hours in department I, 5 hours in department II, and 3 hours in department III. And each type C table saw requires 4 hours in department 1, 2 hours in department II, and 5 hours in department III.

Matrix Notation

Matrices are usually denoted by capital letters. Thus, the matrix

$$B = \begin{bmatrix} 5 & 3 & 1 \\ 8 & 0 & 2 \end{bmatrix}$$

may be referred to by the letter B.

It is sometimes necessary to refer to a general matrix of a given dimension. For example, a general matrix A of dimension 2×3 is

$$A = \begin{bmatrix} a_{11} & a_{12} & a_{13} \\ a_{21} & a_{22} & a_{23} \end{bmatrix}$$

Note that the individual elements of the matrix A are denoted by a_{ij}, where i denotes the row in which the element is located and j denotes the column. Thus, a_{11} denotes the element located in the first row and first column, a_{12} denotes the element in the first row and second column, . . ., and a_{23} denotes the element in the second row and third column. In general, a matrix A of dimension $m \times n$ is denoted by

$$A = \begin{bmatrix} a_{11} & a_{12} & \cdots & a_{1n} \\ a_{21} & a_{22} & \cdots & a_{2n} \\ \vdots & \vdots & & \vdots \\ a_{m1} & a_{m2} & \cdots & a_{mn} \end{bmatrix}$$

Equality of Matrices

Two matrices are **equal** if they are of the same dimension and if their corresponding elements are equal. Thus, if

$$A = \begin{bmatrix} 4 & 3 \\ -2 & 1 \end{bmatrix} \quad \text{and} \quad B = \begin{bmatrix} 8/2 & 3 \\ -2 & 6/6 \end{bmatrix}$$

then $A = B$. However, if $C = [1 \quad 6]$ and $D = [6 \quad 1]$, then $C \neq D$ since corresponding elements are not equal.

Adding and Subtracting Matrices

If two or more matrices are of the same dimension, then they may be *added*. The **sum** of two or more matrices is a matrix where each element is the sum of the corresponding elements of the individual matrices. Similar statements hold for subtraction of matrices. Thus, if

$$A = \begin{bmatrix} 1 & 0 & -5 \\ 8 & -2 & 9 \end{bmatrix} \quad \text{and} \quad B = \begin{bmatrix} 4 & 2 & 3 \\ 5 & 1 & 7 \end{bmatrix}$$

then

$$A + B = \begin{bmatrix} 1+4 & 0+2 & -5+3 \\ 8+5 & -2+1 & 9+7 \end{bmatrix} = \begin{bmatrix} 5 & 2 & -2 \\ 13 & -1 & 16 \end{bmatrix}$$

$$A - B = \begin{bmatrix} 1-4 & 0-2 & -5-3 \\ 8-5 & -2-1 & 9-7 \end{bmatrix} = \begin{bmatrix} -3 & -2 & -8 \\ 3 & -3 & 2 \end{bmatrix}$$

• EXAMPLE 5-19

Matrix N shows the number of dryers shipped from two plants, P_1 and P_2, to three warehouses, W_1, W_2, and W_3, during the month of November.

$$N = \begin{array}{c} \\ P_1 \\ P_2 \end{array} \begin{array}{ccc} W_1 & W_2 & W_3 \\ \begin{bmatrix} 100 & 50 & 70 \\ 300 & 20 & 80 \end{bmatrix} \end{array}$$

Matrix D shows the corresponding shipments made during December.

$$D = \begin{array}{c} \\ P_1 \\ P_2 \end{array} \begin{array}{ccc} W_1 & W_2 & W_3 \\ \begin{bmatrix} 200 & 150 & 80 \\ 400 & 90 & 100 \end{bmatrix} \end{array}$$

Find the matrix showing the combined shipment for both months.

Solution

Here,

$$N + D = \begin{bmatrix} 100+200 & 50+150 & 70+80 \\ 300+400 & 20+90 & 80+100 \end{bmatrix}$$

$$= \begin{bmatrix} 300 & 200 & 150 \\ 700 & 110 & 180 \end{bmatrix}$$

Multiplying a Matrix by a Number

If a matrix A is multiplied by a number k, then the resulting matrix, kA, is determined by multiplying each element of matrix A by k. Specifically, if

$$A = \begin{bmatrix} 6 & 5 \\ 1 & 7 \end{bmatrix}$$

then

$$2A = \begin{bmatrix} 2 \cdot 6 & 2 \cdot 5 \\ 2 \cdot 1 & 2 \cdot 7 \end{bmatrix} = \begin{bmatrix} 12 & 10 \\ 2 & 14 \end{bmatrix}$$

Observe that

$$A + A = \begin{bmatrix} 6 & 5 \\ 1 & 7 \end{bmatrix} + \begin{bmatrix} 6 & 5 \\ 1 & 7 \end{bmatrix} = \begin{bmatrix} 12 & 10 \\ 2 & 14 \end{bmatrix} = 2A$$

• **EXAMPLE 5-20** **Cost Allocation.** _____

The matrix below gives monthly utility costs for each of three plants operated by a company.

$$C = \begin{array}{c} \\ \text{January} \\ \text{February} \\ \text{March} \end{array}$$

	Plant 1	Plant 2	Plant 3	
$C =$	$9000	$8000	$10,000	January
	$9800	$8900	$11,600	February
	$7600	$7900	$9800	March

If 40% of utility costs are attributed to electricity, determine the electricity cost for each plant for each of the above months.

Solution

Electricity costs are given by the matrix

$$0.40C = \begin{bmatrix} (0.40)(\$9000) & (0.40)(\$8000) & (0.40)(\$10,000) \\ (0.40)(\$9800) & (0.40)(\$8900) & (0.40)(\$11,600) \\ (0.40)(\$7600) & (0.40)(\$7900) & (0.40)\ (\$9800) \end{bmatrix}$$

	Plant 1	Plant 2	Plant 3	
$=$	$3600	$3200	$4000	January
	$3920	$3560	$4640	February
	$3040	$3160	$3920	March

•

Exercises 5-4

State the dimension of each of the following matrices.

1. $\begin{bmatrix} 4 & 3 & -1 \\ 8 & 2 & 6 \end{bmatrix}$

2. $\begin{bmatrix} 6 & 8 \\ 5 & -4 \\ 2 & 0 \end{bmatrix}$

3. $\begin{bmatrix} 8 & 4 & 0 \\ 1 & 1 & 0 \\ 2 & 2 & 0 \end{bmatrix}$

4. $\begin{bmatrix} 8 & 4 \\ 6 & -10 \end{bmatrix}$

5. $\begin{bmatrix} 4 & -1 & 6 \end{bmatrix}$

6. $\begin{bmatrix} 7 \\ -1 \end{bmatrix}$

7. $\begin{bmatrix} 5 \\ 0 \\ -1 \\ 4 \end{bmatrix}$

8. $\begin{bmatrix} 3 & 0 & -1 & 5 \end{bmatrix}$

Identify each of the following as either a row matrix or a column matrix.

9. $\begin{bmatrix} 4 & 3 & 0 \end{bmatrix}$

10. $\begin{bmatrix} 7 & -1 \end{bmatrix}$

11. $\begin{bmatrix} 8 \\ 4 \end{bmatrix}$

12. $\begin{bmatrix} 9 \\ 2 \\ 0 \end{bmatrix}$

Which of the following are square matrices?

13. $\begin{bmatrix} 3 & 6 & 1 \\ 8 & 2 & 0 \end{bmatrix}$

14. $\begin{bmatrix} 4 & 3 \\ 2 & 0 \end{bmatrix}$

15. $\begin{bmatrix} 8 & 1 & 0 \\ 4 & 3 & 0 \\ 8 & 2 & 1 \end{bmatrix}$ **16.** $\begin{bmatrix} 8 & 6 & 1 & 0 \\ 2 & 3 & 0 & 0 \end{bmatrix}$

For Exercises 17-20, indicate whether the statement is true or false.

17. If

$$A = \begin{bmatrix} 5 & 3 & 6 \\ 8 & 2 & 1 \end{bmatrix} \quad \text{and} \quad B = \begin{bmatrix} 10/2 & 12/4 & 6 \\ 8 & 14/7 & 9/9 \end{bmatrix}$$

then $A = B$.

18. If

$$C = \begin{bmatrix} 5 & 6 \\ 8 & 4 \end{bmatrix} \quad \text{and} \quad D = \begin{bmatrix} 5 & 6 & 0 \\ 8 & 4 & 0 \end{bmatrix}$$

then $C = D$.

19. If

$$E = \begin{bmatrix} 4 & 8 \\ 6 & 2 \end{bmatrix} \quad \text{and} \quad F = \begin{bmatrix} 8 & 4 \\ 6 & 2 \end{bmatrix}$$

then $E = F$.

20. If

$$H = \begin{bmatrix} 4 & 1 \\ 6 & -2 \end{bmatrix} \quad \text{and} \quad K = \begin{bmatrix} 4 & 8/8 \\ 6 & -2 \end{bmatrix}$$

then $H = K$.

21. Let

$$A = \begin{bmatrix} x \\ y \end{bmatrix} \quad \text{and} \quad B = \begin{bmatrix} 4 \\ -1 \end{bmatrix}$$

Given that $A = B$, what are the values of x and y?

22. Let

$$C = \begin{bmatrix} x_1 \\ x_2 \\ x_3 \end{bmatrix} \quad \text{and} \quad D = \begin{bmatrix} 1 \\ 0 \\ -3 \end{bmatrix}$$

Given that $C = D$, what are the values of x_1, x_2, and x_3?

23. Let

$$H = \begin{bmatrix} x & y \\ z & w \end{bmatrix} \quad \text{and} \quad K = \begin{bmatrix} 1 & -4 \\ 5 & -7 \end{bmatrix}$$

Given that $H = K$, what are the values of x, y, z, and w?

Compute each of the following if

$$A = \begin{bmatrix} 3 & 1 & 2 \\ -1 & 5 & -2 \end{bmatrix} \quad B = \begin{bmatrix} 0 & 4 & 1 \\ 2 & -5 & 3 \end{bmatrix} \quad C = \begin{bmatrix} 4 & 3 & 0 \\ -2 & 5 & -1 \end{bmatrix}$$

24. $A + B$	**25.** $A - B$	**26.** $B - A$
27. $A + C$	**28.** $A - C$	**29.** $C - A$
30. $B + C$	**31.** $B - C$	**32.** $C - B$
33. $A + B + C$	**34.** $A + B - C$	**35.** $A + C - B$
36. $2A$	**37.** $3B$	**38.** $5C$
39. $-3A$	**40.** $-6B$	**41.** $-2C$
42. $C + 2A$	**43.** $A - 3B$	**44.** $B + 5C$
45. $B - 3A$	**46.** $A - 6B + 5C$	**47.** $A + B - 2C$

If $A = [3 \quad -4 \quad 1]$ and $B = [2 \quad 0 \quad -3]$, compute each of the following:

48. $A + B$ **49.** $A - B$ **50.** $B - A$

51. $3A$ **52.** $-2B$ **53.** $A - 2B$

54. $B + 3A$ **55.** $B - 3A$ **56.** $A + 2B$

If $C = \begin{bmatrix} 8 \\ 2 \end{bmatrix}$ and $D = \begin{bmatrix} -7 \\ 1 \end{bmatrix}$, compute each of the following:

57. $C + D$ **58.** $C - D$ **59.** $D - C$

60. $5C$ **61.** $-3D$ **62.** $C - 3D$

63. $5C + D$ **64.** $D - 5C$ **65.** $C + 3D$

Perform the indicated operations.

66. $\begin{bmatrix} 4 & 3 \\ -1 & 2 \end{bmatrix} + \begin{bmatrix} -8 & 0 \\ 2 & 5 \end{bmatrix}$ **67.** $\begin{bmatrix} 1 & -1 \\ 2 & 0 \end{bmatrix} + \begin{bmatrix} -2 & -4 \\ 3 & 9 \end{bmatrix}$

68. $\begin{bmatrix} 8 & 3 & -1 \\ 1 & 0 & 2 \end{bmatrix} - \begin{bmatrix} -1 & 1 & 2 \\ 0 & -2 & -4 \end{bmatrix}$

69. $\begin{bmatrix} -1 & 2 \\ 4 & -3 \\ 0 & -1 \end{bmatrix} - \begin{bmatrix} 4 & -3 \\ 1 & 2 \\ -2 & 6 \end{bmatrix}$

70. $2\begin{bmatrix} 1 & 4 \\ 2 & 1 \end{bmatrix} + \begin{bmatrix} 1 & 0 \\ -1 & 3 \end{bmatrix}$ **71.** $\begin{bmatrix} 4 & 2 \\ -1 & 10 \end{bmatrix} - 3\begin{bmatrix} 1 & -2 \\ 2 & -4 \end{bmatrix}$

72. $-3\begin{bmatrix} -1 & 6 \\ -2 & -1 \end{bmatrix} + 2\begin{bmatrix} 0 & 4 \\ -2 & 1 \end{bmatrix}$ **73.** $2\begin{bmatrix} 10 & 5 \\ 2 & 4 \end{bmatrix} - 3\begin{bmatrix} -1 & -2 \\ 1 & 4 \end{bmatrix}$

74. Let $X = \begin{bmatrix} x_1 \\ x_2 \end{bmatrix}$ and $B = \begin{bmatrix} 6 \\ 15 \end{bmatrix}$. Given that $3X = B$, find X.

75. Let $X = \begin{bmatrix} x_1 \\ x_2 \\ x_3 \end{bmatrix}$ and $C = \begin{bmatrix} 15 \\ 20 \\ 30 \end{bmatrix}$. Given that $5X = C$, find X.

76. If $A = \begin{bmatrix} 4 & 1 \\ 3 & 2 \end{bmatrix}$ and $B = \begin{bmatrix} -1 & 5 \\ 6 & 4 \end{bmatrix}$, verify that $A + B = B + A$.

77. If Z is a matrix whose elements are all zeros, then given that

$$X = \begin{bmatrix} a & b \\ c & d \end{bmatrix}$$

verify the following:
a) $X - X = Z$
b) $X + Z = X$

78. If $A = \begin{bmatrix} 2 & -5 \\ 3 & 1 \end{bmatrix}$, $B = \begin{bmatrix} 2 & 1 \\ 5 & 0 \end{bmatrix}$, and $C = \begin{bmatrix} 2 & -6 \\ 7 & 1 \end{bmatrix}$, verify the following:
a) $A + B = B + A$ (commutative property of addition)
b) $A + (B + C) = (A + B) + C$ (associative property of addition)

Applications

79. *Sales tabulations.* Matrix J shows the number of sofas shipped from two plants, P_1 and P_2, to four warehouses, W_1, W_2, W_3, and W_4, during the month of July.

$$J = \begin{array}{c} \\ P_1 \\ P_2 \end{array} \begin{array}{cccc} W_1 & W_2 & W_3 & W_4 \\ \begin{bmatrix} 200 & 50 & 70 & 100 \\ 300 & 50 & 10 & 0 \end{bmatrix} \end{array}$$

Matrix A shows the corresponding shipments made during August.

$$A = \begin{array}{c} \\ P_1 \\ P_2 \end{array} \begin{array}{cccc} W_1 & W_2 & W_3 & W_4 \\ \begin{bmatrix} 100 & 30 & 10 & 50 \\ 70 & 400 & 200 & 80 \end{bmatrix} \end{array}$$

Find the matrix showing the combined shipment for both months.

80. *Cost analysis.* Larry Merrick operates three fruit stores: S_1, S_2, and S_3. Each store stocks apples, oranges, grapes, and pears. Larry does his buying on Monday, Wednesday, and Friday. Matrix M shows the amounts spent by Larry on each item for each store on Monday.

$$M = \begin{array}{cccc} S_1 & S_2 & S_3 & \\ \begin{bmatrix} \$200 & \$500 & \$300 \\ \$100 & \$400 & \$210 \\ \$500 & \$280 & \$\ 80 \\ \$150 & \$350 & \$250 \end{bmatrix} & \begin{array}{l} \text{apples} \\ \text{oranges} \\ \text{grapes} \\ \text{pears} \end{array} \end{array}$$

Matrices W and F show the corresponding expenditures for Wednesday and Friday, respectively.

$$W = \begin{array}{cccc} S_1 & S_2 & S_3 & \\ \begin{bmatrix} \$150 & \$\ 80 & \$100 \\ \$250 & \$300 & \$150 \\ \$\ 70 & \$\ 50 & \$\ 90 \\ \$120 & \$215 & \$160 \end{bmatrix} & \begin{array}{l} \text{apples} \\ \text{oranges} \\ \text{grapes} \\ \text{pears} \end{array} \end{array}$$

$$F = \begin{array}{cccc} S_1 & S_2 & S_3 & \\ \begin{bmatrix} \$209 & \$180 & \$120 \\ \$310 & \$140 & \$230 \\ \$\ 80 & \$\ 75 & \$\ 55 \\ \$\ 95 & \$\ 90 & \$170 \end{bmatrix} & \begin{array}{l} \text{apples} \\ \text{oranges} \\ \text{grapes} \\ \text{pears} \end{array} \end{array}$$

a) Find the matrix showing the combined purchases for Monday and Wednesday.

b) Find the matrix showing the combined purchases for Wednesday and Friday.

c) Find the matrix showing the combined purchases for Monday, Wednesday, and Friday.

81. *Production.* During a given day, a company made 30 type A, 40 type B, and 60 type C scarves. During the same day, the company also made 25 matching type A, 40 matching type B, and 50 matching type C mittens. Organize this information in a 2×3 matrix.

82. The time requirements (in hours) of a unit of each of three products in each of three departments are given in the matrix below.

	Product 1	Product 2	Product 3
Department 1	5	2	4
Department 2	1	8	3
Department 3	2	1	5

State the number of hours each product requires in each department.

83. *Data.* The weights (in pounds) of six people before taking a weight reduction program were 350, 249, 260, 195, 275, and 295. The weights of these same people after the weight reduction program are 345, 200, 220, 140, 200, and 230, respectively. Summarize this information in a 6×2 matrix.

84. *Commission.* The matrix below gives the total sales of each of three real estate agents at a given agency for the first 3 months of a particular year.

	Mr. Alton	Mrs. Smith	Ms. Harris	
	$160,000	$250,000	$190,000	January
$S =$	$110,000	$180,000	$140,000	February
	$ 90,000	$ 80,000	$ 85,000	March

If the agency pays its agents a commission of 3% based on sales, then write the matrix that gives the commission for each agent for each month.

5-5   • MULTIPLYING MATRICES

In this section, we will learn how to multiply matrices. To begin, we present an application that demonstrates the need for matrix multiplication.

Application

Sales Revenue

A company produces three products: A, B, and C. The number of units produced and sold of each product during each of two given months appears in the matrix below.

Quantity Sold Matrix

	Product A	Product B	Product C
February	100	300	500
March	200	500	400

The unit selling price for each product is given in the matrix below.

Unit Selling Price Matrix

Product A	45
Product B	50
Product C	80

We wish to create a matrix that contains the monthly total sales revenue gained from selling all three products. Since sales revenue is the product of quantity sold and unit selling price, we write the quantity sold and unit selling price matrices next to each other, as shown below.

	Quantity Sold				Unit Selling Price	
	A	B	C			
February	100	300	500	·	45	A
March	200	500	400		50	B
					80	C

To determine February's total sales revenue, we multiply the quantity sold for each product in February by its respective unit selling price and add the products. Thus, we multiply the February entries in the left matrix by the corresponding entries in the right matrix to obtain

$$
\text{February} \quad
\begin{array}{ccc} A & B & C \end{array} \\
[100 \ \ 300 \ \ 500] \cdot
\begin{bmatrix} 45 \\ 50 \\ 80 \end{bmatrix}
\begin{array}{c} A \\ B \\ C \end{array}
= 100(45) + 300(50) + 500(80)
$$

Quantity Sold   Unit Selling Price

$$= 4500 + 15{,}000 + 40{,}000$$
$$= \$59{,}500 \quad \text{February sales revenue}$$

Note that we have multiplied the first entry in the row matrix by the first entry in the column matrix, the second entry in the row matrix by the second entry in the column matrix, and the third entry in the row matrix by the third entry in the column matrix, and then added the products. Such a product of a row matrix and a column matrix is called a **dot product.** We will have more to say about this later.

To determine March's total sales revenue, we multiply the March entries of the quantity sold matrix by the corresponding entries of the unit selling price matrix, as shown below.

$$
\text{March} \quad
\begin{array}{ccc} A & B & C \end{array} \\
[200 \ \ 500 \ \ 400] \cdot
\begin{bmatrix} 45 \\ 50 \\ 80 \end{bmatrix}
\begin{array}{c} A \\ B \\ C \end{array}
= 200(45) + 500(50) + 400(80)
$$

Quantity Sold   Unit Selling Price

$$= 9000 + 25{,}000 + 32{,}000$$
$$= \$66{,}000 \quad \text{March sales revenue}$$

Again, we note that to compute the total sales revenues for February and March, we computed a special type of product between a row matrix and a column matrix. As mentioned earlier, such a product is called a dot product, which we formally define in the box below.

Dot Product

The dot product between a left row matrix and a right column matrix, each containing the same number of entries, is determined by multiplying the first entry of the row matrix by the first entry of the column matrix, the second entry of the row matrix by the second entry of the column matrix, . . . , and the last entry of the row matrix by the last entry of the column matrix, and then adding the products, as shown below. Note that a dot product results in a real number.

$$
[a_1 \ \ a_2 \ \ldots \ a_n] \cdot
\begin{bmatrix} b_1 \\ b_2 \\ \vdots \\ b_n \end{bmatrix}
= a_1 b_1 + a_2 b_2 + \ldots + a_n b_n \quad \text{A real number}
$$

• **EXAMPLE 5-21** _____

Compute the dot product of

$$[2 \quad -1 \quad 0 \quad 3] \quad \text{and} \quad \begin{bmatrix} 4 \\ -5 \\ 1 \\ 8 \end{bmatrix}$$

Solution

The dot product is

$$[2 \quad -1 \quad 0 \quad 3] \begin{bmatrix} 4 \\ -5 \\ 1 \\ 8 \end{bmatrix} = 2(4) + (-1)(-5) + 0(1) + 3(8)$$

$$= 8 + 5 + 0 + 24$$
$$= 37$$

• **EXAMPLE 5-22** _____

A grocery store carries three brands of detergent: Brand X, Brand Y, and Brand Z. The row matrix below represents the number of units of each of these brands sold during the month of June.

	Brand X	Brand Y	Brand Z
Number of units	[100	500	300]

The column matrix below represents the unit selling price of each brand:

$$P = \begin{bmatrix} \$2.00 \\ \$1.00 \\ \$1.50 \end{bmatrix} \begin{matrix} \text{Brand X} \\ \text{Brand Y} \\ \text{Brand Z} \end{matrix}$$

Find the total sales revenue for all these products during the month of June.

Solution

The total sales revenue is given by the dot product of the two matrices, which we compute below. Hence,

$$[100 \quad 500 \quad 300] \begin{bmatrix} \$2.00 \\ \$1.00 \\ \$1.50 \end{bmatrix} = 100(\$2.00) + 500(\$1.00) + 300(\$1.50)$$

$$= \$1150$$

_____ •

Returning to our sales revenue application on page 300, we will illustrate the use of matrices to organize all of the information of the problem. Specifically, we list the February and March total sales revenues in a column matrix next to the quantity and unit selling price matrices, as shown below.

		Quantity Sold			Unit Selling Price		Total Sales Revenue	
		A	B	C				
February		100	300	50	45	A	59,500	February
March		200	500	400	50	B =	66,000	March
					80	C		

As indicated by the equal sign, the total sales revenue matrix is the product of the quantity sold matrix and the unit selling price matrix.

Product Matrices

We now discuss multiplying matrices in general. If

$$A = \begin{bmatrix} 4 & 3 & 2 \\ 5 & 1 & 6 \end{bmatrix} \quad \text{and} \quad B = \begin{bmatrix} 2 & 4 \\ 1 & 0 \\ -1 & 2 \end{bmatrix}$$

then the product matrix AB is determined by the following procedure.

Step 1 Partition the left matrix, A, into rows and the right matrix, B, into columns, as follows:

$$AB = \begin{bmatrix} \boxed{\begin{array}{ccc} 4 & 3 & 2 \end{array}} \\ \boxed{\begin{array}{ccc} 5 & 1 & 6 \end{array}} \end{bmatrix} \begin{bmatrix} \boxed{\begin{array}{c} 2 \\ 1 \\ -1 \end{array}} & \boxed{\begin{array}{c} 4 \\ 0 \\ 2 \end{array}} \end{bmatrix}$$

Step 2 Compute the dot product between each row of the left matrix, A, and each column of the right matrix, B. Write these dot products in a matrix such that the dot product between row i of matrix A and column j of matrix B is located in row i and column j of the new matrix. The resulting new matrix is the product matrix AB.

We illustrate this process by computing the product matrix AB. Looking at the rows and columns of step 1 above, we begin by computing the dot product between row 1 of the left matrix (i.e., matrix A) and column 1 of the right matrix (i.e., matrix B), as shown below.

$$[4 \quad 3 \quad 2] \begin{bmatrix} 2 \\ 1 \\ -1 \end{bmatrix} = 4(2) + 3(1) + 2(-1) = 9 \qquad \text{row 1, column 1}$$

$$\underset{\text{Matrix } A}{\begin{bmatrix} 4 & 3 & 2 \\ 5 & 1 & 6 \end{bmatrix}} \underset{\text{Matrix } B}{\begin{bmatrix} 2 & 4 \\ 1 & 0 \\ -1 & 2 \end{bmatrix}} = \underset{\substack{\text{Product Matrix} \\ AB}}{\begin{bmatrix} 9 & \\ & \end{bmatrix}}$$

Next we find the dot product between row 1 of the left matrix and column 2 of the right matrix, as shown below.

$$[4 \quad 3 \quad 2] \begin{bmatrix} 4 \\ 0 \\ 2 \end{bmatrix} = 4(4) + 3(0) + 2(2) = 20 \qquad \text{row 1, column 2}$$

$$\underset{\text{Matrix } A}{\begin{bmatrix} 4 & 3 & 2 \\ 5 & 1 & 6 \end{bmatrix}} \underset{\text{Matrix } B}{\begin{bmatrix} 2 & 4 \\ 1 & 0 \\ -1 & 2 \end{bmatrix}} = \underset{\substack{\text{Product Matrix} \\ AB}}{\begin{bmatrix} 9 & 20 \\ & \end{bmatrix}}$$

Since we have computed the dot product between row 1 of the left matrix and each of the columns of the right matrix, we now proceed to compute the dot product between row 2 of the left matrix and each column of the right matrix. Thus, we compute the dot product between row 2 and column 1, as shown below.

$$[5 \quad 1 \quad 6]\begin{bmatrix} 2 \\ 1 \\ -1 \end{bmatrix} = 5(2) + 1(1) + 6(-1) = 5 \qquad \text{row 2, column 1}$$

$$\underset{\textit{Matrix A}}{\begin{bmatrix} 4 & 3 & 2 \\ 5 & 1 & 6 \end{bmatrix}} \underset{\textit{Matrix B}}{\begin{bmatrix} 2 & 4 \\ 1 & 0 \\ -1 & 2 \end{bmatrix}} = \underset{\substack{\textit{Product Matrix} \\ AB}}{\begin{bmatrix} 9 & 20 \\ 5 & \end{bmatrix}}$$

Now we compute the dot product between row 2 of the left matrix and column 2 of the right matrix.

$$[5 \quad 1 \quad 6]\begin{bmatrix} 4 \\ 0 \\ 2 \end{bmatrix} = 5(4) + 1(0) + 6(2) = 32 \qquad \text{row 2, column 2}$$

$$\underset{\textit{Matrix A}}{\begin{bmatrix} 4 & 3 & 2 \\ 5 & 1 & 6 \end{bmatrix}} \underset{\textit{Matrix B}}{\begin{bmatrix} 2 & 4 \\ 1 & 0 \\ -1 & 2 \end{bmatrix}} = \underset{\substack{\textit{Product Matrix} \\ AB}}{\begin{bmatrix} 9 & 20 \\ 5 & 32 \end{bmatrix}}$$

Since we have now computed the dot product between each row of the left matrix and each column of the right matrix, we are finished, and, thus, the product matrix AB is given below.

$$\underset{\textit{Product Matrix}}{AB = \begin{bmatrix} 9 & 20 \\ 5 & 32 \end{bmatrix}}$$

Observe that the product matrix AB is defined if and only if the number of columns in the left matrix, A, equals the number of rows in the right matrix, B. Note also that the product matrix has the same number of rows as the left matrix, A, and the same number of columns as the right matrix, B. These details are illustrated as follows:

Dimension of   *Dimension of*
Left Matrix, A   *Right Matrix, B*

2×3 3×2

must be equal

dimension of
product matrix, AB

2×2

Dimensions

In general, if A is an $m \times n$ matrix and B is an $n \times k$ matrix, then the product AB is an $m \times k$ matrix, as shown here:

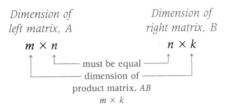

Dimension of left matrix, A   *Dimension of right matrix, B*

$m \times n \qquad\qquad n \times k$

— must be equal —
— dimension of —
product matrix, AB
$m \times k$

A product matrix can be computed only if the number of columns in the left matrix equals the number of rows in the right matrix.

We now summarize the process of matrix multiplication.

Matrix Multiplication

If A is an $m \times n$ matrix and B is an $n \times k$ matrix, the product matrix, AB, is determined as follows.

Step 1 Partition the left matrix into rows and the right matrix into columns.

$$
\begin{array}{c}
\phantom{\text{row 1}} \quad \text{col 1} \quad \text{col 2} \ldots \text{col } n \qquad \text{col 1} \quad \text{col 2} \quad \ldots \quad \text{col } k \\
\begin{array}{c}
\text{row 1} \\
\text{row 2} \\
\\
\text{row } m
\end{array}
\left[\begin{array}{cccc}
a_{11} & a_{12} & \cdots & a_{1n} \\
a_{21} & a_{22} & \cdots & a_{2n} \\
\vdots & \vdots & & \vdots \\
a_{m1} & a_{m2} & \cdots & a_{mn}
\end{array}\right]
\left[\begin{array}{cccc}
b_{11} & b_{12} & \cdots & b_{1k} \\
b_{21} & b_{22} & \cdots & b_{2k} \\
\vdots & \vdots & & \vdots \\
b_{n1} & b_{n2} & \cdots & b_{nk}
\end{array}\right]
\end{array}
$$

Step 2 Compute the dot product between each row of the left matrix and each column of the right matrix. Write these dot products in a matrix such that the dot product between row i of the left matrix and column j of the right matrix is located in row i and column j of the product matrix. Thus, if c_{ij} denotes the entry in row i and column j of the product matrix, then

$$
c_{ij} = [a_{i1} \quad a_{12} \ldots a_{in}]
\begin{bmatrix}
b_{1j} \\
b_{2j} \\
\vdots \\
b_{nj}
\end{bmatrix}
= a_{i1}b_{1j} + a_{i2}b_{2j} + \ldots + a_{in}b_{nj}
$$

continues

Matrix Multiplication—*Continued*

The following tableaus are color coded to illustrate this process. Begin with row 1 of the left matrix, and compute the dot product between row 1 of the left matrix and each respective column of the right matrix, as shown below.

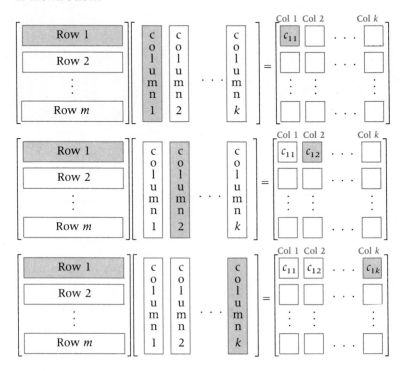

Next compute the dot product between row 2 of the left matrix and each respective column of the right matrix, as shown below.

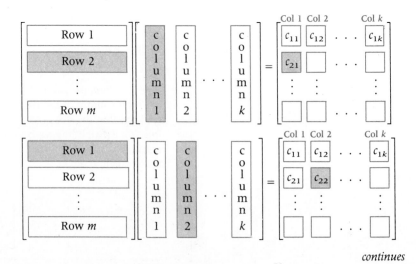

continues

Matrix Multiplication—*Continued*

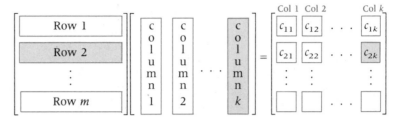

Continuing in this manner, finally, compute the dot product between row m of the left matrix and each respective column of the right matrix, as shown below.

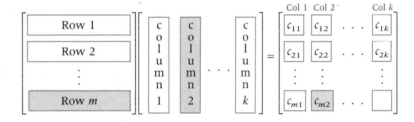

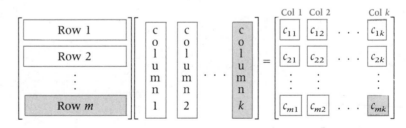

• **EXAMPLE 5-23** _____

Given that

$$F = \begin{bmatrix} 4 & 1 \\ 3 & 5 \\ 0 & 2 \end{bmatrix} \quad \text{and} \quad G = \begin{bmatrix} -3 & 7 \\ 1 & -2 \end{bmatrix}$$

find the product FG.

Solution

Note the following:

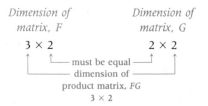

Step 1 Partition the left matrix into rows and the right matrix into columns, as shown below.

$$\begin{bmatrix} \boxed{4 \quad 1} \\ \boxed{3 \quad 5} \\ \boxed{0 \quad 2} \end{bmatrix} \begin{bmatrix} \boxed{\begin{matrix} -3 \\ 1 \end{matrix}} & \boxed{\begin{matrix} 7 \\ -2 \end{matrix}} \end{bmatrix}$$

Step 2 Compute the dot product between each row of the left matrix and each column of the right matrix. We begin with row 1 of the left matrix and compute the dot product between row 1 of the left matrix and each respective column of the right matrix, as shown below.

$$[4 \quad 1]\begin{bmatrix} -3 \\ 1 \end{bmatrix} = 4(-3) + 1(1)$$
$$= -12 + 1$$
$$= -11$$

$$F \qquad G \qquad FG$$
$$\begin{bmatrix} \boxed{4 \quad 1} \\ 3 \quad 5 \\ 0 \quad 2 \end{bmatrix} \begin{bmatrix} \boxed{\begin{matrix} -3 \\ 1 \end{matrix}} & 7 \\ & -2 \end{bmatrix} = \begin{bmatrix} \boxed{-11} & \square \\ \square & \square \\ \square & \square \end{bmatrix}$$

$$[4 \quad 1]\begin{bmatrix} 7 \\ -2 \end{bmatrix} = 4(7) + 1(-2)$$
$$= 28 - 2$$
$$= 26$$

$$F \qquad G \qquad FG$$
$$\begin{bmatrix} \boxed{4 \quad 1} \\ 3 \quad 5 \\ 0 \quad 2 \end{bmatrix} \begin{bmatrix} -3 & \boxed{\begin{matrix} 7 \\ -2 \end{matrix}} \\ 1 & \end{bmatrix} = \begin{bmatrix} -11 & \boxed{26} \\ \square & \square \\ \square & \square \end{bmatrix}$$

Next we find the dot product between row 2 of the left matrix and each respective column of the right matrix, as shown below.

$$[3 \quad 5]\begin{bmatrix} -3 \\ 1 \end{bmatrix} = 3(-3) + 5(1)$$
$$= -9 + 5$$
$$= -4$$

$$F \qquad G \qquad FG$$
$$\begin{bmatrix} 4 \quad 1 \\ \boxed{3 \quad 5} \\ 0 \quad 2 \end{bmatrix} \begin{bmatrix} \boxed{\begin{matrix} -3 \\ 1 \end{matrix}} & 7 \\ & -2 \end{bmatrix} = \begin{bmatrix} -11 & 26 \\ \boxed{-4} & \square \\ \square & \square \end{bmatrix}$$

$$[3 \quad 5]\begin{bmatrix} 7 \\ -2 \end{bmatrix} = 3(7) + 5(-2)$$
$$= 21 - 10$$
$$= 11$$

$$F \qquad G \qquad FG$$
$$\begin{bmatrix} 4 \quad 1 \\ \boxed{3 \quad 5} \\ 0 \quad 2 \end{bmatrix} \begin{bmatrix} -3 & \boxed{\begin{matrix} 7 \\ -2 \end{matrix}} \\ 1 & \end{bmatrix} = \begin{bmatrix} -11 & 26 \\ -4 & \boxed{11} \\ \square & \square \end{bmatrix}$$

Finally, we find the dot product between row 3 of the left matrix and each respective column of the right matrix, as shown below.

$$[0 \quad 2]\begin{bmatrix} -3 \\ 1 \end{bmatrix} = 0(-3) + 2(1)$$
$$= 0 + 2$$
$$= 2$$

$$\begin{array}{cc} & F \\ & \begin{bmatrix} 4 & 1 \\ 3 & 5 \\ \boxed{0 \quad 2} \end{bmatrix} \end{array} \begin{array}{c} G \\ \begin{bmatrix} \boxed{-3} & 7 \\ \boxed{1} & -2 \end{bmatrix} \end{array} = \begin{array}{c} FG \\ \begin{bmatrix} -11 & 26 \\ -4 & 11 \\ \boxed{2} & \end{bmatrix} \end{array}$$

$$[0 \quad 2]\begin{bmatrix} 7 \\ -2 \end{bmatrix} = 0(7) + 2(-2)$$
$$= -4$$

$$\begin{array}{cc} & F \\ & \begin{bmatrix} 4 & 1 \\ 3 & 5 \\ \boxed{0 \quad 2} \end{bmatrix} \end{array} \begin{array}{c} G \\ \begin{bmatrix} -3 & \boxed{7} \\ 1 & \boxed{-2} \end{bmatrix} \end{array} = \begin{array}{c} FG \\ \begin{bmatrix} -11 & 26 \\ -4 & 11 \\ 2 & \boxed{-4} \end{bmatrix} \end{array}$$

Thus, the product matrix FG is

$$\begin{bmatrix} -11 & 26 \\ -4 & 11 \\ 2 & -4 \end{bmatrix}$$

• EXAMPLE 5-24

The Saf-T-Flo Company manufactures two models of faucets: model A and model B. Each model must pass through department I (Assembly) and department II (Polishing). The unit time requirements (in hours) for each model in each department are given by matrix T:

$$\begin{array}{cc} \text{Model A} & \text{Model B} \end{array}$$
$$T = \begin{bmatrix} 3 & 5 \\ 2 & 1 \end{bmatrix} \begin{array}{l} \text{Department I} \\ \text{Department II} \end{array}$$

The production requirements of each model are given by matrix P.

$$P = \begin{bmatrix} 500 \\ 700 \end{bmatrix} \begin{array}{l} \text{Model A} \\ \text{Model B} \end{array}$$

Find the matrix that expresses the total time requirement for each department.

Solution

$$TP = \begin{bmatrix} \boxed{3 \quad 5} \\ \boxed{2 \quad 1} \end{bmatrix} \begin{bmatrix} \boxed{500} \\ \boxed{700} \end{bmatrix} = \begin{bmatrix} 5000 \\ 1700 \end{bmatrix} \begin{array}{l} \text{Total} \\ \text{Time} \\ \\ \text{Department I} \\ \\ \text{Department II} \end{array}$$

Thus, departments I and II need 5000 hours and 1700 hours, respectively, to satisfy production requirements.

• EXAMPLE 5-25

Suppose that the Saf-T-Flo Company of Example 5-24 has two plants: plant X and plant Y. The unit time requirements (in hours) for each model in each department are the same for both plants and are given by matrix T:

$$\begin{array}{cc} \text{Model A} & \text{Model B} \end{array}$$
$$T = \begin{bmatrix} 3 & 5 \\ 2 & 1 \end{bmatrix} \begin{array}{l} \text{Department I} \\ \text{Department II} \end{array}$$

The production requirements of each model in each plant are given by matrix R:

$$R = \begin{bmatrix} 500 & 800 \\ 700 & 300 \end{bmatrix} \begin{matrix} \text{Model A} \\ \text{Model B} \end{matrix}$$

(columns: Plant X, Plant Y)

Find the matrix that expresses the total time requirement for each department in each plant.

Solution

$$TR = \begin{bmatrix} \boxed{3 \quad 5} \\ \boxed{2 \quad 1} \end{bmatrix} \begin{bmatrix} \boxed{\begin{matrix} 500 \\ 700 \end{matrix}} & \boxed{\begin{matrix} 800 \\ 300 \end{matrix}} \end{bmatrix}$$

$$= \begin{bmatrix} 5000 & 3900 \\ 1700 & 1900 \end{bmatrix} \begin{matrix} \text{Department I} \\ \text{Department II} \end{matrix}$$

(columns: Plant X, Plant Y)

Thus, departments I and II of plant X need 5000 hours and 1700 hours, respectively, to satisfy production requirements. Also, departments I and II of plant Y need 3900 hours and 1900 hours, respectively, to satisfy production requirements.

Linear Systems and Matrix Equations

A linear system such as

$$\begin{aligned} 3x + 5y &= 1 \\ -2x + 7y &= -11 \end{aligned}$$

can be rewritten in matrix form as follows:

$$\begin{bmatrix} 3 & 5 \\ -2 & 7 \end{bmatrix} \begin{bmatrix} x \\ y \end{bmatrix} = \begin{bmatrix} 1 \\ -11 \end{bmatrix}$$

If

$$A = \begin{bmatrix} 3 & 5 \\ -2 & 7 \end{bmatrix} \quad X = \begin{bmatrix} x \\ y \end{bmatrix} \quad B = \begin{bmatrix} 1 \\ -11 \end{bmatrix}$$

then the preceding system may be recast as the matrix equation

$$AX = B$$

To verify that the matrix equation $AX = B$ is equivalent to the original system, we first find the product matrix AX. Hence,

$$AX = \begin{bmatrix} 3 & 5 \\ -2 & 7 \end{bmatrix} \begin{bmatrix} x \\ y \end{bmatrix} = \begin{bmatrix} 3x + 5y \\ -2x + 7y \end{bmatrix}$$

Since

$$AX = B$$

then

$$\begin{bmatrix} 3x + 5y \\ -2x + 7y \end{bmatrix} = \begin{bmatrix} 1 \\ -11 \end{bmatrix}$$

Matrix equality requires that corresponding elements of both matrices be equal. Thus,

$$3x + 5y = 1$$
$$-2x + 7y = -11$$

Observe that these are the equations of our original system.

In general, a **linear system**

$$a_{11}x_1 + a_{12}x_2 + \ldots + a_{1n}x_n = b_1$$
$$a_{21}x_1 + a_{22}x_2 + \ldots + a_{2n}x_n = b_2$$
$$\vdots \qquad \vdots \qquad \qquad \vdots \qquad \vdots$$
$$a_{n1}x_1 + a_{n2}x_2 + \ldots + a_{nn}x_n = b_n$$

can be written as the **matrix equation**

$$AX = B$$

as shown below.

$$\begin{bmatrix} a_{11} & a_{12} & \cdots & \cdots & a_{1n} \\ a_{21} & a_{22} & \cdots & \cdots & a_{2n} \\ \vdots & \vdots & & & \vdots \\ a_{n1} & a_{n2} & \cdots & \cdots & a_{nn} \end{bmatrix} \begin{bmatrix} x_1 \\ x_2 \\ \vdots \\ x_n \end{bmatrix} = \begin{bmatrix} b_1 \\ b_2 \\ \vdots \\ b_n \end{bmatrix}$$

Observe that matrix X contains the unknowns of the linear system, whereas matrix A contains the coefficients of the unknowns, and matrix B contains the right-hand-side constants of the linear system.

• **EXAMPLE 5-26** _____

The following is a linear system consisting of three equations and three variables. Rewrite this linear system in the matrix form $AX = B$.

$$4x_1 - 7x_2 + 3x_3 = 16$$
$$9x_1 + 3x_2 - 6x_3 = 5$$
$$-2x_1 - 5x_2 + 8x_3 = 11$$

Solution

Here, we have

$$\underbrace{\begin{bmatrix} 4 & -7 & 3 \\ 9 & 3 & -6 \\ -2 & -5 & 8 \end{bmatrix} \begin{bmatrix} x_1 \\ x_2 \\ x_3 \end{bmatrix}}_{AX} = \underbrace{\begin{bmatrix} 16 \\ 5 \\ 11 \end{bmatrix}}_{B}$$

_____ •

Identity Matrices

The number 1 is called the **multiplicative identity** for real numbers because

$$a \cdot 1 = 1 \cdot a = a$$

for all real numbers a. In other words, the product of any real number a and 1 is the real number a. Similarly, an **identity matrix** is a square matrix I such that

$$AI = IA = A$$

where A is a square matrix of the same dimension as I.

The matrix

$$I = \begin{bmatrix} 1 & 0 \\ 0 & 1 \end{bmatrix}$$

is the multiplicative identity for square matrices of dimension 2×2. If

$$A = \begin{bmatrix} 3 & 5 \\ -2 & 7 \end{bmatrix}$$

then observe that

$$AI = A$$

$$\overset{A}{\begin{bmatrix} 3 & 5 \\ -2 & 7 \end{bmatrix}} \overset{I}{\begin{bmatrix} 1 & 0 \\ 0 & 1 \end{bmatrix}} = \overset{A}{\begin{bmatrix} 3 & 5 \\ -2 & 7 \end{bmatrix}}$$

$$IA = A$$

$$\overset{I}{\begin{bmatrix} 1 & 0 \\ 0 & 1 \end{bmatrix}} \overset{A}{\begin{bmatrix} 3 & 5 \\ -2 & 7 \end{bmatrix}} = \overset{A}{\begin{bmatrix} 3 & 5 \\ -2 & 7 \end{bmatrix}}$$

For square matrices of dimension 3×3, the multiplicative identity is

$$I = \begin{bmatrix} 1 & 0 & 0 \\ 0 & 1 & 0 \\ 0 & 0 & 1 \end{bmatrix}$$

In general, the $n \times n$ matrix

$$I = \begin{bmatrix} 1 & 0 & 0 & \ldots & 0 \\ 0 & 1 & 0 & \ldots & 0 \\ 0 & 0 & 1 & \ldots & 0 \\ \vdots & \vdots & \vdots & & \vdots \\ 0 & 0 & 0 & \ldots & 1 \end{bmatrix}$$

is the multiplicative identity for square matrices of dimension $n \times n$.

• **EXAMPLE 5-27** ──────────────────────

If

$$A = \begin{bmatrix} 1 & -4 & 7 \\ 3 & 2 & -5 \\ -1 & -6 & -8 \end{bmatrix} \quad \text{and} \quad I = \begin{bmatrix} 1 & 0 & 0 \\ 0 & 1 & 0 \\ 0 & 0 & 1 \end{bmatrix}$$

verify that $AI = IA = A$.

Solution

$$AI = \begin{bmatrix} 1 & -4 & 7 \\ 3 & 2 & -5 \\ -1 & -6 & -8 \end{bmatrix} \begin{bmatrix} 1 & 0 & 0 \\ 0 & 1 & 0 \\ 0 & 0 & 1 \end{bmatrix}$$

$$= \begin{bmatrix} 1 & -4 & 7 \\ 3 & 2 & -5 \\ -1 & -6 & -8 \end{bmatrix} = A$$

$$IA = \begin{bmatrix} 1 & 0 & 0 \\ 0 & 1 & 0 \\ 0 & 0 & 1 \end{bmatrix} \begin{bmatrix} 1 & -4 & 7 \\ 3 & 2 & -5 \\ -1 & -6 & -8 \end{bmatrix}$$

$$= \begin{bmatrix} 1 & -4 & 7 \\ 3 & 2 & -5 \\ -1 & -6 & -8 \end{bmatrix} = A$$

Exercises 5-5

Compute the dot product between each pair of matrices.

1. $[1 \quad 2]$ and $\begin{bmatrix} -3 \\ 6 \end{bmatrix}$

2. $[3 \quad -1]$ and $\begin{bmatrix} -2 \\ 7 \end{bmatrix}$

3. $[1 \quad 4 \quad 0 \quad -3]$ and $\begin{bmatrix} 8 \\ -1 \\ 0 \\ 2 \end{bmatrix}$

4. $[-2 \quad 0 \quad 1 \quad -1]$ and $\begin{bmatrix} 1 \\ 2 \\ -1 \\ 4 \end{bmatrix}$

5. *The following problem appeared on a past Uniform CPA Examination.* Dancy, Inc., is going to begin producing a new chemical cleaner containing alcohol, peroxide, and enzyme. Each quart of the new cleaner will require 1/2 quart of alcohol, 1/6 quart of peroxide, and 1/3 quart of enzyme. The cost per quart is $0.40 for alcohol, $0.60 for peroxide, and $0.20 for enzyme. If the requirements are listed in matrix R

$$R = [1/2 \quad 1/6 \quad 1/3]$$

and their unit costs are listed in matrix C

$$C = \begin{bmatrix} 0.40 \\ 0.60 \\ 0.20 \end{bmatrix}$$

then state and perform the matrix operation to determine the cost of producing 1 quart of cleaner.

For each of the following, determine the dimension of the product matrix AB.

6. A is a 2×2 matrix, and B is a 2×4 matrix.
7. A is a 3×4 matrix, and B is a 4×5 matrix.
8. A is a 2×5 matrix, and B is a 5×3 matrix.
9. A is a 4×2 matrix, and B is a 2×4 matrix.
10. A is a 4×4 matrix, and B is a 4×4 matrix.

For each of the following, determine if it is possible to calculate the product matrix CD.

11. C is a 2×5 matrix, and D is a 4×2 matrix.
12. C is a 3×4 matrix, and D is a 2×5 matrix.
13. C is a 2×2 matrix, and D is a 2×2 matrix.

14. *C* is a 2 × 3 matrix, and *D* is a 3 × 7 matrix.

15–18. Repeat Exercises 11-14 for the product matrix *DC*.

Find each of the following matrix products.

19. $\begin{bmatrix} 4 & 3 \\ 2 & 1 \end{bmatrix} \begin{bmatrix} -1 & 1 \\ 5 & -2 \end{bmatrix}$

20. $\begin{bmatrix} 4 & 1 \\ 0 & 2 \end{bmatrix} \begin{bmatrix} 8 & -6 \\ -1 & 4 \end{bmatrix}$

21. $\begin{bmatrix} -1 & 2 \end{bmatrix} \begin{bmatrix} 8 & 3 \\ 1 & 6 \end{bmatrix}$

22. $\begin{bmatrix} 3 & -2 \end{bmatrix} \begin{bmatrix} 2 & 4 \\ -1 & -2 \end{bmatrix}$

23. $\begin{bmatrix} 3 & 4 \\ 2 & 6 \end{bmatrix} \begin{bmatrix} 1 \\ -5 \end{bmatrix}$

24. $\begin{bmatrix} -1 & 2 \\ 0 & 7 \end{bmatrix} \begin{bmatrix} -4 \\ 3 \end{bmatrix}$

25. $\begin{bmatrix} 1 & 2 & -3 \\ -1 & 0 & 2 \\ -2 & 1 & -1 \end{bmatrix} \begin{bmatrix} 2 \\ 4 \\ -4 \end{bmatrix}$

26. $\begin{bmatrix} 2 & 0 & -1 \\ -1 & 3 & -5 \\ 1 & -1 & 2 \end{bmatrix} \begin{bmatrix} -5 \\ 1 \\ -2 \end{bmatrix}$

27. $\begin{bmatrix} 1 & 2 & -3 \\ 0 & -1 & 3 \\ 5 & 0 & -4 \end{bmatrix} \begin{bmatrix} 1 & 3 \\ 2 & 1 \\ -2 & 6 \end{bmatrix}$

28. $\begin{bmatrix} 5 & 4 & -1 \\ -2 & 5 & -3 \\ 1 & 0 & -1 \end{bmatrix} \begin{bmatrix} -2 & 1 \\ 1 & 0 \\ 0 & -3 \end{bmatrix}$

29. $\begin{bmatrix} 4 & 6 \\ 2 & -1 \\ 8 & 0 \end{bmatrix} \begin{bmatrix} 1 & 3 \\ 2 & 4 \end{bmatrix}$

30. $\begin{bmatrix} 8 & 4 \\ -1 & 0 \\ 2 & 1 \end{bmatrix} \begin{bmatrix} 1 & 0 & -1 \\ -2 & 1 & 4 \end{bmatrix}$

31. $\begin{bmatrix} 1 & -4 & 2 \\ 2 & 0 & -1 \\ 3 & 1 & 1 \end{bmatrix} \begin{bmatrix} -2 & 1 & 3 \\ 1 & 2 & -2 \\ 4 & 0 & -1 \end{bmatrix}$

32. $\begin{bmatrix} 2 & 1 & -1 \\ -3 & -1 & 2 \\ 4 & 1 & -2 \end{bmatrix} \begin{bmatrix} 0 & 1 & -1 \\ -2 & 1 & 1 \\ 1 & 4 & -3 \end{bmatrix}$

Given that $A = \begin{bmatrix} 4 & 6 \\ -5 & 2 \end{bmatrix}$ and $B = \begin{bmatrix} 1 & -2 \\ -3 & 4 \end{bmatrix}$

33. Calculate *AB*.

34. Calculate *BA*.

35. Does *AB = BA?*

Given that

$$A = \begin{bmatrix} 1 & 3 & 7 \\ 2 & 4 & 0 \\ -1 & 5 & -2 \end{bmatrix} \quad B = \begin{bmatrix} 1 & 5 \\ 3 & 7 \\ -7 & 2 \end{bmatrix} \quad C = \begin{bmatrix} 2 & -1 & 0 & 6 \\ -1 & 4 & 3 & 2 \end{bmatrix} \quad D = \begin{bmatrix} 1 & 0 & -2 \\ 3 & -1 & 1 \end{bmatrix}$$

calculate, if possible, each of the following.

36. *AB*
37. *BA*
38. *BC*
39. *CB*
40. *BD*
41. *DB*
42. *DA*
43. *AD*
44. *DC*

45. *(AB)C* (*Hint:* Multiply the result of Exercise 36 by *C*. Remember that *C* is written to the right of product matrix *AB*.)

46. *A(BC)* (*Hint:* Multiply the result of Exercise 38 by *A*. Remember that *A* is written to the left of product matrix *BC*.)

47. Verify that the answers to Exercises 45 and 46 are the same. You have just verified the associative property of matrix multiplication, which states that *A(BC) = (AB)C* for matrices *A, B,* and *C,* where these products exist. This is not a mathematical proof, which is beyond the scope of this book. We will, however, accept this property from now on.

48. Given that

$$A = \begin{bmatrix} 2 & -3 \\ 1 & 4 \end{bmatrix} \quad B = \begin{bmatrix} 2 & 0 \\ -1 & 5 \end{bmatrix} \quad C = \begin{bmatrix} 2 & 7 \\ -1 & -3 \end{bmatrix}$$

verify that

a) *A(BC) = (AB)C* (associative property of multiplication)

b) *A(B + C) = AB + AC* (distributive property)

c) *(B + C)A = BA + CA*

We note that the above do not constitute mathematical proofs. However, we will accept these properties from now on.

49. Given that $A = \begin{bmatrix} 4 & 3 \\ 8 & 0 \end{bmatrix}$ and $B = \begin{bmatrix} 7 & -1 \\ -2 & 4 \end{bmatrix}$, verify that $AB \neq BA$. Although this does not constitute a mathematical proof, we will accept this property from now on.

50. If $A^2 = AA$, compute A^2 for each of the following matrices A:

a) $\begin{bmatrix} 2 & 3 \\ -1 & 4 \end{bmatrix}$

b) $\begin{bmatrix} -8 & 0 \\ 1 & 2 \end{bmatrix}$

c) $\begin{bmatrix} 1 & 2 & 1 \\ 4 & -1 & 0 \\ 2 & 0 & 2 \end{bmatrix}$

d) $\begin{bmatrix} -1 & 2 & 3 \\ 5 & -2 & 1 \\ 4 & -4 & 0 \end{bmatrix}$

51. If $A^3 = A^2A$, compute A^3 for each of the matrices of Exercise 50.

52. Compute A^3 for each of the following matrices A:

a) $\begin{bmatrix} 4 & -7 \\ 0 & 1 \end{bmatrix}$

b) $\begin{bmatrix} -2 & -3 \\ 1 & 4 \end{bmatrix}$

c) $\begin{bmatrix} -1 & 0 & 2 \\ -3 & 1 & 1 \\ 2 & -1 & 3 \end{bmatrix}$

d) $\begin{bmatrix} 4 & -1 & -3 \\ 1 & 2 & 1 \\ 0 & 1 & 0 \end{bmatrix}$

53. Using the results of Exercises 50 through 52, define A^n for positive integers n and square matrix A.

Rewrite each of the following linear systems in the matrix form $AX = B$.

54. $\begin{aligned} 2x + 3y &= 7 \\ -4x + 5y &= 9 \end{aligned}$

55. $\begin{aligned} x_1 + 5x_2 &= 6 \\ 4x_1 + 8x_2 &= 11 \end{aligned}$

56. $\begin{aligned} 3x_1 - 7x_2 - 5x_3 &= 11 \\ x_1 + 4x_2 - 2x_3 &= 4 \\ 5x_1 + 9x_2 + 8x_3 &= 16 \end{aligned}$

57. $\begin{aligned} 2x + 3y + z &= 11 \\ x + 2z &= 9 \\ 4y + 5z &= 17 \end{aligned}$

58. $\begin{aligned} 5x - 7y &= 9 \\ -x + 2y &= 1 \end{aligned}$

59. $\begin{aligned} 2x_1 - x_2 &= 6 \\ 3x_1 + 2x_2 &= 9 \end{aligned}$

60. $\begin{aligned} x_1 - 2x_2 + x_3 &= 4 \\ 2x_1 - x_2 &= 8 \\ x_1 + 2x_3 &= 5 \end{aligned}$

61. $\begin{aligned} -x_1 + x_2 - 2x_3 &= 10 \\ 6x_1 + 2x_3 &= 5 \\ x_2 - x_3 &= 9 \end{aligned}$

Write the linear system corresponding to each of the following.

62. $\begin{bmatrix} 2 & 4 \\ -1 & 5 \end{bmatrix} \begin{bmatrix} x \\ y \end{bmatrix} = \begin{bmatrix} 6 \\ -4 \end{bmatrix}$

63. $\begin{bmatrix} 1 & -3 \\ 2 & 4 \end{bmatrix} \begin{bmatrix} x_1 \\ x_2 \end{bmatrix} = \begin{bmatrix} 3 \\ -7 \end{bmatrix}$

64. $\begin{bmatrix} 2 & 1 & 0 \\ 1 & -1 & 3 \\ 3 & 1 & -1 \end{bmatrix} \begin{bmatrix} x_1 \\ x_2 \\ x_3 \end{bmatrix} = \begin{bmatrix} -1 \\ 2 \\ 3 \end{bmatrix}$

65. $\begin{bmatrix} 4 & 1 & -1 \\ 5 & 0 & 2 \\ -2 & 1 & -2 \end{bmatrix} \begin{bmatrix} x_1 \\ x_2 \\ x_3 \end{bmatrix} = \begin{bmatrix} -4 \\ 1 \\ -1 \end{bmatrix}$

66. $\begin{bmatrix} 1 & 0 & -1 \\ 2 & 1 & -3 \\ 5 & -2 & 1 \end{bmatrix} \begin{bmatrix} x_1 \\ x_2 \\ x_3 \end{bmatrix} = \begin{bmatrix} -4 \\ -3 \\ 5 \end{bmatrix}$

67. $\begin{bmatrix} 1 & 4 & -1 \\ 2 & 1 & 0 \\ 4 & 1 & -5 \end{bmatrix} \begin{bmatrix} x_1 \\ x_2 \\ x_3 \end{bmatrix} = \begin{bmatrix} 2 \\ 1 \\ 5 \end{bmatrix}$

68. Given that $A = \begin{bmatrix} 3 & 2 \\ -5 & -6 \end{bmatrix}$ and $I = \begin{bmatrix} 1 & 0 \\ 0 & 1 \end{bmatrix}$, verify that $AI = IA = A$.

69. Given that

$$A = \begin{bmatrix} 4 & 3 & 6 \\ 8 & 2 & 7 \\ -1 & 1 & 4 \end{bmatrix} \quad I = \begin{bmatrix} 1 & 0 & 0 \\ 0 & 1 & 0 \\ 0 & 0 & 1 \end{bmatrix}$$

verify that $AI = IA = A$.

70. Given that $A = \begin{bmatrix} a & b \\ c & d \end{bmatrix}$, where a, b, c, and d are real numbers, and $I = \begin{bmatrix} 1 & 0 \\ 0 & 1 \end{bmatrix}$, verify that $AI = IA = A$.

71. Given that

$$B = \begin{bmatrix} 2 & 3 \\ 7 & 4 \\ 5 & 7 \end{bmatrix} \qquad I = \begin{bmatrix} 1 & 0 \\ 0 & 1 \end{bmatrix}$$

verify that $BI = B$.

72. Given that

$$X = \begin{bmatrix} x_1 \\ x_2 \\ x_3 \end{bmatrix} \qquad A = \begin{bmatrix} 1 & 2 & -1 \\ 4 & 0 & -1 \\ 5 & 1 & 2 \end{bmatrix}$$

verify that $X - AX = (I - A)X$. (*Hint:* Compute the left-hand side and then the right-hand side, and verify that they are equal.)

Applications

73. *Costs.* A company produces three products: A, B, and C. The number of units produced of each product during each of three given months appears in the matrix below.

Production volume

	Product A	Product B	Product C
April	200	500	300
May	400	200	600
June	600	800	900

The variable cost per unit for each product is given in the matrix below.

	Variable cost per unit
Product A	30
Product B	20
Product C	50

Determine the matrix that gives the total variable cost for each of the indicated months.

74. *Production planning.* A company produces two models of a particular product. The time (in hours) required for each model in each of three departments is given in the matrix below.

Department time requirements per unit of model

	Model A	Model B
Department 1	2	3
Department 2	1	2
Department 3	3	4

The projected production volume (in units) for each model for each of the next two months is given in the matrix below.

Projected production volume

	March	April
Model A	6000	8000
Model B	9000	7000

Determine the matrix that gives the projected time requirement for each department for the given months.

75. *Election projection.* A city is divided into four voting districts. Based on a recent survey, the matrix below gives the percentage of each district that plan to vote for a particular party candidate in an upcoming mayoral election.

	District			
	1	2	3	4
Republican	0.30	0.50	0.40	0.10
Democrat	0.60	0.20	0.55	0.86
Independent	0.10	0.30	0.05	0.04

The number of people expected to vote in each district has been projected from past voter turnout. These numbers are given in the matrix below.

	Expected voter turnout
District 1	60,000
District 2	100,000
District 3	70,000
District 4	90,000

Determine the matrix that gives the projected number of votes for the respective party candidates. State the projected winning party.

76. *Data computation.* Matrix operations provide useful methods for performing computations on sets of data. The matrix below gives test grades of four students on each of three exams.

Exam grades

	John	Mary	Pete	Joan
Exam 1	60	80	50	90
Exam 2	90	50	80	70
Exam 3	100	90	70	80

Compute the matrix product

$$[0.20 \quad 0.50 \quad 0.30] \begin{bmatrix} 60 & 80 & 50 & 90 \\ 90 & 50 & 80 & 70 \\ 100 & 90 & 70 & 80 \end{bmatrix}$$

Note that the resulting product matrix gives a weighted average of the exam grades for each student.

a) State the weighted average for each student. How much weight is given to each exam?

b) Give the resulting weighted averages for the weights given by the matrix [0.30 0.10 0.60].

5-6   • INVERSE OF A SQUARE MATRIX

The multiplicative inverse of a real number a is that number $1/a$ that, when multiplied by a, results in the multiplicative identify, 1. Thus,

$$a \cdot \frac{1}{a} = \frac{1}{a} \cdot a = 1 \qquad (\text{for } a \neq 0)$$

We use the multiplicative inverse of a number to solve linear equations of the form $ax = b$, where $a \neq 0$. Specifically, we solve for x by multiplying both sides by $1/a$.

In the previous section, we learned to write linear systems as matrix equations of the form $AX = B$, where A, X, and B are matrices. Thus, in terms of matrices, solving the linear system means solving for the unknown matrix, X. Just as we solve the linear equation $ax = b$ for x by multiplying both sides by the multiplicative inverse of a, $1/a$, we also solve the matrix equation $AX = B$ for X by multiplying both sides by a matrix called the inverse of matrix A, if it exists. We define the inverse of a matrix as follows.

The **multiplicative inverse** (if it exists) of a square matrix A is that square matrix A^{-1} that, when multiplied by A, results in the identity matrix, I. Thus, for a square matrix A, its inverse (if it exists) is denoted by A^{-1} where A^{-1} is that square matrix that satisfies both conditions

$$AA^{-1} = I \qquad \text{and} \qquad A^{-1}A = I$$

We also note that if, for any given matrix, its inverse exists, then it is unique.

• EXAMPLE 5-28

If $A = \begin{bmatrix} 2 & 3 \\ 5 & 4 \end{bmatrix}$, then verifty that $A^{-1} = \begin{bmatrix} -4/7 & 3/7 \\ 5/7 & -2/7 \end{bmatrix}$.

Solution

We must compute the products AA^{-1} and $A^{-1}A$, and then verify that they each yield the identity matrix. Hence,

$$AA^{-1} = \begin{bmatrix} 2 & 3 \\ 5 & 4 \end{bmatrix}\begin{bmatrix} -4/7 & 3/7 \\ 5/7 & -2/7 \end{bmatrix} = \begin{bmatrix} 1 & 0 \\ 0 & 1 \end{bmatrix} = I$$

$$A^{-1}A = \begin{bmatrix} -4/7 & 3/7 \\ 5/7 & -2/7 \end{bmatrix}\begin{bmatrix} 2 & 3 \\ 5 & 4 \end{bmatrix} = \begin{bmatrix} 1 & 0 \\ 0 & 1 \end{bmatrix} = I$$

Thus,

$$AA^{-1} = I = A^{-1}A$$

We note that because of the way matrix multiplication is defined, only square matrices can have inverses.

Computing Matrix Inverses

We now focus on developing a procedure to compute A^{-1}, if it exists, for a square matrix A. We begin with the matrix

$$A = \begin{bmatrix} 2 & 3 \\ 1 & 4 \end{bmatrix}$$

and let

$$A^{-1} = \begin{bmatrix} a & b \\ c & d \end{bmatrix}$$

where a, b, c, and d are unknowns. It is our goal to find values for a, b, c, and d such that

$$AA^{-1} = I$$

or, equivalently,

$$\overset{A}{\begin{bmatrix} 2 & 3 \\ 1 & 4 \end{bmatrix}} \overset{A^{-1}}{\begin{bmatrix} a & b \\ c & d \end{bmatrix}} = \overset{I}{\begin{bmatrix} 1 & 0 \\ 0 & 1 \end{bmatrix}}$$

Multiplying the left-hand side yields

$$\begin{bmatrix} 2a + 3c & 2b + 3d \\ a + 4c & b + 4d \end{bmatrix} = \begin{bmatrix} 1 & 0 \\ 0 & 1 \end{bmatrix}$$

The equality of the above matrices implies that corresponding entries are equal. Hence,

$$2a + 3c = 1 \qquad 2b + 3d = 0$$
$$a + 4c = 0 \qquad b + 4d = 1$$

Observe that the above constitute two linear systems that can be written in tableau form as

$$\overset{a \quad\ c}{\begin{bmatrix} 2 & 3 & | & 1 \\ 1 & 4 & | & 0 \end{bmatrix}} \qquad \overset{b \quad\ d}{\begin{bmatrix} 2 & 3 & | & 0 \\ 1 & 4 & | & 1 \end{bmatrix}}$$

Such tableaus, as we learned in Section 5-2, are also called **augmented matrices.**

We can solve each of the above linear systems by the Gauss-Jordan method. Since the matrix to the left of the vertical line is the same (i.e., it is matrix A) for both of the above tableaus, we can combine the right-hand-side columns of both tableaus and write the two tableaus as a single augmented matrix (or tableau), as illustrated below.

$$\overset{A \qquad\qquad I}{\begin{bmatrix} 2 & 3 & | & 1 & 0 \\ 1 & 4 & | & 0 & 1 \end{bmatrix}} \qquad \text{denoted } [A \mid I]$$

Since matrix A is to the left of the vertical line and the identity matrix is to its right, such an augmented matrix is denoted as $[A \mid I]$.

When we apply the Gauss-Jordan method to such an augmented matrix $[A \mid I]$, we transform it into an equivalent matrix of the form

$$\begin{bmatrix} 1 & 0 & \boxed{A^{-1}} \\ 0 & 1 & \end{bmatrix} \qquad \text{denoted } [I \mid A^{-1}]$$

where A^{-1} appears on the right-hand side. Such a matrix is denoted as $[I \mid A^{-1}]$.

We now apply the Gauss-Jordan method to compute A^{-1}. Remember that this method involves the use of three fundamental row operations, which we repeat:

1. Interchange two rows of a matrix.
2. Multiply a row of a matrix by a nonzero constant.
3. Add a multiple of a row to another row.

Step 1 *Change column 1 of $[A \mid I]$ to* $\begin{bmatrix} 1 \\ 0 \end{bmatrix}$.

We get the 1 first by interchanging Rows 1 and 2 or, in other words, $[R1 \leftrightarrow R2]$. This gives the tableau below.

$$\begin{bmatrix} 1 & 4 & 0 & 1 \\ 2 & 3 & 1 & 0 \end{bmatrix}$$

Now we need a 0 for the second entry in column 1. This is obtained by the row operation

$$-2 \text{ times Row 1, add the result to Row 2,}$$
$$\text{or, in other words, } [(-2)R1 + R2 \rightarrow R2]$$

The resulting tableau is

$$\begin{bmatrix} 1 & 4 & 0 & 1 \\ 0 & -5 & 1 & -2 \end{bmatrix}$$

Step 2 *Change column 2 of the above matrix to* $\begin{bmatrix} 0 \\ 1 \end{bmatrix}$.

We get the 1 first by the row operation

$$\text{Multiply Row 2 by } -1/5,$$
$$\text{or, in other words, } [(-1/5)R2 \rightarrow R2]$$

This gives the tableau

$$\begin{bmatrix} 1 & 4 & 0 & 1 \\ 0 & 1 & -1/5 & 2/5 \end{bmatrix}$$

Now we get a 0 for the first entry in column 2 by the row operation

$$-4 \text{ times row 2, add the result to row 1,}$$
$$\text{or, in other words, } [(-4)R2 + R1 \rightarrow R1]$$

This gives the final tableau

$$\left[\begin{array}{cc|cc} 1 & 0 & 4/5 & -3/5 \\ 0 & 1 & -1/5 & 2/5 \end{array}\right]$$

Thus,

$$A^{-1} = \begin{bmatrix} 4/5 & -3/5 \\ -1/5 & 2/5 \end{bmatrix}$$

We check our result by noting that

$$AA^{-1} = \begin{bmatrix} 2 & 3 \\ 1 & 4 \end{bmatrix}\begin{bmatrix} 4/5 & -3/5 \\ -1/5 & 2/5 \end{bmatrix} = \begin{bmatrix} 1 & 0 \\ 0 & 1 \end{bmatrix}$$

$$A^{-1}A = \begin{bmatrix} 4/5 & -3/5 \\ -1/5 & 2/5 \end{bmatrix}\begin{bmatrix} 2 & 3 \\ 1 & 4 \end{bmatrix} = \begin{bmatrix} 1 & 0 \\ 0 & 1 \end{bmatrix}$$

To Compute a Matrix Inverse

In general, to find the multiplicative inverse of an $n \times n$ matrix, A, we begin with the initial tableau or augmented matrix, $[A \mid I]$:

$$\left[\begin{array}{cccc|cccc} a_{11} & a_{12} & \cdots & a_{1n} & 1 & 0 & \cdots & 0 \\ a_{21} & a_{22} & \cdots & a_{2n} & 0 & 1 & \cdots & 0 \\ \vdots & \vdots & & \vdots & \vdots & \vdots & & \vdots \\ a_{n1} & a_{n2} & \cdots & a_{nn} & 0 & 0 & \cdots & 1 \end{array}\right]$$

and use row operations to obtain the final tableau or augmented matrix, $[I \mid A^{-1}]$:

$$\left[\begin{array}{cccc|c} 1 & 0 & \cdots & 0 & \\ 0 & 1 & \cdots & 0 & \\ \vdots & \vdots & & \vdots & \mathbf{A}^{-1} \\ 0 & 0 & \cdots & 1 & \end{array}\right]$$

• **EXAMPLE 5-29**

If

$$A = \begin{bmatrix} 3 & -1 & 1 \\ 2 & 2 & 0 \\ 0 & 1 & 2 \end{bmatrix}$$

compute A^{-1}.

Solution

We write the initial tableau or augmented matrix, $[A \mid I]$.

$$\left[\begin{array}{ccc|ccc} 3 & -1 & 1 & 1 & 0 & 0 \\ 2 & 2 & 0 & 0 & 1 & 0 \\ 0 & 1 & 2 & 0 & 0 & 1 \end{array}\right]$$

Step 1 *Change column 1 to* $\begin{bmatrix} 1 \\ 0 \\ 0 \end{bmatrix}$.

We show the transformations from one matrix to the next and the appropriate row operations.

$$\begin{bmatrix} 3 & -1 & 1 & | & 1 & 0 & 0 \\ 2 & 2 & 0 & | & 0 & 1 & 0 \\ 0 & 1 & 2 & | & 0 & 0 & 1 \end{bmatrix} \xrightarrow{(-1)R2 + R1 \to R1} \begin{bmatrix} 1 & -3 & 1 & | & 1 & -1 & 0 \\ 2 & 2 & 0 & | & 0 & 1 & 0 \\ 0 & 1 & 2 & | & 0 & 0 & 1 \end{bmatrix}$$

$$\begin{bmatrix} 1 & -3 & 1 & | & 1 & -1 & 0 \\ 2 & 2 & 0 & | & 0 & 1 & 0 \\ 0 & 1 & 2 & | & 0 & 0 & 1 \end{bmatrix} \xrightarrow{(-2)R1 + R2 \to R2} \begin{bmatrix} 1 & -3 & 1 & | & 1 & -1 & 0 \\ 0 & 8 & -2 & | & -2 & 3 & 0 \\ 0 & 1 & 2 & | & 0 & 0 & 1 \end{bmatrix}$$

Step 2 *Change column 2 to* $\begin{bmatrix} 0 \\ 1 \\ 0 \end{bmatrix}$.

$$\begin{bmatrix} 1 & -3 & 1 & | & 1 & -1 & 0 \\ 0 & 8 & -2 & | & -2 & 3 & 0 \\ 0 & 1 & 2 & | & 0 & 0 & 1 \end{bmatrix} \xrightarrow{(-7)R3 + R2 \to R2} \begin{bmatrix} 1 & -3 & 1 & | & 1 & -1 & 0 \\ 0 & 1 & -16 & | & -2 & 3 & -7 \\ 0 & 1 & 2 & | & 0 & 0 & 1 \end{bmatrix}$$

$$\begin{bmatrix} 1 & -3 & 1 & | & 1 & -1 & 0 \\ 0 & 1 & -16 & | & -2 & 3 & -7 \\ 0 & 1 & 2 & | & 0 & 0 & 1 \end{bmatrix} \xrightarrow[\;(-1)R2 + R3 \to R3\;]{(3)R2 + R1 \to R1} \begin{bmatrix} 1 & 0 & -47 & | & -5 & 8 & -21 \\ 0 & 1 & -16 & | & -2 & 3 & -7 \\ 0 & 0 & 18 & | & 2 & -3 & 8 \end{bmatrix}$$

Step 3 *Change column 3 to* $\begin{bmatrix} 0 \\ 0 \\ 1 \end{bmatrix}$.

$$\begin{bmatrix} 1 & 0 & -47 & | & -5 & 8 & -21 \\ 0 & 1 & -16 & | & -2 & 3 & -7 \\ 0 & 0 & 18 & | & 2 & -3 & 8 \end{bmatrix} \xrightarrow{(1/18)R3 \to R3} \begin{bmatrix} 1 & 0 & -47 & | & -5 & 8 & -21 \\ 0 & 1 & -16 & | & -2 & 3 & -7 \\ 0 & 0 & 1 & | & 1/9 & -1/6 & 4/9 \end{bmatrix}$$

$$\begin{bmatrix} 1 & 0 & -47 & | & -5 & 8 & -21 \\ 0 & 1 & -16 & | & -2 & 3 & -16 \\ 0 & 0 & 1 & | & 1/9 & -1/6 & 4/9 \end{bmatrix} \xrightarrow[\;(47)R3 + R1 \to R1\;]{(16)R3 + R2 \to R2} \begin{bmatrix} 1 & 0 & 0 & | & 2/9 & 1/6 & -1/9 \\ 0 & 1 & 0 & | & -2/9 & 1/3 & 1/9 \\ 0 & 0 & 1 & | & \underbrace{1/9 \quad -1/6 \quad 4/9}_{A^{-1}} \end{bmatrix}$$

We leave it for the reader to check that $AA^{-1} = I = A^{-1}A$.

Matrix Inverse May Not Exist

Not all square matrices have inverses. If, during the process of computing the inverse of a matrix A, a row consisting entirely of 0s appears in the left-hand side of the tableau, then the matrix A has no inverse. To illustrate this case, we will attempt to compute the inverse of matrix A where

Initial Tableau, [A | I]

$$A = \begin{bmatrix} 1 & 2 \\ 4 & 8 \end{bmatrix} \qquad \begin{bmatrix} 1 & 2 & | & 1 & 0 \\ 4 & 8 & | & 0 & 1 \end{bmatrix}$$

Since we already have a 1 in the upper left-hand corner, we multiply row 1 by -4 and add the result to row 2. This gives us a 0 in the lower left-hand corner:

$$\begin{bmatrix} 1 & 2 & | & 1 & 0 \\ 0 & 0 & | & -4 & 1 \end{bmatrix}$$

Observe that the left-hand side of row 2 consists entirely of 0s, with at least one nonzero right-hand side entry. This type of situation indicates that the matrix A has *no inverse*. Thus, for this example, A^{-1} does not exist.

Exercises 5-6

Determine whether or not the following matrices are inverses of each other.

1. $\begin{bmatrix} 1 & -3/2 \\ 1 & -2 \end{bmatrix}$ and $\begin{bmatrix} 4 & -3 \\ 2 & -2 \end{bmatrix}$

2. $\begin{bmatrix} 4 & 1 \\ 3 & 0 \end{bmatrix}$ and $\begin{bmatrix} 1 & 2 \\ -1 & 4 \end{bmatrix}$

3. $\begin{bmatrix} 7 & -8 \\ 3 & -3 \end{bmatrix}$ and $\begin{bmatrix} -1 & 8/3 \\ -1 & 7/3 \end{bmatrix}$

4. $\begin{bmatrix} 1 & 3 & 0 \\ 0 & 1 & 0 \\ 1 & 2 & 1 \end{bmatrix}$ and $\begin{bmatrix} 1 & -3 & 0 \\ 0 & 1 & 0 \\ 0 & -2 & 1 \end{bmatrix}$

5. $\begin{bmatrix} 5 & 6 \\ 3 & 4 \end{bmatrix}$ and $\begin{bmatrix} 2 & -3 \\ -3/2 & 5/2 \end{bmatrix}$

6. $\begin{bmatrix} 1 & 0 & 0 \\ 0 & 1 & 0 \\ 2 & 3 & 1 \end{bmatrix}$ and $\begin{bmatrix} 1 & 0 & 0 \\ 0 & 1 & 0 \\ -2 & -3 & 1 \end{bmatrix}$

7. $\begin{bmatrix} 1 & 2 \\ 5 & -1 \end{bmatrix}$ and $\begin{bmatrix} 8 & 0 \\ 4 & 1 \end{bmatrix}$

8. $\begin{bmatrix} 1 & 3 & 2 \\ 0 & 1 & 4 \\ 0 & 0 & 1 \end{bmatrix}$ and $\begin{bmatrix} 1 & -3 & 10 \\ 0 & 1 & -4 \\ 0 & 0 & 1 \end{bmatrix}$

9. Given that $A = \begin{bmatrix} 1 & 5 \\ 2 & 11 \end{bmatrix}$,
  a) Compute A^{-1}.
  b) Verify that $AA^{-1} = A^{-1}A = I$.

10. Given that $B = \begin{bmatrix} 1 & 4 & 5 \\ 0 & 1 & 3 \\ 0 & 1 & 4 \end{bmatrix}$,
  a) Compute B^{-1}.
  b) Verify that $BB^{-1} = B^{-1}B = I$.

Find the inverse of each of the following matrices:

11. $\begin{bmatrix} 5 & -1 \\ -3 & 7 \end{bmatrix}$

12. $\begin{bmatrix} 1 & 3 \\ 2 & -4 \end{bmatrix}$

13. $\begin{bmatrix} 0 & 1 \\ 1 & 1 \end{bmatrix}$

14. $\begin{bmatrix} 1 & -1 & 3 \\ 0 & 2 & -4 \\ -2 & 2 & -5 \end{bmatrix}$

15. $\begin{bmatrix} 3 & 2 & 1 \\ 4 & -3 & 2 \\ 2 & 4 & -3 \end{bmatrix}$

16. $\begin{bmatrix} -1 & 1 & -2 \\ -2 & 0 & -4 \\ 6 & 2 & 10 \end{bmatrix}$

17. $\begin{bmatrix} 3 & 4 \\ 2 & -7 \end{bmatrix}$

18. $\begin{bmatrix} 1 & 3 \\ 2 & 4 \end{bmatrix}$

19. $\begin{bmatrix} 2 & 3 \\ 4 & -1 \end{bmatrix}$

20. $\begin{bmatrix} 1 & 1 & 2 \\ 3 & -1 & 3 \\ 2 & -5 & 2 \end{bmatrix}$

21. $\begin{bmatrix} 1 & 2 & 1 \\ 4 & 1 & 0 \\ 0 & 0 & 1 \end{bmatrix}$

22. $\begin{bmatrix} 1 & 2 & 2 \\ 8 & -6 & 2 \\ 8 & 4 & 4 \end{bmatrix}$

23. Given that $K = \begin{bmatrix} 2 & 3 \\ -10 & -15 \end{bmatrix}$, try to find K^{-1}. Does K^{-1} exist?

24. Given that $H = \begin{bmatrix} 1 & 2 & -1 \\ 2 & 4 & 3 \\ -2 & -4 & 2 \end{bmatrix}$, try to find H^{-1}. Does H^{-1} exist?

Find the inverse, if it exists, of each of the following matrices:

25.
$$\begin{bmatrix} -1 & 1 & 1 & 0 \\ 0 & 0 & 0 & 2 \\ 3 & 3 & 0 & 0 \\ 4 & 2 & 2 & 0 \end{bmatrix}$$

26.
$$\begin{bmatrix} 1 & 2 & 1 & 0 \\ 2 & 2 & 0 & 4 \\ 6 & -3 & 3 & -3 \\ 1 & 1 & 0 & 2 \end{bmatrix}$$

5-7 • SOLVING SQUARE LINEAR SYSTEMS BY MATRIX INVERSES

In order to solve the linear equation

$$ax = b \text{ (where a} \neq 0)$$

for x, we multiply both sides by $1/a$, the multiplicative inverse of a, to obtain

$$\left(\frac{1}{a}\right)ax = \left(\frac{1}{a}\right)b$$

$$x = \left(\frac{1}{a}\right)b$$

Analogously, we may use the multiplicative inverse of a matrix to solve linear systems. Consider the linear system

$$2x_1 + 3x_2 = 9$$
$$5x_1 + 4x_2 = 26$$

Expressing this system in matrix form, $AX = B$, we have

$$\begin{bmatrix} 2 & 3 \\ 5 & 4 \end{bmatrix}\begin{bmatrix} x_1 \\ x_2 \end{bmatrix} = \begin{bmatrix} 9 \\ 26 \end{bmatrix}$$

If we multiply both sides of the matrix equation, $AX = B$, by A^{-1} (assuming that A^{-1} exists), we have

$$A^{-1}(AX) = A^{-1}B$$

Since $A^{-1}(AX) = (A^{-1}A)X$ by the associative property and $A^{-1}A = I$, the left-hand side becomes IX, and the equation reads

$$IX = A^{-1}B$$

Since $IX = X$, we obtain

$$X = A^{-1}B$$

Thus, the solution to a matrix equation $AX = B$ is

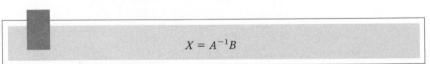

$$X = A^{-1}B$$

Returning to our example,

$$\begin{bmatrix} 2 & 3 \\ 5 & 4 \end{bmatrix} \begin{bmatrix} x_1 \\ x_2 \end{bmatrix} = \begin{bmatrix} 9 \\ 26 \end{bmatrix}$$

we must find A^{-1} by beginning with the augmented matrix or initial tableau, $[A \mid I]$,

$$\begin{bmatrix} 2 & 3 & | & 1 & 0 \\ 5 & 4 & | & 0 & 1 \end{bmatrix}$$

and using row operations to obtain the final tableau, $[I \mid A^{-1}]$,

$$\begin{bmatrix} 1 & 0 & | & -4/7 & 3/7 \\ 0 & 1 & | & 5/7 & -2/7 \end{bmatrix}$$

Hence,

$$A^{-1} = \begin{bmatrix} -4/7 & 3/7 \\ 5/7 & -2/7 \end{bmatrix}$$

Next we find the product $A^{-1}B$:

$$A^{-1}B = \begin{bmatrix} -4/7 & 3/7 \\ 5/7 & -2/7 \end{bmatrix} \begin{bmatrix} 9 \\ 26 \end{bmatrix} = \begin{bmatrix} 6 \\ -1 \end{bmatrix}$$

Thus, the solution is

$$X = A^{-1}B$$
$$\begin{bmatrix} x_1 \\ x_2 \end{bmatrix} = \begin{bmatrix} 6 \\ -1 \end{bmatrix}$$

Therefore, $(6, -1)$ is the solution to our linear system.

SUMMARY

Using a Matrix Inverse to Solve a Square Linear System

Consider a linear system

$$\begin{aligned} a_{11}x_1 + a_{12}x_2 + \ldots\ldots + a_{1n}x_n &= b_1 \\ a_{21}x_1 + a_{22}x_2 + \ldots\ldots + a_{2n}x_n &= b_2 \\ \vdots \qquad \vdots \qquad\qquad \vdots \qquad \vdots \\ a_{n1}x_1 + a_{n2}x_2 + \ldots\ldots + a_{nn}x_n &= b_n \end{aligned}$$

that, when written as the matrix equation

$$AX = B$$

becomes

$$\begin{bmatrix} a_{11} & a_{12} & \ldots\ldots & a_{1n} \\ a_{21} & a_{22} & \ldots\ldots & a_{2n} \\ \vdots & \vdots & & \vdots \\ \vdots & \vdots & & \vdots \\ a_{n1} & a_{n2} & \ldots\ldots & a_{nn} \end{bmatrix} \begin{bmatrix} x_1 \\ x_2 \\ \vdots \\ \vdots \\ x_n \end{bmatrix} = \begin{bmatrix} b_1 \\ b_2 \\ \vdots \\ \vdots \\ b_n \end{bmatrix}.$$

continues

SUMMARY—*Continued*

The **solution** to this linear system is given by the matrix equation

$$X = A^{-1}B$$

where

$$\begin{bmatrix} x_1 \\ x_2 \\ \cdot \\ \cdot \\ x_n \end{bmatrix} = \begin{bmatrix} A^{-1} \end{bmatrix} \begin{bmatrix} b_1 \\ b_2 \\ \cdot \\ \cdot \\ b_n \end{bmatrix}$$

provided that A^{-1} exists.

• **EXAMPLE 5-30**

Use the matrix inverse to solve the linear system

$$x_1 + 3x_2 + 3x_3 = 4$$
$$2x_1 + 7x_2 + 7x_3 = 9$$
$$2x_1 + 7x_2 + 6x_3 = 10$$

Solution

Rewriting the linear system in matrix form, $AX = B$, we have

$$\begin{bmatrix} 1 & 3 & 3 \\ 2 & 7 & 7 \\ 2 & 7 & 6 \end{bmatrix} \begin{bmatrix} x_1 \\ x_2 \\ x_3 \end{bmatrix} = \begin{bmatrix} 4 \\ 9 \\ 10 \end{bmatrix}$$

Hence,

$$A = \begin{bmatrix} 1 & 3 & 3 \\ 2 & 7 & 7 \\ 2 & 7 & 6 \end{bmatrix} \quad X = \begin{bmatrix} x_1 \\ x_2 \\ x_3 \end{bmatrix} \quad B = \begin{bmatrix} 4 \\ 9 \\ 10 \end{bmatrix}$$

We must find A^{-1} by beginning with the initial tableau, $[A \mid I]$,

$$\begin{bmatrix} 1 & 3 & 3 & 1 & 0 & 0 \\ 2 & 7 & 7 & 0 & 1 & 0 \\ 2 & 7 & 6 & 0 & 0 & 1 \end{bmatrix}$$

and using row operations to obtain the final tableau, $[I \mid A^{-1}]$,

$$\begin{bmatrix} 1 & 0 & 0 & 7 & -3 & 0 \\ 0 & 1 & 0 & -2 & 0 & 1 \\ 0 & 0 & 1 & 0 & 1 & -1 \end{bmatrix}$$

Hence,

$$A^{-1} = \begin{bmatrix} 7 & -3 & 0 \\ -2 & 0 & 1 \\ 0 & 1 & -1 \end{bmatrix}$$

We now find the product $A^{-1}B$.

$$A^{-1}B = \begin{bmatrix} 7 & -3 & 0 \\ -2 & 0 & 1 \\ 0 & 1 & -1 \end{bmatrix} \begin{bmatrix} 4 \\ 9 \\ 10 \end{bmatrix} = \begin{bmatrix} 1 \\ 2 \\ -1 \end{bmatrix}$$

Thus, the solution is

$$X = A^{-1}B$$
$$\begin{bmatrix} x_1 \\ x_2 \\ x_3 \end{bmatrix} = \begin{bmatrix} 1 \\ 2 \\ -1 \end{bmatrix}$$

Therefore, $(1, 2, -1)$ is the solution to our linear system.

The method of solving a square linear system $AX = B$ by using A^{-1} (if A^{-1} exists) is relatively inefficient for large square linear systems unless A^{-1} is known beforehand or can easily be determined by using a computer. However, in this age of "cheap computing," most students have access to a computer. Under these circumstances, this method is advantageous for solving square linear systems $AX = B$, especially when matrix B changes and matrix A does not.

Application

PROBLEM

A company manufactures shoes and slippers. Matrix A gives the time requirements (in hours) for each pair of shoes and slippers in departments I and II.

$$A = \begin{matrix} \text{Shoes} \quad \text{Slippers} \\ \begin{bmatrix} 3 & 4 \\ 5 & 2 \end{bmatrix} \end{matrix} \begin{matrix} \text{Department I} \\ \text{Department II} \end{matrix}$$

Matrix B represents the time (in hours) available in each department. All this time must be used.

$$B = \begin{bmatrix} 450 \\ 400 \end{bmatrix} \begin{matrix} \text{Department I} \\ \text{Department II} \end{matrix}$$

We must determine how many pairs of shoes and slippers should be produced if the departments operate at full capacity.

SOLUTION

If the numbers of pairs of shoes and pairs of slippers to be manufactured are represented by the matrix

$$X = \begin{bmatrix} x_1 \\ x_2 \end{bmatrix} \begin{matrix} \text{Pairs of shoes} \\ \text{Pairs of slippers} \end{matrix}$$

then X satisfies the matrix equation

$$\overset{AX = B}{\begin{bmatrix} 3 & 4 \\ 5 & 2 \end{bmatrix} \begin{bmatrix} x_1 \\ x_2 \end{bmatrix} = \begin{bmatrix} 450 \\ 400 \end{bmatrix}}$$

Using row operations, it can be determined that

$$A^{-1} = \begin{bmatrix} -1/7 & 2/7 \\ 5/14 & -3/14 \end{bmatrix}$$

Solving for X yields

$$\overset{X = A^{-1}B}{\begin{bmatrix} x_1 \\ x_2 \end{bmatrix} = \begin{bmatrix} -1/7 & 2/7 \\ 5/14 & -3/14 \end{bmatrix} \begin{bmatrix} 450 \\ 400 \end{bmatrix} = \begin{bmatrix} 50 \\ 75 \end{bmatrix}}$$

Thus, the company should produce

$$x_1 = 50 \text{ pairs of shoes}$$
$$x_2 = 75 \text{ pairs of slippers}$$

The advantage of using A^{-1} to solve this problem becomes apparent when we consider the following change. Suppose matrix B, which represents the time available in each department, changes from

$$\begin{bmatrix} 450 \\ 400 \end{bmatrix} \quad \text{to} \quad \begin{bmatrix} 490 \\ 280 \end{bmatrix}$$

Then, since

$$X = A^{-1} B$$

the new solution X may be determined by multiplying A^{-1} times the new matrix B. Since matrix A is unchanged, it is not necessary to recalculate A^{-1}. For example, if matrix B is changed to

$$B = \begin{bmatrix} 490 \\ 280 \end{bmatrix}$$

then

$$\overset{X = A^{-1}B}{\begin{bmatrix} x_1 \\ x_2 \end{bmatrix} = \begin{bmatrix} -1/7 & 2/7 \\ 5/14 & -3/14 \end{bmatrix} \begin{bmatrix} 490 \\ 280 \end{bmatrix} = \begin{bmatrix} 10 \\ 115 \end{bmatrix}}$$

Thus, the company should produce

$$x_1 = 10 \text{ pairs of shoes}$$
$$x_2 = 115 \text{ pairs of slippers}$$

Exercises 5-7

Find x_1 and x_2 for each of the following.

1. $\begin{bmatrix} x_1 \\ x_2 \end{bmatrix} = \begin{bmatrix} 2 & 1 \\ -1 & 3 \end{bmatrix} \begin{bmatrix} 5 \\ 2 \end{bmatrix}$

2. $\begin{bmatrix} x_1 \\ x_2 \end{bmatrix} = \begin{bmatrix} -1 & 4 \\ 5 & -2 \end{bmatrix} \begin{bmatrix} -3 \\ 6 \end{bmatrix}$

3. $\begin{bmatrix} x_1 \\ x_2 \end{bmatrix} = \begin{bmatrix} 4 & -1 \\ -1 & 3 \end{bmatrix} \begin{bmatrix} 5 \\ 2 \end{bmatrix}$

4. $\begin{bmatrix} x_1 \\ x_2 \end{bmatrix} = \begin{bmatrix} 3 & 1 \\ -2 & 5 \end{bmatrix} \begin{bmatrix} 4 \\ 3 \end{bmatrix}$

Express each of the following linear systems in matrix form $AX = B$. Then compute A^{-1} and use it to solve the linear system.

5.
$$x_1 + 2x_2 = 9$$
$$-x_1 + 3x_2 = 1$$

6.
$$x_1 + x_2 = 9$$
$$2x_1 + 3x_2 = 25$$

7.
$$x_1 \quad\quad + x_3 = 11$$
$$x_2 + 4x_3 = 39$$
$$2x_1 + 3x_2 + x_3 = 22$$

8.
$$x_1 + x_2 + 5x = 21$$
$$x_2 + 3x_3 = 15$$
$$3x_1 + 3x_2 + 16x_3 = 67$$

9.
$$x_1 + x_2 + x_3 = 3$$
$$x_1 + 2x_2 + 3x_3 = 10$$
$$x_2 + 4x_3 = 17$$

10.
$$x_1 - x_2 + x_3 = 8$$
$$x_1 \quad\quad + 4x_3 = 19$$
$$x_2 + 2x_3 = 7$$

11.
$$x_1 + x_2 \quad\quad = 3$$
$$x_2 + 3x_3 = -7$$
$$4x_1 + 6x_2 + 7x_3 = -5$$

12.
$$x_1 + x_2 - 2x_3 = -4$$
$$x_1 + 2x_2 + 3x_3 = 7$$
$$2x_2 + 12x_3 = 26$$

13.
$$2x - 3y = 6$$
$$x - 7y = 25$$

14.
$$4x_1 - 5x_2 = -2$$
$$3x_1 + 2x_2 = -13$$

15.
$$2x + 3y - 5z = -13$$
$$-x + 2y + 3z = -7$$
$$3x - 4y - 7z = 15$$

16.
$$2x_1 - 3x_2 + 4x_3 = 8$$
$$3x_1 + x_2 - 2x_3 = 11$$
$$5x_1 - 2x_2 + 3x_3 = 10$$

17.
$$5x_1 + 7x_2 + x_3 = 1$$
$$3x_1 + 2x_2 + 3x_3 = 8$$
$$2x_1 + 3x_2 + 5x_3 = 19$$

18.
$$3x + 7y + 2z = 2$$
$$4x + 3y + 3z = 8$$
$$x + 2y + 4z = -9$$

19.
$$4x_1 + x_2 = 8$$
$$6x_1 - 2x_2 = -9$$

20.
$$(1/2)x + 5y = 17$$
$$3x + 2y = 18$$

21.
$$2x + y + 3z = 11$$
$$4x + 3y - 2z = -1$$
$$6x + 5y - 4z = -4$$

22.
$$x_1 + x_2 - 5x_3 = -3$$
$$2x_1 + x_2 + 10x_3 = 2$$
$$3x_1 + 2x_2 + 25x_3 = 3$$

23. Express the following linear system in matrix form, $AX = B$. Then compute A^{-1} and use it to solve the linear system.

$$x_1 \quad\quad + x_3 - x_4 = -2$$
$$x_2 - x_3 + 2x_4 = 12$$
$$4x_1 \quad\quad + 5x_3 - 3x_4 = 2$$
$$2x_3 + 3x_4 = 27$$

24. Express the following linear system in matrix form, $AX = B$. Then compute A^{-1} and use it to solve the linear system.

$$x_1 + 2x_2 - x_3 + x_4 = -7$$
$$2x_1 + x_2 + x_3 + 2x_4 = 1$$
$$-3x_1 - x_2 + x_3 - x_4 = 3$$
$$x_1 \quad\quad + 2x_4 = -1$$

25. *Nutrition.* A diet must provide exactly 1200 milligrams of protein and 1000 milligrams of iron. These nutrients will be obtained by eating meat and spinach.

Each pound of meat contains 500 milligrams of protein and 100 milligrams of iron. Each pound of spinach contains 200 milligrams of protein and 800 milligrams of iron.

a) If matrix A lists the number of milligrams of protein and iron obtained from a pound of meat and from a pound of spinach, respectively, then fill in the elements of matrix A.

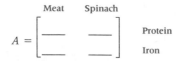

b) If matrix B lists the amounts required of protein and iron, respectively, then fill in the elements of matrix B.

$$B = \begin{bmatrix} \underline{\quad} \\ \underline{\quad} \end{bmatrix} \begin{matrix} \text{Protein} \\ \text{Iron} \end{matrix}$$

c) If $X = \begin{bmatrix} x_1 \\ x_2 \end{bmatrix}$, where x_1 and x_2 represent the number of pounds of meat and spinach, respectively, that should be eaten in order to provide the proper amounts of protein and iron, then write the matrix equation relating A, X, and B.

d) Solve the matrix equation of part c for X and interpret the answer.

e) Repeat parts c and d for $B = \begin{bmatrix} 2300 \\ 3500 \end{bmatrix}$.

26. *Production scheduling.* A company manufactures three products: A, B, and C. Each product must pass through three machines: I, II, and III. Each unit of product A requires 3 hours on I, 2 hours on II, and 4 hours on III. Each unit of product B requires 2 hours on I, 4 hours on II, and 6 hours on III. Each unit of product C requires 3 hours on I, 5 hours on II, and 7 hours on III.

a) If matrix T shows the time requirements of each product on each machine, then fill in the elements of matrix T:

$$T = \begin{matrix} \quad \text{A} \quad \text{B} \quad \text{C} \quad \\ \begin{bmatrix} \underline{\quad} & \underline{\quad} & \underline{\quad} \\ \underline{\quad} & \underline{\quad} & \underline{\quad} \\ \underline{\quad} & \underline{\quad} & \underline{\quad} \end{bmatrix} \begin{matrix} \text{I} \\ \text{II} \\ \text{III} \end{matrix} \end{matrix}$$

b) If machines I, II, and III have available 150, 240, and 360 hours, respectively, then express this information in matrix B:

$$B = \begin{bmatrix} \underline{\quad} \\ \underline{\quad} \\ \underline{\quad} \end{bmatrix} \begin{matrix} \text{I} \\ \text{II} \\ \text{III} \end{matrix}$$

c) If $X = \begin{bmatrix} x_1 \\ x_2 \\ x_3 \end{bmatrix}$, where x_1, x_2, and x_3 represent the numbers of units of products A, B, and C, respectively, produced, then write the matrix equation relating T, X, and B.

d) Solve the matrix equation of part c and interpret the answer.

e) Repeat parts c and d for $B = \begin{bmatrix} 170 \\ 250 \\ 390 \end{bmatrix}$.

27. *Resource allocation.* A company produces two products—XB17 and XB18—for the automotive industry. The matrix below gives the compositions (%) of two raw materials—RM1 and RM2—in each product.

Products

		XB17	XB18
Raw materials	RM1	1	3
	RM2	2	0.5

If 220 units of RM1 and 330 units of RM2 are available next month, how many units of each product can be produced if all available raw materials are to be used?

a) Set up the linear system for this problem.
b) Write the linear system as the matrix equation $AX = B$.
c) Determine A^{-1}.
d) Use A^{-1} to solve the linear system.
e) Suppose next month's availability of RM1 and RM2 is changed to 440 and 110 units, respectively. How many units of each product can be produced if all available raw materials must be used?

28. A company produces dipthelene and triptilene. The matrix below gives the amounts (in liters) of the raw materials zolene and ptolene needed to produce 1 liter of each product.

Products

		Dipthelene	Triptilene
Raw materials	Zolene	2	1
	Ptolene	4	3

The raw materials are highly volatile and must be used immediately. If there are 700 liters of zolene and 2000 liters of ptolene on hand, determine how many liters of each product should be produced.

a) Set up the linear system for this problem.
b) Write the linear system as the matrix equation $AX = B$.
c) Determine A^{-1}.
d) Use A^{-1} to solve the linear system.
e) Suppose additional amounts of 100 liters of zolene and 100 liters of ptolene have just arrived. Determine how many liters of each product should now be produced.

29. *Investment analysis.* An investor has $100,000 to invest. A portion will be invested at 7% and the remainder at 9%. If an annual income of $8500 is desired, determine the amount that should be invested at each rate.

a) Set up the linear system for this problem.
b) Write the linear system as the matrix equation $AX = B$.
c) Determine A^{-1}.
d) Use A^{-1} to solve the linear system.
e) Recalculate your answers to part d if the amount invested changes to $200,000 and the desired annual income changes to $15,000.

5-8   • LEONTIEF'S INPUT-OUTPUT MODEL

Nobel prize winner Wassily Leontief developed a model to study the interdependence among industries of an economy. Since the model assumes that some of the output of an industry is needed as input in other industries of the economy, it is termed **Leontief's input-output model.** The model, which is invaluable to economic planning and development, provides a method for solving the following problem.

SUMMARY

Input-Output Problem

An economy consists of n industries. Some of the output of a given industry is needed by other industries in the economy. This is called **internal demand.** The remainder of such output is needed by industries outside the economy. This is called **final** (or **external**) **demand.** What quantity of output should each of the n industries produce in order to satisfy the total demand for its output? Total demand is the sum of internal demand and final (or external) demand.

As an illustrative example, we consider a simplified economy that produces three commodities: C_1, C_2, and C_3. Production of 1 unit of C_1 requires 0 units of C_1, 1/2 unit of C_2, and 1/4 unit of C_3. This is summarized by the column vector below.

Producing of 1 unit of C_1 requires

$$\begin{bmatrix} 0 \\ 1/2 \\ 1/4 \end{bmatrix} \quad \begin{array}{l} \text{unit of } C_1 \\ \text{unit of } C_2 \\ \text{unit of } C_3 \end{array}$$

The column vectors giving production requirements for C_2 and C_3 are as follows:

Producing of 1 unit of C_2 requires

$$\begin{bmatrix} 1/6 \\ 0 \\ 1/3 \end{bmatrix} \quad \begin{array}{l} \text{unit of } C_1 \\ \text{unit of } C_2 \\ \text{unit of } C_3 \end{array}$$

Producing of 1 unit of C_3 requires

$$\begin{bmatrix} 1/2 \\ 1/8 \\ 0 \end{bmatrix} \quad \begin{array}{l} \text{unit of } C_1 \\ \text{unit of } C_2 \\ \text{unit of } C_3 \end{array}$$

If we write the second column vector alongside the first, and the third alongside the second, we obtain the matrix

$$
\begin{array}{c}
\textit{To produce 1 unit of} \\
\begin{array}{ccc} C_1 & C_2 & C_3 \end{array}
\end{array}
$$

$$
A = \begin{bmatrix} 0 & 1/6 & 1/2 \\ 1/2 & 0 & 1/8 \\ 1/4 & 1/3 & 0 \end{bmatrix}
\begin{array}{l}
\textit{requires} \\
\text{unit of } C_1 \\
\text{unit of } C_2 \\
\text{unit of } C_3
\end{array}
$$

Matrix A is called the **technological** or **input-output** matrix of the economy. The technological matrix of an economy shows the interdependence of its industries or commodities.

Since we wish to determine the number of units of each commodity to be produced, we let

x_1 = number of units of C_1 produced

x_2 = number of units of C_2 produced

x_3 = number of units of C_3 produced

and define matrix X as

$$
X = \begin{bmatrix} x_1 \\ x_2 \\ x_3 \end{bmatrix}
$$

Since matrix X gives the number of units produced of each commodity, it is called the **production** or **total output matrix.**

The final (or external) demand for each commodity (or industry) is given by

d_1 = final (or external) demand for C_1

d_2 = final (or external) demand for C_2

d_3 = final (or external) demand for C_3

Thus, we define the final (or external) demand matrix D as

$$
D = \begin{bmatrix} d_1 \\ d_2 \\ d_3 \end{bmatrix}
$$

The product matrix AX gives the internal demands for the respective commodities, as illustrated below.

$$
AX = \begin{bmatrix} 0 & 1/6 & 1/2 \\ 1/2 & 0 & 1/8 \\ 1/4 & 1/3 & 0 \end{bmatrix} \begin{bmatrix} x_1 \\ x_2 \\ x_3 \end{bmatrix}
$$

$$
= \begin{bmatrix} 0x_1 + \dfrac{1}{6}x_2 + \dfrac{1}{2}x_3 \\[2ex] \dfrac{1}{2}x_1 + 0x_2 + \dfrac{1}{8}x_3 \\[2ex] \dfrac{1}{4}x_1 + \dfrac{1}{3}x_2 + 0x_3 \end{bmatrix}
\begin{array}{l}
\leftarrow \text{number of units of } C_1 \text{ consumed internally} \\
\leftarrow \text{number of units of } C_2 \text{ consumed internally} \\
\leftarrow \text{number of units of } C_3 \text{ consumed internally}
\end{array}
$$

To verify the interpretation of matrix AX, we analyze its first entry below:

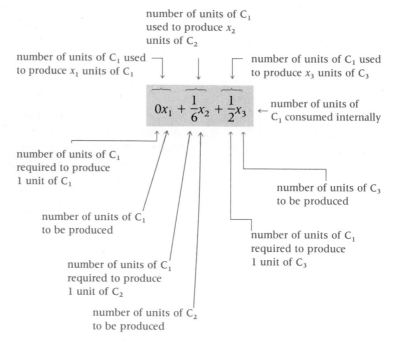

The remaining entries of matrix AX are interpreted analogously. Since

$$\text{total output} = \text{internal demand} + \text{final (or external) demand}$$

we have the corresponding matrix equation

$$X = AX + DZ$$

where X is total output, AX is internal demand, and DZ is final demand.

The basic goal of input-output analysis is to determine the total ouput or production, X, necessary for a given final (or external) demand, D. Thus, the preceding matrix equation must be solved for X. Hence,

$$X = AX + D$$
$$X - AX = D$$
$$(I - A)X = D \qquad \text{(See Exercise 72, Section 5-5)}$$
$$X = (I - A)^{-1}D$$

assuming $(I - A)^{-1}$ exists.

Returning to our example,

$$I - A = \begin{bmatrix} 1 & 0 & 0 \\ 0 & 1 & 0 \\ 0 & 0 & 1 \end{bmatrix} - \begin{bmatrix} 0 & 1/6 & 1/2 \\ 1/2 & 0 & 1/8 \\ 1/4 & 1/3 & 0 \end{bmatrix} = \begin{bmatrix} 1 & -1/6 & -1/2 \\ -1/2 & 1 & -1/8 \\ -1/4 & -1/3 & 1 \end{bmatrix}$$

Using row operations, it is determined that

$$(I - A)^{-1} = \begin{bmatrix} \dfrac{184}{127} & \dfrac{64}{127} & \dfrac{100}{127} \\[2mm] \dfrac{102}{127} & \dfrac{168}{127} & \dfrac{72}{127} \\[2mm] \dfrac{80}{127} & \dfrac{72}{127} & \dfrac{176}{127} \end{bmatrix}$$

Suppose a final (or external) demand of

$$D = \begin{bmatrix} 254 \\ 127 \\ 381 \end{bmatrix} \quad \begin{array}{l} \text{units of } C_1 \\ \text{units of } C_2 \\ \text{units of } C_3 \end{array}$$

is desired. Then a total output of

$$X = (I - A)^{-1}D$$

$$= \begin{bmatrix} \dfrac{184}{127} & \dfrac{64}{127} & \dfrac{100}{127} \\[2mm] \dfrac{102}{127} & \dfrac{168}{127} & \dfrac{72}{127} \\[2mm] \dfrac{80}{127} & \dfrac{72}{127} & \dfrac{176}{127} \end{bmatrix} \begin{bmatrix} 254 \\ 127 \\ 381 \end{bmatrix}$$

$$= \begin{bmatrix} 732 \\ 588 \\ 760 \end{bmatrix} \quad \begin{array}{l} \text{units of } C_1 \\ \text{units of } C_2 \\ \text{units of } C_3 \end{array}$$

is required.

Since our discussion of Leontief's input-output model has assumed the existence of a final (or external) demand, it is called **Leontief's open model.** In other words, an open model assumes that the production of the n industries of an economy is not all consumed internally. An input-output model that assumes all of the production of the n industries of an economy is consumed internally is called a **closed model.**

In a closed model, the final (or external) demand matrix, D, is a matrix of 0s, so that the matrix equation

$$X = AX + D$$

becomes

$$X = AX + 0$$

where 0 denotes a column matrix consisting of n 0s. Solving for X yields.

$$X - AX = 0$$

$$\text{or}$$

$$(I - A)X = 0$$

The above equation has infinitely many solutions if $(I - A)^{-1}$ does not exist. If $(I - A)^{-1}$ does not exist, the infinitely many solutions are expressed parametrically. Of course, if $(I - A)^{-1}$ does exist, the solution matrix X consists of a column of 0s.

SUMMARY

Input-Output Problem

Given a technological matrix A, a total output matrix X, and an external demand matrix D, the following matrix equation holds:

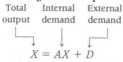

$$X = AX + D$$

The goal of input-output analysis is to determine the total output matrix, X, necessary for a given external demand matrix, D. The **solution** is given by

$$X = (I - A)^{-1}D$$

assuming $(I - A)^{-1}$ exists.

Exercises 5-8

1. A primitive economy has only two commodities: oil and coal. Production of 1 barrel of oil requires 1/2 ton of coal. Production of 1 ton of coal requires 1/4 barrel of oil.

   a) If A is the technological matrix of this economy, then fill in the elements of A:

   $$\begin{array}{cc} & \textit{Requirements for} \\ & \text{1 barrel of oil} \quad \text{1 ton of coal} \end{array}$$

   $$A = \begin{bmatrix} \underline{} & \underline{} \\ \underline{} & \underline{} \end{bmatrix} \begin{array}{l} \text{Oil} \\ \text{Coal} \end{array}$$

   b) If matrix D gives the desired final (or external) demands

   $$D = \begin{bmatrix} 210 \\ 490 \end{bmatrix} \begin{array}{l} \text{Barrels of oil} \\ \text{Tons of coal} \end{array}$$

   then determine the required total output for each commodity.

2. An economy has three commodities: C_1, C_2, and C_3. Production of 1 unit of C_1 requires ¼ unit of C_2. Production of 1 unit of C_2 requires ½ unit of C_1 and 1/3 unit of C_3. Production of 1 unit of C_3 requires 1/4 unit of C_1 and 1/2 unit of C_2.

   a) Write the technological matrix for this economy.

   b) If matrix D gives the desired final (or external) demands

   $$D = \begin{bmatrix} 231 \\ 462 \\ 924 \end{bmatrix} \begin{array}{l} \text{units of } C_1 \\ \text{units of } C_2 \\ \text{units of } C_3 \end{array}$$

   then determine the required total output for each commodity.

3. Given the technological matrix A and the final (or external) demand matrix D for some economy, determine the total output matrix X.

   $$A = \begin{bmatrix} 0.1 & 0.2 \\ 0.3 & 0.1 \end{bmatrix} \qquad D = \begin{bmatrix} 30 \\ 20 \end{bmatrix}$$

4. Given the technological matrix A and the final (or external) demand matrix D for some economy, determine the total output matrix X.

$$A = \begin{bmatrix} 0.1 & 0.4 \\ 0.2 & 0.3 \end{bmatrix} \quad D = \begin{bmatrix} 800 \\ 1000 \end{bmatrix}$$

5. Given the technological matrix A and the final (or external) demand matrix D for some economy, determine the total output matrix X.

$$A = \begin{bmatrix} 0.3 & 0.1 & 0.2 \\ 0.2 & 0.1 & 0.1 \\ 0.2 & 0.1 & 0.1 \end{bmatrix} \quad D = \begin{bmatrix} 50 \\ 30 \\ 90 \end{bmatrix}$$

6. Given the technological matrix A and the final (or external) demand matrix D for some economy, determine the total output matrix X.

$$A = \begin{bmatrix} 0.1 & 0.2 & 0.2 \\ 0.2 & 0.1 & 0.2 \\ 0.2 & 0.2 & 0.1 \end{bmatrix} \quad D = \begin{bmatrix} 100 \\ 200 \\ 180 \end{bmatrix}$$

7. Assume that we have calculated the total output that each of two industries should produce in order to satisfy total demand and that

$$(I - A)^{-1} = \begin{bmatrix} 1.4 & 0.8 \\ 1.1 & 0.9 \end{bmatrix}$$

However, suppose that the final (or external) demands have changed subsequent to our calculation of total output. The matrix ΔD gives the change in final (or external) demand for each industry.

$$\Delta D = \begin{bmatrix} -2 \\ 6 \end{bmatrix} \begin{array}{l} \leftarrow \text{change in final demand for industry 1} \\ \leftarrow \text{change in final demand for industry 2} \end{array}$$

Determine the change in total output needed to meet the changes in the final demands.

Hint: Replace the matrix equation

$$X = (I - A)^{-1}D$$

with

$$\Delta X = (I - A)^{-1}\Delta D$$

where

$$\Delta X = \begin{bmatrix} \Delta x_1 \\ \Delta x_2 \end{bmatrix} \begin{array}{l} \leftarrow \text{change in total output for industry 1} \\ \leftarrow \text{change in total output for industry 2} \end{array}$$

8. Repeat Exercise 7 for

$$\Delta D = \begin{bmatrix} 10 \\ -1 \end{bmatrix}$$

9. Repeat Exercise 7 for

$$(I - A)^{-1} = \begin{bmatrix} 2.3 & 1.5 \\ 0.9 & 1.2 \end{bmatrix} \quad \Delta D = \begin{bmatrix} 4 \\ -1 \end{bmatrix}$$

EXTRA DIVIDENDS

• *Oil Refinery Scheduling—Merco Oil Refinery*

The Merco Oil Refinery owns three oil wells. Oil from the well in Saudi Arabia is refined into 0.2 million barrels of regular gasoline, 0.1 million barrels of unleaded gasoline, and 0.3 million barrels of kerosene each day. Oil from the well in Kuwait is refined into 0.3 million barrels of regular gasoline, 0.2 million barrels of unleaded gasoline, and 0.1 million barrels of kerosene each day. Oil from the well in Egypt is refined into 0.4 million barrels of regular gasoline, 0.1 million barrels of unleaded gasoline, and 0.4 million barrels of kerosene each day. The company needs to produce 19 million barrels of regular gasoline, 10 million barrels of unleaded gasoline, and 20 million barrels of kerosene to meet demand requirements. Assuming that adequate lead time for transportation assures a continual flow, how many days should each well be operated in order to meet the demand requirements?

Exercises

1. Complete the following table, which summarizes the preceding information:

	Well in Saudi Arabia	Well in Kuwait	Well in Egypt	Demand requirements
Regular	(____)	(____)	(____)	(____)
Unleaded	(____)	(____)	(____)	(____)
Kerosene	(____)	(____)	(____)	(____)

2. Define each decision variable, and write the linear system of equations for this problem.
3. Write the linear system in matrix form, $AX = B$.
4. Determine A^{-1} and solve the linear system.
5. Suppose the demand requirements are changed to 20 million barrels of regular gasoline, 10 million barrels of unleaded gasoline, and 15 million barrels of kerosene. How many days should each well be operated in order to meet the demand requirements?

CHAPTER 5 HIGHLIGHTS

• Concepts

Your ability to answer the following questions is one indicator of the depth of your mastery of this chapter's important concepts. Note that the questions are grouped under various topic headings. For any question that you cannot answer, refer to the appropriate section of the chapter indicated by the topic heading. Pay particular attention to the summary boxes within a section.

5-1   LINEAR SYSTEMS (TWO EQUATIONS IN TWO VARIABLES)

1. Graphically, each equation of a linear system in two variables constitutes a(n) _____ _____.

2. The solution to a linear system in two variables is the _____ _____ of the straight lines.

3. If a linear system of two equations in two variables has no solution, this means that the straight lines are _____.

4. If a linear system of two equations in two variables has infinitely many solutions, this means that the straight lines _____.

5. Name two methods that are most efficient for solving linear systems of two equations in two variables.

6. Briefly state the three steps of the problem-solving procedure given in this section.

5-2   LINEAR SYSTEMS; TABLEAUS; PROBLEM FORMULATION

7. Write the format of the final tableau for a linear system consisting of
   a) Two equations in two variables
   b) Three equations in three variables

8. Write the general form of a linear equation in
   a) Two variables   b) Three variables   c) n variables

5-3   GAUSS-JORDAN METHOD OF SOLVING LINEAR SYSTEMS

9. State the three fundamental row operations.

10. Write the format of the final tableau for a linear system of n equations in n unknowns. If this tableau is not obtainable by row operations, then the linear system has either _____ _____ or _____ _____ _____ .

11. Write a tableau that contains an inconsistency.

12. If a final tableau has more _____ than _____, this indicates that there are infinitely many solutions. The infinitely many solutions are expressed by solving for the _____ variables in terms of the _____ variables.

5-4   MATRICES

13. A matrix is a(n) _____ array of numbers.

14. State the conditions for matrices to be equal.

15. In order for matrices to be added or subtracted, they must be of the _____ _____ .

16. How do you multiply a matrix by a number.

5-5   MULTIPLYING MATRICES

17. If A is an $m \times n$ matrix and B is an $n \times r$ matrix, then the product, AB, is a(n) _____ matrix.

18. State the condition that allows the computation of a product of two matrices.

19. Write the 3×3, 4×4, and 5×5 identity matrices.

5-6   INVERSE OF A SQUARE MATRIX

20. Define the inverse of a square matrix.

21. Do all square matrices have inverses?

22. If the inverse of a square matrix exists, is it unique?

5-7   SOLVING SQUARE LINEAR SYSTEMS BY MATRIX INVERSES

23. To solve the linear equation $ax = b$, where $a \neq 0$, we use the _____ _____ of the number a. To solve the matrix equation $AX = B$ for X, we use _____, provided it exists.

24. The solution to a matrix equation $AX = B$ is $X =$ _____, provided that _____ exists.

5-8 **LEONTIEF'S INPUT-OUTPUT MODEL**

25. Given an economy consisting of n industries, the output of a given industry that is needed by other industries in the economy is called _____ _____ . The remainder of such output, needed by industries outside the economy, is called _____ _____.

26. Given the matrix equation $X = AX + D$, interpret
   a) X b) AX c) D

27. For Question 26, the goal of input-output analysis is to determine matrix _____. This matrix is given by the matrix equation _____ , provided that _____ exists.

REVIEW EXERCISES

• *Method of Elimination*

Solve Exercises 1–6 by the method of elimination.

1. $x + 2y = 2$
     $3x - 5y = 17$

2. $2x + 3y = 18$
     $6x + y = 22$

3. $3x - 5y = 8$
     $-6x + 10y = 12$

4. $-5x + 2y = 2$
     $x + 3y = 20$

5. $\dfrac{x}{4} + \dfrac{y}{3} = 6$
     $\dfrac{x}{2} - \dfrac{y}{5} = -1$

6. $\dfrac{x}{3} - \dfrac{y}{5} = 3$
     $\dfrac{x}{4} + y = 8$

• *Method of Substitution*

Solve Exercises 7 and 8 by the method of substitution.

7. $3x + y = 48$
     $y = 5x$

8. $2x + 5y = 27$
     $x = 2y$

• *Linear System Possibilities*

For Exercises 9 and 10,
a) Try to solve the linear system.
b) Verify that the linear system has infinitely many solutions by converting each equation into slope-intercept form.
c) State three solutions to the linear system.

9. $5x - 2y = 20$
     $-15x + 6y = -60$

10. $-6x - 2y = 4$
     $y = -3x - 2$

11. Draw a graph of a linear system (two equations in two variables) that has a unique solution.

12. Draw a graph of a linear system (two equations in two variables) that has no solution.

13. Draw a graph of a linear system (two equations in two variables) that has infinitely many solutions.

• *Gauss-Jordan Method of Row Operations*

Solve Exercises 14–21 by the Gauss-Jordan method of row operations.

14.
$$x + y + 2z = 9$$
$$2x - y + 3z = 12$$
$$3x + 2y + z = 11$$

15.
$$2x_1 + x_2 + 5x_3 = 27$$
$$x_1 + x_3 = 8$$
$$-x_1 + x_2 = -7$$

16.
$$x_1 + 3x_2 + x_3 = 10$$
$$5x_1 + 16x_2 + 9x_3 = 54$$

17.
$$2x_1 + x_2 - x_3 = 8$$
$$-6x_1 - 3x_2 + 3x_3 = 15$$

18.
$$x_1 + x_2 = 3$$
$$2x_1 + x_2 = 1$$
$$4x_1 - x_2 = -13$$

19.
$$x_1 - x_2 = 7$$
$$2x_1 + 3x_2 = 13$$
$$x_1 + x_2 = 6$$

20.
$$3x_1 + 4x_2 - 2x_3 = 10$$
$$x_1 - 2x_2 + x_3 = 2$$
$$2x_1 - 6x_2 + 3x_3 = 7$$

21.
$$x_1 - x_2 + 2x_3 = 5$$
$$-2x_1 + 3x_2 = -2$$
$$-x_1 + x_3 = 4$$

For the tableaus in Exercises 22–27, state the solution to the linear system if a unique solution exists. If there is no solution, state so. If there are infinitely many solutions, express them in terms of t.

22. $\begin{bmatrix} 1 & 0 & 0 & | & 5 \\ 0 & 1 & 0 & | & -2 \\ 0 & 0 & 1 & | & 6 \end{bmatrix}$

23. $\begin{bmatrix} 1 & 0 & 4 & | & 3 \\ 0 & 1 & 0 & | & 5 \\ 0 & 0 & 0 & | & 4 \end{bmatrix}$

24. $\begin{bmatrix} 1 & 0 & 2 & | & 7 \\ 0 & 1 & -1 & | & 8 \\ 0 & 0 & 0 & | & 0 \end{bmatrix}$

25. $\begin{bmatrix} 1 & 0 & | & -3 \\ 0 & 1 & | & 4 \\ 0 & 0 & | & 6 \end{bmatrix}$

26. $\begin{bmatrix} 1 & 0 & -2 & | & 3 \\ 0 & 1 & 6 & | & 4 \end{bmatrix}$

27. $\begin{bmatrix} 1 & 0 & 0 & | & 9 \\ 0 & 1 & 0 & | & -3 \\ 0 & 0 & 0 & | & 0 \end{bmatrix}$

• *Matrices*

If

$$A = \begin{bmatrix} 3 & 4 \\ 1 & -2 \\ 0 & 1 \end{bmatrix} \quad B = \begin{bmatrix} -2 & 3 \\ 1 & -1 \\ 1 & 2 \end{bmatrix} \quad C = \begin{bmatrix} 1 & 2 & 1 \\ 2 & 1 & 0 \end{bmatrix}$$

compute

28. $A + B$　　**29.** $A - B$　　**30.** $B - A$　　**31.** $A - 3B$

32. AC　　**33.** CA　　**34.** BC　　**35.** $(BC)A$

• *Matrix Inverse*

For Exercises 36 and 37
a)　Find the inverse　　　　b)　Verify that your result is correct

36. $\begin{bmatrix} 1 & -2 & 1 \\ 2 & -5 & 0 \\ 0 & 0 & 1 \end{bmatrix}$

37. $\begin{bmatrix} 1 & 2 & 2 \\ 3 & 7 & 1 \\ 0 & 1 & 0 \end{bmatrix}$

Express the linear systems of Exercises 38–41 in matrix form, $AX = B$. Then compute A^{-1} and use it to solve the linear system.

38.
$$x + 2y = 2$$
$$3x - 5y = 17$$

39.
$$2x + 3y = 18$$
$$6x + y = 22$$

40.
$$\begin{aligned} x + y + 2z &= 9 \\ 2x - y + 3z &= 12 \\ 3x + 2y + z &= 11 \end{aligned}$$

41.
$$\begin{aligned} 2x_1 + x_2 + 5x_3 &= 27 \\ x_1 + x_3 &= 8 \\ -x_1 + x_2 &= -7 \end{aligned}$$

Applications

Formulate each of Exercises 42-45 as a linear system, and solve the linear system.

42. *Investment.* An investor has $20,000 to invest in bonds and stocks. For the coming year, bonds and stocks are expected to yield 8% and 10%, respectively. For tax purposes, the investor wants to earn $1900 during the year from the $20,000 invested. How much should be invested in bonds and how much in stocks?

43. *Mixture.* An alloy containing 30% silver is to be mixed with an alloy containing 80% silver to produce 100 pounds of an alloy containing 70% silver. Determine the amount of each alloy needed.

44. *Production planning.* The time requirements (in person-hours) per unit of product for each of three products in each of three departments are given below.

	Product A	Product B	Product C
Department 1	2	1	3
Department 2	1	2	1
Department 3	2	2	1

Departments 1, 2, and 3 have available 80, 80, and 60 person-hours, respectively. How many units of each product should be produced if all available person-hours are to be used?

45. *Transportation problem.* A firm produces desks at two plants. The desks must be transported from the two plants to two distribution centers, as is illustrated below.

	Distribution center 1	Distribution center 2	
Plant 1	x_1	x_2	800 ⌐ Production
Plant 2	x_3	x_4	500 ⌐ capacities
	700	600	

Demands

The production capacity of each plant and the demand of each distribution center are given above. If each plant is to operate at full capacity, how many desks should be shipped from each plant to each distribution center to ensure that the distribution centers' demands are met exactly?

46. *Costs.* A firm produces three products: A, B, and C. The number of units produced of each product during each of three given months appears in the matrix below.

Production volume

	Product A	Product B	Product C
June	300	400	200
July	500	600	800
August	400	300	500

The variable cost per unit for each product is given in the matrix below.

	Variable cost per unit
Product A	50
Product B	70
Product C	60

Determine the matrix that gives the total variable cost for each of the indicated months.

47. *Leontief's input-output model.* Given the technological matrix A and the final (or external) demand matrix D for some economy,
    a) Interpret each entry of the technological matrix
    b) Interpret each entry of the final demand matrix
    c) Determine the total output matrix X and interpret the result

$$A = \begin{bmatrix} 0.4 & 0.2 & 0.3 \\ 0.2 & 0.4 & 0.3 \\ 0.3 & 0.3 & 0.4 \end{bmatrix} \quad D = \begin{bmatrix} 200 \\ 500 \\ 400 \end{bmatrix}$$

6

LINEAR PROGRAMMING: THE GRAPHICAL METHOD

Introductory Application

Linear Programming: Product Mix

Williams Motors, which sells both American cars and imports, is planning its order for the next quarter. Current demand indicates that at least 240, but at most 450 cars should be ordered and that the number of imports ordered should be at least twice the number of American cars ordered. On the average, each American car costs the dealer $9000, and each foreign car costs $12,000. Budgetary and financing constraints limit next quarter's outlay for cars to $5,700,000. If Williams Motors makes an average profit of $600 per American car and $400 per foreign car, determine how many of each type should be ordered for the next quarter in order to maximize profits.

In this chapter, we will develop a procedure for formulating and solving such problems. This problem is solved in Example 6-7.

6-1 • LINEAR INEQUALITIES IN TWO VARIABLES

B. J. Wheels, Inc., makes two models of bicycles: model X and model Y. During any workday, the paint shop at B. J. Wheels has 24 person-hours available for these two models. Each model X bicycle uses 2 person-hours of paint shop time, and each model Y uses 3 person-hours of paint shop time. If, during a given day, the paint shop paints x model X and y model Y bicycles, then the number of person-hours of paint shop time used on these two models is given by the expression

$$2x + 3y$$

Since there are 24 person-hours available daily, then the above expression cannot exceed 24. Hence,

$$2x + 3y \leq 24$$

Note that the inequality $\leq$ implies that not all of the 24 person-hours have to be used.

A statement such as

$$2x + 3y \leq 24$$

is a **linear inequality in two variables.** If the inequality sign ($\leq$) is replaced by the equal sign ($=$), then the above linear inequality becomes the linear equation (equality)

$$2x + 3y = 24$$

Since we have already studied linear equations in Chapter 1, we will define linear inequalities in two variables in terms of linear equations.

SUMMARY

Linear Inequalities in Two Variables

If the equal sign ($=$) of a linear equation in two variables is replaced by an inequality sign ($<$, $>$, $\leq$, $\geq$), the resulting expression is a linear inequality in two variables.

Thus, the statements

$$2x + 3y < 24$$
$$2x + 3y \geq 24$$
$$y \leq 5x - 7$$
$$x > 3y + 4$$

are examples of linear inequalities in two variables. In this section, we discuss the graphing of linear inequalities in two variables.

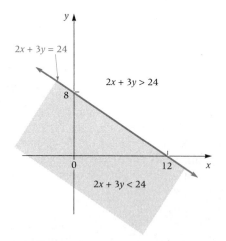

FIGURE 6-1

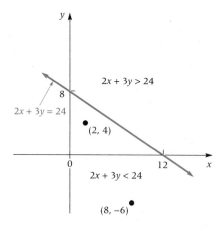

2x + 3y < 24

(2, 4): 2(2) + 3(4) < 24
16 < 24

(8, −6): 2(8) + 3(−6) < 24
−2 < 24

FIGURE 6-2

To graph a linear inequality such as

$$2x + 3y \leq 24$$

we should observe that the corresponding straight line, $2x + 3y = 24$, divides the plane into two regions (see Figure 6-1). One region consists of all points satisfying the inequality $2x + 3y < 24$, whereas the other consists of all points satisfying the inequality $2x + 3y > 24$.

Observing Figure 6-1, note that points *below* the straight line satisfy the linear inequality $2x + 3y < 24$. This can be verified by arbitrarily selecting a few points (x, y) from this region and substituting their coordinates into the inequality $2x + 3y < 24$ (see Figure 6-2). Points lying *above* the straight line satisfy the linear inequality $2x + 3y > 24$. This can be verified by selecting a few points (x, y) from this area above the straight line and substituting their coordinates into the inequality $2x + 3y > 24$ (see Figure 6-3 on page 349). Thus, all points (x, y) satisfying the inequality $2x + 3y \leq 24$ are located either *on or below* the straight line $2x + 3y = 24$ (see Figure 6-4 on page 349). For such points with positive *x*- and *y*-coordinates, the *x*- and *y*-coordinates represent the various combinations of numbers of model X and model Y bicycles that can be serviced by the paint shop during a given workday.

In general, when graphing linear inequalities, we should first sketch the corresponding straight line and then determine whether the points satisfying the inequality lie above or below that straight line. This is such an important procedure that we restate it in the box below.

 To Graph Linear Inequalities

First, graph the corresponding straight line and then determine whether the points (x, y) satisfying the inequality lie **above** or **below** the straight line.

We now illustrate this graphing procedure. As an example, we will graph the linear inequality discussed in this section,

$$2x + 3y \leq 24$$

Since we have already illustrated its graph, let us pretend we have not seen Figure 6-1.

We first find the *y*-intercept of the corresponding straight line by setting $x = 0$ and solving for *y*. Hence,

$$2(0) + 3y \leq 24$$
$$3y \leq 24$$
$$y \leq 8$$

Thus, the *y*-intercept is $(0, 8)$. The inequality $y \leq 8$ indicates that all points $(0, y)$ satisfying the inequality lie on the *y*-axis *at or below* $y = 8$. This result is graphed as an arrow pointing below the marker at $y = 8$ on the *y*-axis in Figure 6-5 on page 350.

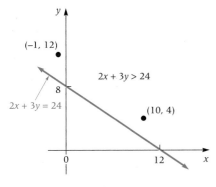

2x + 3y = 24

2x + 3y > 24

(-1, 12)

(10, 4)

8

0   12   x

2x + 3y > 24

(-1, 12): 2(-1) + 3(12) > 24

34 > 24

(10, 4): 2(10) + 3(4) > 24

32 > 24

The fact that a point, arbitrarily chosen from the region **above** the line *satisfies* the inequality indicates that this region (**above** the line) constitutes the graph of the linear inequality $2x + 3y > 24$.

(0, 0): 2(0) + 3(0) $\overset{?}{>}$ 24

0 $\overset{?}{>}$ 24   not true

The fact that a point, arbitrarily chosen from the region **below** the line *does not satisfy* the inequality indicates that the *opposite* region (the region **above** the line) constitutes the graph of the linear inequality $2x + 3y > 24$.

FIGURE 6-3

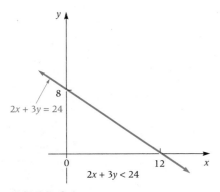

y

8

2x + 3y = 24

0   12   x

2x + 3y < 24

FIGURE 6-4

Now we find the *x*-intercept by setting $y = 0$ and solving for *x*. Hence,

$$2x + 3(0) \leq 24$$

$$2x \leq 24$$

$$x \leq 12$$

Thus, the *x*-intercept is (12, 0). The inequality $x \leq 12$ indicates that all points (*x*, 0) satisfying the inequality lie on the *x*-axis *at or to the left of* $x = 12$. This result is graphed as an arrow pointing to the left of the marker at $x = 12$ on the *x*-axis in Figure 6-5. Connecting the intercepts of Figure 6-5, we obtain the straight line $2x + 3y = 24$, along with the region represented by the inequality $2x + 3y < 24$ (see Figure 6-6 on page 350). Observe that the direction of the arrows indicates whether the associated region is either above or below the straight line.

As we can see in Figure 6-6, the region corresponding to $2x + 3y < 24$ lies below the line $2x + 3y = 24$. We indicate this by *shading the region **not** associated with* $2x + 3y < 24$ and leaving the region corresponding to $2x + 3y < 24$ in white. Although this seems contrary to what one would expect, the reason for this procedure will become apparent later in this section. We will repeat this procedure throughout this chapter, so we restate it in the box below. Since most of the inequalities that we will graph will contain either $\leq$ or $\geq$ inequality signs, we will state the procedure only for these inequality signs. However, we will include a remark regarding < and > inequality signs.

To Graph Linear Inequalities

Shade the Region to Be Discarded

1. *Find the* y-*intercept.* Set $x = 0$ and solve for *y*. This gives a linear inequality of the form $y \leq c$ or $y \geq c$, where *c* is a constant. Mark the *y*-intercept and draw an arrow indicating whether the points (0, *y*) lie above or below the *y*-intercept.

2. *Find the* x-*intercept.* Set $y = 0$ and solve for *x*. This gives an inequality of the form $x \leq c$ or $x \geq c$, where *c* is a constant. Mark the *x*-intercept and draw an arrow indicating whether the points (*x*, 0) lie to the right of or to the left of the *x*-intercept.

3. *Shade the region to be discarded.* Draw a straight line through the intercepts determined in steps 1 and 2. The direction of the arrows (from steps 1 and 2) on the *x*- and *y*-axes indicates the location of the region corresponding to the linear inequality being graphed. Shade the region not associated with the linear inequality. In other words, *shade the region to be discarded.* Thus, the region corresponding to the linear inequality remains in white. Its **boundary** is the straight line previously drawn.

Remark:

a) If a linear inequality contains either < or > inequality signs, its *boundary is **not** included* in its graph and is therefore drawn as a *dotted line.*

b) If a linear inequality contains either $\leq$ or $\geq$ inequality signs, its *boundary **is** included* in its graph and is therefore drawn as a *solid line.*

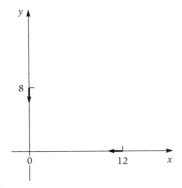

FIGURE 6-5

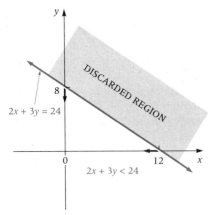

FIGURE 6-6

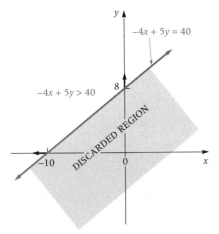

FIGURE 6-7

• EXAMPLE 6-1

Graph $-4x + 5y \geq 40$.

Solution

First, we find the y-intercept by setting $x = 0$ and using the rules of inequalities to solve for y. Hence,

$$-4(0) + 5y \geq 40$$
$$5y \geq 40$$
$$y \geq 8$$

Thus, the y-intercept is $(0, 8)$. The inequality $y \geq 8$ is graphed in Figure 6-7 as an arrow pointing above the marker at $y = 8$ on the y-axis.

Next, we find the x-intercept by setting $y = 0$ and solving for x. Hence,

$$-4x + 5(0) \geq 40$$
$$-4x \geq 40$$
$$x \leq -10$$

Reverse the direction of an inequality when multiplying or dividing both sides by a negative number.

Remember that we reverse the direction of an inequality when we multiply or divide both sides by a negative number. Thus, the x-intercept is $(-10, 0)$. The inequality $x \leq -10$ is graphed in Figure 6-7 as an arrow pointing to the left of the marker at $x = -10$ on the x-axis.

We draw a straight line through the intercepts. The arrows at the intercepts $x = -10$ and $y = 8$ point to the region associated with $-4x + 5y > 40$. As we can see in Figure 6-7, the arrows point to the region *above* the line $-4x + 5y = 40$. Since we shade the region to be discarded, the region corresponding to $-4x + 5y > 40$ remains in white. Thus, the white region plus the straight line $-4x + 5y = 40$ constitutes the graph of $-4x + 5y \geq 40$.

Systems of Linear Inequalities

If we graph a set of points (x, y) satisfying *more than one* linear inequality, we are graphing a **system of linear inequalities.** Specifically, the graph of the system

$$3x + 5y \geq 30$$
$$4x - y \leq 17$$

consists of the set of points (x, y) satisfying *both* inequalities.

To graph a system of two linear inequalities, we graph each inequality on the same axis system and then determine the region common to both. Every point (x, y) in the common region will, of course, satisfy both inequalities. The preceding system of linear inequalities is graphed in Figures 6-8 and 6-9 on page 351.

First, we graph $3x + 5y \geq 30$. Setting $x = 0$ gives $5y \geq 30$, or $y \geq 6$. This is graphed in Figure 6-8 as an arrow pointing above the marker at $y = 6$ on the y-axis. Setting $y = 0$ gives $3x \geq 30$, or $x \geq 10$. This is graphed in Figure 6-8 as an arrow pointing to the right of the marker at $x = 10$ on the x-axis. We draw a straight line through the intercepts. The arrows at the intercepts $x = 10$ and $y = 6$ point to the region associated with $3x + 5y > 30$. Since we *shade the region to be discarded*, the remaining white region of Figure 6-8 is associated with $3x + 5y > 30$. Thus, the white re-

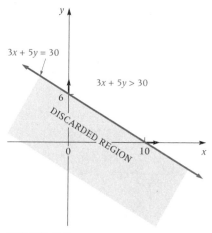

FIGURE 6-8

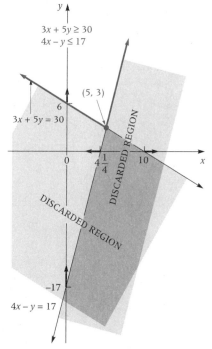

FIGURE 6-9

gion plus the straight line $3x + 5y = 30$ constitutes the graph of $3x + 5y \geq 30$.

Next, we graph $4x - y \leq 17$. Setting $x = 0$ gives $-y \leq 17$, or $y \geq -17$. Remember that we reverse the direction of an inequality when we multiply or divide both sides by a negative number. This is graphed in Figure 6-9 as an arrow pointing above the number $y = -17$ on the y-axis. Setting $y = 0$ gives $4x \leq 17$, or $x \leq 4\frac{1}{4}$. This is graphed in Figure 6-9 as an arrow pointing to the left of the number $x = 4\frac{1}{4}$ on the x-axis. We draw a straight line through the intercepts. The arrows at the intercepts $y = -17$ and $x = 4\frac{1}{4}$ point to the region associated with $4x - y < 17$. We shade the region to be discarded. The *remaining white region and its boundary* in Figure 6-9 comprise the graph of our system of linear inequalities. Observe that this region is *not bounded* on all sides. Thus, it is called an **unbounded region.** Unbounded regions will be discussed in greater detail in Section 6-3.

Vertex Points

The *corner points* on the boundary of a region such as that of Figure 6-9 are called **vertex points.** Observe that the region of Figure 6-9 contains only one vertex point $(5, 3)$. Since this vertex point is the intersection of the straight lines $3x + 5y = 30$ and $4x - y = 17$, its coordinates are determined by solving the associated linear system of equations, using the methods discussed in Chapter 5. Vertex points will take on special importance in the next section of this chapter.

To Graph a System of Linear Inequalities

Graph each inequality on the same set of axes. For each inequality, shade the region to be discarded. The remaining region, the unshaded (white) region, if it exists, constitutes the region associated with the system.

1. If all of the linear inequalities are of the $\leq$ or $\geq$ type, then the *boundary* of the white region *is included* in the region associated with the system.
2. If any linear inequality is of the $<$ or $>$ type, then the portion of the *boundary* (of the white region) corresponding to such an inequality is *not included* in the region associated with the system.

• **EXAMPLE 6-2**

Graph the system

$$4x + 5y \leq 40$$
$$3x - 2y \leq 24$$
$$x \geq 0$$
$$y \geq 0$$

Solution

The system is graphed in Figures 6-10 through 6-13. The region common to all of the inequalities appears in Figure 6-13 on page 353.

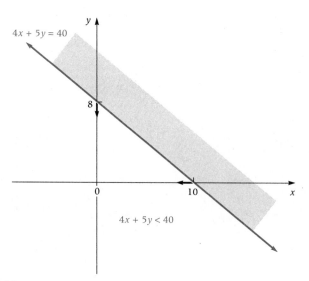

FIGURE 6-10

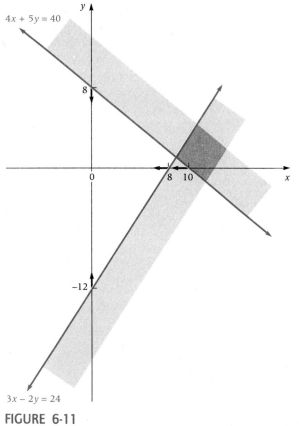

FIGURE 6-11

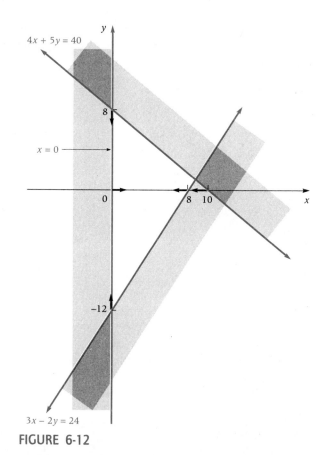

FIGURE 6-12

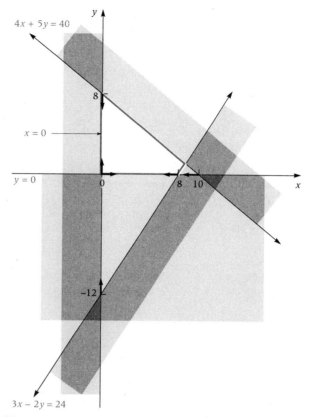

4x + 5y = 40

x = 0

y = 0

3x − 2y = 24

FIGURE 6-13

Note that the inclusion of both inequalities $x \geq 0$ and $y \geq 0$ results in a region that is located within the first quadrant.

• **EXAMPLE 6-3** _____

Graph the system

$$2x + 5y \leq 20$$
$$2x + 5y \geq 30$$

Solution

Both inequalities are graphed on the same set of axes in Figure 6-14 on page 354. Since the shaded region represents the region to be discarded, there is no remaining white region. This means that there are no points satisfying both inequalities. In other words, there are **no solutions** to the system.

_____ •

Throughout this and the next chapter, we will be using the symbols $\leq$ and $\geq$ to write inequalities that express relationships between quantities. Since it is important to use inequality symbols correctly to express relationships that are often stated verbally, we include a summary of phrases associated with each respective inequality symbol.

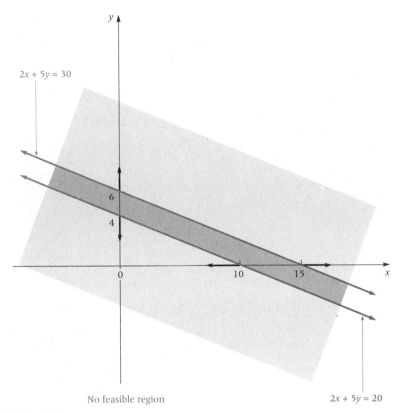

No feasible region

FIGURE 6-14

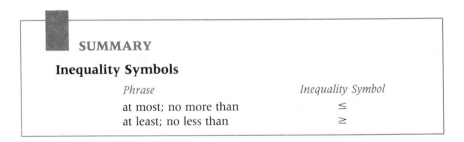

SUMMARY

Inequality Symbols

Phrase	*Inequality Symbol*
at most; no more than	$\leq$
at least; no less than	$\geq$

Application

• **EXAMPLE 6-4** **Product Mix.**

A company makes bicycles and motorbikes, each of which must pass through departments I and II. Department I (Assembly) has at most 450 hours, and department II (Inspection) has at most 400 hours available for both products. Each bicycle requires 3 hours of time in department I and 5 hours of time in department II. Each motorbike requires 4 hours of time in department I and 2 hours of time in department II. How many bicycles and motorbikes can be made in order to satisfy departmental time constraints?

Solution

We apply our problem-solving procedure (see Section 5-1).

Step 1 *Identify the unknowns. Use letters to denote these quantities.*
We let

$$x = \text{number of bicycles to be made}$$

$$y = \text{number of motorbikes to be made}$$

Step 2 *Organize the given information, and write the equations (or inequalities) that express any relationships among the unknowns.*
The given information is listed in the table below.

	x	*y*	Resource capacity
	bicycles	**motorbikes**	
Department I	3 hours/bicycle	4 hours/motorbike	At most 450 hours available
Department II	5 hours/bicycle	2 hours/motorbike	At most 400 hours available

The departmental time constraints are expressed by the inequalities

Department I $3x + 4y \leq 450$

Department II $5x + 2y \leq 400$

$x \geq 0$ Cannot have a negative number of bicycles

$y \geq 0$ Cannot have a negative number of motorbikes

Step 3 *Solve the equations (or inequalities) of step 2.*
We must graph the region corresponding to the system of linear inequalities of step 2. This region is graphed in Figures 6-15 through 6-18. Any point (x, y) in the

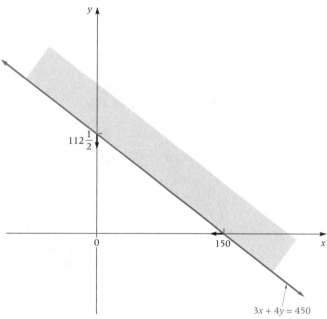

FIGURE 6-15

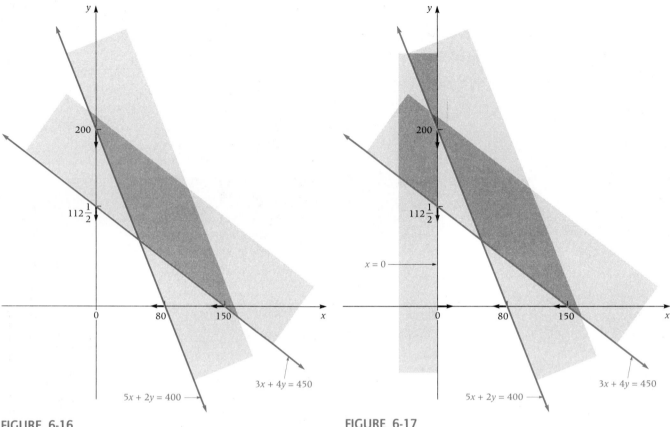

FIGURE 6-16   **FIGURE 6-17**

white region of Figure 6-18 will satisfy the departmental time constraints. In other words, if, for any point (x, y) of the white region of Figure 6-18 on page 357, x bicycles and y motorbikes are made, then the departmental time constraints represented by the linear inequalities will be satisfied.

Also, observe in Figure 6-18 that we have labeled the vertex points with their ordered pairs. Note that the *vertex point (50, 75)* was determined by solving the linear system

$$3x + 4y = 450$$
$$5x + 2y = 400$$

• EXAMPLE 6-5   **Product Mix Continued.** _____

Suppose the company of Example 6-4 receives an order for 10 bicycles and marketing studies indicate that no more than 90 motorbikes should be made. Indicate how these additional restrictions change the graph of Figure 6-18.

Solution

The order for 10 bicycles means that at least 10 bicycles should be produced. This results in the additional inequality

$$x \geq 10$$

That no more than 90 motorbikes should be made results in the additional inequality

$$y \leq 90$$

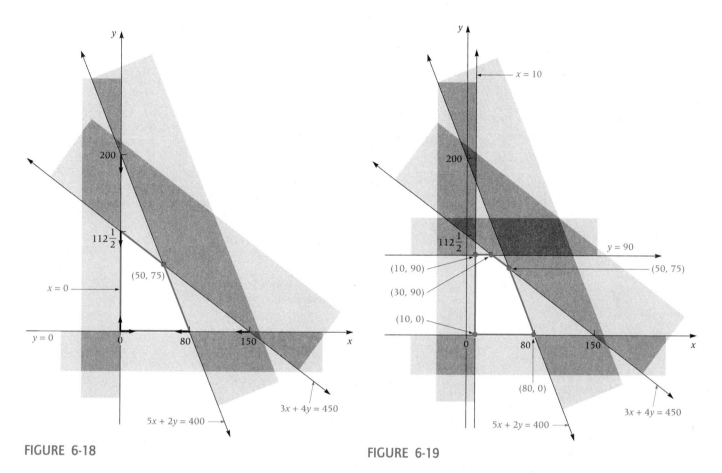

FIGURE 6-18

FIGURE 6-19

Thus, we must graph the region corresponding to the system of linear inequalities

$$3x + 4y \le 450$$
$$5x + 2y \le 400$$
$$x \ge 10$$
$$y \ge 0$$
$$y \le 90$$

These two inequalities can be combined to read $0 \le y \le 90$.

The resulting graph is given in Figure 6-19. Comparing the graph of Figure 6-19 with that of Figure 6-18, observe that the inequality $x \ge 10$ restricts the solution region to the right of the vertical line $x = 10$, while the inequality $y \le 90$ restricts the solution region below the horizontal line $y = 90$. Note that the *vertex point (30, 90)* was determined by solving the linear system

$$3x + 4y = 450$$
$$y = 90$$

Exercises 6-1

Graph each of the following inequalities.

1. $4x + 5y \ge 40$

2. $-3x + 2y \le 12$

3. $x - y \ge 5$

4. $-2x - 4y \ge 16$

5. $2x + y \leq 12$ **6.** $3x - y \leq 15$

7. $x + 3y < 4$ **8.** $-2x + y > 8$

9. $9x - 2y \geq 36$ **10.** $7x - 3y \leq -21$

11. $-4x - 7y \geq -28$ **12.** $x + y < 7$

Graph each of the following systems.

13. $3x + 9y \geq 27$
$2x - 3y \leq 12$

14. $2x + 5y \leq 20$
$x \geq 0$

15. $-3x + 2y \geq -12$
$y \geq -6$

16. $4x - 3y \leq 12$
$x \leq 2$

17. $3x + 4y \leq 48$
$5x + 3y \leq 30$
$x \geq 0$
$y \geq 0$

18. $2x + 7y \geq 28$
$2x + y \geq 8$
$x \geq 0$
$y \geq 0$

19. $6x + 7y \leq 42$
$3x + 5y \leq 25$
$x \geq 0$
$y \geq 0$

20. $6x + 7y \leq 42$
$3x + 5y \leq 25$
$x - y \leq 6$
$x \geq 0$
$y \geq 0$

21. $5x + 2y \geq 30$
$3x + 4y \geq 24$
$x + y \geq 7.6$
$x \geq 0$
$y \geq 0$

22. $3x + y \leq 30$
$2x + 3y \leq 24$
$x \geq 1$
$0 \leq y \leq 7$

Try to graph each of the following systems. What are the results?

23. $3x + 4y \leq 12$
$3x + 4y \geq 24$

24. $x + y \leq 5$
$x - y \geq 5$
$y \geq 1$

25. Model X requires 5 hours in the assembly department, while model Y requires 7 hours in this department. If the assembly department has at most 105 hours available for these two products, write the linear inequality that expresses the relationship between the number of units of each model produced. Graph the inequality.

26. An investor invests x amount of dollars at 8% and y dollars at 9% in order to maintain income of at least $60,000. Write the linear inequality that expresses the relationship between the amounts invested at the different rates. Graph the inequality.

27. Each gadget requires 4 hours in the cutting department, while each widget requires 5 hours in the same department. If the cutting department has at most 80 hours available, write the linear inequality that expresses the relationship between the number of gadgets and widgets produced. Graph the inequality.

28. Each pound of food A contains 500 milligrams of vitamin C, while each pound of food B contains 300 milligrams of vitamin C. A diet consisting of both foods A and B must yield at least 15,000 milligrams of vitamin C. Write the linear inequality that expresses the relationship between the amounts of both foods. Graph the inequality.

29. *Product mix.* A company makes two types of truck tires: type A and type B. Each lot of type A tires requires 2 hours in department 1 and 1 hour in department 2. Each lot of type B tires requires 5 hours in department 1 and 2 hours in department 2. If departments 1 and 2 have available at most 250 and 120 hours, respectively, how many lots of type A and type B tires can be made in order that departmental time constraints are satisfied?

a) Write the corresponding system of linear inequalities.

b) Graph the region.

c) Determine the vertex points.

30. *Investments.* An investor has at most $1,000,000 to allocate among stocks and bonds. Stocks are expected to yield 10% and bonds 8%. How should the amount invested be allocated if the investor wishes to earn at least $85,000?

a) Write the system of linear inequalities.

b) Graph the region.

c) Determine the vertex points.

31. *Marketing research survey.* It costs $30 to survey a family in city 1, while it costs $40 to survey a family in city 2. The maximum amount budgeted for the complete survey is $12,000. At least 100 city 1 families and 120 city 2 families must be surveyed. How many families should be surveyed from each city?

a) Write the system of linear inequalities.

b) Graph the region.

c) Determine the vertex points.

32. *Agriculture.* A farmer has available 2000 acres for the planting of two crops: A and B. Each acre planted with crop A will generate sales revenue of $4000, while each acre planted with crop B will generate sales revenue of $5000. Total sales revenue of at least $9,000,000 is required. If at least 500 acres of crop A and at least 500 acres of crop B must be planted, how many acres of each crop should be planted?

a) Write the system of linear inequalities.

b) Graph the region.

c) Determine the vertex points.

33. *Land use planning.* A parcel of 1,000,000 acres is available for development in a given country. According to an authoritative report, x acres are to be zoned A-2, which means a lot size of 2 acres, and y acres are to be zoned A-3, which means a lot size of 3 acres. At least 480,000 lots are required. There must be at least 200,000 acres zoned A-2 and at least 60,000 acres zoned A-3.

a) Write the system of linear inequalities that shows the possible values of x and y.

b) Graph the region.

c) Determine the vertex points.

6-2 • LINEAR PROGRAMMING

A common problem of most businesses is the optimal allocation of limited resources among competing activities. Linear programming is a method for solving such problems. Historically, linear programming was developed to solve resource allocation problems of the U.S. Air Force during World War II. Much of the development of linear programming is credited to George B. Dantzig, who gave a general formulation of a linear programming problem and a method of solving it. This method is called the simplex method and is discussed in Chapter 7. In this chapter, we will discuss the graphical method for solving linear programming problems.

In this and subsequent sections of this chapter, we will be engaged in the process of formulating and solving linear programming problems. Such problems are special types of word problems that include an overall goal of either maximizing or minimizing some quantity, which can be written as a linear algebraic expression. In order that we have a systematic procedure for approaching such problems, we will present a linear programming problem-solving procedure while solving the following problem. We note that a substantial portion of this process has already been explained in Section 6-1.

PROBLEM

Production Planning

A company that manufactures sneakers and walking shoes must decide how many pairs of each to make during the next week. The company makes profits of $20 on each pair of sneakers and $16 on each pair of walking shoes. Both products are manufactured in the sewing department, which has a limited labor capacity of 480 person-hours for the next week. Each pair of sneakers uses 1 person-hour, and each pair of walking shoes uses 2 person-hours in this department. Another critical constraint, which affects the number of sneakers and walking shoes produced, is imposed by a limited availability of a raw material—XBSL504—which is used in the manufacture of both products. Specifically, each pair of sneakers requires 3 units of XBSL504, and each pair of walking shoes requires 4 units of this raw material. The company has only 1080 units of XBSL504 available during the next week. Finally, one of the company's major outlets has placed an order for 60 pairs of sneakers and 30 pairs of walking shoes. These must be made during the next week. How many pairs of sneakers and walking shoes should the company plan to make next week in order to maximize total profit?

SOLUTION

Step 1 *Identify the quantity to be either maximized or minimized and the related unknowns.*
These unknowns are called **decision variables.** Use letters to denote these quantities. Write an equation for the quantity to be either maximized or minimized.

We seek to maximize total profit. We must determine the number of pairs of sneakers and walking shoes to make next week in order that total profit is maximized. Thus, we let

$$P = \text{total profit for next week}$$
$$x = \text{number of pairs of sneakers}$$
$$y = \text{number of pairs of walking shoes}$$

Then the **objective function** is given by

$$P = 20x + 16y$$

and the objective is to maximize P.

Step 2 *Organize the given information, and write the linear inequalities that express any relationships existing among the unknowns.*

Decision variables

	x sneakers	y walking shoes	Resource capacity
Unit profits	$20/pair	$16/pair	
Sewing department	1 person-hour/pair	2 person-hours/pair	At most 480
Raw material XBSL504	3 units/pair	4 units/pair	At most 1080

Also,

- At least 60 pairs of sneakers must be produced.
- At least 30 pairs of walking shoes must be produced.

Algebraic Formulation

The constraints of the problem yield linear inequalities as derived below.

Sewing Department: Since it takes 1 person-hour to make 1 pair of sneakers, it takes x person-hours to make x pairs of sneakers. Since it takes 3 person-hours to make 1 pair of walking shoes, it takes $3y$ person-hours to make y pairs of walking shoes. Thus, it takes

$$1x + 3y$$

hours to make x pairs of sneakers and y pairs of walking shoes. Since the sewing department has at most 480 person-hours available next week, then

$$x + 3y \leq 480$$

Raw Material XBSL504: Since each pair of sneakers uses 3 units and each pair of walking shoes uses 4 units of XBSL504, then the total number of units of XBSL504 used by x pairs of sneakers and y pairs of walking shoes is given by the expression

$$3x + 4y$$

Since there will be at most 1080 units of XBSL504 available next week, then

$$3x + 4y \leq 1080$$

Demand Requirements: The fact that at least 60 pairs of sneakers must be made next week in order to satisfy demand requirements yields the inequality

$$x \geq 60$$

Also, the fact that at least 30 pairs of walking shoes must be made next week in order to satisfy demand requirements yields the inequality

$$y \geq 30$$

The complete formulation of this problem appears below.

Maximize $P = 20x + 16y$ Objective function

subject to $x + 2y \leq 480$ ⎤

          $3x + 4y \leq 1080$ ⎟   Constraints

              $x \geq 60$ ⎟

              $y \geq 30$ ⎦

Step 3 *Determine the values of* x *and* y *that satisfy the constraints and also maximize the value of the objective function.*

Note that the constraints constitute a system of linear inequalities. If a region corresponding to this system of linear inequalities exists, its graph will reveal a set of points (x, y) that satisfy the constraints of the problem. Figures 6-20 through 6-23 on pages 362-364 illustrate the process of graphing the system of linear inequalities. Remember that, for each figure, the shaded region constitutes the region to be discarded; the white region and its boundary comprise the set of points that satisfy the respective linear inequalities.

Observe that Figure 6-23 reveals the region associated with the constraints of the problem. Since this region consists of a set of points (x, y) that satisfy all the constraints of the problem, it is called the **feasible region.** The coordinates of any point (x, y) of the feasible region constitute a feasible solution to our linear programming problem. In other words, if we choose any point (x, y) of the feasible region and manufacture x pairs of sneakers and y pairs of walking shoes, then this product mix is a feasible solution to the problem. Remember that *feasible* means that all the constraints of the problem are satisfied.

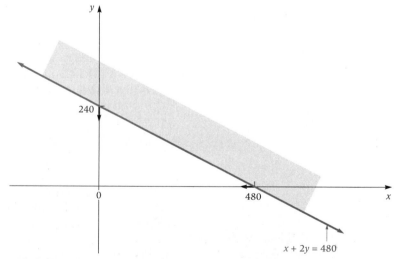

FIGURE 6-20

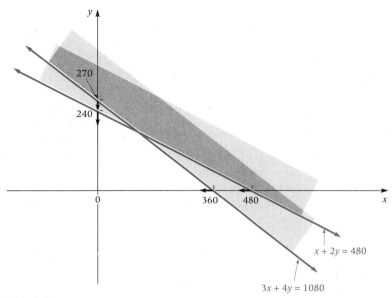

FIGURE 6-21

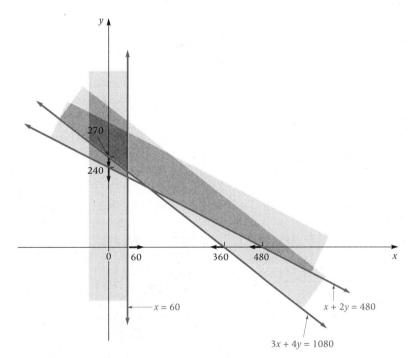

FIGURE 6-22

Optimal Solution

We must now determine which points (x, y) of the feasible region, if substituted into the objective function, yield a maximum value for P. At first glance, it would appear that we must substitute each point (x, y) of the feasible region into the objective function. But, since the feasible region

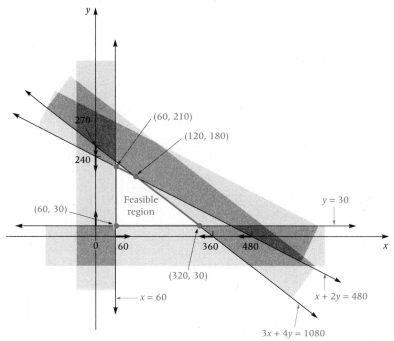

FIGURE 6-23

consists of infinitely many points, this is impossible. However, in the next section of this chapter, we will show the following.

An optimal value of an objective function, if it exists, will occur at one or more of the vertex points or on the boundary of the feasible region.

The feasible region, with its vertex points, is displayed in Figure 6-24. Remember that the vertex points are the corner points located on the boundary of the feasible region. Since each vertex point is an intersection point of a pair of straight lines that correspond to respective constraints of the linear programming problem, then the x- and y-coordinates of each vertex point are determined by solving the linear system associated with each such pair of intersecting straight lines. We state below the linear systems to be solved in order to determine the coordinates of the indicated vertex points.

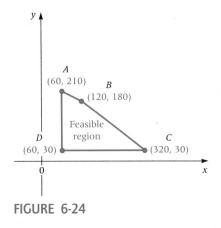

FIGURE 6-24

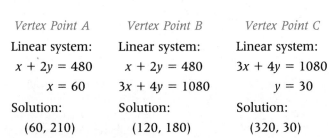

Vertex Point A	*Vertex Point B*	*Vertex Point C*
Linear system:	Linear system:	Linear system:
$x + 2y = 480$	$x + 2y = 480$	$3x + 4y = 1080$
$x = 60$	$3x + 4y = 1080$	$y = 30$
Solution:	Solution:	Solution:
$(60, 210)$	$(120, 180)$	$(320, 30)$

To find the optimal solution, we substitute the coordinates of each vertex point into the objective function to determine which point (or points) yields the maximum profit. Hence,

$$\text{Maximize } P = 20x + 16y \qquad \text{Objective function}$$

Vertex Points

(60, 30)	$P = 20(60) + 16(30) = \$1680$
(60, 210)	$P = 20(60) + 16(210) = \$4560$
(120, 180)	$P = 20(120) + 16(180) = \$5280$
(320, 30)	$P = 20(320) + 16(30) = \$6880$ Maximum profit

Observe that the vertex point (320, 30) yields the maximum profit of \$6880. Therefore, the optimal solution to the linear programming problem is

$$x = 320 \text{ pairs of sneakers}$$
$$y = 30 \text{ pairs of walking shoes}$$
$$\text{Maximum profit } P = \$6880$$

Step 4 *Investigate the implications of the optimal solution.*
This involves substituting the optimal solution values into each constraint inequality.

Sewing Department Constraint:

$$x + 2y \le 480$$
$$320 + 2(30) \le 480$$
$$380 \le 480$$

The left-hand-side value, 380, indicates the actual number of person-hours used in the sewing department to make 320 sneakers and 30 walking shoes. The right-hand-side value, 480, indicates the number of person-hours available in the sewing department. Since the left-hand-side value is less than the right-hand-side value, this indicates that not all of the available 480 person-hours are needed. The unused person-hours are determined by subtracting the left-hand-side value (LHS) from the right-hand-side value (RHS) to obtain

$$\text{RHS} - \text{LHS} = 480 - 380$$
$$= 100 \text{ person-hours}$$

This difference is called **slack** and represents unused capacity in a $\le$ constraint. We formalize this concept in the box below.

SUMMARY

Slack

$\le$ **Constraint.** The difference between the right-hand-side (RHS) and left-hand-side (LHS) values of a $\le$ constraint is called **slack** and represents *unused capacity* for that constraint.

$$\text{Slack} = \text{RHS} - \text{LHS}$$

continues

> **SUMMARY**—*Continued*
>
> If slack = 0 for a constraint, this implies that all of the available capacity or resource of that constraint is being utilized by the optimal solution to the linear programming problem. Such a constraint is called a **binding** constraint.

Raw Material Constraint:

$$3x + 4y \leq 1080$$
$$3(320) + 4(30) \leq 1080$$
$$1080 \leq 1080$$

Since LHS = RHS for this constraint, then slack = 0. Thus, all 1080 units of raw material XBSL504 are being used to make the optimal product mix of sneakers and walking shoes. Thus, this constraint is said to be *binding*, as noted in the box above.

Minimal Sneaker Requirement:

$$x \geq 60$$
$$320 \geq 60$$

The left-hand-side value gives the actual number of pairs of sneakers made. The right-hand-side value indicates the minimum number of pairs of sneakers required. Since the left-hand-side value exceeds the right-hand-side value, there is a **surplus** of sneakers with respect to the minimal requirement. The amount of surplus is determined below.

$$\text{Surplus} = \text{LHS} - \text{RHS}$$
$$= 320 - 60 = 260 \text{ sneakers}$$

We formally present the concept of surplus in the following summary box.

> **SUMMARY**
>
> **Surplus**
>
> $\geq$ **Constraint.** The difference between the left-hand-side (LHS) and right-hand-side (RHS) values of a $\geq$ constraint is called **surplus** and represents the amount by which the minimal requirement of the right-hand side is being exceeded.
>
> $$\text{Surplus} = \text{LHS} - \text{RHS}$$
>
> If surplus = 0 for a constraint, this implies that the minimal requirement of the constraint is being met exactly, but not exceeded. Such a constraint is also called a **binding** constraint.

Minimal Walking Shoe Requirement:

$$y \geq 30$$
$$30 \geq 30$$

Since the left-hand side equals the right-hand side, the minimal walking shoe requirement is being met exactly. In other words, there is no surplus. This constraint is said to be *binding*, as noted in the box above.

Now that we have illustrated the complete process of formulating and solving a linear programming problem, we summarize the linear programming problem-solving procedure in the box below. This is followed by a summary of step 3 of the linear programming problem-solving procedure.

To Solve a Linear Programming Problem

Step 1 Identify the quantity to be optimized and the related decision variables. Write an equation for the quantity to be either maximized or minimized. This equation is called the **objective function.**

Step 2 Write the algebraic formulation for the problem. Organize the given information, and write the linear inequalities that express any relationships existing among the decision variables. These inequalities constitute the constraints of the problem and are usually based on limited resources.

Step 3 Determine an optimal solution, if it exists. Solve the algebraic formulation. In other words, find values of the decision variables that satisfy the inequalities (i.e., constraints) of the problem and optimize the value of the objective function. These decision variable values constitute an optimal solution to the linear programming problem.

Step 4 Investigate the implications of an optimal solution with regard to the constraints. Of course, this assumes that an optimal solution exists.

To Determine an Optimal Solution

A linear programming problem, when formulated algebraically, consists of a linear objective function and a set of linear inequality constraints.

1. First, graph the region corresponding to the system of linear inequality constraints. Since this region, if it exists, consists of a set of points (x, y) that satisfy all the constraints of the problem, it is called the **feasible region.**
2. Second, determine the coordinates of the corner points located on the boundary of the feasible region. Such corner points are called **vertex points.**
3. Finally, substitute the coordinates of each vertex point into the objective function. The vertex point(s) giving the optimal value of the objective function yield(s) the optimal solution to the linear programming problem.

That this procedure produces an optimal solution, if one exists, is due to the result stated below.

Fundamental Theorem of Linear Programming. An optimal solution, if one exists, to a linear programming problem will occur at one or more of the vertex points or on the boundary of the feasible region.

The above result, along with related concepts, will be explained in greater detail in the next section of this chapter.

We now consider, in Example 6-6, a linear programming problem that involves minimizing the value of an objective function.

• EXAMPLE 6-6   Nutritional Requirements. ─────────────

A diet is to include at least 140 milligrams of vitamin A and at least 145 milligrams of vitamin B. These requirements are to be obtained from two types of foods: type I, which contains 10 milligrams of vitamin A and 20 milligrams of vitamin B per pound; and type II, which contains 30 milligrams of vitamin A and 15 milligrams of vitamin B per pound. If type I and type II foods cost $2 and $8 per pound, respectively, how many pounds of each type should be purchased to satisfy the requirements at *minimum cost?*

Solution

Step 1   *Identify the quantity to be optimized and the related decision variables.*
We must determine the number of pounds of type I and type II foods to buy in order that total cost is minimized. Thus, we let

$$C = \text{total food cost}$$
$$x = \text{number of pounds of type I food to be bought}$$
$$y = \text{number of pounds of type II food to be bought}$$

The objective function is given by

$$C = 2x + 8y$$

and the objective is to minimize C.

Step 2   *Organize the given information, and write the linear inequalities that express any relationships existing among the decision variables.*

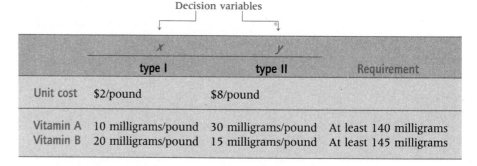

	x type I	y type II	Requirement
Unit cost	$2/pound	$8/pound	
Vitamin A	10 milligrams/pound	30 milligrams/pound	At least 140 milligrams
Vitamin B	20 milligrams/pound	15 milligrams/pound	At least 145 milligrams

Our problem is written algebraically as

$$\begin{aligned} \text{Minimize} \quad & C = 2x + 8y \\ \text{subject to} \quad & 10x + 30y \geq 140 \\ & 20x + 15y \geq 145 \\ & x \geq 0 \\ & y \geq 0 \end{aligned}$$

Note that the first two constraints contain the inequality symbol $\geq$ since 140 milligrams and 145 milligrams are *minimal* requirements of vitamins A and B, respectively.

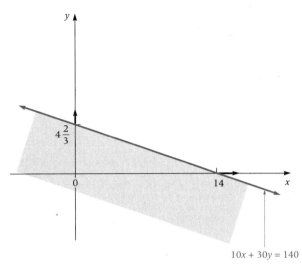

FIGURE 6-25

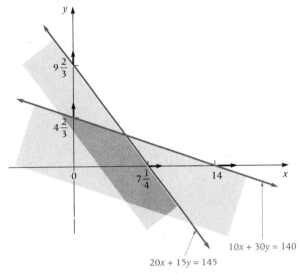

FIGURE 6-26

Step 3 *Determine the optimal solution.*
The feasible region is determined by graphing the linear inequality constraints (see Figure 6-25 through 6-28, pages 369-370). The vertex points are $(0, 9\frac{2}{3})$, $(5, 3)$, and $(14, 0)$. Note that $(5, 3)$ was determined by solving the linear system of equations

$$10x + 30y = 140$$
$$20x + 15y = 145$$

We now substitute the coordinates of each vertex point into the objective function $C = 2x + 8y$ to determine which yields the minimum cost. Hence,

$(0, 9\frac{2}{3})$	$C = 2(0) + 8\left(\dfrac{29}{3}\right) = \$77.33$
$(5, 3)$	$C = 2(5) + 8(3) = \$34.00$
$(14, 0)$	$C = 2(14) + 8(0) = \$28.00$ Minimum cost

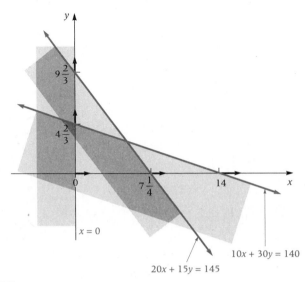

FIGURE 6-27

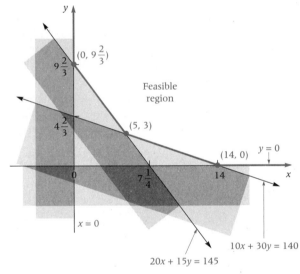

FIGURE 6-28

Since the vertex point (14, 0) yields the minimum cost of $28, then the optimal solution is

$x = 14$ pounds of type I food should be bought

$y = 0$ pounds of type II food should be bought

Step 4 *Investigate the implications of the optimal solution.*
Substituting the optimal solution values into each constraint gives the following.
Vitamin A Constraint:

$$10x + 30y \geq 140$$
$$10(14) + 30(0) \geq 140$$
$$140 \geq 140$$

Since LHS = RHS, *surplus = 0,* and, therefore, the minimal vitamin A requirement is being met exactly. This constraint is binding.

Vitamin B Constraint:

$$20x + 15y \geq 145$$
$$20(14) + 15(0) \geq 145$$
$$280 \geq 145$$

Note that LHS > RHS. Thus,

$$\text{surplus} = \text{LHS} - \text{RHS}$$
$$= 280 - 145 = 135 \text{ milligrams of vitamin B}$$

and, therefore, the minimal vitamin B requirement is being exceeded by 135 milligrams.

•

We conclude this section with the following problem.

• **EXAMPLE 6-7   Product Mix.**

Williams Motors, which sells both American cars and imports, is planning its order for the next quarter. Current demand indicates that at least 240, but at most 450 cars should be ordered and that the number of imports ordered should be at least twice the number of American cars ordered. On the average, each American car costs the dealer $9000, and each foreign car costs $12,000. Budgetary and financing constraints limit next quarter's outlay for cars to $5,700,000. If Williams Motors makes an average profit of $600 per American car and $400 per foreign car, determine how many of each type should be ordered for next quarter.

Solution

Step 1 *Identify the quantity to be optimized and the related decision variables.*
We must determine the number of American and foreign cars to be ordered so that the total profit is maximized. Thus, we let

$$P = \text{total profit}$$
$$x = \text{number of American cars to be ordered}$$
$$y = \text{number of foreign cars to be ordered}$$

The objective function is given by

$$P = 600x + 400y$$

and the objective is to maximize P.

Step 2 *Organize the given information, and write the linear inequalities that express any relationships existing among the decision variables.*
The constraints are formulated as follows. Since at least 240, but at most 450 cars must be ordered, this is formulated as the two constraints

$$x + y \geq 240$$
$$x + y \leq 450$$

Since the number of imports ordered should be at least twice the number of American cars ordered, this is written algebraically as the constraint

$$y \geq 2x$$
$$\text{or} \qquad \text{Add } -2x \text{ to each side.}$$
$$-2x + y \geq 0$$

The budgetary constraint limiting the total outlay to $5,700,000 is written as

$$9000x + 12,000y \leq 5,700,000$$

Thus, the problem is formulated as

$$\text{Maximize } P = 600x + 400y$$

subject to the constraints

$$x + y \geq 240$$
$$x + y \leq 450$$
$$-2x + y \geq 0$$
$$9000x + 12,000y \leq 5,700,000$$
$$x \geq 0$$
$$y \geq 0$$

Step 3 *Determine the optimal solution.*

The constraints are graphed in Figure 6-29, and the region of feasible solutions is unshaded.

The vertex points are (0, 240), (0, 450), (150, 300), and (80, 160). The vertex point (150, 300) was determined by solving the linear system

$$x + y = 450$$
$$-2x + y = 0$$

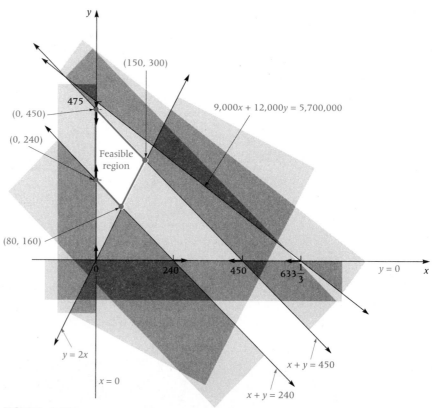

FIGURE 6-29

The vertex point (80, 160) was determined by solving the linear system

$$x + y = 240$$
$$-2x + y = 0$$

We now substitute the coordinates of each vertex point into the objective function $P = 600x + 400y$ to determine which yields the maximum profit. Hence,

(0, 240) $P = 600(0) + 400(240) = \$96,000$

(0, 450) $P = 600(0) + 400(450) = \$180,000$

(150, 300) $P = 600(150) + 400(300) = \$210,000$ Maximum profit

(80, 160) $P = 600(80) + 400(160) = \$112,000$

Note that the vertex point (150, 300) gives the maximum profit of \$210,000. Thus, the optimal solution is

$x = 150$ American cars should be ordered

$y = 300$ foreign cars should be ordered

Step 4 *Investigate the implications of the optimal solution.*

Substituting the optimal solution values into each constraint gives the following.

Number of cars → $x + y \geq 240$

$$150 + 300 \geq 240$$
$$450 \geq 240$$

Surplus = LHS − RHS

$$= 450 - 240 = 210 \text{ cars}$$

Thus, the requirement that at least 240 cars be produced is exceeded by 210 cars.

Number of cars → $x + y \leq 450$

$$150 + 300 \leq 450$$
$$450 \leq 450$$

Slack = RHS − LHS

$$= 450 - 450 = 0$$

The requirement that no more than 450 cars be produced is being met exactly. In other words, the constraint is binding.

Number of foreign cars → $y \geq 2x$ ← Number of American cars

$$300 \geq 2(150)$$
$$300 \geq 300$$

Surplus = LHS − RHS

$$= 300 - 300 = 0$$

The requirement that the number of foreign cars ordered be at least twice the number of American cars ordered is being met exactly. In other words, the constraint is binding.

Budgetary Constraint:

$$9000x + 12,000y \leq 5,700,000$$
$$9000(150) + 12,000(300) \leq 5,700,000$$
$$4,950,000 \leq 5,700,000$$

slack = RHS − LHS

$$= 5,700,000 - 4,950,000$$
$$= \$750,000$$

Thus, of the \$5,700,000 available for the purchase of cars, \$750,000 remains unspent.

Exercises 6-2

For each feasible region and objective function, determine the optimal solutions.

1. Maximize $z = 4x + 7y$ (see Figure 6-30).

2. Minimize $z = 2x + 5y$ (see Figure 6-31).

3. Minimize $z = 0.70x + 0.40y$ (see Figure 6-32).

4. Maximize $z = 5x + 9y$ (see Figure 6-33).

5. Maximize $z = 0.80x + 0.30y$ (see Figure 6-34).

6. Minimize $z = 3x + 10y$ (see Figure 6-35).

Solve each of the following linear programing problems.

7. Maximize $P = 5x + 4y$
subject to $3x + 4y \leq 24$
$2x + y \leq 14$
$x, y \geq 0$

8. Maximize $P = 2x + 7y$
subject to $x + y \leq 10$
$2x + y \leq 18$
$x, y \geq 0$

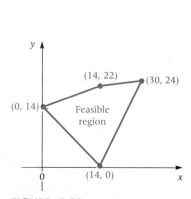

FIGURE 6-30

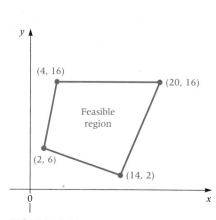

FIGURE 6-31

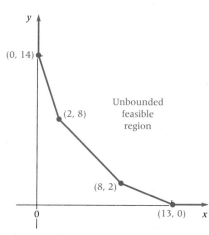

FIGURE 6-32

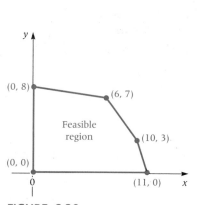

FIGURE 6-33

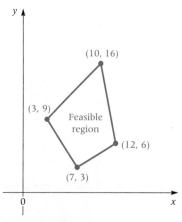

FIGURE 6-34

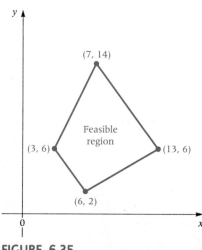

FIGURE 6-35

9. Minimize $C = 4x + 9y$
   subject to $x + y \geq 12$
   $3x + 2y \geq 30$
   $x, y \geq 0$

10. Minimize $C = 8x + 6y$
    subject to $4x + 5y \geq 40$
    $2x + y \geq 18$
    $x, y \geq 0$

11. Maximize $z = 10x + 30y$
    subject to $3x + 5y \leq 30$
    $2x + 4y \leq 22$
    $x, y \geq 0$

12. Maximize $z = 30x + 20y$
    subject to $5x + 7y \leq 70$
    $3x + 2y \leq 30$
    $x, y \geq 0$

13. Minimize $z = 20x + 40y$
    subject to $x + y \geq 10$
    $3x + 4y \geq 36$
    $x + y \leq 40$
    $x, y \geq 0$

14. Minimize $z = 30x + 50y$
    subject to $2x + y \geq 20$
    $x + y \geq 12$
    $x + y \leq 30$
    $x, y \geq 0$

15. Maximize $z = 3x + 5y$
    subject to $2x + y \leq 30$
    $x - 2y \leq 10$
    $x \geq 4$
    $y \geq 1$

16. Maximize $z = 2x + 3y$
    subject to $3x + y \leq 30$
    $2x - y \leq 16$
    $x \geq 2$
    $y \geq 1$

17. Maximize $z = 20x + 30y$
    subject to $x + 4y \leq 20$
    $2x - y \leq 30$
    $-x + y \leq 4$
    $x, y \geq 0$

18. Maximize $z = 40x + 100y$
    subject to $2x + 5y \leq 40$
    $-x + 3y \leq 18$
    $x + y \geq 6$
    $x \geq 0$
    $y \geq 2$

Applications

19. *Production planning.* A company manufactures two types of jackets: casual and formal. The company makes profits of $30 per casual jacket and $50 per formal jacket. Both types of jackets must pass through the cutting department, which has available 960 person-hours during the next week, and the sewing department, which has available 400 person-hours during the next week. Each casual jacket requires 2 person-hours in the cutting department and 1 person-hour in the sewing department. Each formal jacket requires 3 person-hours in the cutting department and 1 person-hour in the sewing department. Additionally, there is an order for 150 casual jackets and 50 formal jackets, which must be made next week. How many of each type of jacket should be made next week in order to maximize total profit and satisfy the above constraints?

a) Fill in the blanks below.

Step 1 $x =$ _____

$y =$ _____

Objective function: Maximize ____ = ____x + ____y

Step 2   ⌐— Decision Variables —⌐

	casual	formal	
Unit profits	____	____	
Cutting department	____ person-hours per jacket	____ person-hours per jacket	At most ____
Sewing department	____ person-hours per jacket	____ person-hours per jacket	At most ____

Also,
- At least ____ casual jackets must be produced.
- At least ____ formal jackets must be produced.

Constraints:

$$\text{Cutting department} \underline{\hspace{3cm}}$$

$$\text{Sewing department} \underline{\hspace{3cm}}$$

$$x \geq \underline{\hspace{1cm}}$$

$$y \geq \underline{\hspace{1cm}}$$

Step 3 Solve the algebraic formulation of steps 1 and 2.

Step 4 Investigate the implications of the optimal solution.

$$\text{Cutting department} \quad \text{slack} = \underline{\hspace{1cm}}$$

$$\text{Sewing department} \quad \text{slack} = \underline{\hspace{1cm}}$$

$$\text{Constraint: } x \geq 150 \quad \text{surplus} = \underline{\hspace{1cm}}$$

$$\text{Constraint: } y \geq 50 \quad \text{surplus} = \underline{\hspace{1cm}}$$

b) How many person-hours are used in the cutting department?
c) How many person-hours are used in the sewing department?

20. *Investment: Portfolio allocation.* An investor has at most $20,000 to be allocated for investment in conservative and aggressive mutual funds. The projected annual rate of return for each mutual fund is given below along with its risk level.

Projected annual rate of return

Conservative mutual fund	Aggressive mutual fund
18%	22%

Risk level

Conservative mutual fund	Aggressive mutual fund
2	6

If the investor wants an average risk level of no more than 3, then how much should be invested in each mutual fund in order to maximize the total projected annual return?

Fill in the blanks below.

Step 1 x = number of dollars invested in the conservative mutual fund

$$y = \underline{\hspace{7cm}}$$

$$\text{Objective function: Maximize} \underline{\hspace{1cm}} = \underline{\hspace{1cm}}x + \underline{\hspace{1cm}}y$$

Step 2 Constraints:
- Total amount invested $\leq 20{,}000$

$$\underline{\hspace{1cm}} + \underline{\hspace{1cm}} \leq 20{,}000$$

- Average risk level ≤ 3

If x dollars are invested at a risk level of 2 and y dollars are invested at a risk level of 6, then the average risk level is given by

$$\frac{2x + 6y}{x + y}$$

Since the average risk level must be no more than 3, this gives the constraint

$$\frac{2x + 6y}{x + y} \le 3$$

Multiplying both sides by $x + y$ (where $x + y > 0$) gives

$$2x + 6y \le 3(\underline{\quad} + \underline{\quad})$$

Using the distributive law and then subtracting $3x$ and $3y$ from both sides results in

$$\underline{\quad}x + \underline{\quad}y \le 0$$

Also, the non-negativity restrictions result in

$$x \ge \underline{\quad}$$
$$y \ge \underline{\quad}$$

Step 3 Solve the algebraic formulation of steps 1 and 2.

Step 4 Investigate the implications of the optimal solution.

      Constraint 1:   Total amount invested = ____

                                        Slack = ____

      Constraint 2:   State the average risk level for the optimal solution.

                    Slack = ____

21. *Investment: Portfolio allocation.* Repeat Exercise 20 under the additional constraints that at least $6000 must be invested in the conservative mutual fund and at most $4000 must be invested in the aggressive mutual fund.

22. *Media selection.* A company executive must determine the optimal mix of radio and TV ads to purchase for next month. Each radio ad costs $1500, and each TV ad costs $2000. There must be a combined total of at least 1200 ads. Also, each radio ad is expected to reach 1000 families, and each TV ad is expected to reach 1500 families. It is required that at least 1,500,000 families be reached.
a) How many of each type of ad should be purchased for next month in order to minimize the total cost?
b) What is the minimum total cost?
c) Determine the surplus for each constraint.
d) How many families will be reached?
e) How many ads will be bought?

23. Repeat Exercise 22 under the assumption that each radio ad costs $1200 and each TV ad costs $2000.

24. *Product mix.* A company manufactures motorcycles and mopeds, each of which must pass through two machines: machine 1 and machine 2. Each motorcycle requires 2 hours on machine 1 and 5 hours on machine 2. Each moped requires 3 hours on machine 1 and 1 hour on machine 2. Machines 1 and 2 have available 90 hours and 160 hours, respectively, for these two products.
a) If the company makes a profit of $120 on each motorcycle and $60 on each moped, how many of each should be produced in order to maximize total profit and satisfy the constraints of the problem? Determine the amount of slack for each constraint.
b) If the company makes only $30 on each motorcycle and $90 on each moped, how many of each should be produced in order to maximize total profit and satisfy the constraints of the problem? Determine the amount of slack for each constraint.

25. *Nutrition.* A diet must provide at least 1200 milligrams of protein and at least 1000 milligrams of iron. These nutrients are to be obtained from eating meat and spinach. Each pound of meat contains 500 milligrams of protein and 100 milligrams of iron. Each pound of spinach contains 200 milligrams of protein and 800 milligrams of iron. If meat and spinach cost $3.00 and $1.50 per pound, respectively, how many pounds of each should be eaten in order to minimize total cost and satisfy the constraints of the problem? Determine the amount of surplus for each constraint.

26. *Product mix.* A manufacturer produces two models of televisions—T140 and T240—each of which must pass through two departments, D1 and D2. Each unit of T140 requires 3 hours in D1 and 4 hours in D2. Each unit of T240 requires 6 hours in D1 and 4 hours in D2. Departments D1 and D2 each have 60 hours available. If the manufacturer makes a profit of $10 per unit on T140 and $30 per unit on T240, then

   a) How many units of each should be made in order to maximize total profit and satisfy the constraints of the problem?
   b) What is the maximum profit?
   c) Determine the amount of slack in each constraint.
   d) How many hours are used in each department?

27. *Agriculture.* A farmer owns a 100-acre farm and wants to plant a combination of two crops: A and B. Crop A requires 60 person-hours of labor per acre, and crop B requires 80 person-hours of labor per acre. The farmer has 6600 person-hours of labor available.

   a) If the farmer makes a profit of $400 per acre on crop A and $500 per acre on crop B, how many acres of each crop should be planted in order to maximize total profit and satisfy the constraints of the problem?
   b) What is the maximum profit?
   c) Determine the amount of slack in each constraint.
   d) How many acres are planted?
   e) How many person-hours of labor are used?

28. Repeat Exercise 27 under the assumption that the farmer makes a profit of $500 per acre on each crop.

29. *Fuel allocation.* A factory uses two types of fuel—F10 and F20—for heating and other purposes. At least 3800 gallons of fuel are needed each day. Some byproducts are produced by the burning of the fuel. Each gallon of F10 leaves a residue of 0.02 pound of ash and 0.06 pound of soot. Each gallon of F20 leaves a residue of 0.05 pound of ash and 0.01 pound of soot. The factory needs at least 120 pounds of ash and at least 136 pounds of soot. If F10 and F20 cost $1.50 and $1.10 per gallon, respectively, then

   a) How many gallons of each type should be purchased in order to minimize total cost and satisfy the constraints of the problem?
   b) What is the minimum cost?
   c) Determine the amount of surplus for each constraint.
   d) How many gallons of fuel are bought daily?
   e) How many pounds of ash are produced daily?
   f) How many pounds of soot are produced daily?

30. *The following problem appeared on a past Uniform CPA Examination.* A company markets two products: Alpha and Gamma. The marginal contributions per gallon are $5 for Alpha and $4 for Gamma. Both products consist of two ingredients: D and K. Alpha contains 80% D and 20% K, while the proportions of the same ingredients in Gamma are 40% and 60%, respectively. The current inventory is 16,000 gallons of D and 6000 gallons of K. The only com-

pany producing D and K is on strike and will neither deliver nor produce them in the foreseeable future.

a) The company wishes to know how many gallons of Alpha and Gamma it should produce with its present stock of raw materials in order to maximize its total revenue.

b) What is the maximum total revenue?

c) Determine the amount of slack for each constraint.

d) How many gallons of D are used?

e) How many gallons of K are used?

31. *The following problem appeared on a past Uniform CPA Examination.* Patsy, Inc., manufactures two products: X and Y. Each product must be processed in each of three departments: machining, assembling, and finishing. The hours needed to produce 1 unit of product per department and the maximum possible hours per department are as follows:

Department	Production hours per unit X	Production hours per unit Y	Maximum capacity (in hours)
Machining	2	1	420
Assembling	2	2	500
Finishing	2	3	600

In addition, $X \geq 50$ and $Y \geq 50$. The objective function is to maximize profits, where profit $= \$4X + \$2Y$. Given the objective and constraints,

a) What is the most profitable number of units of X and Y to manufacture?

b) What is the maximum profit?

c) Determine the slack or surplus for each constraint.

d) How many hours are used in the machining department?

e) How many hours are used in the assembling department?

f) How many hours are used in the finishing department?

32. A pharmaceutical company plans to manufacture two new drugs: diopthelene and gramamine. Each case of diopthelene requires 3 hours of processing time and 1 hour of curing time per week. Each case of gramamine requires 5 hours of processing time and 5 hours of curing time per week. The company's time schedule allows 55 hours of processing time and 45 hours of curing time weekly for the two drugs. Additionally, the company must produce no more than 10 cases of diopthelene and no more than 9 cases of gramamine each week. If the company makes a profit of $400 on each case of diopthelene and $500 on each case of gramamine, then

a) How many cases of each should be produced in order to maximize total profit and satisfy the constraints of the problem?

b) What is the maximum profit?

c) Determine the amount of slack for each constraint.

d) How many hours of processing time are required in total?

e) How many hours of curing time are required in total?

33. *Marketing strategy.* A company markets its product to wholesale and retail outlets with unit profits of $90 and $120, respectively. The company's limited sales force allows for a total marketing effort of at most 17,280 hours for the next month. A past analysis of marketing efforts has revealed that each unit sold to wholesale outlets requires 2.4 hours of sales effort, while each unit sold to retail outlets requires 3.6 hours of sales effort. If next month's production plans call for at most 5600 units of this product, then

a) How many should be distributed to each outlet?
b) What is the maximum profit?
c) Determine the amount of slack for each constraint.
d) How many units of this product will be produced next month?
e) How many hours of marketing effort are expended?

34. Repeat Exercise 33 with the added restriction that the number of wholesale outlets must be less than or equal to 4 times the number of retail outlets.

35. Repeat Exercise 33 with the added restriction that the number of wholesale outlets must be at least 4 times the number of retail outlets.

6-3 • FUNDAMENTAL THEOREM OF LINEAR PROGRAMMING

Having solved linear programming problems in the previous section, we now show why an optimal value of an objective function, if it exists, will occur at one or more of the vertex points or on the boundary of the feasible region. Using the introductory linear programming problem of Section 6-2 as an example, we again illustrate the graph of its region of feasible solutions (see Figure 6-36). Observe that the objective function

$$P = 20x + 16y$$

with its maximum value, $P = 6800$, also appears on the graph as

$$6800 = 20x + 16y$$

Note that it passes through the optimal solution, $(320, 30)$.

Now suppose we substitute some other point of the feasible region into the objective function $P = 20x + 16y$. Choosing $(70, 40)$, we obtain

$$P = 20(70) + 16(40) = \$2040$$

Note that $P = \$2040$ is less than the maximum value, $P = \$6800$. If we include the graph of the objective function $2040 = 20x + 16y$ with the graph of Figure 6-36, we obtain the graph of Figure 6-37. Observe that the graph of the objective function $2040 = 20x + 16y$ is parallel to the graph of the objective function $6800 = 20x + 16y$, but is located closer to the origin.

In general, if we consider the objective function $P = 20x + 16y$ and solve the equation for y to obtain the slope-intercept form

$$y = \frac{-5}{4}x + \frac{P}{16}$$

we note that $P/16$ is the y-intercept of the objective function, as is indicated in Figure 6-37. Studying the graph of the objective function $P = 20x + 16y$ in Figure 6-37, note that P takes on its maximum value over the feasible region at the vertex point $(320, 30)$.

We note that the graph of the objective function must always pass through at least one point of the feasible region. Otherwise, the constraints of the linear programming problem would not be satisfied.

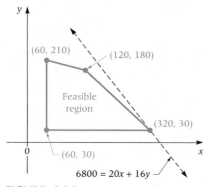

FIGURE 6-36

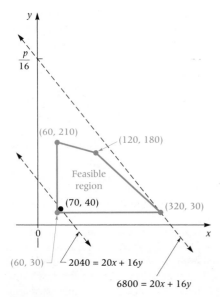

FIGURE 6-37

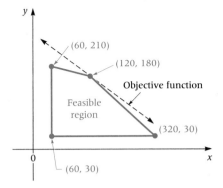

FIGURE 6-38

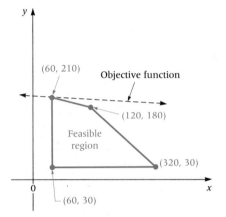

FIGURE 6-39

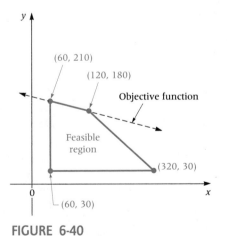

FIGURE 6-40

Note also that if the unit profits were changed so that the slope of the objective function decreased substantially in absolute value, then the vertex point $(120, 180)$ would yield the maximum value of P (see Figure 6-38). If the unit profits were changed so that the slope of the objective function further decreased in absolute value, then the vertex point $(60, 210)$ would yield the maximum value of P (see Figure 6-39).

In addition, if the slope of the objective function equaled the slope of one of the constraints, then more than one vertex point would yield an optimal solution (see Figure 6-40). In fact, both vertex points and all points on the straight line between them yield optimal values for P. Thus, in the present example, the vertex points $(60, 210)$ and $(120, 180)$ and all points on the straight line between them yield optimal values of P (see Figure 6-40).

Also, if our goal were to minimize the value of the objective function, then the vertex point $(60, 30)$ would yield an optimal solution, as shown in Figure 6-41.

The discussions in the previous paragraphs have demonstrated what we have already stated in the shaded box on page 367. Since the importance of this statement should not be underestimated, we restate it below.

SUMMARY

Fundamental Theorem of Linear Programming

An optimal value of an objective function, if it exists, will occur at one or more of the vertex points or on the boundary of the region of feasible solutions.

We now consider Example 6-6 of Section 6-2, a linear programming problem that involves minimizing the value of an objective function. Its feasible region is given in Figure 6-42. Observing the graph of Figure 6-42, note that the feasible region is **unbounded.** That is, it is not completely enclosed by its boundary lines. If our goal were to maximize the value of the objective function $C = 2x + 8y$, as indicated in Figure 6-43 on page 382,

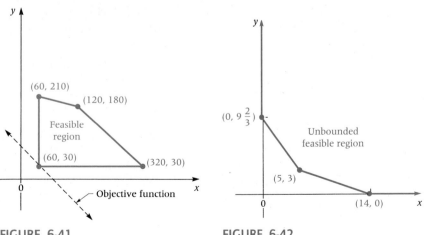

FIGURE 6-41

FIGURE 6-42

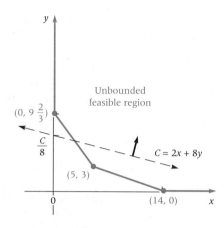

FIGURE 6-43

then there would be no optimal solution to this problem since the value of C increases indefinitely as the objective function moves in the direction of the arrow. However, since our goal in Example 6-6 was to minimize the value of C, then we observe that the vertex point $(14, 0)$ yields the optimal solution to the linear programming problem.

Thus, we can understand that the following statements are true for linear programming problems.

1. If a feasible region is *bounded,* then there is always an optimal solution to the associated linear programming problem. Such an optimal solution will occur at one or more vertex points or on the boundary interval between two vertex points.
2. If a feasible region is *unbounded,* then there may or may not be an optimal solution to the associated linear programming problem.

The following box contains a complete summary of different situations that can be encountered when solving linear programming problems.

SUMMARY

Linear Programming

When solving a linear programming problem, one of the following situations will occur:

1. An **optimal solution** exists at a *single vertex point.*
2. There is **more than one optimal solution.** This situation occurs when the objective function line is parallel to a constraint line. Thus, optimal solutions exist at two vertex points and on the connecting boundary interval.
3. There is **no optimal solution** because a *feasible region does not exist.*
4. There is **no optimal solution** because the *feasible region is unbounded,* and, therefore, a best solution does not exist because there is always a better solution. We note, however, that unbounded feasible regions may or may not yield optimal solutions. This depends on the graph of the unbounded feasible region and the optimal direction of movement of the graph of the objective function.

Exercises 6-3

Each of the following graphs illustrates a feasible region and an objective function (labeled *z*) for a linear programming problem. Each objective function (*z*) has an arrow that indicates its direction of optimal movement. For each of the following, state the optimal solution(s) or identify whichever linear programming situation occurs.

1.

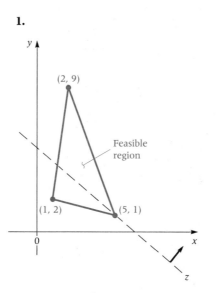

2.

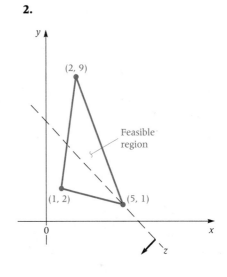

3.

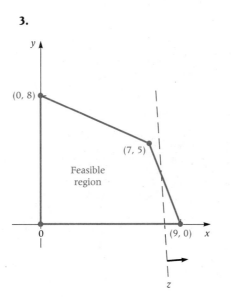

4.

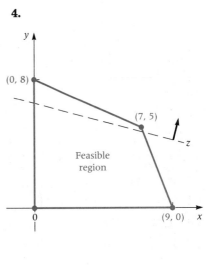

5.

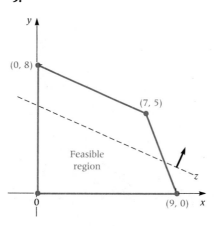

6.

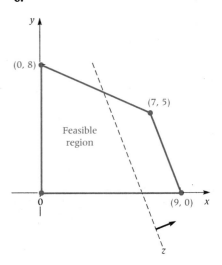

7.

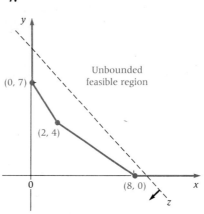

8.

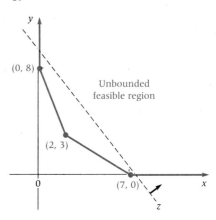

9.

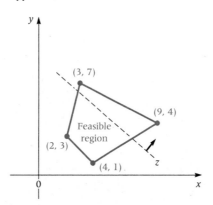

10.

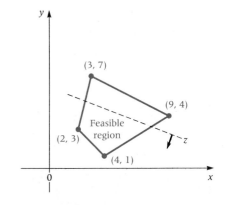

11.

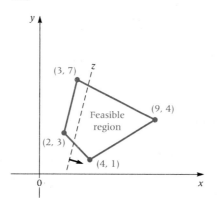

12.

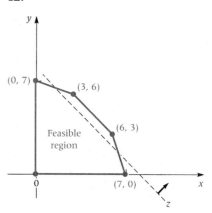

13.

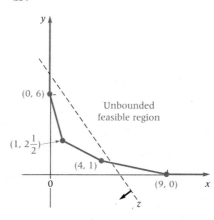

14.

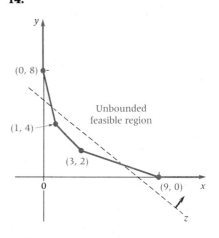

Which linear programming situation occurs for each of the problems below?

15. Maximize $z = 3x + 5y$
subject to $x + y \leq 5$
$x + y \geq 7$
$x \geq 0$
$y \geq 0$

16. Maximize $z = 5x + 2y$
subject to $7x + 5y \leq 35$
$x + y \geq 8$
$x \geq 0$
$y \geq 0$

17. Minimize $z = 12x + 15y$
subject to $3x + 2y \leq 48$
$x \geq 4$
$0 \leq y \leq 20$

18. Minimize $z = 10x + 4y$
subject to $5x + 2y \geq 60$
$x \geq 4$
$y \geq 6$

19. Maximize $z = 10x + 20y$
subject to $3x + 4y \geq 60$
$x \geq 4$
$y \geq 3$

CHAPTER 6 HIGHLIGHTS

• *Concepts*

Your ability to answer the following questions is one indicator of the depth of your mastery of this chapter's important concepts. Note that the questions are grouped under various topic headings. For any question that you cannot answer, refer to the appropriate section of the chapter indicated by the topic heading. Pay particular attention to the summary boxes within a section.

6-1 LINEAR INEQUALITIES IN TWO VARIABLES

1. Write the general form of a linear inequality in two variables.
2. Give the procedure to graph a linear inequality.
3. Give the procedure to graph a system of linear inequalities.

6-2 LINEAR PROGRAMMING

4. State the four steps of the linear programming problem-solving procedure.
5. Give the graphical procedure for determining the optimal solution to a linear programming problem.
6. Give the formula for slack and interpret the result.
7. To what type of constraint is slack relevant?
8. If, for a particular constraint, slack = 0, the constraint is called a(n) _____. Interpret this result.
9. Give the formula for surplus and interpret the result.
10. To what type of constraint is surplus relevant?
11. If, for a particular constraint, surplus = 0, the constraint is called a(n) _____. Interpret this result.

6-3 FUNDAMENTAL THEOREM OF LINEAR PROGRAMMING

12. State the fundamental theorem of linear programming.
13. If a feasible region is bounded, does an optimal solution exist for the corresponding linear programming problem?
14. If a feasible region is unbounded, what possibilities exist regarding an optimal solution for the corresponding linear programming problem?
15. If an objective function line is parallel to a constraint line, what does this imply with regard to an optimal solution?
16. What is the cause of an unbounded solution?
17. If a feasible region does not exist for a linear programming problem, what does this imply with regard to an optimal solution?

REVIEW EXERCISES

• *Graphing Linear Inequalities*

Graph each of the following.

1. $3x + 2y \le 24$
2. $-2x + 5y \le 40$
3. $5x + 4y \ge 40$
4. $3x - 7y \ge 42$

• Graphing Systems of Linear Inequalities

Graph each linear system.

5. $x + y \leq 12$
       $8x + 4y \leq 64$

6. $-5x + 2y \geq 20$
               $y \geq 5$

7. $2x + 3y \leq 12$
       $6x + 5y \leq 30$
             $x \geq 0$
             $y \geq 0$

8. $x + y \geq 20$
            $y \geq x$
            $x \geq 0$
           $y \geq 12$

• Linear Programming

Solve each of the following.

9. Maximize $z = 2x + 5y$
   subject to $2x + y \leq 40$
             $3x + y \leq 48$
               $x, y \geq 0$

10. Maximize $z = 6x + 4y$
    subject to $2x + 3y \leq 30$
                 $x \geq 3$
                 $y \geq 2$

11. Minimize $z = 5x + 2y$
   subject to $x + y \geq 20$
             $x + 3y \geq 30$
               $x, y \geq 0$

12. Minimize $z = 4x + 5y$
    subject to $4x + 3y \geq 24$
                 $x \leq 5$
                 $y \leq 6$
               $x, y \geq 0$

Applications

Exercises 13-15 are adapted from problems that appeared on past Uniform CPA Examinations.

a) Formulate the linear programming problem.
b) Solve.
c) Investigate the implications of the optimal solution.

13. The Sanch Company plans to expand its sales force by opening several new branch offices. Sanch has $5,200,000 in capital available for new branch offices. Sanch will consider opening only two types of branches: 10-person branches (type A) and 5-person branches (type B). Expected initial cash outlays are $650,000 for a type A branch and $335,000 for a type B branch. Expected annual cash inflow, net of income taxes, is $46,000 for a type A branch and $18,000 for a type B branch. Sanch will hire no more than 100 employees for the new branch offices. How many of each type should be opened?

14. Repeat Exercise 13 under the added constraint that Sanch will not open more than 10 branch offices.

15. The raw material requirements for a unit of each of two products are given below.

	Product A	Product B
Raw material 1	3	4
Raw material 2	7	2
Unit profit	$10	$4

If 300 units of raw material 1 and 400 units of raw material 2 are available, how many units of each product should be produced?

16. *Investment: Portfolio allocation.* An investor has at least $30,000 to be allocated for investment in bond and stock mutual funds. The projected annual rate of return for each mutual fund is given below, along with its risk level.

Projected annual rate of return

Bond fund	Stock fund
15%	20%

Risk level

Bond fund	Stock fund
3	5

If the investor wants an annual rate of return of at least 16%, how much should be invested in each fund in order to minimize the total risk?

• *Fundamental Theorem of Linear Programming*

Draw a graph of a feasible region and an objective function that illustrates each of the following.

17. An optimal solution exists at a single vertex point.
18. There is more than one optimal solution.
19. There is no optimal solution because a feasible solution does not exist.
20. There is no optimal solution because the feasible region is unbounded.

7

LINEAR PROGRAMMING: THE SIMPLEX METHOD

Introductory Application

Investment: Portfolio Selection

In this chapter, we discuss a method for solving linear programming problems with more than two decision variables. One such problem is presented below.

An investor has $600,000 to allocate among the following investment alternatives:

Investment alternatives	Rate of return	Risk level
Government Bonds	7.5%	0
Money Market Funds	8.6	2
Hi-tech Stock	13.5	9
Municipal Bonds	7.8	1

The investor has stated the following investment criteria:

1. The full amount of $600,000 is to be invested.
2. The average risk is to be no more than 3.5.
3. At least $100,000 is to be invested in government bonds.
4. At least $100,000 is to be invested in money market funds.
5. At least $60,000 is to be invested in hi-tech stock.
6. At least $50,000 is to be invested in municipal bonds.

PROBLEM

We must determine the amount that should be invested in each investment alternative in order to maximize the annual return.

SOLUTION

The solution to this problem is given in Section 7-4.

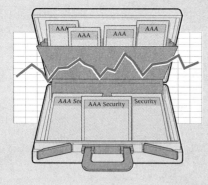

7-1

• A GEOMETRIC INTRODUCTION AND THE SIMPLEX TABLEAU

In the preceding chapter, we solved linear programming problems graphically. Our procedure was to graph the region of feasible solutions, determine its vertex points, and substitute the coordinates of each vertex point into the objective function to determine the optimal solution.

The principle of finding vertex points and substituting values into an objective function carries over into larger problems, but a graphical approach is impractical. The graphical approach for solving linear programming problems is not viable when the number of variables exceeds two, and since most real-world linear programming problems have many variables, its applicability is very limited. Fortunately, there exists an *algebraic* method of determining the vertex points of the region of feasible solutions. This algebraic method is called the **simplex method.** It enables us to determine the vertex points of the region of feasible solutions without having to graph the region. In fact, the simplex method allows us to proceed systematically from one vertex point to another and improve the value of the objective function at each step until an optimal solution has been found. This systematic feature of the simplex method enhances its suitability for computer solution.

Maximization Problem: Slack Variables

As an illustrative example, we consider the problem of determining an optimal mix of two products. The raw material and time requirement for each product for each resource are given in Table 7-1. Here,

$$x_1 = \text{number of units of product A to be produced}$$
$$x_2 = \text{number of units of product B to be produced}$$
$$Z = \text{total profit (in dollars)}$$

Decision variables

TABLE 7-1

	x_1	x_2	
	product A	**product B**	Resource capacity
Unit profit	$20	$24	
Raw material	1 pound per unit of A	2 pounds per unit of B	At most 850 pounds of raw material
Department 1	2 person-hours per unit of A	2 person-hours per unit of B	At most 1000 person-hours
Department 2	3 person-hours per unit of A	9 person-hours per unit of B	At most 3600 person-hours

The corresponding algebraic formulation is

$$\text{Maximize} \quad Z = 20x_1 + 24x_2$$
$$\text{subject to} \quad x_1 + 2x_2 \le 850$$
$$2x_1 + 2x_2 \le 1000 \quad \quad (1)$$
$$3x_1 + 9x_2 \le 3600$$
$$\text{where } x_1 \text{ and } x_2 \ge 0$$

Standard Maximization Form

A linear programming maximization problem written in the above form is said to be in standard maximization form. In general, a linear programming maximization problem is in *standard maximization form* if

  1. The objective function is to be maximized and is of the linear form

$$Z = c_1x_1 + c_2x_2 + \ldots + c_nx_n$$

  2. All variables are non-negative (i.e., $x_i \ge 0$).
  3. All constraints are linear inequalities of the form

$$a_1x_1 + a_2x_2 + \ldots + a_nx_n \le b$$

where $b \ge 0$.

Henceforth in this section, we consider only linear programming problems that are in standard maximization form.

Slack Variables

The first step in applying the simplex method to a linear programming problem involves restating the linear inequality constraints as equations. For a $\le$ constraint, this is accomplished by introducing a slack variable. In Section 6-2, we discussed the concept of slack. Recall that for a $\le$ constraint, slack (the difference between the right-hand side and the left-hand side of the constraint) represents the amount of unused resource capacity in the constraint. Thus, we let

Slack variables
$$s_1 = \text{slack in constraint 1}$$
(the amount of unused raw material)
$$s_2 = \text{slack in constraint 2}$$
(the amount of unused person-hours in department 1)
$$s_3 = \text{slack in constraint 3}$$
(the amount of unused person-hours in department 2)

where s_1, s_2, and s_3 are non-negative. The variables s_1, s_2, and s_3 are called **slack variables.**

We now restate the linear inequalities as linear equations by including the slack variables as given below.

$$x_1 + 2x_2 + s_1 \quad \quad = 850$$
$$2x_1 + 2x_2 \quad + s_2 \quad = 1000$$
$$3x_1 + 9x_2 \quad \quad + s_3 = 3600$$

Note that

- If $s_1 = 0$, then $x_1 + 2x_2 = 850$. This means that all 850 gallons of raw material are being used to produce x_1 units of product A and x_2 units of product B.
- If $s_2 = 0$, then $2x_1 + 2x_2 = 1000$. This means that all 1000 person-hours of department 1 are being used to produce x_1 units of product A and x_2 units of product B.
- If $s_3 = 0$, then $3x_1 + 9x_2 = 3600$. This means that all 3600 person-hours of department 2 are being used to produce x_1 units of product A and x_2 units of product B.

Feasible Solutions

The complete problem is now stated algebraically as follows:

$$\text{Maximize } Z = 20x_1 + 24x_2$$
$$\begin{aligned} \text{subject to} \quad x_1 + 2x_2 + s_1 \qquad\qquad &= 850 \\ 2x_1 + 2x_2 \qquad + s_2 \qquad &= 1000 \\ 3x_1 + 9x_2 \qquad\qquad + s_3 &= 3600 \end{aligned} \qquad (2)$$
$$\text{where } x_1, x_2, s_1, s_2, s_3 \geq 0$$

A **feasible solution** to the above problem consists of values of

$$x_1 = \underline{\quad}, x_2 = \underline{\quad}, s_1 = \underline{\quad}, s_2 = \underline{\quad}, s_3 = \underline{\quad}$$

such that values of the above variables satisfy the constraints. This is the algebraic equivalent of points located in the feasible region, as illustrated in Figure 7-1 on page 394. Figure 7-1 gives a graphical portrayal of the feasible region for this problem. Note that only the x_1 and x_2 coordinates are expressed graphically in Figure 7-1.

Basic Feasible Solutions

In our discussion of the graphical method of solving linear programming problems, we learned the following, which we restate below.

SUMMARY

Fundamental Theorem of Linear Programming

An optimal value of an objective function, if it exists, will occur at one or more of the vertex points or on the boundary of the region of feasible solutions.

We must now discuss the algebraic equivalent of the vertex points of the region of feasible solutions. Algebraic equivalents of the vertex points of a feasible region are called **basic feasible solutions.** A *basic feasible solution* is a feasible solution in which the number of nonzero variables is equal to the number of constraint equations; the remaining variables must

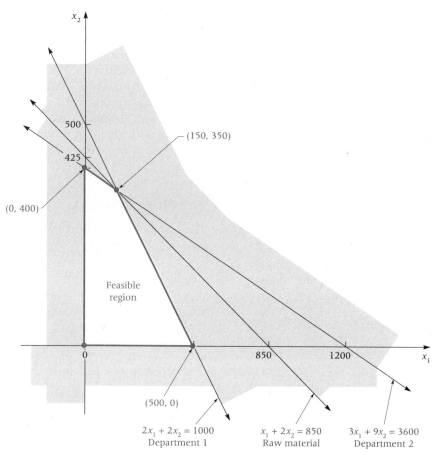

FIGURE 7-1

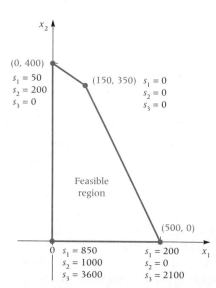

Basic feasible solutions

FIGURE 7-2

equal 0. In other words, if there are m constraint equations, then a basic feasible solution contains exactly m nonzero variables; the remaining variables must equal 0.*

For our illustrative problem, a possible basic feasible solution is given by

$$x_1 = 0, \ x_2 = 0, \ s_1 = 850, \ s_2 = 1000, \ s_3 = 3600$$

Note that since $x_1 = 0$ and $x_2 = 0$, this basic feasible solution corresponds to the vertex point $(0, 0)$, as is graphically illustrated in Figure 7-2. Observe that, in Figure 7-2, we give the basic feasible solutions corresponding to all the vertex points of the feasible region.

The simplex method provides a process for proceeding systematically from one basic feasible solution (or vertex point) to another to improve the value of the objective function at each step until an optimal solution is found.

---

*Actually, a basic feasible solution can contain fewer nonzero variables than the number of constraint equations. When this happens, the solution is termed **degenerate.** Since degeneracies do not occur very often, for practical purposes they are not considered in our definition of a basic feasible solution. We will encounter a degeneracy in the next section.

Basic and Nonbasic Variables

The *nonzero variables* of a basic feasible solution are called **basic variables,** or simply **basis,** whereas the *zero variables* are called **nonbasic variables.** We illustrate these terms below by using the preceding basic feasible solution.

Basic Feasible Solution

$$\underbrace{x_1 = 0,\, x_2 = 0,}_{\text{Nonbasic variables}}\quad \underbrace{s_1 = 850,\, s_2 = 1000,\, s_3 = 3600}_{\substack{\text{Basic variables} \\ \text{or basis}}}$$

We summarize as follows.

SUMMARY

Standard Maximization Form. A linear programming problem is in standard maximization form if

1. The objective function is to be maximized and is of the linear form

$$z = c_1 x_1 + c_2 x_2 + \ldots + c_n x_n$$

2. All variables are non-negative (i.e., $x_i \geq 0$).
3. All constraints are linear inequalities of the form

$$a_1 x_1 + a_2 x_2 + \ldots + a_n x_n \leq b$$

where $b \geq 0$.

Basic Feasible Solutions. A basic feasible solution to a linear programming problem, written in standard form with slack variables included, is a feasible solution in which the number of nonzero variables is equal to the number of constraint equations; the remaining variables equal 0.

Basic and Nonbasic Variables. The *nonzero variables* of a basic feasible solution are called **basic variables,** or simply **basis.** The variables that *equal zero* are called **nonbasic variables.**

Optimal Solution. An optimal solution, if one exists, to a linear programming problem is a basic feasible solution.

Simplex Tableau

We now prepare the algebraic formulation (2) of our linear programming problem for solution by the simplex method. Referring to the formulation (2), first rewrite the objective function so that all the terms are on its left-hand side. This gives

$$-20x_1 - 24x_2 + Z = 0$$

which we write below the constraints as follows.

$$
\begin{aligned}
x_1 + 2x_2 + s_1 &= 850 \\
2x_1 + 2x_2 + s_2 &= 1000 \\
3x_1 + 9x_2 + s_3 &= 3600 \\
-20x_1 - 24x_2 + Z &= 0
\end{aligned}
$$

Now write the coefficients of the above formulation as the matrix below. Note that each column is labeled with its variable.

$$
\begin{array}{cccccc}
x_1 & x_2 & s_1 & s_2 & s_3 & Z \\
\end{array}
$$

$$
\left[
\begin{array}{cccccc|c}
1 & 2 & 1 & 0 & 0 & 0 & 850 \\
2 & 2 & 0 & 1 & 0 & 0 & 1000 \\
3 & 9 & 0 & 0 & 1 & 0 & 3600 \\
\hline
-20 & -24 & 0 & 0 & 0 & 1 & 0 \\
\end{array}
\right]
$$

Objective function value

Such a matrix is called a **simplex tableau.** This tableau or matrix represents a linear system for which we seek a solution that maximizes Z.

It is beneficial to learn how to read a simplex tableau. In the above simplex tableau, note that we have drawn a line between the constraint rows and the objective function row. This distinguishes the objective function from the constraints. Also, note that the identity matrix columns of the constraint coefficients denote the basic variables of the tableau. These are shaded, and arrows indicate the values of the basic variables. Thus, for the above tableau, the basic variables are

Basic variables
$$s_1 = 850$$
$$s_2 = 1000$$
$$s_3 = 3600$$

The remaining variables are nonbasic, and, therefore, their solution values are zero. Hence,

Nonbasic variables
$$x_1 = 0$$
$$x_2 = 0$$

Also, note that the solution value for Z is given below the solution values for the basic variables. Hence, $Z = 0$ is the current value of the objective function for this basic feasible solution. Although Z is included in the solution, it is neither a basic nor a nonbasic variable; it is the objective function value that we seek to optimize.

We now consider some examples.

• **EXAMPLE 7-1**

Consider the following linear programming problem.

$$\text{Maximize } Z = 3x_1 + 5x_2 + 2x_3$$
$$\text{subject to } x_1 + x_2 + 2x_3 \leq 440$$
$$x_1 + 4x_3 \leq 420$$
$$3x_1 + 2x_2 \leq 480$$
$$\text{where } x_1, x_2, \text{ and } x_3 \geq 0$$

a) Prepare this problem for solution by the simplex method.
b) Write the simplex tableau.
c) State the basic feasible solution and the current value of the objective function.

Solutions

a) We include slack variables s_1, s_2, and s_3 and rewrite the objective function so that all terms are on its left-hand side. Also, we write the objective function below the constraints. Hence,

$$
\begin{aligned}
x_1 + x_2 + 2x_3 + s_1 &= 440 \\
x_1 \quad\quad + 4x_3 \quad\quad + s_2 &= 420 \\
3x_1 + 2x_2 \quad\quad\quad\quad + s_3 &= 480 \\
-3x_1 - 5x_2 - 2x_3 \quad\quad\quad\quad\quad + Z &= 0 \quad \longleftarrow \text{Objective function}
\end{aligned}
$$

b) The corresponding simplex tableau is given below.

$$
\begin{array}{ccccccc}
x_1 & x_2 & x_3 & s_1 & s_2 & s_3 & Z \\
\end{array}
$$

$$
\left[
\begin{array}{ccccccc|c}
1 & 1 & 2 & 1 & 0 & 0 & 0 & 440 \\
1 & 0 & 4 & 0 & 1 & 0 & 0 & 420 \\
3 & 2 & 0 & 0 & 0 & 1 & 0 & 480 \\
\hline
-3 & -5 & -2 & 0 & 0 & 0 & 1 & 0
\end{array}
\right]
\begin{array}{l}
\\ \\ \\ \text{Objective} \\ \text{function} \\ \text{value}
\end{array}
$$

c) The basic feasible solution and the current value of the objective function are given below.

Basic Feasible Solution

$$
\underbrace{x_1 = 0, \quad x_2 = 0, \quad x_3 = 0,}_{\text{Nonbasic variables}} \quad \underbrace{s_1 = 440, \quad s_2 = 420, \quad s_3 = 480,}_{\text{Basic variables, or basis}} \quad \underbrace{Z = 0}_{\substack{\text{Objective} \\ \text{function value}}}
$$

• EXAMPLE 7-2

The following is a simplex tableau for some maximization linear programming problem.

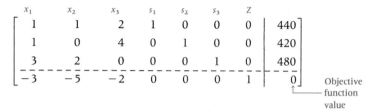

$$
\begin{array}{cccccccc}
x_1 & x_2 & x_3 & s_1 & s_2 & s_3 & s_4 & Z \\
\end{array}
$$

$$
\left[
\begin{array}{cccccccc|c}
2 & 1 & -1 & 0 & 0 & -5 & 0 & 0 & 45 \\
-5 & 0 & 0 & 0 & 1 & 9 & 0 & 0 & 30 \\
3 & 0 & 0 & 1 & 0 & 5 & 0 & 0 & 80 \\
-1 & 0 & 0 & 0 & 0 & 2 & 1 & 0 & 60 \\
\hline
-28 & 0 & 5 & 0 & 0 & 9 & 0 & 1 & 7890
\end{array}
\right]
$$

State the basic feasible solution and the current value of the objective function.

Solution

Remember that the identity matrix columns of the constraint coefficients identify the basic variables. These are shaded in the tableau, and arrows indicate the values of the basic variables. Hence,

Basic Feasible Solution

$$
\underbrace{x_1 = 0, \quad x_3 = 0, \quad s_3 = 0,}_{\text{Nonbasic variables}} \quad \underbrace{x_2 = 45, \quad s_1 = 80, \quad s_2 = 30, \quad s_4 = 60,}_{\text{Basic variables, or basis}} \quad \underbrace{Z = 7890}_{\substack{\text{Objective} \\ \text{function} \\ \text{value}}}
$$

• EXAMPLE 7-3

The following tableau was derived from that of the previous example by applying the simplex method.

x_1	x_2	x_3	s_1	s_2	s_3	s_4	Z	
1	1/2	−1/2	0	0	−5/2	0	0	22.5
0	5/2	−5/2	0	1	−7/2	0	0	142.5
0	−3/2	3/2	1	0	25/2	0	0	12.5
0	1/2	−1/2	0	0	−1/2	1	0	82.5
0	14	−9	0	0	−61	0	1	8520

State the basic feasible solution and the current value of the objective function.

Solution

Remember that the identity matrix columns of the constraint coefficients identify the basic variables. These are shaded in the tableau, and arrows indicate the values of the basic variables. Hence,

Basic Feasible Solution

$$x_2 = 0,\, x_3 = 0,\, s_3 = 0, \quad x_1 = 22.5,\, s_1 = 12.5,\, s_2 = 142.5,\, s_4 = 82.5, \quad Z = 8520$$

Nonbasic variables • Basic variables, or basis • Objective function value

---

Exercises 7-1

For each of the following:
a)   Prepare the problem for solution by the simplex method.
b)   Write the simplex tableau.
c)   State the basic feasible solution and the current value of the objective function.

1.   Maximize $Z = 120x_1 + 60x_2$
     subject to $2x_1 + 3x_2 \leq 90$
     $\quad\quad\quad\quad 5x_1 + x_2 \leq 160$
     where x_1 and $x_2 \geq 0$

2.   Maximize $Z = 10x_1 + 30x_2$
     subject to $3x_1 + 6x_2 \leq 60$
     $\quad\quad\quad\quad 4x_1 + 4x_2 \leq 60$
     where x_1 and $x_2 \geq 0$

3.   Maximize $Z = 400x_1 + 500x_2$
     subject to $\quad x_1 + \quad x_2 \leq 100$
     $\quad\quad\quad\quad 60x_1 + 80x_2 \leq 6600$
     where x_1 and $x_2 \geq 0$

4.   Maximize $Z = 5x_1 + 6x_2 + 2x_3$
     subject to $2x_1 + 3x_2 + 5x_3 \leq 20$
     $\quad\quad\quad\quad 6x_1 + 2x_2 + 3x_3 \leq 50$
     $\quad\quad\quad\quad\ x_1 + 3x_2 + 4x_3 \leq 24$
     where $x_1, x_2,$ and $x_3 \geq 0$

5.   Maximize $Z = 20x_1 + 42x_2 + 56x_3$
     subject to $2x_1 + 3x_2 + \quad x_3 \leq 6$
     $\quad\quad\quad\quad 4x_1 + 2x_2 + 3x_3 \leq 12$
     $\quad\quad\quad\quad 4x_1 + 2x_2 + \quad x_3 \leq 8$
     where $x_1, x_2,$ and $x_3 \geq 0$

6.   Maximize
     $Z = 80x_1 + 10x_2 + 16x_3 + 12x_4$
     subject to
     $\quad\quad x_1 + x_2 + \quad x_3 + x_4 \leq 40$
     $\quad\quad 2x_1 + x_2 + 4x_3 + x_4 \leq 80$
     where $x_1, x_2, x_3,$ and $x_4 \geq 0$

Each of the following is a simplex tableau for some maximization linear programming problem. State the basic feasible solution and the current value of the objective function.

7.

x_1	x_2	x_3	s_1	s_2	s_3	Z	
0	−5	1	8	0	2	0	6
1	4	0	6	0	5	0	3
0	2	0	3	1	4	0	5
0	−5	0	4	0	2	1	5670

8.

x_1	x_2	x_3	s_1	s_2	s_3	Z	
3	0	6	1	5	0	0	80
4	1	5	0	7	0	0	90
3	0	2	0	8	1	0	70
5	0	−4	0	9	0	1	600

9.

x_1	x_2	x_3	s_1	s_2	s_3	Z	
1	6	0	6	4	5	0	75
0	4	1	7	3	2	0	60
0	9	0	−5	6	−1	1	50

10.

x_1	x_2	x_3	x_4	s_1	s_2	s_3	Z	
0	1	7	6	5	0	5	0	5
1	0	5	3	2	0	6	0	7
0	0	4	2	3	1	5	0	9
0	0	−3	9	−8	0	4	1	45

7-2 • SIMPLEX METHOD: MAXIMIZATION

Since we will use the illustrative problem of the previous section, we restate it here.

$$\text{Maximize } Z = 20x_1 + 24x_2$$
$$\text{subject to } \quad x_1 + 2x_2 \leq 850$$
$$2x_1 + 2x_2 \leq 1000$$
$$3x_1 + 9x_2 \leq 3600$$
$$\text{where } x_1 \text{ and } x_2 \geq 0$$

Recall that, in the previous section, we prepared this problem for solution by the simplex method. Specifically, this entailed

1. Rewriting the linear inequalities as linear equations by including slack variables.
2. Rewriting the objective function so that all terms are on its left-hand side and placing it below the constraints.

This resulted in the formulation below.

$$x_1 + 2x_2 + s_1 \qquad\qquad = 850$$
$$2x_1 + 2x_2 \qquad + s_2 \qquad\quad = 1000$$
$$3x_1 + 9x_2 \qquad\qquad + s_3 \qquad = 3600$$
$$-20x_1 - 24x_2 \qquad\qquad\qquad + Z = 0$$

which is written as the simplex tableau below.

$$
\begin{array}{cccccc}
x_1 & x_2 & s_1 & s_2 & s_3 & Z \\
\end{array}
$$

$$
\left[\begin{array}{cccccc|c}
1 & 2 & 1 & 0 & 0 & 0 & 850 \\
2 & 2 & 0 & 1 & 0 & 0 & 1000 \\
3 & 9 & 0 & 0 & 1 & 0 & 3600 \\
\hline
-20 & -24 & 0 & 0 & 0 & 1 & 0
\end{array}\right] \quad (1)
$$

$\leftarrow$ Objective function

Indicators

Recall that the *basic feasible solution* for this tableau is

$$x_1 = 0, x_2 = 0, \qquad s_1 = 850, \quad s_2 = 1000, s_3 = 3600, \qquad Z = 0$$

Nonbasic variables   Basic variables, or basis   Objective function value

Optimizing the Value of the Objective Function

We must now search for a basic feasible solution that improves the value of the objective function. This requires that we increase the value of each nonbasic variable, one at a time, and consider the resulting effects on the value of the objective function. Remember that the value of each nonbasic variable is zero, and, currently, x_1 and x_2 are the nonbasic variables. Thus, at this point, we need to answer the following question.

QUESTION

Which nonbasic variable should be increased in order to provide the largest increase in the value of the objective function, Z?

ANSWER

To answer this question, we analyze the last row, the objective function row, of our simplex tableau. Specifically, we must determine the effects of increases in x_1 and x_2, one at a time, on the value of Z. Remember that the objective function can be written as

$$Z = 20x_1 + 24x_2$$

Thus, if x_1 is increased by 1 unit, Z will increase by 20 units. Also, if x_2 is increased by 1 unit, Z will increase by 24 units. Therefore, increasing x_2 results in the largest per unit increase in Z. This analysis can be done directly from the simplex tableau by studying the coefficients of the last row, the objective function row. Specifically, the variable with the most negative coefficient is increased in order to provide the largest per unit increase in the value of Z. Thus, each coefficient in the last row, with the exception of the coefficient of Z, indicates the effect on the value of Z of a unit increase in the value of the corresponding variable. For this reason, the coefficients in the last row of any simplex tableau are called indicators and are labeled as such in (1).

We state the following criterion for choosing the variable to be increased.

Choosing the Variable to Be Increased

For a simplex tableau corresponding to a linear programming maximization problem, in order to improve the value of the objective function by the largest amount, we *increase the value of the variable with the most negative indicator.*

Note: In the event of ties, we arbitrarily choose either of the tied variables.

Therefore, as stated earlier in this discussion, we must increase x_2 in order to increase the value of Z by the largest amount. Specifically, for each unit increase in x_2, Z will increase by 24 units. In order to increase x_2, we rewrite our tableau so that x_2 is a basic variable. This means that the x_2 column of constraint coefficients becomes an identity matrix column. In other words, the entries of the x_2 column are changed to one of the following:

$$
\begin{array}{ccc}
1 & 0 & 0 \\
0 \ \text{or} \ 1 \ \text{or} \ 0 \\
0 & 0 & 1
\end{array}
$$

Row operations are used to accomplish the above. More will be said about this later. The column corresponding to the variable to be increased is called the **pivot column.** Thus, at this point in this example, the x_2 column is the pivot column. Now we must determine which entry in the x_2 column is to be changed to 1. Since we will have to make such a determination very often during the simplex method procedure, we state the above as a question in general context and then provide an explanation for the answer.

QUESTION

Once we have determined the variable to be increased, its column of coefficients is called the pivot column. We then ask the following: Which entry in the pivot column should be changed to 1?

ANSWER

To answer this question, we write the constraint equations

$$
\begin{aligned}
x_1 + 2x_2 + s_1 \qquad\qquad &= 850 \\
2x_1 + 2x_2 \qquad + s_2 \qquad &= 1000 \\
3x_1 + 9x_2 \qquad\qquad + s_3 &= 3600
\end{aligned}
$$

and solve for the current basic variables as follows:

$$s_1 = 850 - x_1 - 2x_2$$
$$s_2 = 1000 - 2x_1 - 2x_2 \qquad (2)$$
$$s_3 = 3600 - 3x_1 - 9x_2$$

Remember that x_1 and x_2 are both equal to zero since they are nonbasic variables. This means that if we replace x_1 and x_2 above with zeros, then $s_1 = 850$, $s_2 = 1000$, and $s_3 = 3600$. This conforms with our earlier statement of the current basic feasible solution. Now, since x_1 is zero and x_2 is to be increased, we delete the x_1 column in (2) to obtain

$$s_1 = 850 - 2x_2$$
$$s_2 = 1000 - 2x_2$$
$$s_3 = 3600 - 9x_2$$

We now analyze the above for a unit increase in x_2. Specifically, for each unit increase in x_2,

- The first equation indicates that s_1 will decrease by 2 units,
- The second equation indicates that s_2 will decrease by 2 units, and
- The third equation indicates that s_3 will decrease by 9 units.

We now determine by how many units x_2 can increase before s_1, s_2, or s_3 becomes negative. (Remember that x_1, x_2, s_1, s_2, and $s_3 \geq 0$.) Thus,

- For the equation $s_1 = 850 - 2x_2$, the quotient $850/2$, or 425, gives the amount by which x_2 can increase before s_1 becomes negative;
- For the equation $s_2 = 1000 - 2x_2$, the quotient $1000/2$, or 500, gives the amount by which x_2 can increase before s_2 becomes negative; and
- For the equation $s_3 = 3600 - 9x_2$, the quotient $3600/9$, or 400, gives the amount by which x_2 can increase before s_3 becomes negative.

Therefore, in order for s_1, s_2, and s_3 to remain non-negative, x_2 cannot be increased by more than the minimum quotient, 400, which was obtained from the third equation.

If we relate the above quotients to the simplex tableau, note that these quotients are obtained by dividing the right-hand-side values by the pivot column coefficients as shown below.

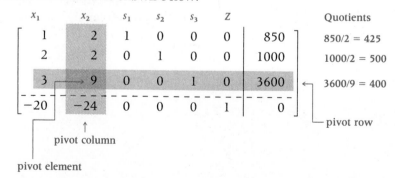

In general, such quotients are found only for the positive coefficients of the pivot column. This is because a negative coefficient allows the increasing variable to increase indefinitely. For any tableau, we never compute a quotient for the objective function row. The row corresponding to the *minimum quotient* is called the **pivot row.** It is in the pivot row that the pivot column coefficient must be changed to 1. This coefficient, *which is to be changed to 1*, is called the **pivot element.** For this example, the pivot element is 9, as we indicate in the above tableau.

We summarize as follows.

Choosing the Pivot Element

Once the variable to be increased is chosen, its column of coefficients is called the **pivot column.** To choose the pivot element,

1. For each positive pivot column coefficient, divide the corresponding right-hand-side value by the pivot column coefficient. Determine the *minimum such quotient. Note:* In the event of ties, arbitrarily choose either of the tied quotients.*
2. Locate the row corresponding to the *minimum quotient.* This is called the **pivot row.** Circle the pivot column coefficient in this row. This is called the **pivot element.** It is the pivot element that must be changed to 1 by a row operation. *Note:* This procedure ensures that the right-hand-side values (in other words, the solution values) are non-negative.

Returning to our illustrative example, we now use row operations to change the pivot element to 1 and the remaining pivot column coefficients to 0s. There are only two permissible row operations that we can use. These are stated in the following box.

Permissible Row Operations

1. Multiply a row by a nonzero constant.
2. Add a multiple of a row to another row.

Thus, to change the pivot element, 9, to 1, we multiply row 3 by 1/9 [i.e., $(1/9)R3 \to R3$] to obtain the equivalent tableau.

$$
\begin{array}{cccccc}
x_1 & x_2 & s_1 & s_2 & s_3 & Z \\
\end{array}
$$

$$
\left[
\begin{array}{cccccc|c}
1 & 2 & 1 & 0 & 0 & 0 & 850 \\
2 & 2 & 0 & 1 & 0 & 0 & 1000 \\
1/3 & 1 & 0 & 0 & 1/9 & 0 & 400 \\
\hline
-20 & -24 & 0 & 0 & 0 & 1 & 0 \\
\end{array}
\right]
$$

*This results in a degeneracy. Degeneracies will be explained on page 412.

Now we must change the remaining entries of the pivot column to 0s. This also includes the indicator, -24. We now state the row operations to accomplish this goal.

1. The indicator, -24, is changed to 0 by the following row operation:

24 times row 3, add the result to row 4,

or, in other words, $[(24)R3 + R4 \rightarrow R4]$

2. The 2 in row 2 is changed to 0 by the following row operation:

-2 times row 3, add the result to row 2,

or, in other words, $[(-2)R3 + R2 \rightarrow R2]$

3. The 2 in row 1 is changed to 0 by the following row operation:

-2 times row 3, add the result to row 1,

or, in other words, $[(-2)R3 + R1 \rightarrow R1]$

These result in the following equivalent tableau.

$$
\begin{array}{c}
\begin{array}{cccccc}
x_1 & x_2 & s_1 & s_2 & s_3 & Z
\end{array} \\
\left[
\begin{array}{cccccc|c}
1/3 & 0 & 1 & 0 & -2/9 & 0 & 50 \\
4/3 & 0 & 0 & 1 & -2/9 & 0 & 200 \\
\hline
1/3 & 1 & 0 & 0 & 1/9 & 0 & 400 \\
\hline
-12 & 0 & 0 & 0 & 24/9 & 1 & 9600
\end{array}
\right]
\end{array}
\qquad (3)
$$

 — negative indicator

In the above tableau, (3), note that x_1 has a negative indicator. This means that the current solution is not optimal, and, therefore, we must increase the variable with the most negative indicator. Thus, we must increase the value of x_1. However, before we do so, we state the following.

Optimality Criterion

For a maximization linear programming problem, a simplex tableau yields an *optimal solution* if there are *no negative indicators*. As long as a negative indicator exists, the value of the objective function can be increased by increasing the variable corresponding to a negative indicator. As stated earlier, if there is more than one negative indicator, *increase the variable corresponding to the most negative indicator.*

Since we must increase the value of x_1, its column is now the pivot column. To determine the pivot row, we divide each right-hand-side value by its corresponding pivot column coefficient. As stated earlier, we do this only for the positive entries of the pivot column. The row corresponding to the minimum such quotient is the pivot row, and the pivot column entry in the pivot row is the pivot element. These results are indicated in the following tableau.

	x_1	x_2	s_1	s_2	s_3	Z		Quotients
	1/3	0	1	0	−2/9	0	50	$50 \div \frac{1}{3} = 150$
	4/3	0	0	1	−2/9	0	200	$200 \div \frac{4}{3} = 150$
	1/3	1	0	0	1/9	0	400	$400 \div \frac{1}{3} = 1200$
	−12	0	0	0	24/9	1	9600	

⤒— pivot column

Note that two quotients are tied for the minimum. *Such a situation is called a **degeneracy** and will lead to one or more basic variables equaling zero in the next tableau.* In choosing the pivot row, we may choose either of the rows that correspond to the minimum quotients. In other words, the choice is arbitrary.

We choose row 2. Thus, the pivot element is 4/3 and must be changed to 1 by the following row operation:

Multiply row 2 by 3/4, or, in other words, [(3/4)R2 → R2]

This gives the following equivalent tableau.

	x_1	x_2	s_1	s_2	s_3	Z	
	1/3	0	1	0	−2/9	0	50
	1	0	0	3/4	−1/6	0	150
	1/3	1	0	0	1/9	0	400
	−12	0	0	0	24/9	1	9600

⤒— pivot column

We change the remaining pivot column entries to 0 by the following row operations:

1. The indicator, −12, is changed to 0 by the row operation:

12 times row 2, add the result to row 4,

or, in other words, [(12)R2 + R4 → R4]

2. The 1/3 in row 3 is changed to 0 by the row operation:

−1/3 times row 2, add the result to row 3,

or, in other words, [(−1/3)R2 + R3 → R3]

3. The 1/3 in row 1 is changed to 0 by the row operation;

−1/3 times row 2, add the result to row 1,

or, in other words, [(−1/3)R2 + R1 → R1]

These result in the following equivalent tableau.

$$
\begin{array}{c}
\begin{array}{cccccc}
x_1 & x_2 & s_1 & s_2 & s_3 & Z
\end{array} \\
\left[
\begin{array}{cccccc|c}
0 & 0 & 1 & -1/4 & -1/6 & 0 & 0 \\
1 & 0 & 0 & 3/4 & -1/6 & 0 & 150 \\
0 & 1 & 0 & -1/4 & 1/6 & 0 & 350 \\
\hline
0 & 0 & 0 & 9 & 2/3 & 1 & 11{,}400
\end{array}
\right]
\end{array}
\qquad (4)
$$

Since there are no negative indicators, this tableau yields an optimal solution and is therefore called an **optimal tableau.** Note that, as we mentioned earlier, one of the basic variables equals zero (i.e., $s_1 = 0$). Such a solution, where one or more basic variables equal zero, is called a *degenerate solution.* Sometimes a degeneracy is resolved in a subsequent tableau. In other words, a subsequent tableau no longer has a degenerate solution. Other times, as in this example, a degenerate solution remains in the optimal tableau. Such an optimal solution is called an **optimal degenerate solution.** We provide a summary of comments regarding degeneracies at the end of this section. It is intended to be used for reference purposes. At this point, we proceed with an analysis of the above optimal solution, which is stated below.

Optimal Solution

$$ s_2 = 0, \quad s_3 = 0, \qquad x_1 = 150, \quad x_2 = 350, \quad s_1 = 0, \qquad Z = 11{,}400 $$

Nonbasic variables   Basic variables, or basis   Objective function value

We now summarize the implications of the optimal solution for the original problem outlined in Table 7-1 of Section 7-1. We look at Table 7-1 as we present the following results.

IMPLICATIONS OF OPTIMAL SOLUTION

- $x_1 = 150$ units of product A should be produced.
- $x_2 = 350$ units of product B should be produced.
- $s_1 = 0$, $s_2 = 0$, and $s_3 = 0$ imply that, for the above optimal product mix, there is no slack in any of the constraints. As we learned in the previous chapter, such constraints are called binding constraints. Specifically, this means that all 850 pounds of raw material, all 1000 department 1 person-hours, and all 3600 department 2 person-hours are used to produce the optimal product mix of 150 units of product A and 350 units of product B.
- $Z = 11{,}400$ is the maximum profit (in dollars).

Comparison with Graphical Method

Figure 7-3 is a restatement of the feasible region and vertex points for the above problem. The arrows indicate the progression of the simplex method from vertex point $(0, 0)$ to $(0, 400)$ to $(150, 350)$, as is determined by looking at tableaus (1), (3), and (4).

The simplex method is summarized on pages 409-410. We suggest a review of this summary before proceeding to the next example.

Basic feasible solutions

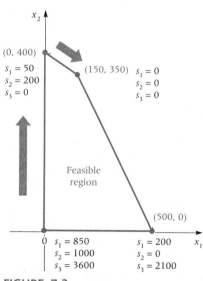

FIGURE 7-3

• EXAMPLE 7-4

Solve, by the simplex method, the following problem, where Z denotes the profit (in thousands of dollars) gained from producing x_1, x_2, and x_3 units of products A, B, and C, respectively. The right-hand-side value, 60, is a person-hour constraint; the right-hand-side value, 100, is a raw material constraint.

$$\text{Maximize } Z = 2x_1 + 5x_2 + 4x_3$$
$$\text{subject to} \quad x_1 + 3x_2 + 2x_3 \leq 60 \qquad \text{Person-hours}$$
$$4x_1 + 2x_2 + x_3 \leq 100 \qquad \text{Raw Material}$$
$$\text{where } x_1, x_2, \text{ and } x_3 \geq 0$$

Solution

Simplex Tableau.

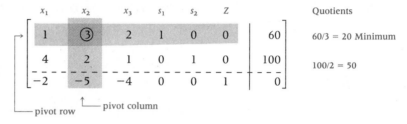

The pivot element is circled.

Row Operations. The following row operations, in the order of their listing, are used to change the above tableau into the equivalent tableau below.

$$[(1/3)R1 \to R1], \qquad [(-2)R1 + R2 \to R2], \qquad [(5)R1 + R3 \to R3]$$

	x_1	x_2	x_3	s_1	s_2	Z		Quotients
→	1/3	1	2/3	1/3	0	0	20	$20 \div \frac{2}{3} = 30$
	10/3	0	−1/3	−2/3	1	0	60	No quotient here due to negative pivot column entry, −1/3
	−1/3	0	−2/3	5/3	0	1	100	

pivot row — pivot column

Row Operations. The following row operations, in the order of their listing, are used to change the above tableau into the equivalent tableau below.

$$[(3/2)R1 \to R1], \qquad [(1/3)R1 + R2 \to R2], \qquad [(2/3)R1 + R3 \to R3]$$

	x_1	x_2	x_3	s_1	s_2	Z	
	1/2	3/2	1	1/2	0	0	30
	7/2	1/2	0	−1/2	1	0	70
	0	1	0	2	0	1	120

(5)

No negative indicators

Since there are no negative indicators, this tableau yields an optimal solution, which we list below.

Optimal Solution

$$\underbrace{x_1 = 0,\, x_2 = 0,\, s_1 = 0,}_{\text{Nonbasic variables}} \quad \underbrace{x_3 = 30,\, s_2 = 70}_{\text{Basic variables}} \quad \underbrace{Z = 120}_{\text{Objective function value}}$$

IMPLICATIONS OF OPTIMAL SOLUTION

- $x_1 = 0$ units of product A should be produced.
- $x_2 = 0$ units of product B should be produced.
- $x_3 = 30$ units of product C should be produced.
- $s_1 = 0$ units of slack in the person-hours constraint. This means that all of the available 60 person-hours are used to produce the optimal product mix.
- $s_2 = 70$ units of slack in the raw material constraint. This means that 70 of the available 100 units of raw material remain unused.
- $Z = 120$ is the maximum profit (in thousands of dollars).

Alternate Optimal Solutions

Studying the optimal tableau, (5), note the zero indicator corresponding to the nonbasic variable x_1. This implies that x_1 can be increased without increasing the objective function value. Thus, if we increase the value of x_1, we would obtain another solution with the same optimal objective function value. Such a solution is called an **alternate optimal solution.** We find this alternate optimal solution and investigate its implications in Example 7-5.

> ### Alternate Optimal Solutions
>
> If, in an optimal tableau, a *nonbasic variable has a zero indicator,* then an alternate optimal solution exists that is determined by increasing the variable with the zero indicator.

• **EXAMPLE 7-5** ──────────────────────────────

Return to the optimal tableau of Example 7-4.

a) Determine the alternate optimal solution by increasing the value of x_1.
b) Investigate the implications of the alternate optimal solution.

Solution

a) The optimal tableau from Example 7-4 is restated. The quotients, along with the pivot column and row, are given.

	x_1	x_2	x_3	s_1	s_2	Z		Quotients
	1/2	3/2	1	1/2	0	0	30	$30 \div \frac{1}{2} = 60$
→	7/2	1/2	0	−1/2	1	0	70	$70 \div \frac{7}{2} = 20$ Minimum
	0	1	0	2	0	1	120	

pivot row ↑ pivot column

The pivot element is circled.

Row Operations. The following row operations, in the order of their listing, are used to change the above tableau into the following equivalent tableau.

$$[(2/7)R2 \rightarrow R2], \qquad [(-1/2)R2 + R1 \rightarrow R1]$$

$$
\begin{array}{cccccc|c}
x_1 & x_2 & x_3 & s_1 & s_2 & Z & \\
0 & 10/7 & 1 & 4/7 & -1/7 & 0 & 20 \\
1 & 1/7 & 0 & -1/7 & 2/7 & 0 & 20 \\
\hline
0 & 1 & 0 & 2 & 0 & 1 & 120
\end{array}
$$

Optimal Solution

$$\underbrace{x_2 = 0,\ s_1 = 0,\ s_2 = 0,}_{\text{Nonbasic variables}} \quad \underbrace{x_1 = 20,\ x_3 = 20,}_{\text{Basic variables, or basis}} \quad \underbrace{Z = 120}_{\text{Objective function value}}$$

b)   IMPLICATIONS OF OPTIMAL SOLUTION

- $x_1 = 20$ units of product A should be produced.
- $x_2 = 0$ units of product B should be produced.
- $x_3 = 20$ units of product C should be produced.
- $s_1 = 0$ units of slack in the person-hours constraint.
- $s_2 = 0$ units of slack in the raw material constraint.
- $Z = 120$ is the maximum profit (in thousands of dollars).

Note that all available resouces (person-hours and raw materials) are used to produce the optimal product mix. This is in contrast to the optimal solution of Example 7-4, where 70 units of raw material remained unused. Also, as indicated earlier, the maximum profit is the same for both solutions.

SUMMARY

Simplex Method: Problems in Standard Maximization Form

Simplex Tableau. Rewrite the linear inequalities as linear equations by including slack variables. Rewrite the *objective function below the constraints* so that all terms are on its left-hand side. Write the simplex tableau corresponding to this linear system.

Choose the Variable to Be Increased (Pivot Column). The last row of a simplex tableau contains indicators. Increase the value of the variable with the *most negative indicator*.

    Note: In the event of ties, arbitrarily choose either of the tied variables.

Choose the Pivot Element (Row). Once the variable to be increased is chosen, its column of coefficients is the pivot column. To choose the pivot element,

1. For each positive pivot column coefficient, divide the corresponding right-hand-side value by the pivot column coefficient. Determine the *minimum such quotient. Note:* In the event of ties, arbitrarily choose either of the tied quotients.
2. Locate the row corresponding to the minimum quotient. This is called the pivot row. Circle the pivot column coefficient in this row. This is called the pivot element. It is the *pivot element* that *must be changed to 1* by a row operation.

    Note: This procedure ensures that the right-hand-side values (in other words, the solution values) are non-negative.

continues

> **SUMMARY**—*Continued*
>
> **Row Operations.** Use the following permissible row operations to change the pivot element to 1 and the remaining pivot column coefficients, including the objective function coefficient, to Os:
> 3. Multiply a row by a nonzero constant.
> 4. Add a multiple of a row to another row.
>
> **Apply the Optimality Criterion.** Check the indicators of the new tableau for negative values.
> 5. If there are *no negative indicators*, then the most recent tableau yields an *optimal solution*. State the optimal solution, and investigate its implications for the problem.
> 6. If there are negative indicators, then return to the step entitled "Choose the Variable to Be Increased (Pivot Column)" and repeat the subsequent steps until there are no negative indicators.

• **EXAMPLE 7-6   Campaign Spending: Media Selection.** ——

The state chairman of a political party must allocate an advertising budget of $3,000,000 among three media: radio, television, and newspaper. The expected number of votes gained per dollar spent on each advertising medium is given below.

Expected votes per dollar spent

Radio	Television	Newspaper
3	5	2

Since these data are valid within limited amounts spent on each medium, the chairman has imposed the following restrictions:

- No more than $500,000 may be spent on television ads.
- No more than $1,200,000 may be spent on radio ads.
- No more than $2,400,000 may be spent on television and newpaper ads combined.

How much should be spent on each medium in order to maximize the expected number of votes gained?

Solution

If x_1, x_2, and x_3 denote the number of dollars spent on radio, television, and newspaper advertising, respectively, then the formulated problem is given as follows.

$$\text{Maximize } Z = 3x_1 + 5x_2 + 2x_3 \qquad \text{Expected Number of Votes}$$

$$\begin{aligned}
\text{subject to} \quad & x_1 + x_2 + x_3 \le 3{,}000{,}000 && \text{Budget Constraint} \\
& x_1 \qquad\qquad\quad \le \quad 500{,}000 && \text{Television Constraint} \\
& \qquad x_2 \qquad\quad \le 1{,}200{,}000 && \text{Radio Constraint} \\
& \qquad x_2 + x_3 \le 2{,}400{,}000 && \text{Combined Television and} \\
& && \text{Newspaper Constraint}
\end{aligned}$$

where x_1, x_2, and $x_3 \ge 0$.

Simplex Tableau.

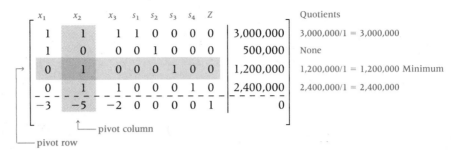

x_1	x_2	x_3	s_1	s_2	s_3	s_4	Z		Quotients
1	1	1	1	0	0	0	0	3,000,000	3,000,000/1 = 3,000,000
1	0	0	0	1	0	0	0	500,000	None
0	1	0	0	0	1	0	0	1,200,000	1,200,000/1 = 1,200,000 Minimum
0	1	1	0	0	0	1	0	2,400,000	2,400,000/1 = 2,400,000
−3	−5	−2	0	0	0	0	1	0	

↑—— pivot column
—— pivot row

Row Operations. The following row operations, in the order of their listing, are used to change the above tableau into the following equivalent tableau.

$$[((-1)R3 + R1 \rightarrow R1], \qquad [(-1)R3 + R4 \rightarrow R4], \qquad [(5)R3 + R5 \rightarrow R5]$$

x_1	x_2	x_3	s_1	s_2	s_3	s_4	Z		Quotients
1	0	1	1	0	−1	0	0	1,800,000	1,800,000/1 = 1,800,000
1	0	0	0	1	0	0	0	500,000	500,000/1 = 500,000 Minimum
0	1	0	0	0	1	0	0	1,200,000	None
0	0	1	0	0	−1	1	0	1,200,000	None
−3	0	−2	0	0	5	0	1	6,000,000	

↑—— pivot column
—— pivot row

Row Operations. The following row operations, in the order of their listing, are used to change the above tableau into the following equivalent tableau.

$$[(-1)R2 + R1 \rightarrow R1], \qquad [(3)R2 + R5 \rightarrow R5]$$

x_1	x_2	x_3	s_1	s_2	s_3	s_4	Z		Quotients
0	0	1	1	−1	−1	0	0	1,300,000	1,300,000/1 = 1,300,000
1	0	0	0	1	0	0	0	500,000	None
0	1	0	0	0	1	0	0	1,200,000	None
0	0	1	0	0	−1	1	0	1,200,000	1,200,000/1 = 1,200,000 Minimum
0	0	−2	0	3	5	0	1	7,500,000	

↑—— pivot column
—— pivot row

Row Operations. The following row operations, in the order of their listing, are used to change the above tableau into the following equivalent tableau.

$$[(-1)R4 + R1 \rightarrow R1], \qquad [(2)R4 + R5 \rightarrow R5]$$

x_1	x_2	x_3	s_1	s_2	s_3	s_4	Z	
0	0	0	1	−1	0	−1	0	100,000
1	0	0	0	1	0	0	0	500,000
0	1	0	0	0	1	0	0	1,200,000
0	0	1	0	0	−1	1	0	1,200,000
0	0	0	0	3	3	2	1	9,900,000

No negative indicators

Since there are no negative indicators, this tableau yields an optimal solution, which we list below.

Optimal Solution

$$\underbrace{s_2 = 0, \quad s_3 = 0, \quad s_4 = 0,}_{\text{Nonbasic variables}} \quad \underbrace{\begin{aligned} x_1 &= 500{,}000, \quad x_2 = 1{,}200{,}000, \\ x_3 &= 1{,}200{,}000, \quad s_1 = 100{,}000, \end{aligned}}_{\text{Basic variables}} \quad \underbrace{Z = 9{,}900{,}000}_{\substack{\text{Objective} \\ \text{function value}}}$$

IMPLICATIONS OF OPTIMAL SOLUTION

- $x_1 = \$500{,}000$ should be spent on radio ads.
- $x_2 = \$1{,}200{,}000$ should be spent on television ads.
- $x_3 = \$1{,}200{,}000$ should be spent on newspaper ads.
- $s_1 = \$100{,}000$ slack in the budget constraint. This means that $100,000 of the $3,000,000 budgeted for advertising remains unused.
- $s_2 = \$0$ slack in the television constraint.
- $s_3 = \$0$ slack in the radio constraint.
- $s_4 = \$0$ slack in the combined television and newspaper constraint.
- $Z = 9{,}900{,}000$ is the maximum expected number of votes gained.

SUMMARY

Degeneracy

1. A degeneracy occurs when, for some tableau, one or more of the basic variables are zero. Such a solution is called a **degenerate solution.**

   - This arises when two or more quotients are tied for a pivot row choice. In such a situation, arbitrarily choose a pivot row from the tied contestants.
   - This may result in a subsequent tableau where the objective function value does not improve from that of a previous tableau.

2. A degeneracy may or may not be resolved in a later tableau. When a degeneracy is in the optimal tableau, the solution is called an **optimal degenerate solution.**

3. A degeneracy may result in subsequent tableaus that enter a loop and repeat sequentially without ever reaching an optimal solution. Such a condition is called *cycling* or *circling*. Procedures are available for dealing with this condition. However, this condition is rare and will not be pursued.

4. Graphically, degeneracies usually occur when more than two constraint lines pass through an individual vertex point, with a redundancy occurring. (A constraint is redundant if its removal does not change the feasible region.) This is illustrated in Figure 7-1, where the vertex point (150, 350) has three constraint lines passing through it.

Exercises 7-2

1. On page 402, the following equations and quotients were given:

Equations	Quotients
$s_1 = 850 - 2x_2$	$850/2 = 425$
$s_2 = 1000 - 2x_2$	$1000/2 = 500$
$s_3 = 3600 - 9x_2$	$3600/9 = 400$

It was stated that in order for s_1, s_2, and s_3 to remain non-negative, x_2 cannot increase by more than the minimum quotient, 400. Verify this statement by substituting each of the above quotients into the equations for s_1, s_2, and s_3. Note which quotient results in non-negative solution values for all three variables, s_1, s_2, and s_3.

2. Given the following constraint equations for some linear programming problem:

$$2x_1 + 3x_2 + x_3 + s_1 \qquad\qquad = 240$$
$$-4x_1 + 5x_2 + 2x_3 \qquad + s_2 \qquad = 400$$
$$6x_1 + x_2 + 5x_3 \qquad\qquad + s_3 = 600$$

where x_1, x_2, x_3, s_1, s_2, and $s_3 \geq 0$ and s_1, s_2, and s_3 are slack variables.
a) If x_1, x_2, and x_3 each equal zero, state the values of s_1, s_2, and s_3.
b) If x_1 and x_2 remain equal to zero, determine for each equation the maximum amount by which x_3 can increase before the corresponding slack variable becomes negative. (*Hint:* Delete x_1 and x_2 from the linear system, and solve the resulting equations for s_1, s_2, and s_3.)
c) Substitute the results of part b into the equations for s_1, s_2, and s_3, and state the substitution that results in non-negative values for all three variables s_1, s_2, and s_3.

3. Consider the constraint equations of Exercise 2.
a) If x_2 and x_3 each equal zero, determine for each equation the maximum amount by which x_1 can increase before the corresponding slack variable becomes negative. (*Hint:* Delete x_2 and x_3 from the linear system, and solve the resulting equations for s_1, s_2, and s_3.) *Note:* For the second equation, since the coefficient of x_1 is negative, x_1 can increase indefinitely without s_2 becoming negative.
b) Substitute the results of part a into the equations for s_1, s_2, and s_3, and state the substitution that results in non-negative values for all three variables, s_1, s_2, and s_3.

Solve Exercises 4–16 by the simplex method.

4. Maximize $Z = 120x_1 + 60x_2$
subject to $2x_1 + 3x_2 \leq 90$
$\qquad\qquad 4x_1 + x_2 \leq 160$
where x_1 and $x_2 \geq 0$

5. Maximize $Z = 10x_1 + 30x_2$
subject to $3x_1 + 6x_2 \leq 60$
$\qquad\qquad 4x_1 + 4x_2 \leq 60$
where x_1 and $x_2 \geq 0$

6. Maximize $Z = 400x_1 + 500x_2$
subject to $x_1 + x_2 \leq 100$
$\qquad\qquad 60x_1 + 80x_2 \leq 6600$
where x_1 and $x_2 \geq 0$

7. Maximize $Z = 5x_1 + 6x_2 + x_3$
subject to $2x_1 + 3x_2 + 5x_3 \leq 30$
$\qquad\qquad 6x_1 + 2x_2 + 3x_3 \leq 14$
$\qquad\qquad x_1 + 3x_2 + 4x_3 \leq 24$
where x_1, x_2, and $x_3 \geq 0$

8. Maximize $Z = 20x_1 + 42x_2 + 56x_3$
subject to $2x_1 + 3x_2 + x_3 \le 6$
$4x_1 + 2x_2 + 4x_3 \le 12$
$4x_1 + 2x_2 + x_3 \le 8$
where $x_1, x_2,$ and $x_3 \ge 0$

9. Maximize
$Z = 80x_1 + 10x_2 + 16x_3 + 12x_4$
subject to
$x_1 + x_2 + x_3 + x_4 \le 40$
$2x_1 + x_2 + 4x_3 + x_4 \le 90$
where $x_1, x_2, x_3,$ and $x_4 \ge 0$

10. Maximize $Z = 60x_1 - 30x_2 + 40x_3$
subject to $x_1 + x_2 + x_3 \le 90$
$2x_1 + 4x_2 + 2x_3 \le 120$
$3x_1 + 2x_2 + 5x_3 \le 190$
where $x_1, x_2,$ and $x_3 \ge 0$

11. Maximize $Z = 5x_1 + 8x_2 - 9x_3$
subject to $4x_1 + 2x_2 + 6x_3 \le 60$
$2x_1 + 2x_2 + 4x_3 \le 120$
$x_1 + 2x_2 + 3x_3 \le 90$
where $x_1, x_2,$ and $x_3 \ge 0$

12. Maximize $Z = 3x_1 + 4x_2 + 6x_3$
subject to $x_1 + x_2 + x_3 \le 140$
$2x_1 + x_2 + 9x_3 \le 270$
where $x_1, x_2,$ and $x_3 \ge 0$.

13. Maximize $Z = 8x_1 + 5x_2 + 2x_3$
subject to $x_1 + 2x_2 + x_3 \le 50$
$2x_1 + 4x_2 + 2x_3 \le 120$
$x_1 \le 20$
where $x_1, x_2,$ and $x_3 \ge 0$

14. Maximize $Z = 6x_1 + 8x_2 + 9x_3$
subject to $x_1 + x_2 + x_3 \le 120$
$6x_1 + 3x_2 + 3x_3 \le 240$
$x_3 \le 50$
where $x_1, x_2,$ and $x_3 \ge 0$

15. Maximize $Z = 5x_1 + 3x_2 + x_3$
subject to $x_1 + x_2 + x_3 \le 150$
$x_1 \le 30$
$x_2 \le 40$
$x_3 \le 60$
where $x_1, x_2,$ and $x_3 \ge 0$

16. Maximize $Z = 5x_1 + 9x_2 + 2x_3$
subject to $2x_1 + x_2 + 2x_3 \le 80$
$x_1 + x_2 + x_3 \le 100$
$x_1 \le 30$
$x_2 \le 50$
where $x_1, x_2,$ and $x_3 \ge 0$

Alternate Optimal Solutions

For Exercises 17 and 18:
a) Solve by the simplex method.
b) State the nonbasic variable that has a zero indicator in the optimal tableau.
c) Determine the alternate optimal solution by increasing the value of the nonbasic variable determined in part b.
d) Investigate the implications of the alternate optimal solution.

17. Maximize $Z = 3x_1 + 4x_2 + 5x_3$
subject to
$x_1 + x_2 + x_3 \le 100$
$5x_1 + 8x_2 \le 180$
$x_1 + 10x_3 \le 50$
where $x_1, x_2,$ and $x_3 \ge 0$

18. Maximize $Z = 2x_1 + 4x_2 + 6x_3$
subject to
$x_1 + x_2 + x_3 \le 200$
$3x_1 + 2x_2 \le 150$
$-2x_1 + 3x_3 \le 140$
where $x_1, x_2,$ and $x_3 \ge 0$

Graphical Approach and the Simplex Method

19. Solve

$$\text{Maximize } Z = 10x_1 + 15x_2$$
$$\text{subject to } 2x_1 + 4x_2 \le 100$$
$$x_1 + 3x_2 \le 90$$
$$x_1 \le 80$$
$$x_2 \le 40$$
$$\text{where } x_1 \text{ and } x_2 \ge 0$$

by the graphical method and then the simplex method. For the basic feasible solution of each simplex tableau, state the corresponding vertex point from the graph of the feasible region. Finally, from the graph of the feasible region, trace the path from the vertex point corresponding to the first simplex tableau to those of successive tableaus to that of the optimal tableau.

20. Solve

$$\text{Maximize } Z = 400x_1 + 500x_2$$

$$\text{subject to} \quad 3x_1 + 5x_2 \leq 55$$
$$x_1 + 5x_2 \leq 45$$
$$x_1 \leq 10$$
$$x_2 \leq 9$$

$$\text{where } x_1 \text{ and } x_2 \geq 0$$

by the graphical method and then the simplex method. For the basic feasible solution of each simplex tableau, state the corresponding vertex point from the graph of the feasible region. Finally, from the graph of the feasible region, trace the path from the vertex point corresponding to the first simplex tableau to those of successive tableaus to that of the optimal tableau.

Note:

- The second tableau contains a *degeneracy* that is resolved prior to the optimal tableau.
- The vertex point $(0, 9)$ has more than two constraint lines passing through it, with the constraint $x_2 \leq 9$ being redundant. This is the reason for the occurrence of the degeneracy.

Applications

For Exercises 21-32, formulate as a linear programming problem. Then solve by the simplex method and investigate the implications of the optimal solution.

21. *Product mix.* A firm produces products A, B, and C, each of which passes through the assembly and inspection departments. The number of person-hours required by a unit of each product in each department is given in the following table.

Person-hours per unit of product

	Product A	Product B	Product C
Assembly	2	4	2
Inspection	3	2	1

During a given week, the assembly and inspection departments have available at most 1500 and 1200 person-hours, respectively. If the unit profits for products A, B, and C are $50, $40, and $60, respectively, determine the number of units of each product that should be produced in order to maximize the total profit and satisfy the constraints of the problem.

22. *Product mix.* Repeat Exercise 21 under the additional constraint that there must be no more than 500 units of product C produced.

23. *Investment: Portfolio allocation.* An investor has at most $2,000,000 to be allocated for investment in stocks, bonds, and money market funds. The projected annual rate of return for each investment vehicle is given below.

Projected annual rate of return

Stocks	Bonds	Money market funds
10%	8%	6%

The investor wants no more than $1,000,000 invested among a combination of stocks and bonds. Also, no more than $1,200,000 is to be invested among a combination of bonds and money market funds. How much should be invested in each of the above categories in order to maximize the total projected annual return?

24. *Investment: Portfolio allocation.* Repeat Exercise 23 under the additional constraint that the amount invested in stocks must not exceed $600,000.

25. *Transportation.* A company must transport its product from two plants to two retail outlets. The unit costs of this product differ for each plant and are given in the following table. Also, the unit selling prices of this product differ for each retail outlet, as given in the following table.

	Retail outlet 1	Retail outlet 2
Unit selling price	$15	$18
Plant 1		
Unit cost: $10	x_1	x_2
Plant 2		
Unit cost: $12	x_3	x_4

Plants 1 and 2 have at most 1000 and 1800 units, respectively, available for shipping to the retail outlets. Due to limited demand, retail outlets 1 and 2 are to receive no more than 1200 and 2000 units, respectively. If, as indicated in the above table,

x_1 = number of units shipped from plant 1 to retail outlet 1

x_2 = number of units shipped from plant 1 to retail outlet 2

x_3 = number of units shipped from plant 2 to retail outlet 1

x_4 = number of units shipped from plant 2 to retail outlet 2

determine the values of x_1, x_2, x_3, and x_4 that maximize the total profit gained from the product shipped.

26. *Agriculture: Crop allocation.* A farmer has 1000 acres to be allocated among three crops. The number of person-hours per acre required for each crop and its profit per acre are given in the following table.

Person-hours per acre

Crop A	Crop B	Crop C
3	5	4

Profit per acre

Crop A	Crop B	Crop C
$600	$300	$500

If the farmer has at most 6000 person-hours available, determine the number of acres of each crop that should be planted in order to maximize the total profit.

27. *Agriculture: Crop allocation.* Repeat Exercise 26 under the addtional constraints that there should be no more than 500 and 300 acres of crops A and C, respectively.

28. *Nutrition.* A nutrition counselor must determine how many units of each of three food types to include in a diet so that the protein intake is maximized for a particular patient. The following table gives the amounts of relevant nutrients contained per unit of each type food.

Milligrams per unit of food type

	Food A	Food B	Food C
Protein	4	6	5
Iron	6	9	7
Calcium	5	3	2

Also, the amount of calories for each food is given below.

Calories per unit of food type

	Food A	Food B	Food C
Calories	500	1000	300

If the diet is to include at most 300 milligrams of iron, at most 40 milligrams of calcium, and at most 2000 calories, determine the number of units of each type of food that should be given to the person in order to maximize the protein intake.

29. *Marketing strategy.* A company markets one of its products through two retail outlets and one wholesale outlet. The unit profits differ at each outlet and are given below.

Unit profit

Retail outlet 1	Retail outlet 2	Wholesale outlet
$400	$350	$300

The marketing effort in person-hours per unit required for each outlet is given below.

Marketing effort in person-hours per unit

Retail outlet 1	Retail outlet 2	Wholesale outlet
1.5	1	0.5

The company's limited sales force allows for a total marketing effort of at most 8000 person-hours. Production plans call for at most 10,000 units of this product to be produced. How many units of this product should be marketed through each outlet in order to maximize the total profit and satisfy all problem constraints?

30. *Marketing strategy.* Repeat Exercise 29 under the additional constraint that no more than 5000 units will be marketed through the wholesale outlet.

31. *Election polling.* A polling firm can hire professional and semiprofessional pollsters for election-day polling at two locations. The total cost per pollster for the entire day at each location is given below.

Cost per pollster per day

	Professional	Semiprofessional
Location 1	$500	$200
Location 2	500	200

The number of voters surveyed per day for each type of pollster at each location is given below.

Number of voters surveyed per day

	Professional	Semiprofessional
Location 1	100	60
Location 2	100	60

If the polling firm has $3000 budgeted for location 1 and $5000 budgeted for location 2 on election day, then determine how many professional and semiprofessional pollsters should be hired at each location in order to maximize the total number of voters surveyed subject to the budgetary constraints.

32. *Election polling.* Repeat Exercise 31 under the additional constraint that there are at most 20 semiprofessional pollsters available.

7-3 • MINIMIZATION; THE DUAL; SHADOW PRICES

In this section, we will consider linear programming minimization problems where

1. The objective function is to be minimized and is of the linear form

$$Z = c_1x_1 + c_2x_2 + \ldots + c_nx_n$$

2. All constraints are linear inequalities of the $\geq$ type. In other words, they are of the form

$$a_1x_1 + a_2x_2 + \ldots + a_nx_n \geq b$$

3. All variables are non-negative (i.e., $x_i \geq 0$).

As a typical example, we consider an agricultural problem, formulated below, where Z denotes the total cost of using a daily feed mix consisting of x_1 and x_2 pounds of feed A and feed B, respectively. Here, the per pound costs of feeds A and B are $4 and $9, respectively. The farmer must determine the optimal feed mix such that minimal nutritional requirements as given by the two constraints are satisfied. Thus, the farmer must determine the number of pounds of feeds A and B that should be used in order to minimize the total cost and ensure that at least 200 units of nutrient 1 and at least 750 units of nutrient 2 are derived from the feed mix.

The formulation is given below.

Minimize $Z = 4x_1 + 9x_2$ Total cost

subject to $x_1 + 2x_2 \geq 200$ Nutrient 1 (minimal requirement)

$2x_1 + 6x_2 \geq 750$ Nutrient 2 (minimal requirement)

where x_1 and $x_2 \geq 0$

Such linear programming minimization problems can be solved directly by the simplex method. However, the $\geq$ constraints cause complications that result in unwieldy computations when performed without a computer. In this section, we show how the optimal solution to a minimization problem is determined by solving a companion problem associated with the minimization problem. The companion problem is called the **dual** of the minimization problem. The original problem is called the **primal.** We now show how to find the dual.

Dual

The dual of a minimization problem with $\geq$ constraints is a maximization problem with $\leq$ constraints. The variables of the dual problem are called **dual variables** and will be denoted by $y_1, y_2, \ldots$, etc., whereas the variables of the original (or primal) problem are denoted by $x_1, x_2, \ldots$, etc.

Using the above problem as our illustrative example, we begin to find its dual by first placing the objective function below the constraints and then writing the corresponding matrix, as shown below on the right.

Original (Primal) Problem

$$
\begin{aligned}
x_1 + 2x_2 &\geq 200 \\
2x_1 + 6x_2 &\geq 750 \\
4x_1 + 9x_2 &= Z
\end{aligned}
\qquad
\begin{array}{cc}
^{x_1} & ^{x_2} \\
\left[\begin{array}{cc|c}
1 & 2 & 200 \\
2 & 6 & 750 \\
\hline
4 & 9 & Z
\end{array}\right]
\end{array}
$$

To find the dual of the above problem, we assign a dual variable to each primal constraint, insert the $\leq$ symbol above each objective function coefficient, and read the matrix vertically, as illustrated below.

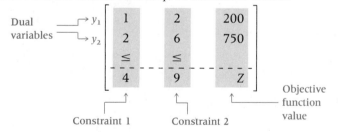

The associated *dual* problem is

$$
\begin{aligned}
y_1 + 2y_2 &\leq 4 \quad &&\text{Constraint 1} \\
2y_1 + 6y_2 &\leq 9 \quad &&\text{Constraint 2} \\
200y_1 + 750y_2 &= Z \quad &&\text{Objective Function}
\end{aligned}
$$

Note the following relationships between the primal and the dual. Specifically, the first column of the primal matrix becomes the first row of the dual, the second column of the primal matrix becomes the second row of the dual, and so on until the right-hand-side values of the primal become the dual objective function coefficients.

We state the dual problem so that its objective function is written before the constraints.

Dual

$$\text{Maximize } Z = 200y_1 + 750y_2$$
$$\text{subject to } \quad y_1 + 2y_2 \leq 4$$
$$2y_1 + 6y_2 \leq 9$$
$$\text{where } y_1 \text{ and } y_2 \geq 0$$

We summarize as follows.

To Find the Dual

Given a minimization (primal) problem with $\geq$ constraints:

1. Place the objective function below the constraints, and write the corresponding matrix.
2. Assign a dual variable to each primal constraint, and read the matrix vertically so that column 1 of the primal becomes row 1 of the dual, column 2 of the primal becomes row 2 of the dual, and so on until the right-hand-side values of the primal become the dual objective function coefficients.
3. For the dual, the objective function is to be maximized, and all constraints are of the $\leq$ type.
   Note: The dual of a maximization problem with $\leq$ constraints is a minimization problem with $\geq$ constraints. Also, the dual of a dual equals the primal.

• **EXAMPLE 7-7** ─────────────────────────────

Find the dual of the problem

$$\text{Minimize } Z = 5x_1 + 6x_2 + 2x_3$$
$$\text{subject to } 4x_1 + 5x_2 + 3x_3 \geq 80$$
$$x_1 + 2x_2 + 7x_3 \geq 60$$
$$\text{where } x_1, x_2, \text{ and } x_3 \geq 0$$

Solution

Step 1

	Primal			*Matrix*		

$$
\begin{array}{l}
4x_1 + 5x_2 + 3x_3 \geq 80 \\
x_1 + 2x_2 + 7x_3 \geq 60 \\
5x_1 + 6x_2 + 2x_3 = Z
\end{array}
\qquad
\left[\begin{array}{ccc|c}
4 & 5 & 3 & 80 \\
1 & 2 & 7 & 60 \\
\hline
5 & 6 & 2 & Z
\end{array}\right]
$$

Step 2

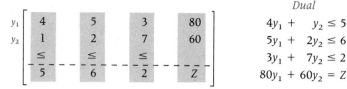

$$y_1 \begin{bmatrix} 4 & 5 & 3 & 80 \\ 1 & 2 & 7 & 60 \\ \le & \le & \le & \\ 5 & 6 & 2 & Z \end{bmatrix}$$

Dual

$4y_1 + y_2 \le 5$
$5y_1 + 2y_2 \le 6$
$3y_1 + 7y_2 \le 2$
$80y_1 + 60y_2 = Z$

Step 3

The dual is stated as follows:

$$\text{Maximize } Z = 80y_1 + 60y_2$$
$$\text{subject to } 4y_1 + y_2 \le 5$$
$$5y_1 + 2y_2 \le 6$$
$$3y_1 + 7y_2 \le 2$$
$$\text{where } y_1 \text{ and } y_2 \ge 0$$

At this point, we state a theorem that reveals why we can determine the solution to a primal by solving its dual, and vice versa.

SUMMARY

Fundamental Theorem of Duality

1. If either the primal or the dual problem has an optimal solution, then they both have optimal solutions. If an optimal solution exists, both primal and dual objective functions have the same optimal value.
2. The optimal solution values of the primal variables $x_1, x_2, \ldots,$ etc., are given by the indicators corresponding to the slack variables in the dual optimal tableau.

We now solve the dual of our illustrative example. Both the primal and dual are given below.

Primal

Minimize $Z = 4x_1 + 9x_2$
subject to $x_1 + 2x_2 \ge 200$
$2x_1 + 6x_2 \ge 750$
where x_1 and $x_2 \ge 0$

Dual

Maximize $Z = 200y_1 + 750y_2$
subject to $y_1 + 2y_2 \le 4$
$2y_1 + 6y_2 \le 9$
where y_1 and $y_2 \ge 0$

The dual simplex tableau is given below.

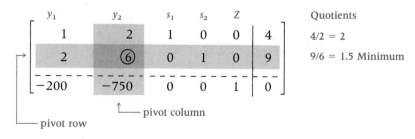

	y_1	y_2	s_1	s_2	Z		Quotients
	1	2	1	0	0	4	$4/2 = 2$
→	2	⑥	0	1	0	9	$9/6 = 1.5$ Minimum
	−200	−750	0	0	1	0	

pivot row   pivot column

The pivot element is circled. Note that the pivot column has been determined and the quotients used to choose the pivot row.

The following row operations, in the order of their listing, are used to change the above tableau into the equivalent tableau below.

$$[(1/6)R2 \to R2], \qquad [(-2)R2 + R1 \to R1], \qquad [(750)R2 + R3 \to R3]$$

$$
\begin{array}{ccccc}
y_1 & y_2 & s_1 & s_2 & Z \\
\end{array}
$$

$$
\left[
\begin{array}{ccccc|c}
1/3 & 0 & 1 & -1/3 & 0 & 1 \\
1/3 & 1 & 0 & 1/6 & 0 & 3/2 \\
\hline
50 & 0 & 0 & 125 & 1 & 1125 \\
\end{array}
\right]
$$

Since the above tableau has no negative indicators, it yields an optimal solution to the dual problem.

Optimal Solution (Dual)

$$\underbrace{y_1 = 0, \quad s_2 = 0,}_{\text{Nonbasic variables}} \qquad \underbrace{y_2 = 3/2, \quad s_1 = 1,}_{\text{Basic variables, or basis}} \qquad \underbrace{Z = 1125}_{\substack{\text{Objective} \\ \text{function value}}}$$

Optimal Solution to Primal

As stated in the Fundamental Theorem of Duality, the optimal solution values of the primal variables $x_1, x_2, \ldots$, etc., are given by the indicators corresponding to the slack variables in the dual optimal solution. Also, the optimal objective function values are equal for both problems. We restate the optimal tableau for the illustrative problem of this section to show these results.

Optimal Tableau (Dual)

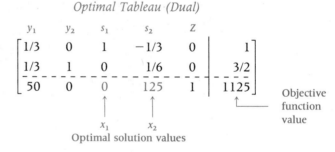

Thus, the optimal solution values for the primal variables x_1 and x_2 are $x_1 = 0$ and $x_2 = 125$. The optimal value of the objective function is 1125. This is a minimum value for the primal objective function and a maximum value for the dual objective function.

IMPLICATIONS OF OPTIMAL SOLUTION

We restate the primal problem and investigate the implications of the optimal solution.

Primal Problem

$$\text{Minimize } Z = 4x_1 + 9x_2$$
$$\text{subject to } \quad x_1 + 2x_2 \geq 200$$
$$2x_1 + 6x_2 \geq 750$$
$$\text{where } x_1 \text{ and } x_2 \geq 0$$

Constraint 1.

$$x_1 + 2x_2 \geq 200$$

Substitute the optimal values for x_1 and x_2 to get

$$(0) + 2(125) \geq 200$$
$$250 \geq 200$$
$$\text{Surplus} = \text{LHS} - \text{RHS}$$
$$= 250 - 200 = 50$$

There are 50 units of surplus in this constraint.

Constraint 2.

$$2x_1 + 6x_2 \geq 750$$

Substitute the optimal values for x_1 and x_2 to get

$$2(0) + 6(125) \geq 750$$
$$750 \geq 750$$

Since LHS = RHS, there is no surplus in this constraint. In other words, it is a *binding constraint.*

Interpretation of a Dual Optimal Solution: Shadow Prices

We now give meaning to the optimal values of the dual variables y_1, y_2, . . . , etc. To do so, we restate the primal and dual problems.

Primal	*Dual*
Minimize $Z = 4x_1 + 9x_2$	Maximize $Z = 200y_1 + 750y_2$
subject to $x_1 + 2x_2 \geq 200$	subject to $y_1 + 2y_2 \leq 4$
$2x_1 + 6x_2 \geq 750$	$2y_1 + 6y_2 \leq 9$
where x_1 and $x_2 \geq 0$	where y_1 and $y_2 \geq 0$

Notice that the dual objective function, $200y_1 + 750y_2$, contains the right-hand-side values, 200 and 750, of the primal constraints. The optimal values of y_1 and y_2 are $y_1 = 0$ and $y_2 = 3/2$. Thus, the optimal value of either objective function is given by

$$Z = 200y_1 + 750y_2$$
$$= 200(0) + 750(3/2) = 1125$$

Note that the values of y_1 and y_2 indicate the effects on the optimal value of the objective function of changes in the primal right-hand-side values of 200 and 750, respectively. Specifically, if the right-hand-side value, 200, of the first primal constraint increases by 1 unit, the optimal objective function value, 1125, changes by 0 units. If the right-hand-side value, 750, of the second primal constraint increases by 1 unit, the optimal objective function value, 1125, will increase by 3/2, or $1.50. Of course, if the right-hand-side value, 750, decreases by 1 unit, the optimal objective function value will decrease by $1.50. In other words, if the minimal requirement for nutrient 2 is lowered by 1 unit, the total cost will decrease by $1.50. Thus, if the farmer were to pay an amount of money to be able to lower the minimal nutritional requirement, the farmer should pay no more than $1.50 per unit of decrease in the requirement. It is for this reason that the optimal values of the dual variables, $y_1 = 0$ and $y_2 = 3/2$, or 1.5, are called **shadow prices.** We caution that the above interpretation of the shadow prices is valid only to the extent that the primal right-hand-side values, 200 and 750, can be changed without changing the feasibility of the optimal basis. We will have more to say about this in Section 7-5. We summarize as follows.

SUMMARY

Shadow Prices

1. The optimal values of the dual variables are called **shadow prices.**
2. A shadow price represents the amount of change in the optimal value of an objective function resulting from a change in the right-hand-side value of a primal constraint.

Caution: A shadow price is valid only for a specific interval within which a right-hand-side value can vary.

We now present some applications.

Applications

A Transportation Problem

A company makes fuel-efficient furnaces at two plants. The furnaces must be transported from the two plants to two distribution centers, as illustrated in Table 7-2. The plants are called **supply points,** and the distribution centers are called **demand points.** Studying Table 7-2, note that plants 1 and 2 have production capacities of 800 and 500 furnaces, respectively. Distribution centers 1 and 2 have demand requirements of at least 900 and 300 furnaces, respectively. The numbers in the upper left-hand corner of each cell represent the cost of transporting a furnace from the corresponding plant to the respective dis-

TABLE 7-2   Demand points

		Distribution center 1	Distribution center 2	Plant capacities
Supply points →	Plant 1	10 x_1	8 x_2	≤ 800
→	Plant 2	6 x_3	9 x_4	≤ 500
	Demands	≥ 900	≥ 300	

tribution center. Specifically, it costs \$10 to ship a furnace from plant 1 to distribution center 1, \$8 from plant 1 to distribution center 2, \$6 from plant 2 to distribution center 1, and \$9 from plant 2 to distribution center 2.

PROBLEM

The company must determine how many furnaces to ship from each plant to each distribution center in order to minimize the total transportation cost and satisfy all constraints.

SOLUTION

In Table 7-2, let

x_1 = number of furnaces shipped from plant 1 to distribution center 1

x_2 = number of furnaces shipped from plant 1 to distribution center 2

x_3 = number of furnaces shipped from plant 2 to distribution center 1

x_4 = number of furnaces shipped from plant 2 to distribution center 2

The total transportation cost is given by

$$Z = 10x_1 + 8x_2 + 6x_3 + 9x_4$$

The limited production capacity of plant 1 indicates that

$$\underbrace{x_1 + x_2}_{\text{number shipped from plant 1}} \leq 800$$

The limited production capacity of plant 2 indicates that

$$\underbrace{x_3 + x_4}_{\text{number shipped from plant 2}} \leq 500$$

The demand requirement of distribution center 1 indicates that

$$\underbrace{x_1 + x_3}_{\text{number shipped to distribution center 1}} \geq 900$$

The demand requirement of distribution center 2 indicates that

$$\underbrace{x_2 + x_4}_{\text{number shipped to distribution center 2}} \geq 300$$

Thus, our problem is formulated below.

$$\begin{aligned}
\text{Minimize } Z = 10x_1 &+ 8x_2 + 6x_3 + 9x_4 \\
\text{subject to } x_1 &+ x_2 && \leq 800 \\
& && x_3 + x_4 \leq 500 \\
x_1 & && + x_3 \geq 900 \\
& x_2 && + x_4 \geq 300
\end{aligned}$$

where x_1, x_2, x_3, and $x_4 \geq 0$

We determine the solution to this problem by solving its dual. However, all constraints must be of the $\geq$ type. So we multiply both sides of the first two constraints by -1 to obtain the formulation below.

$$\text{Minimize } Z = 10x_1 + 8x_2 + 6x_3 + 9x_4$$

$$
\begin{aligned}
\text{subject to } -x_1 - x_2 \quad\quad\quad &\geq -800 \\
-x_3 - x_4 &\geq -500 \\
x_1 \quad\quad + x_3 \quad\quad &\geq 900 \\
x_2 \quad\quad + x_4 &\geq 300
\end{aligned}
$$

where $x_1, x_2, x_3,$ and $x_4 \geq 0$

We find the dual.

The dual is

$$\text{Maximize } Z = -800y_1 - 500y_2 + 900y_3 + 300y_4$$

$$
\begin{aligned}
\text{subject to } -y_1 \quad\quad + y_3 \quad\quad &\leq 10 \\
-y_1 \quad\quad\quad\quad + y_4 &\leq 8 \\
-y_2 + y_3 \quad\quad &\leq 6 \\
-y_2 \quad\quad + y_4 &\leq 9
\end{aligned}
$$

where $y_1, y_2, y_3,$ and $y_4 \geq 0$

We now list each simplex tableau preceded by the row operations used to get that tableau. The first tableau is called the initial tableau.

Initial Tableau (Dual)

y_1	y_2	y_3	y_4	s_1	s_2	s_3	s_4	Z	
-1	0	1	0	1	0	0	0	0	10
-1	0	0	1	0	1	0	0	0	8
0	-1	1	0	0	0	1	0	0	6
0	-1	0	1	0	0	0	1	0	9
800	500	-900	-300	0	0	0	0	1	0

$$[(-1)R3 + R1 \to R1], \quad [(900)R3 + R5 \to R5]$$

y_1	y_2	y_3	y_4	s_1	s_2	s_3	s_4	Z	
-1	1	0	0	1	0	-1	0	0	4
-1	0	0	1	0	1	0	0	0	8
0	-1	1	0	0	0	1	0	0	6
0	-1	0	1	0	0	0	1	0	9
800	-400	0	-300	0	0	900	0	1	5400

$$[(1)R1 + R3 \rightarrow R3], \qquad [(1)R1 + R4 \rightarrow R4], \qquad [(400)R1 + R5 \rightarrow R5]$$

$$\begin{bmatrix} -1 & 1 & 0 & 0 & 1 & 0 & -1 & 0 & 0 & | & 4 \\ -1 & 0 & 0 & 1 & 0 & 1 & 0 & 0 & 0 & | & 8 \\ -1 & 0 & 1 & 0 & 1 & 0 & 0 & 0 & 0 & | & 10 \\ -1 & 0 & 0 & 1 & 1 & 0 & -1 & 1 & 0 & | & 13 \\ \hline 400 & 0 & 0 & -300 & 400 & 0 & 500 & 0 & 1 & | & 7000 \end{bmatrix}$$

$$[(-1)R2 + R4 \rightarrow R4], \qquad [(300)R2 + R5 \rightarrow R5]$$

Optimal Tableau (Dual)

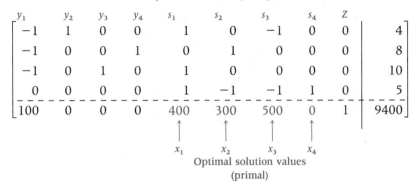

y_1	y_2	y_3	y_4	s_1	s_2	s_3	s_4	Z	
-1	1	0	0	1	0	-1	0	0	4
-1	0	0	1	0	1	0	0	0	8
-1	0	1	0	1	0	0	0	0	10
0	0	0	0	1	-1	-1	1	0	5
100	0	0	0	400	300	500	0	1	9400

$$\uparrow \qquad \uparrow \qquad \uparrow \qquad \uparrow$$
$$x_1 \qquad x_2 \qquad x_3 \qquad x_4$$

Optimal solution values
(primal)

Dual Optimal Solution

$\underbrace{y_1 = 0, s_1 = 0, s_2 = 0, s_3 = 0,}_{\text{Nonbasic variables}} \quad \underbrace{y_2 = 4, y_3 = 10, y_4 = 8, s_4 = 5,}_{\text{Basic variables, or basis}} \quad \underbrace{Z = 9400}_{\substack{\text{Optimal value} \\ \text{of objective} \\ \text{function}}}$

IMPLICATIONS OF OPTIMAL SOLUTION

- $x_1 = 400$ furnaces are shipped from plant 1 to distribution center 1.
- $x_2 = 300$ furnaces are shipped from plant 1 to distribution center 2.
- $x_3 = 500$ furnaces are shipped from plant 2 to distribution center 1.
- $x_4 = 0$ furnaces are shipped from plant 2 to distribution center 2.

Slack/Surplus

Constraint 1. $x_1 + x_2 \leq 800$
$400 + 300 \leq 800$
$700 \leq 800$ Slack = 100 means excess plant
capacity at Plant 1.

Constraint 2. $x_3 + x_4 \leq 500$
$500 + 0 \leq 500$
$500 \leq 500$ Slack = 0 means no excess plant
capacity at Plant 2.

Constraint 3. $x_1 + x_3 \geq 900$
$400 + 500 \geq 900$
$900 \geq 900$ Surplus =0

Constraint 4.
$$x_2 + x_4 \geq 300$$
$$300 + 0 \geq 300$$
$$300 \geq 300 \qquad \text{Surplus} = 0$$

Shadow Prices

Focus on the dual objective function

$$Z = -800y_1 - 500y_2 + 900y_3 + 300y_4$$

remembering that the coefficients are the right-hand-side values of the primal constraints.

- $y_1 = 0$ means that for each unit increase (decrease) in the right-hand-side value, -800, the transportation cost changes by $0. Thus, a change in the plant capacity of plant 1 results in no change in the total transportation cost.

- $y_2 = 4$ means that for each unit increase (decrease) in the right-hand-side value, -500, the total transportation cost increases (decreases) by $4. Note that if -500 increases by 1, it becomes -499. This means that the original primal constraint becomes $x_3 + x_4 \leq 499$. Thus, a 1-unit increase in -500 is equivalent to a 1-unit decrease in plant 2's capacity, and this results in a $4 increase in total transportation cost.

- $y_3 = 10$ means that for each unit increase (decrease) in the demand requirement, 900, for distribution center 1, the total transportation cost increases (decreases) by $10.

- $y_4 = 8$ means that for each unit increase (decrease) in the demand requirement, 300, for distribution center 2, the total transportation cost increases (decreases) by $8.

Caution: Remember that each shadow price is valid only for a specific interval within which its corresponding right-hand-side value can vary. We will discuss such intervals in Section 7-5.

We now consider another application.

Blending Problem

A company manufactures two types of plant food—type A and type B—packaged in 50-pound bags. Each type is a blend of two raw materials: raw material 1 and raw material 2. Raw material 1 contains 70% nitrogen and 10% phosphorus. Raw material 2 contains 20% nitrogen and 40% phosphorus. Type A must contain at least 55% nitrogen. Type B must contain at least 15% phosphorus. The season's demand is for at least 50,000 bags for type A and at least 20,000 bags for Type B. If each pound of raw material 1 costs $0.60 and each pound of raw material 2 costs $0.45, how many pounds of each raw material should be ordered to satisfy demand at minimum cost?

Here, we let

x_1 = number of pounds of raw material 1 used for type A food

x_2 = number of pounds of raw material 1 used for type B food

x_3 = number of pounds of raw material 2 used for type A food

x_4 = number of pounds of raw material 2 used for type B food

See Figure 7-4. Since the objective is to minimize the total cost of the raw materials, the objective function is defined by

$$\text{Minimize } Z = 0.60x_1 + 0.60x_2 + 0.45x_3 + 0.45x_4$$

Since we must have at least 50,000 50-pound bags of type A, then

$$x_1 + x_3 \geq 50,000(50)$$

Since we must have at least 20,000 50-pound bags of type B, then

$$x_2 + x_4 \geq 20,000(50)$$

Since type A must contain at least 55% nitrogen, then

$$0.70x_1 + 0.20x_3 \geq 0.55(x_1 + x_3)$$

or

$$0.15x_1 - 0.35x_3 \geq 0$$

Since type B must contain at least 15% phosphorus, then

$$0.10x_2 + 0.40x_4 \geq 0.15(x_2 + x_4)$$

or

$$-0.05x_2 + 0.25x_4 \geq 0$$

Thus, the linear programming problem is stated as

$$\text{Minimize } Z = 0.60x_1 + 0.60x_2 + 0.45x_3 + 0.45x_4$$

$$\begin{aligned}
\text{subject to} \quad x_1 \quad\quad + \quad x_3 \quad\quad\quad &\geq 2{,}500{,}000 \\
x_2 \quad\quad + \quad x_4 &\geq 1{,}000{,}000 \\
0.15x_1 \quad\quad - \; 0.35x_3 \quad\quad &\geq 0 \\
-0.05x_2 \quad\quad + \; 0.25x_4 &\geq 0
\end{aligned}$$

where x_1, x_2, x_3, and $x_4 \geq 0$

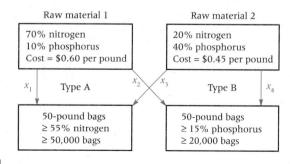

FIGURE 7-4

We determine the solution to this problem by solving its dual, which we determine below.

$$
\begin{array}{c}
\begin{array}{ccccc}
\quad x_1 & \quad x_2 & \quad x_3 & \quad x_4 &
\end{array}\\
\begin{array}{c}
y_1\\ y_2\\ y_3\\ y_4\\ \\ \\ \\
\end{array}
\left[
\begin{array}{ccccc}
1 & 0 & 1 & 0 & 2{,}500{,}000\\
0 & 1 & 0 & 1 & 1{,}000{,}000\\
0.15 & 0 & -0.35 & 0 & 0\\
0 & -0.05 & 0 & 0.25 & 0\\
\leq & \leq & \leq & \leq & \\
0.60 & 0.60 & 0.45 & 0.45 & Z
\end{array}
\right]
\end{array}
$$

Dual

Maximize $Z = 2{,}500{,}000y_1 + 1{,}000{,}000y_2 + 0y_3 + 0y_4$

subject to

$$
\begin{aligned}
y_1 \quad\quad + 0.15y_3 \quad\quad &\leq 0.60\\
y_2 \quad\quad\quad\quad - 0.15y_4 &\leq 0.60\\
y_1 \quad\quad - 0.35y_3 \quad\quad &\leq 0.45\\
y_2 \quad\quad\quad\quad + 0.25y_4 &\leq 0.45
\end{aligned}
$$

where $y_1, y_2, y_3,$ and $y_4 \geq 0$

We now list each simplex tableau, preceded by the row operations used to derive the tableau from the preceding tableau.

Initial Tableau (Dual)

	y_1	y_2	y_3	y_4	s_1	s_2	s_3	s_4	Z	
	1	0	0.15	0	1	0	0	0	0	0.60
	0	1	0	-0.05	0	1	0	0	0	0.60
	1	0	-0.35	0	0	0	1	0	0	0.45
	0	1	0	0.25	0	0	0	1	0	0.45
	-2,500,000	-1,000,000	0	0	0	0	0	0	1	0

$$[(-1)R3 + R1 \rightarrow R1], \quad [(2{,}500{,}000)R3 + R5 \rightarrow R5]$$

0	0	0.50	0	1	0	-1	0	0		0.15
0	1	0	-0.05	0	1	0	0	0		0.60
1	0	-0.35	0	0	0	1	0	0		0.45
0	1	0	0.25	0	0	0	1	0		0.45
0	-1,000,000	-875,000	0	0	0	2,500,000	0	1		1,125,000

$$[(-1)R4 + R2 \rightarrow R2], \quad [(1{,}000{,}000)R4 + R5 \rightarrow R5]$$

0	0	0.50	0	1	0	-1	0	0		0.15
0	0	0	-0.30	0	1	0	-1	0		0.15
1	0	-0.35	0	0	0	1	0	0		0.45
0	1	0	0.25	0	0	0	1	0		0.45
0	0	-875,000	250,000	0	0	2,500,000	1,000,000	1		1,575,000

$$[(2)R1 \rightarrow R1], \quad [(0.35)R1 + R3 \rightarrow R3], \quad [(875,000)R1 + R5 \rightarrow R5]$$

Optimal Tableau (Dual)

y_1	y_2	y_3	y_4	s_1	s_2	s_3	s_4	z	
0	0	1	0	2	0	−2	0	0	0.30
0	0	0	−0.30	0	1	0	−1	0	0.15
1	0	0	0	0.70	0	0.30	0	0	0.55
0	1	0	0.25	0	0	0	1	0	0.45
0	0	0	250,000	1,750,000	0	750,000	1,000,000	1	1,837,500

$$\qquad\qquad \uparrow \qquad\quad \uparrow \quad \uparrow \qquad\qquad \uparrow$$
$$\qquad\qquad x_1 \qquad\quad x_2 \quad x_3 \qquad\qquad x_4$$

Optimal solution values
(primal)

Dual Optimal Solution

$y_4 = 0, s_1 = 0, s_3 = 0,$	$y_1 = 0.55, y_2 = 0.45, y_3 = 0.30,$	$Z = 1,837,500$
$s_4 = 0,$	$s_2 = 0.15,$	Optimal value of objective function
Nonbasic variables	Basic variables, or basis	

IMPLICATIONS OF OPTIMAL SOLUTION

Using Figure 7-4,

- $x_1 = 1,750,000$ pounds of raw material 1 is used for type A food.
- $x_2 = 0$ pounds of raw material 1 is used for type B food.
- $x_3 = 750,000$ pounds of raw material 2 is used for type A food.
- $x_4 = 1,000,000$ pounds of raw material 2 is used for type B food.

Surplus

Constraint 1.

$$x_1 + x_3 \geq 2,500,000 \text{ pounds of type A food}$$
$$1,750,000 + 750,000 \geq 2,500,000$$
$$2,500,000 \geq 2,500,000 \qquad \text{No surplus}$$

Constraint 2.

$$x_2 + x_4 \geq 1,000,000 \text{ pounds of type B food}$$
$$0 + 1,000,000 \geq 1,000,000 \qquad \text{No surplus}$$

Constraint 3. Type A food must contain at least 55% nitrogen.

$$0.15x_1 - 0.35x_3 \geq 0$$
$$0.15(1,750,000) - 0.35(750,000) \geq 0$$
$$0 \geq 0 \qquad \text{No surplus}$$

Constraint 4.   Type B food must contain at least 15% phosphorus.

$$-0.05x_2 + 0.25x_4 \geq 0$$
$$-0.05(0) + 0.25(1,000,000) \geq 0$$
$$250,000 \geq 0 \qquad \text{Surplus} = 250,000$$

Type B food contains 250,000 pounds more phosphorus than the minimal requirement.

Shadow Prices

Focus on the dual objective function

$$Z = 2,500,000y_1 + 1,000,000y_2 + 0y_3 + 0y_4$$

remembering that the coefficients are the right-hand-side values of the primal constraints.

Constraint 1. $y_1 = 0.55$ means that for each 1-pound increase (decrease) in the minimal type A food requirement of 2,500,000 pounds, the total cost will increase (decrease) by $0.55.

Constraint 2. $y_2 = 0.45$ means that for each 1-pound increase (decrease) in the minimal type B food requirement of 1,000,000 pounds, the total cost will increase (decrease) by $0.45.

Constraint 3. $y_3 = 0.30$ means that for each unit increase (decrease) in the right-hand-side value of 0, the total cost will increase (decrease) by $0.30.

Constraint 4. $y_4 = 0$ means that for each unit increase (decrease) in the right-hand-side value of 0, the total cost will increase (decrease) by $0.

Caution: Remember that each shadow price is valid only for a specific interval within which its corresponding right-hand-side value can vary. We will discuss such intervals in Section 7-5.

Exercises 7-3

For Exercises 1–12:
a)   Find the dual.
b)   Solve the dual.
c)   Find the solution to the primal problem from the dual optimal tableau.
d)   State the amount of surplus in each primal constraint.
e)   Identify and interpret the shadow prices.

1. Minimize $Z = 40x_1 + 60x_2$
subject to $2x_1 + x_2 \geq 6$
$4x_1 + 6x_2 \geq 8$
where x_1 and $x_2 \geq 0$

2. Minimize $Z = 120x_1 + 320x_2$
subject to $4x_1 + 2x_2 \geq 8$
$6x_1 + 8x_2 \geq 10$
where x_1 and $x_2 \geq 0$

3. Minimize $Z = 300x_1 + 150x_2$
subject to $4x_1 + 2x_2 \geq 120$
$x_1 + 8x_2 \geq 100$
where x_1 and $x_2 \geq 0$.

4. Minimize $Z = 5x_1 + 2x_2 + x_3$
subject to $x_1 + 2x_2 + x_3 \geq 20$
$3x_1 + 3x_2 + 6x_3 \geq 24$
where $x_1, x_2,$ and $x_3 \geq 0$

5. Minimize $Z = 200x_1 + 240x_2$
subject to $x_1 + 2x_2 \geq 6$
$\qquad\quad x_1 + 6x_2 \geq 8$
$\qquad\quad x_1 + 4x_2 \geq 4$
where x_1 and $x_2 \geq 0$

6. Minimize $Z = 180x_1 + 120x_2$
subject to $6x_1 + x_2 \geq 9$
$\qquad\quad x_1 + 2x_2 \geq 2$
$\qquad\quad 4x_1 + 2x_2 \geq 7$
where $x_1, x_2,$ and $x_3 \geq 0$

7. Minimize $Z = 80x_1 + 100x_2 + 10x_3$
subject to $2x_1 + x_2 + x_3 \geq 6$
$\qquad\quad 4x_1 + 2x_2 \geq 9$
$\qquad\qquad\quad 2x_2 \geq 5$
where $x_1, x_2,$ and $x_3 \geq 0$

8. Minimize $Z = 480x_1 + 280x_2 + 360x_3$
subject to $4x_1 + x_2 + \geq 100$
$\qquad\qquad\quad x_2 + 2x_3 \geq 80$
$\qquad\quad 6x_1 + 6x_3 \geq 90$
where $x_1, x_2,$ and $x_3 \geq 0$

9. Minimize $Z = 600x_1 + 460x_2 + 600x_3 + 800x_4$
subject to $2x_1 + x_2 + x_3 \geq 40$
$\qquad\quad x_1 + 2x_2 + x_3 + x_4 \geq 60$
$\qquad\quad 2x_1 + 2x_2 + x_4 \geq 50$
where $x_1, x_2, x_3,$ and $x_4 \geq 0$

10. Minimize $Z = 80x_1 + 60x_2 + 70x_3 + 90x_4$
subject to $x_1 + x_3 \geq 6$
$\qquad\quad x_1 + x_4 \geq 5$
$\qquad\qquad\quad x_2 + x_3 \geq 4$
$\qquad\qquad\quad x_2 + x_4 \geq 4$
where $x_1, x_2, x_3,$ and $x_4 \geq 0$

11. Minimize $Z = 90x_1 + 100x_2 + 60x_3 + 80x_4$
subject to $x_1 + x_3 \geq 7$
$\qquad\quad x_1 + x_4 \geq 8$
$\qquad\qquad\quad x_2 + x_4 \geq 9$
$\qquad\qquad\quad x_2 + x_3 \geq 10$
where $x_1, x_2, x_3,$ and $x_4 \geq 0$

12. Minimize $Z = 100x_1 + 120x_2 + 200x_3$
subject to $x_1 + x_2 \geq 4$
$\qquad\quad x_1 + x_3 \geq 6$
$\qquad\quad x_1 + x_2 \geq 5$
$\qquad\qquad\qquad x_3 \geq 1$
where $x_1, x_2,$ and $x_3 \geq 0$

Applications

For Exercises 13–20:
a) Formulate the problem.
b) Rewrite the formulation so that each constraint is of the $\geq$ type, and then find the dual of the result.
c) Solve the dual.
d) Find the solution to the primal problem from the dual optimal tableau.
e) State the amount of slack or surplus in each primal constraint.
f) Identify and interpret the shadow prices.

13. *Transportation.* A company makes water heaters at two plants. The water heaters must be transported from the two plants to two distribution centers, as illustrated in the following table.

	Distribution center 1	Distribution center 2	Plant capacities
Plant 1	$6 x_1	$8 x_2	≤ 500
Plant 2	$10 x_3	$9 x_4	≤ 600
Demands	≥ 400	≥ 650	

Note that plants 1 and 2 have production capacities of 500 and 600 water heaters, respectively. Distribution centers 1 and 2 have demand requirements of 400 and 650 water heaters, respectively. The numbers in the upper left-hand corner of each cell represent the cost of transporting a water heater from the corresponding plant to the respective distribution center. Also, the numbers of water heaters to be shipped from respective plants to respective distribution centers are denoted by x_1, x_2, x_3, and x_4. The company must determine how many water heaters to ship from each plant to each distribution center in order to minimize the total transportation cost.

14. *Transportation.* A company makes wood-burning stoves at two plants. The stoves must be transported from the two plants to two distribution centers, as illustrated in the table below.

	Distribution center 1	Distribution center 2	Plant capacities
Plant 1	$20 x_1	$15 x_2	≤ 900
Plant 2	$18 x_3	$30 x_4	≤ 600
Demands	≥ 500	≥ 800	

Note that plants 1 and 2 have production capacities of 900 and 600 stoves, respectively. Distribution centers 1 and 2 have demand requirements of 500 and 800 stoves, respectively. The numbers in the upper left-hand corner of each cell represent the cost of transporting a stove from the corresponding plant to the respective distribution center. Also, the numbers of stoves to be shipped from respective plants to respective distribution centers are denoted by x_1, x_2, x_3, and x_4. The company must determine how many stoves to ship from each plant to each distribution center in order to minimize the total transportation cost.

15. *Production assignment.* A company produces two products at each of two plants. The following table gives the manufacturing cost per unit for each product at each plant, along with plant capacities and demand requirements for each product. The company must determine how many units of each product should be produced at each plant in order to minimize the total manufacturing cost. Note that the variables x_1, x_2, x_3, and x_4 denote the number of units of the respective product to be produced at the respective plant.

Manufacturing cost per unit

	Product A	Product B	Plant capacities
Plant 1	$8 x_1	$10 x_2	≤ 450
Plant 2	$15 x_3	$9 x_4	≤ 600
Demands	≥ 400	≥ 500	

16. *Blending problem.* A company manufactures two types of liquid fertilizer: type A and type B. Each type is a blend of two raw materials: raw material 1 and raw material 2. Raw material 1 contains 60% nitrogen and 20% phosphorus. Raw material 2 contains 30% nitrogen and 40% phosphorus. Type A must contain at least 40% nitrogen, and type B must contain at least 18% phosphorus. The season's demand is for at least 100,000 gallons of Type A and at least 70,000 gallons of type B. If raw material 1 costs $0.80 per gallon and raw material 2 costs $0.55 per gallon, how many pounds of each raw material should be ordered to satisfy demand at minimum cost?

17. *Nutrition: Diet.* A dietician must determine how many units of each of three food types to include in a diet so that the total number of calories is minimized and nutritional requirements are realized. The following table gives the amounts of relevant nutrients contained per unit of each food type.

Milligrams per unit of food type

	Food A	Food B	Food C
Protein	5	4	2
Calcium	10	5	8
Iron	2	1	3

Calories per unit of food type

Food A	Food B	Food C
800	500	600

Minimal nutritional requirements (in milligrams)

Protein	25
Calcium	60
Iron	10

18. *Nutrition: Diet.* Repeat Exercise 17 with the objective of minimizing the cost of the diet. Delete the objective of minimizing the total number of calories. The unit cost of each food type is given in the following table.

Cost per unit of food type

Food A	Food B	Food C
$15	$20	$30

19. *Election polling.* A polling firm can hire professional and semiprofessional poll-sters for election-day polling at two locations. The total cost per pollster for the entire day at each location is given below.

Cost per pollster per day

	Professional	Semiprofessional
Location 1	$400	$300
Location 2	400	300

The number of voters surveyed per day for each type of pollster at each location is given below.

Number of voters surveyed per day

	Professional	Semiprofessional
Location 1	80	50
Location 2	80	50

The polling firm wants to survey at least 440 and 800 voters from locations 1 and 2, respectively. At least 200 voters are to be surveyed by semiprofessional pollsters. How many professional and semiprofessional pollsters should be hired at each location in order to minimize the total polling cost?

20. *Election polling.* Repeat Exercise 19 under the additional constraint that at least 600 voters must be surveyed by professional pollsters.

7-4 • MIXED CONSTRAINTS; SHADOW PRICES (PRIMAL); COMPUTER SOLUTION

In the previous sections of this chapter, we have discussed standard maximization and minimization problems. Specifically, a standard maximization problem has $\leq$ constraints and an objective function that must be maximized; a minimization problem has $\geq$ constraints and an objective function that must be minimized. In the previous section, we determined solutions to minimization problems by solving their duals.

In this section, we consider maximization and minimization problems that contain any combination of $\leq$, $\geq$, and $=$ constraints. We will show how to prepare such problems for solution by the simplex method. Specifically, we will show how to rewrite $\geq$ constraints as equations. We will refer to a specialized method for solving such problems. However, because this method involves unwieldy computations, we will not solve such problems by hand computation. Instead, we will present optimal tableaus and show how to determine shadow prices from optimal primal tableaus. In other words, we will discuss the determination of shadow prices without the use of the dual. Finally, we will discuss computer solutions and their interpretation.

Mixed Constraints

We begin by discussing the preparation of the problem

$$\text{Maximize } Z = 3x_1 + 4x_2 + x_3$$
$$\text{subject to } x_1 + 2x_2 + 3x_3 \leq 8$$
$$2x_1 + x_2 + 4x_3 \geq 10$$
$$\text{where } x_1, x_2, \text{ and } x_3 \geq 0$$

for solution by the simplex method. We first restate the constraints as linear equations. We add a slack variable to the left-hand side of the $\leq$ constraint, as we learned in Section 7-1. Thus, the first constraint becomes

$$x_1 + 2x_2 + 3x_3 + s_1 = 8$$

where s_1 denotes the amount of slack in the constraint.

The second constraint is of the $\geq$ type. Recall from Chapter 6 that a $\geq$ constraint contains surplus that indicates the amount by which the left-hand side exceeds the right-hand side. Thus, to restate a $\geq$ constraint as an equation, we must subtract a surplus variable from its left-hand side. Thus, the second constraint becomes

$$2x_1 + x_2 + 4x_3 - s_2 = 10$$

where s_2 denotes the amount of surplus in the constraint.

If we write the equations corresponding to the constraints, we have

$$x_1 + 2x_2 + 3x_3 + s_1 = 8$$
$$2x_1 + x_2 + 4x_3 - s_2 = 10$$

where $x_1, x_2, x_3, s_1,$ and $s_2 \geq 0$. A *basic solution* includes

$$\underbrace{x_1 = 0, \quad x_2 = 0, \quad x_3 = 0,}_{\text{Nonbasic variables}} \qquad \underbrace{s_1 = 8, \quad s_2 = -10}_{\substack{\text{Basic variables,} \\ \text{or basis}}}$$

Note that s_2 *is negative* because s_2, being a surplus variable, is subtracted from the left-hand side of the constraint. However, the fact that s_2 is negative violates the non-negativity restrictions stated above, and, thus, the above basic solution is not feasible. So we must introduce another non-negative variable in the second equation (which came from the $\geq$ constraint) in order to obtain a positive solution value. Such a non-negative variable is called an **artificial variable** and is denoted by a_1. Thus, the second constraint is written as

$$2x_1 + x_2 + 4x_3 - s_2 + a_1 = 10$$

We note that artificial variables, such as a_1 in this example, have no meaning and must be driven to zero by the time the simplex process yields an optimal tableau, if it exists. To ensure that an artificial variable is driven to zero, we multiply it by $-M$, where M is an **arbitrarily large positive constant**, and add the result to the objective function. Thus, for the above example, the objective function would become

$$\text{Maximize } Z = 3x_1 + 4x_2 + x_3 + 0s_1 + 0s_2 - Ma_1$$

The addition of $-Ma_1$ where $a_1 > 0$ and M is an arbitrarily large positive constant, decreases the value of the objective function (the opposite of what we want) unless $a_1 = 0$. Since the simplex method is maximizing Z, the only way in which this can occur is for a_1 to equal zero.

Thus, our problem is restated as

$$\text{Maximize } Z = 3x_1 + 4x_2 + x_3 + 0s_1 + 0s_2 - Ma_1$$
$$\text{subject to } x_1 + 2x_2 + 3x_3 + s_1 \qquad = 8$$
$$2x_1 + x_2 + 4x_3 + \qquad - s_2 + a_1 = 10$$
$$\text{where } x_1, x_2, x_3, s_1, s_2, \text{ and } a_1 \geq 0$$

Looking at the constraints, a *basic feasible solution* includes

$$\underbrace{x_1 = 0, \quad x_2 = 0, \quad x_3 = 0, \quad s_2 = 0,}_{\text{Nonbasic variables}} \qquad \underbrace{s_1 = 8, \quad a_1 = 10}_{\substack{\text{Basic variables,} \\ \text{or basis}}}$$

Note that the inclusion of a_1 provides the identity matrix column $\begin{bmatrix} 0 \\ 1 \end{bmatrix}$. This, along with the identity matrix column $\begin{bmatrix} 1 \\ 0 \end{bmatrix}$ for the variable s_1, yields the stated basic feasible solution with basic variables s_1 and a_1.

At this point, we summarize the formulation of linear programming problems for solution by the simplex method.

SUMMARY

Slack, Surplus, and Artificial Variables

To prepare a formulated problem for solution by the simplex method:

1. Add a slack variable to the left-hand side of any $\leq$ constraint.
2. Subtract a surplus variable from the left-hand side of any $\geq$ constraint, and, also, add an artificial variable to the left-hand side of such constraint.
3. Add an artificial variable to the left-hand side of any = constraint.
4. Assign 0s as objective function coefficients of all slack and/or surplus variables.

continues

SUMMARY—*Continued*

5. Assign objective function coefficients to artificial variables as follows:

- $-M$ if the objective function is to be maximized
- M if the objective function is to be minimized

where M is an arbitrarily large positive number. This drives the values of the artificial variables to 0.

• EXAMPLE 7-7

Prepare this problem for solution by the simplex method.

$$\text{Minimize } Z = 4x_1 + 5x_2 + 7x_3$$
$$\text{subject to } x_1 + 4x_2 + x_3 \leq 90$$
$$x_1 + x_2 + x_3 = 200$$
$$2x_1 + x_2 + 6x_3 \geq 70$$
$$\text{where } x_1, x_2, \text{ and } x_3 \geq 0$$

Solution

$$\text{Minimize } Z = 4x_1 + 5x_2 + 7x_3 + 0s_1 + Ma_1 + 0s_2 + Ma_2$$
$$\text{subject to } x_1 + 4x_2 + x_3 + s_1 = 90$$
$$x_1 + x_2 + x_3 + a_1 = 200$$
$$2x_1 + x_2 + 6x_3 - s_2 + a_2 = 70$$
$$\text{where } x_1, x_2, x_3, s_1. s_2, a_1, \text{ and } a_2 \geq 0$$

Here s_1 is a slack variable, s_2 is a surplus variable, and a_1 and a_2 are artificial variables. Note that the inclusion of a_1 and a_2 provides the identity matrix columns $\begin{bmatrix} 0 \\ 1 \\ 0 \end{bmatrix}$ and $\begin{bmatrix} 0 \\ 0 \\ 1 \end{bmatrix}$. These, along with the identity matrix column $\begin{bmatrix} 1 \\ 0 \\ 0 \end{bmatrix}$ for s_1, yield the basic variables $s_1 = 90$, $a_1 = 200$, and $a_2 = 70$ for the basic feasible solution

$$\underbrace{x_1 = 0, \quad x_2 = 0, \quad x_3 = 0, \quad s_2 = 0,}_{\text{Nonbasic variables}} \quad \underbrace{s_1 = 90, \quad a_1 = 200, \quad a_2 = 70}_{\text{Basic variables, or basis}}$$

•

At the beginning of this section, we stated that we would not compute the solutions to such problems by hand since the Ms cause unwieldy computations. We have discussed the use of slack, surplus, and artificial variables because most computer programs use these concepts. Later we will discuss the computer output of solutions to linear programming problems.

Shadow Prices and the Optimal Primal Tableau

At this point, we give the optimal tableau to the problem

$$\text{Maximize } Z = 3x_1 + 4x_2 + x_3$$
$$\text{subject to } x_1 + 2x_2 + 3x_3 \leq 8$$
$$2x_1 + x_2 + 4x_3 \geq 10$$
$$\text{where } x_1, x_2, \text{ and } x_3 \geq 0$$

noting that the artificial variable column has been deleted because the artificial variable has been driven to 0 by the simplex method.

Optimal Tableau

$$
\begin{array}{ccccc}
x_1 & x_2 & x_3 & s_1 & s_2 \\
\end{array}
$$

$$
\left[
\begin{array}{ccccc|c}
0 & 3 & 2 & 2 & 1 & 6 \\
\hline
1 & 2 & 3 & 1 & 0 & 8 \\
\hline
0 & 2 & 8 & 3 & 0 & 24 \\
\end{array}
\right] \tag{1}
$$

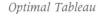
shadow prices

Optimal Solution

$$\underbrace{x_2 = 0, \quad x_3 = 0, \quad s_1 = 0,}_{\text{Nonbasic variables}} \quad \underbrace{x_1 = 8, \quad s_2 = 6,}_{\substack{\text{Basic variables,}\\\text{or basis}}} \quad \underbrace{Z = 24}_{\substack{\text{Objective}\\\text{function value}}}$$

Shadow Prices. In the previous section, we learned that the optimal values of dual variables are shadow prices and that a shadow price represents the amount of change in the optimal value of an objective function resulting from a change in the right-hand-side value of a primal constraint. Here we note that shadow prices are also given among the indicators corresponding to the slack and/or surplus variables of an optimal primal tableau. These are indicated in the optimal tableau for the above problem.

In the optimal primal tableau, (1), note that

1. The first shadow price, 3, corresponds to s_1, the slack variable for constraint 1. Thus, this shadow price represents the amount of change in the optimal value of the objective function resulting from a change in the right-hand-side value of constraint 1. Recall that constraint 1 is given by

$$x_1 + 2x_2 + 3x_3 \le 8$$

and, obviously, its right-hand-side value is 8. Thus, the shadow price is specifically interpreted as follows:

For each unit increase (decrease) in 8, the optimal value of the objective function, 24, increases (decreases) by 3 units.

2. The second shadow price, 0, corresponds to s_2, the surplus variable for constraint 2. Recall that constraint 2 is given by

$$2x_1 + x_2 + 4x_3 \ge 10$$

Since the shadow price is 0, this means that any change in 10, the right-hand-side value, does not result in a change in the optimal value of the objective function.

We caution that a shadow price is valid only for a specific interval within which a right-hand-side value can vary. The determination of such an interval is discussed in Section 7-5.

SUMMARY

Shadow Prices from an Optimal Primal Tableau

1. A **shadow price** represents the *amount of change in the optimal value of an objective function* resulting from a *change in the right-hand-side value* of a primal constraint.
2. *Shadow prices are given among the* indicators *corresponding to* slack *and/or* surplus variables *of an* optimal primal tableau.
   Caution: A shadow price is valid only for a specific interval within which a right-hand-side value can vary.

Computer Solution

We now discuss the use of a computer solution to the following linear programming problem.

Portfolio Selection

An investor has $600,000 to allocate among these investment alternatives:

Investment alternatives	Rate of return	Risk level
Government Bonds	7.5%	0
Money Market Funds	8.6	2
Hi-tech Stock	13.5	9
Municipal Bonds	7.8	1

The investor has stated the following investment criteria:

1. The full amount of $600,000 is to be invested.
2. The average risk is to be no more than 3.5.
3. At least $100,000 is to be invested in government bonds.
4. At least $100,000 is to be invested in money market funds.
5. At least $60,000 is to be invested in hi-tech stock.
6. At least $50,000 is to be invested in municipal bonds.

PROBLEM

We must determine the amount that should be invested in each investment alternative in order to maximize the annual return.

SOLUTION

Let

x_1 = amount invested in government bonds
x_2 = amount invested in money market funds
x_3 = amount invested in hi-tech stock
x_4 = amount invested in municipal bonds
Z = annual return

Since the objective is to maximize the annual return, the objective function is given by

$$\text{Maximize } Z = 0.075x_1 + 0.086x_2 + 0.135x_3 + 0.078x_4$$

subject to constraints that are determined as follows.

Constraint 1. Since the full amount of $600,000 must be invested, this gives

$$x_1 + x_2 + x_3 + x_4 = 600,000$$

Constraint 2. Since the average risk must be at most 3.5, this is formulated as follows. Using the risk levels given in the table, x_1, x_2, x_3, and x_4 dollars will be subjected to risk levels of 0, 2, 9, and 1, respectively. Thus, the average risk level, which must be at most 3.5, is given by

$$\frac{0x_1 + 2x_2 + 9x_3 + x_4}{600,000} \leq 3.5$$

Multiplying both sides of the above inequality by 600,000 gives

$$0x_1 + 2x_2 + 9x_3 + x_4 \leq 3.5(600,000)$$

or, equivalently,

$$2x_2 + 9x_3 + x_4 \leq 2,100,000$$

Constraint 3. Since at least $100,000 must be invested in government bonds, this gives

$$x_1 \geq 100,000$$

Constraint 4. Since at least $100,000 must be invested in money market funds, this gives

$$x_2 \geq 100,000$$

Constraint 5. Since at least $60,000 must be invested in hi-tech stock, this gives

$$x_3 \geq 60,000$$

Constraint 6. Since at least $50,000 must be invested in municipal bonds, this gives

$$x_4 \geq 50,000$$

Thus, our problem is formulated as

$$\text{Maximize } Z = 0.075x_1 + 0.086x_2 + 0.135x_3 + 0.078x_4$$

$$\text{subject to } x_1 + x_2 + x_3 + x_4 = 600,000$$

$$2x_2 + 9x_3 + x_4 \leq 2,100,000$$

$$x_1 \qquad\qquad\qquad \geq 100,000$$

$$x_2 \qquad\qquad \geq 100,000$$

$$x_3 \qquad \geq 60,000$$

$$x_4 \geq 50,000$$

where x_1, x_2, x_3, and $x_4 \geq 0$

Table 7-3 gives a computer solution to our linear programming problem. We proceed to the columns below the objective function value entitled "Variable" and "Value" and note the following.

INTERPRETATION OF THE COMPUTER SOLUTION

The optimal solution indicates the following:

- $x_1 = 244,444.469$ means that \$244,444.47 is invested in government bonds.

- $x_2 = 100,000$ means that \$100,000 is invested in money market funds.

- $x_3 = 205,555.547$ means that \$205,555.55 is invested in hi-tech stock.

- $x_4 = 50,000$ means that \$50,000 is invested in municipal bonds.

- The optimal annual return for this portfolio is given by the objective function value, \$58,583.34.

TABLE 7-3   Computer solution for portfolio selection problem

```
        Objective Function Value = 58583.336000

        Variable                    Value

          X1                   244444.469000
          X2                   100000.000000
          X3                   205555.547000
          X4                    50000.000000

        Constraint           Slack/Surplus          Dual Prices

          1                     0.000000              0.075000
          2                     0.000000              0.006667
          3                144444.469000              0.000000
          4                     0.000000             -0.002333
          5                145555.547000              .000000
          6                     0.000000             -0.003667
```

Objective Coefficient Ranges

Variable	Lower Limit	Current Value	Upper Limit
X1	0.072000	0.075000	0.135000
X2	No Lower Limit	0.086000	0.088333
X3	0.124500	0.135000	No Upper Limit
X4	No Lower Limit	0.078000	0.081667

Right-Hand-Side Ranges

Constraint	Lower Limit	Current Value	Upper Limit
1	455555.530000	600000.000000	No Upper Limit
2	790000.120000	2100000.000000	3400000.200000
3	No Lower Limit	100000.000000	244444.469000
4	0.000000	100000.000000	285714.3100000
5	No Lower Limit	60000.000000	205555.547000
6	0.000000	50000.000000	212500.031000

We now proceed to the "Slack/Surplus" and "Dual Prices" columns of the computer output and note that the dual prices are, in effect, shadow prices subject to the following interpretation.

SUMMARY

Dual Prices

1. The **dual price** for a constraint gives the *improvement in the optimal value of the objective function* resulting from a *1-unit increase in the right-hand-side value* of the constraint.

2. The meaning of the word *improvement* depends on whether the objective function is to be maximized or minimized. Specifically, if the objective function is to be

   - Maximized, improvement means an increase in its value.
   - Minimized, improvement means a decrease in its value.

3. Also,

   - A *positive dual price* means that the optimal value of an objective function will *improve*
   - A *negative dual price* means that the optimal value of an objective function will *not improve*

   as a result of an increase in the right-hand-side value of the associated constraint.

We return to the "Slack/Surplus" and "Dual Prices" columns of the computer output in Table 7-3. Note that for each constraint, its slack or surplus and dual price are given. Since, at this point, the interpretation of slack/surplus is obvious, we will not include these in our discussion. Our attention will be directed to the dual prices, which are interpreted as follows.

Constraint 1. Dual price = 0.075. This means that for each 1-unit increase in the right-hand-side value, 600,000, the optimal value of the objective function, $58,583.34, will improve by $0.075. (Remember, for an objective function that is to be maximized, to improve means to increase.) In other words, for each additional dollar invested, the optimal value of the objective function will increase by $0.075.

Constraint 2. Dual price = 0.006667. This means that for each 1-unit increase in the right-hand-side value, 2,100,000, the optimal value of the objective function will improve (increase) by 0.006667. Since the right-hand-side value, 2,100,000, is the product of the maximal tolerable risk level, 3.5, and 600,000 (return to the formulation of this problem to see this), then the above interpretation can be stated equivalently in terms of an increase in the maximal tolerable risk level as follows. Note that if the risk level, 3.5, is increased by 1 unit, then the right-hand-side value, 2,100,000, of the constraint is increased by 600,000 since $(3.5 + 1)(600,000) = 3.5(600,000) + 1(600,000)$. Thus, the product of the dual price, 0.006667, and 600,000, or

4000.20, gives the increase in the optimal value of the objective function resulting from a 1-point increase in the maximal tolerable risk level.

Constraint 3.   Dual price = 0.   Thus, a change in the right-hand-side value of this constraint has no effect on the value of the objective function. This coincides with the fact that this constraint is not binding.

Constraint 4.   Dual price = −0.002333.   This means that for each 1-unit increase in the right-hand-side value, 100,000, the optimal value of the objective function will not improve; in other words, it will decrease by $0.002333. (Remember that a negative dual price means the objective function will not improve.)

Constraint 5.   Dual price = 0.   Thus, a change in the right-hand-side value of this constraint has no effect on the value of the objective function. Again, this coincides with the fact that this constraint is not binding.

Constraint 6.   Dual price = −0.003667.   This means that for each unit increase in the right-hand-side value, 50,000, the optimal value of the objective function will not improve; in other words, it will decrease by $0.003667. (Remember that a negative dual price means the objective function will not improve.)

Note that binding constraints have nonzero dual prices, and nonbinding constraints have zero dual prices.

We will not discuss the portions of computer output labeled "Objective Coefficient Ranges" and "Right Hand Side Ranges." These topics are discussed in the next section.

Exercises 7-4

For each of the following:
a) Prepare the problem for solution by the simplex method; include slack, surplus, and artificial variables where needed.
b) Given the indicated optimal tableau (artificial variable columns are deleted), state the optimal solution.

1. Maximize $Z = 5x_1 + 8x_2 + 6x_3$
subject to
$$2x_1 + x_2 + 4x_3 \leq 190$$
$$x_1 + 2x_2 + 4x_3 \geq 20$$
$$x_1 + x_2 + x_3 = 160$$
where $x_1, x_2,$ and $x_3 \geq 0$

Optimal Tableau

x_1	x_2	x_3	s_1	s_2	Z	
1	0	−2	0	1	0	300
1	0	3	1	0	0	30
1	1	1	0	0	0	160
3	0	2	0	0	1	1280

2. Maximize $Z = 6x_1 + 2x_2 + 8x_3$
   subject to $4x_1 + 2x_2 + x_3 \leq 70$
   $\qquad\qquad 3x_1 + x_2 + 2x_3 \geq 15$
   where x_1, x_2, and $x_3 \geq 0$

Optimal Tableau

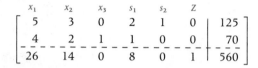

$$\begin{bmatrix} x_1 & x_2 & x_3 & s_1 & s_2 & Z & \\ 5 & 3 & 0 & 2 & 1 & 0 & 125 \\ 4 & 2 & 1 & 1 & 0 & 0 & 70 \\ \hline 26 & 14 & 0 & 8 & 0 & 1 & 560 \end{bmatrix}$$

For each of the following problems, the optimal tableau is given.
a) State the optimal solution.
b) Investigate the implications of the optimal solution.
c) Identify and interpret the shadow prices.

3. Maximize $Z = 10x_1 + 5x_2 + 9x_3$
   subject to $3x_1 + 2x_2 + 4x_3 \leq 100$
   $\qquad\qquad 2x_1 + 3x_2 + x_3 \leq 150$
   $\qquad\qquad x_1 + 5x_2 + 2x_3 \leq 160$
   where x_1, x_2, and $x_3 \geq 0$

Optimal Tableau

$$\begin{bmatrix} x_1 & x_2 & x_3 & s_1 & s_2 & s_3 & Z & \\ 1 & 0.667 & 1.333 & 0.333 & 0 & 0 & 0 & 33.333 \\ 0 & 1.667 & -1.667 & -0.667 & 1 & 0 & 0 & 83.333 \\ 0 & 4.333 & 0.667 & -0.333 & 0 & 1 & 0 & 126.667 \\ \hline 0 & 1.667 & 4.333 & 3.333 & 0 & 0 & 1 & 333.333 \end{bmatrix}$$

4. Maximize $Z = 20x_1 + 30x_2 + 15x_3$
   subject to $x_1 + x_2 + x_3 \leq 100$
   $\qquad\qquad 2x_1 + x_2 + 4x_3 \leq 260$
   $\qquad\qquad 3x_1 + 4x_2 + 5x_3 \leq 380$
   where x_1, x_2, and $x_3 \geq 0$

Optimal Tableau

$$\begin{bmatrix} x_1 & x_2 & x_3 & s_1 & s_2 & s_3 & Z & \\ 0.25 & 0 & -0.25 & 1 & 0 & -0.25 & 0 & 5 \\ 1.25 & 0 & 2.75 & 0 & 1 & -0.25 & 0 & 165 \\ 0.75 & 1 & 1.25 & 0 & 0 & 0.25 & 0 & 95 \\ \hline 2.5 & 0 & 22.5 & 0 & 0 & 7.5 & 1 & 2850 \end{bmatrix}$$

5. Maximize $Z = 4x_1 + 5x_2 + 7x_3$
   subject to $5x_1 + 8x_2 + 4x_3 \leq 180$
   $\qquad\qquad 2x_1 + x_2 + 5x_3 \leq 200$
   where x_1, x_2, and $x_3 \geq 0$

Optimal Tableau

$$\begin{bmatrix} x_1 & x_2 & x_3 & s_1 & s_2 & Z & \\ 0.472 & 1 & 0 & 0.139 & -0.111 & 0 & 2.778 \\ 0.306 & 0 & 1 & -0.028 & 0.222 & 0 & 39.444 \\ \hline 0.5 & 0 & 0 & 0.5 & 1 & 1 & 290 \end{bmatrix}$$

6. Maximize $Z = 50x_1 + 60x_2 + 90x_3$
subject to $7x_1 + 8x_2 + 9x_3 \leq 460$
$\qquad 5x_1 + 8x_2 + 2x_3 \leq 390$
where x_1, x_2, and $x_3 \geq 0$

Optimal Tableau

$$
\begin{array}{cccccc|c}
x_1 & x_2 & x_3 & s_1 & s_2 & Z & \\
0.778 & 0.889 & 1 & 0.111 & 0 & 0 & 51.111 \\
3.444 & 6.222 & 0 & -0.222 & 1 & 0 & 287.778 \\
\hline
20 & 20 & 0 & 10 & 0 & 1 & 4600
\end{array}
$$

Computer Solutions

For each of the following, a computer solution is given.
a)   State the optimal solution.
b)   Investigate the implications of the optimal solution.
c)   Interpret the dual prices.

7. Maximize $Z = 70x_1 + 90x_2 + 60x_3$
subject to $2x_1 + 5x_2 + 7x_3 \leq 560$
$\qquad 3x_1 + 5x_2 + 2x_3 \geq 100$
$\qquad x_1 + x_2 + x_3 = 200$
where x_1, x_2, and $x_3 \geq 0$

Optimal Solution

```
Objective Function Value =         15066.666000
        Variable              Value
```

Variable	Value
X1	146.666656
X2	53.333344
X3	0.000000

Constraint	Slack/Surplus	Dual Prices
1	0.000000	6.666664
2	606.666690	0.000000
3	0.000000	56.666672

8. Maximize $Z = 4x_1 + 6x_2 + 7x_3$
subject to $5x_1 + 8x_2 + 6x_3 = 150$
$\qquad 2x_1 + 5x_2 + 6x_3 \leq 600$
$\qquad x_1 + 3x_2 + 4x_3 \geq 100$
where x_1, x_2, and $x_3 \geq 0$

Optimal Solution

```
Objective Function Value =         175.000015
        Variable              Value
```

Variable	Value
X1	0.000000
X2	0.000000
X3	25.000004

Constraint	Slack/Surplus	Dual Prices
1	0.000000	1.166667
2	450.000000	0.000000
3	0.000000	0.000000

9. Minimize $Z = 10x_1 + 20x_2 + 15x_3$
subject to $x_1 + x_2 + x_3 \geq 100$
$2x_1 + x_2 + 4x_3 \leq 250$
$x_1 + 3x_2 + 2x_3 \geq 120$
where x_1, x_2, and $x_3 \geq 0$

Optimal Solution

```
Objective Function Value =        1100.000000
        Variable                Value
```

Variable	Value
X1	90.000008
X2	9.999992
X3	0.000000

Constraint	Slack/Surplus	Dual Prices
1	0.000000	−5.000000
2	59.999985	0.000000
3	0.000000	−5.000000

10. Minimize $Z = 5x_1 + 6x_2 + 4x_3$
subject to $2x_1 + 8x_2 + 5x_3 \leq 360$
$x_1 + 2x_2 + x_3 \geq 90$
$3x_1 + x_2 + 4x_3 \geq 70$
where x_1, x_2, and $x_3 \geq 0$

Optimal Solution

```
Objective Function Value =        280.526310
        Variable                Value
```

Variable	Value
X1	2.631581
X2	41.052631
X2	5.263157

Constraint	Slack/Surplus	Dual Prices
1	0.000000	0.473684
2	0.000000	−4.684211
3	0.000000	−0.421053

11. Minimize $Z = 6x_1 + 3x_2 + 5x_3$
subject to $3x_1 + 6x_2 + 8x_3 \geq 80$
$x_1 + 5x_2 + 8x_3 \leq 140$
$3x_1 + x_2 + 4x_3 \geq 130$
where x_1, x_2, and $x_3 \geq 0$

Optimal Solution

```
Objective Function Value =        216.500000
        Variable                Value
```

Variable	Value
X1	24.000002
X2	0.000000
X3	14.499999

Constraint	Slack/Surplus	Dual Prices
1	107.999992	0.000000
2	0.000000	0.450000
3	0.000000	−2.150000

12. Maximize $Z = 5x_1 + 4x_2 + 6x_3$
subject to $2x_1 + 6x_2 + 9x_3 \leq 390$
$\qquad\qquad x_1 + 3x_2 + 2x_3 \geq\ \ 50$
$\qquad\quad 4x_1 +\ \ x_2 +\ \ x_3 \leq 160$
where x_1, x_2, and $x_3 \geq 0$

Optimal Solution

```
Objective Function Value =              373.235320
         Variable                   Value
```

Variable	Value
X1	30.882355
X2	0.000000
X3	36.470589

Constraint	Slack/Surplus	Dual Prices
1	0.000000	0.558824
2	53.823532	0.000000
3	0.000000	0.970588

Applications

13. *Product mix.* The Comfort House Furniture Company manufactures three products: chairs, desks, and tables. The production process involves passing each product through each of three departments: cutting, assembly, and finishing and inspection. The available time (per month) for each department and the time requirements for each type of furniture are as follows:

Time requirements (hours)

Department	Chairs	Desks	Tables	Time availability (hours per month)
Cutting	30	20	10	46,000
Assembly	20	60	20	32,000
Finishing and Inspection	10	40	90	26,000

The profit per chair is $30, the profit per desk is $100, and the profit per table is $160. Management wishes to determine the quantity of each type of furniture to be produced in order to maximize profit and satisfy the departmental time constraints.

a) Formulate as a linear programming problem. The computer solution is given, and the formulation is given as part of the solution. Note that the computer solution uses $<$ to mean $\leq$ and $>$ to mean $\geq$.

b) Interpret the computer solution.

c) Investigate the implications of the optimal solution with regard to slack.

d) If additional hours are made available in the cutting department, what is the maximum amount that should be paid for each such hour?

e) If additional hours are made available in the assembly department, what is the maximum amount that should be paid for each such hour?

f) If additional hours are made available in the finishing and inspection department, what is the maximum amount that should be paid for each such hour?

COMPUTER SOLUTION

Linear Programming Problem

```
MAX 30x1 + 100x2 + 160x3
    S.T.
      1) 30x1 + 20x2 + 10x3 < 46000
      2) 20x1 + 60x2 + 20x3 < 32000
      3) 10x1 + 40x2 + 90x3 < 26000
```

Optimal Solution

Objective Function Value =   64250.008000

Variable	Value
X1	1475.000000
X2	0.000000
X3	125.000000

Constraint	Slack/Surplus	Dual Prices
1	500.001460	0.000000
2	0.000000	0.687500
3	0.000000	1.625000

14.   *Product mix.* Repeat Example 13 with the additional constraint that at least 40 desks (i.e., $x_2 \geq 40$) must be produced. The computer solution is given, and the formulation is given as part of the output. Note that the computer solution uses < in place of $\leq$ and > in place of $\geq$. Also, add part g to the list of questions repeated from Exercise 13.

g) If the right-hand-side value, 40, of constraint 4 is increased by 1 unit, how is the profit affected?

COMPUTER SOLUTION

Linear Programming Problem

```
MAX 30x1 + 100x2 + 160x3
    S.T.
      1) 30x1 + 20x2 + 10x3 <46000
      2) 20x1 + 60x2 + 20x3 <32000
      3) 10x1 + 40x2 + 90x3 <26000
      4) x2 >40
```

Optimal Solution

Objective Function Value =   64000.008000

Variable	Value
X1	1360.000000
X2	40.000000
X3	120.000000

Constraint	Slack/Surplus	Dual Prices
1	3200.001700	0.000000
2	0.000000	0.687500
3	0.000000	1.625000
4	0.000000	−6.250000

15. *Investment: Portfolio allocation.* A trust officer has $800,000 to allocate among the following investment alternatives.

Investment alternative	Rate of return	Risk factor
Treasury Bills	8.3%	0
Municipal Bonds	9.8	1
Real Estate	15.9	3
Mutual Fund	16.3	4
Energy Stocks	18.4	6

The investor will tolerate an average risk of no more than 5.7 and will invest no more than $200,000 in energy stocks. If the objective is to maximize annual return subject to the stated restrictions, how much should be allocated among the various investment alternatives?

a) Formulate as a linear programming problem. The computer solution is given, and the formulation is given as part of the solution. Note that the computer solution uses $<$ to mean $\leq$ and $>$ to mean $\geq$.

b) Interpret the computer solution.

c) Investigate the implications of the optimal solution with regard to slack.

d) If the amount invested, $800,000, is increased by $1, how is annual return affected?

e) If the restriction that no more than $200,000 can be invested in energy stocks is lifted, then each additional dollar invested in such stocks has what effect on the annual return? *Note:* This assumes that each such additional dollar is reallocated from the original portfolio of $800,000.

COMPUTER SOLUTION

Linear Programming Problem

```
MAX 0.083x1 + 0.098x2 + 0.159x3 + 0.163x4 + 0.184x5
    S.T.

    1) x1 + x2 + x3 + x4 + x5 = 800000
    2) 0x1 + x2 + 3x3 + 4x4 + 6x5 < 45600000
    3) x5 < 200000
```

Optimal Solution

```
Objective Function Value =     134600.000000
       Variable              Value
```

Variable	Value
X1	0.000000
X2	0.000000
X3	0.000000
X4	600000.000000
X5	200000.000000

Constraint	Slack Surplus	Dual Prices
1	0.000000	0.163000
2	960000.000000	0.000000
3	0.000000	0.021000

16. *Investment: Portfolio allocation.* Repeat Exercise 15 under the additional restriction that at least 40% of the invested money is to be allocated between Treasury bills and municipal bonds. The computer solution is given, and the formulation is given as part of the output. Note that the computer solution uses < in place of ≤ and > in place of ≥. Also, add part f to the list of questions repeated from Exercise 15.

f) If the right-hand-side value, 320,000, of constraint 4 is increased by 1 unit, what effect will this have on the annual return?

COMPUTER SOLUTION

Linear Programming Problem

```
MAX 0.083x1 + 0.098x2 + 0.159x3 + 0.163x4 + 0.184x5

    S.T.

    1) x1 + x2 + x3 + x4 + x5 = 800000
    2) 0x1 + x2 + 3x3 + 4x4 + 6x5 < 45600000
    3) x5 < 200000
    4) x1 + x2 > 320000

OPTIMAL SOLUTION

Objective Function Value =        113800.000000
```

Variable	Value
X1	0.000000
X2	320000.000000
X3	0.000000
X4	280000.000000
X5	200000.000000

Constraint	Slack/Surplus	Dual Prices
1	0.000000	0.163000
2	42960000.000000	0.000000
3	0.000000	0.021000
4	0.000000	−0.065000

17. *Transportation.* A company ships reprocessed polystyrene from two plants to three distribution centers, as illustrated below.

	Distribution center 1	Distribution center 2	Distribution center 3	Plant capacities
Plant 1	$400 x_1	$800 x_2	$600 x_3	≤ 50
Plant 2	$500 x_4	$700 x_5	$900 x_6	≤ 40
Demands	≥ 20	≥ 50	≥ 15	

Note that plants 1 and 2 have capacities of 50 and 40 truckloads, respectively. Distribution centers 1, 2, and 3 have demands of 20, 50, and 15 truckloads, respectively. The number in the upper left-hand corner of each cell represents the cost of shipping a truckload of reprocessed polystyrene from the corresponding plant to the corresponding distribution center. The number of truckloads of reprocessed polystyrene shipped from respective plants to respective distribution centers are denoted by x_1, x_2, x_3, x_4, x_5, and x_6. The company must determine how many truckloads to ship from each plant to each distribution center in order to minimize the total transportation cost.

a) Formulate as a linear programming problem. The computer solution is given, and the formulation is given as part of the solution. Note that the computer solution uses < to mean ≤ and > to mean ≥.

b) Interpret the computer solution.

c) Investigate the implications of the optimal solution with regard to slack and surplus.

d) Should plant 1 increase its plant capacity? Why or why not?

e) Should plant 2 increase its plant capacity? Why or why not?

f) If distribution center 1 increases its demand by 1 truckload, what effect will this have on the total transportation cost?

g) If distribution center 2 increases its demand by 1 truckload, what effect will this have on the total transportation cost?

h) If distribution center 3 increases its demand by 1 truckload, what effect will this have on the total transportation cost?

i) If there is a decrease in demand, from which distribution center will such a decrease result in the greatest reduction in the total transportation cost?

COMPUTER SOLUTION

Linear Programming Problem

```
MIN 400x1 + 800x2 + 600x3 + 500x4 + 700x5 + 900x6

    S.T.

      1) x1 + x2 + x3 < 50
      2) x4 + x5 + x6 < 40
      3) x1 + x4 > 20
      4) x2 + x5 > 50
      5) x3 + x6 > 15


OPTIMAL SOLUTION

Objective Function Value =        53000.000000
```

Variable	Value
X1	20.000000
X2	10.000000
X3	15.000000
X4	0.000000
X5	40.000000
X6	0.000000

Constraint	Slack/Surplus	Dual Prices
1	5.000000	0.000000
2	0.000000	100.000000
3	0.000000	−400.000000
4	0.000000	−800.000000
5	0.000000	−600.000000

18. *Break-even analysis.* The unit selling price, the variable cost per unit, and the fixed cost are given in the table below for each of three products produced by a company. The break-even point for each product is also given for intuitive purposes only since it will not be needed for subsequent computations or formulation.

	Selling price per unit	Variable cost per unit	Fixed cost	Break-even point
Product 1	$50	$30	$50,000	2500
Product 2	80	50	30,000	1000
Product 3	40	25	30,000	2000

The company wishes to determine how many units of each product it must produce and sell in order to break even and minimize the total variable cost subject to the following restrictions:

- Marketing research has indicated that no more than 4000 units of product 1 should be produced.
- The company has an order for 600 units of product 2. Thus, at least 600 units of product 2 must be produced and sold.
- The company has an order for 700 units of product 3. Thus, at least 700 units of product 3 must be produced and sold.

If x_1, x_2, and x_3 denote the number of units produced and sold of products 1, 2, and 3, respectively, then the requirement that the company *break even* means that

$$\text{total sales revenue} = \text{total cost}$$

where total sales revenue is given by the expression

$$50x_1 + 80x_2 + 40x_3 \quad \leftarrow \text{Total sales revenue}$$

and total cost is given by the expression

$$30x_1 + 50x_2 + 25x_3 + (50,000 + 30,000 + 30,000)$$
$$30x_1 + 50x_2 + 25x_3 + 110,000 \quad \leftarrow \text{Total cost}$$

Thus, to break even means that x_1, x_2, and x_3 satisfy the equation

$$\text{total sales revenue} = \text{total cost}$$
$$50x_1 + 80x_2 + 40x_3 = 30x_1 + 50x_2 + 25x_3 + 110,000$$

or, equivalently,

$$20x_1 + 30x_2 + 15x_3 = 110,000 \quad \leftarrow \text{Break-even constraint}$$

a) Formulate as a linear programming problem. The computer solution is given, and the formulation is given as part of the solution. Note that the computer solution uses $<$ to mean $\leq$ and $>$ to mean $\geq$.
b) Interpret the computer solution.
c) Investigate the implications of the optimal solution with regard to slack and surplus.
d) If the total fixed cost, $110,000, increases by $1, what effect will this have on the minimal total variable cost.
e) If the right-hand-side value, 4000, of the second constraint is increased by $1, what effect will this have on the minimal total variable cost?

COMPUTER SOLUTION

Linear Programming Problem

```
MIN 30x1 + 50x2 + 25x3
    S.T.
    1) 20x1 + 30x2 +15x3 = 110000
    2) x1 < 4000
    3) x2 > 600
    4) x3 > 700
```

```
OPTIMAL SOLUTION
Objective Function Value = 170000.000000
        Variable                Value
```

Variable	Value
X1	4000.000000
X2	650.000000
X3	700.000000

Constraint	Slack/Surplus	Dual Prices
1	0.000000	−1.666667
2	0.000000	3.333336
3	50.000000	0.000000
4	0.000000	0.000000

19. *Personnel scheduling.* Under normal conditions, the police officers of a certain town work 8-hour shifts. However, since the first shift starts at midnight, the second at 4:00 A.M., the third at 8:00 A.M., etc., as illustrated in the following table, there are 6 such 8-hour shifts.

Shift schedule

Shift	Starting time	Ending time
1	Midnight	8:00 A.M.
2	4:00 A.M.	Noon
3	8:00 A.M.	4:00 P.M.
4	Noon	8:00 P.M.
5	4:00 P.M.	Midnight
6	8:00 P.M.	4:00 A.M.

For personnel requirements, each 24-hour day is divided into 6 4-hour time intervals, as illustrated in the following table.

Personnel requirements

Times	Minimum number of police officers required
Midnight–4:00 A.M.	3
4:00 A.M.–8:00 A.M.	5
8:00 A.M.–noon	14
Noon–4:00 P.M.	16
4:00 P.M.–8:00 P.M.	14
8:00 P.M.–midnight	10

The problem is to determine how many officers should work each shift in order to minimize the total number of officers needed and satisfy the personnel requirements.

If

x_1 = number of officers working shift 1 (starting at midnight)

x_2 = number of officers working shift 2 (starting at 4:00 A.M.)

x_3 = number of officers working shift 3 (starting at 8:00 A.M.)

x_4 = number of officers working shift 4 (starting at noon)

x_5 = number of officers working shift 5 (starting at 4:00 P.M.)

x_6 = number of officers working shift 6 (starting at 8:00 P.M.)

this problem can be organized in terms of the following table.

Midnight to 4:00 A.M.	4:00 A.M. to 8:00 A.M.	8:00 A.M. to Noon	Noon to 4:00 P.M.	4:00 P.M. to 8:00 P.M.	8:00 P.M. to Midnight
x_1	x_1 x_2	x_2 x_3	x_3 x_4	x_4 x_5	x_5 x_6
x_6					
≥ 3	≥ 5	≥ 14	≥ 16	≥ 14	≥ 10

Minimal personnel requirements

a) Formulate as a linear programming problem. The computer solution is given, and the formulation is given as part of the solution. Note that the computer solution uses $<$ to mean $\leq$ and $>$ to mean $\geq$.
b) Inpterpret the computer solution.
c) State the total number of officers needed to satisfy minimal personnel requirements.
d) Investigate the implications of the optimal solution with regard to surplus.
e) If an additional police officer is needed during the 4:00 A.M.-8:00 A.M. time interval, what effect will this have on the total number of officers needed to satisfy personnel requirements?
f) If an additional officer is needed during the 8:00 A.M.-noon time interval, what effect will this have on the total number of officers needed to satisfy personnel requirements?

COMPUTER SOLUTION

Linear Programming Problem

```
MIN x1 + x2 + x3 + x4 + x5 + x6

    S.T.

        1) x1 + x6 > 3
        2) x1 + x2 > 5
        3) x2 + x3 > 14
        4) x3 + x4 > 16
        5) x4 + x5 > 14
        6) x5 + x6 > 10

OPTIMAL SOLUTION

Objective Function Value =        31.000000
```

Variable	Value
X1	3.000000
X2	2.000000
X3	12.000000
X4	4.000000
X5	10.000000
X6	0.000000

Constraint	Slack/Surplus	Dual Prices
1	0.000000	0.000000
2	0.000000	−1.000000
3	0.000000	0.000000
4	0.000000	−1.000000
5	0.000000	0.000000
6	0.000000	−1.000000

20. *Assignment problem.* Three workers are to be assigned to three jobs, so that each worker is assigned to only one job and each job has only one assigned worker. The cost of assigning a specific worker to a specific job is given in the upper left-hand corner of each cell in following table.

	Job 1	Job 2	Job 3	Capacities
Worker 1	$120 x_1	$150 x_2	$100 x_3	= 1
Worker 2	$170 x_4	$110 x_5	$140 x_6	= 1
Worker 3	$130 x_7	$160 x_8	$180 x_9	= 1
Demands	= 1	= 1	= 1	

In the above table, the variables x_1, x_2, x_3, x_4, x_5, and x_6 have values of either 0 or 1, depending on whether a specific worker is assigned to a specific job. In particular,

$$x_1 = \begin{cases} 1 & \text{if worker 1 is assigned to job 1} \\ 0 & \text{otherwise} \end{cases}$$

.
.
.

$$x_8 = \begin{cases} 1 & \text{if worker 3 is assigned to job 2} \\ 0 & \text{otherwise} \end{cases}$$

Note that an assignment problem can be viewed as a special case of a transportation problem where each supply is 1 and each demand is 1. This is why we have written = 1 in the rows corresponding to the workers (supply points) and the columns corresponding to the jobs (demand points). The problem is to determine which worker should be assigned to which job in order to minimize the total assignment cost.

a) Formulate as a linear programming problem. The computer solution is given, and the formulation is given as part of the solution. Note that the computer solution uses < to mean ≤ and > to mean ≥. We have written comments below in order to give insight to the meaning of some of the constraints.

b) Interpret the computer solution.

c) State the minimum total assignment cost.

Notes:

- Since there is only 1 of each worker and 1 of each job, the right-hand-side values of the constraints cannot change from 1. Thus, the dual variables, although given as part of the computer solution, have no meaning.

• Other specialized methods exist for solving assignment problems. These are discussed in management science and operations research texts.

COMPUTER SOLUTION

Linear Programming Problem

```
MIN 120x1 + 150x2 + 100x3 + 170x4 + 110x5 + 140x6 + 130x7
              + 160x8 + 180x9

    S.T.

    1) x1 + x2 + x3 = 1
    2) x4 + x5 + x6 = 1
    3) x7 + x8 + x9 = 1
    4) x1 + x4 + x7 = 1
    5) x2 + x5 + x8 = 1
    6) x3 + x6 + x9 = 1
```

Optimal Solution

Objective Function Value =   410.000000

Variable	Value
X1	1.000000
X2	0.000000
X3	0.000000
X4	0.000000
X5	1.000000
X6	0.000000
X7	0.000000
X8	0.000000
X9	1.000000

Constraint	Slack/Surplus	Dual Prices
1	0.000000	-135.000000
2	0.000000	-105.000000
3	0.000000	-145.000000
4	0.000000	15.000000
5	0.000000	-5.000000
6	0.000000	35.000000

7-5 • SENSITIVITY ANALYSIS

We begin by considering the following illustrative example.

Agriculture: Product Mix

A farmer has 55 acres available to grow tomatoes and peppers. Fertilizer requirements for each acre of tomatoes and peppers are 2 and 5 bags, respectively. The total number of bags of fertilizer must not exceed 200. Also, no more than 40 and 38 acres can be planted with tomatoes and peppers, respectively. The profits (in thousands of dollars) per acre for tomatoes and peppers are 3 and 6, respectively. The farmer wishes to determine the number of acres that should be planted with each crop in order to maximize the total profit.

The formulation for this problem is given below. Let

x_1 = number of acres planted with tomatoes

x_2 = number of acres planted with peppers

Z = total profit

Maximize $Z = 3x_1 + 6x_2$ Total profit

subject to $x_1 + x_2 \leq 55$ Acres

$2x_1 + 5x_2 \leq 200$ Bags of fertilizer

$x_1 \leq 40$ Tomatoes

$x_2 \leq 38$ Peppers

where x_1 and $x_2 \geq 0$

For reference purposes, we give the optimal tableau.

Optimal Tableau

slack variables

x_1	x_2	s_1	s_2	s_3	s_4	
0	0	2/3	−1/3	0	1	8
1	0	5/3	−1/3	0	0	25
0	0	−5/3	1/3	1	0	15
0	1	−2/3	1/3	0	0	30
0	0	1	1	0	0	255

Optimal Solution

$s_1 = 0, \quad s_2 = 0,$ $x_1 = 25, \quad x_2 = 30, \quad s_3 = 15, \quad s_4 = 8,$ $Z = 255$

Nonbasic variables   Basic variables, or basis   Objective function value

Thus, according to the optimal tableau,

x_1 = 25 acres of tomatoes should be planted

x_2 = 30 acres of peppers should be planted

This results in a maximum profit of 255 thousand dollars.

Sensitivity Analysis

After an optimal solution to a linear programming problem has been found, it is often desirable to study the effects of changes in the original problem. Such changes include the following:

1. Changes in the objective function coefficients
2. Changes in the right-hand-side values of the constraints
3. Changes in the constraint coefficients
4. The inclusion of additional variables to the problem
5. The inclusion of additional constraints to the problem

Discussion of most of these changes is usually reserved for more advanced texts in management science and operations research.

In this text, we discuss only the first two changes listed above. We note that discussion of changes in the objective coefficients and changes in the right-hand-side values is warranted as these coefficients are often estimates of their actual values. For example, in our agricultural product-mix problem, the objective function coefficients, 3 and 6, may not accurately represent the profits (in thousands of dollars) per acre for the two crops, so the farmer must be able to determine the effects on the optimal solution of changes in the objective function coefficients. A similar concern exists for the right-hand-side values of the constraints and also for the constraint coefficients.

Changes in the Objective Function Coefficients.   We begin by considering the effects of changes in the objective function coefficients for our illustrative agricultural example. Although we have stated the optimal tableau for this problem, we will use the graphical approach to explain these concepts. Thus, we give the graphical solution to our problem in Figure 7-5. Note that Figure 7-5(a) illustrates the determination of the feasible region and Figure 7-5(b) gives the feasible region, its vertex points, and the objective function.

We observe Figure 7-6 to study the effects of changes in the objective

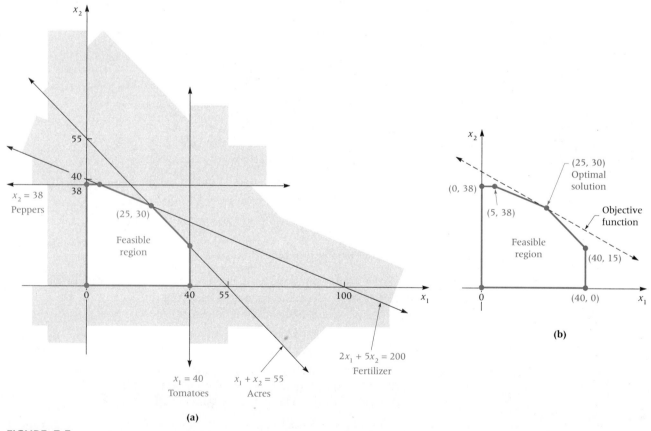

FIGURE 7-5

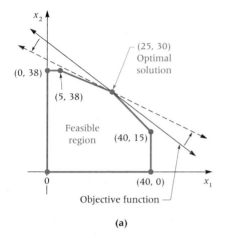

(a)

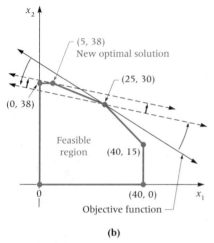

(b)

FIGURE 7-6

coeffients. First, we rewrite the equation of the objective function in slope-intercept form by solving for x_2 to obtain

$$x_2 = -\frac{3}{6}x_1 + \frac{Z}{6}$$

We consider the effects of a change in the objective function coefficient, 3, by noting that if 3 decreases, the slope of the objective function line becomes less steep and its graph rotates counterclockwise, as illustrated in Figure 7-6(a). Studying Figure 7-6(a), observe that if the graph of the objective function rotates so that it becomes the dotted line in Figure 7-6(a), the current optimal vertex point, (25, 30), remains optimal. In terms of the optimal tableau, this means that there is no change in the basic variables and their solution values. There would be a change in the optimal value of the objective function as one of its coefficients is changed. However, if the objective function coefficient, 3, decreases to the extent that the graph of the objective function becomes the dotted line of Figure 7-6(b), then a different vertex point, (5, 38), yields the optimal solution. In terms of the optimal tableau, this means that some of the basic variables might change and the solution values would change. Of course, the optimal value of the objective function would most likely change.

If the objective function coefficient, 3, increases, then its slope becomes steeper, and its graph would rotate clockwise, as illustrated in Figure 7-7(a) on page 462. Studying Figure 7-7(a), observe that if the graph of the objective function rotates so that it becomes the dotted line of Figure 7-7(a), then the current optimal vertex point, (25, 30), remains optimal. In terms of the optimal tableau, this means that there is no change in the basic variables and their solution values. The optimal value of the objective function would change as one of its coefficient is changed. However, if the objective function coefficient, 3, increases to the extent that its graph becomes the dotted line of Figure 7-7(b), then a different vertex point, (40, 15), yields the optimal solution. In terms of the optimal tableau, this means that basic variables might change and the solution values would change. Also, the optimal value of the objective function would most likely change.

Similar analyses could be performed regarding changes in the objective coefficient, 6, with analogous results. Thus, we state the following fundamental question regarding changes in an objective function coefficient.

QUESTION

By what amount can an objective function coefficient change in order that the optimal basis (in other words, the vertex point) remains optimal?

ANSWER

We consider this question for each objective function coefficient, one at a time. The answer involves the determination of a range (in other words, an interval) within which an objective function coefficient can vary without causing a change in the optimal basis (vertex point). More advanced texts in management science and operations research provide methods for computing such a range within which an objective function coefficient can vary without causing a change in the optimal basis. In this

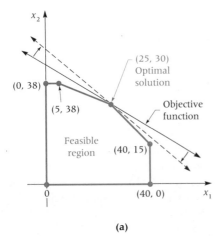

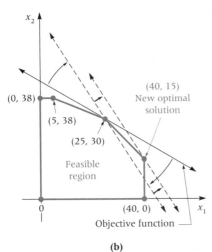

FIGURE 7-7

TABLE 7-4 **Computer solution for agriculture products-mix problem**

Linear Programming Problem

```
MAX  3x1 + 6x2
     S.T.
     1) x1 + x2 < 55
     2) 2x1 + 5x2 < 200
     3) x1 < 40
     4) x2 < 38
```

Optimal Solution

Objective Function Value =   254.999969

Variable	Value
X1	25.000000
X2	30.000004

Constraint	Slack/Surplus	Dual Prices
1	0.000000	1.000000
2	0.000000	1.000000
3	15.000000	0.000000
4	7.999996	0.000000

Objective Coefficient Ranges

Variable	Lower Limit	Current Value	Upper Limit
X1	2.400000	3.000000	5.999999
X2	3.000001	6.000000	7.500000

Right-Hand-Side Ranges

Constraint	Lower Limit	Current Value	Upper Limit
1	43.000008	55.000000	64.000000
2	155.000000	200.000000	223.999985
3	25.000000	40.000000	No Upper Limit
4	30.000004	38.000000	No Upper Limit

text, we will use computer results to determine such a range for each objective function coefficient.

COMPUTER SOLUTION

The computer solution for our illustrative agricultural product-mix problem is given in Table 7-4. Refer to the section of computer output entitled "Objective Coefficient Ranges," which we restate below.

Objective Coefficient Ranges

Variable	Lower Limit	Current Value	Upper Limit
X1	2.400000	3.000000	5.999999
X2	3.000001	6.000000	7.500000

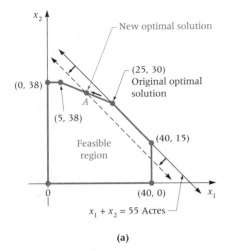

(a)

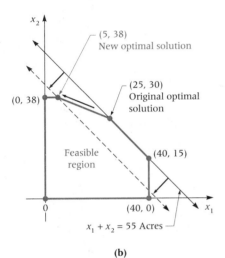

(b)

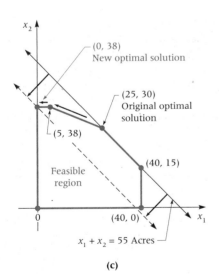

(c)

FIGURE 7-8

Observe that

1. For the objective function coefficient of x_1, its lower limit is 2.400000, its current value is 3.000000, and its upper limit is 5.999999. This means that the coefficient of x_1, the profit (in thousands of dollars) per acre for tomatoes, can vary anywhere between 2.4 and 5.999999 without causing a change in the optimal basis (vertex point). This assumes that the objective function coefficient of x_2, 6, remains constant.

2. For the objective function coefficient of x_2, its lower limit is 3.000001, its current value is 6.000000, and its upper limit is 7.500000. This means that the coefficient of x_2, the profit (in thousands of dollars) per acre for peppers, can vary anywhere between 3.000001 and 7.5 without causing a change in the optimal basis (vertex point).

We summarize as follows.

SUMMARY

Objective Coefficient Ranges

For a given variable, the **objective coefficient range** gives the interval within which the corresponding objective coefficient can vary without causing a change in the optimal basis (vertex point).

We now discuss changes in the right-hand-side values of the constraints.

Changes in the Right-Hand-Side Values. Refer to Figure 7-8, which gives the feasible region for the agricultural product-mix problem. Consider the effect of change in the right-hand-side value, 55, of the constraint $x_1 + x_2 \leq 55$. Observe that if 55 decreases, the constraint line becomes the dotted line of Figure 7-8(a), and the vertex point yielding the optimal solution shifts to point A. Observe that the feasible region has decreased in size. If 55 is decreased still further, as illustrated in Figure 7-8(b), the optimal vertex point shifts to (5, 38). In terms of the optimal tableau, this means that the optimal basis still contains x_1 and x_2, albeit with different solution values. At this point, $x_1 = 5$ and $x_2 = 38$. If 55 is decreased still further, so that the corresponding constraint line becomes the dotted line of Figure 7-8(c), the optimal vertex point shifts to (0, 38). In terms of the optimal tableau, this means that x_1 has now been driven to 0 and is no longer a basic variable. Thus, x_1 would be removed from the basis in the optimal tableau. Analogously, a similar analysis could be performed when considering an increase in the right-hand-side value, 55, of the first constraint. Also, similar analyses could be performed for changes in the right-hand-side values of the other constraints. We will not discuss these other changes since an understanding of the analysis regarding Figures 7-8 is sufficient for the development of an intuitive conception of changes in the right-hand-side value of a constraint. Thus, when we consider changes in the right-hand-side value of a constraint, we ask the following question.

QUESTION

By what amount can the right-hand-side value of a constraint change in order that the optimal basis remains feasible and, thus, the respective shadow price (or dual price) interpretation remains applicable?

Note that, as we stated in previous sections of this chapter, shadow (or dual) price interpretations are valid only for specific ranges within which the right-hand-side values can vary. Thus when we answer the above question, we are also finding the range within which the respective shadow (or dual) price interpretation is valid. Thus, the answer to the above question involves a range (in other words, an interval) within which the right-hand-side value can vary. As was the case for the objective coefficient ranges, the answer for each right-hand-side value presumes no change in the right-hand-side values of the other constraints.

ANSWER: COMPUTER SOLUTION

The answer to the above question is given within the computer solution of Table 7-4 in the section entitled "Right Hand Side Ranges." For convenience, we restate this portion below.

Right-Hand-Side Ranges

Constraint	Lower Limit	Current Value	Upper Limit
1	43.000008	55.000000	64.000000
2	155.000000	200.000000	223.999985
3	25.000000	40.000000	No Upper Limit
4	30.000004	38.000000	No Upper Limit

As with the objective coefficient ranges, here we are given a range for the right-hand-side value of each constraint. Thus, for each constraint, as long as its right-hand-side value is varied anywhere between the lower and the upper limits, the optimal basis remains feasible, and the shadow (or dual) price interpretation remains applicable. Note that for constraints 3 and 4, there is no upper limit. This means that the right-hand-side value for each of these constraints can increase indefinitely without causing the optimal basis to become infeasible.

We summarize as follows.

SUMMARY

Right-Hand-Side Ranges

For a given constraint, the **right-hand-side range** gives the interval within which the right-hand-side value can vary in order that the optimal basis remains feasible and the shadow (or dual) price interpretation remains valid.

DECISION-MAKING IMPLICATIONS

Using results from the computer solution of Table 7-4, we note the following:

Constraint 1. This constraint has no slack, it has a dual price of 1, and its right-hand-side value can vary anywhere from 43 to 64 for the shadow (or dual) price interpretation to be valid. Remember that the right-hand-side value, 55, represents the total number of acres available for planting, Since the slack in this constraint is 0, then all 55 acres are planted. The dual price, 1, means that for each additional acre planted (beyond the 55 acres), the total profit will increase by 1 thousand dollars. (Remember that profit was given in terms of thousands of dollars.) Thus, if the farmer can buy or lease additional acres, each such acre is worth at most 1 thousand dollars. In other words, an opportunity exists for the farmer to increase total profit if the farmer can buy or lease additional acreage for less than 1 thousand dollars per acre. This is valid up to a total of 64 (the upper right-hand-side range) acres.

Constraint 2. This constraint has no slack, it has dual price of 1, and its right-hand-side range has lower and upper limits of 155 and 223.999985, respectively. Remember that the right-hand-side value, 200, represents the total number of bags of fertilizer available. Since the slack in this constraint is 0, then all 200 bags of fertilizer are used. The dual price, 1, means that for each additional bag of fertilizer used (beyond the original 200 bags), the total profit will increase by 1 thousand dollars. (Remember that profit was given in terms of thousands of dollars.) In other words, each additional bag of fertilizer is worth at most 1 thousand dollars. This is valid up to a total amount of 223.999985, or approximately 224 (the upper right-hand-side range) bags. Thus, another opportunity exists for the farmer to increase profits if additional bags of fertilizer can be purchased for less than 1 thousand dollars per bag.

Exercises 7-5

For each of the following, a computer solution is given.
a) State the optimal solution.
b) Investigate the implications of the optimal solution with regard to slack and/or surplus.
c) Interpret the dual prices.
d) Interpret the objective function coefficient ranges.
e) Interpret the right-hand-side value ranges.

1. Maximize $Z = 4x_1 + 6x_2 + 8x_3$
subject to $2x_1 + 6x_2 + 5x_3 \leq 100$
$5x_1 + 2x_2 + x_3 \leq 180$
$5x_1 - 6x_2 + x_3 \leq 150$
where $x_1, x_2,$ and $x_3 \geq 0$
The computer solution is given on page 475.

2. Maximize $Z = 4x_1 + 9x_2 + 6x_3$
subject to $4x_1 - 2x_2 + 7x_3 \leq 70$
$2x_1 + 4x_2 + 6x_3 \leq 180$
$x_1 - 4x_2 + 9x_3 \geq 50$
where $x_1, x_2,$ and $x_3 \geq 0$
The computer solution is given on page 476.

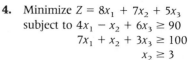

3. Minimize $Z = 8x_1 + 5x_2 + 9x_3$
subject to $2x_1 + 9x_2 + 5x_3 \geq 20$
$6x_1 + 4x_2 + x_3 \geq 60$
$x_1 - 2x_2 + 4x_3 \geq 40$
where $x_1, x_2,$ and $x_3 \geq 0$
The computer solution is given
on pages 476-477.

4. Minimize $Z = 8x_1 + 7x_2 + 5x_3$
subject to $4x_1 - x_2 + 6x_3 \geq 90$
$7x_1 + x_2 + 3x_3 \geq 100$
$x_2 \geq 3$
where $x_1, x_2,$ and $x_3 \geq 0$
The computer solution is given
on page 477.

5. Maximize $Z = 9x_1 + 8x_2 + 6x_3$
subject to $4x_1 + 2x_2 - x_3 \leq 70$
$5x_1 + 6x_2 + 8x_3 \leq 190$
$x_3 \geq 5$
where $x_1, x_2,$ and $x_3 \geq 0$
The computer solution is given
on page 478.

6. Minimize $Z = 9x_1 + 7x_2 + 5x_3$
subject to $6x_1 + 4x_2 + x_3 \geq 30$
$6x_1 - 8x_2 + 5x_3 \geq 20$
$x_2 \geq 2$
where $x_1, x_2,$ and $x_3 \geq 0$
The computer solution is given
on pages 478-479.

Applications

7. *Product mix.* A firm wishes to determine how many units of each of three products to produce during a given time period in order to maximize total profit and satisfy departmental labor constraints. The following table gives the person-hour requirements for each product in each department.

Person-hour requirements per unit of product

	Product A	Product B	Product C	Department capacity
Department 1	2	3	1	760
Department 2	1	2	4	600
Department 3	2	1	2	660

Profit per unit of product

Product A	Product B	Product C
$50	$40	$60

a) Formulate as a linear programming problem. The computer solution is given on page 479, and the formulation is given as part of the solution. Note that the computer solution uses < to mean ≤ and > to mean ≥.
b) Interpret the computer solution.
c) Investigate the implications of the optimal solution with regard to slack.
d) If additional person-hours are made available in department 1, what is the maximum amount that should be paid for each such hour?
e) Within what range of department 1's labor capacity is the answer to part d valid?
f) Which department's per unit increase in labor capacity yields the largest increase in total profit? An increase of 1 person-hour in this department has what effect on total profit? What is the upper limit on labor capacity in this department in order that these answers are valid?
g) Within what range can the unit profit for product B vary in order that the optimal basis remains the same?

8. *Product mix.* Repeat Exercise 7 under the added constraints that at least 80 and 55 units of products B and C must be produced, respectively. The computer solution is given on page 480.

9. *Diet.* A dietician must determine how many units of each of three food types to include in a diet so that the cost is minimized and nutritional requirements are realized. The following table gives the amounts of relevant nutrients contained per unit of each type of food.

Milligrams per unit of food type

	Food A	Food B	Food C
Protein	3	5	6
Calcium	6	12	5
Iron	4	2	1

Cost per unit of food type

Food A	Food B	Food C
$30	$20	$35

Minimal nutritional requirements (in milligrams)

Protein	30
Calcium	72
Iron	15

a) Formulate as a linear programming problem. The computer solution is given on pages 480-481, and the formulation is given as part of the solution. Note that the computer solution uses < to mean ≤ and > to mean ≥.

b) Interpret the computer solution.

c) Investigate the implications of the optimal solution with regard to surplus.

d) If the minimal protein requirement is decreased by 1 milligram, what effect will this have on the optimal diet cost?

e) A 1-milligram decrease in which minimal nutritional requirement yields the largest decrease in the optimal diet cost? State the amount of this decrease in diet cost. How low can the minimal requirement for this nutrient get in order that these answers are valid?

f) Within what range can the unit cost of food B vary in order that the optimal basis remains the same?

g) Within what range can the unit cost of food C vary in order that the optimal basis remains the same?

10. *Transportation problem.* The costs of shipping a unit of product from plants to warehouses are given in the upper left-hand corners of the cells in the following table. Also given are plant capacity and minimal demand requirements.

	Warehouse 1	Warehouse 2	Capacities
Plant 1	$80 x_1	$120 x_2	≤ 800
Plant 2	$100 x_3	$110 x_4	≤ 600
Demands	≥ 500	≥ 700	

The company must determine how many units to ship from each plant to each warehouse in order to minimize the total transportation cost and satisfy plant capacity and demand requirements.

a) Formulate as a linear programming problem. The computer solution is given on pages 481-482, and the formulation is given as part of the solution. Note that the computer solution uses $<$ to mean $\leq$ and $>$ to mean $\geq$.

b) Interpret the computer solution.

c) Investigate the implications of the optimal solution with regard to slack and surplus.

d) Which plant's capacity should be increased so that the optimal transportation cost can be further decreased? A unit increase in this plant's capacity decreases the optimal transportation cost by how much? State the upper limit on this plant's capacity in order that these answers are valid.

e) Within what range can the unit transportation cost of $80 vary in order that the optimal basis remains the same?

f) Within what range can the unit transportation cost of $100 vary in order that the optimal basis remains the same?

11. *Production assignments.* The unit costs of producing each of three products at each of two plants are given in the upper left-hand corners of the cells in the following table. Also given are plant capacity and demand requirements for the products. We must determine how many units of each product should be produced at each plant in order to minimize the total production cost and satisfy capacity and demand requirements. The solutions are denoted by x_1, x_2, x_3, x_4, x_5, and x_6 in the following table.

Unit costs

	Product A	Product B	Product C	Capacities
Plant 1	$80 x_1	$100 x_2	$150 x_3	≤ 900
Plant 2	$90 x_4	$70 x_5	$60 x_6	≤ 1000
Demands	≥ 800	≥ 600	≥ 400	

a) Formulate as a linear programming problem. The computer solution is given on pages 482-483, and the formulation is given as part of the solution. Note that the computer solution uses $<$ to mean $\leq$ and $>$ to mean $\geq$.

b) Interpret the computer solution.

c) Investigate the implications of the optimal solution with regard to slack and surplus.

d) Should management increase the capacity of either plant in order to further decrease the minimal production cost? Why or why not?

e) If the minimal demand requirement for product C is increased by 1 unit, what effect will this have on the optimal production cost?

f) If the minimal demand requirement for product B is decreased by 1 unit, what effect will this have on the optimal production cost?

g) The per unit decrease in the minimal requirement for which product would result in the largest decrease in the optimal production cost? Give the amount of the decrease. What is the lower limit on the minimal requirement for this product in order that these answers are valid?

h) The cost of producing product A at plant 2 can vary within what range in order that the optimal basis remains the same?

i) The cost of producing product C at plant 2 can vary within what range in order that the optimal basis remains the same?

12. *Marketing research: Survey planning?.* A pharmaceutical firm plans to survey two types of medical doctors in two cities. The costs of interviewing each type of doctor in each city are given in the upper left-hand corners of the corresponding cells in the following table. Also indicated are the requirements that at least 150 general practitioners and at least 120 specialists must be interviewed and that at most 200 and 250 doctors from cities 1 and 2, respectively, must be interviewed. The firm must determine how many of each type of doctor in each city should be interviewed in order to minimize the total interview cost and satisfy the stated requirements. Note that $x_1, x_2, x_3,$ and x_4 denote the solution values.

	City 1	City 2	Minimum number to be interviewed (by type)
General Practitioners	$50 x_1	$70 x_2	≥ 150
Specialists	$60 x_3	$90 x_4	≥ 120
Maximum Number to be Interviewed (by city)	≤ 200	≤ 250	

a) Formulate as a linear programming problem. The computer solution is given on page 483, and the formulation is given as part of the solution. Note that the computer solution uses $<$ to mean $\leq$ and $>$ to mean $\geq$.

b) Interpret the computer solution.

c) Investigate the implications of the optimal solution with regard to slack and surplus.

d) If the maximum number of doctors to be interviewed from city 1, 200, is increased by 1, what effect will this have on the total interview cost? Within what range is this answer valid?

e) If the minimal number of specialists to be interviewed, 120, is increased by 1, what effect will this have on the total interview cost? Within what range is this answer valid?

f) Within what range can the cost of interviewing a general practitioner in city 2 vary in order that the optimal basis remains the same?

13. *Marketing research: Survey planning.* Repeat Exercise 12 under the added requirement that at least 20 specialists in city 2 must be interviewed. The computer solution is given on page 484.

14. *Investment: Portfolio allocation.* An investor has $8,000,000 to allocate among the following investment alternatives.

Investment alternative	Projected rate of return	Maximum amount invested
Bonds	10%	$2,500,000
Stocks	20	4,000,000
Real Estate	15	2,000,000
Collectibles	25	500,000

The maximum amounts to be invested in the various investment alternatives are also stated above. How much should be invested in each alternative in order to maximize the projected annual return and satisfy the stated restrictions?

a) Formulate as a linear programming problem. The computer solution is given on pages 484-485, and the formulation is given as part of the solution. Note that the computer solution uses < to mean ≤ and > to mean ≥.

b) Interpret the computer solution.

c) Investigate the implications of the optimal solution with regard to slack.

d) If the constraint on the amount invested in bonds, $2,500,000, is increased by $1, what effect will this have on the optimal projected annual return? Within what range is this answer valid?

e) If the constraint on the amount invested in collectibles, $500,000, is increased by $1, what effect will this have on the optimal projected annual return? Within what range is this answer valid?

f) Within what range can the rate of return on bonds vary in order that the optimal basis remains the same?

g) Within what range can the rate of return on stocks vary in order that the optimal basis remains the same?

15. *Investment: Portfolio allocation.* A financial planner has $5,000,000 to invest for a client. This is to be allocated among the following investment alternatives.

Investment alternative	Projected rate of return	Risk factor
Money Market Funds	7%	0
Mutual Funds	15	3
Growth and Income Stocks	18	5
Aggressive Growth Stocks	25	9

If the investor wants an average risk no larger than 4.7, how much should be invested in each alternative in order to maximize the projected annual return?

a) Formulate as a linear programming problem. The computer solution is given on pages 485-486, and the formulation is given as part of the solution. Note that the computer solution uses < to mean ≤ and > to mean ≥.

b) Interpret the computer solution.

c) Investigate the implications of the optimal solution with regard to slack.

d) If the constraint on the total amount invested, $5,000,000, is increased by $1, what effect will this have on the optimal projected annual return? Within what range is this answer valid?

e) Within what range can the projected rate of return for aggressive growth stocks vary in order that the optimal basis remains the same?

16. *Investment: Portfolio allocation.* Repeat Exercise 15 under the added constraint that at least $700,000 must be invested in growth and income stocks. The computer solution is given on page 486.

17. *Break-even analysis.* The unit selling price, the variable cost per unit, and the fixed cost are given in the following table for each of three products produced

by a company. The break-even point for each product is also given for intuitive purposes only since it will not be needed for subsequent computations or formulation.

	Selling price per unit	Variable cost per unit	Fixed cost	Break-even point
Product 1	$80	$30	$15,000	300
Product 2	120	50	28,000	400
Product 3	90	50	20,000	500

The company wishes to determine how many units of each product it must produce and sell in order to break even and minimize the total variable cost subject to the following restrictions:

- The company has orders for 200 units of product 1 and 400 units of product 3. Thus, at least 200 and 400 units of products 1 and 2, respectively, must be produced.
- Marketing research has indicated that no more than 300 units of product 2 should be produced.

a) Formulate as a linear programming problem. The computer solution is given on page 487, and the formulation is given as part of the solution. Note that the computer solution uses < to mean ≤ and > to mean ≥.

b) Interpret the computer solution.

c) Investigate the implications of the optimal solution with regard to slack.

d) If the total fixed cost, $63,000, is increased by $1, what effect will this have on the optimal total variable cost? Within what range is this answer valid?

e) If the right-hand-side value, 400, of the product 3 constraint decreases by $1, what effect will this have on the optimal total variable cost? Within what range is this answer valid?

f) Within what range can the variable cost per unit for product 1 vary in order that the optimal basis remains the same?

g) Within what range can the variable cost per unit for product 3 vary in order that the optimal basis remains the same?

18. *Scheduling: Personnel requirements.* Under normal conditions, waiters and waitresses at a 24-hour restaurant work 8-hour shifts. Since the first shift starts at midnight, the second at 4:00 A.M., the third at 8:00 A.M., etc., as illustrated in the following table, there are 6 such 8-hour shifts.

Shift schedule

Shift	Starting time	Ending time
1	Midnight	8:00 A.M.
2	4:00 A.M.	Noon
3	8:00 A.M.	4:00 P.M.
4	Noon	8:00 P.M.
5	4:00 P.M.	Midnight
6	8:00 P.M.	4:00 A.M.

For personnel requirements, each 24-hour day is divided into 6 4-hour time intervals, as illustrated in the following table.

Personnel requirements

Times	Minimum number of waiters and/or waitresses required
Midnight–4:00 A.M.	30
4:00 A.M.–8:00 A.M	35
8:00 A.M.–Noon	70
Noon–4:00 P.M.	45
4:00 P.M.–8:00 P.M.	55
8:00 P.M.–midnight	20

The problem is to determine how many waiters and/or waitresses should work each shift in order to minimize the total number needed and satisfy the personnel requirements.

If

x_1 = number of waiters and/or waitresses working shift 1 (starting at midnight)

x_2 = number of waiters and/or waitresses working shift 2 (starting at 4:00 A.M.)

x_3 = number of waiters and/or waitresses working shift 3 (starting at 8:00 A.M.)

x_4 = number of waiters and/or waitresses working shift 4 (starting at noon)

x_5 = number of waiters and/or waitresses working shift 5 (starting at 4:00 P.M.)

x_6 = number of waiters and/or waitresses working shift 6 (starting at 8:00 P.M.)

This problem can be organized in terms of the following table.

Midnight to 4:00 A.M.	4:00 A.M. to 8:00 A.M.	8:00 A.M. to noon	Noon to 4:00 P.M.	4:00 P.M. to 8:00 P.M.	8:00 P.M. to midnight
x_1	x_1				
	x_2	x_2			
		x_3	x_3		
			x_4	x_4	
				x_5	x_5
x_6					x_6
≥ 30	≥ 35	≥ 70	≥ 45	≥ 55	≥ 20

Minimal personnel requirements

a) Formulate as a linear programming problem. The computer solution is given on pages 487-488, and the formulation is given as part of the solution. Note that the computer solution uses < to mean ≤ and > to mean ≥.

b) Interpret the computer solution.

c) State the total number of waiters and/or waitresses needed to satisfy minimal personnel requirements.

d) Investigate the implications of the optimal solution with regard to surplus.

e) If an additional waiter or waitress is needed during the 4:00 A.M.–8:00 A.M. time interval, what effect would this have on the total number needed to satisfy personnel requirements? Within what range is this answer valid?

f) If an additional waiter or waitress is needed during the 8:00 A.M.-noon time interval, what effect would this have on the total number needed to satisfy personnel requirements? Within what range is this answer valid?

Computer Exercises

Use a computer software package to solve the following exercises.

19. *Product mix.* A company makes three products, each of which uses three raw materials, as outlined below.

Raw material requirements (in pounds) per unit of product

	Product A	Product B	Product C
Raw Material 1	3	2	5
Raw Material 2	2	4	6
Raw Material 3	4	2	7

Profit per unit of product

Product A	Product B	Product C
$90	$60	$70

Raw material capacity (in pounds)

Raw Material 1	30,000
Raw Material 2	33,000
Raw Material 3	37,000

Minimal product demand (in units)

Product A	800
Product B	400
Product C	500

The company must determine how many units of each product to produce in order to maximize profit and satisfy raw material and product demand constraints.

a) Formulate as a linear programming problem.

b) Solve by using a computer software package.

c) Interpret the computer solution.

d) Investigate the implications of the optimal solution with regard to slack and surplus.

e) If additional pounds of raw material 1 are made available, what is the maximum amount that should be paid for each such pound?

f) If additional pounds of raw material 2 are made available, what is the maximum amount that should be paid for each such pound? This answer is valid for how many additional pounds of raw material 2?

g) For which raw material does a per unit increase yield the largest increase in total profit? An increase of 1 unit of this raw material has what effect on total profit? What is the upper limit on the amount available of this raw material in order that these answers are valid?

h) Within what range can the unit profit for product B vary in order that the optimal basis remains the same?

20. *Production planning.* A production manager must decide how many units of each of three products to produce on each of three machines. The same number of units of a particular product need not be produced on all three machines. Relevant information is given below. Here x_1, x_2, x_3, x_4, x_5, x_6, x_7, x_8, and x_9 denote the solution values.

Per unit cost of each product on each machine

	Product A	Product B	Product C
Machine 1	$10 x_1	$8 x_2	$12 x_3
Machine 2	$15 x_4	$9 x_5	$13 x_6
Machine 3	$12 x_7	$11 x_8	$15 x_9

Per unit labor requirements (In person-hours) for each product on each machine

	Product A	Product B	Product C
Machine 1	0.50 x_1	0.80 x_2	0.20 x_3
Machine 2	0.60 x_4	1.00 x_5	0.40 x_6
Machine 3	0.70 x_7	0.90 x_8	0.30 x_9

Labor capacity (in person-hours)

Machine 1	1600
Machine 2	2400
Machine 3	1800

Minimal product demand (in units)

Product A	2700
Product B	2400
Product C	3400

The production manager must determine how many units of each product to produce on each machine in order to minimize the total production cost and satisfy labor capacity and demand constraints.

a) Formulate as a linear programming problem.
b) Solve by using a computer software package.
c) Interpret the computer solution.
d) Investigate the implications of the optimal solution with regard to slack and surplus.

e) If additional person-hours are made available on machine 1, what is the maximum amount that should be paid for each such person-hour? This answer is valid for how many additional person-hours?

f) If additional person-hours are made available on machine 3, what is the maximum amount that should be paid for each such person-hour? This answer is valid for how many additional person-hours?

g) For which machine does a per unit increase in person-hours yield the largest increase in total profit? An increase of 1 person-hour in the labor capacity of this machine has what effect on total profit? What is the upper limit on this machine's labor capacity in order that these answers are valid?

h) Within what range can the unit cost for product B on machine 1 vary in order that the optimal basis remains the same?

i) Within what range can the unit cost for product A on machine 3 vary in order that the optimal basis remains the same?

Computer Solutions

Computer Solution for Exercise 1

Linear Programming Problem

```
MAX 4x1 + 6x2 + 8x3

    S.T.

    1) 2x1 + 6x2 + 5x3 < 100
    2) 5x1 + 2x2 + x3 ≤ 180
    3) 5x1 - 6x2 + x3 < 150
```

Optimal Solution

Objective Function Value =   182.608704

Variable	Value
X1	28.260870
X2	0.000000
X3	8.695653

Constraint	Slack/Surplus	Dual Prices
1	0.000000	1.565217
2	30.000000	0.000000
3	0.000000	0.173913

Objective Coefficient Ranges

Variable	Lower Limit	Current Value	Upper Limit
X1	3.200000	4.000000	5.500000
X2	No Lower Limit	6.000000	8.347826
X3	6.714285	8.000000	10.000000

Right-Hand-Side Ranges

Constraint	Lower Limit	Current Value	Upper Limit
1	59.999996	100.000000	750.000000
2	150.000000	180.000000	No Upper Limit
3	20.000000	150.000000	180.000000

Computer Solution for Exercise 2

Linear Programming Problem

```
MAX 4x1 + 9x2 + 6x3
    S.T.

    1) 4x1 - 2x2 + 7x3 < 70
    2) 2x1 + 4x2 + 6x3 < 180
    3) x1 - 4x2 + 9x3 > 50
```

Optimal Solution

Objective Function Value =   292.222230

Variable	Value
X1	2.222222
X2	21.555553
X3	14.888887

Constraint	Slack/Surplus	Dual Prices
1	0.000000	0.333333
2	0.000000	1.694444
3	0.000000	-0.722222

Objective Coefficient Ranges

Variable	Lower Limit	Current Value	Upper Limit
X1	3.000000	4.000000	34.500000
X2	-1.517241	9.000000	14.000002
X3	-15.785715	6.000000	11.000002

Right-Hand-Side Ranges

Constraint	Lower Limit	Current Value	Upper Limit
1	63.333332	70.000000	293.333310
2	46.206909	180.000000	220.000000
3	-84.000000	50.000000	60.000000

Computer Solution for Exercise 3

Linear Programming Problem

```
MIN 8x1 + 5x2 + 9x3
    S.T.

    1) 2x1 + 9x2 + 5x3 > 20
    2) 6x1 + 4x2 + x3 > 60
    3) x1 - 2x2 + 4x3 > 40
```

Optimal Solution

Objective Function Value =   140.000000

Variable	Value
X1	8.695652
X2	0.000000
X3	7.826086

Constraint	Slack/Surplus	Dual Prices
1	36.521736	0.000000
2	0.000000	-1.000000
3	0.000000	-2.000000

Objective Coefficient Ranges

Variable	Lower Limit	Current Value	Upper Limit
X1	2.250000	8.000000	14.388889
X2	0.000000	5.000000	No Upper Limit
X3	1.812500	9.000000	32.000000

Right-Hand-Side Ranges

Constraint	Lower Limit	Current Value	Upper Limit
1	No Lower Limit	20.000000	56.521736
2	10.000000	60.000000	239.999969
3	10.000004	40.000000	240.000000

Computer Solution for Exercise 4
Linear Programming Problem

```
MIN 8x1 + 7x2 + 5x3
    S.T.
    1) 4x1 - x2 + 6x3 >  90
    2) 7x1 + x2 + 3x3 > 100
    3) x2 > 3
```

Optimal Solution

Objective Function Value =   145.633331

Variable	Value
X1	10.100001
X2	3.000000
X3	8.766666

Constraint	Slack/Surplus	Dual Prices
1	0.000000	-0.366667
2	0.000000	-0.933333
3	0.000000	-6.433333

Objective Coefficient Ranges

Variable	Lower Limit	Current Value	Upper Limit
X1	3.333333	8.000000	11.666665
X2	0.566667	7.000000	No Upper Limit
X3	3.428572	5.000000	12.000000

Right-Hand-Side Ranges

Constraint	Lower Limit	Current Value	Upper Limit
1	52.428574	90.000000	191.000000
2	49.499996	100.000000	165.750000
3	0.000000	3.000000	36.666668

Computer Solution for Exercise 5
Linear Programming Problem

```
MAX 9x1 + 8x2 + 6x3
    S.T.
    1) 4x1 + 2x2 - x3 < 70
    2) 6x1 + 6x2 + 8x3 < 190
    3) x3 > 5
```

Optimal Solution

Objective Function Value = 255.000000

Variable	Value
X1	10.714285
X2	16.071430
X3	5.000000

Constraint	Slack/Surplus	Dual Prices
1	0.000000	1.000000
2	0.000000	1.000000
3	0.000000	-0.999999

Objective Coefficient Ranges

Variable	Lower Limit	Current Value	Upper Limit
X1	6.666666	9.000000	9.636363
X2	7.621622	8.000000	10.800001
X3	No Lower Limit	6.000000	6.999999

Right-Hand-Side Ranges

Constraint	Lower Limit	Current Value	Upper Limit
1	45.000000	70.000000	115.000015
2	133.750000	190.000000	265.000000
3	0.000000	5.000000	11.081082

Computer Solution for Exercise 6
Linear Programming Problem

```
MIN 9x1 + 7x2 + 5x3
    S.T.
    1) 6x1 + 4x2 + x3 > 30
    2) 6x1 - 8x2 + 5x3 > 20
    3) x2 > 2
```

Optimal Solution

Objective Function Value = 59.250000

Variable	Value
X1	3.083334
X2	2.000000
X3	3.500000

Constraint	Slack/Surplus	Dual Prices
1	0.000000	-0.625000
2	0.000000	-0.875000
3	0.000000	-11.499999

Objective Coefficient Ranges

Variable	Lower Limit	Current Value	Upper Limit
X1	6.000000	9.000000	18.857142
X2	-4.499999	7.000000	No Upper Limit
X3	1.500000	5.000000	7.500001

Right-Hand-Side Ranges

Constraint	Lower Limit	Current Value	Upper Limit
1	15.200000	30.000000	44.000000
2	6.000000	30.000000	92.999992
3	0.833333	2.000000	4.642857

Computer Solution for Exercise 7
Linear Programming Problem

```
MAX 50x1 + 40x2 + 60x3
    S.T.
    1) 2x1 + 3x2 + x3 < 760
    2) x1 + 2x2 + 4x3 < 600
    3) 2x1 + x2 + 2x3 < 660
```

Optimal Solution

Objective Function Value =   18160.000000

Variable	Value
X1	240.000000
X2	75.999969
X3	51.999992

Constraint	Slack/Surplus	Dual Prices
1	0.000000	4.000000
2	0.000000	4.666664
3	0.000000	18.666668

Objective Coefficient Ranges

Variable	Lower Limit	Current Value	Upper Limit
X1	21.999998	50.000000	63.999992
X2	30.000000	40.000000	80.000000
X3	42.500008	60.000000	80.000000

Right-Hand-Side Ranges

Constraint	Lower Limit	Current Value	Upper Limit
1	570.000060	760.000000	1020.000000
2	405.000000	600.000000	1320.000000
3	300.000000	660.000000	822.857060

Computer Solution for Exercise 8

Linear Programming Problem

```
MAX 50x1 + 40x2 + 60x3
    S.T.
      1) 2x1 + 3x2 + x3 < 760
      2) x1 + 2x2 + 4x3 < 600
      3) 2x1 + x2 + 2x3 < 660
      4) x2 > 80
      5) x3 > 55
```

Optimal Solution

Objective Function Value =   17500.000000

Variable	Value
X1	220.000000
X2	80.000000
X3	55.000000

Constraint	Slack/Surplus	Dual Prices
1	25.000000	0.000000
2	0.000000	50.000000
3	30.000000	0.000000
4	0.000000	-60.000000
5	0.000000	-140.000000

Objective Coefficient Ranges

Variable	Lower Limit	Current Value	Upper Limit
X1	20.000000	50.000000	No Upper Limit
X2	No Lower Limit	40.000000	100.000000
X3	No Lower Limit	60.000000	200.000000

Right-Hand-Side Ranges

Constraint	Lower Limit	Current Value	Upper Limit
1	735.000000	760.000000	No Upper Limit
2	380.000000	600.000000	612.500000
3	630.000000	660.000000	No Upper Limit
4	70.000000	80.000000	190.000000
5	51.428570	55.000000	110.000000

Computer Solution for Exercise 9

Linear Programming Problem

```
MIN 30x1 + 20x2 + 35x3
    S.T.
      1) 3x1 + 5x2 + 6x3 > 30
      2) 6x1 + 12x2 + 5x3 > 72
      3) 4x1 + 2x2 + x3 > 15
```

Optimal Solution

```
Objective Function Value =    140.000015
```

Variable	Value
X1	1.000000
X2	5.500000
X3	0.000000

Constraint	Slack/Surplus	Dual Prices
1	0.499998	0.000000
2	0.000000	-0.555556
3	0.000000	-6.666667

Objective Coefficient Ranges

Variable	Lower Limit	Current Value	Upper Limit
X1	10.000002	30.000000	40.000004
X2	14.999998	20.000000	59.999996
X3	9.444445	35.000000	No Upper Limit

Right-Hand-Side Ranges

Constraint	Lower Limit	Current Value	Upper Limit
1	No Lower Limit	30.000000	30.499998
2	70.714287	72.000000	90.000000
3	12.000011	15.000000	48.000000

Computer Solution for Exercise 10

Linear Programming Problem

```
MIN 80x1 + 120x2 + 100x3 + 110x4
    S.T.
    1) x1 + x2 < 800
    2) x3 + x4 < 600
    3) x1 + x3 > 500
    4) x2 + x4 > 700
```

Optimal Solution

```
Objective Function Value =    118000.000000
```

Variable	Value
X1	500.000000
X2	100.000000
X3	0.000000
X4	600.000000

Constraint	Slack/Surplus	Dual Prices
1	200.000000	0.000000
2	0.000000	10.000000
3	0.000000	-80.000000
4	0.000000	-120.000000

Objective Coefficient Ranges

Variable	Lower Limit	Current Value	Upper Limit
X1	0.000000	80.000000	110.000000
X2	110.000000	120.000000	No Upper Limit
X3	70.000000	100.000000	No Upper Limit
X4	No Lower Limit	110.000000	120.000000

Right-Hand-Side Ranges

Constraint	Lower Limit	Current Value	Upper Limit
1	600.000000	800.000000	No Upper Limit
2	400.000000	600.000000	700.000000
3	0.000000	500.000000	700.000000
4	600.000000	700.000000	900.000000

Computer Solution for Exercise 11

Linear Programming Problem

```
MIN 80x1 + 100x2 + 150x3 + 90x4 + 70x5 + 60x6
    S.T.
      1) x1 + x2 + x3 < 900
      2) x4 + x5 + x6 < 1000
      3) x1 + x4 > 800
      4) x2 + x5 > 600
      5) x3 + x6 > 400
```

Optimal Solution

Objective Function Value =   110000.000000

Variable	Value
X1	800.000000
X2	0.000000
X3	0.000000
X4	0.000000
X5	600.000000
X6	400.000000

Constraint	Slack/Surplus	Dual Prices
1	100.000000	0.000000
2	0.000000	0.000000
3	0.000000	-80.000000
4	0.000000	-70.000000
5	0.000000	-60.000000

Objective Coefficient Ranges

Variable	Lower Limit	Current Value	Upper Limit
X1	0.000000	80.000000	90.000000
X2	70.000000	100.000000	No Upper Limit
X3	60.000000	150.000000	No Upper Limit
X4	80.000000	90.000000	No Upper Limit
X5	0.000000	70.000000	100.000000
X6	0.000000	60.000000	150.000000

Right-Hand-Side Ranges

Constraint	Lower Limit	Current Value	Upper Limit
1	800.000000	900.000000	No Upper Limit
2	1000.000000	1000.000000	No Upper Limit
3	0.000000	800.000000	900.000000
4	0.000000	600.000000	600.000000
5	0.000000	400.000000	400.000000

Computer Solution for Exercise 12

Linear Programming Problem

```
MIN 50x1 + 70x2 + 60x3 + 90x4
    S.T.
      1) x1 + x2 > 150
      2) x3 + x4 > 120
      3) x1 + x3 < 200
      4) x2 + x4 < 250
```

Optimal Solution

Objective Function Value =   16100.000000

Variable	Value
X1	80.000000
X2	70.000000
X3	120.000000
X4	0.000000

Constraint	Slack/Surplus	Dual Prices
1	0.000000	−70.000000
2	0.000000	−80.000000
3	0.000000	20.000000
4	180.000000	0.000000

Objective Coefficient Ranges

Variable	Lower Limit	Current Value	Upper Limit
X1	40.000000	50.000000	70.000000
X2	50.000000	70.000000	80.000000
X3	−20.000000	60.000000	70.000000
X4	80.000000	90.000000	No Upper Limit

Right-Hand-Side Ranges

Constraint	Lower Limit	Current Value	Upper Limit
1	80.000000	150.000000	330.000000
2	50.000000	120.000000	200.000000
3	120.000000	200.000000	270.000000
4	70.000000	250.000000	No Upper Limit

Computer Solution for Exercise 13

Linear Programming Problem

```
MIN 50x1 + 70x2 + 60x3 + 90x4
    S.T.
      1) x1 + x2 > 150
      2) x3 + x4 > 120
      3) x1 + x3 < 200
      4) x2 + x4 < 250
      5) x4 > 20
```

Optimal Solution

```
Objective Function Value =    16300.000000
```

Variable	Value
X1	100.000000
X2	50.000000
X3	100.000000
X4	20.000000

Constraint	Slack/Surplus	Dual Prices
1	0.000000	−70.000000
2	0.000000	−80.000000
3	0.000000	20.000000
4	180.000000	0.000000
5	0.000000	−10.000000

Objective Coefficient Ranges

Variable	Lower Limit	Current Value	Upper Limit
X1	40.000000	50.000000	70.000000
X2	50.000000	70.000000	80.000000
X3	−20.000000	60.000000	70.000000
X4	80.000000	90.000000	No Upper Limit

Right-Hand-Side Ranges

Constraint	Lower Limit	Current Value	Upper Limit
1	100.000000	150.000000	330.000000
2	70.000000	120.000000	220.000000
3	100.000000	200.000000	250.000000
4	70.000000	250.000000	No Upper Limit
5	0.000000	20.000000	70.000000

Computer Solution for Exercise 14

Linear Programming Problem

```
MAX .10x1 + .20x2 + .15x3 + .25x4
    S.T.
      1) x1 + x2 + x3 + x4 = 8000000
      2) x1 < 2500000
      3) x2 < 4000000
      4) x3 < 2000000
      5) x4 < 500000
```

Optimal Solution

```
Objective Function Value =    1375000.000000
        Variable                  Value
```

Variable	Value
X1	1500000.000000
X2	4000000.000000
X3	2000000.000000
X4	500000.000000

Constraint	Slack/Surplus	Dual Prices
1	0.000000	0.100000
2	1000000.000000	0.000000
3	0.000000	0.100000
4	0.000000	0.050000
5	0.000000	0.150000

Objective Coefficient Ranges

Variable	Lower Limit	Current Value	Upper Limit
X1	No Lower Limit	0.100000	0.150000
X2	0.100000	0.200000	No Upper Limit
X3	0.100000	0.150000	No Upper Limit
X4	0.100000	0.250000	No Upper Limit

Right-Hand-Side Ranges

Constraint	Lower Limit	Current Value	Upper Limit
1	6500000.000000	8000000.000000	9000000.000000
2	1500000.000000	2500000.000000	No Upper Limit
3	3000000.000000	4000000.000000	5500000.000000
4	1000000.000000	2000000.000000	3500000.000000
5	0.000000	500000.000000	2000000.000000

Computer Solution for Exercise 15

Linear Programming Problem

```
MAX .07X1 + .15X2 + .18X3 + .25X4
   S.T.
    1) X1 + X2 + X3 + X4 = 5000000
    2) 0X1 + 3X2 + 5X3 + 9X4 < 23500000
```

Optimal Solution

```
Objective Function Value =    891666.690000
        Variable                  Value
```

Variable	Value
X1	0.000000
X2	3583333.800000
X3	0.000000
X4	1416666.500000

Constraint	Slack/Surplus	Dual Prices
1	0.000000	0.100000
2	0.000000	0.016667

Objective Coefficient Ranges

Variable	Lower Limit	Current Value	Upper Limit
X1	No Lower Limit	0.070000	0.100000
X2	0.145000	0.150000	0.250000
X3	No Lower Limit	0.180000	0.183333
X4	0.240000	0.250000	0.310000

Right-Hand-Side Ranges

Constraint	Lower Limit	Current Value	Upper Limit
1	2611111.000000	5000000.000000	7833333.000000
2	15000001.000000	23500000.000000	45000000.000000

Computer Solution for Exercise 16

Linear Programming Problem

```
MAX .07X1 + .15X2 + .18X3 + .25X4
   S.T.
    1) X1 + X2 + X3 + X4 = 5000000
    2) 0X1 + 3X2 + 5X3 + 9X4 < 23500000
    3) X3 > 700000
```

Optimal Solution

Objective Function Value =   889333.380000

Variable	Value
X1	0.000000
X2	3116667.000000
X3	700000.000000
X4	1183333.120000

Constraint	Slack/Surplus	Dual Prices
1	0.000000	0.100000
2	0.000000	0.016667
3	0.000000	−0.003333

Objective Coefficient Ranges

Variable	Lower Limit	Current Value	Upper Limit
X1	No Lower Limit	0.070000	0.100000
X2	0.145000	0.150000	0.250000
X3	No Lower Limit	0.180000	0.183333
X4	0.240000	0.250000	0.310000

Right-Hand-Side Ranges

Constraint	Lower Limit	Current Value	Upper Limit
1	2922222.000000	5000000.000000	7366666.000000
2	16400002.000000	23500000.000000	42200000.000000
3	0.000000	700000.000000	4249999.000000

Computer Solution for Exercise 17

Linear Programming Problem

```
MIN 30x1 + 50x2 + 50x3
    S.T.
      1) 50x1 + 70x2 + 40x3 = 63000
      2) x1 > 200
      3) x2 < 300
      4) x3 > 400
```

Optimal Solution

Objective Function Value =   48199.996000

Variable	Value	Reduced Costs
X1	940.000000	0.000002
X2	0.000000	8.000004
X3	400.000000	0.000000

Constraint	Slack/Surplus	Dual Prices
1	0.000000	−0.600000
2	740.000000	0.000000
3	300.000000	0.000000
4	0.000000	−26.000002

Objective Coefficient Ranges

Variable	Lower Limit	Current Value	Upper Limit
X1	No Lower Limit	30.000000	35.714287
X2	41.999996	50.000000	No Upper Limit
X3	23.999998	50.000000	No Upper Limit

Right-Hand-Side Ranges

Constraint	Lower Limit	Current Value	Upper Limit
1	26000.000000	63000.000000	No Upper Limit
2	No Lower Limit	200.000000	940.000000
3	0.000000	300.000000	No Upper Limit
4	0.000000	400.000000	1325.000000

Computer Solution for Exercise 18

Linear Programming Problem

```
MIN x1 + x2 + x3 + x4 + x5 + x6
    S.T.
      1) x1 + x6 > 30
      2) x1 + x2 > 35
      3) x2 + x3 > 70
      4) x3 + x4 > 45
      5) x4 + x5 > 55
      6) x5 + x6 > 20
```

Optimal Solution

```
Objective Function Value =    155.000000
          Variable              Value
```

Variable	Value
X1	30.000000
X2	60.000000
X3	10.000000
X4	35.000000
X5	20.000000
X6	0.000000

Constraint	Slack/Surplus	Dual Prices
1	0.000000	−1.000000
2	55.000000	0.000000
3	0.000000	−1.000000
4	0.000000	0.000000
5	0.000000	−1.000000
6	0.000000	0.000000

Objective Coefficient Ranges

Variable	Lower Limit	Current Value	Upper Limit
X1	0.000000	1.000000	1.000000
X2	1.000000	1.000000	1.000000
X3	1.000000	1.000000	1.000000
X4	1.000000	1.000000	1.000000
X5	1.000000	1.000000	1.000000
X6	1.000000	1.000000	No Upper Limit

Right-Hand-Side Ranges

Constraint	Lower Limit	Current Value	Upper Limit
1	0.000000	30.000000	No Upper Limit
2	No Lower Limit	35.000000	90.000000
3	15.000000	70.000000	No Upper Limit
4	35.000000	45.000000	100.000000
5	20.000000	55.000000	65.000000
6	10.000000	20.000000	55.000000

CHAPTER 7 HIGHLIGHTS

• *Concepts*

Your ability to answer the following questions is one indicator of the depth of your mastery of this chapter's important concepts. Note that the questions are grouped under various topic headings. For any question that you cannot answer, refer to the appropriate section of the chapter indicated by the topic heading. Pay particular attention to the summary boxes within a section.

7-1 **A GEOMETRIC INTRODUCTION AND THE SIMPLEX TABLEAU**

1. Explain the following terms: slack variables, feasible solution, basic feasible solution, basic variables, nonbasic variables, standard maximization form, simplex tableau.

2. If a slack variable equals zero, what does this imply with regard to the constraint.

7-2 **SIMPLEX METHOD: MAXIMIZATION**

3. Explain the following terms: pivot column, pivot row, pivot element, indicators, degeneracy.
4. State the rule for determining the variable to be increased (i.e., the pivot column).
5. Give the rule for determining the pivot row (i.e., the pivot element).
6. State the permissible row operations for the simplex method.
7. How do you determine when an optimal tableau is attained?
8. How do you determine if alternate optimal solutions exist?

7-3 **MINIMIZATION; THE DUAL; SHADOW PRICES**

9. Explain the following terms: minimization problem, primal, dual.
10. Give the procedure for finding the dual of a minimization problem.
11. Explain the Fundamental Theorem of Duality.
12. The optimal values of the dual variables are called _____ _____ . Interpret this term and state any restrictions that apply.
13. If a particular constraint has zero surplus, it is called a(n) _____ _____ . What does this imply with regard to the constraint?

7-4 **MIXED CONSTRAINTS; SHADOW PRICES (PRIMAL); COMPUTER SOLUTION**

14. Explain the term *mixed constraints*.
15. Explain the need for an artificial variable in a constraint.
16. What types of constraints need
   a) Slack variables
   b) Surplus variables
   c) Artificial variables
17. Give the rule for assigning objective function coefficients to artificial variables.
18. Slack and surplus variables are assigned objective function coefficients of _____ .
19. Where are the shadow prices given in an optimal primal tableau?

Computer Solution

20. Explain the dual prices that are given in the computer output of a computer software package.

7-5 **SENSITIVITY ANALYSIS**

21. Explain the following terms: sensitivity analysis, objective coefficient range, right-hand-side range.

REVIEW EXERCISES

• *Simplex Tableau*

Exercises 1 and 2 are each a simplex tableau for some maximization problem.
a) State the basic feasible solution and the current value of the objective function.

b) State whether the solution is optimal. Give the reason for your conclusion.

1.

$$\begin{array}{ccccccc} x_1 & x_2 & x_3 & s_1 & s_2 & s_3 & Z \end{array}$$

$$\begin{bmatrix} -3 & 0 & 1 & 4 & 2 & 0 & 0 & 7 \\ 2 & 1 & 0 & -1 & 3 & 0 & 0 & 4 \\ -1 & 0 & 0 & 5 & 4 & 1 & 0 & 9 \\ \hline -3 & 0 & 0 & 6 & 9 & 0 & 1 & 856 \end{bmatrix}$$

2.

$$\begin{array}{ccccccc} x_1 & x_2 & x_3 & s_1 & s_2 & s_3 & Z \end{array}$$

$$\begin{bmatrix} 1 & 8 & 0 & -1 & 0 & 4 & 0 & 5 \\ 0 & -2 & 1 & 2 & 0 & 5 & 0 & 3 \\ 0 & 3 & 0 & 5 & 1 & -3 & 0 & 6 \\ \hline 0 & 4 & 0 & 7 & 0 & 3 & 1 & 450 \end{bmatrix}$$

• Simplex Method (Maximization)

Solve Exercises 3–6 by the simplex method.

3. Maximize $Z = 5x_1 + 8x_2 + 6x_3$
subject to $x_1 + x_2 + x_3 \le 30$
$2x_1 + x_2 + 2x_3 \le 40$
where x_1, x_2, and $x_3 \ge 0$

4. Maximize $Z = 9x_1 + 7x_2 + 6x_3$
subject to $2x_1 + 4x_2 + x_3 \le 30$
$x_1 + 2x_2 + x_3 \le 24$
where x_1, x_2, and $x_3 \ge 0$

5. Maximize $Z = 6x_1 + 8x_2 + 4x_3$
subject to $x_1 + 4x_2 + 8x_3 \le 40$
$2x_1 + x_2 + 6x_3 \le 30$
$x_1 + x_2 + x_3 \le 16$
where x_1, x_2, and $x_3 \ge 0$

6. Maximize $Z = 5x_1 + 2x_2 + 6x_3$
subject to $x_1 + 4x_2 + 8x_3 \le 32$
$2x_1 + x_2 + 4x_3 \le 30$
$2x_1 + 4x_2 + 2x_3 \le 28$
where x_1, x_2, and $x_3 \ge 0$

• Alternate Optimal Solutions

For Exercises 7 and 8:
a) Solve by the simplex method.
b) State the nonbasic variable that has a zero indicator in the optimal tableau.
c) Determine the alternate optimal solution by increasing the value of the nonbasic variable determined in part b.
d) Investigate the implications of the alternate optimal solution.

7. Maximize $Z = 8x_1 + 4x_2$
subject to $20x_1 + 10x_2 \le 220$
$10x_1 + 12x_2 \le 194$
where x_1 and $x_2 \ge 0$

8. Maximize $Z = 20x_1 + 40x_2$
subject to $x_1 + x_2 \le 20$
$15x_1 + 30x_2 \le 450$
where x_1 and $x_2 \ge 0$

• Degeneracy

For Exercises 9 and 10:
a) Solve by the simplex method and note the degeneracy.
b) Graph the feasible region and indicate the reason for the occurrence of the degeneracy.

9. Maximize $Z = 6x_1 + 4x_2$
subject to $x_1 + x_2 \le 30$
$20x_1 + 40x_2 \le 800$
$60x_1 + 15x_2 \le 1800$
where x_1 and $x_2 \ge 0$

10. Maximize $Z = 22x_1 + 24x_2$
subject to $x_1 + x_2 \le 50$
$40x_1 + 60x_2 \le 2400$
$5x_1 + 6x_2 \le 270$
where x_1 and $x_2 \ge 0$

• *Dual (Minimization)*

For Exercises 11–14:
a) Find the dual.
b) Solve the dual.
c) Find the solution to the primal problem from the dual optimal tableau.
d) State the amount of slack or surplus in each primal constraint.
e) Identify and interpret the shadow prices.

11. Minimize $Z = 4x_1 + 8x_2 + 2x_3$
subject to $x_1 + x_2 + x_3 \geq 10$
$4x_1 + x_2 + 2x_3 \geq 12$
$x_1 + 2x_2 + 2x_3 \geq 8$
where $x_1, x_2,$ and $x_3 \geq 0$

12. Minimize $Z = 8x_1 + 4x_2 + 2x_3$
subject to $4x_1 + 4x_2 + 2x_3 \geq 12$
$8x_1 + 2x_2 + 4x_3 \geq 16$
$x_1 + 2x_2 + 4x_3 \geq 8$
where $x_1, x_2,$ and $x_3 \geq 0$

13. Minimize $Z = 96x_1 + 64x_2 + 48x_3$
subject to $2x_1 + x_2 + 2x_3 \geq 5$
$6x_1 + 4x_2 + x_3 \geq 7$
$4x_1 + 2x_2 + x_3 \geq 6$
where $x_1, x_2,$ and $x_3 \geq 0$

14. Minimize $Z = 24x_1 + 36x_2 + 18x_3$
subject to $3x_1 + 2x_2 + x_3 \geq 9$
$6x_1 + x_2 + 2x_3 \geq 7$
$x_1 + 4x_2 + x_3 \geq 8$
where $x_1, x_2,$ and $x_3 \geq 0$

• *Shadow Prices (Dual)*

Exercises 15 and 16 each give a primal problem and its corresponding dual optimal tableau.
a) State the solution to the primal problem from the dual optimal tableau.
b) State the amount of surplus in each primal constraint.
c) Identify and interpret the shadow prices.

15. *Primal problem.*
Minimize $Z = 40x_1 + 15x_2 + 12x_3$
subject to $5x_1 + x_2 + 2x_3 \geq 7$
$4x_1 + 2x_2 + x_3 \geq 5$
$x_1 + x_2 + 3x_3 \geq 6$
where $x_1, x_2,$ and $x_3 \geq 0$

Dual Optimal Tableau

y_1	y_2	y_3	s_1	s_2	s_3	Z	
0	0	−6	1	−1	−2	0	1
0	1	−.333	0	.667	−.333	0	6
1	0	1.667	0	−.333	.667	0	3
0	0	4	0	1	3	1	51

16. *Primal problem.*
Minimize $Z = 20x_1 + 30x_2 + 25x_3$
subject to $x_1 + 2x_2 + 4x_3 \geq 4$
$5x_1 + x_2 + 2x_3 \geq 3$
$6x_1 + 5x_2 + x_3 \geq 5$
where $x_1, x_2,$ and $x_3 \geq 0$

Dual Optimal Tableau

y_1	y_2	y_3	s_1	s_2	s_3	Z	
0	.783	1	.173	0	−.043	0	2.391
0	−3.522	0	−.783	1	−.304	0	6.739
1	.304	0	−.043	0	.261	0	5.652
0	2.13	0	.696	0	.826	1	34.565

• Shadow Prices (Primal)

For Exercises 17–19, a primal problem and its optimal tableau are given.

a) State the optimal solution.
b) Investigate the implications of the optimal solution.
c) Identify and interpret the shadow prices.

17. Maximize $Z = 6x_1 + 5x_2 + 6x_3$
subject to $5x_1 + 4x_2 + x_3 \leq 40$
$x_1 + 2x_2 + x_3 \leq 15$
$2x_1 + x_2 + 3x_3 \leq 12$
where $x_1, x_2,$ and $x_3 \geq 0$

Optimal Tableau

x_1	x_2	x_3	s_1	s_2	s_3	Z	
0	0	−6	1	−1	−2	0	1
0	1	−.333	0	.607	−.333	0	6
1	0	1.667	0	−.333	.667	0	3
0	0	2.333	0	1.333	2.333	1	48

18. Maximize $Z = 25x_1 + 30x_2 + 18x_3$
subject to $5x_1 + 3x_2 + 2x_3 \leq 36$
$2x_1 + 5x_2 + x_3 \leq 40$
$4x_1 + x_2 + 2x_3 \leq 28$
where $x_1, x_2,$ and $x_3 \geq 0$

Optimal Tableau

x_1	x_2	x_3	s_1	s_2	s_3	Z	
2.714	0	1	.714	−.429	0	0	8.571
−.143	1	0	−.143	.286	0	0	6.286
−1.286	0	0	−1.286	.571	1	0	4.571
19.571	0	0	8.571	.857	0	1	342.857

19. Maximize $Z = 30x_1 + 40x_2 + 25x_3$
subject to $2x_1 + x_2 + 3x_3 \leq 70$
$x_1 + 3x_2 + 4x_3 \leq 60$
$4x_1 + x_2 + 5x_3 \leq 80$
where $x_1, x_2,$ and $x_3 \geq 0$

Optimal Tableau

x_1	x_2	x_3	s_1	s_2	s_3	Z	
0	0	0	1	−.182	−.455	0	22.727
0	1	1	0	.364	−.091	0	14.545
1	0	1	0	−.091	.273	0	16.364
0	0	45	0	11.818	4.545	1	1072.72

• Slack, Surplus, and Artificial Variables

For Exercises 20–23, prepare the problem for solution by the simplex method; include slack, surplus, and artificial variables where needed. Do not solve.

20. Maximize $Z = 4x_1 + 5x_2 + 6x_3$
subject to $x_1 + x_2 + 5x_3 \leq 70$
$x_1 + 3x_2 + 5x_3 = 80$
$5x_1 + 7x_2 + x_3 \geq 10$
where $x_1, x_2,$ and $x_3 \geq 0$

21. Maximize $Z = 19x_1 + 17x_2 + 15x_3$
subject to $5x_1 + x_2 + 5x_3 \geq 15$
$3x_1 + 6x_2 + 8x_3 \leq 90$
$2x_1 + 5x_2 + 8x_3 = 180$
where $x_1, x_2,$ and $x_3 \geq 0$

22. Minimize $Z = 6x_1 + 8x_2 + 4x_3$
subject to $3x_1 + 5x_2 + 6x_3 \geq 15$
$4x_1 + 6x_2 + x_3 = 20$
$x_1 + 5x_2 + 6x_3 \leq 90$
where x_1, x_2, and $x_3 \geq 0$

23. Minimize $Z = 5x_1 + 9x_2 + 8x_3$
subject to $x_1 + 5x_2 + 8x_3 \leq 100$
$x_1 + 15x_2 + 8x_3 = 160$
$2x_1 + 3x_2 + 9x_3 \geq 50$
where x_1, x_2, and $x_3 \geq 0$

• *Computer Solutions*

For Exercises 24 and 25, a computer solution is given.
a) State the optimal solution.
b) Investigate the implications of the optimal solution.
c) Interpret the dual prices.

24. Maximize $Z = 10x_1 + 12x_2 + 15x_3$
subject to $4x_1 + 7x_2 + 5x_3 \leq 30$
$2x_1 + 6x_2 + x_3 \geq 20$
$x_1 + x_2 + x_3 \leq 90$
where x_1, x_2, and $x_3 \geq 0$

Optimal Solution

```
Objective Function Value =          64.000008
        Variable              Value
```

Variable	Value
X1	4.000000
X2	2.000001
X3	0.000000

Constraint	Slack/Surplus	Dual Prices
1	0.000000	3.600001
2	0.000000	−2.200001
3	84.000000	0.000000

25. Minimize $Z = 8x_1 + 4x_2 + 6x_3$
subject to $3x_1 + x_2 + 4x_3 \geq 20$
$x_1 + 4x_2 + x_3 = 70$
$2x_1 + x_2 + 8x_3 \leq 160$
where x_1, x_2, and $x_3 \geq 0$

Optimal Solution

```
Objective Function Value =          73.333336
        Variable              Value
```

Variable	Value
X1	0.000000
X2	17.333334
X3	0.666667

Constraint	Slack/Surplus	Dual Prices
1	0.000000	−1.333333
2	0.000000	−0.666667
3	137.333328	0.000000

• *Computer Exercises*

Use a computer software package to solve Exercises 26 and 27.
a) State the optimal solution.

b) Investigate the implications of the optimal solution.
c) Interpret the dual prices.

26. Minimize $Z = 5x_1 + 9x_2 + 7x_3$
subject to $2x_1 + 7x_2 + 6x_3 \geq 50$
$3x_1 + x_2 + 8x_3 \leq 150$
$4x_1 + x_2 + 2x_3 \geq 100$
where $x_1, x_2,$ and $x_3 \geq 0$

27. Maximize $Z = 7x_1 + 5x_2 + 9x_3$
subject to $9x_1 + 5x_2 + x_3 \leq 50$
$3x_1 + x_2 + 2x_3 \geq 20$
$x_1 + 3x_2 + 4x_3 = 60$
where $x_1, x_2,$ and $x_3 \geq 0$

• *Sensitivity Analysis*

Computer output giving sensitivity analysis results for Exercises 28 and 29 is presented below, along with the linear programming problem.
a) Interpret each objective coefficient range.
b) Interpret each right-hand-side range.

28. *Linear Programming Problem*

```
MAX 10x1 + 12x2 + 15x3
    S.T.

    1) 4x1 + 7x2 + 5x3 < 30
    2) 2x1 + 6x2 + x3 > 20
    3) x1 + x2 + 3x3 < 90
```

Objective Coefficient Ranges

Variable	Lower Limit	Current Value	Upper Limit
X1	9.652173	10.000000	No Upper Limit
X2	No Lower Limit	12.000000	13.333338
X3	No Lower Limit	15.000000	15.800003

Right-Hand-Side Ranges

Constraint	Lower Limit	Current Value	Upper Limit
1	23.333334	30.000000	40.000000
2	14.999999	20.000000	25.714285
3	6.000000	90.000000	No Upper Limit

29. *Linear Programming Problem*

```
MIN 8x1 + 4x2 + 6x3
    S.T.

    1) 3x1 + x2 + 4x3 > 20
    2) x1 + 4x2 + x3 = 70
    3) 2x1 + x2 + 8x3 < 160
```

Objective Coefficient Ranges

Variable	Lower Limit	Current Value	Upper Limit
X1	4.666667	8.000000	No Upper Limit
X2	No Lower Limit	4.000000	24.000002
X3	1.000000	6.000000	10.545454

Right-Hand-Side Ranges

Constraint	Lower Limit	Current Value	Upper Limit
1	17.500000	20.000000	86.451607
2	5.000000	70.000000	80.000000
3	22.666672	160.000000	No Upper Limit

Applications

Use a computer software package to solve each of the following. For Exercises 30–33:
a) Formulate the problem.
b) State the optimal solution.
c) Investigate the implications of the optimal solution.
d) Interpret the dual prices.
e) Interpret the objective coefficient ranges.
f) Interpret the right-hand-side ranges.

30. *Product mix.* A firm makes three models of microwave ovens—MCWO1, MCWO2, and MCWO3—with unit profits of $100, $150, and $200, respectively. For the next month, the firm can produce a total of 500 microwave ovens. The microwave ovens require two crucial components that are in limited supply. The number of each such component required by each model is given below.

Component requirements per unit of model

	Model MCWO1	Model MCWO2	Model MCWO3
Component A	2	1	3
Component B	1	2	2

The available supply of each component is given below.

Available supply

Component A	400
Component B	600

How many of each model should be produced in order to maximize profit and satisfy the problem constraints?

31. *Product mix.* Solve Exercise 30 under the additional constraint that the firm must produce at least twice as many MCWO3 models as MCWO2 models.

32. *Purchasing.* The Swenson Company makes videocassette recorders (VCRs). Each VCR requires two specialized components for proper functioning. These two components are purchased from outside suppliers. Since no one supplier can meet Swenson's needs, the two components are purchased from three different suppliers. The unit prices of the components from the respective suppliers are given below.

Price per unit

	Supplier 1	Supplier 2	Supplier 3
Component 1	$40	$45	$50
Component 2	60	50	70

The total number of components (component 1 + component 2) that can be supplied by any single supplier is limited, as indicated below.

Supplier total capacity (component 1 + component 2)

Supplier 1	600
Supplier 2	800
Supplier 3	700

If the Swenson Company needs at least 1000 and 900 units of components 1 and 2, respectively, how many should be purchased from each supplier in order to minimize the total cost?

33. *Blending problem.* An oil company blends two types of crude oil to produce two types of gasoline: regular and premium. Both types of crude oil contain different proportions of two ingredients, as given below.

	Crude 1	Crude 2
Ingredient A	15%	45%
Ingredient B	50	40

The cost per gallon for each type of crude is given below.

Cost per gallon

Crude 1	Crude 2
$0.20	$0.25

At least 30% of each gallon of regular gasoline must be ingredient A; at most 45% of each gallon of premium must be ingredient B. Demand requirements are such that the oil company must produce at least 900,000 gallons of regular and at least 1,200,000 gallons of premium per day. Determine the number of gallons of each type of crude that must be blended to produce each type of gasoline in order to meet the minimal demand requirements at minimum cost.

8

PROBABILITY

Introductory Application

The following problem appeared on a past Uniform CPA examination.

PROBLEM

Clay Company operates 3 shipping terminals, referred to as X, Y, and Z. Of the total cargo shipped, terminals X, Y, and Z handle approximately 60%, 30%, and 10%, respectively, with error rates of 3%, 4%, and 6%, respectively. Clay's internal auditor randomly selects 1 shipping document, ascertaining that this document contains an error. The probability that the error occurred in terminal X is

a) 60%   **b)** 50%   **c)** 23%   **d)** 3%

	Terminal X	Terminal Y	Terminal Z
Shipping volume	60%	30%	10%
Error rate	3%	4%	6%

The solution to this problem involves a result known as Bayes' formula. We will solve this problem and discuss Bayes' formula in Section 8-5 of this chapter.

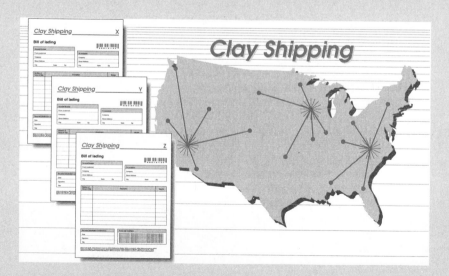

In this chapter, we will discuss *probability*—the likelihood of occurrence of chance events. Since probability will be presented by using sets, we begin the chapter with a review of sets.

8-1 • SETS

A **set** is a collection of things. Examples of sets exist everywhere in our daily lives. Some specific sets are the following:

- The collection of letters of the English alphabet
- The collection of vowels in the English alphabet
- The collection of integers 1 through 9

Sets are usually written using set braces, { }. Thus, the preceding sets may be expressed as

$$\{\text{letters in the English alphabet}\}$$
$$\{a, e, i, o, u\}$$
$$\{1, 2, 3, 4, 5, 6, 7, 8, 9\}$$

Sets are often named by capital letters. The objects belonging to a set are called **elements** of that set. The phrase "is an element of" is written in shorthand by the symbol $\in$. Thus, if

$$A = \{a, e, i, o, u\}$$

then

$$a \in A \quad e \in A \quad i \in A \quad o \in A \quad u \in A$$

The fact that s "is not an element of" A is written in shorthand as

$$s \notin A$$

It is frequently necessary to count the number of elements in a set. Again, consider set A:

$$A = \{a, e, i, o, u\}$$

The statement "the number of elements in set A is 5" may be written in shorthand notation as

$$n(A) = 5$$

• **EXAMPLE 8-1** _____

If

$$B = \{4, 3, 0, 2, 8, 1\}$$

then $n(B) = 6$.

Empty Set

The **empty set,** or **null set,** is a set containing no elements. The empty set is commonly represented by either of the following symbols: $\emptyset$, { }. Hence, $n(\emptyset) = 0$.

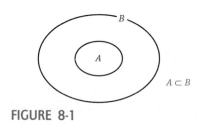

FIGURE 8-1

Subset

If there exist two sets A and B such that every element of A is also an element of B, then A is a **subset** of B. The statement of "A is a subset of B" is written in shorthand as $A \subset B$.

• **EXAMPLE 8-2**

If
$$A = \{1, 4, 6\} \qquad B = \{1, 2, 4, 6, 8\}$$
then $A \subset B$, but $B \not\subset A$.

Note that the symbol $\not\subset$ means "is not a subset of."

The concept of subset is pictorially illustrated by the **Venn Diagram** of Figure 8-1. Note that set A is completely contained inside set B. Hence, each element of A is also in B.

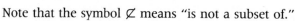
• **EXAMPLE 8-3**

If
$$A = \{\text{members of the U.S. Congress}\}$$
$$B = \{\text{members of the U.S. Senate}\}$$
$$C = \{\text{members of the U.S. House of Representatives}\}$$
then $B \subset A$ and $C \subset A$.

It can be proven that the empty set is a subset of every set. Also, any set is a subset of itself.

Equality of Sets

Two sets are **equal** if they contain exactly the same elements. If A and B represent equal sets, then we may write $A = B$.

• **EXAMPLE 8-4**

If
$$A = \{1, 3, 4\} \qquad B = \{3, 4, 1\}$$
then $A = B$.

Note that if two sets are equal, then each is a subset of the other.

SUMMARY

Sets

A set A is said to be a **subset** of a set B if each element of A is also an element of B. This is written as $A \subset B$. The concept of subset is illustrated by the Venn diagram of Figure 8-2.

continues

SUMMARY—*Continued*

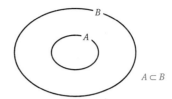

FIGURE 8-2

The **empty set,** $\varnothing$, is a *subset of every set.* In other words, for any set A.

$$\varnothing \subset A$$

Any set A is a subset of itself. In other words, for any set A,

$$A \subset A$$

Two sets are **equal** if they contain exactly the same elements. Also, if A and B are any two sets, then $A = B$ means that $A \subset B$ and $B \subset A$, and vice versa.

• **EXAMPLE 8-5** _____

If $A = \{a, b, c\}$, list all the subsets of A.

Solution

$$\varnothing, \{a, b, c\}, \{a, b\}, \{a, c\}, \{b, c\}, \{a\}, \{b\}, \{c\}$$

We note, without proof, that a set containing n elements has 2^n subsets. Thus, for the above example, since set A contains 3 elements, then there should be $2^3 = 8$ subsets. Note that this is confirmed because 8 subsets are listed.

_____ •

Universal Set

Usually when discussing a specific problem involving sets, a universal set is identified. A **universal set** contains all elements of all sets of a given problem. In other words, every set of the given problem is subset of the universal set for that problem. The letter U will represent the universal set.

• **EXAMPLE 8-6** _____

Let

$$U = \{1, 2, 3, 4, 5, 6\} \qquad A = \{1, 3, 4\} \qquad B = \{6\}$$

Note that $A \subset U$ and $B \subset U$. The Venn diagram of Figure 8-3 pictorially illustrates these sets.

_____ •

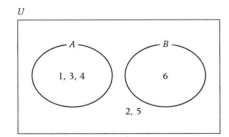

FIGURE 8-3

We now consider set operations.

Intersection

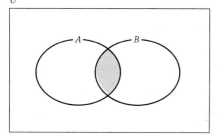

$A \cap B$ = shaded area

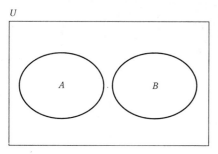

$A \cap B = \varnothing$
Disjoint sets

FIGURE 8-4

Union

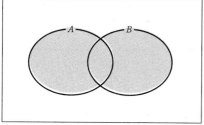

$A \cup B$ = shaded area

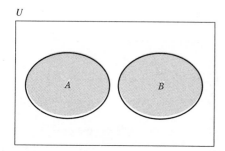

$A \cup B$ = shaded area

FIGURE 8-5

Intersection of Sets

Let A and B represent two sets. The **intersection** of the two sets, written $A \cap B$, is the set of elements belonging to *both* A *and* B. The intersection of two sets consists of elements common to both.

- **EXAMPLE 8-7**

  If

  $$A = \{1, 3, 5, 7\} \qquad B = \{2, 3, 4, 5, 9\}$$

  then $A \cap B = \{3, 5\}$. Note that in order for an element to belong to $A \cap B$, it must belong to both A and B.

- **EXAMPLE 8-8**

  If

  $$A = \{2, 3, 4\} \qquad B = \{1, 5, 6, 9\}$$

  then $A \cap B = \varnothing$. Since the two sets A and B have no elements in common, their intersection is empty. Such sets are called **disjoint sets.**

The Venn diagrams of Figure 8-4 pictorially illustrate the concept of intersection.

Union of Sets

Let A and B represent two sets. The **union** of the two sets, written $A \cup B$, is the set of elements belonging to *either* A *or* B *or both*. When we "union" two sets, we "join them together."

- **EXAMPLE 8-9**

  If

  $$A = \{1, 3, 5, 7\} \qquad B = \{2, 3, 4, 5, 9\}$$

  then $A \cup B = \{1, 2, 3, 4, 5, 7, 9\}$. Note that in order for an element to belong to $A \cup B$, it must belong to either A or B or both.

- **EXAMPLE 8-10**

  If

  $$A = \{2, 3, 4\} \qquad B = \{1, 5, 6, 9\}$$

  then $A \cup B = \{1, 2, 3, 4, 5, 6, 9\}$.

The Venn diagrams of Figure 8-5 pictorially illustrate the concept of union.

Complement of a Set

Let A represent a set and U represent a universal set. The **complement** of A, written A', is the set of all elements of U that *do not belong to A*.

Complement

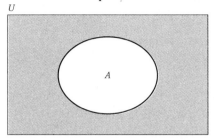

$A' =$ shaded area

FIGURE 8-6

• **EXAMPLE 8-11**

If

$$U = \{0, 1, 2, 3, 4, 5\} \qquad A = \{1, 3, 5\}$$

then $A' = \{0, 2, 4\}$.

•

The Venn diagram of Figure 8-6 pictorially illustrates the concept of complement.

SUMMARY

Intersection. The intersection of sets A and B, written **$A \cap B$,** is the set of elements common to **both A and B.** This is illustrated in terms of the Venn diagrams in Figure 8-7.

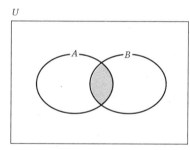
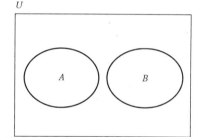

$A \cap B =$ shaded area $A \cap B = \varnothing$
                                  Disjoint sets

FIGURE 8-7

Union. If A and B are sets, then A union B, written **$A \cup B$,** is the set of elements belonging to **either A or B or both.** When we union sets, we "join them together." This is illustrated in terms of the Venn diagrams in Figure 8-8.

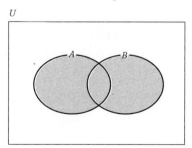
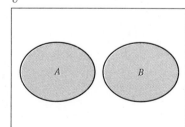

$A \cup B =$ shaded area $A \cup B =$ shaded area

FIGURE 8-8

continues

SUMMARY—*Continued*

Complement. The complement of a set A, written A', is the set of elements of U that are **not in A.** This is illustrated in terms of the Venn diagram in Figure 8-9.

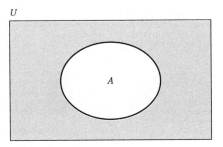

$A' =$ shaded area

FIGURE 8-9

• **EXAMPLE 8-12**

If $A = \{a, b, c, d, e\}$, $B = \{b, d, e, g, h\}$, and $C = \{a, d, e, j\}$, then list the elements of

a) $A \cap B \cap C$.   **b)** $A \cup B \cup C$.

Solutions

a) $A \cap B \cap C$ is the set of elements common to all three sets: A, B, and C. Hence,

$$A \cap B \cap C = \{d, e\}$$

b)   To find $A \cup B \cup C$, we join the sets A, B, and C. Hence,

$$A \cup B \cup C = \{a, b, c, d, e, g, h, j\}$$

Use of Parentheses

Sometimes parentheses are used to indicate set operations. For example, suppose it is given that $U = \{a, b, c, d, e, f, g, h\}$, $A = \{a, b, c, h\}$, $B = \{b, d, g, h\}$, and $C = \{a, b, g\}$; then the parentheses in the expression

$$(A \cup B)'$$

imply that to determine the elements of $(A \cup B)'$, we should first list the elements of $A \cup B$ and then determine the complement of $A \cup B$. Hence,

$$A \cup B = \{a, b, c, d, g, h\}$$

Looking at U and listing those elements of U that are not in $A \cup B$ gives

$$(A \cup B)' = \{e, f\}$$

• **EXAMPLE 8-13**

Using sets U, A, B, and C as defined in the paragraph preceding this example, list the elements of

a) $(A \cap B) \cup C$.   **b)** $A \cap (B' \cup C)$.

Solutions

a) The parentheses of the expression $(A \cap B) \cup C$ indicate that we should first determine the set enclosed by the parentheses. Hence,

$$A \cap B = \{b, h\}$$

Then we determine the union of the above result with set C to get

$$(A \cap B) \cup C = \{a, b, g, h\}$$

b) The parentheses of the expression $A \cap (B' \cup C)$ indicate that we should first determine the set enclosed by the parentheses. Thus, we determine $B' \cup C$. However, in order to do this, we must determine the elements of B'. Hence,

$$B' = \{a, c, e, f\}$$

Now, we determine

$$B' \cup C = \{a, b, c, e, f, g\}$$

Finally, we find the intersection of the above result with set A to get

$$A \cap (B' \cup C) = \{a, b, c\}$$

• **EXAMPLE 8-14** _____

A survey of a mathematics class containing 37 students reveals the indicated responses to the following questions:

- "How many class members are marketing majors?" *Response:* 23 students
- "How many class members are accounting majors?" *Response:* 18 students
- "How many class members are both marketing and accounting majors?" *Response:* 7 students

a) If $U = \{$students in the mathematics class$\}$, $M = \{$marketing majors$\}$, and $A = \{$accounting majors$\}$, express the above results in a Venn diagram.

b) How many class members are either marketing majors or accounting majors?

c) How many class members are accounting majors, but not marketing majors?

d) Of the class members who are marketing majors, what percentage are accounting majors?

$n(U) = 37$

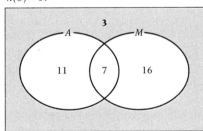

$(A \cup M)' =$ shaded region

FIGURE 8-10

Solutions

a) The class members who are both marketing and accounting majors constitute set $A \cap M$. Thus, $n(A \cap M) = 7$, and we write this number in the region representing $A \cap M$ in the Venn diagram of Figure 8-10. Also, $n(A) = 18$, and $n(M) = 23$. The number of accounting majors who are not marketing majors is given by $n(A) - n(A \cap M) = 18 - 7 = 11$. This number is written inside set A, but outside set M. Also, the number of marketing majors who are not accounting majors is given by $n(M) - n(A \cap M) = 23 - 7 = 16$. This number is written inside set M, but outside set A. Thus, $n(A \cup M) = 16 + 7 + 11 = 34$. Since there are 37 students in the class, then there are $37 - 34 = 3$ students outside the union of set A and set M. In other words, $(A \cup M)'$ has three elements, as is illustrated in Figure 8-10.

b) We want the number of students in $M \cup A$. As stated in part a, $n(M \cup A) = 34$.

c) We want the number of students in set A, but not in set M. In other words, we want $n(A \cap M')$. Looking at Figure 8-10, note that $n(A \cap M') = n(A) - n(A \cap M) = 18 - 7 = 11$.

d) Of the 23 marketing majors, 7 are also accounting majors. Thus, $n(A \cap M)/n(M) = 7/23 = 30.43\%$ of the marketing majors are accounting majors. This is illustrated in the Venn diagram of Figure 8-11.

U

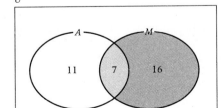

FIGURE 8-11

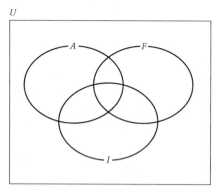

FIGURE 8-12

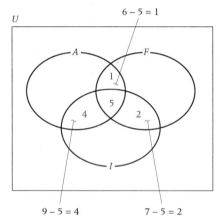

$6 - 5 = 1$

$9 - 5 = 4$ $7 - 5 = 2$

FIGURE 8-13

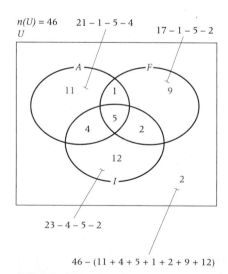

$n(U) = 46$ $21 - 1 - 5 - 4$ $17 - 1 - 5 - 2$

$23 - 4 - 5 - 2$

$46 - (11 + 4 + 5 + 1 + 2 + 9 + 12)$

FIGURE 8-14

• **EXAMPLE 8-15**   **Labor Planning.**

The production process for a given product involves three processes: assembly, finishing, and inspection. The production department's work force consists of 46 employees classified as follows:

- 21 can do assembly.
- 17 can do finishing.
- 23 can do inspection.
- 6 can do both assembly and finishing.
- 9 can do both assembly and inspection.
- 7 can do both finishing and inspection.
- 5 can do all three processes.

If

$$U = \{\text{production department employees}\}$$
$$A = \{\text{employees who can do assembly}\}$$
$$F = \{\text{employees who can do finishing}\}$$
$$I = \{\text{employees who can do inspection}\},$$

then

a) Fill in the number of employees belonging to each region of the Venn diagram of Figure 8-12.

b) Determine how many employees cannot do any of the three processes.

c) Determine how many employees can do only assembly.

Solutions

a) We fill in the Venn diagram by first filling in the intersection of all three sets, then each intersection of two sets, and then the individual sets until all regions are filled in. Hence,

- $n(A \cap F \cap I) = 5$ These are the 5 employees who can do all three processes.
- $n(F \cap I) = 7$ These are the 7 employees who can do both finishing and inspection.
- $n(A \cap I) = 9$ These are the 9 employees who can do both assembly and inspection.
- $n(A \cap F) = 6$ These are the 6 employees who can do both assembly and finishing.

Studying the Venn diagram of Figure 8-13, note that we have filled in the region corresponding to $A \cap F \cap I$ with 5. Then, since $n(F \cap I) = 7$, and since $F \cap I$ includes $A \cap F \cap I$, we have filled in the portion of $F \cap I$ that excludes $A \cap F \cap I$ with $7 - 5$, or 2. Analogously, we have filled in all regions composing $A \cap I$ and $A \cap F$. Note in Figure 8-13 that, for the regions corresponding to $A \cap I$ and $A \cap F$, $n(A \cap I) = 4 + 5 = 9$, and $n(A \cap F) = 5 + 1 = 6$, respectively.

Now we fill in the portion of I that excludes the intersection of I with either A or F. Since $n(I) = 23$, and since the 23 includes the 4, 5, and 2 employees from the intersections of I with the other sets, then the portion of I that excludes the intersection of I with either A or F has $23 - 4 - 5 - 2$, or 12 employees (see Figure 8-14). These 12 employees can do only inspection. Analogously, the number of employees who can do only finishing is given by $n(F) - 1 - 5 - 2 = 17 - 1 - 5 - 2 = 9$, and the number of employees who can do only assembly is given by $n(A) - 1 - 5 - 4 = 21 - 1 - 5 - 4 = 11$ (see Figure 8-14).

Finally, we determine the number of employees who cannot do any of the three processes. This is given by $n[(A \cup F \cup I)']$. Since $n(U) = 46$, then

$$n[(A \cup F \cup I)'] = N(U) - n(A \cup F \cup I) = 46 -$$
$$(11 + 4 + 5 + 1 + 2 + 9 + 12) = 46 - 44 = 2.$$

Note that $n(A \cup F \cup I)$ was determined by adding the numbers of the regions composing $A \cup F \cup I$ (see Figure 8-14).

b) This is given by $n[(A \cup F \cup I)']$ of Figure 8-14. In part a above, we determined that $n[(A \cup F \cup I)'] = 2$.

c) In part a above, we determined that this was given in Figure 8-14 by the portion of A that excludes the intersection of A with either F or I. The number of employees in this region is 11 (see Figure 8-14).

Cross-Classification Tables

A marketing research survey includes two questions, as shown in Table 8-1.

TABLE 8-1 Survey

Please check the appropriate answer.
  1. Sex

      Male _____   Female _____
  2. Have you purchased a television during the past 3 years?

      Yes _____   No _____

TABLE 8-2

Sex	Purchased TV		
	Y yes	*N* no	
M Male	120	35	155 } row
F Female	30	15	45 } totals
	150	50	

column totals

The results of 200 responses to these two questions are given in Table 8-2. Such a table that exhibits a classification of individuals with respect to various attributes or groups is called a **cross-classification table.** A cross-classification table can be analyzed by using set concepts. For example, in the table above, if $M = \{$male respondents$\}$, $F = \{$female respondents$\}$, $Y = \{$yes respondents$\}$, $N = \{$no respondents$\}$, and $U = \{$all survey respondents$\}$, then $n(U) = 200$, $n(M) = 155$, $n(F) = 45$, $n(Y) = 150$, and $n(N) = 50$, as is illustrated in Table 8-3 on page 508. Each cell entry denotes the intersection of the respective row and column sets. For example, $n(M \cap Y) = 120$ implies that 120 respondents answered yes and are males; $n(M \cap N) = 35$ implies that 35 respondents answered no and are males;

TABLE 8-3

	Sex	Purchased TV			
		Y yes	N no		
$n(M \cap Y)$ →	M Male	120	35	155 ← $n(M)$	$n(M \cap N)$
$n(F \cap Y)$ →	F Female	30	15	45 ← $n(F)$	$n(F \cap N)$
		150	50	200	

$n(Y)$ $n(N)$

TABLE 8-4 **Column percentages**

Sex	Purchased TV		
	yes	no	
Male	$\frac{120}{150} = 80\%$	$\frac{35}{50} = 70\%$	$\frac{155}{200} = 77.5\%$
Female	$\frac{30}{150} = 20\%$	$\frac{15}{50} = 30\%$	$\frac{45}{200} = 22.5\%$
	$\frac{150}{150} = 100\%$	$\frac{50}{50} = 100\%$	$\frac{200}{200} = 100\%$

$n(F \cap Y) = 30$ implies that 30 respondents answered yes and are females; $n(F \cap N) = 15$ implies that 15 respondents answered no and are females. Note that $Y \cap N = \varnothing$ and also $M \cap F = \varnothing$.

Let's see what interesting information can be gained from a cross-classification table. We first divide each table entry by its respective column total, as illustrated in Table 8-4. We denote the resulting table by the name "Column Percentages." Looking at the "Yes" column of Table 8-4, note that of the respondents who answered yes, 80% are males and 20% are females. Looking at the "No" column, note that of the respondents who answered no, 70% are males and 30% are females. Looking at the right-most column (the column containing row totals), note that of all the respondents, 77.5% are males and 22.5% are females.

Now we return to Table 8-3 and divide each entry by its respective row total. The resulting table is titled "Row Percentages" and is given in Table 8-5. Looking at the "Male" row, note that of the male respondents, 77.4% purchased a TV and 22.6% did not. Looking at the "Female" row, note that of the female respondents, 66.7% purchased a TV and 33.3% did not. Looking at the bottom row (the row containing column totals), note that of all the respondents, 75% purchased a TV and 25% did not. A marketing researcher, noting the fact that 77.4% of the males and 66.7% of the

TABLE 8-5 **Row percentages**

Sex	Purchased TV		
	yes	**no**	
Male	$\dfrac{120}{155} = 77.4\%$	$\dfrac{35}{155} = 22.6\%$	$\dfrac{155}{155} = 100\%$
Female	$\dfrac{30}{45} = 66.7\%$	$\dfrac{15}{45} = 33.3\%$	$\dfrac{45}{45} = 100\%$
	$\dfrac{150}{200} = 75\%$	$\dfrac{50}{200} = 25\%$	$\dfrac{200}{200} = 100\%$

females purchased TVs, might conclude the almost equal proportions of males and females purchased TVs during the past 3 years. This could result in advertising directed toward both males and females instead of advertising directed toward one group.

Counting

Let's return to the above cross-classification table, which we repeat in Table 8-6 on page 510. Suppose we are asked to determine the number of respondents that *either answered yes or are females*. In terms of sets, we are seeking $n(F \cup Y)$. We already know that $n(F) = 45$, $n(Y) = 150$, and $n(F \cap Y) = 30$. Thus, we need a rule that will enable us to determine the number of elements contained in the union of two sets, given the number of elements in each set and in their intersection. Such a rule is given in the box below.

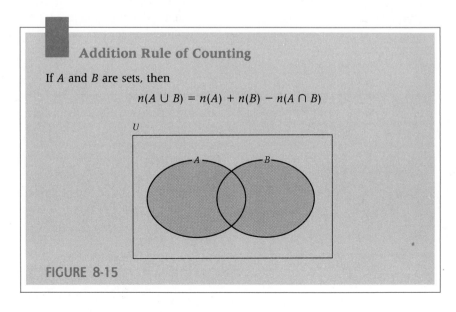

Addition Rule of Counting

If A and B are sets, then

$$n(A \cup B) = n(A) + n(B) - n(A \cap B)$$

FIGURE 8-15

U

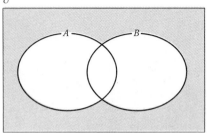

$(A \cup B)' =$ shaded region

(a)

U

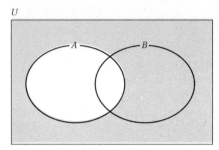

$A' =$ shaded region

(b)

U

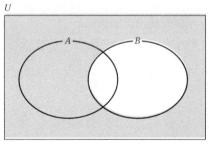

$B' =$ shaded region

(c)

U

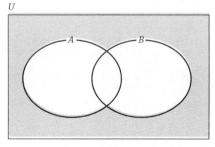

$A' \cap B' =$ shaded region

(d)

FIGURE 8-16

TABLE 8-6

Sex	Purchased TV		
	Y yes	*N* no	
M Male	120	35	155 ⟵ n(M)
F Female	30	15	45 ⟵ n(F)
	150	50	200
	↑ n(Y)	↑ n(N)	

If we apply this rule to solve our problem, we obtain

$$n(F \cup Y) = n(F) + n(Y) - n(F \cap Y)$$
$$= 45 + 150 - 30$$
$$= 165$$

Notice that we subtract $n(F \cap Y)$ from the sum of $n(F)$ and $n(Y)$. This is because when we add $n(F)$ and $n(Y)$, we have twice included $n(F \cap Y)$—once within $n(F)$ and again within $n(Y)$. Since $n(F \cap Y)$ should be included only once, we subtract it from the sum of $n(F)$ and $n(Y)$ to obtain $n(F \cup Y)$.

De Morgan's Laws

We now verify that the following two statements are true for any sets A and B:

$$(A \cup B)' = A' \cap B'$$
$$(A \cap B)' = A' \cup B'$$

These two statements are called **De Morgan's laws.** Literally, the first law states that the complement of a union of two sets equals the intersection of the individual complements. The second law states that the complement of an intersection of two sets equals the union of the individual complements.

We will verify the first law and note that similar reasoning is used to verify the second law. We begin with the Venn diagram of Figure 8-16(a). Our procedure will be to show that the region of the Venn diagram corresponding to the left-hand-side, $(A \cup B)'$, of the first De Morgan's law is equal to the region corresponding to the right-hand side, $A' \cap B'$. Thus, in Figure 8-16(a), we shade the region corresponding to the complement of $A \cup B$. In Figure 8-16(b), we shade the region corresponding to A'. In Figure 8-16(c), we shade the region corresponding to B'. The shaded region of Figure 8-16(d) is the region common to both A' and B', or $A' \cap B'$. Note that the shaded region of Figure 8-16(d) is the same as the shaded region corresponding to $(A \cup B)'$ in Figure 8-16(a). Thus, we have verified the first De Morgan's law

$$(A \cup B)' = A' \cap B'$$

We note that $A' \cap B'$ literally means *not* A *and not* B, or *neither* A *nor* B. The above law is often useful in evaluating statements of the form "neither A nor B." Using this law, we can replace $A' \cap B'$, a difficult set to determine in many instances, with $(A \cup B)'$, an easy set to determine because it is simply the complement of $A \cup B$.

As an example, consider the cross-classification table below.

	A	B	
C	200	80	280
D	50	70	120
	250	150	400

$\longleftarrow n(U)$

Suppose we want to determine the number of elements that are neither As nor Ds or, in other words, $n(A' \cap D')$. Since, by De Morgan's law, $(A \cup D)' = A' \cap D'$, we first determine $n(A \cup D)$, as shown below.

$$n(A \cup D) = n(A) + n(D) - n(A \cap D)$$
$$= 250 + 120 - 50$$
$$= 320$$

Next we find $n[(A \cup D)']$ as follows:

$$n[(A \cup D)'] = n(U) - n(A \cup D)$$
$$= 400 - 320$$
$$= 80$$

Since $(A \cup D)' = A' \cap D'$, then our answer is

$$n(A' \cap D') = n[(A \cup D)']$$
$$= 80$$

Exercises 8-1

1. If $A = \{0, 1, 2, 3, 4\}$, state whether each of the following is true or false:
   a) $0 \in A$ b) $1 \in A$
   c) $2 \in A$ d) $3 \in A$
   e) $4 \in A$ f) $7 \in A$
   g) $n(A) = 4$ h) $8 \in A$
2. If $A = \{5, 6, 7\}$ and $B = \{5, 6, 7, 8, 9\}$, answer each of the following:
   a) Is $A \subset B$?   b) Is $B \subset A$?   c) Does $A = B$?
3. If $A = \{7, 9, 10\}$ and $B = \{7, 10, 9\}$, answer each of the following:
   a) Is $A \subset B$?   b) Is $B \subset A$?   c) Does $A = B$?

If $U = \{1, 2, 3, 4, 5, 6, 7, 8, 9\}$, $A = \{2, 3, 4, 5\}$, and $B = \{4, 5, 6, 7\}$, find each of the following.

4. $A \cup B$	5. $A \cap B$	6. A'	7. $n(B)$
8. $A' \cap B$	9. $A \cap B'$	10. $(A \cup B)'$	11. $(A \cap B)'$
12. $A' \cap B'$	13. $A' \cup B'$	14. $n(A \cap B)$	15. $n(B')$

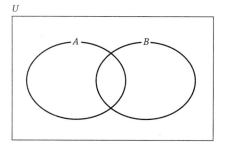

FIGURE 8-17

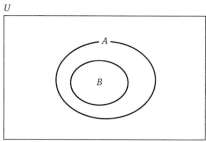

(a)

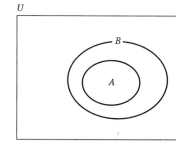

(b)

(c)

FIGURE 8-18

(d)

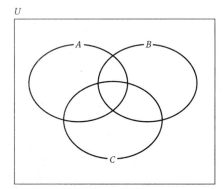

FIGURE 8-19

For the Venn diagram of Figure 8-17, shade the region corresponding to each of the following.

16. $A \cup B$ **17.** $(A \cup B)'$ **18.** $A \cap B$
19. $(A \cap B)'$ **20.** A' **21.** $A' \cap B$
22. B' **23.** $B' \cap A$ **24.** $A' \cap B'$

If $U = \{a, b, c, d, e, f, g, h, i, j\}$, $A = \{a, c, d, g, j\}$, $B = \{a, b, g, j\}$,
$C = \{a, b, c, g, i, j\}$, and $D = \{a, d, f, g, i, j\}$, find each of the following.

25. $A \cap B$ **26.** $A \cup B$ **27.** $C \cap D$ **28.** $C \cup D$
29. A' **30.** B' **31.** $A' \cap B$ **32.** $B' \cup D$
33. $D' \cup A$ **34.** $A \cap B \cap C$ **35.** $A \cup C \cup D$ **36.** $(A \cap B) \cup D$
37. $A \cup (B \cap D)$ **38.** $(A \cap D) \cup C$ **39.** $A \cup (C' \cap D)$ **40.** $B \cap (C \cup D)$
41. $(A \cap B) \cup (C \cap D)$
42. $(B \cup C) \cap (D \cup A)$

43. For each of the Venn diagrams in Figure 8-18, shade the region corresponding to $A \cap B$.
44. For each of the Venn diagrams of Exercise 43, shade the region corresponding to $A \cup B$.
45. For each of the Venn diagrams of Exercise 43, shade the region corresponding to A'.
46. For each of the Venn diagrams of Exercise 43, shade the region corresponding to B'.

For the Venn diagram of Figure 8-19, shade the region corresponding to each of the following.

47. $A \cup B$ **48.** $A \cup C$ **49.** $A \cap B$
50. $B \cap C$ **51.** $A \cap B \cap C$ **52.** $A \cup B \cup C$

53. $A \cap B'$ **54.** $(A \cup B)'$ **55.** $(A \cap B)'$

56. $A' \cup B$ **57.** $A' \cap B'$ **58.** $A \cap (B \cup C)'$

59. $A \cap (B \cap C)'$ **60.** $A' \cap (B \cap C)$ **61.** $C' \cap (A \cap B)$

62. $B' \cap (A \cap C)$ **63.** $(A \cup B)' \cap C$ **64.** $(A \cup C)' \cap B$

65. $(A \cup B \cup C)'$

66. In a certain mathematics class containing 33 students, 8 take a science course, 20 take an English course, and 4 take both.

     a) Express the above results in a Venn diagram.

     b) How many students from this class take either science or English?

     c) How many take an English course, but not a science course?

     d) How many take a science course, but not an English course?

     e) How many do not take English?

     f) How many do not take science?

     g) How many take neither science nor English?

67. *Health care.* In a certain hospital ward containing 100 patients, 40 need psychological counseling, 70 need medical care, and 25 need both.

     a) Express the above results in a Venn diagram.

     b) How many do not need psychological counseling?

     c) How many do not need medical care?

     d) How many do not need both medical care and psychological counseling?

     e) How many need either psychological counseling or medical care?

     f) How many need psychological counseling, but not medical care?

     g) How many need medical care, but not psychological counseling.

     h) How many need neither psychological counseling nor medical care?

68. *Marketing research.* A survey of 60 executives revealed the following results:

     • 40 read *The Wall Street Journal*.

     • 30 read *Barron's*.

     • 20 read both *Barron's* and *The Wall Street Journal*.

     a) Express the above information in a Venn diagram.

     b) How many read either *The Wall Street Journal* or *Barron's*?

     c) How many do not read *Barron's*?

     d) How many read only *The Wall Street Journal*?

     e) How many read only *Barron's*?

     f) How many read neither *Barron's* nor *The Wall Street Journal*?

     g) Of those who read *Barron's*, what percentage also read *The Wall Street Journal?*

     h) Of those who read *The Wall Street Journal*, what percentage also read *Barron's?*

69. In a group of 200 physicians attending a conference, 80 were family practitioners, 130 were specialists, and 40 were both.

     a) Express the above information in a Venn diagram.

     b) How many were either family practitioners or specialists?

     c) How many were neither family practitioners nor specialists?

     d) How many were family practitioners, but not specialists?

     e) How many were specialists, but not family practitioners?

     f) How many were not specialists?

     g) What percentage of the specialists were also family practitioners?

     h) What percentage of the family practitioners were also specialists?

70. *Quality control.* A set of 1000 washers contains 200 that are too small, 300 that are too thin, and 50 that are too small and too thin.

     a) Express the above information in a Venn diagram.

     b) How many washers are either too small or too thin?

     c) How many washers are not too small?

     d) How many washers are neither too small nor too thin?

e) Of those washers that are too small, what percentage are too thin?

f) Of those washers that are too thin, what percentage are too small?

g) How many washers are too small, but not too thin?

71. *Financial planning.* An investment firm commissioned a survey of 500 families that revealed the following results:

- 300 had savings accounts.
- 200 had mutual fund accounts.
- 115 had brokerage accounts.
- 150 had both savings and mutual fund accounts.
- 70 had both savings and brokerage accounts.
- 60 had both brokerage and mutual fund accounts.
- 20 had all three types of accounts.

a) Express the above information in a Venn diagram.

b) How many families did not have any of these three types of accounts?

c) How many families had both savings and brokerage accounts, but not mutual fund accounts?

d) How many families had both savings and mutual fund accounts, but not brokerage accounts?

e) How many families had only savings accounts?

f) How many families had only mutual fund accounts?

g) How many families had either savings or mutual fund accounts?

72. *Blood types.* An antigen is a substance that, when introduced into the body (as in the bloodstream), causes the production of an antibody. There are three possible antigens—A, B, and Rh—that may be present in a person's blood. A person's blood may have none, one, two, or all three of these antigens. A person's blood type is indicative of the antigens it contains. Specifically,

- type A+   Blood has both A and Rh, but not the B antigen.
- type A−   Blood has the A antigen, but not the B and not the Rh antigens.
- type B+   Blood has both B and Rh, but not the A antigen.
- type B−   Blood has the B antigen, but not the A and not the Rh antigens.
- type AB+   Blood has all three antigens.
- type AB−   Blood has both A and B, but not the Rh antigen.
- type O+   Blood has the Rh antigen, but not the A and not the B antigens.
- type O−   Blood does not have any of the three antigens.

Fill in the blood type that corresponds to each of the regions in the Venn diagram of Figure 8-20.

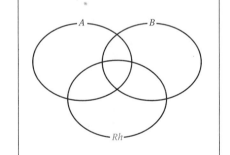

FIGURE 8-20

Answer the following for each cross-classification table in Exercises 73 and 74:

a) $n(D)$ b) $n(A \cap C)$ c) $n(B \cap D)$

d) $n(A \cup C)$ e) $n(B \cup D)$ f) $n(B')$

g) $n(A \cap B)$ h) $n(D')$ i) $n(C \cup D)$

j) What percentage of the *B*s are also *C*s?

k) What percentage of the *A*s are also *D*s?

l) What percentage of the *C*s are also *A*s?

73.

	A	B	
C	90	100	190
D	60	150	210
	150	250	400

74.

	A	B	
C	130	110	240
D	170	90	260
	300	200	500

75. *Survey analysis.* The results of a survey of 50 residents of Hilltop Manor Exclusive Apartments are expressed in the following table:

	Doctors	Lawyers	Business people	
Single	6	3	1	10
Married	18	7	15	40
	24	10	16	50

Let $D = \{doctors\}$, $L = \{lawyers\}$, $B = \{business\ people\}$, $J = \{singles\}$, and $M = \{marrieds\}$.

a) Find $n(D)$.　　　b) Find $n(L)$.　　　c) Find $n(B)$.

d) Find $n(D \cap J)$.　　e) Find $n(D \cap M)$.　　f) Find $n(L \cap J)$.

g) Find $n(D \cup J)$.　　h) Find $n(B \cup M)$.　　i) Find $n(L \cup J)$.

j) Find $n(B')$.　　　k) Find $n(J')$.　　　l) Find $n(D' \cap J)$.

m) Of those residents who are single, what percentage are doctors?

n) Of those residents who are doctors, what percentage are single?

o) Of those residents who are lawyers, what percentage are married?

p) Of those residents who are married, what percentage are lawyers?

76. *Credit screening.* A group of mortgage applicants is cross-classified as given in the table below.

Credit rating	Income		
	under $20,000	$20,000 or more	
Excellent	10	40	50
Good	20	70	90
Fair	50	10	60
	80	120	200

a) How many applicants have either an excellent credit rating or an income under $20,000?

b) How many applicants have either a good credit rating or an income of $20,000 or more?

c) How many applicants have both an excellent credit rating and an income under $20,000?

d) How many applicants have both an excellent credit rating and an income of $20,000 or more?

e) Of those applicants with incomes of $20,000 or more, what percentage have excellent credit ratings?

f) Of those applicants with incomes under $20,000, what percentage have excellent credit ratings?

g) Of those applicants having good credit ratings, what percentage have incomes of $20,000 or more?

h) Of those applicants having fair credit ratings, what percentage have incomes under $20,000?

i) Construct the corresponding "Column Percentages" table, and interpret the result.

j) Construct the corresponding "Row Percentages" table, and interpret the result.

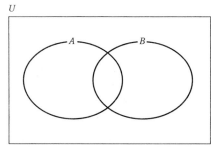

FIGURE 8-21

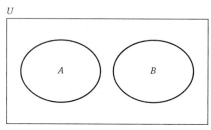

FIGURE 8-22

77. Referring to the Venn diagram of Figure 8-21, explain why
$$n(A \cup B) = n(A) + n(B) - n(A \cap B)$$

78. Referring to the Venn diagram of Figure 8-22, explain why
$$n(A \cup B) = n(A) + n(B)$$

79. If $n(A) = 28$, $n(B) = 20$, and $n(A \cap B) = 5$, find $n(A \cup B)$.

80. If $n(A) = 40$, $n(B) = 30$, and $n(A \cap B) = 12$, find $n(A \cup B)$.

81. If $n(A) = 45$, $n(B) = 22$, and $n(A \cap B) = 0$, find $n(A \cup B)$.

82. If $n(U) = 100$, $n(A) = 30$, $n(B) = 10$, and $n(A \cap B) = 5$, find
a) $n(A \cup B)$.   b) $n[(A \cup B)']$.

83. If $n(U) = 70$, $n(A) = 30$, $n(B) = 18$, and $n(A \cap B) = 11$, find
a) $n(A \cup B)$.   b) $n[(A \cup B)']$.

84–85. For each cross-classification table in Exercises 73 and 74, find
a) $n(A' \cap C')$.   b) $n(D' \cap B')$.
c) $n(A' \cap D')$.   d) $n(D' \cap C')$.

86. For the cross-classification table of Exercise 75, find
a) The number of residents who are neither doctors nor single.
b) The number of residents who are neither lawyers nor married.
c) The number of residents who are neither married nor doctors.

87. For the cross-classification table of Exercise 76, find
a) The number of applicants who have neither an excellent credit rating nor an income under $20,000.
b) The number of applicants who have neither $20,000 or more income nor a good credit rating.
c) The number of applicants who have neither a fair credit rating nor an income under $20,000.

8-2 • COUNTING, PERMUTATIONS, AND COMBINATIONS

Many times we must determine how many possible ways a given sequence of operations can be performed. We often do this by using principles of counting. The following experiment will illustrate a basic principle of counting called the **multiplication rule.**

PROBLEM

Consider two sets, A and B, containing 4 and 2 elements, respectively. In how many different ways can we first select an element from A and then one from B?

SOLUTION

The tree diagram of Figure 8-23 shows all the possible outcomes for this experiment. Note that, for the sake of illustration, we let $A = \{a, b, c, d\}$ and $B = \{e, f\}$. Observe that there are $4 \cdot 2 = 8$ possible ways of first selecting an element from A and then selecting an element from B. This result can be generalized to any number of sets to yield the **multiplication rule of counting.**

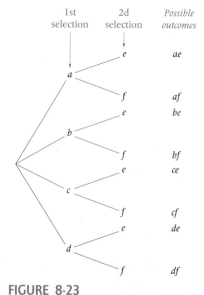

FIGURE 8-23

Multiplication Rule of Counting

Suppose a task consists of 2 operations, O_1 and O_2, to be performed in sequence. If there are n_1 possible outcomes for the first operation, O_1, and n_2 possible outcomes for the second operation, O_2, then there are

$$n_1 \cdot n_2$$

possible ways of first performing O_1 and then performing O_2.

This is generalized to m operations below.

Suppose a task consists of m operations, $O_1, O_2, \ldots, O_m$ to be performed in sequence. If there are n_1 possible outcomes for O_1, n_2 possible outcomes for O_2, . . . , and n_m possible outcomes for O_m, then there are

$$n_1 \cdot n_2 \ldots \cdot n_m$$

possible ways of first performing O_1, then O_2, . . . , and finally O_m.

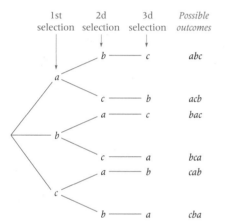

Books are labeled a, b, and c.

FIGURE 8-24

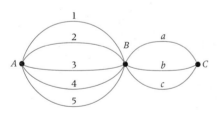

FIGURE 8-25

• EXAMPLE 8-16

A student must arrange 3 books on a shelf. How many possible arrangements are there?

Solution

By the multiplication rule of counting, there are

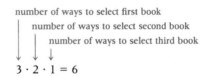

possible arrangements. The tree diagram of Figure 8-24 illustrates all possible arrangements.

• EXAMPLE 8-17

A trip is to consist of driving from city A to city B and then from city B to city C. There are 5 possible routes from city A to city B and 3 possible routes from city B to city C, as illustrated in Figure 8-25. How many different ways can this trip be driven?

Solution

By the multiplication rule of counting, there are

number of ways to drive from city A to city B

number of ways to drive from city B to city C

$$5 \cdot 3 = 15$$

different ways that this trip can be driven.

Factorial

In Example 8-16, we determined that there are $3 \cdot 2 \cdot 1 = 6$ different arrangements of 3 books. Note that $3 \cdot 2 \cdot 1$ is a product of all consecutive integers from 1 to 3. There are many chance experiments where the number of possible outcomes is a product of all consecutive integers from 1 to n. Such a product is called **n factorial** and is denoted by the symbol **$n!$.** Thus, for any counting number n,

$$n! = n(n - 1)(n - 2) \ldots (3)(2)(1)$$

Hence, the phrase "5 factorial" is denoted by the symbol 5! and implies the product

$$5! = 5 \cdot 4 \cdot 3 \cdot 2 \cdot 1$$

And the phrase "7 factorial" is denoted by 7! and implies the product

$$7! = 7 \cdot 6 \cdot 5 \cdot 4 \cdot 3 \cdot 2 \cdot 1$$

By definition, $0! = 1$.

• **EXAMPLE 8-18**

Evaluate each of the following:

a) 6!   b) 7!   c) $\dfrac{9!}{7!}$ d) $\dfrac{30!}{3!27!}$

Solutions

a) $6! = 6 \cdot 5 \cdot 4 \cdot 3 \cdot 2 \cdot 1 = 720$
b) $7! = 7 \cdot 6 \cdot 5 \cdot 4 \cdot 3 \cdot 2 \cdot 1$
     $= 7 \cdot 6!$ (We know from part a that 6! = 720.)
     $= 7(720)$
     $= 5040$
c) $\dfrac{9!}{7!} = \dfrac{9 \cdot 8 \cdot 7!}{7!} = 72$
d) $\dfrac{30!}{3!27!} = \dfrac{30 \cdot 29 \cdot 28 \cdot 27!}{3 \cdot 2 \cdot 1 \cdot 27!} = 4060$

Comments

1. Observe below that $n!$ gets very large very quickly.

    $3! = 6$
    $5! = 120$
    $7! = 5040$
    $10! = 3,628,800$
    $13! = 6,227,020,800$

2. Some calculators have an $n!$ key.

• **EXAMPLE 8-19   Ranking.**

Five artists are to submit one painting each for judging by a panel of peers. The paintings are to be ranked first (best), second (next best), . . . , etc. Assuming no ties, how many possible outcomes are there?

Solution

By the multiplication rule of counting, there are

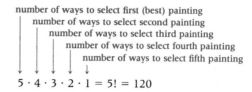

$$5 \cdot 4 \cdot 3 \cdot 2 \cdot 1 = 5! = 120$$

possible ways of ranking the 5 paintings.

• **EXAMPLE 8-20**

How many different batting orders does the manager of a baseball team (9 players) have to choose from?

Solution

The first selection is made from a set of 9 players, the second from a set of 8 players, the third from a set of 7 players, etc., and so, by the multiplication rule of counting, there are

$$9 \cdot 8 \cdot 7 \cdot 6 \cdot 5 \cdot 4 \cdot 3 \cdot 2 \cdot 1 = 9! = 362,880$$

possible batting orders.

• **EXAMPLE 8-21**

Referring to Example 8-20, suppose the star hitter must be third in the batting order and the pitcher must be sixth in the batting order. How many different batting orders are there under these restrictions?

Solution

Since the star hitter must bat third and the pitcher must bat sixth, these two players are fixed in their respective batting orders. Thus, the first selection is made from a set of 7 players, the second from a set of 6 players, the third from a set of 1 player (the star hitter), the fourth from a set of 5 players, the fifth from a set of 4 players, the sixth from a set of 1 player (the pitcher), the seventh from a set of 3 players, the eighth from a set of 2 players, and the ninth from a set of 1 player. Thus, by the multiplication rule of counting, there are

$$7 \cdot 6 \cdot 1 \cdot 5 \cdot 4 \cdot 1 \cdot 3 \cdot 2 \cdot 1 = 5040$$

possible batting orders.

•

Permutations

Suppose we want to select 2 letters without replacement from the set $\{a, b, c, d, e\}$ where the order of selection is important. Since there are 5 possibilities for the first selection and 4 possibilities for the second selection, then by the multiplication rule of counting, there are $5 \cdot 4 = 20$ possible outcomes. The tree diagram of Figure 8-26 illustrates all the possible outcomes for this experiment.

Observing the outcomes of Figure 8-26, we note two important characteristics of this counting problem:

Possible outcomes

	b	ab
	c	ac
a	d	ad
	e	ae
	a	ba
	c	bc
b	d	bd
	e	be
	a	ca
	b	cb
c	d	cd
	e	ce
	a	da
	b	db
d	c	dc
	e	de
	a	ea
	b	eb
e	c	ec
	d	ed

FIGURE 8-26

1. No letter is repeated. In other words, a selected letter is not replaced before a subsequent selection.

2. The order of selection makes a difference. That is, despite the fact that *ab* and *ba* consist of the same 2 letters, they are considered different outcomes because the order of the 2 letters is different.

Counting problems that consist of selecting *r* elements out of a set of *n* elements and that satisfy these two characteristics are called **permutations of *n* elements taken *r* at a time.**

The number of **permutations** of *n* elements taken *r* at a time ($r \leq n$) is the number of all possible ways of selecting *r* elements from a set of *n* elements where *order of selection is important* and replacement between selections is not allowed. This quantity is denoted by the symbol $P(n, r)$.

We now derive a formula for $P(n, r)$, the number of possible ways of selecting *r* elements from a set of *n* elements where order of selection is important and replacement between selections is not allowed. Since the first selection has *n* possibilities, the second selection has $n - 1$ possibilities, the third selection has $n - 2$ possibilities, etc., by the multiplication rule of counting, there will be

$$\underbrace{n(n - 1)(n - 2) \ldots (n - r + 1)}_{r \text{ factors}}$$

possible arrangements. Thus,

$$P(n, r) = \underbrace{n(n - 1)(n - 2) \ldots (n - r + 1)}_{r \text{ factors}}$$

For example, referring to the counting problem of Figure 8-26, where $n = 5$ and $r = 2$, we saw that there were

$$P(5, 2) = \underbrace{5 \cdot 4}_{r = 2 \text{ factors}}$$

arrangements of 5 elements taken 2 at a time. Note that the product $5 \cdot 4$ can be written in factorial notation as follows:

$$5 \cdot 4 = \frac{5 \cdot 4 \cdot 3 \cdot 2 \cdot 1}{3 \cdot 2 \cdot 1}$$

$$= \frac{5!}{3!}$$

$$= \frac{5!}{(5 - 2)!}$$

In general, the product

$$P(n, r) = \underbrace{n(n - 1)(n - 2) \ldots (n - r + 1)}_{r \text{ factors}}$$

may be written in factorial notation as

$$P(n, r) = \frac{n!}{(n - r)!}$$

Thus, we conclude the following.

Permutations

The number of permutations of n elements taken r at a time $(0 \leq r \leq n)$ is denoted by $P(n, r)$, where

$$P(n, r) = \frac{n!}{(n - r)!}$$

• **EXAMPLE 8-22** _____

Four board members of some organization are to be chosen from a group of 7 candidates. The first person chosen becomes president, the second becomes vice president, the third becomes treasurer, and the fourth becomes secretary. No one person can hold two offices. If the 4 people selected constitute a board, how many possible boards can be selected from the 7 candidates?

Solution

The number of ways of selecting 4 elements out of 7 where order is important and replacement is not allowed is given by

$$
\begin{aligned}
P(7, 4) &= \frac{7!}{(7 - 4)!} \\
&= \frac{7!}{3!} \\
&= \frac{7 \cdot 6 \cdot 5 \cdot 4 \cdot 3!}{3!} \\
&= 840 \qquad \text{Number of possible boards}
\end{aligned}
$$

•

Combinations

Consider all possible ways of selecting 3 letters from the 4-element set $\{a, b, c, d\}$ where order makes a difference and replacement is not allowed. Thus, we are considering all possible permutations of 4 elements taken 3 at a time, or

$$P(4, 3) = \frac{4!}{(4 - 3)!} = 24$$

abc	acb	bac	bca	cab	cba
abd	adb	bad	bda	dab	dba
acd	adc	cad	cda	dac	dca
bcd	bdc	cbd	cdb	dbc	dcb

24 permutations of 4 elements
taken 3 at a time

FIGURE 8-27

possible outcomes. Figure 8-27 illustrates the 24 permutations.

Suppose we want to determine the number of possible ways of selecting 3 elements out of 4 elements where order makes *no* difference and replacement is not allowed. Here we are seeking the number of combinations of 4 elements taken 3 at a time. This quantity is denoted by the symbol $\binom{4}{3}$. In general, counting problems that consist of selecting r elements out of a set of n elements where the order of selection makes no difference and replacement is not allowed are called **combinations of *n* elements taken *r* at a time.**

> The number of **combinations** of *n* elements taken *r* at a time ($0 \le r \le n$) is the number of all possible ways of selecting *r* elements from a set of *n* elements where order of selection makes no difference and replacement between selections is not allowed. This quantity is denoted by the symbol $\binom{n}{r}$ or $C(n, r)$.

We now derive a formula for $\binom{n}{r}$. Observing the 24 permutations of 4 elements taken 3 at a time of Figure 8-27, note that the outcomes of each row contain the same 3 letters. Since 3 letters can be arranged in 3! different orders, each row has $3! = 6$ outcomes that are now considered equal since order makes no difference. Thus, the number of combinations of 4 elements taken 3 at a time, or $\binom{4}{3}$, is found by dividing the number of permutations by 3!. Hence, we have

$$C(4, 3) = \binom{4}{3} = \frac{P(4, 3)}{3!}$$

In general, the number of combinations of *n* elements taken *r* at a time is

$$C(n, r) = \binom{n}{r}$$
$$= \frac{P(n, r)}{r!}$$
$$= \frac{n!}{r!(n - r)!}$$

Thus, we conclude the following.

> **Combinations**
>
> The number of combinations of *n* elements taken *r* at a time ($0 \le r \le n$) is denoted by $\binom{n}{r}$ or $C(n, r)$, where
>
> $$C(n, r) = \binom{n}{r} = \frac{n!}{r!(n - r)!}$$

• **EXAMPLE 8-23**

How many 3-element subsets can be selected from a set containing 5 elements?

Solution

This situation is equivalent to selecting 3 elements out of 5 where order makes no difference and replacement is not allowed. Thus, there are

$$C(5, 3) = \binom{5}{3}$$

$$= \frac{5!}{3!(5-3)!}$$

$$= \frac{5!}{3!2!}$$

$$= \frac{5 \cdot 4 \cdot 3!}{3!2!}$$

$$= 10$$

possible subsets or combinations of 5 elements taken 3 at a time.

• **EXAMPLE 8-24** ────────────────────────

In how many ways can a committee of 5 be chosen from a group of 9 persons?

Solution

We seek the number of combinations of 9 elements taken 5 at a time. There are

$$C(9, 5) = \binom{9}{5}$$

$$= \frac{9!}{5!(9-5)!}$$

$$= \frac{9!}{5!4!}$$

$$= \frac{9 \cdot 8 \cdot 7 \cdot 6 \cdot 5!}{5! \cdot 4 \cdot 3 \cdot 2 \cdot 1}$$

$$= 126$$

such combinations.

──────────────────────────────────── •

Since students sometimes have difficulty discerning the difference between permutations and combinations, we provide a summary of both concepts. An example demonstrating both concepts follows the summary.

SUMMARY

Permutations and Combinations

Permutations. Order of selection is important. The number of permutations of n elements taken r at a time $(0 \le r \le n)$ is given by

$$P(n, r) = \frac{n!}{(n-r)!}$$

Combinations. Order of selection is not important. The number of combinations of n elements taken r at a time $(0 \le r \le n)$ is given by

$$C(n, r) = \binom{n}{r} = \frac{n!}{r!(n-r)!}$$

• **EXAMPLE 8-25** _____

a) *Ranking.* How many ways can we select 3 elements from a set of 7 elements where the selected elements are ranked?

b) How many ways can we select 3 elements from a set of 7 elements?

Solution

a) Since the selected elements are ranked, this means that order of selection is important. Therefore, we want the number of permutations of 7 elements taken 3 at a time, or

$$P(7, 3) = \frac{7!}{(7 - 3)!}$$

$$= \frac{7!}{4!} = 210$$

b) Since order of selection is not important, we want the number of combinations of 7 elements taken 3 at a time, or

$$C(7, 3) = \frac{7!}{3!(7 - 3)!}$$

$$= \frac{7!}{3!4!} = 35$$

• **EXAMPLE 8-26** _____

How many bridge hands (13 cards) contain exactly 3 queens?

Solution

We want our hand (13 cards) to contain 3 queens and 10 nonqueens. Since the 3 queens must be chosen from 4 queens in a deck, there are $C(4, 3)$ ways of doing this. The 10 nonqueens must be chosen from the 48 nonqueens (remember there are 52 cards in a deck) of the deck. There are $C(48, 10)$ ways of doing this. Thus, by the multiplication rule of counting, there are

$$C(4, 3) \cdot C(48, 10) = \frac{4!}{3!1!} \cdot \frac{48!}{10!38!}$$

$$= 26{,}162{,}860{,}000$$

such bridge hands.

_____ •

The type of problem given in Example 8-26 occurs so often that we provide a summary of its main points. Since this model involves the multiplication rule of counting and combinations, we will call it the **MRCC model.**

SUMMARY

MRCC Model

1. We begin with an n-element set that is divided into two subsets, the first containing n_1 elements and the second containing n_2 elements, where $n_1 + n_2 = n$. See Figure 8-28.

continues

SUMMARY—*Continued*

2. We select a sample of r elements from the n-element set. We want the sample to contain r_1 elements from the n_1-element subset and r_2 elements from the n_2-element subset, as illustrated in Figure 8-28. Also, note that $r_1 + r_2 = r$. Since there are $C(n_1, r_1)$ ways of selecting r_1 elements from n_1 elements and $C(n_2, r_2)$ ways of selecting r_2 elements from n_2 elements, then, by the multiplication rule of counting, there are

$$\binom{n_1}{r_1} \cdot \binom{n_2}{r_2}$$

ways of selecting such an r-element subset.

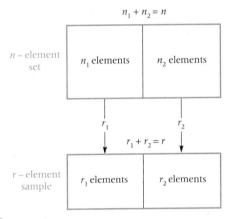

FIGURE 8-28

We proceed with more examples.

• **EXAMPLE 8-27   Quality Control.** _____

A production lot contains 20 radios, 4 of which are defective. A sample of 5 radios is to be selected from the lot.

a) How many possible samples are there?
b) Suppose we want the sample of 5 radios to contain all nondefective radios. In how many ways can this happen?

Solutions

a) Since we are selecting 5 elements out of a set of 20 elements where order makes no difference and replacement is not allowed, there are

$$\binom{20}{5} = \frac{20!}{5!(20-5)!}$$
$$= \frac{20 \cdot 19 \cdot 18 \cdot 17 \cdot 16 \cdot 15!}{5 \cdot 4 \cdot 3 \cdot 2 \cdot 1 \cdot 15!}$$
$$= 15{,}504$$

possible samples.

b) Since the production lot contains 4 defectives, we want the sample of 5 radios to be selected from 16 nondefective radios. There are

$$\binom{16}{5} = \frac{16!}{5!11!}$$
$$= 4368$$

possible ways of doing this.

• EXAMPLE 8-28

In Example 8-27, suppose we want the 5-element sample to contain exactly 3 defectives. How many such samples are possible?

Solution

We want the sample to contain 3 defectives and 2 nondefectives. Since the 3 defectives must be chosen from the 4 defectives in the production lot, and since the 2 nondefectives must be chosen from the 16 nondefectives of the production lot, then, by the MRCC model, there are

$$\binom{4}{3} \cdot \binom{16}{2} = 4 \cdot 120$$
$$= 480$$

defectives ⎤
nondefectives ⎦

possible samples that contain exactly 3 defectives.

• EXAMPLE 8-29

Suppose, in Example 8-27, we want the 5-element subset to contain at least 3 defectives. How many such samples are possible?

Solution

In Example 8-28, we determined that there are

$$\binom{4}{3} \cdot \binom{16}{2} = 4 \cdot 120$$
$$= 480$$

defectives ⎤
nondefectives ⎦

possible samples containing exactly 3 defectives. Using similar reasoning, we determine that there are

$$\binom{4}{4} \cdot \binom{16}{1} = 1 \cdot 16$$
$$= 16$$

defectives ⎤
nondefectives ⎦

possible samples containing exactly 4 defectives. Since the production lot contains only 4 defectives, we cannot consider getting 5 defectives for this 5-element sample.

Thus, the number of possible samples containing at least 3 defectives is given by the sum of the above two quantities, or

$$\binom{4}{3} \cdot \binom{16}{2} + \binom{4}{4} \cdot \binom{16}{1} = 480 + 16$$
$$= 496$$

Exercises 8-2

Evaluate each of the following.

1. $4!$ **2.** $0!$ **3.** $1!$ **4.** $2!$ **5.** $6!$

6. $\dfrac{8!}{5!}$ **7.** $\dfrac{4!}{0!}$ **8.** $\dfrac{9!}{3!6!}$ **9.** $\dfrac{10!}{3!7!}$

10. $\dfrac{6!}{2!(6-2)!}$ **11.** $\dfrac{10!}{4!(10-4)!}$ **12.** $\dfrac{14!}{9!(14-9)!}$

13. $\dfrac{18!}{0!(18-0)!}$ **14.** $\dfrac{19!}{19!(19-19)!}$ **15.** $\dfrac{20!}{2!(20-2)!}$

16. A student must arrange 4 books on a shelf. How many possible arrangements are there?

17. A trip is to consist of driving from city A to city B and then from city B to city C. There are 6 possible routes from city A to city B and 4 possible routes from city B to city C. How many different ways can this trip be taken?

18. Five bakers each submit 1 pie for judging. In how many ways can these 5 pies be ranked?

19. A multiple-choice quiz has 10 questions. Each question has 5 possible choices. How many different sets of 10 answers are possible?

20. A restaurant offers a choice of 7 different types of sandwiches, 3 different types of desserts, and 5 different types of beverages. If a lunch consists of a sandwich, a dessert, and a beverage, how many different lunches are available?

21. *Career placement.* A placement officer analyzes a job applicant's personality by rating that applicant on each of 4 different characteristics. If each characteristic has 6 different ratings, how many different personality types are possible?

22. *Product options.* A new car model provides 3 choices of color, 2 possible types of engines, and 5 interior options. How many different types of this model are possible?

23. *License plates.* For a given state, a typical license plate consists of 2 letters followed by a 3-digit number. How many different such license plates can be produced if
  a) Repetitions of letters and digits are allowed.
  b) Repetitions of digits are allowed, but repetitions of letters are not allowed.
  c) Repetitions of letters are allowed, but repetitions of digits are not allowed.

24. *Serial numbers.* A producer of hi-tech equipment assigns serial numbers to its products. Each serial number consists of 3 letters followed by 6 digits. How many different serial numbers are allowed if
  a) Repetitions of letters and digits are allowed.
  b) Repetitions of digits are allowed, but repetitions of letters are not allowed.
  c) Repetitions of letters are allowed, but repetitions of digits are not allowed.

25. *Nutrition counseling.* A dietician, in planning a low-calorie diet, has a choice of 4 types of meats, 5 types of vegetables, 6 types of fruits, and 3 types of cereals. If a diet consists of a meat, a vegetable, a fruit, and a cereal, then how many different diets are possible?

26. *Computer science.* In computer science, a **bit** (or **binary digit**) consists of either a **0** or **1**. An **n-bit string** is a series of *n* bits. Specifically, 1 0 0 1 0 is an example of a 5-bit string. Bit strings are used to store information in computers.
  a) How many possible 5-bit strings are there?
  b) How many possible 8-bit strings are there?
  c) How many possible 8-bit strings beginning with 1 are there?
  d) How many possible 8-bit strings beginning and ending with 0 are there?

Evaluate each of the following.

27. $P(5, 3)$ **28.** $P(4, 2)$ **29.** $P(7, 6)$

30. $P(5, 2)$ **31.** $P(6, 4)$ **32.** $P(9, 3)$

33. $C(5, 2)$ **34.** $C(6, 4)$ **35.** $C(9, 3)$

36. $C(8, 2)$ **37.** $C(8, 6)$ **38.** $C(9, 6)$

39. $C(8, 8)$ **40.** $C(5, 1)$ **41.** $C(4, 4)$

42. $\binom{9}{5}$ **43.** $\binom{6}{3}$ **44.** $\binom{10}{7}$

45. $\binom{5}{5}$ **46.** $\binom{6}{0}$ **47.** $\binom{9}{2}$

48. $C(8, 2) \cdot C(5, 3)$ **49.** $C(5, 1) \cdot C(4, 2)$

50. $\binom{7}{5} \cdot \binom{6}{2}$ **51.** $\binom{9}{7} \cdot \binom{5}{3}$

52. $\binom{9}{5} \cdot \binom{9}{3}$ **53.** $\binom{10}{6} \cdot \binom{10}{4}$

54. $\binom{8}{4} \cdot \binom{7}{2}$ **55.** $\binom{13}{6} \cdot \binom{12}{10}$

56. After evaluating $\binom{6}{4}$ and $\binom{6}{2}$, explain why, in general,

$$\binom{n}{r} = \binom{n}{n - r}$$

57. In how many ways can 5 letters be selected from $\{a, b, c, d, e\}$ if the order of selection makes a difference?

58. In how many ways can 5 people be seated in a row of 5 seats?

59. In how many ways can 3 letters be chosen from $\{a, b, c, d, e\}$ if the order of selection makes a difference?

60. In how many ways can 3 people be seated in a row of 5 seats?

61. In how many ways can 3 letters be selected from $\{a, b, c, d, e\}$ if the order of selection makes no difference?

62. *Committee selection.* In how many ways can a committee of 3 be chosen from a group of 5 people?

63. Given that 2 points determine a straight line, how many straight lines are determined by a set of 5 points, no 3 of which are collinear?

64. How many ways can we select 5 elements from a set of 9 elements where the selected elements are
  a) Ranked.   b) Not ranked.

65. *Ranking.* Six out of 9 cars are to be ranked on performance. How many possibilities are there?

66. *Ranking.* Seven out of 10 cars are to be ranked on interior design. How many possibilities are there?

67. A deck of cards contains 52 cards. A bridge hand contains 13 cards. How many possible hands are there?

68. With a 52-card deck, how many 5-card hands are possible?

69. *Team building.* A construction crew consists of 7 workers. How many 3-worker teams are possible?

70. Suppose a code word consists of any 4 letters selected from the first 6 letters of the alphabet. How many such code words are possible if
  a) Letters cannot be repeated?
  b) Letters can be repeated?

71. Ten bicycle riders are competing for the top 4 finishes in a race. Assuming that there are no ties, how many possibilities are there?

72. Twelve runners are competing for the top 3 finishes in a race. Assuming that there are no ties, how many possibilities are there?

73. How many 5-card poker hands are possible with a standard deck (52 cards)?

74. How many 5-card poker hands containing 3 aces and 2 kings are possible with a standard deck (52 cards)?

75. In how many ways can a committee of 3 women and 2 men be selected from a group containing 10 women and 9 men?

76. A city council is composed of 4 Democrats and 3 Republicans. How many possible committees consisting of 2 Democrats and 2 Republicans are there?

77. *Telephone numbers.* How many 7-digit telephone numbers are possible if the first digit cannot be 0 and

   a) Repetitions of digits are allowed?

   b) Repetitions of digits are not allowed?

78. A box contains 5 red and 7 blue marbles.

   a) How many possible 4-marble samples can be selected?

   b) How many possible 4-marble samples contain 2 red and 2 blue marbles?

   c) How many possible 4-marble samples contain 1 red and 3 blue marbles?

79. *Zip codes.* How many possible 5-digit zip codes are there if

   a) Repetitions of digits are allowed?

   b) Repetitions of digits are not allowed?

80. How many bridge hands (13 cards) contain exactly 2 queens?

81. How many bridge hands (13 cards) contain at least 2 queens?

82. How many bridge hands (13 cards) contain at least 2 aces?

83. *Audit sampling.* An auditor selects a sample of 8 accounts from a set of 30 accounts receivable for the purpose of balance confirmation. Of the 30 accounts receivable, 4 are in error.

   a) How many possible samples are there?

   b) How many possible samples contain exactly 1 account in error?

   c) How many possible samples contain exactly 2 accounts in error?

   d) How many possible samples contain at least 2 accounts in error?

   e) How many possible samples contain at most 2 accounts in error?

84. *Quality control.* A shipment of 24 television sets contains 5 defectives. A sample of 6 televisions is to be selected from this shipment.

   a) How many possible samples are there?

   b) How many possible samples contain exactly 1 defective?

   c) How many possible samples contain no defectives?

   d) How many possible samples contain exactly 2 defectives?

   e) How many possible samples contain at least 4 defectives?

   f) How many possible samples contain at most 1 defective?

85. *Senate committees.* A committee of 12 senators is to be selected from the body of the U.S. Senate (100 members). How many such possible committees are there?

86. *Committee selection.* A committee of 4 men and 4 women is to be selected from a group containing 7 men and 10 women. How many possible such committees are there?

8-3

• PROBABILITY; ADDITION AND COMPLEMENT RULES; ODDS

Basic Probability Formula

In the remaining sections of this chapter, we will encounter happenings whose outcomes are uncertain. Happenings with uncertain outcomes are

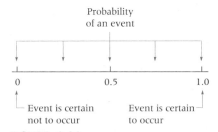

Probability
of an event

0   0.5   1.0

Event is certain   Event is certain
not to occur   to occur

FIGURE 8-29

called **chance experiments.** The start of a new day with its unknown weather, the rolling of a pair of dice, the flipping of a coin, and the selection of a card from a deck are some examples of chance experiments. In the remaining sections of this chapter, we will encounter many chance experiments. Given a chance experiment, we will determine the likelihood of occurrence of certain chance events. The likelihood of occurrence of a chance event is called its **probability.**

The probability of a chance event is a number between 0 and 1. The closer the number is to 1, the more likely it is that the event will occur. The closer the number is to 0, the less likely it is that the event will occur. If an event is certain to occur, then its probability is 1. If event is certain not to occur, then its probability is 0 (see Figure 8-29).

To determine probabilities of events, we must define the following terms.

A **sample space, S,** is the set of all possible outcomes of a chance experiment.

An **event, E,** is a subset of a sample space.

• **EXAMPLE 8-30**

A fair coin is flipped.* H = heads; T = tails.

a) Write the sample space, S, for this chance experiment.
b) Write the set E that represents the event of a head occurring.

Solutions

a) $S = \{H, T\}$
b) $E = \{H\}$

• **EXAMPLE 8-31**

Two fair dice—one red, the other blue—are rolled.†

a) Write the sample space, S, for this chance experiment.
b) Write the set E that represents the event of getting a 1 on the red die.
c) Write the set E that represents the event of getting a sum of 5.

---

*A coin is fair if, when flipped, either of its two sides is equally likely to come up.
†A die is fair if, when rolled, any one of its six faces is equally likely to come up.

Solutions

a) Table 8-7 lists the 36 elements of *S*.

TABLE 8-7

		Blue die					
		⚀	⚁	⚂	⚃	⚄	⚅
	⚀	(1, 1)	(1, 2)	(1, 3)	(1, 4)	(1, 5)	(1, 6)
	⚁	(2, 1)	(2, 2)	(2, 3)	(2, 4)	(2, 5)	(2, 6)
Red	⚂	(3, 1)	(3, 2)	(3, 3)	(3, 4)	(3, 5)	(3, 6)
die	⚃	(4, 1)	(4, 2)	(4, 3)	(4, 4)	(4, 5)	(4, 6)
	⚄	(5, 1)	(5, 2)	(5, 3)	(5, 4)	(5, 5)	(5, 6)
	⚅	(6, 1)	(6, 2)	(6, 3)	(6, 4)	(6, 5)	(6, 6)

b) The event, *E*, of getting a 1 on the red die is represented by

$$E = \{(1, 1), (1, 2), (1, 3), (1, 4), (1, 5), (1, 6)\}$$

c) The event, *E*, of getting a sum of 5 is represented by

$$E = \{(1, 4), (4, 1), (2, 3), (3, 2)\}$$

In general, the relationship between an event, *E*, and its sample space, *S*, is illustrated in Figure 8-30. Observe that a sample space, *S*, is a universal set for a given experiment. An event, *E*, is simply a subset of a sample space.

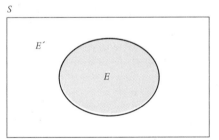

S

FIGURE 8-30

Probabilities of Events

The probability of an event, *E*, occurring will be denoted by the symbol

$$P(E)$$

If $n(S)$ is the number of elements of a finite sample space whose outcomes are equally likely to occur, and if $n(E)$ is the number of elements of an event set, *E*, then $P(E)$, the probability of event *E* occurring, is given by

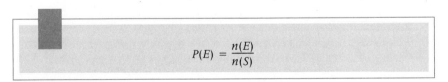

$$P(E) = \frac{n(E)}{n(S)}$$

This expression is called the **basic probability formula.**

• **EXAMPLE 8-32** _____

If a fair coin is flipped once, find the probability of a head occurring.

Solution

In Example 8-30, we determined that $S = \{H, T\}$ and that $E = \{H\}$. Since $n(S) = 2$ and $n(E) = 1$, then

$$P(E) = \frac{n(E)}{n(S)} = \frac{1}{2}, \text{ or } .50$$

• **EXAMPLE 8-33** _____

If two fair dice—one red, the other blue— are rolled, find the probability of getting

a) A 1 on the red die.
b) A sum of 5.

Solutions

In part a of Example 8-31, we determined that $n(S) = 36$.

a) In part b of Example 8-31, we determined that

$$E = \{(1, 1), (1, 2), (1, 3), (1, 4), (1, 5), (1, 6)\}$$

Since $n(E) = 6$, then

$$P(E) = \frac{n(E)}{n(S)} = \frac{6}{36} = \frac{1}{6}, \text{ or } 16\frac{2}{3}\%$$

b) In part c of Example 8-31, we determined that

$$E = \{(1, 4), (4, 1), (2, 3), (3, 2)\}$$

Since $n(E) = 4$, then

$$P(E) = \frac{n(E)}{n(S)} = \frac{4}{36} = \frac{1}{9}, \text{ or } 11\frac{1}{9}\%$$

• **EXAMPLE 8-34** _____

Two fair coins are flipped.

a) Determine the sample space.
b) Determine the probability that exactly 1 head occurs.
c) Determine the probability that at most 1 head occurs.

Solutions

a) Since this experiment consists of flipping more than one coin, we will determine the sample space by using a **tree diagram** (see Figure 8-31). From the tree diagram of Figure 8-31, we obtain

$$S = \{HH, HT, TH, TT\}$$

b) The event of *getting exactly 1 head* is represented by the event set

$$E = \{HT, TH\}$$

Since $n(E) = 2$ and $n(S) = 4$, then

$$P(E) = \frac{n(E)}{n(S)} = \frac{2}{4}, \text{ or } 50\%$$

c) The event of *getting at most 1 head* is represented by the event set

$$E = \{TT, HT, TH\}$$

Since $n(E) = 3$ and $n(S) = 4$, then

$$P(E) = \frac{n(E)}{n(S)} = \frac{3}{4}, \text{ or } 75\%$$

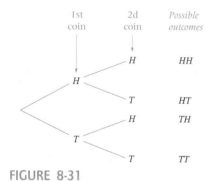

1st coin   2d coin   *Possible outcomes*

H
   H   *HH*
   T   *HT*
T
   H   *TH*
   T   *TT*

FIGURE 8-31

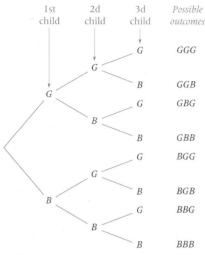

1st child 2d child 3d child *Possible outcomes*

G — GGG
G
B — GGB
G
G — GBG
B
B — GBB
G — BGG
G
B — BGB
B
G — BBG
B
B — BBB

FIGURE 8-32

• **EXAMPLE 8-35   Family Planning.** _____

A newly married couple plans to have 3 children. If we assume that no multiple births will occur and that the events "having a boy," *B*, and "having a girl," *G*, are equally likely to occur, then

a) Use a tree diagram to determine a sample space for this chance experiment.
b) Determine the probability of having 2 girls and 1 boy in that order.
c) Determine the probability of having 2 girls and 1 boy in any order.
d) Determine the probability of having at least 2 boys.

Solutions

a) The sample space is determined from the tree diagram of Figure 8-32.

From this diagram, we obtain

$$S = \{GGG, GGB, GBG, GBB, BGG, BGB, BBG, BBB\}$$

We note that the outcomes of this sample space are equally likely to occur since the events "having a boy" and "having a girl" are equally likely to occur.

b) We seek outcomes of *S* containing 2 girls and 1 boy in that order. There is only one such outcome. Hence, the event set

$$E = \{GGB\}$$

Since $n(E) = 1$ and $n(S) = 8$, then

$$P(E) = \frac{n(E)}{n(S)} = \frac{1}{8}, \text{ or } 12.5\%$$

c) We seek outcomes of *S* containing 2 girls and 1 boy in any order. Hence,

$$E = \{GGB, GBG, BGG\}$$

Since $n(E) = 3$ and $n(S) = 8$, then

$$P(E) = \frac{n(E)}{n(S)} = \frac{3}{8}, \text{ or } 37.5\%$$

d) We seek outcomes of *S* containing either 2 boys or 3 boys. Hence,

$$E = \{GBB, BGB, BBG, BBB\}$$

Since $n(E) = 4$ and $n(S) = 8$, then

$$P(E) = \frac{n(E)}{n(S)} = \frac{4}{8}, \text{ or } 50\%$$

Interpreting Probabilities

In this section, we have calculated probabilities of various events. In Example 8-32, we determined that if a coin is flipped, the probability of a head occurring is 1/2, or 50%. This may be interpreted objectively as follows: If a coin is repeatedly flipped, then the ratio

$$\frac{\text{total number of heads}}{\text{total number of flips}}$$

will approach 1/2 as the number of flips increases (see Figure 8-33). This interpretation is based on the *law of large numbers*.

The above concept is used to approximate probabilities of events. For example, suppose we have a biased coin. Out of 100 flips, the coin shows 70 heads (or 70% heads); out of 200 flips, the coin shows 116 heads (or

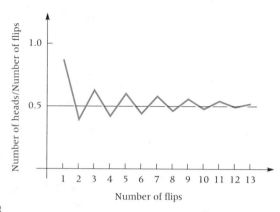

FIGURE 8-33

58% heads); out of 500 flips, the coin shows 315 heads (or 63% heads); out of 1000 flips, the coin shows 600 heads (or 60% heads). We could conclude that the probability of a head occurring with this coin is approximately .60, or 60%. Such a probability approximation derived from actual experience is called an **empirical probability.**

Empirical Probability

If an event, E, occurs m times out of n trials, then

$$P(E) \approx \frac{m}{n}$$

where the approximation gets better as n gets larger and larger. The ratio m/n is called the **relative frequency** of event E after n trials.

Sometimes probabilities of certain events must be assigned subjectively. Such probabilities are called **subjective probabilities.** For example, suppose a supermarket chain is planning to open a new market in a developing community. Management has no past record of success or failure at this location. However, using personal judgment, hunches, or perhaps past experience with a similar location, management assigns an 80% probability of success to the new market. The 80% probability is a subjective probability.

Probability Distributions

Up to this point in this section we have used the formula $P(E) = n(E)/n(S)$ to determine probabilities of events. As previously noted, this formula applies to situations where outcomes of a finite sample space are equally likely to occur. Also, we must be able to determine $n(E)$ and $n(S)$. However, sometimes we encounter situations where the outcomes of a finite sample space are not equally likely to occur, or $n(E)$ and $n(S)$ cannot be determined. For such situations, we consider a sample space, S, consisting of n outcomes, $e_1, e_2, \ldots, e_n$, where the outcomes are assigned the respective probabilities, $p_1, p_2, \ldots, p_n$, such that $p_1 + p_2 + \ldots + p_n = 1$. If an event $E = \{e_1, e_2, e_3\}$, then $P(E)$ is determined by adding the respective probabilities, or, in other words, $P(E) = p_1 + p_2 + p_3$. If $E = \{e_3, e_4, e_5, e_6\}$, then $P(E) = p_3 + p_4 + p_5 + p_6$. We generalize in the box below.

SUMMARY

Probability Distributions

1. If $S = \{e_1, e_2, \ldots, e_n\}$, where the outcomes of S are assigned probabilities as given in the table below, then such a table is called a probability distribution for the sample space, S.

Outcome	Probability	
e_1	p_1	$0 \le p_1 \le 1$
e_2	p_2	$0 \le p_2 \le 1$
.	.	.
.	.	.
.	.	.
e_n	p_n	$0 \le p_n \le 1$
		$p_1 + p_2 + \ldots + p_n = 1$
	1	

2. $P(S) = 1$; $P(\varnothing) = 0$.
3. If event $E = \{e_1, e_2, \ldots, e_m\}$, where $m \le n$, then
$$P(E) = p_1 + p_2 + \ldots + p_m$$

4. If the outcomes are *equally likely* to occur, then we assign each outcome the probability $1/n$. In other words,
$$p_1 = p_2 = \ldots = p_n = \frac{1}{n}$$

• **EXAMPLE 8-36   Marketing Research.** _____

A marketing researcher counts the number of people entering a department store during a specified 4-hour time period on Friday afternoons. The results, for a total of 50 Friday afternoons, are recorded below.

Number of people		Frequency of occurrence	Probability
e_1:	≤ 300	2	2/50 = .04
e_2:	301–400	3	3/50 = .06
e_3:	401–500	30	30/50 = .60
e_4:	501–600	10	10/50 = .20
e_5:	> 600	5	5/50 = .10
		50	1.00

number of
trials

Studying the above table, note that on 2 Friday afternoons, at most 300 people entered the store; on 3 Friday afternoons, at least 301, but at most 400 people entered the store; on 30 Friday afternoons, at least 401, but at most 500 people entered the store; on 10 Friday afternoons, at least 501, but at most 600 people entered the store; on 5 Friday afternoons, more than 600 people entered the store. Note that we have divided the frequency of occurrence of each outcome by the number of trials, 50, to obtain the empirical probability of each outcome.

We now consider the following:

a) Find the probability that at most 500 people enter the store on a Friday afternoon during the specified time period.

b) Find the probability that at least 401, but at most 600 people enter the store on a Friday afternoon during the specified time period.

Solutions

a) $E = \{e_1, e_2, e_3\}$ and

$$P(E) = .04 + .06 + .60$$
$$= .70, \text{ or } 70\%$$

Thus, 70% of the time, at most 500 people enter the store, as specified above.

b) $E = \{e_3, e_4\}$ and

$$P(E) = .60 + .20$$
$$= .80, \text{ or } 80\%$$

Thus, 80% of the time, at least 401, but at most 600 people enter the store, as specified before.

Addition Rules

We now discuss probability rules that are used to determine probabilities of events written with the word "or." In other words, if A and B are events, then sometimes we must determine the probability of event A or event B, written as $P(A \text{ or } B)$. Such an event, A or B, is the union of A and B and is therefore written as $P(A \cup B)$. Thus, $P(A \text{ or } B)$ means the same as $P(A \cup B)$.

We now state a rule for determining $P(A \cup B)$.

Addition Rule

If A and B are events, then

$$P(A \cup B) = P(A) + P(B) - P(A \cap B)$$

Note:

1. $P(A \cup B)$ is the same as $P(A \text{ or } B)$.
2. $P(A \cap B)$ is the same as $P(A \text{ and } B)$.

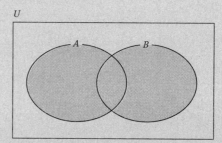

$A \cup B = $ shaded region

FIGURE 8-34

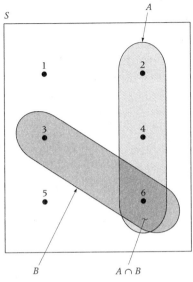

S

A

B $A \cap B$

FIGURE 8-35

Observing Figure 8-34, note that $P(A \cup B)$ is determined by adding $P(A)$ and $P(B)$ and then subtracting $P(A \cap B)$. We subtract $P(A \cap B)$ because it has been counted twice, once within $P(A)$ and again within $P(B)$. We note that the addition rule of probability defines $P(A \cup B)$ for any events A and B.

• **EXAMPLE 8-37** ——————————————————————

A fair die is rolled once. The sample space is

$$S = \{1, 2, 3, 4, 5, 6\}$$

Determine the probability of rolling

a) An even number.
b) A number that is divisible by 3.
c) An even number **and** a number that is divisible by 3.
d) An even number **or** a number that is divisible by 3.

Solutions

a) The event of *rolling an even number* is defined by set $A = \{2, 4, 6\}$, as shown in Figure 8-35. Since $n(A) = 3$ and $n(S) = 6$, then the probability of rolling an even number is

$$P(A) = \frac{n(A)}{n(S)} = \frac{3}{6} = \frac{1}{2}$$

b) The event of *rolling a number that is divisible by 3* is defined by set $B = \{3, 6\}$, as shown in Figure 8-35. Since $n(B) = 2$, then the probability of rolling a number that is divisible by 3 is

$$P(B) = \frac{n(B)}{n(S)} = \frac{2}{6} = \frac{1}{3}$$

c) The event of *rolling an even number **and** a number that is divisible by 3* is defined by set $A \cap B = \{6\}$, as shown in Figure 8-35. Since $n(A \cap B) = 1$, then the probability of rolling an even number and a number that is divisible by 3 is

$$P(A \cap B) = \frac{n(A \cap B)}{n(S)} = \frac{1}{6}$$

d) The event of *rolling either an even number **or** a number that is divisible by 3* is defined by $A \cup B$. Thus, the probability of rolling an even number or a number that is divisible by 3 is given by

$$P(A \cup B) = P(A) + P(B) - P(A \cap B)$$
$$= \frac{1}{2} + \frac{1}{3} - \frac{1}{6}$$
$$= \frac{4}{6} = \frac{2}{3}$$

•

Mutually Exclusive Events. If events A and B are such that they are disjoint, then $A \cap B = \varnothing$ (see Figure 8-36 on page 538), and events A and B are called **mutually exclusive events.** Since $A \cap B = \varnothing$, then $P(A \cap B) = 0$, and the addition rule becomes

$$P(A \cup B) = P(A) + P(B)$$

We summarize in the following box.

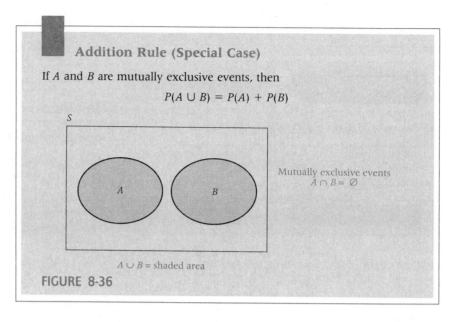

Addition Rule (Special Case)

If A and B are mutually exclusive events, then

$$P(A \cup B) = P(A) + P(B)$$

Mutually exclusive events
$A \cap B = \varnothing$

$A \cup B$ = shaded area

FIGURE 8-36

•   **EXAMPLE 8-38**

We return to the chance experiment of rolling a fair die once. The sample space is repeated in Figure 8-37. Determine the probability of rolling

a)   An odd number.
b)   A 4.
c)   Either an odd number **or** a 4.

Solutions

a)   The event of *rolling an odd number* is defined by set $C = \{1, 3, 5\}$, as shown in Figure 8-38. Thus, we seek $P(C)$ and

$$P(C) = \frac{n(C)}{n(S)} = \frac{3}{6} = \frac{1}{2}$$

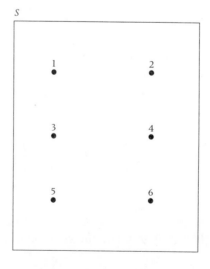

FIGURE 8-37

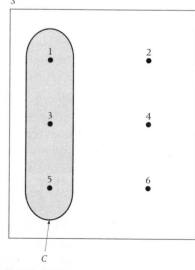

FIGURE 8-38

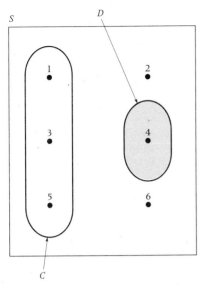

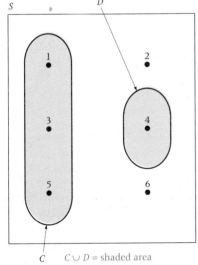

FIGURE 8-39

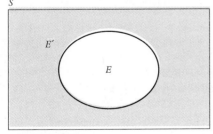

$C \cup D$ = shaded area

FIGURE 8-40

Complement of an event

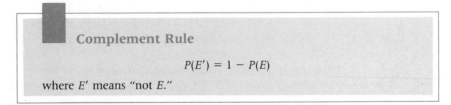

FIGURE 8-41

b) The event of *rolling a 4* is defined by set $D = \{4\}$, as shown in Figure 8-39. Thus, we seek $P(D)$ and

$$P(D) = \frac{n(D)}{n(S)} = \frac{1}{6}$$

c) The event of *rolling either an odd number or a 4* is defined by the set $C \cup D$. Since C and D are mutually exclusive events, as we see from Figure 8-40, then by the special case addition rule,

$$P(C \cup D) = P(C) + P(D)$$
$$= \frac{1}{2} + \frac{1}{6}$$
$$= \frac{4}{6} = \frac{2}{3}$$

Complement of an Event

The Venn diagram of Figure 8-41 illustrates the relationship between an event, E, and its sample space, S. The **complement** of an event, E, consists of the set of elements of S that are not in E. The complement of E is denoted by E', read "not E."

We now derive a formula for $P(E')$ by noting that E and E' are disjoint sets (or, in other words, mutually exclusive events), and, therefore, $E \cap E' = \emptyset$. Also, $E \cup E' = S$, and, thus,

$$P(S) = P(E \cup E')$$
$$= P(E) + P(E') \qquad \text{Special Case Addition Rule}$$

Since $P(S) = 1$, the above becomes

$$1 = P(E) + P(E')$$

Solving for $P(E')$ gives the *complement rule*

$$P(E') = 1 - P(E)$$

We summarize as follows.

> **Complement Rule**
>
> $$P(E') = 1 - P(E)$$
>
> where E' means "not E."

• **EXAMPLE 8-39**

If the probability of a supermarket succeeding at a given location is .70, find the probability of its failing at that location.

Solution

By the complement rule, we have

$$P(\text{failing}) = 1 - P(\text{succeeding})$$
$$= 1 - .70$$
$$= .30$$

We now consider more examples using the rules of this section.

• **EXAMPLE 8-40**   **Weather Forecasting.** _____

According to a weather forecaster, the probability of rain tomorrow is .60, the probability of hail is .10, and the probability of both rain and hail is .08. Find the probability of

a)   Either rain or hail tomorrow.
b)   Neither rain nor hail tomorrow.

Solution

a)   Let

$$R = \text{event of rain tomorrow}$$
$$H = \text{event of hail tomorrow}$$
$$R \text{ and } H = \text{event of both rain and hail tomorrow}$$

Thus, $P(R) = .60$ and $P(H) = .10$. Since $P(R \text{ and } H)$ is equivalent to $P(R \cap H)$, then $P(R \cap H) = .08$. We seek $P(R \text{ or } H)$. Since $P(R \text{ or } H)$ is equivalent to $P(R \cup H)$, we use the addition rule to obtain

$$P(R \cup H) = P(R) + P(H) - P(R \cap H)$$
$$= .60 + .10 - .08$$
$$= .62$$

b)   We seek $P(\text{neither } R \text{ nor } H)$ or, in other words, $P(\text{not } R \text{ and not } H)$. This can be written as $P(R' \text{ and } H')$ or $P(R' \cap H')$. Using one of De Morgan's laws, $R' \cap H' = (R \cup H)'$. Thus, we seek $P[(R \cup H)']$. Since we have determined that $P(R \cup H) = .62$ in part a, then by the complement law

$$P[(R \cup H)'] = 1 - P(R \cup H)$$
$$= 1 - .62$$
$$= .38$$

• **EXAMPLE 8-41**   **Quality Control.** _____

A production lot of 1000 ball bearings contains 50 that are too small, 30 that are not perfectly round, and 10 that are both too small and not perfectly round. If a ball bearing is selected from this production lot, determine the probability that it is

a)   Too small.
b)   Not perfectly round.
c)   Both too small **and** not perfectly round.
d)   Either too small **or** not perfectly round.
e)   Either too small **or** not perfectly round, but **not both.**

Solutions

a)   Let

$$S = \text{sample space of 1000 ball bearings}$$
$$A = \text{event that the selected ball bearing is too small}$$
$$B = \text{event that the selected ball bearing is not perfectly round}$$
$$A \cap B = \text{event that the selected ball bearing is both too small and}$$
$$\text{not perfectly round}$$

$n(S) = 1000$

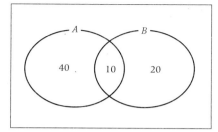

FIGURE 8-42

$n(S) = 1000$

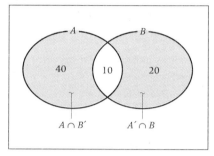

$(A \cap B') \cup (A' \cap B) = $ shaded region

FIGURE 8-43

as illustrated in the Venn diagram of Figure 8-42. Thus, we seek $P(A)$ and

$$P(A) = \frac{n(A)}{n(S)} = \frac{50}{1000} = .05$$

b) We seek $P(B)$ and

$$P(B) = \frac{n(B)}{n(S)} = \frac{30}{1000} = .03$$

c) We seek $P(A \cap B)$ and

$$P(A \cap B) = \frac{n(A \cap B)}{n(S)} = \frac{10}{1000} = .01$$

d) We seek $P(A \cup B)$ and

$$P(A \cup B) = P(A) + P(B) - P(A \cap B)$$
$$= .05 + .03 - .01$$
$$= .07$$

e) The set corresponding to the event of *selecting a ball-bearing that is either too small or not perfectly round, but not both* is given by $(A \cap B') \cup (A' \cap B)$, as illustrated in the Venn diagram of Figure 8-43. Studying Figure 8-43, note that the events $A \cap B'$ and $A' \cap B$ are mutually exclusive. Thus, by the special case addition rule,

$$P[(A \cap B') \cup (A' \cap B)] = P(A \cap B') + P(A' \cap B)$$
$$= \frac{40}{1000} + \frac{20}{1000}$$
$$= .04 + .02$$
$$= .06$$

• **EXAMPLE 8-42**   **Market Analysis.** _____

The manager of an automobile dealership has analyzed the past week's sales. The results are given in Table 8-8. If a person is selected from this group, what is the probability that the selected person

a) Paid cash.
b) Bought a full-size car.

TABLE 8-8

		Buyers of automobiles		
		A paid cash	*B* used financing	
F	Bought full-size car	50	30	80
M	Bought mid-size car	10	76	86
C	Bought compact	5	29	34
		65	135	200 ←—$n(S)$

c) Paid cash **and** bought a full-size car.
d) Paid cash **or** bought a full-size car.
e) Paid cash **or** bought a full-size car, but **not both.**
f) Bought a full-size car **or** a compact.
g) **Neither** paid cash **nor** bought a full-size car.

Solutions

a) We seek $P(A)$ and

$$P(A) = \frac{n(A)}{n(S)} = \frac{65}{200} = .325$$

b) We seek $P(F)$ and

$$P(F) = \frac{n(F)}{n(S)} = \frac{80}{200} = .40$$

c) We seek $P(A$ and $F)$ or, equivalently, $P(A \cap F)$, as illustrated in Table 8-9.

$$P(A \cap F) = \frac{n(A \cap F)}{n(S)} = \frac{50}{200} = .25$$

d) We seek $P(A$ or $F)$ or, equivalently, $P(A \cup F)$, as indicated by the shaded area in Table 8-9. Using the addition rule, we have

$$P(A \cup F) = P(A) + P(F) - P(A \cap F)$$
$$= .325 + .40 - .25$$
$$= .475$$

e) The set corresponding to this event is $(A \cap F') \cup (A' \cap F)$ and is shaded in Table 8-10. Note that the events $A \cap F'$ and $A' \cap F$ are mutually exclusive. Thus, by the special case addition rule,

$$P[(A \cap F') \cup (A' \cap F)] = P(A \cap F') + P(A' \cap F)$$
$$= \frac{n(A \cap F')}{n(S)} + \frac{n(A' \cap F)}{n(S)}$$
$$= \frac{15}{200} + \frac{30}{200}$$
$$= \frac{45}{200}$$
$$= .225$$

TABLE 8-9

		A paid cash	B used financing	
	Buyers of automobiles			
F	Bought full-size car	50	30	80
M	Bought mid-size car	10	76	86
C	Bought compact	5	29	34
		65	135	200 ← $n(S)$

$n(A)$ $n(B)$

$n(A \cap F)$

TABLE 8-10

		A paid cash	B used financing	
	Buyers of automobiles			
F	Bought full-size car	50	30	80
M	Bought mid-size car	10	76	86
C	Bought compact	5	29	34
		65	135	200 ⟵ $n(S)$

$A \cap F'$ $n(A)$ $n(B)$ $A' \cap F$

$(A \cap F') \cup (A' \cap F)$ = shaded area

f) We seek $P(F \text{ or } C)$. The set corresponding to this event is shaded in Table 8-11. Since F and C are mutually exclusive events, we use the special case addition rule to obtain

$$P(F \text{ or } C) = P(F) + P(C)$$
$$= \frac{n(F)}{n(S)} + \frac{n(C)}{n(S)}$$
$$= \frac{80}{200} + \frac{34}{200}$$
$$= .40 + .17$$
$$= .57$$

g) We seek $P(\text{neither } A \text{ nor } F)$ or, in other words, $P(\text{not } A \text{ and not } F)$. This can be written as $P(A' \text{ and } F')$ or $P(A' \cap F')$. Using one of De Morgan's laws,

TABLE 8-11

		A paid cash	B used financing	
	Buyers of automobiles			
F	Bought full-size car	50	30	80 ⟵ $n(F)$
M	Bought mid-size car	10	76	86
C	Bought compact	5	29	34 ⟵ $n(C)$
		65	135	200 ⟵ $n(S)$

$n(A)$ $n(B)$

$F \cup C$ = shaded area

$A' \cap F' = (A \cup F)'$. Thus, we seek $P[(A \cup F)']$. Since we have determined that $P(A \cup F) = .475$ in part d, then, by the complement rule,

$$P[(A \cup F)'] = 1 - P(A \cup F)$$
$$= 1 - .475$$
$$= .525$$

We now consider an example involving rules of counting and combinations.

• **EXAMPLE 8-43   Quality Control Planning.** _____

A production lot of 20 personal computers contains 3 that are defective. A planned quality control procedure is to consist of sampling and then inspecting 4 computers from the production lot. Determine the probability that such a sample contains

a) Exactly 1 defective.
b) At most 1 defective.
c) More than 1 defective.

Solutions

a) We need to determine $n(S)$, the number of 4-element samples from a 20-element set. There are $\binom{20}{4}$ such samples. Hence,

$$n(S) = \binom{20}{4}$$
$$= \frac{20!}{4!16!}$$
$$= 4845$$

Next, we must determine $n(E)$, the number of 4-element samples containing exactly 1 defective. Since our sample must contain 1 defective and 3 nondefectives selected from 3 defectives and 17 nondefectives, respectively, then, by the MRCC model, there are $\binom{3}{1} \cdot \binom{17}{3}$ such samples. Hence,

$$n(E) = \binom{3}{1} \cdot \binom{17}{3}$$

↑_____↑ nondefectives
└_____ defectives

$$= \frac{3!}{1!2!} \frac{17!}{3!14!}$$
$$= 2040$$

and

$$P(E) = \frac{n(E)}{n(S)}$$
$$= \frac{2040}{4845}$$
$$= .42, \text{ or } 42\%$$

b) Note that

$$P\binom{\text{at most}}{\text{1 defective}} = P\binom{\text{exactly}}{\text{0 defective}} + P\binom{\text{exactly}}{\text{1 defective}}$$

We have already computed $P\binom{\text{exactly}}{\text{1 defective}}$ in part a. Thus, we compute $P\binom{\text{exactly}}{\text{0 defective}}$. Since $n(S)$ is the same as that in part a, we compute $n(E)$, the number of 4-element samples containing 0 defective computers. This means that all 4 computers of the sample must be selected from the 17 nondefective computers. There are $\binom{17}{4}$ such samples. Hence,

$$n(E) = \binom{17}{4}$$
$$= \frac{17!}{4!13!}$$
$$= 2380$$

and

$$P\binom{\text{exactly}}{\text{0 defective}} = P(E) = \frac{n(E)}{n(S)}$$
$$= \frac{2380}{4845}$$
$$= .49$$

Thus,

$$P\binom{\text{at most}}{\text{1 defective}} = P\binom{\text{exactly}}{\text{0 defective}} + P\binom{\text{exactly}}{\text{1 defective}}$$
$$= .42 + .49$$
$$= .91, \text{ or } 91\%$$

c) The event of *getting more that 1 defective* is the complement of the event of *getting at most 1 defective*. Thus, by the complement rule,

$$P\binom{\text{getting more}}{\text{than 1 defective}} = 1 - P\binom{\text{getting at}}{\text{most 1 defective}}$$
$$= 1 - .91$$
$$= .09, \text{ or } 9\%$$

Odds and Probability

People often express the likelihood of events in terms of odds. Some examples are given below.

- The odds of inflation recurring next year are 5 to 4.
- The odds of rain tomorrow are 1 to 5.

Odds can be translated into probabilities, as shown in the box below.

Odds and Probability

Translating Odds Into Probabilities. If the odds in favor of an event, E, are a to b, then the probability of event E occurring is given by

$$P(E) = \frac{a}{a + b}$$

Returning to the above examples, then

$$P(\text{inflation recurring}) = \frac{5}{5 + 4} = \frac{5}{9}$$

$$P(\text{rain tomorrow}) = \frac{1}{1 + 5} = \frac{1}{6}$$

In the above examples, we translated odds into probabilities. Sometimes it is necessary to translate probabilities into odds. We summarize as follows.

Odds and Probability

Translating Probabilities Into Odds. If E is some event and $P(E)$ its probability, then the

$$\text{odds in favor of } E = \frac{P(E)}{P(E')} \qquad [P(E) \neq 1]$$

where $P(E') = 1 - P(E)$.

Thus, if

$$P(\underbrace{\text{interest rates rising}}_{E}) = .60$$

then the

$$\text{odds in favor of } \textit{interest rates rising} = \frac{P(E)}{P(E')}$$

$$= \frac{.60}{.40}$$

$$= \frac{3}{2} \qquad \text{which can be written ``3 to 2''}$$

Thus, the odds are 3 to 2 that interest rates will rise.

At this point, we summarize the results of this chapter by presenting a procedure for finding probabilities of events.

To Find Probabilities of Events

1. **Focus on the event.** Look for the rollowing key words:

or → Addition rules:
$P(A \text{ or } B) = P(A) + P(B) - P(A \cap B)$
If A and B are mutually exclusive events,
$P(A \text{ or } B) = P(A) + P(B)$

not → Complement rule:
$P(\text{not } E) = 1 - P(E)$

neither A nor B → Use De Morgan's law:
$A' \cap B' = (A \cup B)'$
Then determine $P(A \cup B)$ and, finally, use the complement rule to find
$P[(A \cup B)'] = 1 - P(A \cup B)$

either A or B,
but not both → This event is defined by the set
$(A \cap B') \cup (A' \cap B)$
which corresponds to the shaded region in Figure 8-44. Since $A \cap B'$ and $A' \cap B$ are mutually exclusive, we use the special case addition rule to obtain
$P[(A \cap B') \cup (A' \cap B)] = P(A \cap B') + P(A' \cap B)$

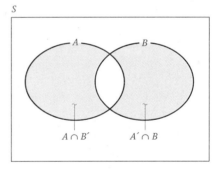

$(A \cap B') \cup (A' \cap B)$ = shaded region

FIGURE 8-44

Note: If the outcomes are equally likely to occur, you may have to use the formula $P(E) = n(E)/n(S)$ within a given rule.

2. If the above approaches do not work and the outcomes are equally likely to occur, try to determine $n(S)$ and $n(E)$ by using counting procedures (i.e., permutations, combinations, and the MRCC model) so that the formula $P(E) = n(E)/n(S)$ can be used.
3. You may have to use the concept of probability distributions.

Exercises 8-3

1. Each letter of the word "money" is written on a separate slip of paper, and the slips are placed in a box. A chance experiment consists of selecting 2 slips without replacement from the box.
   a) Determine the sample space.
   b) What is the probability of getting "o" on the first selection?

    c) What is the probability of getting "n" on the second selection?

    d) What is the probability of getting the same letter for both selections?

2. Repeat Exercise 1 under the assumption that the first slip is replaced before the second is selected.

3. A boy has a penny, a nickel, a dime, and a quarter in his pocket. Upon entering a candy store, he takes 2 coins out of his pocket—first one, then another.

    a) Determine the sample space.

    b) What is the probability the boy selects a total of 35 cents?

    c) What is the probability of getting the same coin for both selections?

4. Repeat Exercise 3 under the assumption that the first coin is replaced before the second is selected.

5. A fair coin is tossed 4 times.

    a) Determine the sample space.

    b) Find the probability of getting exactly 3 heads.

    c) Find the probability of getting at most 3 heads.

    d) Find the probability of getting at least 3 heads.

    e) Find the probability of getting the same result on all four trials.

A placement office in a large company received applications from recent college graduates with the following racial origins: 65 whites, 15 blacks, 10 Hispanics, 5 Asians, and 5 American Indians. If 1 applicant is screened out, find the probability that the selected applicant's racial origin is each of the following.

6.	White	**7.**	Nonwhite
8.	Black	**9.**	Nonblack
10.	Hispanic or Asian	**11.**	Asian or American Indian

12. If there is a 30% chance of a stock price increase tomorrow, what is the probability that it will not increase tomorrow?

If two fair dice are rolled, find the probability of getting each of the following.

13. A 3 on the second die

14. A sum of 10

15. An even number on the first die and an odd number on the second die

16. Even numbers on both

17. A sum of 13

18. A sum of 7

19. A sum not equal to 7

A card is selected from an ordinary deck of 52 cards. Find the probability that the selected card is each of the following.

20.	A king	**21.**	A queen
22.	Not a queen	**23.**	A red card
24.	A jack	**25.**	Not a jack
26.	A black jack	**27.**	The ace of spades
28.	Not a red king	**29.**	Either a jack or a queen

Determine $P(E)$ if the odds in favor of event E occurring are as follows.

30.	1 to 3	**31.**	5 to 3	**32.**	7 to 2
33.	3 to 8	**34.**	6 to 4	**35.**	2 to 5

Determine the odds in favor of event E occurring if $P(E)$ is given as follows.

36.	.30	**37.**	.80	**38.**	.90
39.	5/9	**40.**	1/3	**41.**	6/7

Translate each of the following into probabilities.

42. The odds in favor of a recession next year are 5 to 3.

43. The odds in favor of a Democratic victory in next year's mayoral contest are 2 to 5.
44. The odds in favor of an expanding economy are 2 to 3.

Translate each of the following into odds.

45. The probability of snow tomorrow is .70.
46. The probability of a higher stock market next month is 5/7.
47. The probability of growth in consumer spending next year is .10.

Which of the following probability distributions are in error and, for such, state the error.

48.

Outcome	Probability
e_1	.4
e_2	.3
e_3	.2
e_4	.1

49.

Outcome	Probability
e_1	.3
e_2	−.2
e_3	.4
e_4	.1

50.

Outcome	Probability
e_1	.1
e_2	.2
e_3	−.1
e_4	.3
e_5	.1

51.

Outcome	Probability
e_1	.1
e_2	.2
e_3	.3
e_4	.2
e_5	.3

52.

Outcome	Probability
e_1	1/4
e_2	1/2
e_3	1/8
e_4	1/8

53.

Outcome	Probability
e_1	1/2
e_2	1/4
e_3	3/8
e_4	1/8

54. For the probability distribution at the bottom left, if $E_1 = \{e_1, e_2\}$ and $E_2 = \{e_2, e_4, e_5\}$, then determine
   a) $P(E_1)$ b) $P(E_2)$
55. For the second probability distribution at the bottom right, if $E_1 = \{e_1, e_3\}$ and $E_2 = \{e_1, e_4, e_5\}$, then determine
   a) $P(E_1)$ b) $P(E_2)$

Outcome	Probability
e_1	.05
e_2	.15
e_3	.30
e_4	.40
e_5	.10

Outcome	Probability
e_1	.10
e_2	.15
e_3	.25
e_4	.30
e_5	.20

56. *Standardized testing.* A standardized mathematics exam was given to 1000 students nationwide. The table below gives the numbers of students who scored within the given ranges.

Score	Number of students
e_1: Below 50	10
e_2: 50–59	18
e_3: 60–69	300
e_4: 70–79	500
e_5: 80–89	150
e_6: 90–99	20
e_7: 100	2
	1000

a) Convert the above table to a probability distribution.
b) Determine the probability of a student scoring below 70.
c) Determine the probability of a student scoring above 89.
d) Determine the probability of a student scoring in the 70s.

57. *Opinion survey.* A pollster surveys 200 people with regard to their opinions on the construction of a waste-to-energy power plant in their community. The results are given in the table below.

Opinion	Number of people
Strongly in favor	40
Somewhat in favor	100
Neutral	10
Somewhat opposed	20
Strongly opposed	30
	200

a) Assuming that the 200 people are a representative sample of the community, convert the above table to a probability distribution.
b) Determine the probability of a community member being strongly in favor of the plant.
c) Determine the probability of a community member being opposed to the plant.
d) Determine the probability of a community member being in favor of the plant.

58. A fair die is rolled. If A is the event of *getting an even number* and B is the event of *getting a number less than or equal to 4,* find each of the following:
a) $P(A)$ b) $P(B)$
c) $P(A \cap B)$ d) $P(A \cup B)$

59. Two fair dice are rolled.
a) Write the sample space for this chance experiment.
b) Let A be the event that *a sum of at most 5 is obtained.* Circle this event set in the sample space of part a and determine $P(A)$.
c) Let B be the event that *both dice come up the same.* Circle this event set in the sample space of part a and determine $P(B)$.

    d) Are events *A* and *B* mutually exclusive? Why or why not?

    e) Use the addition rule to determine $P(A \text{ or } B)$.

    f) Let *C* be the event that *a sum of 6 comes up*. Circle this event set in the sample space of part a and determine $P(C)$.

    g) Let *D* be the event *a sum of 9 comes up*. Circle this event set in the sample space of part a and determine $P(D)$.

    h) Are events *C* and *D* mutually exclusive? Why or why not?

    i) Use the addition rule to determine $P(C \text{ or } D)$.

60. A card is selected from an ordinary deck of cards (52 cards). Determine the probability of getting

    a) A red card.

    b) A king.

    c) A jack.

    d) A queen.

    e) A 9.

    f) A 5.

    g) Either a red card or a king. (Are these two events mutually exclusive?)

    h) Either a jack or a queen. (Are these two events mutually exclusive?)

    i) Either a black card or a 9.

    j) Either a 9 or a 5.

61. A box contains 100 marbles: 20 red, 30 green, 40 orange, and 10 blue. A person is to select 1 marble from the box. Find the probability of getting

    a) A red marble.

    b) A blue marble.

    c) Either a red or a blue marble. (Are these two events mutually exclusive?)

    d) Either a green or an orange marble. (Are these two events mutually exclusive?)

62. The probability that a student passes mathematics is .60; the probability that he or she passes sociology is .50; and the probability that he or she passes both subjects is .30. Find the probability that the student passes either mathematics or sociology.

63. *Weather forcasting.* The probability of snow tomorrow is .50; the probability of sleet tomorrow is .30; and the probability of both is .10. Find the probability of either sleet or snow tomorrow.

64. *Risk analysis.* A pest exterminator that offers warranties against pest infestation has determined that, for a given geographic area, the probability of a home becoming infested with carpenter ants is .30; the probability of a home becoming infested with termites is .20; and the probability of a home becoming infested with both carpenter ants and termites is .11. Determine the probability of a home becoming infested with

    a) Either carpenter ants or termites.

    b) Either carpenter ants or termites, but not both.

    c) Neither carpenter ants nor termites.

65. A survey of 60 executives of Montcalf Corporation revealed the following results:

    • 40 read *The Wall Street Journal*.

    • 30 read *Barron's*.

    • 20 read both *The Wall Street Journal* and *Barron's*.

If a person is selected from this group, find the probability that he or she

    a) Reads *The Wall Street Journal*.

    b) Reads *Barron's*.

    c) Reads both.

    d) Reads either *The Wall Street Journal* or *Barron's*.

    e) Reads either *The Wall Street Journal* or *Barron's*, but not both.

    f) Reads neither *The Wall Street Journal* nor *Barron's*.

	A	B	C	
D	90	80	20	190
E	60	120	30	210
	150	200	50	400

66. Given the cross-classification table to the left, find

a) $P(A)$ b) $P(B)$
c) $P(D)$ d) $P(E)$
e) $P(A \cap E)$ f) $P(D \cap B)$
g) $P(A \cap C)$ h) $P(D \cap E)$
i) $P(A \cup E)$ (Are A and E mutually exclusive events?)
j) $P(D$ or $B)$ (Are D and B mutually exclusive events?)
k) $P(A \cup C)$ (Are A and C mutually exclusive events?)
l) $P(B \cup C)$ (Are B and C mutually exclusive events?)
m) $P(A' \cap C')$ n) $P(B' \cap C')$
o) P(neither A nor E) p) P(neither D nor B)
q) $P(A$ or E but not both) r) $P(D$ or B but not both)

67. *Market analysis.* An analysis of 50 occupants of an office building is given in the cross-classification table below.

	Doctors	Lawyers	Business executives	
Occupy 2-room suite	0	30	6	36
Occupy 3-room suite	5	10	25	40
Occupy 4-room suite	15	5	4	24
	20	45	35	100

If an occupant is selected from this group, find the probability of selecting

a) A doctor.
b) A business executive
c) An occupant of a 2-room suite.
d) An occupant of a 4-room suite.
e) Both a doctor and an occupant of a 4-room suite.
f) Both a lawyer and an occupant of a 2 room suite.
g) Both a business executive and an occupant of a 3-room suite.
h) Both a doctor and an occupant of a 2-room suite.
i) Either a doctor or an occupant of a 4-room suite.
j) Either a lawyer or an occupant of a 2-room suite.
k) Either a business executive or an occupant of a 3-room suite.
l) Either a doctor or a lawyer.
m) Either an occupant of a 2-room suite or an occupant of a 4-room suite.
n) Either a doctor or an occupant of a 3-room suite, but not both.
o) Either a lawyer or an occupant of a 4-room suite, but not both.
p) Neither a lawyer nor an occupant of a 3-room suite.
q) Neither a business executive nor an occupant of a 2-room suite.

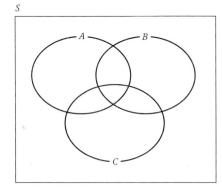

FIGURE 8-45

68. Using the Venn diagram of Figure 8-45, verify that
$$P(A \cup B \cup C) = P(A) + P(B) + P(C) - P(A \cap B) - P(A \cap C)$$
$$- P(B \cap C) + P(A \cap B \cap C).$$

69. The Heavenly Flavor Ice Cream Company surveyed 100 families to determine flavor preferences. The results were as follows:
- 40 families liked vanilla.
- 34 families liked strawberry.
- 52 families liked coffee.
- 21 families liked both vanilla and strawberry.
- 15 families liked both coffee and strawberry.
- 17 families liked both vanilla and coffee.
- 10 families liked all three flavors.

If a family is selected from this group, find the probability that it likes
a) Vanilla.
b) Both vanilla and strawberry.
c) Either vanilla or strawberry.
d) Either vanilla or strawberry or coffee.

70. Three individuals are applying for the position of manager in a large company. Candidates A and B have the same chance of being hired. The probability of candidate C being hired is twice that of candidate A. Find the probability that
a) Candidate A is hired.
b) Candidate B is hired.
c) Candidate C is hired.

71. Determine the probability that a 4-card hand contains
a) All aces.   b) All red cards.

72. Determine the probability that a 5-card hand contains
a) All hearts (this is called a *heart flush*).
b) All spades (this is called a *spade flush*).
c) 3 aces and 2 fives.

73. What is the probability that a bridge hand (13 cards) will contain
a) Exactly 2 queens?
b) Exactly 4 queens?
c) At least 2 queens?

74. What is the probability that a bridge hand (13 cards) will contain
a) No queens?
b) Exactly 1 queen?
c) At most 1 queen?

75. What is the probability that a 5-digit zip code starts with 1 if
a) Repetitions of digits are allowed?
b) Repetitions of digits are not allowed?

76. What is the probability that a 7-digit telephone number ends with 3 if the first digit cannot be 0 and
a) Repetitions of digits are allowed?
b) Repetitions of digits are not allowed?

77. A sample of 5 marbles is selected from a box containing 6 red and 4 blue marbles. Determine the probability that the sample contains
a) Exactly 1 red marble.
b) Exactly 2 red marbles.
c) At most 2 red marbles.
d) More that 2 red marbles.

78. *Quality control.* A shipment of 24 televisions contains 5 defectives. A sample of 6 televisions is to be selected from this shipment.
a) How many possible samples are there?
b) Determine the probability that the sample contains all nondefective televisions.
c) What is the probability that the sample contains 6 nondefective televisions?
d) Find the probability that the sample contains exactly 1 defective television.
e) Find the probability that the sample contains at most 1 defective television.
f) Find the probability that the sample contains at most 2 defective televisions.
g) Find the probability that the sample contains more than 2 defective televisions.

79. *Auditing.* An auditor is selecting a sample of 8 accounts from a set of 30 accounts receivable for the purpose of balance confirmation. Of the 30 accounts receivable, 4 are in error.

a) How many possible samples are there?

b) What is the probability that the sample contains all correct accounts?

c) What is the probability that the sample contains exactly 1 account in error?

d) What is the probability that the sample contains exactly 2 accounts in error?

e) What is the probability that the sample contains at most 2 accounts in error?

f) What is the probability that the sample contains at least 3 accounts in error?

80. *Birthday problem.* A group of 6 people is to be selected at random. Find the probability that at least 2 of them have the same birthday. Assume that there are 365 days to a year. Parts a through c offer a step-by-step solution to this problem.

a) Since each person has 365 possible days for a birthday, we are selecting 1 element from each of 6 sets where each set has 365 elements. Thus, by the multiplication rule of counting, there are _____ possible outcomes in the sample space, S.

b) Since it is difficult to calculate $n(E)$, the number of ways in which at least 2 selected people have the same birthday, we calculate $n(E')$, the number of ways in which all 6 birthdays are different. If all 6 birthdays are to be different, the first selection has 365 possibilities, the second has 364, the third has _____, the fourth has _____, the fifth has _____, and the sixth has _____. Thus, by the multiplication rule of counting, there are _____ ways in which all 6 selected birthdays are different.

c) Hence, $P(E') = n(E')/n(S) = $ _____ and $P(E) = $ _____. So the probability that at least 2 selected people have the same birthday is _____ .

81. *Birthday problem.* Repeat Exercise 80 for 5 selected people.

8-4 • CONDITIONAL PROBABILITY AND INDEPENDENCE

An automobile producer, after surveying 500 buyers of its various models, has constructed the following cross-classification table (Table 8-12). A chance experiment consists of selecting one buyer of a mid-size model. Note that the buyer is not to be selected from the full sample space, S. The buyer is to be selected from M, where

$$M = \{\text{buyers of mid-size models}\}$$

Thus, M is called the restricted sample space for this chance experiment. Suppose we want to find the probability of selecting a buyer whose automobile needed major repair, given that the automobile was a mid-size model. Such a probability is called a **conditional probability** since a restricted sample space is involved. Since

$$H = \{\text{buyers whose automobiles needed major repairs}\}$$

TABLE 8-12

Model	Repair category			
	H major repair needed	*J* minor repair needed	*K* no repair needed	
F Full-size	40	30	20	90
M Mid-size	20	60	50	130
C Compact	90	160	30	280
	150	250	100	500

$n(S)$

then this conditional probability is denoted as

$$P(H|M)$$

restricted sample space

Note that the restricted sample space is written after the vertical line in the notation $P(H|M)$.

The conditional probability $P(H|M)$ implies that we want to find the probability of getting a buyer from set H, given that we are making our selection from a restricted sample space, set M in this problem, instead of the full sample space, S. This is illustrated in Table 8-13. Studying Table 8-13, note that the probability of getting a buyer from set H, given that the selection is made from set M, is determined by the formula

$$P(H|M) = \frac{n(H \cap M)}{n(M)}$$

restricted sample space

$$= \frac{20}{130} \text{, or approximately } 15.38\%.$$

Note that the conditional probability, 15.38%, also means that approximately 15.38% of mid-size automobile buyers bought automobiles that needed major repair.

TABLE 8-13

Model	Repair category			
	H major repair needed	*J* minor repair needed	*K* no repair needed	
F Full-size	40	30	20	90
M Mid-size	20	60	50	130
C Compact	90	160	30	280
	150	250	100	500

$n(S)$

SUMMARY

Conditional Probability

If a chance experiment has equally likely outcomes, and if A and B are events in a sample space, S, then the conditional probability $P(A|B)$ is determined below.

$$P(A|B) = \frac{n(A \cap B)}{n(B)}$$

restricted sample space

provided that $n(A \cap B)$ and $n(B)$ are known and $n(B) \neq 0$.

If we begin with the formula $P(A|B) = n(A \cap B)/n(B)$ and divide both numerator and denominator by $n(S)$, the number of elements in the sample space, we obtain

$$P(A|B) = \frac{\dfrac{n(A \cap B)}{n(S)} \longleftarrow P(A \cap B)}{\dfrac{n(B)}{n(S)} \longleftarrow P(B)}$$

$$= \frac{P(A \cap B)}{P(B)}$$

Thus, if $P(A \cap B)$ and $P(B)$ are known and $P(B) \neq 0$, then $P(A|B)$ may be calculated by the formula

$$P(A|B) = \frac{P(A \cap B)}{P(B)}$$

This formula defines the conditional probability, $P(A|B)$, for any events A and B. Returning to Table 8-13, observe that

$$P(H|M) = \frac{P(H \cap M)}{P(M)} = \frac{\dfrac{20}{500}}{\dfrac{130}{500}} = \frac{20}{130} = 15.38\%$$

We generalize below.

SUMMARY

Conditional Probability

If A and B are events in a sample space, S, then

$$P(A|B) = \frac{P(A \cap B)}{P(B)}$$

restricted sample space

continues

SUMMARY—*Continued*

provided $P(A \cap B)$ and $P(B)$ are known and $P(B) \neq 0$. This is illustrated in terms of the Venn diagram in Figure 8-46.

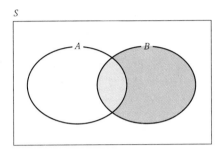

FIGURE 8-46

• **EXAMPLE 8-44** _____

Consider the cross-classification table of Table 8-14. Determine the probability of selecting

a) A mid-size automobile buyer, given that the automobile needed major repair.

b) A person who is both a mid-size automobile buyer and a buyer whose automobile needed major repair.

Solutions

a) We seek $P(M|H)$. As illustrated in Table 8-14,

$$P(M|H) = \frac{n(M \cap H)}{n(H)}$$

$$= \frac{20}{150} \approx 13.33\%$$

Note that this also means that approximately 13.33% of the automobiles that needed major repairs were mid-size.

TABLE 8-14

Model	Repair category			
	H major repair needed	*J* minor repair needed	*K* no repair needed	
F Full-size	40	30	20	90
M Mid-size	20	60	50	130
C Compact	90	160	30	280
	150	250	100	500 ⟵ *n(S)*

b) We seek $P(M$ and $H)$, or, equivalently, $P(M \cap H)$. Since this is not a conditional probability, the implication is that the selection is made from the full sample space, S. Hence,

$$P(M \cap H) = \frac{n(M \cap H)}{n(S)}$$

$$= \frac{20}{500} = 4\%$$

Thus, 4% of all the surveyed buyers bought a mid-size automobile and needed major repairs.

• **EXAMPLE 8-45 Political Science.** _____

In a voting district of a large city, 60 percent of the voters are Democrats, 30% of the voters plan to vote for candidate A in an upcoming election, and 12% of the voters both plan to vote for candidate A and are Democrats. If D denotes the event of *a voter being a Democrat* and A denotes the event of *a voter planning to vote for candidate A*, then determine the probability that a selected voter

a) Is a Democrat and plans to vote for candidate A.
b) Plans to vote for candidate A, knowing that the voter is a Democrat.
c) Is a Democrat, given that the voter plans to vote for candidate A.

Solutions

a) We seek $P(D$ and $A)$ or, equivalently, $P(D \cap A)$.

$$P(D \cap A) = .12$$

b) We seek $P(A|D)$ and

$$P(A|D) = \frac{P(A \cap D)}{P(D)}$$

$$= \frac{.12}{.60}$$

$$= 1/5, \text{ or } 20\%$$

This also means that 20% of the Democrats plan to vote for candidate A (see Figure 8-47).

c) We seek $P(D|A)$ and

$$P(D|A) = \frac{P(D \cap A)}{P(A)}$$

$$= \frac{.12}{.30}$$

$$= .40, \text{ or } 40\%$$

This also means that 40% of those who plan to vote for candidate A are Democrats (see Figure 8-48).

Sometimes conditional probabilities must be calculated without using the formula $P(A|B) = P(A \cap B)/P(B)$. Example 8-46 involves such a case.

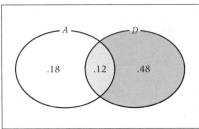

$P(A|D) = \dfrac{.12}{.60} = 20\%$ of Democrats plan to vote for candidate A

FIGURE 8-47

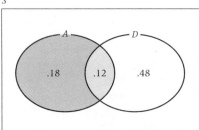

$P(D|A) = \dfrac{.12}{.30} = 40\%$ of those planning to vote for candidate A are Democrats

FIGURE 8-48

• **EXAMPLE 8-46** _____

A chance experiment consists of two selections without replacement from the box of marbles illustrated here.

Box of Marbles

30 red
70 blue

a) Find the probability of selecting a red marble on the first selection.
b) Find the probability of selecting a red marble on the second selection, given that a red marble was obtained on the first selection.

Solutions

a) If R_1 represents the event of *selecting a red marble on the first selection*, then since there are 30 red marbles out of a total of 100 marbles, we have

$$P(R_1) = \frac{30}{100}$$

b) If R_2 represents the event of *getting a red marble on the second selection*, then we seek $P(R_2|R_1)$. If a red marble is obtained on the first selection, then, for the second selection, there are only 29 red marbles out of a total of 99 marbles. Thus, we obtain

$$P(R_2|R_1) = \frac{29}{99}$$

•

Product Rules

Up to this point, whenever we have had to determine $P(A$ and $B)$ where A and B are events in some sample space, S, we have used the formula $P(A \cap B) = n(A \cap B)/n(S)$. However, there are times when we must determine $P(A \cap B)$ where $n(A \cap B)$ is not known. For such situations, we use the product rule that we now derive.

The product rule gives another formula to determine $P(A$ and $B)$. To derive this rule, we begin with the formula for conditional probability

$$P(A|B) = \frac{P(A \cap B)}{P(B)}$$

and multiply both sides by $P(B)$ to get

$$P(A \cap B) = P(B)P(A|B)$$

Had we started with the formula

$$P(B|A) = \frac{P(A \cap B)}{P(A)}$$

and multiplied both sides by $P(A)$, we would have obtained

$$P(A \cap B) = P(A)P(B|A)$$

These two formulas, written in color, are called the **product rules.** We generalize below.

Product Rules

If A and B are events with nonzero probabilities, then
$$P(A \cap B) = P(A)P(B|A)$$
or
$$P(A \cap B) = P(B)P(A|B)$$
where $A \cap B$ means the same as A *and* B.

The product rules define $P(A \cap B)$ for events A and B. They are usually used to determine $P(A$ and $B)$ for chance experiments consisting of multiple trials, as we illustrate in the following examples.

• **EXAMPLE 8-47** _____

A chance experiment consists of selecting two marbles without replacement from the following box:

Box of Marbles

| 40 red |
| 60 blue |

Find the probability of selecting

a) Two red marbles.
b) Two blue marbles.
c) A red on the first selection and a blue on the second.
c) A blue on the first selection and a red on the second.
d) One of each color.

Solutions

a) If R_1 represents the event of *getting a red on the first selection* and R_2 represents the event of *getting a red on the second,* then we seek $P(R_1$ and $R_2)$. Using the product rule, we have

$$P(R_1 \text{ and } R_2) = P(R_1)P(R_2|R_1)$$
$$= \frac{40}{100} \cdot \frac{39}{99}$$
$$= \frac{26}{165}$$

b) If B_1 and B_2 represent the events of *getting a blue on the first and second selections,* respectively, then we calculate

$$P(B_1 \text{ and } B_2) = P(B_1)P(B_2|B_1)$$
$$= \frac{60}{100} \cdot \frac{59}{99}$$
$$= \frac{59}{165}$$

c) Using the preceding notation, we seek $P(R_1$ and $B_2)$. By the product rule, we have

$$P(R_1 \text{ and } B_2) = P(R_1)P(B_2|R_1)$$
$$= \frac{40}{100} \cdot \frac{60}{99}$$
$$= \frac{40}{165} = \frac{8}{33}$$

d) Here we seek $P(B_1 \text{ and } R_2)$.

$$P(B_1 \text{ and } R_2) = P(B_1)P(R_2|B_1)$$

$$= \frac{60}{100} \cdot \frac{40}{99}$$

$$= \frac{40}{165} = \frac{8}{33}$$

e) Here we seek $P[(R_1 \text{ and } B_2) \text{ or } (B_1 \text{ and } R_2)]$. Since the events $(R_1 \text{ and } B_2)$ and $(B_1 \text{ and } R_2)$ are mutually exclusive, then, by the special case addition rule,

$$P[(R_1 \text{ and } B_2) \text{ or } (B_1 \text{ and } R_2)] = P(R_1 \text{ and } B_2) + P(B_1 \text{ and } R_2)$$

In parts c and d of this example, we determined that

$$P(R_1 \text{ and } B_2) = \frac{8}{33}$$

$$P(B_1 \text{ and } R_2) = \frac{8}{33}$$

Thus,

$$P[(R_1 \text{ and } B_2) \text{ or } (B_1 \text{ and } R_2)] = P(R_1 \text{ and } B_2) + P(B_1 \text{ and } R_2)$$

$$= \frac{8}{33} + \frac{8}{33}$$

$$= \frac{16}{33}$$

The possible outcomes of this chance experiment are illustrated by the tree diagram of Figure 8-49. Since the events are not equiprobable, the probability of each event is written along its respective branch of the diagram. The probability of each outcome is calculated at the far right. Note that the sum of these probabilities is 1. Thus, all possible outcomes are included in the tree diagram.

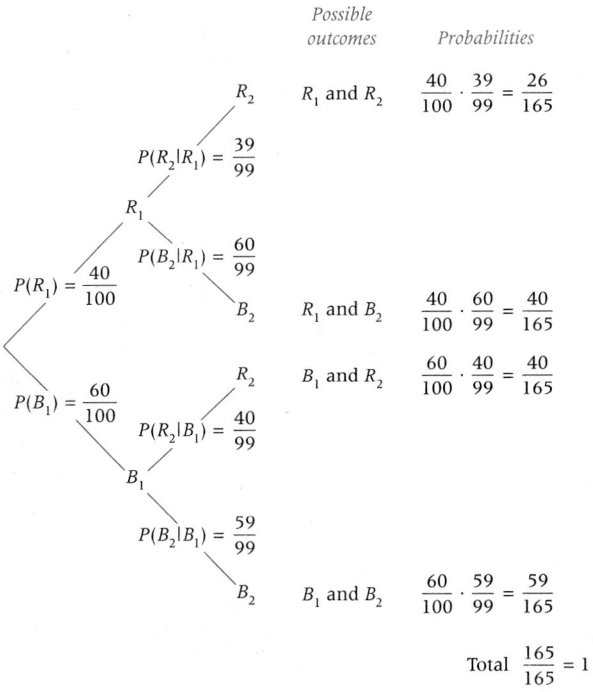

	Possible outcomes	Probabilities
R_2	$R_1 \text{ and } R_2$	$\frac{40}{100} \cdot \frac{39}{99} = \frac{26}{165}$
$P(R_2|R_1) = \frac{39}{99}$		
R_1		
$P(B_2|R_1) = \frac{60}{99}$		
B_2	$R_1 \text{ and } B_2$	$\frac{40}{100} \cdot \frac{60}{99} = \frac{40}{165}$
$P(R_1) = \frac{40}{100}$		
R_2	$B_1 \text{ and } R_2$	$\frac{60}{100} \cdot \frac{40}{99} = \frac{40}{165}$
$P(B_1) = \frac{60}{100}$ $P(R_2|B_1) = \frac{40}{99}$		
B_1		
$P(B_2|B_1) = \frac{59}{99}$		
B_2	$B_1 \text{ and } B_2$	$\frac{60}{100} \cdot \frac{59}{99} = \frac{59}{165}$
	Total	$\frac{165}{165} = 1$

FIGURE 8-49

The product rule can be generalized to three or more events, as we show in the box below.

SUMMARY

Product Rules: Three or More Events

If A_1, A_2, and A_3 are events, then

$$P(A_1 \cap A_2 \cap A_3) = P(A_1)P(A_2|A_1)P(A_3|A_1 \cap A_2)$$

Remember that the intersection symbol, $\cap$, can be replaced with the word "and." Also, note that $P(A_3|A_1 \cap A_2)$ denotes the conditional probability of A_3, given that both A_1 and A_2 have occurred.

If A_1, A_2, A_3, . . . , A_n are events, then

$P(A_1 \cap A_2 . . . \cap A_n)$
$\qquad = P(A_1)P(A_2|A_1)P(A_3|A_1 \cap A_2) . . . P(A_n|A_1 \cap A_2 . . . \cap A_{n-1})$

• **EXAMPLE 8-48   Auditing.** ⎯⎯⎯⎯⎯⎯⎯⎯⎯⎯⎯⎯⎯⎯

A set of 50 invoices contains 7 that have errors. An auditor selects without replacement a sample of 3 invoices. Using the product rule, determine the probability that all 3 contain errors.

Solution

Let

E_1 = event that the first selected invoice contains errors
E_2 = event that the second selected invoice contains errors
E_3 = event that the third selected invoice contains errors

Then we seek $P(E_1$ and E_2 and $E_3)$ or, equivalently,

$P(E_1 \cap E_2 \cap E_3)$ and $P(E_1 \cap E_2 \cap E_3) = P(E_1)P(E_2|E_1)P(E_3|E_1 \cap E_2)$

$$= \frac{7}{50} \cdot \frac{6}{49} \cdot \frac{5}{48}$$

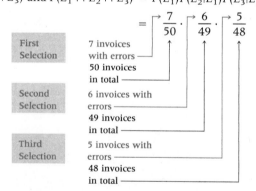

First Selection — 7 invoices with errors — 50 invoices in total

Second Selection — 6 invoices with errors — 49 invoices in total

Third Selection — 5 invoices with errors — 48 invoices in total

• **EXAMPLE 8-49** ⎯⎯⎯⎯⎯⎯⎯⎯⎯⎯⎯⎯⎯⎯⎯⎯⎯⎯⎯⎯

If the auditor of Example 8-48 selects a sample of 4 invoices, find the probability that the first 2 contain errors, the third does not, and the fourth does contain errors.

Solution

If

E_4 = event that the fourth selected invoice contains errors, then we seek $P(E_1 \cap E_2 \cap E_3' \cap E_4)$. Note that

E_3' = event that the third selected invoice does not contain errors

Thus,

$$P(E_1 \cap E_2 \cap E_3' \cap E_4) = P(E_1)P(E_2|E_1)P(E_3'|E_1 \cap E_2)P(E_4|E_1 \cap E_2 \cap E_3')$$

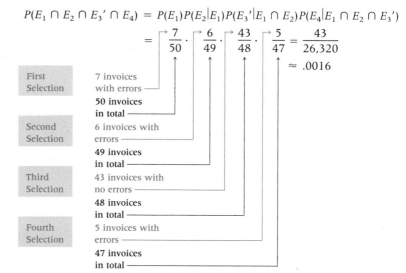

$$= \frac{7}{50} \cdot \frac{6}{49} \cdot \frac{43}{48} \cdot \frac{5}{47} = \frac{43}{26,320}$$
$$\approx .0016$$

First Selection — 7 invoices with errors — 50 invoices in total

Second Selection — 6 invoices with errors — 49 invoices in total

Third Selection — 43 invoices with no errors — 48 invoices in total

Fourth Selection — 5 invoices with errors — 47 invoices in total

Independent Events

Two events, A and B, where $P(B) \neq 0$, are independent if

$$P(A|B) = P(A)$$

Intuitively, two events are independent if the occurrence of one does not change the probability of the occurrence (or nonoccurrence) of the other. If two events are not independent, then they are dependent. As a specific example, consider the chance experiment of selecting with replacement 2 marbles from the box of Example 8-47, which is repeated here for reference.

Box of Marbles

| 40 red |
| 60 blue |

Recall from Example 8-47 that the probability of selecting a red marble on the second selection, given that a red occurred on the first selection, is

$$P(R_2|R_1) = \frac{39}{99}$$

Since we are now selecting the 2 marbles with replacement, the first marble selected is replaced before selecting the second marble. Thus,

$$P(R_2|R_1) = P(R_2) = \frac{40}{100}$$

and the events of *getting a red marble on the second selection* and *getting a red marble on the first selection* are independent.

If two events, *A* and *B,* are independent, the product rule

$$P(A \cap B) = P(A)P(B|A)$$

becomes

$$P(A \cap B) = P(A)P(B)$$

since $P(B|A) = P(B)$. The result in the box below is a special case of the product rule. It must be remembered that this law applies only to independent events. The special case product rule defines $P(A \cap B)$ for independent events *A* and *B.*

Product Rule (Special Case)

If *A* and *B* are independent events, then

$$P(A \cap B) = P(A)P(B)$$

where $A \cap B$ means the same as *A and B.*

• **EXAMPLE 8-50** _____

A chance experiment consists of selecting 2 marbles with replacement from the following box:

Box of Marbles

40 red
60 blue

Find the probability of selecting

a) Two red marbles.
b) Two blue marbles.
c) A red on the first selection and a blue on the second.
d) A blue on the first selection and a red on the second.
e) One of each color.

Solutions

Since the selections are made with replacement, the resulting events are independent. Using the special case product rule, we have

a) $P(R_1 \text{ and } R_2) = P(R_1)P(R_2)$
$$= \frac{40}{100} \cdot \frac{40}{100}$$
$$= .16$$

b) $P(B_1 \text{ and } B_2) = P(B_1)P(B_2)$
$$= \frac{60}{100} \cdot \frac{60}{100}$$
$$= .36$$

c) $P(R_1 \text{ and } B_2) = P(R_1)P(B_2)$
$$= \frac{40}{100} \cdot \frac{60}{100}$$
$$= .24$$

d) $P(B_1 \text{ and } R_2) = P(B_1)P(R_2)$

$$= \frac{60}{100} \cdot \frac{40}{100}$$

$$= .24$$

e) Using the special case addition rule, we have

$$P[(R_1 \text{ and } B_2) \text{ or } (B_1 \text{ and } R_2)] = P(R_1 \text{ and } B_2) + P(B_1 \text{ and } R_2)$$

$$= .24 + .24$$

$$= .48$$

The special case of the product rule can be generalized to n independent events, as given in the box below.

> ### Product Rule (Special Case)
>
> If events $A_1, A_2, \ldots, A_n$ are independent, then
>
> $$P(A_1 \cap A_2 \cap \ldots \cap A_n) = P(A_1)P(A_2) \ldots P(A_n)$$

Thus, if a box contains 30 red marbles and 70 blue marbles, then the probability of obtaining 3 red marbles out of 3 selections made with replacement is determined by using the special case of the product rule, as indicated below:

$$P(R_1 \text{ and } R_2 \text{ and } R_3) = P(R_1)P(R_2)P(R_3)$$

$$= (.3)(.3)(.3)$$

 30 red marbles out
of a total of 100 marbles $\longrightarrow$ ↑ ↑ ↑

$$= .027$$

Sometimes we must use the addition rules, product rules, and conditional probability formulas to solve certain problems. Example 8-51 illustrates such a case.

• EXAMPLE 8-51   Healthcare.

In a certain hospital, 60% of the patients are smokers, 30% of the patients have lung cancer, and 40% of those who are smokers have lung cancer. If 1 patient is to be selected from this group, find the probability that he or she

a) Is a smoker and has lung cancer.
b) Is a smoker, given that he or she has lung cancer.
c) Is a smoker or has lung cancer.

Solutions

If

$$S = \text{event of selecting a smoker}$$

$$L = \text{event of selecting a patient with lung cancer}$$

then

$$P(S) = .60 \qquad P(L) = .30 \qquad P(L|S) = .40$$

a) $P(S \text{ and } L) = P(S)P(L|S)$

$$= (.60)(.40)$$

$$= .24$$

b) $P(S|L) = \dfrac{P(S \text{ and } L)}{P(L)}$

$= \dfrac{.24}{.30} = \dfrac{.08}{.10}$

$= .80$

c) $P(S \text{ or } L) = P(S) + P(L) - P(S \text{ and } L)$

$= .60 + .30 - .24$

$= .66$

We now update the procedure for finding probabilities of events that was included at the end of Section 8-3.

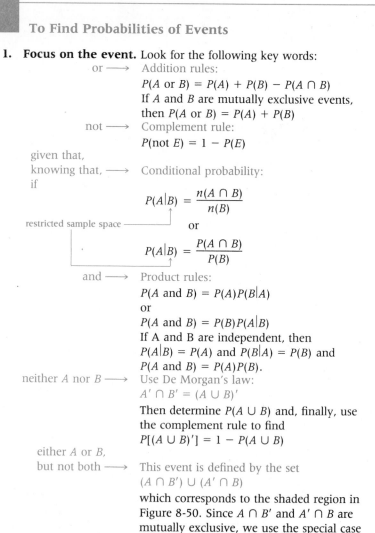

To Find Probabilities of Events

1. **Focus on the event.** Look for the following key words:

or ⟶ Addition rules:

$P(A \text{ or } B) = P(A) + P(B) - P(A \cap B)$

If A and B are mutually exclusive events, then $P(A \text{ or } B) = P(A) + P(B)$

not ⟶ Complement rule:

$P(\text{not } E) = 1 - P(E)$

given that,

knowing that, ⟶ Conditional probability:

if

$P(A|B) = \dfrac{n(A \cap B)}{n(B)}$

restricted sample space ⟶ ↑   or

$P(A|B) = \dfrac{P(A \cap B)}{P(B)}$
↑

and ⟶ Product rules:

$P(A \text{ and } B) = P(A)P(B|A)$

or

$P(A \text{ and } B) = P(B)P(A|B)$

If A and B are independent, then $P(A|B) = P(A)$ and $P(B|A) = P(B)$ and $P(A \text{ and } B) = P(A)P(B)$.

neither A nor B ⟶ Use De Morgan's law:

$A' \cap B' = (A \cup B)'$

Then determine $P(A \cup B)$ and, finally, use the complement rule to find

$P[(A \cup B)'] = 1 - P(A \cup B)$

either A or B,

but not both ⟶ This event is defined by the set

$(A \cap B') \cup (A' \cap B)$

which corresponds to the shaded region in Figure 8-50. Since $A \cap B'$ and $A' \cap B$ are mutually exclusive, we use the special case addition rule to obtain

$P[(A \cap B') \cup (A' \cap B)] = P(A \cap B') + P(A' \cap B)$

continues

To Find Probabilities of Events—*Continued*

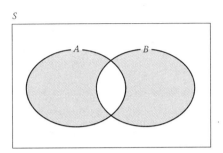

FIGURE 8-50

Note: Within a given rule (or law), you may have to use the formula $P(E) = n(E)/n(S)$.

2. If the above approach does not work, try to determine $n(S)$ and $n(E)$ so that the formula $P(E) = n(E)/n(S)$ can be used. You may have to use counting procedures (i.e., permutations, combinations, and the MRCC model) or the concept of probability distributions.

Exercises 8-4

Market research. A survey of recent buyers of automobiles revealed the information presented in the following table:

	Bought compact car	Bought full-size car	Total
Paid cash	50	30	80
Paid credit	100	20	120
Total	150	50	200

If a person is selected from this group, find the probability of getting

1. A full-size car buyer, given that he or she used credit.
2. A credit user, given that he or she bought a full-size car.
3. A full-size car buyer and a credit user.
4. Either a full-size car buyer or a credit user.

Human resources. A survey of employees at a large company reveals the following information.

	M Male	*F* Female	Total
W White-collar workers	15%	25%	40%
B Blue-collar workers	50%	10%	60%
Total	65%	35%	100%

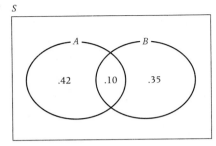

FIGURE 8-51

Determine each of the following probabilities:

5. $P(M|W)$ **6.** $P(W|M)$ **7.** $P(F|B)$
8. $P(B|F)$ **9.** $P(B$ and $F)$ **10.** $P(B$ or $F)$
11. $P(M|B)$ **12.** $P(B|M)$ **13.** $P(M$ and $B)$
14. $P(M$ or $B)$ **15.** $P(M$ and $W)$ **16.** $P(M$ or $W)$

Referring to the Venn diagram of Figure 8-51, determine each of the following probabilities:

17. $P(A)$ **18.** $P(B)$ **19.** $P(A \cup B)$
20. $P(A|B)$ **21.** $P(B|A)$ **22.** $P(A \cap B)$
23. $P(A')$ **24.** $P(B')$ **25.** $P[(A \cap B)']$

26. *Investments.* A bond broker is considering using a list of stockholders for direct mail advertising. She knows that 60% of the investors hold stocks, that 30% hold bonds, and that 20% hold both.
 a) If an investor is a stockholder, what is the probability that he or she is also a bondholder?
 b) If an investor is a bondholder, what is the probability that he or she is also a stockholder?

27. *Market analysis.* In a certain store, 40% of entering customers buy washers, 30% buy dryers, and 20% buy both washers and dryers.
 a) If a customer has bought a washer, find the probability that he or she also buys a dryer.
 b) If a customer has bought a dryer, find the probability that he or she also buys a washer.

28. *Brand preference.* In a given small town, 40% of the drivers buy Mercurys, 70% buy Oldsmobiles, and 30% buy both.
 a) If a driver buys a Mercury, find the probability that he or she also buys an Oldsmobile.
 b) If a driver buys an Oldsmobile, find the probability that he or she also buys a Mercury.
 c) What percentage of the drivers buy either an Oldsmobile or a Mercury?

29. A box of marbles contains 40 red and 60 green marbles. A chance experiment consists of 2 selections without replacement from the box. Find the probability of selecting
 a) A red marble on the first selection.
 b) A red marble on the second selection, given that a red marble was picked on the first selection.
 c) A green marble on the second selection, given that a red marble was picked on the first selection.

30. Repeat Exercise 29 under the assumption that the 2 selections are made with replacement.

31. *Quality control.* A production lot of 200 spark plugs contains 20 defectives. A quality control check consists of selecting 3 spark plugs without replacement from the lot. Find the probability of selecting.
 a) A defective spark plug on the first selection.
 b) A defective spark plug on the second selection, given that a defective was obtained on the first selection.
 c) A defective spark plug on the third selection, given that defectives were obtained on the first two selections.
 d) A defective spark plug on the third selection, given that nondefectives were obtained on the first 2 selections.

32. *Quality control.* Repeat Exercise 31 under the assumption that the 3 selections are made with replacement.

33. Three cards are selected without replacement from an ordinary deck. Determine the probability of getting
  a) A red card on the first selection.
  b) A red card on the second selection, given that a red card was gotten on the first selection.
  c) A red card on the third selection, given that red cards were gotten on the first 2 selections.
  d) A red card on the third selection, given that black cards were gotten on the first 2 selections.

34. Given that events A and B are mutually exclusive, find $P(A|B)$ and $P(B|A)$. (*Hint:* A Venn diagram will be helpful.)

35. At a given college, 35% of the students are under 20. Also, 80% of the students are male, and 25% of the males are under 20. Using a cross-classification table, answer each of the following:
  a) What percentage of the students are female and 20 or over?
  b) Given that a student is a female, what is the probability that she is under 20?

36. A box contains 50 white balls, 110 green balls, and 40 red balls. A chance experiment consists of selecting 2 balls without replacement from the box. Find the probability of getting
  a) Two red balls.
  b) Two white balls.
  c) First a red, then a green.
  d) First a green, then a red.
  e) A red and a green.

37. Repeat Exercise 36 under the assumption that the selections are made with replacement.

38. *Market research.* Of the households of a given city, 30% have electric dryers, 40% have electric stoves, and 25% of those that have electric stoves also have electric dryers. Find the probability that
  a) A household has both an electric dryer and an electric stove.
  b) A household with an electric dryer also has an electric stove.

39. *Sales analysis.* Analyzing the sales of a given product in a retail store, we discover that 10% of the purchases were made by men and 20% of the purchases were over $10 in value. Given that 80% of the male customers make purchases over $10, find what percentage of the purchases
  a) Were over $10 and were made by men.
  b) Were over $10 or were made by men.
  c) Over $10 were made by men.

40. The probability of a husband not voting in an election is .30. The probability of a wife voting, given that her husband votes, is .80. Find the probability that both a husband and a wife vote.

41. *Medical care.* Sixty percent of the patients at a medical center are female, and 55 percent are over 40. Ten percent are male and over 40. If a patient is selected from this group, find the probability that he or she is
  a) Male and 40 or under.
  b) Female and over 40.
  c) Female and 40 or under.
  d) Over 40.
  (*Hint:* Use a cross-classification table.)

42. *Emergency response.* A private ambulance service keeps 2 vehicles in readiness for emergencies. The probability that a given vehicle is available when needed is .90. If the availability of one vehicle is independent of the availability of the other, find the probability that

a) Both vehicles will be available in the event of 2 emergencies occurring at the same time.
b) A vehicle will be available when a call is received for service (i.e., the probability that either vehicle will be available for service).
c) Neither vehicle is available for service.

43. If events A and B are independent, and if $P(A) = .3$ and $P(B) = .6$, find each of the following:

a) $P(A \text{ and } B)$ b) $P(A \text{ or } B)$
c) $P(A|B)$ d) $P(B|A)$

44. Given that $P(A) = .6$, $P(B) = .7$, and $P(A \cap B) = .4$,

a) Find $P(A \cup B)$.   b) Find $P(A|B)$.
c) Find $P(B|A)$.   d) Are events A and B independent? Why or why not?

45. A chance experiment consists of selecting 4 marbles without replacement from a box containing 20 red marbles and 80 blue marbles. Find the probability of selecting

a) Four blue marbles.
b) Three reds, then a blue.
c) First a red, then 3 blues.
d) First a blue, then 2 reds, then a blue.

46. Repeat Exercise 45 under the assumption that the selections are made with replacement.

47. *Auditing.* A set of 80 invoices contains 10 that have errors. An auditor selects (without replacement) a sample of 4 invoices. Determine the probability that

a) All 4 contain errors.
b) The first 3 contain errors and the fourth does not.
c) The first 2 contain errors, the third does not, and the fourth does.
d) All 4 do not contain errors.

48. *Auditing.* Repeat Exercise 47 under the assumption that the selections are made with replacement.

49. *Quality control.* A production lot of 60 spark plugs contains 9 that are defective. A quality control check consists of selecting 4 spark plugs without replacement from the lot. Determine the probability that

a) All 4 spark plugs are defective.
b) The first 2 are not defective and the last 2 are.
c) The first 1 is defective and the last 3 are not.
d) All 4 spark plugs are not defective.

50. *Quality control.* Repeat Exercise 49 under the assumption that the selections are made with replacement.

8-5   • BAYES' FORMULA

In the previous section, we encountered conditional probabilities such as $P(A|B)$, $P(B|A)$, etc. Sometimes we come across situations where we know, for example, $P(A|B)$ and wish to determine $P(B|A)$. Such a problem is usually solved by using **Bayes' formula.** We now proceed to develop this famous useful expression.

The following problem appeared on a past Uniform CPA examination.

PROBLEM

Clay Company operates 3 shipping terminals, referred to as X, Y, and Z. Of the total cargo shipped, terminals X, Y, and Z handle approximately 60%, 30%, and 10%, respectively, with error rates of 3%, 4%, and 6%, respectively. Clay's internal auditor randomly selects 1 shipping document, ascertaining that this document contains an error. The probability that the error occurred in terminal X is

a) 60%   **b)** 50%   **c)** 23%   **d)** 3%

SOLUTION

We let

B_1 = event that the document came from terminal X

B_2 = event that the document came from terminal Y

B_3 = event that the document came from terminal Z

E = event that a shipping document contains an error

Since terminals X, Y, and Z handle 60%, 30%, and 10%, respectively, of the shipping volume, then

$$P(B_1) = .60 \qquad P(B_2) = .30 \qquad P(B_3) = .10$$

Also, since terminals X, Y, and Z have error rates of 3%, 4%, and 6%, respectively, then

$$P(E|B_1) = .03 \qquad P(E|B_2) = .04 \qquad P(E|B_3) = .06$$

We seek to answer the following:

Given that a shipping document contains an error, what is the probability that the error occurred in terminal X?

Thus, we must determine $P(B_1|E)$.

Using the formula for conditional probability

$$P(B_1|E) = \frac{P(B_1 \cap E)}{P(E)}$$

where $P(B_1 \cap E)$ is determined by the product rule as indicated below.

$$P(B_1 \cap E) = P(B_1)P(E|B_1)$$
$$= (.60)(.03) = .018 \qquad (1)$$

Now we must determine $P(E)$. At this point, we use a Venn diagram. Note that B_1, B_2, and B_3 are mutually exclusive events such that their probabilities sum to 1. This implies that, in terms of Venn diagrams, the sample space, S, is partitioned as illustrated in Figure 8-52 on page 572. Observe that event E is the union of mutually exclusive subsets

$$B_1 \cap E \qquad B_2 \cap E \qquad B_3 \cap E$$

and, therefore, by the special addition rule

$$P(E) = P(B_1 \cap E) + P(B_2 \cap E) + P(B_3 \cap E)$$

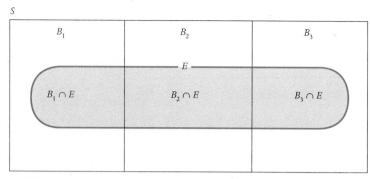

FIGURE 8-52

The above equation, sometimes called the **law of total probability,** is re-written by using the product rule to determine the probabilities $P(B_1 \cap E)$, $P(B_2 \cap E)$, and $P(B_3 \cap E)$ as follows:

$$P(B_1 \cap E) = P(B_1)P(E|B_1)$$
$$P(B_2 \cap E) = P(B_2)P(E|B_2)$$
$$P(B_3 \cap E) = P(B_3)P(E|B_3)$$

Substituting these results into the law of total probability gives

$$P(E) = P(B_1)P(E|B_1) + P(B_2)P(E|B_2) + P(B_3)P(E|B_3)$$

Recall that $P(B_1) = .60$, $P(B_2) = .30$, $P(B_3) = .10$, $P(E|B_1) = .03$, $P(E|B_2) = .04$, and $P(E|B_3) = .06$. Substituting these results into the above formula for $P(E)$ gives

$$
\begin{aligned}
P(E) &= (.60)(.03) + (.30)(.04) + (.10)(.06) \\
&= .018 + .012 + .006 \\
&= .036
\end{aligned}
\tag{2}
$$

Remember that our goal is to determine $P(B_1|E)$, using the formula

$$P(B_1|E) = \frac{P(B_1 \cap E)}{P(E)} \tag{3}$$

Note that we have determined $P(B_1 \cap E) = .018$ in equation (1). Substituting this result into the numerator and the result of equation (2) into the denominator of equation (3) gives

$$P(B_1|E) = \frac{.018}{.036} = .50, \text{ or } 50\% \tag{4}$$

Thus, the probability that the error occurred in terminal X is 50%.

Note that if, in the formula for $P(B_1|E)$,

$$P(B_1|E) = \frac{P(B_1 \cap E)}{P(E)}$$

$P(B_1 \cap E)$ is replaced by $P(B_1)P(E|B_1)$ and $P(E)$ is replaced by $P(B_1)P(E|B_1)$ + $P(B_2)P(E|B_2)$ + $P(B_3)P(E|B_3)$, the result is

$$P(B_1|E) = \frac{P(B_1)P(E|B_1)}{P(B_1)P(E|B_1) + P(B_2)P(E|B_2) + P(B_3)P(E|B_3)} \quad \longleftarrow \text{law of total probability}$$

The above formula for $P(B_1|E)$ is a special case of **Bayes' formula.** Note that the law of total probability gives the denominator of Bayes' formula.

We now present a general expression of Bayes' formula.

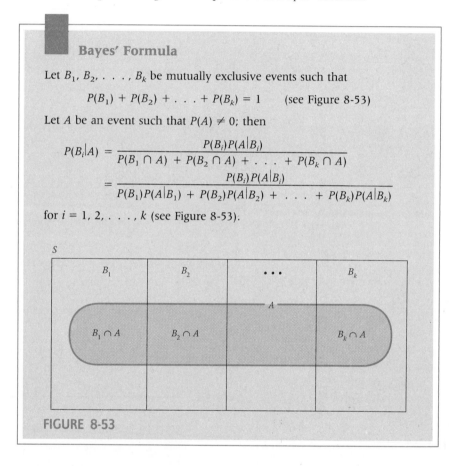

Bayes' Formula

Let $B_1, B_2, \ldots, B_k$ be mutually exclusive events such that

$$P(B_1) + P(B_2) + \ldots + P(B_k) = 1 \quad \text{(see Figure 8-53)}$$

Let A be an event such that $P(A) \neq 0$; then

$$P(B_i|A) = \frac{P(B_i)P(A|B_i)}{P(B_1 \cap A) + P(B_2 \cap A) + \ldots + P(B_k \cap A)}$$

$$= \frac{P(B_i)P(A|B_i)}{P(B_1)P(A|B_1) + P(B_2)P(A|B_2) + \ldots + P(B_k)P(A|B_k)}$$

for $i = 1, 2, \ldots, k$ (see Figure 8-53).

FIGURE 8-53

Figure 8-54 on page 574 contains a tree diagram illustration of Bayes' formula. Observe that $B_1, B_2, \ldots, B_k$ are mutually exclusive events, one of which must occur. Also, $P(A|B_1), P(A|B_2), \ldots, P(A|B_k)$ are known probabilities. Bayes' formula calculates the probabilities $P(B_i|A)$ for $i = 1, 2, \ldots, k$.

• **EXAMPLE 8-52** _____

Referring to the illustrative CPA problem of this section, find the probability that the shipping document error

a) Occurred in terminal Y.   **b)** Occurred in terminal Z.

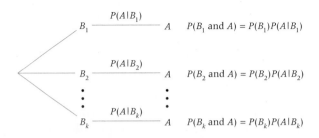

$$P(B_1 \text{ and } A) = P(B_1)P(A|B_1)$$

$$P(B_2 \text{ and } A) = P(B_2)P(A|B_2)$$

$$P(B_k \text{ and } A) = P(B_k)P(A|B_k)$$

Bayes' formula

$$P(B_i|A) = \frac{P(B_i)P(A|B_i)}{P(B_1)P(A|B_1) + P(B_2)P(A|B_2) + \cdots + P(B_k)P(A|B_k)}$$

for $i = 1, 2, \ldots, k$

FIGURE 8-54

Solution

a) We seek $P(B_2|E)$ which, according to Bayes' formula, is given by

$$P(B_2|E) = \frac{P(B_2)P(E|B_2)}{P(B_1)P(E|B_1) + P(B_2)P(E|B_2) + P(B_3)P(E|B_3)}$$

We note that the denominator is unchanged from that of our illustrative example. Nevertheless, we show our substitutions into the above formula. Hence,

$$P(B_2|E) = \frac{(.30)(.04)}{(.60)(.03) + (.30)(.04) + (.10)(.06)}$$

$$= \frac{.012}{.036} = \frac{1}{3}, \text{ or } 33\frac{1}{3}\%$$

b) We seek $P(B_3|E)$ which, according to Bayes' formula, is given by

$$P(B_3|E) = \frac{P(B_3)P(E|B_3)}{P(B_1)P(E|B_1) + P(B_2)P(E|B_2) + P(B_3)P(E|B_3)}$$

$$= \frac{(.10)(.06)}{(.60)(.03) + (.30)(.04) + (.10)(.06)}$$

$$= \frac{.006}{.036} = \frac{1}{6}, \text{ or } 16\frac{2}{3}\%$$

To Use Bayes' Formula

1. Determine the mutually exclusive events $B_1, B_2, \ldots, B_k$ and their respective probabilities $P(B_1), P(B_2), \ldots, P(B_k)$. Remember that

$$P(B_1) + P(B_2) + \ldots + P(B_k) = 1$$

2. Determine event A, usually the event that has already occurred, and the probabilities $P(A|B_1), P(A|B_2), \ldots, P(A|B_k)$.

3. Substitute the above results into the formula for $P(B_i|A)$ to determine

$$P(B_i|A) = \frac{P(B_i)P(A|B_i)}{P(B_1)P(A|B_1) + P(B_2)P(A|B_2) + \ldots + P(B_k)P(A|B_k)}$$

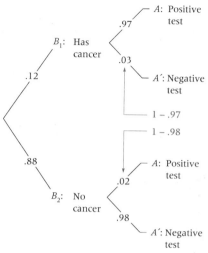

FIGURE 8-55

• EXAMPLE 8-53   Test Reliability.

A pharmaceutical company has a new test for detecting colon cancer. In an attempt to evaluate the test, it was given to a group of 15,000 people, 12% of whom are known to have colon cancer and 88% of whom are known not to have colon cancer. Of those known to have colon cancer, the test correctly identified 97%; of those known not to have colon cancer, the test correctly identified 98%. Determine each of the following probabilities:

a) If a person tests positive, the person really has colon cancer.

b) If a person tests negative, the person really does not have colon cancer.

Solutions

Here

$$B_1 = \text{event that a person has colon cancer}$$
$$B_2 = \text{event that a person does not have colon cancer}$$
$$A = \text{event that the test is positive}$$
$$A' = \text{event that the test is negative}$$

Then $P(B_1) = .12$, $P(B_2) = .88$, $P(A|B_1) = .97$, and $P(A'|B_2) = .98$. These results are summarized in the tree diagram of Figure 8-55.

a) We seek $P(B_1|A)$ which, by Bayes' formula, is given by

$$P(B_1|A) = \frac{P(B_1)P(A|B_1)}{P(B_1)P(A|B_1) + P(B_2)P(A|B_2)}$$

$$= \frac{(.12)(.97)}{(.12)(.97) + (.88)(.02)}$$

$$\uparrow \text{—— } 1 - .98, \text{ as found in Figure 8-55}$$

$$= \frac{.1164}{.1340} \approx .8687, \text{ or } 86.87\%$$

Thus, if a person tests positive, there is approximately an 86.87% probability that the person really has colon cancer.

b) We seek $P(B_2|A')$ which, by Bayes' formula, is given by

$$P(B_2|A') = \frac{P(B_2)P(A'|B_2)}{P(B_1)P(A'|B_1) + P(B_2)P(A'|B_2)}$$

$$= \frac{(.88)(.98)}{(.12)(.03) + (.88)(.98)}$$

$$\uparrow \text{—— } 1 - .97, \text{ as found in Figure 8-55}$$

$$= \frac{.8624}{.8660} \approx .9958, \text{ or } 99.58\%$$

Thus, if a person tests negative, there is approximately a 99.58% probability that the person really does not have colon cancer.

• EXAMPLE 8-54   Credit Screening.

A credit information bureau classifies credit card users into 3 groups: high risk, medium risk, and low risk. The bureau has classified 20%, 30%, and 50% of credit card users as high risk, medium risk, and low risk, respectively. Also, the bureau has determined that 80% of the high-risk group, 20% of the medium-risk group, and 5% of the low-risk group will become delinquent in credit card payments. If a credit card user from this group becomes delinquent, then find the probability that this credit card user was classified in the medium-risk group.

Solution

Let

B_1 = event that a credit-card user is classified in the high-risk group

B_2 = event that a credit-card user is classified in the medium-risk group.

B_3 = event that a credit-card user is classified in the low-risk group

A = event that a credit-card user is delinquent in payments

Then

$$P(B_1) = .20, \; P(B_2) = .30, \; P(B_3) = .50$$
$$P(A|B_1) = .80, \; P(A|B_2) = .20, \; P(A|B_3) = .05$$

We seek $P(B_2|A)$. Using Bayes' formula,

$$P(B_2|A) = \frac{(P(B_2)P(A|B_2)}{P(B_1)P(A|B_1) + P(B_2)P(A|B_2) + P(B_3)P(A|B_3)}$$
$$= \frac{(.30)(.20)}{(.20)(.80) + (.30)(.20) + (.50)(.05)}$$
$$= \frac{.06}{.16 + .06 + .025}$$
$$\approx .24$$

Exercises 8-5

Box 1 contains 5 red and 3 green marbles, and Box 2 contains 1 yellow, 7 red, and 2 green marbles. A chance experiment consists of first selecting a box and then selecting a marble from that box.

1. Find the probability of getting a red marble.
2. Find the probability of getting a green marble.
3. Find the probability of getting a yellow marble.
4. If a red marble is selected, find the probability that it came from Box 1.
5. If a green marble is selected, find the probability that it came from Box 1.
6. If a red marble is selected, find the probability that it came from Box 2.
7. If a green marble is selected, find the probability that it came from Box 2.
8. If a yellow marble is selected, find the probability that it came from Box 2.

Quality assurance. A company that manufactures mopeds has 3 plants. Plant 1 produces 40% of the output, plant 2 produces 35%, and plant 3 produces 25%. Of the mopeds, 2% produced by plant 1 are defective, 1% produced by plant 2 are defective, and 3% produced by plant 3 are defective. If a moped is selected from this company's output and found to be defective, find the probability that it came from each of the following.

9. Plant 1   10. Plant 2   11. Plant 3

12. *Medical screening.* If a person with a certain disease is given a screening, there is a 90% probability that the disease will be detected. If a person without this disease is given the same screening, there is a 20% probability that the person will be diagnosed incorrectly as having this disease. In a given community, 15% of the residents have this disease. If a resident of this community is diagnosed as having this disease, what is the probability that he or she actually has the disease?

Consumer behavior. A given city is divided into submarkets for consumer behavior. Submarket 1 contains 30% of the consumers, submarket 2 contains 25%, submarket 3 contains 21%, and submarket 4 contains 24%. Of the consumers, 40% from submarket 1 usually favor foreign-made cars, as do 20% from submarket 2, 35% from submarket 3, and 50% from submarket 4.

13. If a consumer is chosen at random, what is the probability that he or she will favor foreign-made cars?

14. If a chosen consumer has favored foreign-made cars, what is the probability that he or she came from submarket 1?

Risk analysis. The following table shows the accident rates for various age groups insured with a particular insurance company.

Age group	Proportion of total insured	Accident rate
Under 21	.10	.08
21–30	.15	.05
31–40	.35	.03
41–50	.25	.02
Over 50	.15	.04

If a policyholder reports an accident, what is the probability that he or she is in each of the following age groups?

15. Under 21

16. 31–40

17. *Customer returns.* A local department store has classified 90% of its credit customers as "Good Payers" and 10% as "Poor Payers." From past experience, it has been determined that 98% of the "Good Payers" do not return any items purchased, whereas only 30% of the "Poor Payers" do not return any items purchased. If a credit customer returns a purchased item, what is the probability that he or she is a "Poor Payer"?

18. *Quality assurance.* A mail-order house has two workers filling orders. Worker 1 usually fills 70% of all orders, and worker 2 fills the remaining 30%. Worker 1 has an error rate of 5%, and worker 2 has an error rate of 3%. If an order is returned due to an error, what is the probability that it was filled by worker 1?

Quality assurance. A distributor carries three brands of tires: brand B_1, brand B_2, and brand B_3. Of all the tires, 50% are brand B_1, 30% are brand B_2, and 20% are brand B_3. Percentages of defectives are as follows: 10% of brand B_1, 5% of brand B_2, and 8% of brand B_3.

19. If the distributor selects a tire from this inventory, find the probability that the tire is a defective.

20. If the distributor selects a tire and gets a defective, find the probability that the tire is a brand B_2 tire.

Test reliability. A test for detecting a particular disease was given to a very large group of people, 15% of whom are known to have the disease and 85% of whom are known not to have the disease. Of those who have the disease, the test correctly identified 98%; of those known not to have the disease, the test correctly identified 96%. Determine each of the following probabilities.

21. If a person tests positive, the person really has the disease.

22. If a person tests negative, the person really does not have the disease.

23. If a person tests negative, the person really has the disease.

24. If a person tests positive, the person really does not have the disease.

EXTRA DIVIDENDS

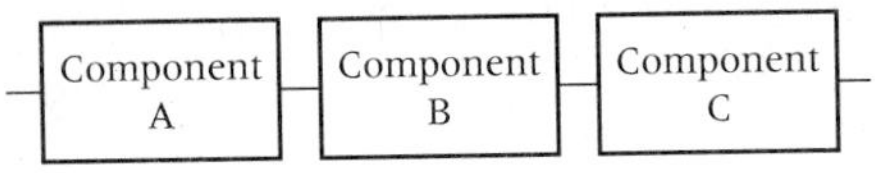

Series configuration

FIGURE 8-56

• *System Reliability*

A **system**—such as an aircraft flight control system, a manufacturing system, or an emergency response system (i.e., a fire department or ambulance service)—consists of components arranged in various configurations. As an example, we consider a firm producing a hi-tech device used in the hardware of computers. The production process for this device is a system consisting of 3 components: component A, a soldering process; component B, an assembly process; and component C, a cleaning process. We will be concerned with determining the production process's **system reliability** or, in other words, the probability that the system (i.e., production process) produces a device that works.

A characteristic of this system (i.e., production process) is that the system will produce a device that works only if all 3 components do not fail. In other words, the failure of any component (A, B, or C) will result in the system producing a defective device. This characteristic implies that the 3 components of the system are arranged in the configuration shown in Figure 8-56. Such a configuration of system components is called a **series configuration.** Remember that a series configuration of system components results when the failure of any one component causes the system to fail.

If we let

$P(A)$ = probability that component A does not fail
(i.e., the reliability of component A)

$P(B)$ = probability that component B does not fail
(i.e., the reliability of component B)

$P(C)$ = probability that component C does not fail
(i.e., the reliability of component C)

$P(S)$ = probability that the system
(i.e., production process) works

then, since the system works only if all 3 components do not fail, the system reliability is given by

$$P(S) = P(A \text{ and } B \text{ and } C)$$

We assume that the components are independent of each other. In other words, whether one component fails or not has no effect on whether the others fail or not. Thus, we can use the special law of multiplication to obtain

$$P(S) = P(A)P(B)P(C)$$

If the reliabilities of components A, B, and C are .95, .97, and .96, respectively, the reliability of the system is given by

$$P(S) = (.95)(.97)(.96)$$
$$= .88$$

We now consider some other system consisting of 2 components: component A and component B. This system possesses the characteristic

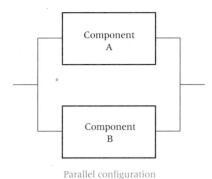

Parallel configuration

FIGURE 8-57

that the system will fail only if both components fail. The diagram of Figure 8-57 gives the configuration of these two components. Such a configuration is called a **parallel configuration.** A parallel configuration implies the concept of redundancy. In other words, referring to the diagram of Figure 8-57, component A and component B are both performing the same function. If one of them fails, the other can still perform the function. A redundancy is used to improve the reliability of a system.

Again, we let

$$P(A) = \text{probability that component A does not fail}$$
$$\text{(i.e., the reliability of component A)}$$

$$P(B) = \text{probability that component B does not fail}$$
$$\text{(i.e., the reliability of component B)}$$

$$P(S) = \text{probability that the system works}$$

and we assume that components A and B are independent of each other. We determine the system reliability, $P(S)$, by first determining the probability of both components failing and then taking the complement of that result. Hence,

$$P(S') = P(A' \text{ and } B')$$
$$= P(A')P(B')$$

Since $P(S) = 1 - P(S')$, then

$$P(S) = 1 - P(A')P(B')$$

If the reliabilities of components A and B are .93 and .98, respectively, then $P(A') = 1 - .93 = .07$ and $P(B') = 1 - .98 = .02$, so that the reliability of the system is given by

$$P(S) = 1 - P(A')P(B')$$
$$= 1 - (.07)(.02)$$
$$= 1 - .0014$$
$$= .9986$$

Exercises

1. Given that the reliabilities of components A, B, C, and D are .98, .96, .94, and .99 respectively, determine the reliability of the system of Figure 8-58.

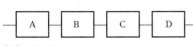

FIGURE 8-58

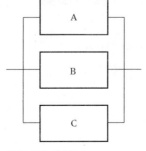

FIGURE 8-59

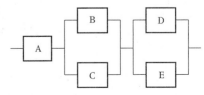

FIGURE 8-60

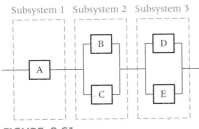

FIGURE 8-61

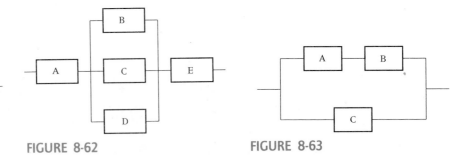

FIGURE 8-62   **FIGURE 8-63**

2. If the reliabilities of components A, B, and C are .94, .98, and .96, respectively, determine the reliability of the system of Figure 8-59 on page 579.

3. If the reliabilities of components A, B, C, D, and E are .96, .95, .98, .94, and .93, respectively, determine the reliability of the system of Figure 8-60. *Hint:* Break up the system into subsystems, as illustrated in Figure 8-61 on page 579, and determine the reliability of each subsystem. Then look at the system as a series configuration of the 3 subsystems and determine its reliability.)

4. Verify that the reliability of the system of Figure 8-62 is given by the formula

$$P(S) = P(A)(1 - [1 - P(B)][1 - P(C)][1 - P(D)])P(E)$$

5. Verify that the reliability of the system of Figure 8-63 is given by

$$P(S) = 1 - ([1 - P(A)P(B)][1 - P(C)])$$

CHAPTER 8 HIGHLIGHTS

• *Concepts*

Your ability to answer the following questions is one indicator of the depth of your mastery of this chapter's important concepts. Note that the questions are grouped under various topic headings. For any question that you cannot answer, refer to the appropriate section of the chapter indicated by the topic heading. Pay particular attention to the summary boxes within a section.

8-1 SETS

1. Explain the following terms: set, empty set, null set, equality of sets, subset, universal set, intersection of sets, union of sets, disjoint sets, complement of a set, De Morgan's laws, cross-classification table, Venn diagram.

8-2 COUNTING, PERMUTATIONS, AND COMBINATIONS

2. Explain the following terms: multiplication rule of counting, factorial, permutation, combination.
3. State the difference between a permutation and a combination.
4. Explain the MRCC model.

8-3 PROBABILITY; ADDITION AND COMPLEMENT RULES; ODDS

5. Explain the following terms: chance experiment, sample space, event, probability, law of large numbers, empirical probability, subjective probability, probability distribution.
6. Explain the basic probability formula and its restrictions.

7. State the addition rule. Give the key word that is associated with the addition rule.
8. State the special case addition rule, and specify when it is used.
9. State the key word that is associated with the complement rule.
10. Explain the term *odds.*
11. Give the formula that translates odds into probabilities.
12. Give the formula that translates probabilities into odds.

8-4 CONDITIONAL PROBABILITY AND INDEPENDENCE

13. Explain the term *conditional probability,* and give two formulas for finding conditional probabilities.
14. State the product rules, and indicate when they are used. Specify the key word associated with the product rules.
15. Explain the term *independence;* state the special case product rule, and specify when it is used.

8-5 BAYES' FORMULA

16. Explain Bayes' formula.

REVIEW EXERCISES

• Sets

1. Of the most recent 50 invoices at an appliance store, 20 were for an electric range, 35 were for a refrigerator, and 9 were for both.
   a) Express the above information in a Venn diagram.
   b) How many invoices were not for an electric range?
   c) How many invoices were for either an electric range or a refrigerator?
   d) How many invoices were for neither an electric range nor a refrigerator?
   e) Of those invoices that included refrigerators, what percentage included electric ranges?
   f) Of those invoices that included electric ranges, what percentage included refrigerators?
   g) How many invoices included an electric range, but not a refrigerator?

2. The Heavenly Flavor Ice Cream Company surveyed 100 families to determine flavor preferences. The results were as follows:
   - 40 families liked vanilla.
   - 34 families liked strawberry.
   - 52 families liked coffee.
   - 21 families liked both vanilla and strawberry.
   - 15 families liked both coffee and strawberry.
   - 17 families liked both vanilla and coffee.
   - 10 families liked all three flavors.
   a) Express the above information in a Venn diagram.
   b) How many families liked both vanilla and strawberry, but not coffee?
   c) How many families liked both strawberry and coffee, but not vanilla?
   d) How many families liked both vanilla and coffee, but not strawberry?
   e) How many families liked only vanilla?
   f) How many families liked only strawberry?
   g) How many families liked only coffee?
   h) How many families liked none of the three flavors?

• Cross-Classification Table

3. The table below gives employees' sentiments regarding working conditions at a particular plant.

| | Sentiments: Working conditions | | | |
	good	average	poor	Total
Male	320	40	200	560
Female	160	60	220	440
Total	480	100	420	1000

   a) Construct the corresponding "Column Percentages" table, and interpret the results.
   b) Construct the corresponding "Row Percentages" table, and interpret the results.
   c) What percentage of the respondents are female and feel that working conditions are poor?
   d) What percentage of the respondents are either male or feel that working conditions are average?
   e) What percentage of the respondents feel that working conditions are not good?
   f) What percentage of the respondents feel that working conditions are either good or average?

• Counting, Permutations, and Combinations

Evaluate Exercises 4–11.

4. 8!   5. 1!   6. 0!   7. 4!
8. $P(9, 4)$ 9. $P(7, 2)$ 10. $C(9, 4)$ 11. $C(8, 5)$

12. A trip is to consist of driving from city 1 to city 2 and then from city 2 to city 3. There are 5 possible routes from city 1 to city 2 and 3 possible routes from city 2 to city 3. How many different ways can this trip be taken?

13. *Committee selection.* In how many ways can a committee of 4 be chosen from a group of 7 people if
   a) The first person chosen becomes president, the second becomes vice president, the third becomes treasurer, and the fourth becomes secretary?
   b) The order of selection makes no difference?

14. *Serial numbers.* A bicycle maker assigns a serial number to each bicycle. Each serial number consists of 4 letters followed by 7 digits. How many different serial numbers are allowed if
   a) Repetitions of letters and digits are allowed?
   b) Repetitions of digits are allowed, but repetitions of letters are not allowed?
   c) Repetitions of letters are allowed, but repetitions of digits are not allowed?

15. *Quality control.* A production lot of 30 computers contains 6 defective computers. A sample of 5 computers is to be selected from this production lot.
   a) How many possible samples are there?
   b) How many possible samples contain exactly 2 defective computers?
   c) How many possible samples contain no defective computers?
   d) How many possible samples contain at least 4 defective computers?

• *Probability, Addition and Complement Rules, Odds*

16. A card is selected from an ordinary deck of 52 cards. Find the probability that the selected card is

a) An ace.   b) A jack.   c) Not an ace.   d) Not a jack.

e) Either a jack or a black card.   f) A red jack.

g) Neither a jack nor a red card.

17. Of 200 employees of the Beta Company, 120 got a promotion, 180 got a raise, and 100 got both during the past 2 years. If a person is selected from this group, determine the probability that the selected person

a) Got a raise.

b) Got a promotion.

c) Got both a raise and a promotion.

d) Got either a raise or a promotion.

e) Got either a raise or a promotion, but not both.

f) Got neither a raise nor a promotion.

18. Given the following cross-classification table,

	A	B	C	Total
D	20	30	40	90
E	80	60	10	150
Total	100	90	50	240

find

a) $P(A)$.   b) $P(E)$.   c) $P(A$ or $C)$.   d) $P(B$ and $D)$.

e) $P(B$ or $D)$.   f) $P(A$ and $C)$.   g) P(neither E nor A).

19. *Quality control.* A production lot of 40 computers contains 8 that are defective. A sample of 6 computers is selected from this production lot. Determine the probability that the sample contains

a) All nondefective computers.

b) Exactly 3 defective computers.

c) At most 3 defective computers.

d) At least 5 defective computers.

20. For the probability distribution at the left, if $E_1 = \{e_1, e_3\}$ and $E_2 = \{e_2, e_3, e_4\}$, then determine

a) $P(E_1)$.   b) $P(E_2)$.

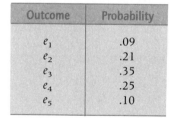

Outcome	Probability
e_1	.09
e_2	.21
e_3	.35
e_4	.25
e_5	.10

• *Odds*

Determine $P(E)$ if the odds in favor of event E occurring are as follows:

21. 1 to 5   **22.** 6 to 3   **23.** 3 to 7   **24.** 5 to 2

Determine the odds in favor of event E occurring if $P(E)$ is given as follows:

25. .80   **26.** 7/9   **27.** .30   **28.** 2/9

Translate the following into probabilities.

29. The odds in favor of inflation recurring are 5 to 2.

30. The odds in favor of interest rates rising are 7 to 3.

Translate the following into odds.

31. The probability of rain tomorrow is .60.

32. The probability of unemployment rising during the next quarter is .90.

• Conditional Probability and Independence

33. *Brand preference.* At a given supermarket, 60% of the shoppers buy brand A detergent, 30% buy brand B, and 10% buy both.
  a) If a shopper buys brand A, find the probability that he or she also buys brand B.
  b) If a shopper buys brand B, find the probability that he or she also buys brand A.
  c) What percentage of the shoppers buy either brand A or brand B?

34. *Market research.* Of the households in a given city, 90% have Touch-Tone telephones, 70% have videocassette recorders (VCRs), and 80% of those that have Touch-Tone telephones also have VCRs. Find the probability that
  a) A household has both a Touch-Tone telephone and a VCR.
  b) A household with a VCR also has a Touch-Tone telephone.

35. *Quality control.* A production lot of 500 tires contains 40 defective tires. A quality control procedure consists of selecting 3 tires without replacement from the production lot. Find the probability of selecting
  a) A defective tire on the first selection.
  b) A defective tire on the second selection, given that a nondefective tire was selected on the first selection.
  c) Three defective tires.

36. *Quality control.* Repeat Exercise 35 under the assumption that the 3 selections are made with replacement.

• Bayes' Formula

37. *Quality assurance.* A retail outlet carries 3 brands of refrigerators; A, B, and C. Of all the refrigerators, 40% are brand A, 50% are brand B, and 10% are brand C. The percentages of defectives are as follows: 6% of brand A, 10% of brand B, and 7% of brand C.
  a) If a refrigerator is selected from inventory, find the probability that it is defective.
  b) If a refrigerator is selected and found to be defective, find the probability that it is a brand A refrigerator.

Algebra Refresher

EXPONENTS

Rational Exponents

$$x^{1/n} = \sqrt[n]{x}$$

Examples: $\quad x^{1/2} = \sqrt{x} \qquad x^{1/3} = \sqrt[3]{x} \qquad x^{1/4} = \sqrt[4]{x}$

Worksheet

Fill in the blanks.

$x^{1/5} = \sqrt[\ ]{x}$ Answer: $\sqrt[5]{x}$ $\qquad$ $\sqrt[7]{x} = x^{-/-}$ Answer: $x^{1/7}$

$x^{1/9} = \sqrt[\ ]{x}$ Answer: $\sqrt[9]{x}$ $\qquad$ $\sqrt[8]{x} = x^{-/-}$ Answer: $x^{1/8}$

$$x^{m/n} = \sqrt[n]{x^m}$$

Examples: $\quad x^{5/2} = \sqrt{x^5} \qquad x^{5/3} = \sqrt[3]{x^5} \qquad x^{7/4} = \sqrt[4]{x^7}$

Worksheet

Fill in the blanks.

$x^{2/3} = \sqrt[3]{x^{-}}$ Answer: $\sqrt[3]{x^2}$ $\qquad$ $x^{9/4} = \sqrt[\ ]{x^{-}}$ Answer: $\sqrt[4]{x^9}$

$\sqrt[5]{x^8} = x^{-/-}$ Answer: $x^{8/5}$ $\qquad$ $\sqrt[7]{x^6} = x^{-/-}$ Answer: $x^{6/7}$

Negative Exponents

$$x^{-n} = \frac{1}{x^n}$$

Examples: $\quad x^{-2} = \dfrac{1}{x^2} \qquad x^{-1/3} = \dfrac{1}{\sqrt[3]{x}} \qquad x^{-5/4} = \dfrac{1}{\sqrt[4]{x^5}}$

Worksheet

Fill in the blanks.

$x^{-3} = $ _____   Answer: $\dfrac{1}{x^3}$ $\qquad$ $x^{-1/4} = $ _____   Answer: $\dfrac{1}{\sqrt[4]{x}}$

$x^{-1/5} = $ _____   Answer: $\dfrac{1}{\sqrt[5]{x}}$ $\qquad$ $x^{-5/3} = $ _____   Answer: $\dfrac{1}{\sqrt[3]{x^5}}$

$x^{-4/3} = $ _____   Answer: $\dfrac{1}{\sqrt[3]{x^4}}$ $\qquad$ $\dfrac{1}{\sqrt[5]{x^6}} = $ _____   Answer: $x^{-6/5}$

$\dfrac{1}{\sqrt{x^7}} = $ _____   Answer: $x^{-7/2}$ $\qquad$ $\dfrac{1}{\sqrt[4]{x^7}} = $ _____   Answer: $x^{-7/4}$

The contents of this page and other exponent laws are discussed in Section R-3.

9

DIFFERENTIATION

Introductory Application

Marginal Revenue

Given the demand equation

$$p = -x + 10 \qquad (0 \le x \le 10)$$

where p denotes the unit selling price and x denotes the number of units demanded of some product,

a) Determine the equation for total sales revenue, $R(x)$.
b) Determine the equation for marginal revenue.
c) Determine the marginal revenue at sales level $x = 3$ units. Interpret the result.

In Chapter 2, we learned to determine the equation of a sales revenue function, given a demand equation. In this chapter, we will learn that marginal revenue represents the additional revenue gained from the sale of one more unit of product.

The above problem is solved in Example 9-28.

In the remaining chapters of this text, we will study calculus. **Calculus** is the branch of mathematics that concerns itself with the *rate of change* of one quantity with respect to another quantity. Calculus is considered to have been invented by Isaac Newton and Gottfried Wilhelm von Leibnitz working independently at the close of the seventeenth century. Calculus is separated into two parts: **differential calculus** and **integral calculus.** Differential calculus is involved with a certain quantity called a **derivative.** In this chapter, we will learn what a derivative is, how to calculate a derivative, and how a derivative is used. Integral calculus will be considered in Chapters 13 and 14.

9-1   • LIMITS

The concept of limit is very important for the formal development of calculus. In this section, we will give a brief introduction to limits.

When we apply the concept of limit, we examine what happens to the *y*-values of a function $f(x)$ as *x* gets closer and closer to (but does not reach) some particular number, called *a*. If the *y*-values also get closer and closer to a single number, L, then the number L is said to be the *limit of the function as x approaches a.* Thus, we say that L **is the limit of $f(x)$ as x approaches *a*.** This is written in mathematical shorthand as

$$\lim_{x \to a} f(x) = L$$

where the symbol $\to$ stands for the word *approaches*. If the *y*-values of the function do not get closer and closer to a single number as *x* gets closer and closer to *a*, then the function has no limit as *x* approaches *a*. Figure 9-1 gives the graph of the function

$$f(x) = 2x + 1$$

along with a table of *x* and $f(x)$ values.

We wish to determine the limit of f(x) = 2x + 1 *as* x *approaches 3.*

To determine $\lim_{x \to 3} f(x)$, we let *x* take on values that approach 3 from the left and record the corresponding $f(x)$ values, as illustrated in the table of Figure 9-1. Note that as *x* approaches 3 from the left (i.e., $x < 3$), $f(x)$ approaches 7. This is a **left-hand limit** and is written as

$$\lim_{x \to 3^-} f(x) = 7$$

x approaches 3 ——————⌐   ⌐—————— left-hand limit
from the left.

Also, we let *x* take on values that approach 3 from the right and record corresponding $f(x)$ values, as shown in the table of Figure 9-1. Note that as

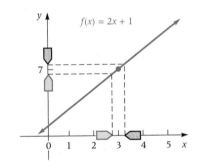

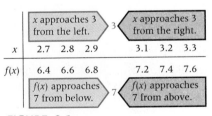

FIGURE 9-1

	x approaches 3 from the left.		3	x approaches 3 from the right.	
x	2.7 2.8 2.9			3.1 3.2 3.3	
$f(x)$	6.4 6.6 6.8			7.2 7.4 7.6	
	$f(x)$ approaches 7 from below.		7	$f(x)$ approaches 7 from above.	

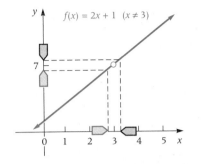

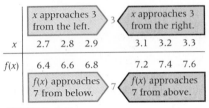

FIGURE 9-2

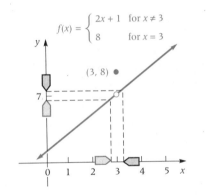

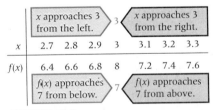

FIGURE 9-3

x approaches 3 from the right (i.e., $x > 3$) $f(x)$ approaches 7. This is a **right-hand limit** and is written as

$$\lim_{x \to 3^+} f(x) = 7$$

x approaches 3 from the right.   right-hand limit

Since the left-hand limit, 7, equals the right-hand limit, 7, then we say that 7 is the limit of $f(x)$ as x approaches 3. In other words, the $f(x)$ values approach the same number—in this case, 7—as x approaches 3 from both sides. Thus, we write

$$\lim_{x \to 3} f(x) = 7$$

We note that if the point (3, 7) is omitted from the function $f(x)$, then the $\lim_{x \to 3} f(x)$ is unaffected and is still 7, as is shown in Figure 9-2.

Also, if the function $f(x)$ is assigned a value different from 7 when $x = 3$, as illustrated in Figure 9-3, then the $\lim_{x \to 3} f(x)$ is unaffected and is still 7, as we show in Figure 9-3.

Nonexistence of Limits

We now give an example where a *limit does not exist* at a particular point. We consider an income tax function, $T(x)$, which gives the amount of federal income tax for taxable income x. This tax function was under consideration during a past tax reform movement. We note that present-day tax functions possess a somewhat similar structure. Thus, $T(x)$ is defined below, and its graph is given in Figure 9-4.

Tax Function

$$T(x) = \begin{cases} 0.15x & \text{for } 0 \le x \le 29{,}300 \\ 0.27x - 3561 & \text{for } x > 29{,}300 \end{cases}$$

Studying the tax function $T(x)$, note that for taxable income up to and including \$29,300, the federal income tax is 15% of such income. However, for taxable income in excess of \$29,300, the federal income tax is 27% of such income, minus \$3561.

We want to determine the limit, if it exists, of T(x) *as* x *approaches 29,300.*

Thus, we let x take on values that approach 29,300 from the left and record the corresponding $T(x)$ values, as illustrated in the table of Figure 9-4. Note that as x approaches 29,300 from the left, $T(x)$ approaches 4395. Thus,

$$\lim_{x \to 29{,}300^-} T(x) = 4395$$

x approaches 29,300 from the left.   left-hand limit

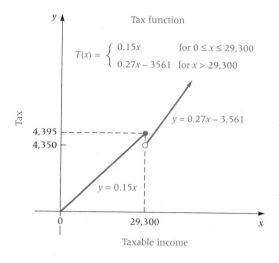

FIGURE 9-4

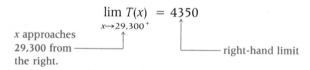

Also, we let x take on values that approach 29,300 from the right and record the corresponding $T(x)$ values, as illustrated in Figure 9-4. Observe that as x approaches 29,300 from the right, $T(x)$ approaches 4350. Thus,

$$\lim_{x \to 29,300^+} T(x) = 4350$$

x approaches 29,300 from the right. — right-hand limit

Since the left-hand limit, 4395, does not equal the right-hand limit, 4350, then

$$\lim_{x \to 29,300} T(x) \qquad does\ not\ exist.$$

• **EXAMPLE 9-1**

Find the limit of the function $f(x) = x^2$ as x approaches 3.

Solution

Table 9-1 on page 592 contains a listing of x and y values of $f(x) = x^2$ as x takes on values near 3. Observe that as x gets closer and closer to 3 from each side, $f(x)$ gets closer to 9 from each side. Thus, we say that 9 is the limit of $f(x)$ as x approaches 3. This is written in mathematical shorthand as

$$\lim_{x \to 3} f(x) = 9$$

Since $f(x) = x^2$, this expression may also be written as

$$\lim_{x \to 3} x^2 = 9$$

TABLE 9-1 $y = f(x) = x^2$

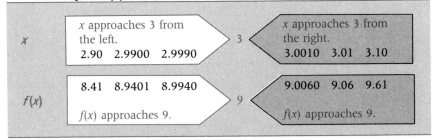

x	x approaches 3 from the left. 2.90 2.9900 2.9990	3	x approaches 3 from the right. 3.0010 3.01 3.10
$f(x)$	8.41 8.9401 8.9940 $f(x)$ approaches 9.	9	9.0060 9.06 9.61 $f(x)$ approaches 9.

We now give the following definition of limit.

Limit

1. Let a and L be numbers and $f(x)$ a function. If, as x approaches the number a from each side, the values of $f(x)$ approach the single value L, then L is said to be the **limit of $f(x)$ as x approaches a.** We write this in mathematical shorthand as

$$\lim_{x \to a} f(x) = L$$

2. This means that the left-hand limit equals the right-hand limit or, in other words,

$$\lim_{x \to a^-} f(x) = L = \lim_{x \to a^+} f(x)$$

3. The $\lim_{x \to a} f(x)$ does not depend on the value of $f(x)$ at $x = a$. Whether or not the function, $f(x)$ is defined at $x = a$ does not affect the limit or its existence or nonexistence at $x = a$.

4. In other words,

$$\lim_{x \to a} f(x) = L$$

means that the values of $f(x)$ approach, without necessarily being equal to, L as x approaches, without necessarily being equal to, a.

• **EXAMPLE 9-2**

If $f(x) = x$, find $\lim_{x \to 4} f(x)$ or, in other words, $\lim_{x \to 4} x$.

Solution

We make a table of x and y values as x approaches 4 (see Table 9-2). Note that as x approaches 4 from each side, the values of $f(x)$ approach 4. Thus, $4 = \lim_{x \to 4} f(x)$ or, equivalently, $4 = \lim_{x \to 4} x$.

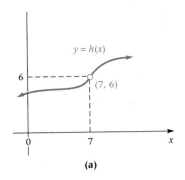

(a)

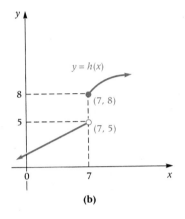

(b)

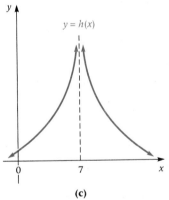

(c)

FIGURE 9-5

TABLE 9-2 $y = f(x) = x$

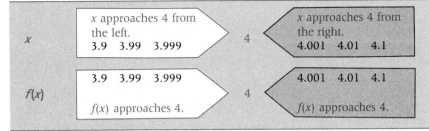

x	x approaches 4 from the left. 3.9 3.99 3.999	4	x approaches 4 from the right. 4.001 4.01 4.1
$f(x)$	3.9 3.99 3.999 $f(x)$ approaches 4.	4	4.001 4.01 4.1 $f(x)$ approaches 4.

We now look at situations where the function is not given as a formula. Instead, we have only the graph. We can still find the limit, if it exists.

• EXAMPLE 9-3

For each of the graphs of Figure 9-5, determine if $\lim_{x \to 7} h(x)$ exists. If the limit exists, state its numerical value.

Solutions

a) As x gets closer and closer to 7 from each side, the values of $h(x)$ get closer and closer to the single value 6. Thus, $\lim_{x \to 7} h(x) = 6$. Note that this function has a limit at all other values of x shown on this graph.

b) As x gets closer and closer to 7 from the left, the values of $h(x)$ get closer and closer to 5. As x gets closer and closer to 7 from the right, the values of $h(x)$ get closer and closer to 8. Since the values of $h(x)$ do not approach the same value from each side, the function has no limit as $x \to 7$. Note that this function has a limit at all other values of x shown on this graph.

c) As x gets closer and closer to 7, the values of $h(x)$ get larger and larger and do not approach a single number. Thus, $\lim_{x \to 7} h(x)$ does not exist. Note that this function has a limit at all other values of x shown on this graph.

Limit Properties

In the previous examples of this section, we determined the limits of functions by applying the definition of limit. Many times, limits of functions are determined in a much simpler manner by using **limit properties.** The following limit properties are stated without verification.

Limit Properties   For each of the following, assume that $\lim_{x \to a} f(x)$ and $\lim_{x \to a} g(x)$ both exist. Also, let a, c, k, and r be constant real numbers, with $r > 0$.

Property 1   *Limit of a Constant.*

$$\lim_{x \to a} c = c$$

This property states that the limit of a constant function is the constant value. Thus, for example, we write

$$\lim_{x \to 2} 5 = 5 \qquad \lim_{x \to -1} 8 = 8 \qquad \lim_{x \to a} -4 = -4 \qquad \lim_{x \to 6} 9 = 9$$

Property 2   *Limit of a Sum or Difference.*

$$\lim_{x \to a} [f(x) \pm g(x)] = \lim_{x \to a} f(x) \pm \lim_{x \to a} g(x)$$

This property states that the limit of a sum or difference is the sum or difference of the individual limits, provided that these limits exist. Thus, if $f(x) = x$ and $g(x) = 5$, then

$$\begin{aligned}
\lim_{x \to 4} [f(x) + g(x)] &= \lim_{x \to 4} (x + 5) \\
&= \lim_{x \to 4} x + \lim_{x \to 4} 5 \\
&= 4 + 5 \\
&= 9 \\
\lim_{x \to 4} [f(x) - g(x)] &= \lim_{x \to 4} (x - 5) \\
&= \lim_{x \to 4} x - \lim_{x \to 4} 5 \\
&= 4 - 5 \\
&= -1
\end{aligned}$$

Property 3   *Limit of a Constant Times a Function.*

$$\lim_{x \to a} kf(x) = k \lim_{x \to a} f(x)$$

This property states that the limit of a constant times a function is the constant times the limit of the function, provided, of course, that the limit exists. Thus, if $f(x) = x$ and $k = 3$, then

$$\begin{aligned}
\lim_{x \to 4} kf(x) &= \lim_{x \to 4} 3x \\
&= 3 \lim_{x \to 4} x \\
&= 3(4) \\
&= 12
\end{aligned}$$

Property 4   *Limit of a Function to a Power.*

$$\lim_{x \to a} [f(x)]^r = \left[\lim_{x \to a} f(x) \right]^r$$

This property states that the limit of a function raised to a power is the power of the limit, provided, of course, that the limit exists. Thus, if $f(x) = x$ and $r = 3$, then

$$\begin{aligned}
\lim_{x \to 4} [f(x)]^r &= \lim_{x \to 4} x^3 \\
&= \left[\lim_{x \to 4} x \right]^3 \\
&= 4^3 \\
&= 64
\end{aligned}$$

Property 5   *Limit of a Product.*

$$\lim_{x \to a} [f(x)g(x)] = \left[\lim_{x \to a} f(x) \right]\left[\lim_{x \to a} g(x) \right]$$

This property states that the limit of a product is the product of the limits, provided that these limits exist. Thus, if $f(x) = x^3$ and $g(x) = x + 5$, then

$$\lim_{x \to 4} [f(x)g(x)] = \lim_{x \to 4} x^3(x + 5)$$
$$= \left[\lim_{x \to 4} x^3\right]\left[\lim_{x \to 4} (x + 5)\right]$$
$$= 4^3(4 + 5)$$
$$= 64(9)$$
$$= 576$$

Note that we have previously determined that $\lim_{x \to 4} x^3 = 4^3 = 64$ and that $\lim_{x \to 4}(x + 5) = 4 + 5 = 9$.

Property 6   *Limit of a Quotient.*
If $\lim_{x \to a} g(x) \neq 0$, then

$$\lim_{x \to a} \frac{f(x)}{g(x)} = \frac{\lim_{x \to a} f(x)}{\lim_{x \to a} g(x)}$$

This property states that the limit of a quotient is the quotient of the limits, provided that the limits exist and that the limit of the denominator is not zero. Thus, if $f(x) = x^3$ and $g(x) = x + 5$, then

$$\lim_{x \to 4} \frac{f(x)}{g(x)} = \lim_{x \to 4} \frac{x^3}{x + 5}$$
$$= \frac{\lim_{x \to 4} x^3}{\lim_{x \to 4} (x + 5)}$$
$$= \frac{4^3}{(4 + 5)}$$
$$= \frac{64}{9}$$

Again, recall that we have previously determined that $\lim_{x \to 4} x^3 = 4^3 = 64$ and that $\lim_{x \to 4}(x + 5) = 9$.

• **EXAMPLE 9-4** _____

Compute the following limits:

a) $\lim_{x \to 5} x$ b) $\lim_{x \to 5} x^4$

c) $\lim_{x \to 5} 3x^4$ d) $\lim_{x \to 5}(3x^4 - 275)$

e) $\lim_{x \to 5} \sqrt{3x^4 - 275}$ f) $\lim_{x \to 5} \dfrac{\sqrt{3x^4 - 275}}{x^3}$

Solutions

a) In Example 9-2, we showed that $\lim_{x \to 4} x = 4$. In a similar manner, we could show that $\lim_{x \to 5} x = 5$.

b) $\lim_{x \to 5} x^4 = \left(\lim_{x \to 5} x\right)^4$ By Property 4
$$= 5^4 \qquad \text{By Part a}$$
$$= 625$$

c) $\lim\limits_{x\to5} 3x^4 = 3 \lim\limits_{x\to5} x^4$ **By Property 3**

$$= 3(625) \quad \text{By Part b}$$
$$= 1875$$

d) $\lim\limits_{x\to5} (3x^4 - 275) = \lim\limits_{x\to5} 3x^4 - \lim\limits_{x\to5} 275$ **By Property 2**

Since $\lim_{x\to5} 3x^4 = 1875$ by part c and $\lim_{x\to5} 275 = 275$ by property 1, the result is

$$\lim_{x\to5}(3x^4 - 275) = 1875 - 275$$
$$= 1600$$

e) $\lim\limits_{x\to5} \sqrt{3x^4 - 275} = \lim\limits_{x\to5}(3x^4 - 275)^{1/2}$

$$= \left[\lim_{x\to5}(3x^4 - 275)\right]^{1/2} \quad \text{By Property 4}$$

Since $\lim_{x\to5}(3x^4 - 275) = 1600$ from part d, then we have

$$\left[\lim_{x\to5}(3x^4 - 275)\right]^{1/2} = 1600^{1/2}$$
$$= 40$$

f) $\lim\limits_{x\to5} \dfrac{\sqrt{3x^4 - 275}}{x^3} = \dfrac{\lim\limits_{x\to5}\sqrt{3x^4 - 275}}{\lim\limits_{x\to5} x^3}$ **By Property 6**

In part e, we determined that $\lim_{x\to5} \sqrt{3x^4 - 275} = 40$. By Property 4 and part a, we determine that $\lim_{x\to5} x^3 = (\lim_{x\to5} x)^3 = 5^3 = 125$. Hence, we obtain

$$\frac{\lim\limits_{x\to5}\sqrt{3x^4 - 275}}{\lim\limits_{x\to5} x^3} = \frac{40}{125} = \frac{8}{25}$$

• **EXAMPLE 9-5** _____

If

$$f(x) = \frac{x^2 - 36}{x - 6}$$

compute $\lim_{x\to6} f(x)$.

Solution

Note that $f(x)$ is not defined at $x = 6$ since $f(6) = (6^2 - 36)/(6 - 6) = 0/0$, which is undefined. However, we can consider $\lim_{x\to6} f(x)$ since the limit as x approaches 6 depends only on values of x *near* 6 without consideration of the value at $x = 6$. To evaluate $\lim_{x\to6} f(x)$, note that if $x \neq 6$,

$$\frac{x^2 - 36}{x - 6} = \frac{(x - 6)(x + 6)}{x - 6}$$
$$= x + 6$$

Hence,

$$\lim_{x\to6} \frac{x^2 - 36}{x - 6} = \lim_{x\to6}(x + 6)$$
$$= 12$$

A graph of $f(x)$ appears in Figure 9-6. Observing this figure, note that the graph of $f(x)$ is the graph of the straight line $y = x + 6$ with the point (6, 12) excluded. The open circle at (6, 12) indicates that this point is excluded from the graph.

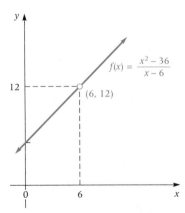

FIGURE 9-6

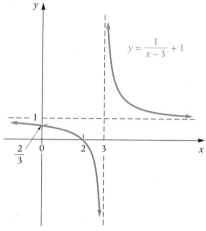

FIGURE 9-7

Infinity and Limits

Consider the function

$$f(x) = \frac{1}{x-3} + 1$$

The graph of this function appears in Figure 9-7. Observing this figure, note that as x takes on larger and larger positive numbers (i.e., as x increases without bound), the value of $f(x)$ approaches 1. (Recall that the horizontal line $y = 1$ is a *horizontal asymptote* in this case.) For such a situation, we say that 1 is the limit of $f(x)$ as x approaches infinity. The statement "x increases without bound" is equivalently expressed in mathematical terms as "x approaches infinity." Infinity is denoted by the symbol ∞. Thus, $x \to \infty$ means that x is increasing without bound (i.e., x exceeds any positive number). Similarly, $x \to -\infty$ means that x is decreasing without bound (i.e., x is getting more and more negative). Therefore, the fact that the values of $f(x)$ of Figure 9-7 approach 1 as x approaches ∞ is written as

$$\lim_{x \to \infty} f(x) = 1$$

Observe also that as x becomes more and more negative (i.e., as x decreases without bound), the value of $f(x)$ approaches 1. Thus, we say that the limit of $f(x)$ as x approaches negative infinity is 1 and write

$$\lim_{x \to -\infty} f(x) = 1$$

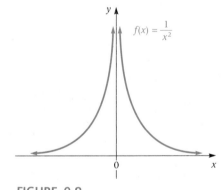

FIGURE 9-8

• **EXAMPLE 9-6** _____

Observe the graph of $f(x) = 1/x^2$ in Figure 9-8. Determine

$$\lim_{x \to -\infty} \frac{1}{x^2}$$

Solution

Since $1/x^2$ approaches 0 as x decreases without bound, we obtain

$$\lim_{x \to -\infty} \frac{1}{x^2} = 0$$

_____ •

Observing Figure 9-8, note that $1/x^2$ approaches 0 as x increases without bound. Thus, we can say

$$\lim_{x \to \infty} \frac{1}{x^2} = 0$$

Similar results would be obtained for the functions $1/x$, $1/x^3$, . . . , $1/x^n$, where n is any positive real number. Thus, we state the following in the box below.

For any positive real number n

$$\lim_{x \to -\infty} \frac{1}{x^n} = 0 \text{ and } \lim_{x \to \infty} \frac{1}{x^n} = 0$$

Also, by limit property 5,

$$\lim_{x \to -\infty} \frac{k}{x^n} = 0 \text{ and } \lim_{x \to \infty} \frac{k}{x^n} = 0$$

for any constant k.

• **EXAMPLE 9-7** _____

Determine

$$\lim_{x \to \infty} \frac{3}{x^2 + 5}$$

Solution

As x increases without bound, so does $x^2 + 5$. Thus, the fraction $3/(x^2 + 5)$ approaches 0 as x approaches ∞. Hence, we have

$$\lim_{x \to \infty} \frac{3}{x^2 + 5} = 0$$

• **EXAMPLE 9-8** _____

Determine

$$\lim_{x \to \infty} \frac{x^2 + 3x}{4x^2 + 9}$$

Solution

Note that as x increases without bound, so do both the numerator and the denominator. To determine the limit of their quotient, we factor out the highest power of x in the numerator and also the highest power of x in the denominator to obtain

$$\frac{x^2 + 3x}{4x^2 + 9} = \frac{x^2 \left(1 + \dfrac{3}{x}\right)}{x^2 \left(4 + \dfrac{9}{x^2}\right)}$$

$$= \frac{1 + \dfrac{3}{x}}{4 + \dfrac{9}{x^2}}$$

Now, as x increases without bound, $3/x$ and $9/x^2$ both approach 0, so the numerator, $1 + 3/x$, approaches 1, and the denominator, $4 + 9/x^2$, approaches 4. Thus, using property 6, we calculate

$$\lim_{x \to \infty} \frac{x^2 + 3x}{4x^2 + 9} = \frac{1}{4}$$

Exercises 9-1

For each of the following functions $f(x)$, determine whether or not $\lim_{x \to 5} f(x)$ exists. If $\lim_{x \to 5} f(x)$ does exist, state its value.

1.

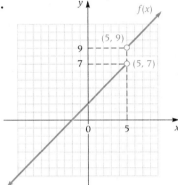

2.

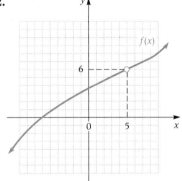

3.

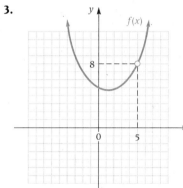

4.

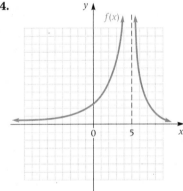

For each of the following functions $h(x)$, determine whether or not $\lim_{x \to 7} h(x)$ exists. If $\lim_{x \to 7} h(x)$ does exist, state its value.

5.

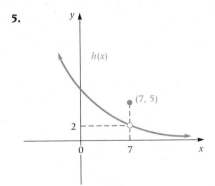

6.

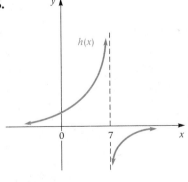

7.

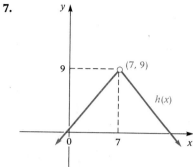

8.

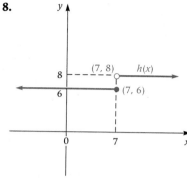

For each of the following functions $f(x)$, determine whether or not $\lim_{x \to \infty} f(x)$ exists. If $\lim_{x \to \infty} f(x)$ does exist, state its value.

9.

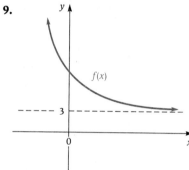

10.

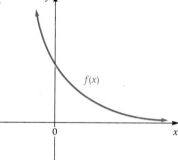

11.

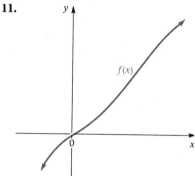

12.

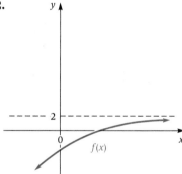

For each of the following functions $g(x)$, determine whether or not $\lim_{x \to -\infty} g(x)$ exists. If $\lim_{x \to -\infty} g(x)$ does exist, state its value.

13.

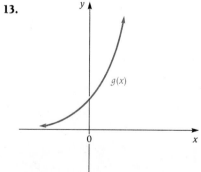

14.

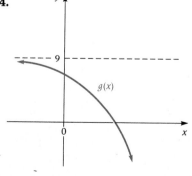

15.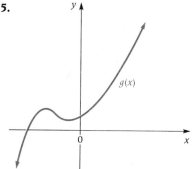

16.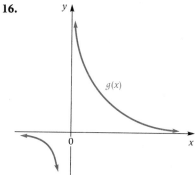

Determine the value of each of the following limits. If the limit does not exist, then state this.

17. $\lim\limits_{x \to 2}(4x + 7)$

18. $\lim\limits_{x \to 1}\dfrac{2x^2 - 2x}{x - 1}$

19. $\lim\limits_{x \to 5}\dfrac{x}{x - 5}$

20. $\lim\limits_{x \to 2}\sqrt{3x^2 + 4}$

21. $\lim\limits_{x \to 0}\dfrac{x^2 - 5x}{x}$

22. $\lim\limits_{x \to 5}\dfrac{x^2 - 25}{x - 5}$

23. $\lim\limits_{x \to 3}\dfrac{x^2 - x - 6}{x - 3}$

24. $\lim\limits_{x \to 8}\dfrac{1}{(x - 8)^2}$

25. $\lim\limits_{x \to \infty}\dfrac{9}{x^3}$

26. $\lim\limits_{x \to \infty}\dfrac{5x^3 - 4x}{2x^3 - 3}$

27. $\lim\limits_{x \to \infty}\dfrac{4}{3x - 7}$

28. $\lim\limits_{x \to \infty}\dfrac{6x^4 - 8x^2}{3x^3 + 2x}$

29. $\lim\limits_{x \to 1}(8x - 5)$

30. $\lim\limits_{x \to 3}\sqrt{5x^2 + 4}$

31. $\lim\limits_{x \to -3}\dfrac{x}{x + 3}$

32. $\lim\limits_{x \to 8}\dfrac{x^2 - 64}{x - 8}$

33. $\lim\limits_{x \to 2}\dfrac{x^2 + 3x - 10}{x - 2}$

34. $\lim\limits_{x \to 5}\dfrac{1}{x^2 - 25}$

35. $\lim\limits_{x \to 0}\dfrac{x^3 - 4x^2 + 5x}{x}$

36. $\lim\limits_{x \to \infty}\dfrac{2x + 3}{x + 7}$

37. $\lim\limits_{x \to -\infty}\dfrac{1}{x^2}$

38. $\lim\limits_{x \to -\infty}\dfrac{5}{x^3}$

39. $\lim\limits_{x \to \infty}\dfrac{3x^2 - 2x}{5x^3 + x}$

40. $\lim\limits_{x \to \infty}\dfrac{5x^3 - 7x}{2x^2 + 3}$

41. Determine whether or not $\lim_{x \to 0} |x|/x$ exists by filling in the table below. If the limit does exist, give its value.

	x approaches 0 from the left.				x approaches 0 from the right.				
x	-2	-1.5	-1	-0.5	-0.0001	0.0001	0.5	1	1.5	2
$f(x) = \dfrac{|x|}{x}$										
	$f(x)$ approaches ?					$f(x)$ approaches ?				

42. Determine whether or not $\lim_{x \to 1} |x - 1|/(x - 1)$ exists by filling in the table below. If the limit does exist, give its value.

	x approaches 1 from the left.				x approaches 1 from the right.			
x	0.25	0.50	0.75	0.95	1.05	1.25	1.50	1.75
$f(x) = \dfrac{|x - 1|}{x - 1}$								
	$f(x)$ approaches ?				$f(x)$ approaches ?			

43. Using a calculator, determine whether or not $\lim_{x \to 4} (\sqrt{x} - 2)/(x - 4)$ exists by filling in the table below. If the limit does exist, give its value.

	x approaches 4 from the left.				x approaches 4 from the right.		
x	3	3.5	3.75	3.95	4.05	4.25	4.5
$f(x) = \dfrac{\sqrt{x} - 2}{x - 4}$							
	$f(x)$ approaches ?				$f(x)$ approaches ?		

44. Using a calculator, determine whether or not $\lim_{x \to 9} (\sqrt{x} - 3)/(x - 9)$ exists. If the limit does exist, give its value.

	x approaches 9 from the left.				x approaches 9 from the right.		
x	8	8.5	8.75	8.95	9.05	9.25	9.5
$f(x) = \dfrac{\sqrt{x} - 3}{x - 9}$							
	$f(x)$ approaches ?				$f(x)$ approaches ?		

45. In Section 3-1, we learned that the expression $(1 + 1/x)^x \to e$ as x gets larger and larger, where e = 2.718281828 to nine decimal places. Thus, we can say

$$\lim_{x \to \infty} (1 + 1/x)^x = e$$

Use a calculator to verify this limit by filling in the following table.

	x approaches ∞				
x	1,000	10,000	100,000	1,000,000	10,000,000
$f(x) = (1 + 1/x)^x$					

f(x) approaches ?

46. Verify that $\lim_{x \to \infty} 1/x = 0$ by filling in the table below. Illustrate graphically.

	x approaches ∞				
x	100	1,000	10,000	100,000	1,000,000
$f(x) = 1/x$					

f(x) approaches ?

47. Verify that $\lim_{x \to \infty} 1/x^2 = 0$ by filling in the table below. Illustrate graphically.

	x approaches ∞				
x	100	1,000	10,000	100,000	1,000,000
$f(x) = 1/x^2$					

f(x) approaches ?

48. *Tax function.* For taxable income, x, where $0 \leq x \leq 155,320$, the amount of federal income tax due for a tax year is given by

$$T(x) = \begin{cases} 0.15x & \text{for } 0 \leq x \leq 30,950 \\ 0.28x - 4023.5 & \text{for } 30,950 < x \leq 74,850 \\ 0.33x - 7766 & \text{for } 74,850 < x \leq 155,320 \end{cases}$$

a) Graph the function $T(x)$.
b) Determine $\lim_{x \to 30,950} T(x)$.
c) Determine $\lim_{x \to 74,850} T(x)$.

49. *Tax function.* For taxable income x, the amount of tax due is given by

$$T(x) = \begin{cases} 0.20x & \text{for } 0 \leq x \leq 40,000 \\ 0.30x - 3800 & \text{for } x > 40,000 \end{cases}$$

a) Graph the function $T(x)$.
b) Determine $\lim_{x \to 40,000} T(x)$.

Computer Exercises

Use a computer to generate a table of x and $f(x)$ values to determine each of the following.

50. $\lim\limits_{x \to 2} \dfrac{x - 2}{x^2 - 4}$

51. $\lim\limits_{x \to 6} \dfrac{x^2 - 36}{x - 6}$

52. $\lim\limits_{x \to \infty} x^{1/x}$

53. $\lim\limits_{x \to 0^+} x^x$

54. $\lim\limits_{x \to 1} \dfrac{x^3 + x^2 - 2x}{x^3 - x}$

55. $\lim\limits_{x \to 3} \dfrac{x^3 + 2x^2 - 15x}{x^3 - x^2 - 6x}$

9-2 • CONTINUITY

Look at the graphs in Figure 9-9. Notice that the graph of $y = x^2$ has no breaks, whereas the graph of $y = 1/(x - 3)^2$ has a break at $x = 3$. Since the graph of the function defined by $y = x^2$ has no breaks, it is said to be continuous at all values of x. In other words, we can trace this graph without lifting our pencil from the paper. Since the graph of the function defined by $y = 1/(x - 3)^2$ has a break at $x = 3$, it is said to be discontinuous at $x = 3$.

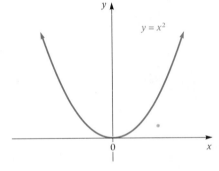

> In general, a function $f(x)$ is **continuous** at $x = a$ if its graph has no break at $x = a$.

This definition is a graphical approach to the concept of continuity. Continuity can be defined in terms of limits. Specifically, a function $f(x)$ is continuous at $x = a$ if

$$\lim_{x \to a} f(x) = f(a)$$

The above statement implies that a function is continuous at $x = a$ if the limit of the function as x approaches a equals the value of the function at $x = a$. This also implies that the function must be defined at $x = a$ and that the limit of the function as x approaches a must exist. We summarize below.

FIGURE 9-9

> **Limits and Continuity**
>
> A function $f(x)$ is continuous at $x = a$ if
>
> 1. $f(a)$ exists.
> 2. $\lim\limits_{x \to a} f(x)$ exists.
> 3. $\lim\limits_{x \to a} f(x) = f(a)$.

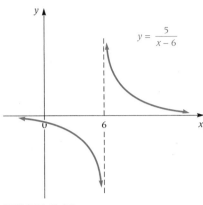

$$y = \frac{5}{x - 6}$$

FIGURE 9-10

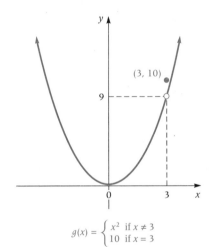

$$g(x) = \begin{cases} x^2 & \text{if } x \neq 3 \\ 10 & \text{if } x = 3 \end{cases}$$

• **EXAMPLE 9-9** _____

Look at the graph of $f(x) = 5/(x - 6)$ in Figure 9-10.

a)   Is $f(x)$ continuous at $x = 8$?
b)   Is $f(x)$ continuous at $x = 6$?

Solutions

a)   The function is continuous at $x = 8$ since its graph has no break at $x = 8$.
b)   The function is not continuous at $x = 6$ since its graph has a break at $x = 6$. In terms of limits, the function is not continuous at $x = 6$ because $f(6)$ is undefined (does not exist). This violates condition 1 of our definition on page 604.

Continuity Over an Interval

Observing the graph of Figure 9-10, note that the function is continuous at all values of x to the right of $x = 6$. Another way of stating this is to say that $f(x)$ *is continuous over the interval* x > 6. Also, note in Figure 9-10, that the function $f(x)$ is continuous at all values of x to the left of $x = 6$. Thus, we say that $f(x)$ *is continuous over the interval* x < 6. Thus, we state the following.

> A function is **continuous over an interval** if it is continuous at each point in the interval.

• **EXAMPLE 9-10** _____

A function is defined as follows:

$$g(x) = \begin{cases} x^2 & \text{if } x \neq 3 \\ 10 & \text{if } x = 3 \end{cases}$$

The graph of $g(x)$ appears in Figure 9-11.

a)   Is $g(x)$ continuous at $x = 2$?
b)   Where is $g(x)$ discontinuous? Where is $g(x)$ continuous?

Solutions

a)   This function is continuous at $x = 2$ since its graph has no break at $x = 2$.
b)   This function is discontinuous at $x = 3$ since its graph has a break at $x = 3$. In terms of limits, $g(x)$ is discontinuous at $x = 3$ because condition 3 of our definition of continuity on page 604 is violated. In other words, $\lim_{x \to 3} g(x) \neq g(3)$ since $\lim_{x \to 3} g(x) = 9$, but $g(3) = 10$. We note that $g(x)$ is continuous over the intervals $x < 3$ and $x > 3$.

• **EXAMPLE 9-11** _____

Where is $f(x) = (x^2 - 4)/(x - 2)$ discontinuous? Since

$$\frac{x^2 - 4}{x - 2} = \frac{(x - 2)(x + 2)}{(x - 2)} = x + 2$$

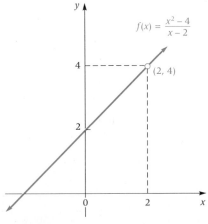

FIGURE 9-12

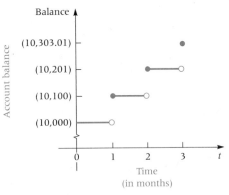

FIGURE 9-13

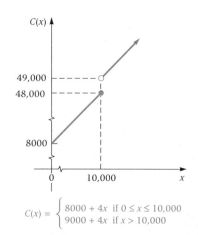

$$C(x) = \begin{cases} 8000 + 4x & \text{if } 0 \le x \le 10{,}000 \\ 9000 + 4x & \text{if } x > 10{,}000 \end{cases}$$

FIGURE 9-14

$f(x) = x + 2$ if $x \ne 2$. The graph of $f(x)$ is the straight line $y = x + 2$ minus the point $(2, 4)$ (see Figure 9-12). Since the graph of $f(x)$ has a break at $x = 2$, $f(x)$ is discontinuous at $x = 2$. In terms of limits, $f(x)$ is discontinuous at $x = 2$ because $f(2)$ is undefined (does not exist). Therefore, condition 1 of our definition of continuity on page 604 is violated. Thus, $g(x)$ is continuous over the intervals $x < 2$ and $x > 2$.

• **EXAMPLE 9-12** **Compound Interest.** ────────────

Ten thousand dollars is deposited into a savings account for 3 months at an interest rate of 12% compounded monthly. The interest rate per compounding period is 12%/12, or 1% per month. A full month must pass before interest is added.

At the end of the first month, the account's balance is

$$10{,}000 + 10{,}000(.01) = \$10{,}100$$

At the end of the second month, the account's balance is

$$10{,}100 + 10{,}100(.01) = \$10{,}201$$

At the end of the third month, the account's balance is

$$10{,}201 + 10{,}201(.01) = \$10{,}303.01$$

A graph of the *account's balance* versus *time, t (in months)*, appears in Figure 9-13. Where is the graph discontinuous?

Solution

Since the graph has breaks at $t = 1$, $t = 2$, and $t = 3$, it is discontinuous at $t = 1$, $t = 2$, and $t = 3$. These discontinuities occur at the end of each month when interest is computed and added to the account's balance.

• **EXAMPLE 9-13** **Cost Analysis.** ────────────

Technic, Inc., manufactures electronic circuitry for computers. For a particular unit, the TE104, there is a variable cost of $4 per unit and a fixed cost of $8000 for the first 10,000 units produced. If the number of units manufactured exceeds 10,000, the fixed cost increases by $1000.

a) Define the cost function.
b) Graph the cost function.
c) Where is the cost function discontinuous?

Solutions

a) If $C(x)$ is the cost of manufacturing x units of TE104,

$$C(x) = \begin{cases} 8000 + 4x & \text{if } 0 \le x \le 10{,}000 \\ 9000 + 4x & \text{if } x > 10{,}000 \end{cases}$$

b) The graph of $C(x)$ appears in Figure 9-14.
c) Since the graph of $C(x)$ has a break at $x = 10{,}000$, then $C(x)$ is discontinuous at $x = 10{,}000$.

──────────────────────────────── •

In the previous section, we stated limit properties, which we used to determine limits of some functions. Similar properties hold for continuity. We state these in the box below.

SUMMARY

Continuity Properties

1. *Constant function.* If $f(x) = k$ where k is a constant, then $f(x)$ is continuous for all x. In other words, a constant function is continuous for all values of x.
2. *Power functions.* Functions of the form $f(x) = x^n$ and $g(x) = \sqrt[n]{x}$, where n is a positive integer, are continuous for all values x of their respective domains.
3. *Sum, difference, and product.* If $f(x)$ and $g(x)$ are continuous at a point, then $f(x) + g(x), f(x) - g(x)$, and $f(x) \cdot g(x)$ are continuous at that point.
4. *Quotient.* If $f(x)$ and $g(x)$ are continuous at a point, then $f(x)/g(x)$ is continuous at that point provided that $g(x) \neq 0$ at the point.

We also include the following statement about continuity regarding polynomial and rational functions. This statement follows directly from the continuity properties.

Continuity for Polynomial and Rational Functions

Any polynomial function is continuous at all values of x. Any rational function is continuous at all values of x, where its denominator does not equal 0.

Exercises 9-2

Which of the following functions are continuous at $x = a$?

1.
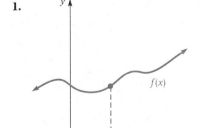

2.
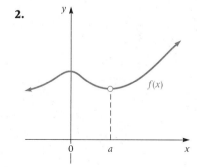

3.

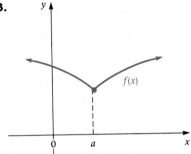

4.

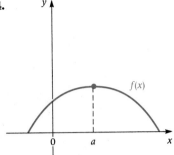

5.

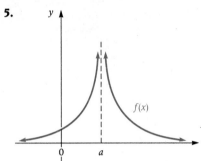

6.

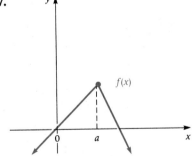

7.

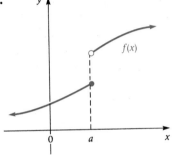

8.

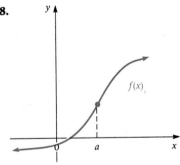

9.

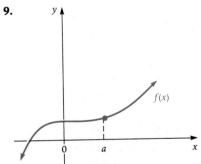

10.

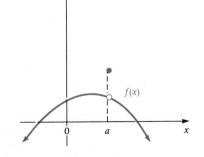

11.

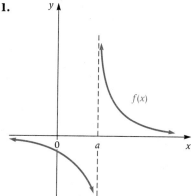

12.

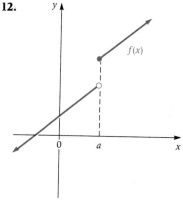

13. Graph $f(x) = 5/x^3$. Where is this function discontinuous?

14. Graph $f(x) = 4/x^2$. Where is this function discontinuous?

15. Graph the following function:

$$f(x) = \begin{cases} x^3 & \text{if } x \neq 2 \\ 10 & \text{if } x = 2 \end{cases}$$

Where is this function discontinuous?

16. Graph the following function:

$$g(x) = \begin{cases} x^4 & \text{if } x \neq 1 \\ 2 & \text{if } x = 1 \end{cases}$$

Where is this function discontinuous?

17. Graph $f(x) = (x^2 - 25)/(x - 5)$. Where is this function discontinuous?

18. Graph $g(x) = (x^2 - 81)/(x + 9)$. Where is this function discontinuous?

19. *Compound interest.* One-hundred thousand dollars is deposited into a savings account for 1 year at 12% compounded quarterly. If interest is added at the end of each quarter,

   a) Find the account's balance for each quarter.

   b) Draw a graph of the account's balance versus time, t (in quarters).

   c) Where is the graph in part b discontinuous?

20. *Cost analysis.* Gameron, Inc., manufactures games for computers. For a particular game, there is a variable cost of $10 per unit and a fixed cost of $20,000 for the first 100,000 units produced. If the number of units produced exceeds 100,000, the fixed cost increases by $5000.

   a) Define the cost function.

   b) Graph the cost function.

   c) Where is the cost function discontinuous?

21. *Cost analysis.* A company makes office supplies. For one of its products, there is a variable cost of $30 per unit and a fixed cost of $40,000 for the first 50,000 units produced. If the number of units produced exceeds 50,000, the fixed cost increases by $10,000.

   a) Define the cost function.

   b) Graph the cost function.

   c) Where is the cost function discontinuous?

22. The **greatest integer function** is defined as:

$$f(x) = [x] = \begin{cases} \text{the greatest integar that} \\ \text{is less than or equal to } x \end{cases}$$

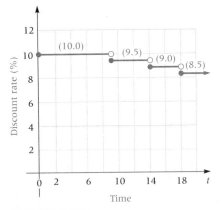

FIGURE 9-15

Specifically, $f(4.73) = [4.73] = 4, f(8.641) = [8.641] = 8,$ and $f(-2.315) = [-2.315] = -3$, etc. For a positive number, x, this function cuts off the decimal portion of x. For a negative non-integer, x, this function associates the next lower integer.

a) Graph $f(x)$ for $-2 \le x \le 4$.
b) Where is this function discontinuous?

23. *Tax function.* Consider the tax function of Figure 9-4.
a) Where is this function discontinuous?
b) Where is this function continuous?

24. *Discount rate.* The interest rate charged by Federal Reserve banks for direct loans to member banks is called the *discount rate*. Figure 9-15 gives a graph of the discount rate for some time period. Where is the function discontinuous?

25. *Chemical production.* A chemical company discovers that the yield, y, of a given chemical process is dependent on its temperature, x (in degrees Celsius), as by the function

$$f(x) = \begin{cases} -(x - 120)^2 + 600 & \text{for } 100 \le x \le 120 \\ -(x - 140)^2 + 1050 & \text{for } 120 < x \le 140 \end{cases}$$

a) Graph $f(x)$.
b) For which value(s) of x is $f(x)$ discontinuous?

9-3 • AVERAGE RATE OF CHANGE

At the same instant that a test driver begins his journey around a track, a stopwatch is started. The function defined by

$$y = f(x) = 10x^2 \qquad (x \ge 0)$$

expresses the total distance, y (in miles), traveled by the driver during the first x hours. Thus, during the first 3 hours, the driver has traveled a total distance of

$$y = f(3) = 10(3)^2 = 90 \text{ miles}$$

During the first 5 hours, the driver has traveled a total distance of

$$y = f(5) = 10(5)^2 = 250 \text{ miles}$$

We now pose the following question:

What is the driver's average speed during the time interval between the end of the third hour and the end of the fifth hour?

Figure 9-16 gives a graph of $y = f(x) = 10x^2$, where $x \ge 0$. Since the driver has traveled 90 miles during the first 3 hours and 250 miles during the first 5 hours, he has traveled

$$\Delta y = 250 - 90 = 160 \text{ miles}$$

during the time interval $\Delta x = 5 - 3 = 2$ from $x = 3$ to $x = 5$ (see Figure 9-16). Dividing by the length of the time interval, we have

$$\frac{\Delta y}{\Delta x} = \frac{250 - 90}{5 - 3} = \frac{160}{2} = 80 \text{ miles per hour}$$

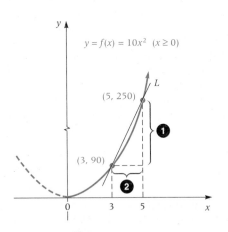

❶ $\Delta y = 250 - 90 = 160$

❷ $\Delta x = 5 - 3 = 2$

$$\frac{\Delta y}{\Delta x} = \frac{160}{2} = 80$$

FIGURE 9-16

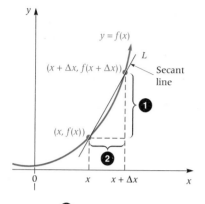

$$\begin{array}{l}\textbf{1}\quad \Delta y = f(x + \Delta x) - f(x)\\[4pt] \textbf{2}\quad \Delta x\end{array}$$

$$\frac{\Delta y}{\Delta x} = \frac{f(x + \Delta x) - f(x)}{\Delta x}$$

FIGURE 9-17

as the **average speed,** or **average rate of change** of distance with respect to time. Note that the average speed (or average rate of change of distance with respect to time) is the slope of the straight line, L, passing through the points $(3, 90)$ and $(5, 250)$ of the graph of $y = f(x) = 10x^2$ in Figure 9-16. Such a straight line intersecting the graph in at least two points is called a **secant line** (Figure 9-17).

In general, the slope of a secant line passing through two points of the graph of a function is the average rate of change of that function over the respective interval. Observing Figure 9-17, note that the secant line passes through the points $(x, f(x))$ and $(x + \Delta x, f(x + \Delta x))$. Thus, the average rate of change of the function $y = f(x)$ over the interval from x to $x + \Delta x$ is given by the expression

$$\frac{f(x + \Delta x) - f(x)}{\Delta x}$$

Note that Δx is the horizontal distance between the two points $(x, f(x))$ and $(x + \Delta x, f(x + \Delta x))$. We summarize below.

Average Rate of Change

The average rate of change of a function $f(x)$ is given by the formula

$$\frac{f(x + \Delta x) - f(x)}{\Delta x} \qquad (\Delta x \neq 0)$$

The above expression, called the **difference quotient,** gives the slope of the secant line passing through $(x, f(x))$ and $(x + \Delta x, f(x + \Delta x))$, as illustrated in Figure 9-17.

We now give a procedure for determining a general formula for the difference quotient for any given function $f(x)$.

To Determine a Formula for the Difference Quotient

Step 1   Given a formula for $f(x)$, replace x with $x + \Delta x$ to obtain

$$f(x + \Delta x)$$

Step 2   Subtract $f(x)$ from the result of step 1 (and simplify) to obtain

$$\Delta y = f(x + \Delta x) - f(x)$$

Step 3   Divide the result of step 2 by Δx (and simplify) to obtain a formula for the difference quotient

$$\frac{\Delta y}{\Delta x} = \frac{f(x + \Delta x) - f(x)}{\Delta x}$$

This result gives a formula for the *average rate of change* for the given function $f(x)$ as we move from x to $x + \Delta x$.

As an example, we compute a formula for the difference quotient (i.e., the average rate of change) of the function defined by

$$y = f(x) = 10x^2$$

Step 1   We replace x with $x + \Delta x$ to obtain

$$
\begin{aligned}
f(x + \Delta x) &= 10(x + \Delta x)^2 \\
&= 10[x^2 + 2x(\Delta x) + (\Delta x)^2] \\
&= 10x^2 + 20x(\Delta x) + 10(\Delta x)^2
\end{aligned}
$$

Step 2   We subtract $f(x)$ from the result of step 1 to obtain

$$
\begin{aligned}
y &= f(x + \Delta x) - f(x) \\
\end{aligned}
$$

$$
= \underbrace{10x^2 + 20x(\Delta x) + 10(\Delta x)^2}_{f(x + \Delta x)} - \underbrace{10x^2}_{f(x)}
$$

$$
= 20x(\Delta x) + 10(\Delta x)^2
$$

Step 3   We divide the result of step 2 by Δx to obtain

$$
\begin{aligned}
\frac{\Delta y}{\Delta x} &= \frac{f(x + \Delta x) - f(x)}{\Delta x} \\
&= \frac{20x(\Delta x) + 10(\Delta x)^2}{\Delta x} \\
&= 20x + 10(\Delta x) \qquad \text{\small\textbf{Formula for Difference Quotient}}
\end{aligned}
$$

This result gives a formula for the *average rate of change* between any two points of the function $f(x)$.

Thus, if we want to determine the average rate of change (that is, the slope of the secant line) between the points $(3, 90)$ and $(5, 250)$ of $f(x) = 10x^2$, we let $x = 3$ and $\Delta x = 5 - 3 = 2$. Then

$$
\begin{aligned}
\frac{\Delta y}{\Delta x} &= 20x + 10(\Delta x) \\
&= 20(3) + 10(2) \\
&= 80
\end{aligned}
$$

is the average rate of change from $x = 3$ to $x + \Delta x = 3 + 2 = 5$. Note that this equals the result previously determined in Figure 9-16.

If $x = 3$ and $\Delta x = 1$, then

$$
\begin{aligned}
\frac{\Delta y}{\Delta x} &= 20x + 10(\Delta x) \\
&= 20(3) + 10(1) \\
&= 70
\end{aligned}
$$

is the average rate of change from $x = 3$ to $x + \Delta x = 3 + 1 = 4$. In other words, during the interval from $x = 3$ to $x = 4$, the average speed was 70 miles per hour. Observe, in Figure 9-18, that this is the slope of the secant line passing through the points $(3, 90)$ and $(4, 160)$.

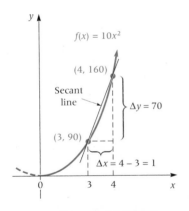

Slope of secant line:
$$\frac{\Delta y}{\Delta x} = 70$$

FIGURE 9-18

• **EXAMPLE 9-14**   **Revenue Function.** _____

The total sales revenue R, gained from selling x units of a product is given by

$$R(x) = -0.2x^2 + 8000x \qquad (0 \le x \le 20{,}000)$$

a) Determine the formula for the average rate of change of sales revenue with respect to x.

b) Use the result of part a to determine the average rate of change of sales revenue with respect to x as x changes from $x = 10{,}000$ to $x = 14{,}000$.

c) Interpret the result of part b.

Solutions

a) The formula for average rate of change (i.e., the difference quotient) is determined by finding

$$\frac{\Delta R}{\Delta x} = \frac{R(x + \Delta x) - R(x)}{\Delta x}$$

This quantity is determined as follows.

Step 1   Replace x in $R(x)$ with $x + \Delta x$ to obtain

$$R(x + \Delta x) = -0.2(x + \Delta x)^2 + 8000(x + \Delta x)$$
$$= -0.2[x^2 + 2x(\Delta x) + (\Delta x)^2] + 8000x + 8000(\Delta x)$$
$$= -0.2x^2 - 0.4x(\Delta x) - 0.2(\Delta x)^2 + 8000x + 8000(\Delta x)$$

Step 2   Subtract $R(x)$ from the result of step 1 to obtain

$$\Delta R = R(x + \Delta x) - R(x)$$

$$\overbrace{= -0.2x^2 - 0.4x(\Delta x) - 0.2(\Delta x)^2 + 8000x + 8000(\Delta x)}^{R(x + \Delta x)}$$

$$\underbrace{- (-0.2x^2 + 8000x)}_{R(x)}$$

$$= -0.4x(\Delta x) - 0.2(\Delta x)^2 + 8000(\Delta x)$$

Step 3   Divide the result of step 2 by Δx to obtain

$$\frac{\Delta R}{\Delta x} = \frac{R(x + \Delta x) - R(x)}{\Delta x}$$
$$= \frac{-0.4x(\Delta x) - 0.2(\Delta x)^2 + 8000(\Delta x)}{\Delta x}$$
$$= -0.4x - 0.2(\Delta x) + 8000 \qquad \text{Formula for Difference Quotient}$$

This result gives the formula for the average rate of change of sales revenue with respect to x.

b) Since x changes from $x = 10{,}000$ to $x = 14{,}000$, then $\Delta x = 14{,}000 - 10{,}000 = 4000$. Substituting $x = 10{,}000$ and $\Delta x = 4000$ into the result of part a gives

$$\frac{\Delta R}{\Delta x} = -0.4x - 0.2(\Delta x) + 8000$$
$$= -0.4(10{,}000) - 0.2(4000) + 8000$$
$$= 3200$$

as the average rate of change of sales revenue with respect to x as x changes from $x = 10{,}000$ to $x = 14{,}000$. This result is illustrated graphically in Figure 9-19. Observe that the average rate of change, 3200, is the slope of the secant line in Figure 9-19.

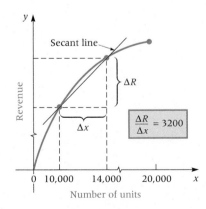

$R(x) = -0.2x^2 + 8000x \quad (0 \le x \le 20{,}000)$

FIGURE 9-19

c) The result of part b is interpreted as follows: As x changes from $x = 10,000$ to $x = 14,000$, an additional unit sold yields \$3200 of sales revenue, on the average.

• ——————————————————————————————————— •

Direct Computation of Average Rate of Change

The average rate of change between two specific points of a function can be computed directly without having to determine the general formula for the difference quotient.

As an example, we return to the function defined by

$$y = f(x) = 10x^2$$

and compute the *average rate of change* from $x = 3$ to $x = 4$. Using the formula

$$\frac{\Delta y}{\Delta x} = \frac{f(x + \Delta x) - f(x)}{\Delta x}$$

we substitute $x = 3$ and $\Delta x = 4 - 3 = 1$ into the above formula to obtain

$$\frac{\Delta y}{\Delta x} = \frac{f(3 + 1) - f(3)}{1}$$

$$= \frac{f(4) - f(3)}{1}$$

Since $f(4) = 10(4^2) = 160$ and $f(3) = 10(3^2) = 90$, the above formula becomes

$$\frac{\Delta y}{\Delta x} = \frac{160 - 90}{1}$$

$$= \frac{70}{1} = 70 \qquad \text{Average Rate of Change}$$

Note that this result agrees with that previously obtained in Figure 9-18.

• **EXAMPLE 9-15** ———————————————————————————————— 🗑

Look at the graph of
$$f(x) = x^3$$
given in Figure 9-20. Use a calculator to compute the slopes of the secant lines corresponding to the respective values of Δx, and write the results in the Table 9-3.

Solutions

For $x = 1$ and $\Delta x = 0.75$,

$$\frac{\Delta y}{\Delta x} = \frac{f(x + \Delta x) - f(x)}{\Delta x}$$

$$= \frac{f(1 + 0.75) - f(1)}{0.75}$$

$$= \frac{f(1.75) - f(1)}{0.75}$$

Calculator
$f(1.75) = (1.75)^3 \approx 5.3594$
$f(1) = (1)^3 = 1$

$$= \frac{5.3594 - 1}{0.75} \approx 5.8125 \qquad \text{Answer}$$

TABLE 9-3

x	Δx	$\dfrac{f(x + \Delta x) - f(x)}{\Delta x}$
1	0.75	
1	0.50	
1	0.25	

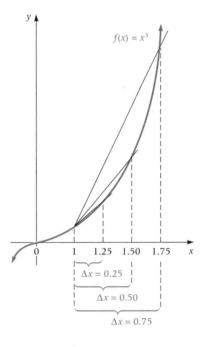

FIGURE 9-20

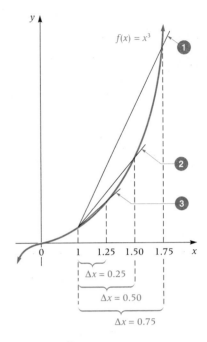

1 Slope = 5.8125

2 Slope = 4.75

3 Slope = 3.8124

FIGURE 9-21

For $x = 1$ and $\Delta x = 0.50$,

$$\frac{\Delta y}{\Delta x} = \frac{f(x + \Delta x) - f(x)}{\Delta x}$$

$$= \frac{\overbrace{f(1 + 0.50)}^{1.5} - f(1)}{0.50}$$

> Calculator
> $f(1.5) = (1.5)^3$
> $= 3.375$

$$= \frac{3.375 - 1}{0.50} = 4.75$$

For $x = 1$ and $\Delta x = 0.25$,

$$\frac{\Delta y}{\Delta x} = \frac{f(x + \Delta x) - f(x)}{\Delta x}$$

$$= \frac{\overbrace{f(1 + 0.25)}^{1.25} - f(1)}{0.25}$$

> Calculator
> $f(1.25) = (1.25)^3$
> ≈ 1.9531

$$\approx \frac{1.9531 - 1}{0.25} = 3.8124 \quad \text{Answer}$$

The above results are entered in Table 9-4 and also in Figure 9-21.

TABLE 9-4

x	Δx	$\dfrac{f(x + \Delta x) - f(x)}{\Delta x}$
1	0.75	5.8125
1	0.50	4.75
1	0.25	3.8124

Exercises 9-3

1. *Prime rate.* The *prime interest rate,* often called the *prime rate,* is the interest rate that banks charge their most credit-worthy borrowers. Table 9-5 gives the prime rate for a succession of weeks during a past time period.

TABLE 9-5

t time (weeks)	1	2	3	4	5	6	7	8	9	10
y prime rate (%)	15¼	16½	16¾	17¼	17¾	18½	19	19½	20	19½

Determine the average rate of change of the prime rate over the time interval from
a) $t = 2$ to $t = 6$.
b) $t = 1$ to $t = 9$.

2. *Medical research.* In a study attempting to measure bodily response to stress, a person's *systolic blood pressure* (SBP) is recorded at 1-minute intervals following a stress-inducing stimulus. The results are given in Table 9-6.

TABLE 9-6

x minutes	1	2	3	4	5	6	7	8	9	10
y SBP	160	200	190	185	180	172	156	150	148	148

Determine the average rate of change in SBP over the interval from
a) $x = 1$ to $x = 2$.
b) $x = 3$ to $x = 8$.

3. *Dow Jones average.* The graph of Figure 9-22 illustrates the Dow Jones industrial average (DJIA) during a past time period. Find the average rate of change of the DJIA over the indicated time interval.

4. *Dow Jones average.* The graph of Figure 9-23 illustrates the Dow Jones industrial average (DJIA) during a past time period. Find the average rate of change of the DJIA over the indicated time interval.

5. *Yield curve.* The graph of Figure 9-24 gives the yields on U.S. Treasury securities of various maturities on a given day. Determine the average rate of change of yield with respect of maturity from
a) $x = 2$ to $x = 10$.
b) $x = ¼$ to $x = 30$.

6. *Yield curve.* The graph of Figure 9-25 gives the yields on U.S. Treasury securities of various maturities on a given day. Determine the average rate of change of yield with respect to maturity from
a) $x = 2$ to $x = 10$.
b) $x = 2$ to $x = 30$.

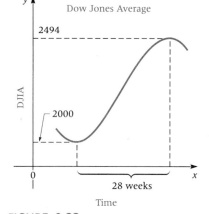

FIGURE 9-22

y ↑
Dow Jones Average
2494
DJIA
2000
0
28 weeks
Time
x

FIGURE 9-23

y ↑
Dow Jones Average
2722
DJIA
1739
0
8 weeks
Time
x

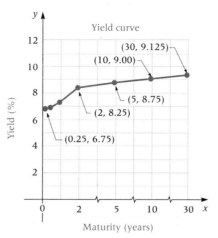

FIGURE 9-24

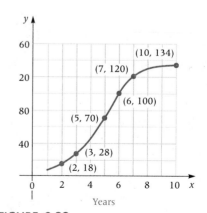

FIGURE 9-25

7. *Inflation rate.* A graph of the annual inflation rate for China is given in Figure 9-26. Determine the average rate of change of the inflation rate from
   a) $x = 3$ to $x = 8$.
   b) $x = 6$ to $x = 8$.
   c) $x = 3$ to $x = 5$.

8. *Learning curve.* The number of nondefectives produced by a newly hired apprentice at Hi-Tech Industries is given in Figure 9-27. Determine the average rate of change of nondefectives from
   a) $x = 2$ to $x = 5$.
   b) $x = 5$ to $x = 10$.

9. *Population growth.* The graph of Figure 9-28 gives the population of a city during a given time period. Determine the average rate of change of the population during the time interval from
   a) $x = 2$ to $x = 6$.
   b) $x = 3$ to $x = 7$.
   c) $x = 5$ to $x = 10$.

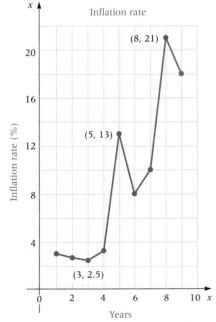

FIGURE 9-26

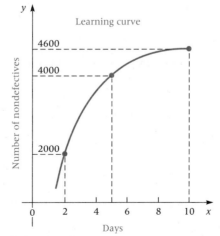

FIGURE 9-27

FIGURE 9-28

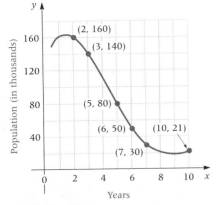

FIGURE 9-29

10. *Population decline.* The graph of Figure 9-29 gives the population of a city during a given time period. Determine the average rate of change of the population during the time interval from
a) $x = 2$ to $x = 5$.
b) $x = 3$ to $x = 7$.
c) $x = 6$ to $x = 10$.

For each of the following, determine the formula for the difference quotient.

11. $f(x) = 3x$ **12.** $f(x) = -6x$
13. $f(x) = -2x + 5$ **14.** $f(x) = 4x - 7$
15. $f(x) = 4x^2$ **16.** $f(x) = -6x^2$
17. $f(x) = x^2 - 5x + 8$ **18.** $f(x) = -2x^2 + 3x$
19. $f(x) = -5x^2 + 9$ **20.** $f(x) = 3x^2 - 4$
21. $f(x) = x^2 - 2x + 1$ **22.** $f(x) = x^2 + 5x - 3$
23. $f(x) = 2x^2 - x + 4$ **24.** $f(x) = -3x^2 + 2x + 1$
25. $f(x) = x^3$ **26.** $f(x) = x^3 - 6x$
27. $f(x) = x^4$ **28.** $f(x) = x^4 - 3x^2 + 1$
29. $f(x) = x^4 + x^2 + 4x$ **30.** $f(x) = x^4 - 2x^2 + 3x$

For each of the following, first determine the formula for the average rate of change of y with respect to x over the interval from x to $x + \Delta x$. Then use this result to calculate the average rate of change over the given interval, and interpret this result graphically.

31. $f(x) = x^2 - 4x + 5$ from $x = 2$ to $x = 6$
32. $f(x) = x^2 - 3x$ from $x = 1$ to $x = 3$
33. $f(x) = 4x + 7$ from $x = 2$ to $x = 3$
34. $f(x) = -2x^2 + 8$ from $x = 1$ to $x = 4$
35. $f(x) = -3x^2 - 2x + 1$ from $x = 2$ to $x = 5$
36. $f(x) = x^3 - 16x$ from $x = 0$ to $x = 2$

37. *Sales revenue.* The Great Glove Company manufactures gloves. Its total sales revenue, R, is given by

$$R = f(x) = x^2 - 6x + 9 \qquad (x \geq 3)$$

where x is the number of pairs of gloves sold. Find the average rate of change of sales revenue with respect to number of pairs of gloves sold over the interval $4 \leq x \leq 6$. Show the graphical interpretation.

38. *Cost.* The total cost of producing x units of some product is given by

$$C(x) = 3x^2 + 80,000 \qquad (0 \leq x \leq 100)$$

Find the average rate of change of cost with respect to the number of units produced as x changes from $x = 50$ to $x = 55$. Interpret graphically.

39. *Cost.* The total cost, C (in millions of dollars), of producing x (in hundreds) units of a product is given by

$$C(x) = 0.5x^2 + 10,000 \qquad (0 \leq x \leq 1000)$$

Find the average rate of change of cost with respect to x as x changes from $x = 200$ to $x = 220$. Interpret graphically.

40. *Projectile.* A ball is projected vertically into the air. The function defined by

$$S(t) = -16t^2 + 192t \qquad (0 \leq t \leq 12)$$

gives the height of the ball (in feet) above the ground at time, t (in seconds). Find the average rate of change of height with respect to time as t changes from $t = 1$ to $t = 4$. Interpret graphically.

41. *Profit.* The profit, P (in millions of dollars), gained from selling x (in thousands) units of a product is given by

$$P(x) = -0.1x^2 + 4x - 30 \qquad (10 \leq x \leq 30)$$

TABLE 9-7

x	Δx	$\dfrac{f(x + \Delta x) - f(x)}{\Delta x}$
2	0.80	
2	0.40	
2	0.20	

TABLE 9-8

x	Δx	$\dfrac{f(x + \Delta x) - f(x)}{\Delta x}$
4	0.75	
4	0.50	
4	0.25	

TABLE 9-9

x	Δx	$\dfrac{f(x + \Delta x) - f(x)}{\Delta x}$
2	0.80	
2	0.40	
2	0.20	

TABLE 9-10

x	Δx	$\dfrac{f(x + \Delta x) - f(x)}{\Delta x}$
1	0.60	
1	0.40	
1	0.20	

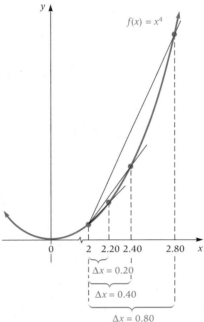

FIGURE 9-30

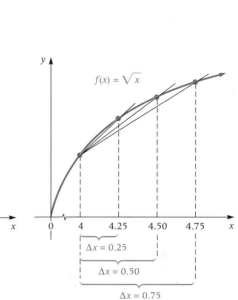

FIGURE 9-31

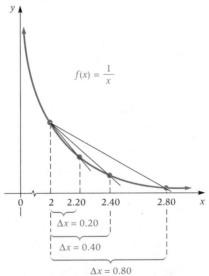

FIGURE 9-32

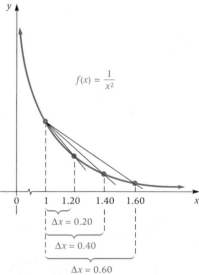

FIGURE 9-33

Find the average rate of change of profit with respect to x as x changes from $x = 12$ to $x = 15$. Interpret graphically.

42. Look at the graph of $f(x) = x^4$, given in Figure 9-30. Use a calculator to compute the slopes of the secant lines corresponding to the respective values of Δx, and write the results in Table 9-7.

43. Look at the graph of $f(x) = \sqrt{x}$, given in Figure 9-31. Use a calculator to compute the slopes of the secant lines corresponding to the respective values of Δx, and write the results in Table 9-8.

44. Look at the graph of $f(x) = 1/x$, given in Figure 9-32. Use a calculator to compute the slopes of the secant lines corresponding to the respective values of Δx, and write the results in Table 9-9.

45. Look at the graph of $f(x) = 1/x^2$, given in Figure 9-33 on page 619. Use a calculator to compute the slopes of the secant lines corresponding to the respective values of Δx, and write the results in Table 9-10.

9-4 • THE DERIVATIVE

In the previous section, we discussed the relationship between the distance, y (in miles), traveled by a driver and the time elapsed, x (in hours). These two quantities are related by the equation

$$y = f(x) = 10x^2 \qquad (x \geq 0)$$

Instantaneous Rate of Change

The formula for the average rate of change of y with respect to x over the interval from x to $x + \Delta x$ is given by

$$\frac{f(x + \Delta x) - f(x)}{\Delta x} = 20x + 10(\Delta x)$$

The average rate of change of y with respect to x when x changes from $x = 3$ to $x = 5$ is determined by substituting $x = 3$ and $\Delta x = 5 - 3 = 2$ into the formula for average rate of change, $20x + 10(\Delta x)$, to give

$$20(3) + 10(2) = 80$$

Thus, the driver's average speed during the time interval from $x = 3$ to $x = 5$ is 80 miles per hour. Graphically, this is the slope of the secant line, passing through $(3, 90)$ and $(5, 250)$ of Figure 9-34.

The driver's average speed (i.e., average rate of change of y with respect to x) during the time interval from $x = 3$ to $x = 4$ is determined by substituting $x = 3$ and $\Delta x = 4 - 3 = 1$ into the formula for average rate of change, $20x + 10(\Delta x)$, to give

$$20(3) + 10(1) = 70$$

Thus, the driver's average speed during the time interval from $x = 3$ to $x = 4$ is 70 miles per hour. Graphically, this is the slope of the secant line M, passing through $(3, 90)$ and $(4, 160)$ in Figure 9-34.

Now what is the driver's speed at $x = 3$? This result is called the **instantaneous speed** or **instantaneous rate of change** of y with respect to x at $x = 3$. It is determined by first calculating a formula for the instantaneous rate of change of y with respect to x at point $(x, f(x))$. This formula is determined by calculating the average rate of change

$$\frac{f(x + \Delta x) - f(x)}{\Delta x} = 20x + 10(\Delta x)$$

letting Δx get very small (i.e., we let $\Delta x \to 0$) to obtain

$$20x + 10(0) = 20x$$

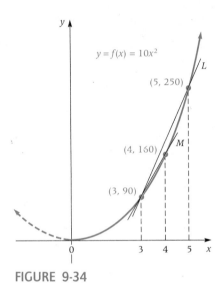

FIGURE 9-34

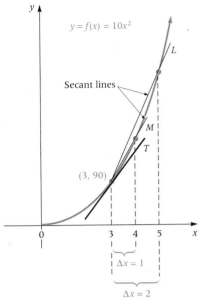

Observe:

As $\Delta x \to 0$, secant lines approach the tangent line T.

$f'(3) = 60$ is the slope of tangent line T.

FIGURE 9-35

This result, $20x$, is called the **derivative** of the function $f(x) = 10x^2$ and is denoted by **$f'(x)$.** Thus, the derivative

$$f'(x) = 20x$$

gives the formula for the instantaneous rate of change of y with respect to x at any point $(x, f(x))$ of the function defined by $y = f(x) = 10x^2$.

To determine the instantaneous rate of change at $x = 3$, we evaluate the derivative at $x = 3$ to obtain

$$f'(3) = 20(3) = 60$$

Thus, the driver's speed at $x = 3$ is 60 miles per hour. That is, at $x = 3$, the car's speedometer reading indicated a speed of 60 miles per hour. Graphically, this is the limit of the slopes of the secant lines L and M in Figure 9-35 as Δx approaches zero. As Δx approaches zero, the slopes of the secant lines L and M approach the slope of tangent line T. Thus, the slope of tangent line T is $f'(3)$, which equals 60. Tangent line T touches the curve $y = 10x^2$ at the point $(3, 90)$.

The instantaneous rate of change of y with respect to x at any point $(x, f(x))$ on the graph of a function $f(x)$ is given by the derivative of $f(x)$. The derivative is denoted by $f'(x)$ and is determined by calculating

$$\frac{f(x + \Delta x) - f(x)}{\Delta x}$$

and letting Δx approach zero (i.e., $\Delta x \to 0$). In other words, the derivative or the instantaneous rate of change of y with respect to x is the limit of the average rate of change as $\Delta x \to 0$ (provided this limit exists). This written as

$$f'(x) = \lim_{\Delta x \to 0} \frac{f(x + \Delta x) - f(x)}{\Delta x}$$

In summary, we state the following.

  SUMMARY

Instantaneous Rate of Change

The **instantaneous rate of change of y with respect to x** at any point $(x, f(x))$ on the graph of a function $y = f(x)$ is given by the **derivative $f'(x)$** which is defined by

$$f'(x) = \lim_{\Delta x \to 0} \frac{f(x + \Delta x) - f(x)}{\Delta x}$$

provided this limit exists. Graphically, the *derivative is the slope of the straight line tangent to the graph of the function at $(x, f(x))$*, as shown in Figure 9-36. The derivative, $f'(x)$, is determined by the following procedure:

Step 1 Calculate the difference quotient

$$\frac{f(x + \Delta x) - f(x)}{\Delta x}$$

continues

SUMMARY—*Continued*

Step 2 Let $\Delta x \to 0$ and calculate the resulting limit.

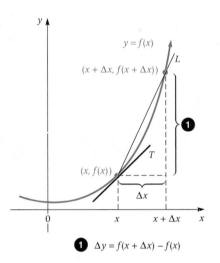

1 $\Delta y = f(x + \Delta x) - f(x)$

> As $\Delta x \to 0$, then
> $$\frac{f(x + \Delta x) - f(x)}{\Delta x} \to f'(x)$$ where $f'(x)$ is the slope of tangent line, T

FIGURE 9-36

• **EXAMPLE 9-16** _____

For the function defined by

$$y = f(x) = x^3$$

a) Calculate $f'(x)$.
b) Determine the instantaneous rate of change of y with respect to x at $x = 2$.
c) Find the equation of the tangent line to the graph of $f(x)$ at $x = 2$.

Solutions

a) **Step 1** Since

$$f(x + \Delta x) = (x + \Delta x)^3$$
$$= x^3 + 3x^2(\Delta x) + 3x(\Delta x)^2 + (\Delta x)^3$$

then

$$\frac{f(x + \Delta x) - f(x)}{\Delta x} = \frac{\overbrace{x^3 + 3x^2(\Delta x) + 3x(\Delta x)^2 + (\Delta x)^3}^{f(x + \Delta x)} - \overbrace{x^3}^{f(x)}}{\Delta x}$$

$$= 3x^2 + 3x(\Delta x) + (\Delta x)^2$$

Step 2 Letting $\Delta x \to 0$, we have

$$f'(x) = 3x^2$$

which we call the derivative of $f(x) = x^3$.

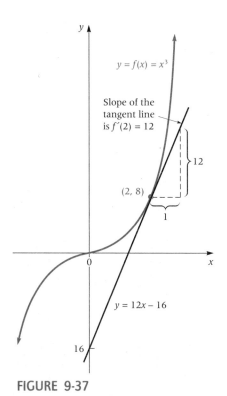

$y = f(x) = x^3$

Slope of the tangent line is $f'(2) = 12$

12

$(2, 8)$

1

0

x

$y = 12x - 16$

16

FIGURE 9-37

TABLE 9-11(a)

x	Δx	$\dfrac{f(x + \Delta x) - f(x)}{\Delta x}$
2	0.1	12.610000
2	0.01	12.060100
2	0.001	12.006001
2	0.0001	12.000600
2	0.00001	12.000014

approaching 12

TABLE 9-11(b)

x	Δx	$\dfrac{f(x + \Delta x) - f(x)}{\Delta x}$
2	−0.1	11.410000
2	−0.01	11.940100
2	−0.001	11.994001
2	−0.0001	11.999397
2	−0.00001	11.999954

approaching 12

b) Evaluating $f'(x)$ at $x = 2$ gives

$$f'(2) = 3(2)^2$$
$$= 12$$

c) The slope of the tangent line at $x = 2$ is given by $f'(2) = 12$, as shown in Figure 9-37. Since $f(2) = 2^3 = 8$, then the point of tangency is $(2, f(2)) = (2, 8)$. Thus, the tangent line passes through $(2, 8)$ and has a slope of 12. Using the slope-intercept form, $y = mx + b$, of the equation of a straight line, we have

$$y = 12x + b$$

We determine b by substituting the coordinates of $(2, 8)$ into this equation and solving for b to obtain

$$8 = 12(2) + b$$
$$b = -16$$

Thus, the equation of the tangent line is $y = 12x - 16$.

Numerical Computation

The derivative of a function at a point can be approximated by numerical computation. As an example, we consider approximating the derivative of

$$f(x) = x^3$$

at $x = 2$ by using a calculator to compute the value of the difference quotient

$$\frac{f(x + \Delta x) - f(x)}{\Delta x}$$

at $x = 2$ and smaller and smaller values of Δx, as illustrated in Table 9-11(a) and (b) and Figure 9-38(a) and (b) on page 624.

Observe that Table 9-11(a) has positive Δx-values, and, therefore, the secant lines are drawn to the right of $x = 2$, as illustrated in Figure 9-38(a). On the other hand, Table 9-11(b) has negative Δx-values, and, therefore, the secant lines are drawn to the left of $x = 2$, as illustrated in Figure 9-38(b). Note that as $\Delta x \to 0$, the difference quotient, $[f(x + \Delta x) - f(x)]/\Delta x$, approaches 12 for both positive and negative Δx-values. Graphically, the slopes of the secant lines to both the *right* and the *left* of $x = 2$ are approaching 12. Recall that this agrees with our previous computation of $f'(2)$ in Example 9-16.

Round-Off Error

Computers are also used to numerically approximate derivatives. We hasten to mention that numerical approximation of derivatives via the difference quotient—whether by calculator or by computer—entails consideration of round-off error. Round-off error is the result of the fact that a computer or calculator stores, processes, and displays numbers to a limited number of significant digits. Although further discussion of this issue is beyond the scope of this text, it should be noted that computer or calculator results of the numerical approximation of derivatives should always be checked for reasonableness.

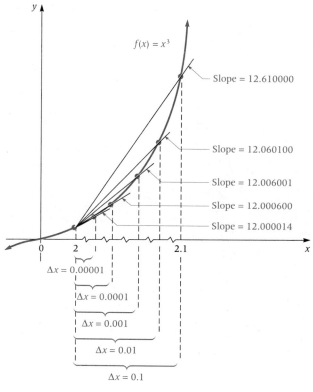

(a)

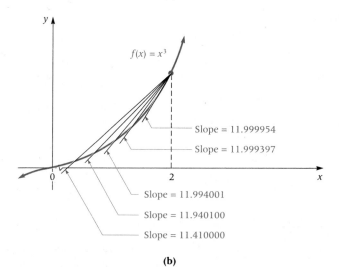

(b)

FIGURE 9-38

Exercises 9-4

For each of the following functions, find the formula for $f'(x)$.

1. $f(x) = x^2$ 2. $f(x) = 4x^2$
3. $f(x) = 6x^3$ 4. $f(x) = x^3$
5. $f(x) = x^4$ 6. $f(x) = -3x^4$
7. $f(x) = 3x$ 8. $f(x) = 5x$
9. $f(x) = x^2 - 5x + 7$ 10. $f(x) = x^2 + 3x + 1$
11. $f(x) = -3x^2 + 4x$ 12. $f(x) = -2x^2 + 6x$
13. $f(x) = 5x^2 + 6$ 14. $f(x) = 3x^2 + 11$
15. $f(x) = x^3 - x^2 + 5x$ 16. $f(x) = x^3 + 2x^2 + 9x$

For each of the following functions, find $f'(1)$, $f'(2)$, and $f'(-2)$.

17. $f(x) = x^2 - 4x + 1$ 18. $f(x) = x^2 + 3x + 2$
19. $f(x) = x^2 + 6x$ 20. $f(x) = x^2 - 4x$
21. $f(x) = -3x^2 + 5$ 22. $f(x) = -2x^2 + 9$
23. $f(x) = x^2 - 5x + 4$ 24. $f(x) = x^2 - 5x + 2$
25. $f(x) = x^3 - 5x^2 + 7$ 26. $f(x) = x^3 - 2x^2 + 5$
27. $f(x) = 2x^3 - 3x^2 + 9$ 28. $f(x) = 4x^3 - 3x^2 + 1$

For each of the following functions, find the instantaneous rate of change of y with respect to x at each of the given points. Illustrate graphically.

29. $y = f(x) = x^2 - 10x$ at $x = 2$ and $x = 3$
30. $y = f(x) = x^3 + 2$ at $x = 3$ and $x = 4$
31. $y = f(x) = 5x + 7$ at $x = 4$ and $x = 5$
32. $y = f(x) = -x^2 + 8$ at $x = 1$ and $x = 3$

Find the derivative of each of the following.

33. $y = f(x) = 3x^2 - 5$
34. $y = f(x) = 2x^3 + 8$
35. $y = f(x) = 5x^2 - 3x + 1$
36. $y = f(x) = 4x - 6$
37. $y = f(x) = x^2 - 3x + 5$
38. $y = f(x) = x^4 - 5$

For each of the following functions, find the instantaneous rate of change of y with respect to x at the given point. Also, find the equation of the tangent line. Then graph the function and its tangent line on the same axis system.

39. $y = f(x) = x^2 - 4x + 5$ at $x = 2$
40. $y = f(x) = x^2 - 3x$ at $x = 1$
41. $y = f(x) = 4x + 7$ at $x = 2$
42. $y = f(x) = -2x^2 + 8$ at $(1, 6)$
43. $y = f(x) = x^2 - 16x$ at $x = 1$
44. $y = f(x) = x^4 - 36x^2$ at $x = 3$

45. *Sales revenue.* The Quality Hat Company manufactures hats. Its total sales revenue, y, is given by

$$y = f(x) = -3x^2 + 60x \qquad (0 \le x \le 20)$$

where x is the number of hats sold.

a) Calculate $f'(x)$
b) Calculate the instantaneous rate of change of sales revenue with respect to the number of hats sold at $x = 3$.
c) Find the equation of the tangent line to the graph of $y = f(x) = -3x^2 + 60x$ at $x = 3$.

Numerical Computation

46. Look at the graph of $f(x) = x^4$ in Figure 9-39 on page 627. Use a calculator to approximate $f'(2)$ by filling in the difference quotient columns of Table 9-12(a) and (b). Draw the graph for Table 9-12(b). As $\Delta x \to 0$, the values of the difference quotient appear to be approaching what number?

TABLE 9-12(a)

x	Δx	$\dfrac{f(x + \Delta x) - f(x)}{\Delta x}$
2	0.1	
2	0.01	
2	0.001	
2	0.0001	
2	0.00001	

TABLE 9-12(b)

x	Δx	$\dfrac{f(x + \Delta x) - f(x)}{\Delta x}$
2	−0.1	
2	−0.01	
2	−0.001	
2	−0.0001	
2	−0.00001	

approaching ?

47. Look at the graph of $f(x) = \sqrt{x}$ in Figure 9-40 on page 627. Use a calculator to approximate $f'(4)$ by filling in the difference quotient columns of Tables 9-13(a) and (b). Draw the graph for Table 9-13(b). As $\Delta x \to 0$, the values of the difference quotient appear to be approaching what number?

TABLE 9-13(a)

x	Δx	$\dfrac{f(x + \Delta x) - f(x)}{\Delta x}$
4	0.1	
4	0.01	
4	0.001	
4	0.0001	
4	0.00001	

TABLE 9-13(b)

x	Δx	$\dfrac{f(x + \Delta x) - f(x)}{\Delta x}$
4	−0.1	
4	−0.01	
4	−0.001	
4	−0.0001	
4	−0.00001	

approaching ?

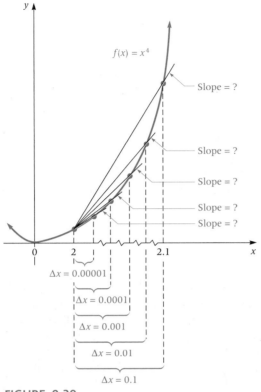

FIGURE 9-39

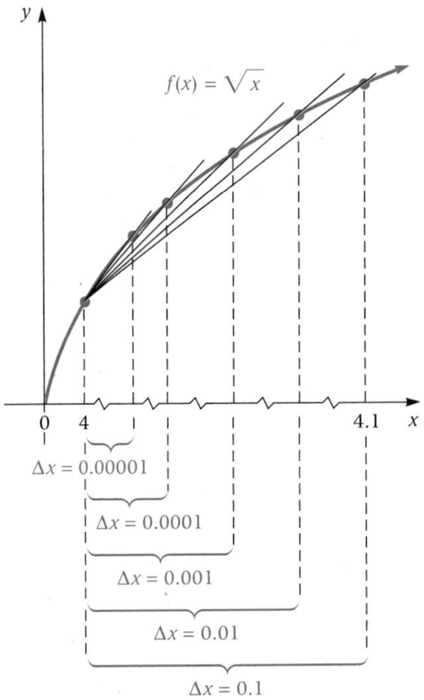

FIGURE 9-40

Computer Exercises

48. If $f(x) = 1/x$, use a computer to approximate $f'(2)$ by filling in the difference quotient columns of Table 9-14(a) and (b).

49. If $f(x) = 1/x^2$, use a computer to approximate $f'(1)$ by filling in the difference quotient columns of Table 9-15 (a) and (b).

TABLE 9-14(a)

x	Δx	$\dfrac{f(x + \Delta x) - f(x)}{\Delta x}$
2	0.1	
2	0.01	
2	0.001	
2	0.0001	
2	0.00001	

TABLE 9-14(b)

x	Δx	$\dfrac{f(x + \Delta x) - f(x)}{\Delta x}$
2	−0.1	
2	−0.01	
2	−0.001	
2	−0.0001	
2	−0.00001	

TABLE 9-15(a)

x	Δx	$\dfrac{f(x + \Delta x) - f(x)}{\Delta x}$
1	0.1	
1	0.01	
1	0.001	
1	0.0001	
1	0.00001	

TABLE 9-15(b)

x	Δx	$\dfrac{f(x + \Delta x) - f(x)}{\Delta x}$
1	−0.1	
1	−0.01	
1	−0.001	
1	−0.0001	
1	−0.00001	

Use a computer to approximate the derivative of each of the following functions at the indicated value of x.

50. $f(x) = 3x + 4$, $x = 5$

51. $f(x) = 7x - 2$, $x = -1$

52. $f(x) = 5x^2 + 3x - 2$, $x = 2$

53. $f(x) = 3x^2 - 2x + 5$, $x = 1$

54. $f(x) = (3x + 4)/(x - 5)$, $x = 1$

55. $f(x) = (4x - 7)/(x + 3)$, $x = 2$

56. $f(x) = \sqrt{5x + 4}$, $x = 1$

57. $f(x) = \sqrt{2x + 10}$, $x = 3$

58. $f(x) = 3/(\sqrt{x} + 5)$, $x = 4$

59. $f(x) = 5/(\sqrt{x} + 8)$, $x = 9$

9-5 • DIFFERENTIABILITY AND CONTINUITY

Up to this point, we have defined the derivative of a function $f(x)$ to be

$$f'(x) = \lim_{\Delta x \to 0} \frac{f(x + \Delta x) - f(x)}{\Delta x}$$

Differentiability

If this limit does not exist at certain values of x, the function $f(x)$ does not have a derivative at those values of x. In general, if a function $f(x)$ has a derivative at $x = a$, then $f(x)$ is said to be **differentiable** at $x = a$.

In this section, we will show situations where a function is not differentiable at a value of x—say, $x = a$. Recall that the derivative of a function $f(x)$ evaluated at $x = a$ is the slope of the tangent line to the graph of the function at $(a, f(a))$. Thus, if the graph of the function has a vertical tangent line at $x = a$, the function is not differentiable at $x = a$ since the slope of a vertical line is undefined.

We summarize as follows.

Differentiability

A function is said to be differentiable at a point if its derivative exists at that point.

Graphical Interpretation. A function is said to be differentiable at a point if its graph has a unique nonvertical tangent line at that point.

As an example, consider the function

$$f(x) = x^{2/3}$$

Its graph appears in Figure 9-41. Observe that the graph of $f(x)$ has unique nonvertical tangent lines at all values of x except $x = 0$. At $x = 0$, notice how the graph of $f(x)$ comes to a sharp point, and, therefore, we can draw many tangent lines, one of which is the (vertical) y-axis. Let us see what happens to the derivative at $x = 0$. Since $f(x) = x^{2/3}$, then, as will be shown in Example 9-20, we determine that

$$f'(x) = \frac{2}{3}x^{-1/3}$$

$$= \frac{2}{3\sqrt[3]{x}}$$

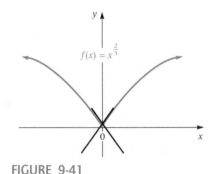

$f(x) = x^{\frac{2}{3}}$

FIGURE 9-41

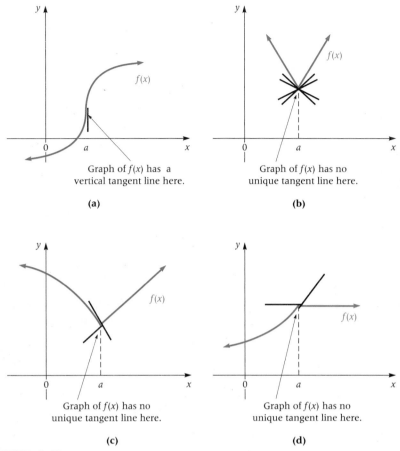

(a)
Graph of $f(x)$ has a vertical tangent line here.

(b)
Graph of $f(x)$ has no unique tangent line here.

(c)
Graph of $f(x)$ has no unique tangent line here.

(d)
Graph of $f(x)$ has no unique tangent line here.

FIGURE 9-42

Hence, we have

$$f'(0) = \frac{2}{3\sqrt[3]{0}} \qquad \text{which is undefined}$$

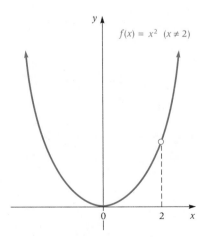

$f(x) = x^2 \ (x \neq 2)$

FIGURE 9-43

Thus, the function $f(x)$ has no derivative at $x = 0$. Observe that $f(x)$ has a derivative at all other values of x since the ratio $2/3\sqrt[3]{x}$ is defined for all values of x except $x = 0$. Figure 9-42(a) contains the graph of another function that has a vertical tangent line at $x = a$ and, thus, is not differentiable at $x = a$.

If the graph of a function has no tangent line at $x = a$, the function is not differentiable at $x = a$. Figures 9-42(b), (c), and (d) contains graphs of functions that do not have tangent lines at $x = a$ and, hence, are not differentiable at $x = a$.

If a function is not defined at a value of x, then it is not differentiable there. Specifically, let us consider the function defined by $f(x) = x^2$ for all values of x except $x = 2$. The graph of this function is the parabola $y = x^2$ excluding the point $(2, 4)$ (see Figure 9-43). Since the point $(2, 4)$ does not belong to the function $f(x)$ as defined, the graph of $f(x)$ has a break at

(2, 4). Thus, we cannot evaluate $f(2)$ to use in the definition of the derivative $f'(x) = \lim_{\Delta x \to 0} [f(x + \Delta x) - f(x)]/\Delta x$. Hence, there is no tangent line to the graph of $f(x)$ at (2, 4), and $f(x)$ is not differentiable there.

Continuity

The graph of Figure 9-43 again brings up the topic of **continuity.** Recall that a function $f(x)$ is continuous at all values of x if its graph has no breaks. Thus, the function in Figure 9-43 is not continuous at $x = 2$, but is continuous at all other values of x.

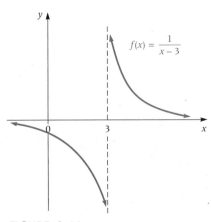

$$f(x) = \frac{1}{x - 3}$$

FIGURE 9-44

Continuity and Differentiability

Observe that the rational function

$$f(x) = \frac{1}{x - 3}$$

whose graph appears in Figure 9-44, is continuous at all values of x except $x = 3$. Note that its derivative (which will be determined in Example 9-34), is

$$f'(x) = \frac{-1}{(x - 3)^2}$$

and is undefined at $x = 3$.

The functions in Figures 9-43 and 9-44 illustrate the fact that if a function $f(x)$ is not continuous at a value of x, then it is not differentiable there. Do not misinterpret this statement by concluding that if a function $f(x)$ is continuous at a value of x, then it is differentiable there. This is not necessarily true. If we observe the graph in Figure 9-41, we see a function, $f(x) = x^{2/3}$, which is continuous at $x = 0$, but not differentiable there. An inspection of the graphs in Figure 9-42 reveals functions continuous at $x = a$, but not differentiable there.

We now state, without proof, the following facts, which are usually proven in more formal calculus texts.

1. If a function is differentiable at a point, then it is continuous at that point.
2. If a function is not continuous at a point, then it is not differentiable at that point.

We now summarize on pages 631-632 situations where a function is not differentiable.

• **EXAMPLE 9-17** _____

For each of the following functions, study its derivative and state where the derivative does not exist. The solutions are given at the bottom of page 632.

Function	*Derivative*

a) $f(x) = (x - 7)^{5/2}$ $f'(x) = \dfrac{5}{2}(\sqrt{x - 7})^3$

b) $f(x) = (8 - x)^{1/5}$ $f'(x) = \dfrac{-1}{5(\sqrt[5]{8 - x})^4}$

continues

SUMMARY

Situations Where a Function Is Not Differentiable
A function is not differentiable
  1. Where the graph of the function has a *sharp point* (see Figure 9-45).

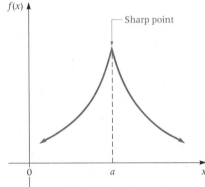

The function does not have a derivative at $x = a$.

FIGURE 9-45

  2. Where the graph of the function has a *vertical tangent line* (see Figure 9-46).

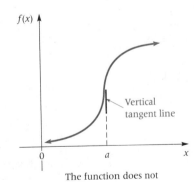

The function does not have a derivative at $x = a$.

FIGURE 9-46

continues

SUMMARY—*Continued*

3. Where the function is *not continuous* (see Figure 9-47).

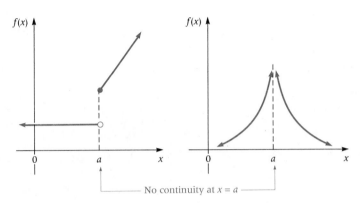

No continuity at $x = a$

Both functions do not have derivatives at $x = a$.

FIGURE 9-47

4. Where the function is *not defined* (see Figure 9-48).

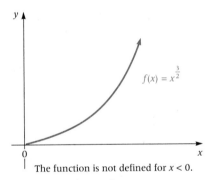

The function is not defined for $x < 0$.

$$f'(x) = \frac{3}{2} x^{\frac{1}{2}} = \frac{3}{2} \sqrt{x}$$

The derivative does not exist for $x < 0$.

FIGURE 9-48

Solutions to Example 9-17

a) Since the square root (or, for that matter, any even root) of a negative number is undefined, the derivative $f'(x) = \frac{5}{2}(\sqrt{x-7})^3$ does not exist at values of x where $x - 7 < 0$. Since $x - 7 < 0$ for $x < 7$, then $f'(x)$ does not exist for $x < 7$.

b) Here the derivative does not exist at values of x where the denominator equals 0. Since this occurs at $x = 8$, then the derivative does not exist at $x = 8$. Note that since the root is an odd root, we do not have to be concerned about where $8 - x$ is negative because an odd root of a negative number does exist.

Exercises 9-5

1. Which of the functions in Figure 9-49 are differentiable at $x = a$?
2. Which of the functions in Figure 9-50 on page 634 are continuous at $x = a$, but not differentiable at $x = a$?
3. Given the function defined by

$$f(x) = \frac{1}{(x - 5)^2}$$

with

$$f'(x) = \frac{-2}{(x - 5)^3}$$

a) Graph $f(x)$.
b) For which value(s) of x is $f(x)$ not continuous?
c) For which value(s) of x is $f(x)$ not differentiable?

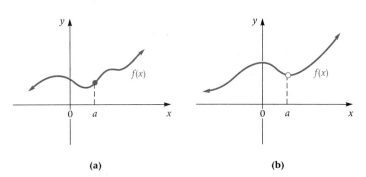

(a) (b)

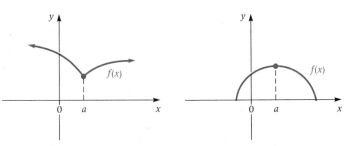

(c) (d)

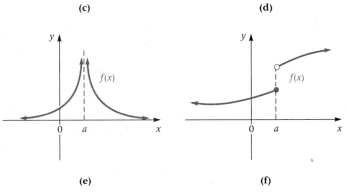

(e) (f)

FIGURE 9-49

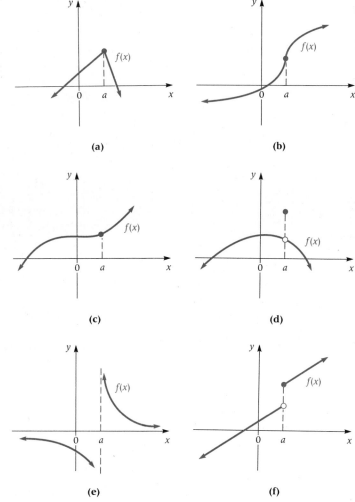

FIGURE 9-50

4. Given the function defined by

$$f(x) = \frac{1}{(x - 3)^2(x + 5)}$$

   with

$$f'(x) = \frac{-(3x + 7)}{(x - 3)^3(x + 5)^2}$$

   a) For which value(s) of x is $f(x)$ not continuous?
   b) For which value(s) of x is $f(x)$ not differentiable?

5. Given the function defined by

$$f(x) = x^{1/3}$$

   with

$$f'(x) = \frac{1}{3\sqrt[3]{x^2}}$$

   For which value(s) of x is $f(x)$ not differentiable?

6. Given that
$$f(x) = \begin{cases} x^2 & \text{if } x \neq 3 \\ 10 & \text{if } x = 3 \end{cases}$$

   a) Graph $f(x)$.
   b) Where is this function discontinuous?
   c) Where is this function not differentiable?

7. Given that
$$f(x) = \begin{cases} x^2 + 5 & \text{if } x \neq 4 \\ 20 & \text{if } x = 4 \end{cases}$$

   a) Graph $f(x)$.
   b) Where is this function discontinuous?
   c) Where is this function not differentiable?

8. Given that $f(x) = (x^2 - 25)/(x - 5)$
   a) Graph $f(x)$.
   b) Where is this function discontinuous?
   c) Where is this function not differentiable?

9. Given that $f(x) = (x^2 - 81)/(x + 9)$
   a) Graph $f(x)$.
   b) Where is this function discontinuous?
   c) Where is this function not differentiable?

10. For what values of x is the absolute value function, $f(x) = |x|$, not differentiable?

For each of the following functions, study its derivative and state where the derivative does not exist.

Function	*Derivative*
11. $f(x) = \sqrt{x - 5}$	$f'(x) = \dfrac{1}{2\sqrt{x - 5}}$
12. $f(x) = \sqrt{x + 3}$	$f'(x) = \dfrac{1}{2\sqrt{x + 3}}$
13. $f(x) = \dfrac{1}{x - 2}$	$f'(x) = \dfrac{-1}{(x - 2)^2}$
14. $f(x) = \dfrac{1}{x - 9}$	$f'(x) = \dfrac{-1}{(x - 9)^2}$
15. $f(x) = \dfrac{x + 5}{x - 1}$	$f'(x) = \dfrac{-6}{(x - 1)^2}$
16. $f(x) = \dfrac{x - 2}{x + 1}$	$f'(x) = \dfrac{3}{(x + 1)^2}$
17. $f(x) = \dfrac{1}{\sqrt{x - 3}}$	$f'(x) = \dfrac{-1}{2\sqrt{(x - 3)^3}}$
18. $f(x) = (2x - 1)^{1/3}$	$f'(x) = \dfrac{2}{3\sqrt[3]{(2x - 1)^2}}$
19. $f(x) = (7 - x)^{4/5}$	$f'(x) = \dfrac{-4}{5\sqrt[5]{7 - x}}$
20. $f(x) = (9 - x)^{1/5}$	$f'(x) = \dfrac{-1}{5\sqrt[5]{(9 - x)^4}}$
21. $f(x) = (4x - 1)^{3/5}$	$f'(x) = \dfrac{12}{5\sqrt[5]{(4x - 1)^2}}$
22. $f(x) = (x + 4)^{3/2}$	$f'(x) = \dfrac{3}{2}\sqrt{x + 4}$
23. $f(x) = (x - 6)^{5/2}$	$f'(x) = \dfrac{5}{2}(\sqrt{x - 6})^3$

9-6

• RULES FOR FINDING DERIVATIVES

Alternative Notations for the Derivative

The derivative of a function $y = f(x)$ is a function that is denoted by the symbol $f'(x)$. Alternative notations are

$$\frac{dy}{dx} \qquad y' \qquad \frac{d}{dx}[f(x)] \qquad D_x y \qquad D_x[f(x)]$$

Thus, the derivative $f'(x) = 20x$ of the function $y = f(x) = 10x^2$ may also be expressed with any of the following notations:

$$\frac{dy}{dx} = 20x \qquad y' = 20x \qquad \frac{d}{dx}(10x^2) = 20x \qquad D_x y = 20x \qquad D_x(10x^2) = 20x$$

Up to this point, we have been calculating derivatives of functions $y = f(x)$ by using the definition of the derivative $f'(x) = \lim_{\Delta x \to 0}[f(x + \Delta x) - f(x)]/\Delta x$. Since this is a tedious process, we will introduce some rules to expedite the calculation of derivatives.

The first rule pertains to calculating the derivative of a function defined by an equation of the form

$$f(x) = k$$

where k is a constant. Such a function is called a **constant function.** Since

$$\frac{f(x + \Delta x) - f(x)}{\Delta x} = \frac{k - k}{\Delta x} = \frac{0}{\Delta x} = 0$$

and $\lim_{\Delta x \to 0}(0) = 0$, then $f'(x) = 0$. Thus, we state the **constant function rule.**

Constant Function Rule

If $f(x) = k$, where k is a constant, then
$$f'(x) = 0$$

The constant function rule states that the derivative of a constant function is 0. Thus, if $f(x) = 5$, then $f'(x) = 0$. If $y = -7$, then $dy/dx = 0$.

Another useful rule pertains to derivatives of functions defined by equations of the form

$$f(x) = x^n$$

where n is a real number. It is called the **power rule** and is stated in the following box. The proof of the case where n is a positive integer appears in Appendix A.

Power Rule

If $f(x) = x^n$, where n is a real number, then

$$f'(x) = nx^{n-1}$$

Note that the derivative of x^n is found by writing the exponent, n, as the coefficient of x with an exponent that is 1 less than n, as illustrated below.

$$f(x) = x^n$$

$$f'(x) = nx^{n-1} \quad \longleftarrow \quad \text{This exponent is 1 less than that of } x^n.$$

The following are illustrations of the use of the power rule:

- If $f(x) = x^3$, then $f'(x) = 3x^{3-1} = 3x^2$.
- If $f(x) = x^6$, then $f'(x) = 6x^{6-1} = 6x^5$.
- If $f(x) = x^{-8}$, then $f'(x) = -8x^{-8-1} = -8x^{-9}$ or $-8/x^9$.
- If $f(x) = x$, then $f'(x) = 1x^{1-1} = 1x^0 = 1$.

• **EXAMPLE 9-18** _____

If $y = f(x) = \sqrt{x}$, find the following.

a) dy/dx

b) $f'(16)$

Solutions

a) Since $y = f(x) = \sqrt{x} = x^{1/2}$, then, using the power rule, we have

$$\frac{dy}{dx} = \frac{1}{2}x^{1/2-1} = \frac{1}{2}x^{-1/2} = \frac{1}{2\sqrt{x}}$$

b) Since $dy/dx = f'(x)$, then

$$f'(16) = \frac{1}{2\sqrt{16}} = \frac{1}{(2)(4)} = \frac{1}{8}$$

• **EXAMPLE 9-19** _____

If $y = 1/x^2$, find dy/dx.

Solution

Since $y = 1/x^2 = x^{-2}$, using the power rule, we have

$$\frac{dy}{dx} = -2x^{-2-1} = -2x^{-3} = \frac{-2}{x^3}$$

• **EXAMPLE 9-20** _____

If $f(x) = x^{2/3}$, find $f'(x)$.

Solution

By the power rule, we calculate

$$f'(x) = \frac{2}{3}x^{2/3-1} = \frac{2}{3}x^{-1/3} = \frac{2}{3\sqrt[3]{x}}$$

Using the power rule, we may easily calculate the derivative of a function of the form $y = x^n$, where n is a real number. However, additional rules are needed if we wish to determine the derivatives of such functions as

$$y = 3x^7$$
$$y = 6x^3 - 4x^2 + 8x - 5$$
$$y = (x^3 + 7)(x^2 - 3x + 5)$$

One such rule, the **constant multiplier rule,** is stated here.

Constant Multiplier Rule

If $y = kf(x)$, where k is a constant and $f'(x)$ exists, then

$$\frac{dy}{dx} = kf'(x)$$

The constant multiplier rule states that the derivative of a constant times a function is the constant times the derivative of the function.

To prove the constant multiplier rule, we let $y(x) = kf(x)$ and note that

$$\frac{dy}{dx} = \lim_{\Delta x \to 0} \frac{y(x + \Delta x) - y(x)}{\Delta x}$$

$$= \lim_{\Delta x \to 0} \frac{kf(x + \Delta x) - kf(x)}{\Delta x}$$

$$= \lim_{\Delta x \to 0} k\frac{f(x + \Delta x) - f(x)}{\Delta x}$$

By limit property 3, this result becomes

$$\frac{dy}{dx} = k \lim_{\Delta x \to 0} \frac{f(x + \Delta x) - f(x)}{\Delta x}$$

$$= kf'(x)$$

As previously stated, the constant multiplier rule states that if a function, $f(x)$, is multiplied by a constant, k, then the derivative of the new function, $kf(x)$, is k times the derivative of the original function.

Thus, if $y = 3x^7$, we have

$$\frac{dy}{dx} = 3(7x^6) = 21x^6$$

• **EXAMPLE 9-21**

If $f(x) = 6/x^3$, find $f'(x)$.

Solution

Since $f(x) = 6x^{-3}$, then by the constant multiplier rule and the power rule,

$$f'(x) = 6(-3x^{-3-1}) = -18x^{-4} = \frac{-18}{x^4}$$

Another useful rule for finding derivatives, the **sum or difference rule,** is stated here.

> **Sum or Difference Rule**
>
> If $y = f(x) \pm g(x)$, where $f(x)$ and $g(x)$ are differentiable functions at x, then
>
> $$\frac{dy}{dx} = f'(x) \pm g'(x)$$

The sum or difference rule states that the derivative of a sum or a difference of two functions is the sum or difference of their derivatives. It may be generalized to more than two functions.

Thus, the function

$$y = 6x^4 + 8x^2$$

is of the form

$$y = f(x) + g(x)$$

with $f(x) = 6x^4$ and $g(x) = 8x^2$. Since $f'(x) = 24x^3$ and $g'(x) = 16x$, then according to the sum rule,

$$\frac{dy}{dx} = f'(x) + g'(x)$$

$$= 24x^3 + 16x$$

To prove the sum or difference rule, we let $y(x) = f(x) \pm g(x)$ and note that

$$\frac{dy}{dx} = \lim_{\Delta x \to 0} \frac{y(x + \Delta x) - y(x)}{\Delta x}$$

$$= \lim_{\Delta x \to 0} \frac{[f(x + \Delta x) \pm g(x + \Delta x)] - [f(x) \pm g(x)]}{\Delta x}$$

$$= \lim_{\Delta x \to 0} \frac{[f(x + \Delta x) - f(x)] \pm [g(x + \Delta x) - g(x)]}{\Delta x}$$

$$= \lim_{\Delta x \to 0} \left[\frac{f(x + \Delta x) - f(x)}{\Delta x} \pm \frac{g(x + \Delta x) - g(x)}{\Delta x} \right]$$

By limit property 2, this result becomes

$$\frac{dy}{dx} = \lim_{\Delta x \to 0} \frac{f(x + \Delta x) - f(x)}{\Delta x} \pm \lim_{\Delta x \to 0} \frac{g(x + \Delta x) - g(x)}{\Delta x}$$

$$= f'(x) \pm g'(x)$$

• **EXAMPLE 9-22** ―――――――――――――――――――

If $y = x^3 - 4x^2 + 15x - 10$, find dy/dx.

Solution

$$\frac{dy}{dx} = \frac{d}{dx}(x^3) + \frac{d}{dx}(-4x^2) + \frac{d}{dx}(15x) + \frac{d}{dx}(-10)$$
$$= 3x^2 - 8x + 15 + 0$$
$$= 3x^2 - 8x + 15$$

• **EXAMPLE 9-23** ―――――――――――――――――――

If

$$y = x^5 - 8x^2 + \frac{6}{x^2} + 50$$

find dy/dx.

Solution

First rewrite the equation as

$$y = x^5 - 8x^2 + 6x^{-2} + 50$$

Then

$$\frac{dy}{dx} = \frac{d}{dx}(x^5) + \frac{d}{dx}(-8x^2) + \frac{d}{dx}(6x^{-2}) + \frac{d}{dx}(50)$$
$$= 5x^4 - 16x - 12x^{-3} + 0$$
$$= 5x^4 - 16x - \frac{12}{x^3}$$

• **EXAMPLE 9-24** ―――――――――――――――――――

Find the equation of the tangent line to $f(x) = 3x^2 - 12x + 13$ at $x = 3$.

Solution

The slope of the tangent line for $x = 3$ is given by $f'(3)$. Calculating $f'(x)$, we have

$$f'(x) = 6x - 12 \qquad \text{Derivative of function}$$

Hence,

$$f'(3) = 6(3) - 12$$
$$= 6 \qquad \text{Slope of tangent line}$$

The point of tangency is $(3, f(3))$. Since

$$f(3) = 3(3)^2 - 12(3) + 13$$
$$= 4 \qquad y\text{-Coordinate of point of tangency}$$

the point of tangency is $(3, 4)$. Using the slope-intercept form, $y = mx + b$, of the equation of a straight line, we have

$$y = 6x + b$$

We determine b by substituting the coordinates of $(3, 4)$ into this equation and solving for b to obtain

$$4 = 6(3) + b$$
$$b = -14$$

Thus, the equation of the tangent line is $y = 6x - 14$ (see Figure 9-51). We could have found the equation of the tangent line by using the point-slope form. This method is used in Example 9-26.

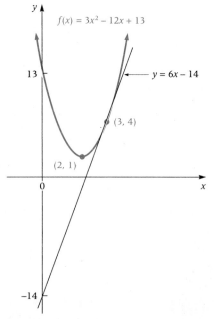

FIGURE 9-51

Notation

Given that $y = f(x) = 3x^2 - 4x + 5$, the instantaneous rate of change of y with respect to x is given by $f'(x)$ or

$$\frac{dy}{dx} = 6x - 4$$

If we wish to evaluate dy/dx [or $f'(x)$] at $x = 3$, this is indicated by $f'(3)$ or, alternatively, by

$$\frac{dy}{dx}\bigg|_{x=3} = 6(3) - 4 = 14$$

Thus, given a function $y = f(x)$, its derivative evaluated at $x = a$ is given by either

$$f'(a) \quad \text{or} \quad \frac{dy}{dx}\bigg|_{x=a}$$

sometimes letters other than x and y appear in equations. If $q = z^3 + 8z^2 + 10z + 9$, then the *instantaneous rate of change of q with respect to z* is given by dq/dz where

$$\frac{dq}{dz} = \frac{d}{dz}(z^3) + \frac{d}{dz}(8z^2) + \frac{d}{dz}(10z) + \frac{d}{dz}(9)$$

$$= 3z^2 + 16z + 10 + 0$$

$$= 3z^2 + 16z + 10$$

• **EXAMPLE 9-25** _____

A ball moves in the path of a straight line. The distance, S (in feet), of the ball from its starting point after t seconds have elapsed is given by

$$S = -3t^2 + 48t \quad (0 \le t \le 16)$$

a) Find the formula giving the ball's instantaneous speed.
b) Find the ball's instantaneous speed at $t = 2$.

Solutions

a) The ball's instantaneous speed is given by the rate of change of distance with respect to time or ds/dt.

$$\frac{ds}{dt} = \frac{d}{dt}(-3t^2) + \frac{d}{dt}(48t)$$

$$= -6t + 48$$

b) $\dfrac{ds}{dt}\bigg|_{t=2} = -6(2) + 48 = 36$

Thus, at $t = 2$, the ball's instantaneous speed is 36 feet per second.

• **EXAMPLE 9-26** **Investment Portfolio.** _____

The value, y (in millions of dollars), of an investment portfolio is related to time, x (in years), since inception by the equation

$$y = f(x) = 5x^2 \quad (x \ge 0)$$

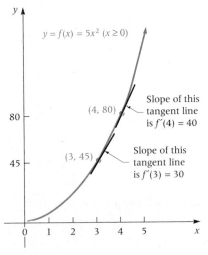

FIGURE 9-52

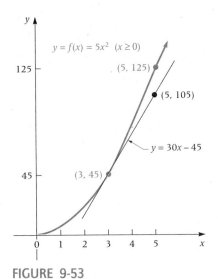

FIGURE 9-53

a) Calculate $f'(x)$.

b) Determine the instantaneous rate of change of value with respect to time at $x = 3$ and at $x = 4$. Illustrate these results graphically. Is the instantaneous rate of change the same for each year?

c) If the instantaneous rate of change of value with respect to time were to remain constant for $x \geq 3$, determine the portfolio's value at $x = 5$. (This is, of course, a different portfolio for $x > 3$ than the original.)

Solutions

a) $f'(x) = 10x$

b) Since $f'(3) = 10(3) = 30$, the portfolio's value is increasing at the rate of $30 million per year at $x = 3$.

Since $f'(4) = 10(4) = 40$, the portfolio's value is increasing at the rate of $40 million per year at $x = 4$.

The rate of change is not the same for each year. These results are graphically illustrated in Figure 9-52.

c) If the rate of change of value with respect to time were to remain constant for $x \geq 3$, then the new portfolio's value will be given by the equation of the tangent line in Figure 9-53 for $x \geq 3$. The slope of the tangent line at $x = 3$ is given by $f'(3) = 30$. Since $f(3) = 5(3^2) = 45$, then the point of tangency is $(3, f(3)) = (3, 45)$. Thus, the tangent line passes through $(3, 45)$ and has a slope of 30.

Using the point-slope form of the equation of a straight line

$$y - y_1 = m(x - x_1)$$

where $m = 30$ and $(x_1, y_1) = (3, 45)$

we have

$$y - 45 = 30(x - 3) \qquad \text{Point-slope form}$$

Solving for y gives the slope-intercept form. Hence,

$$y - 45 = 30x - 90$$
$$y = 30x - 45 \qquad \text{Equation of tangent line}$$

Thus, the equation of the tangent line is $y = 30x - 45$.

The new portfolio's value at $x = 5$ is determined by substituting 5 into the equation of the tangent line to yield

$$y = 30(5) - 45$$
$$= 105$$

Thus, if the instantaneous rate of change of value with respect to time remains constant for $x \geq 3$, the new portfolio's value at $x = 5$ is $105 million. If the instantaneous rate of change does not remain constant, but varies according to the derivative, then the original portfolio's value at $x = 5$ is $125 million (i.e., $f(5) = 5(5^2) = 125$), as shown in Figure 9-53.

$\bullet$

Marginal Cost and Marginal Revenue

Suppose the total cost of producing x units of some commodity is given by the cost function

$$C(x) = -0.01x^2 + x + 175 \qquad (0 \leq x \leq 50)$$

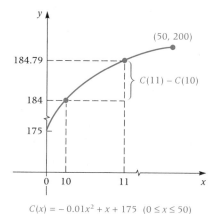

$C(x) = -0.01x^2 + x + 175 \quad (0 \le x \le 50)$

FIGURE 9-54

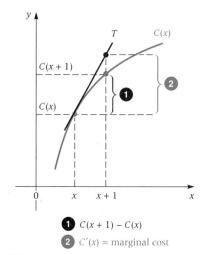

① $C(x + 1) - C(x)$
② $C'(x) =$ marginal cost

FIGURE 9-55

Then the total cost of producing 10 units is

$$C(10) = -0.01(10)^2 + 10 + 175$$
$$= \$184$$

Thus, at production level $x = 10$, the total cost is \$184.

If we want to determine the additional cost of producing 1 more unit at production level $x = 10$, we must calculate the total cost of producing $10 + 1 = 11$ units and subtract from this result the total cost of producing 10 units. Hence, we find

$$C(11) = -0.01(11)^2 + 11 + 175$$
$$= \$184.79$$

And the additional cost of producing 1 more unit is

$$C(11) - C(10) = 184.79 - 184$$
$$= \$0.79$$

Observing Figure 9-54, note that $C(11) - C(10)$ is the *vertical distance* between the points $(10, 184)$ and $(11, 184.79)$ of the cost function.

In general, for a cost function, $C(x)$, the additional cost of producing *1 more unit* at production level x is

$$C(x + 1) - C(x)$$

In practice, this quantity is usually approximated by the derivative $C'(x)$, which is called the **marginal cost.** Observing Figure 9-55, note that the marginal cost, $C'(x)$, is the slope of the tangent line, T. However, since the horizontal distance between x and $x + 1$ is 1, then $C'(x)$ is the vertical distance indicated. Note that $C'(x)$ is an approximation of $C(x + 1) - C(x)$. Thus, returning to the cost function

$$C(x) = -0.01x^2 + x + 175$$

the marginal cost at production level $x = 10$ is $C'(10)$ and is determined by

$$C'(x) = -0.02x + 1$$
$$C'(10) = -0.02(10) + 1$$
$$= \$0.80$$

Thus, at production level $x = 10$, 1 more unit costs approximately \$0.80.

Similarly, given a revenue function, $R(x)$, its derivative, $R'(x)$, is called the **marginal revenue.** It approximates the quantity $R(x + 1) - R(x)$, which is the additional revenue derived from producing and selling 1 more unit.

We summarize in the following boxes.

SUMMARY

Marginal Cost

If

$C(x)$ = the *total cost* of producing x units of some product

then its derivative,

$C'(x)$ = the *marginal cost*

which is the approximate cost of producing 1 more unit when the production level is x units. The graphical interpretation appears in Figure 9-56.

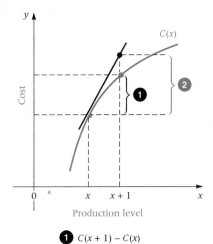

① $C(x + 1) - C(x)$

② $C'(x)$ = marginal cost

FIGURE 9-56

SUMMARY

Marginal Revenue

If

$R(x)$ = the *total revenue* gained from selling x units of some product

then its derivative,

$R'(x)$ = the *marginal revenue*

which is the approximate revenue gained from selling 1 more unit when the sales level is x units. The graphical interpretation appears in Figure 9-57.

continues

SUMMARY—*Continued*

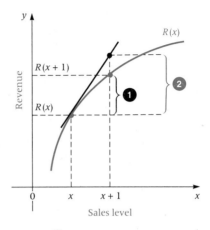

1 $R(x + 1) - R(x)$

2 $R'(x)$ = marginal revenue

FIGURE 9-57

Comment. Given a demand equation

$$p = f(x)$$

where p denotes the unit price of some product and x denotes the number of units demanded, the equation for total sales revenue is given by

$$R(x) = \text{(number of units sold)}\text{(unit price)}$$

$$= xp$$

$$R(x) = x \cdot f(x)$$

Replace p with $f(x)$ from the demand equation $p = f(x)$.

• **EXAMPLE 9-27** _____

The total cost of producing x units of some product is given by

$$C(x) = -0.02x^2 + 4x + 8000 \qquad (0 \le x \le 100)$$

a) Find the equation for marginal cost.

b) Find the marginal cost at a production level of $x = 60$ units. Interpret the result.

Solutions

a) The equation for marginal cost is given by

$$C'(x) = -0.04x + 4$$

b) The marginal cost at $x = 60$ is

$$C'(60) = -0.04(60) + 4$$
$$= \$1.60$$

Thus, at production level $x = 60$, 1 more unit costs approximately $1.60.

• **EXAMPLE 9-28** _____

Given the demand equation

$$p = -x + 10 \qquad (0 \le x \le 10)$$

where p denotes the unit selling price and x denotes the number of units demanded of some product,

a) Determine the equation for total sales revenue, $R(x)$.
b) Determine the equation for marginal revenue.
c) Determine the marginal revenue at sales level $x = 3$ units. Interpret the result.

Solutions

a) The *total sales revenue* is given by

$$R(x) = (\text{number of units sold})(\text{unit price})$$

$$= xp$$
$$= x(-x + 10)$$

From the demand equation $p = -x + 10$

$$R(x) = -x^2 + 10x \qquad (0 \le x \le 10)$$

b) The equation for *marginal revenue* is given by

$$R'(x) = -2x + 10$$

c) The *marginal revenue at* $x = 3$ is given by

$$R'(3) = -2(3) + 10$$
$$= \$4$$

Thus, at sales level $x = 3$ units, approximately \$4 of revenue is gained from selling 1 more unit.

_____

Exercises 9-6

For each of the following, find dy/dx.

1. $y = x^3$ **2.** $y = x^{10}$ **3.** $y = x^{20}$
4. $y = x^{1/5}$ **5.** $y = 4x$ **6.** $y = x^{-3}$
7. $y = 1/x^6$ **8.** $y = 1/x$ **9.** $y = x^5$
10. $y = x^9$ **11.** $y = 1/x^3$ **12.** $y = 1/\sqrt{x^5}$
13. $y = x^{-1/4}$ **14.** $y = -40$ **15.** $y = 6$

For each of the following, find $f'(x)$.

16. $f(x) = x^5$ **17.** $f(x) = -x^8$
18. $f(x) = 4x^2$ **19.** $f(x) = -3/x^2$
20. $f(x) = 4/x$ **21.** $f(x) = 5/\sqrt{x^3}$
22. $f(x) = -2/(\sqrt[3]{x})^4$ **23.** $f(x) = 1/6$

For each of the following, find $f'(4)$.

24. $f(x) = 3\sqrt{x}$ **25.** $f(x) = 5/\sqrt{x}$
26. $f(x) = -2/\sqrt{x^3}$ **27.** $f(x) = 8\sqrt{x^3}$
28. $f(x) = 5/x^2$ **29.** $f(x) = -2/x^3$

For each of the following, find dy/dx.

30. $y = 3x^2 - 2x + 5$

31. $y = x^2 - 8x$

32. $y = -4x^2 + 6$

33. $y = 8x^2 + 10$

34. $y = x^3 + 4x^2 + 1$

35. $y = x^3 + 2x^2 + 9$

Find the derivative of each of the following.

36. $f(x) = 5x^7 - 8x^3 + 6x - 8$

37. $y = x^6 - x^5 + 4/x^2 + 9$

38. $f(x) = -8x^3 + 6x^2 - 6x + 9$

39. $y = -5x^3 - 6x^2 + 8x - 4$

40. $y = x(x^3 - 4x^2 + 3x - 8)$

41. $y = x^3(x^2 - 6x + 8)$

Find each of the following.

42. $\dfrac{d}{dx}(4x^2 - 5)$

43. $\dfrac{d}{dx}(3x^2 + 7)$

44. $\dfrac{d}{dx}(5x^2 + 2)$

45. $\dfrac{d}{dx}(-2x^2 + 1)$

46. $\dfrac{d}{dx}(8x^2 - 3)$

47. $\dfrac{d}{dx}(-3x^3 + 4)$

48. $\dfrac{d}{dx}(x^2 - 2x)$

49. $\dfrac{d}{dx}(x^3 - 4x^2 + 5)$

50. $\dfrac{d}{dx}(\sqrt{x} + 1/x)$

51. $\dfrac{d}{dx}(1/\sqrt{x} + 4\sqrt{x})$

Determine each of the following.

52. $\dfrac{d}{dt}(t^3 - t^2 + 8)$

53. $\dfrac{d}{dt}(-3t^2 + 8t + 7)$

54. $\dfrac{d}{dz}(z^4 - 8z^2 + 1)$

55. $\dfrac{d}{dw}(w^3 - 5w + 8)$

For each of the following, find $\dfrac{dy}{dx}\Big|_{x=1}$.

56. $y = x^2 - 3x + 5$

57. $y = -2x^3 + 4x$

58. $y = 3\sqrt{x} + 4$

59. $y = -6/\sqrt{x} + 7$

For each of the following, find $\dfrac{dy}{dx}\Big|_{x=4}$.

60. $y = 4x^2 - 8x + 5$

61. $y = -3x^3 + 7x$

62. $y = 6x^2 - \sqrt{x}$

63. $y = \sqrt{x} - 4/\sqrt{x}$

Determine y' for each of the following.

64. $y = 8x^2 - 3x + 5$

65. $y = -3x^2 + 2x + 1$

66. $y = -x^3 - 2x^2 + 5x + 1$

67. $y = x^3 + 6x^2 + 8x + 7$

68. $y = x^4 - 5x^2 - 7x + 8$

69. $y = x^5 - 6x^3 + 6x + 5$

Determine each of the following.

70. $D_x(30x^3)$

71. $D_x(5x^{10})$

72. $D_x(9/x^4)$

73. $D_x(-3/x^2)$

74. $D_x(8x^2 - 4x + 6)$

75. $D_x(4x^3 - 6x^2 + 4x + 8)$

76. Find the equation of the tangent line to $f(x) = x^2 - 10x + 28$ at $x = 7$. Illustrate graphically.

77. Find the equation of the tangent line to $f(x) = 2x^3 + 5$ at $x = 1$. Illustrate graphically.

78. Find the equation of the tangent line to $f(x) = -3x^2 + 18x$ at $x = 4$. Illustrate graphically.

Applications

79. *Annual profits.* A company's annual profit, P, is related to time, x, by the equation

$$P(x) = 0.03x^2 + 5 \qquad (x \geq 0)$$

where $P(x)$ is the profit (in millions of dollars) for the xth year the company has been operating.
a) Find the rate of change of profit at the second year. Interpret the result.
b) Find the rate of change of profit at $x = 3$. Interpret the result.
c) If the rate of change of profit remains constant at and beyond the third year, find the equation relating P and x for $x \geq 3$. Calculate the profit for the seventh year.

80. *Investment portfolio.* The value, y (in millions of dollars), of an investment portfolio is related to time, x (in years), since inception by the equation

$$y = f(x) = 4x^2 \qquad (x \geq 0)$$

a) Calculate $f'(x)$.
b) Determine the instantaneous rate of change of value with respect to time at $x = 2$ and at $x = 3$. Illustrate these results graphically. Is the instantaneous rate of change the same for each year?
c) If the instantaneous rate of change of value with respect to time were to remain constant for $x \geq 2$, determine the portfolio's value at $x = 4$. (We are assuming a different portfolio for $x > 2$ than the original.)

81. *Investment portfolio.* The value, y (in millions of dollars), of an investment portfolio is related to time, x (in years), since inception by the equation

$$y = f(x) = 6x^2 \qquad (x \geq 0)$$

a) Calculate $f'(x)$.
b) Determine the instantaneous rate of change of value with respect to time at $x = 2$ and at $x = 3$. Illustrate these results graphically. Is the rate of change the same for each year?
c) If the rate of change of value with respect to time remains constant for $x \geq 3$, determine the portfolio's value at $x = 5$. (We are assuming a different portfolio for $x > 3$ than the original.)

82. *Production cost.* The cost of producing x units of some commodity is given by the cost function defined by

$$C(x) = 5x^2 + 100 \qquad (x \geq 0)$$

a) Find the equation for marginal cost.
b) Find the marginal cost at $x = 3$. Interpret the result.
c) Illustrate the graphical interpretation of the answer to part b.

83. *Sales revenue.* The revenue derived from selling x units of some item is given by the revenue function defined by

$$R(x) = -2x^2 + 60x \qquad (0 \leq x \leq 30)$$

a) Find the equation for marginal revenue.
b) Find the marginal revenue at $x = 10$. Interpret the result.
c) Illustrate the graphical interpretation of the answer to part b.

84. *Sales revenue.* The demand for tricycles, x, is related to the price per tricycle, p, by the equation

$$p = -2x + 40 \qquad (0 \le x \le 20)$$

a) Find the revenue function, $R(x)$.
b) Find the equation for marginal revenue.
c) Find the marginal revenue at $x = 5$. Interpret the result.
d) Find the marginal revenue at $x = 7$. Interpret the result.
e) Illustrate the graphical interpretation of the answers to parts c and d.

85. *Projectile.* At the same instant a ball is projected into the air, a stopwatch is started. The function defined by

$$S(x) = -16x^2 + 64x \qquad (0 \le x \le 4)$$

expresses the height (in feet) above the ground of the ball after x seconds have elapsed.

a) At what speed (in feet per second) is the ball traveling after 1 second has elapsed (i.e., at $x = 1$)?
b) At what speed is the ball traveling at $x = 2$?
c) At what speed is the ball traveling at $x = 3$?
d) Sketch $S(x)$ and illustrate the graphical interpretations of parts a through c.

86. *Production cost.* The Ding Dong Company manufactures ornamental bells. The function

$$C(x) = x^2 - 100x + 2900 \qquad (x \ge 0)$$

relates total daily production cost, C, with daily production, x, of bells.

a) Find the equation for marginal cost.
b) Find the marginal cost at $x = 40$. Interpret the result.
c) Find the marginal cost at $x = 50$. Interpret the result.
d) Find the marginal cost at $x = 70$. Interpret the result.

87. *Profit.* Consider the profit function defined by

$$P(x) = 4x - \frac{x^3}{1{,}000{,}000} \qquad (0 \le x \le 2000)$$

Marginal profit is defined in the same manner as marginal revenue and marginal cost.

a) Find the equation for marginal profit.
b) Find the marginal profit at $x = 100$. Interpret the result.
c) Find the marginal profit at $x = 1900$. Interpret the result.

88. *Sales revenue.* Consider the revenue function defined by

$$R(x) = -\frac{1}{100}x^3 + 16x \qquad (0 \le x \le 40)$$

a) Find the equation for marginal revenue.
b) Find the marginal revenue at $x = 10$. Interpret the result.
c) Find the marginal revenue at $x = 30$. Interpret the result.

89. *Learning curve.* The number of units produced, y, by a trainee after x hours of instruction is given by

$$y = 90 \sqrt{x} \qquad (x \ge 0)$$

a) Determine the equation for the trainee's production rate.
b) Determine the trainee's production rate after 4 hours of instruction.
c) Determine the trainee's production rate after 9 hours of instruction.

90. *Air pollution.* In a given geographical region, the concentration of pollution (in parts per million) in the air is given by

$$y = \frac{0.3}{x^2} \qquad (x > 0)$$

where x denotes the distance (in miles) from a large industrial area. Determine the instantaneous rate of change of concentration at
a) $x = 1$ mile.   b) $x = 3$ miles.

91. *Population growth.* The population, P, of a certain city is related to time, t (in years), by the function

$$P(t) = 4000t^2 + 200{,}000$$

where $t = 0$ denotes the year 19*X*0, $t = 1$ denotes the year 19*X*1, etc.
a) Determine the formula for the instantaneous rate of change of the population with respect to time.
b) Determine the instantaneous rate of change of the population at $t = 3$.
c) Determine the instantaneous rate of change of the population at $t = 6$.

9-7 • THE PRODUCT AND QUOTIENT RULES

Often we must find the derivative of a product of functions such as

$$y = (x^3 - 8x)(x^4 - 15)$$

The derivative, dy/dx, may be determined by the **product rule,** which is stated as follows. Its proof appears in Appendix A.

> **Product Rule**
>
> If $y = f(x)s(x)$, where $f(x)$ and $s(x)$ are differentiable functions at x, then
>
> $$\frac{dy}{dx} = f(x)s'(x) + s(x)f'(x)$$

The product rule states that the derivative of the product $f(x)s(x)$ is $f(x)$ times the derivative of $s(x)$ plus $s(x)$ times the derivative of $f(x)$. In other words, the derivative dy/dx of the product of two functions is given by

$$\frac{dy}{dx} = (\text{first})\binom{\text{derivative}}{\text{of second}} + (\text{second})\binom{\text{derivative}}{\text{of first}}$$

Thus, for the function

$$y = (x^3 - 8x)(x^4 - 15)$$

we note that $f(x) = x^3 - 8x$ is the first function and $s(x) = x^4 - 15$ is the second function. Hence,

$$\begin{aligned}
\frac{dy}{dx} &= (\text{first})\binom{\text{derivative}}{\text{of second}} + (\text{second})\binom{\text{derivative}}{\text{of first}} \\
&= (x^3 - 8x)(4x^3) + (x^4 - 15)(3x^2 - 8) \\
&= 7x^6 - 40x^4 - 45x^2 + 120
\end{aligned}$$

• **EXAMPLE 9-29** _____

If $y = (x^5 - 6x^3 + 5)(x^{10} - 8x^2)$, find dy/dx.

Solution

The first function of our product is $f(x) = x^5 - 6x^3 + 5$, and the second function is $s(x) = x^{10} - 8x^2$. By the product rule, we have

$$\frac{dy}{dx} = (\text{first})\begin{pmatrix}\text{derivative}\\\text{of second}\end{pmatrix} + (\text{second})\begin{pmatrix}\text{derivative}\\\text{of first}\end{pmatrix}$$
$$= (x^5 - 6x^3 + 5)(10x^9 - 16x) + (x^{10} - 8x^2)(5x^4 - 18x^2)$$
$$= 15x^{14} - 78x^{12} + 50x^9 - 120x^6 + 240x^4 - 80x$$

• **EXAMPLE 9-30** _____

If $g(x) = (5x + 3)(2x - 1)$, find $g'(x)$

a) By using the product rule.
b) Without using the product rule.

Solutions

a) Using the product rule, we have

$$g'(x) = (5x + 3)(2) + (2x - 1)(5)$$
$$= (10x + 6) + (10x - 5)$$
$$= 20x + 1$$

b) Without using the product rule, we must multiply the binomial factors $5x + 3$ and $2x - 1$ of $g(x)$ to obtain

$$g(x) = 10x^2 + x - 3$$

Since the result is a polynomial, its derivative is

$$g'(x) = 20x + 1$$

Observe that this result agrees with the final answer for part a.

Application

• **EXAMPLE 9-31   Agriculture: Peach Growing.**

If a peach grower harvests her peach crop now, she will pick on the average 200 pounds per tree, and she will get $0.72 per pound for her peaches. From past experience, the grower has learned that for each additional week that she waits, the yield per tree will increase by 20 pounds, while the price will decrease by $0.04 per pound.

a) Write the equation that gives the total sales revenue per tree, R, as a function of the number of weeks, x, that the peach grower should wait before harvesting.
b) Determine the formula for dR/dx.
c) Evaluate dR/dx at $x = 2$ and interpret the result.

Solutions

a) We must determine an equation for the total sales revenue per tree, R. Hence,

$$R = (\text{price per pound})(\text{number of pounds})$$

TABLE 9-16

Decision	Price per pound
Harvest now	$0.72
Wait 1 week	$0.72 − 0.04
Wait 2 weeks	$0.72 − 0.04(2)
Wait 3 weeks	$0.72 − 0.04(3)
.	.
.	.
.	.
Wait x weeks	$0.72 − 0.04$x$

TABLE 9-17

Decision	Number of pounds
Harvest now	200
Wait 1 week	200 + 20
Wait 2 weeks	200 + 20(2)
Wait 3 weeks	200 + 20(3)
.	.
.	.
.	.
Wait x weeks	200 + 20x

Let's focus on the *price per pound*. If the peach grower harvests now, the price per pound is $0.72. For each additional week that she waits, the price per pound decreases by $0.04. This is illustrated in Table 9-16.

Thus, the sales revenue equation is

$$R = \text{(price per pound)(number of pounds)}$$
$$= (0.72 − 0.04x)\text{(number of pounds)}$$

Now we focus on the *number of pounds*. If the peach grower harvests now, she will harvest 200 pounds per tree. For each week that she waits, the number of pounds harvested per tree increases by 20 pounds. This is illustrated in Table 9-17.

Thus, the sales revenue equation is

$$R = \text{(price per pound)(number of pounds)}$$

$$R = (0.72 − 0.04x)(200 + 20x)$$

b) Using the product rule, we find

$$\frac{dR}{dx} = (0.72 − 0.04x)(20) + (200 + 20x)(−0.04)$$
$$= −1.6x + 6.4$$

c)
$$\frac{dR}{dx}\bigg|_{x = 2} = −1.6(2) + 6.4 = 3.2$$

Thus, after 2 weeks have elapsed, the sales revenue per tree is increasing at the rate of $3.20 per tree.

Quotient Rule

To find the derivative of the quotient of functions such as

$$y = \frac{x^5 − 9x}{3x^2 − 8}$$

we must use the **quotient rule,** which is stated as follows. Its proof appears in Appendix A.

Quotient Rule

If $y = n(x)/d(x)$, where $n(x)$ and $d(x)$ are differentiable functions at x and $d(x) \neq 0$, then

$$\frac{dy}{dx} = \frac{d(x)n'(x) − n(x)d'(x)}{[d(x)]^2}$$

The quotient rule states that the derivative dy/dx of a quotient of two functions is given by

$$\frac{dy}{dx} = \frac{\text{(denominator)}\left(\begin{array}{c}\text{derivative}\\\text{of numerator}\end{array}\right) − \text{(numerator)}\left(\begin{array}{c}\text{derivative}\\\text{of denominator}\end{array}\right)}{\text{(denominator)}^2}$$

Thus, for the function

$$y = \frac{x^5 - 9x}{3x^2 - 8}$$

the numerator is $n(x) = x^5 - 9x$, and the denominator is $d(x) = 3x^2 - 8$. By the quotient rule, we have

$$\frac{dy}{dx} = \frac{(\text{denominator})\left(\begin{array}{c}\text{derivative}\\\text{of numerator}\end{array}\right) - (\text{numerator})\left(\begin{array}{c}\text{derivative}\\\text{of denominator}\end{array}\right)}{(\text{denominator})^2}$$

$$= \frac{(3x^2 - 8)(5x^4 - 9) - (x^5 - 9x)(6x)}{(3x^2 - 8)^2}$$

$$= \frac{9x^6 - 40x^4 + 27x^2 + 72}{(3x^2 - 8)^2}$$

• **EXAMPLE 9-32** _____

If

$$y = \frac{x^8 - 3x}{2x^5 - 9}$$

find dy/dx.

Solution

The numerator is $n(x) = x^8 - 3x$, and the denominator is $d(x) = 2x^5 - 9$. By the quotient rule,

$$\frac{dy}{dx} = \frac{(\text{denominator})\left(\begin{array}{c}\text{derivative}\\\text{of numerator}\end{array}\right) - (\text{numerator})\left(\begin{array}{c}\text{derivative}\\\text{of denominator}\end{array}\right)}{(\text{denominator})^2}$$

$$= \frac{(2x^5 - 9)(8x^7 - 3) - (x^8 - 3x)(10x^4)}{(2x^5 - 9)^2}$$

$$= \frac{6x^{12} - 72x^7 + 24x^5 + 27}{(2x^5 - 9)^2}$$

• **EXAMPLE 9-33** _____

If

$$f(x) = \frac{6x^4 - 8x^2}{x}$$

find $f'(x)$

a) By using the quotient rule.
b) Without using the quotient rule.

Solutions

a) Using the quotient rule, we have

$$f'(x) = \frac{(x)(24x^3 - 16x) - (6x^4 - 8x^2)(1)}{x^2}$$

$$= \frac{24x^4 - 16x^2 - 6x^4 + 8x^2}{x^2}$$

$$= \frac{18x^4 - 8x^2}{x^2}$$

$$= 18x^2 - 8$$

b) Without using the quotient rule, we must divide $6x^4 - 8x^2$ by x to obtain

$$f(x) = 6x^3 - 8x$$

Hence, the derivative of the resulting polynomial is

$$f'(x) = 18x^2 - 8$$

Observe that this result agrees with the final answer for part a.

• **EXAMPLE 9-34**

Find the equation of the straight line tangent to $f(x) = 1/(x - 3)$ at $x = 4$.

Solution

The slope of the tangent line is given by $f'(4)$. Using the quotient rule, we calculate

$$f'(x) = \frac{(x - 3)(0) - (1)(1)}{(x - 3)^2}$$

$$= \frac{-1}{(x - 3)^2} \qquad \text{Derivative of Function}$$

Hence,

$$f'(4) = \frac{-1}{(4 - 3)^2} = -1 \qquad \text{Slope of Tangent Line}$$

The point of tangency is $(4, f(4))$. Since

$$f(4) = \frac{1}{4 - 3} = 1 \qquad y - \text{Coordinate of Point of Tangency}$$

the point of tangency is $(4, 1)$. Using the slope-intercept form, $y = mx + b$, of the equation of a straight line, we have

$$y = -1x + b$$

We determine b by substituting the coordinates of $(4, 1)$ into the equation and solving for b to obtain

$$1 = -1(4) + b$$

$$b = 5$$

Thus, the equation of the tangent line is $y = -x + 5$ (see Figure 9-58).

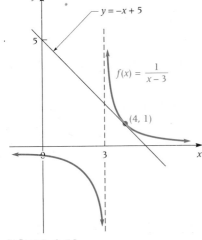

FIGURE 9-58

Application

• **EXAMPLE 9-35 Average Cost.**

If $C(x) = $ total cost of producing x units of some product, then the **average cost per unit** is given by

$$\overline{C}(x) = \frac{C(x)}{x} \qquad (x > 0)$$

Given the cost function defined by

$$C(x) = 8x + 100$$

a) Determine the equation for average cost, $\overline{C}(x)$.
b) Determine the formula for $\overline{C}'(x)$.
c) Compute $\overline{C}'(5)$ and interpret the result.

Solutions

a) $\quad \overline{C}(x) = \dfrac{C(x)}{x}$

$\qquad = \dfrac{8x + 100}{x} \qquad (x > 0)$

b) Using the quotient rule, we find

$$\overline{C}'(x) = \frac{x(8) - (8x + 100)(1)}{x^2}$$

$$= \frac{-100}{x^2}$$

c) $\quad \overline{C}'(5) = \dfrac{-100}{5^2} = -4$

Thus, at a production level of 5 units, the average cost per unit is decreasing by \$4 per unit.

Sometimes we must use the product and quotient rules together within a single problem. Example 9-36 illustrates such a situation.

• **EXAMPLE 9-36** _____

If

$$y = \frac{(x^2 - 3x + 5)(4x - 1)}{x + 3}$$

find dy/dx.

Solution

Note that the formula for y is a quotient, the numerator of which is a product. Thus, we begin by using the quotient rule.

$$\frac{dy}{dx} = \frac{(\text{denominator})\left(\begin{array}{c}\text{derivative}\\\text{of numerator}\end{array}\right) - (\text{numerator})\left(\begin{array}{c}\text{derivative}\\\text{of denominator}\end{array}\right)}{(\text{denominator})^2}$$

$$= \frac{(x + 3)\dfrac{d}{dx}[(x^2 - 3x + 5)(4x - 1)] - (x^2 - 3x + 5)(4x - 1)\dfrac{d}{dx}(x + 3)}{(x + 3)^2}$$

Note that we must use the product rule in the numerator of the above to find d/dx $[(x^2 - 3x + 5)(4x - 1)]$. Thus, the above expression becomes

$$\frac{dy}{dx} = \frac{(x + 3)\,[(x^2 - 3x + 5)(4) + (4x - 1)(2x - 3)] - (x^2 - 3x + 5)(4x - 1)(1)}{(x + 3)^2}$$

$$= \frac{(x + 3)(4x^2 - 12x + 20 + 8x^2 - 2x - 12x + 3) - (4x^3 - 13x^2 + 23x - 5)}{(x + 3)^2}$$

$$= \frac{(x + 3)(12x^2 - 26x + 23) - 4x^3 + 13x^2 - 23x + 5}{(x - 3)^2}$$

$$= \frac{12x^3 + 10x^2 - 55x + 69 - 4x^3 + 13x^2 - 23x + 5}{(x - 3)^2}$$

$$= \frac{8x^3 + 23x^2 - 78x + 74}{(x - 3)^2}$$

In Example 9-36, we began with the quotient rule since the function was written as a quotient of two expressions. Since one of these expressions was a product, we had to use the product rule within the quotient rule. Sometimes we encounter examples where the function is a product of expressions, one or more of which are quotients. For such cases, we would have to begin with the product rule and then use the quotient rule within the product rule. We will encounter such problems in the exercises.

Exercises 9-7

Find the derivative of each of the following.

1. $y = (x^2 + 4x + 5)(x^3 - 2x^2 + 7)$
2. $y = (4x^5 - 9x^3 + 7x)(x^7 - 8x^6 + 4)$
3. $f(x) = (x^3 - 2x + 6)(x^2 - 3x + 2)$
4. $g(x) = (5x^3 + 6)(x^2 - 8x + 4)$
5. $y = (x^3 - x^2 - 2)(x^2 - x - 1)$

For each of the following, find dy/dx.

6. $y = (x^3 - 8x + 4)(3x^2 - 6x + 1)$
7. $y = (x^7 - 6x^2)(4x^2 - 3x + 4)$
8. $y = (8x + 4)(6x^3 + 4x)$
9. $y = (5x^2 - 3x + 1)(3x^4 - 7)$
10. $y = (3\sqrt{x} + 4x^2)(4/\sqrt{x} + x)$

Find the derivative of each of the following.

11. $y = \dfrac{x^2 - 4x + 5}{x^3 - 3x + 9}$

12. $y = \dfrac{x^3 - x^2 + 5x}{x^2 - 2x + 1}$

13. $f(x) = \dfrac{x^3}{x + 5}$

14. $y = \dfrac{x + 6}{x^4}$

15. $g(x) = \dfrac{x^3 + 7}{x^4}$

16. $y = \dfrac{x^3}{x^2 - 3}$

17. $y = 8 - \dfrac{6}{x - 2} + \dfrac{3x}{5x + 1}$

18. $y = 4 + \dfrac{2}{x + 5} - \dfrac{5x}{6x - 7}$

19. $y = \dfrac{x^3 + 9}{x^2 - 9}$

20. $y = \dfrac{x^4 - 6}{x^3 + 1}$

For each of the following, find dy/dx.

21. $y = \dfrac{1}{x^2 - 3x}$

22. $y = \dfrac{1}{x^4 - 5x}$

23. $y = \dfrac{4x + 1}{3x^2 - 2x}$

24. $y = \dfrac{3x + 2}{5x^2 - 3x}$

25. $y = \dfrac{5x^3 - 2x + 1}{\sqrt[5]{x}}$

26. $y = \dfrac{4x^2 - x + 7}{\sqrt[3]{x}}$

27. $y = \dfrac{x^4 - 8x^3 + 5x + 1}{5x^3 - 7x^2 + 3}$

28. $y = \dfrac{x^3 - 8x^2 + 3x + 1}{x^2 - 6x + 1}$

29. $y = \dfrac{\sqrt{x} + x}{x - 1/\sqrt{x}}$

30. $y = \dfrac{x + 1/\sqrt{x}}{\sqrt{x} - 1}$

For each of the following, find $\dfrac{dy}{dx}\bigg|_{x=1}$.

31. $y = \dfrac{x^2 - 3x + 1}{x^3 - 2x}$

32. $y = \dfrac{x^3 - 4x^2 + 2}{x^2 + 6x + 1}$

33. $y = \dfrac{\sqrt{x} + 6x}{x - 2/\sqrt{x}}$

34. $y = \dfrac{5x - 2}{2x^3 + 3}$

Find the derivatives of each of the following.

35. $y = (x^3 - 4x^2 + 5)(x^2 - 8x + 7)$

36. $y = \dfrac{x^2 - 3x}{x^3 + 16}$

37. $y = \dfrac{(x^3 - 4x + 7)(x^2 - 2x)}{x^3 - 6x + 1}$

38. $f(x) = \dfrac{x^4 - 8x^2 + 6}{(x^3 + 5)(x^2 - 3x)}$

39. $y = \dfrac{(x^3 - 6x^2 + 5)(x^2 - 4x)}{(x^5 - 8x^2)(x^3 + 1)}$

40. $f(x) = (x^3 + 4)\left(\dfrac{x^4 - 2}{x^5 + 1}\right)$

41. $g(t) = (t^5 - 4)\left(\dfrac{t^3 + 6}{t^4 + 7}\right)$

42. $f(x) = \dfrac{\dfrac{5}{4x} - 3}{\dfrac{6}{x^5} + 9}$

43. $y = (x^2 - 4x + 1)\left(\dfrac{x^3 - 5x}{x^2 + 6}\right)$

44. If $f(x) = -4/x^3$, find $f'(x)$ by using
   a) The power rule.
   b) The quotient rule.

45. If $y = x^3(x^6 - 8x^2)$, find dy/dx
   a) Without using the product rule.
   b) By using the product rule.

46. If $f(x) = (x - 1)/(x + 3)$, find $f'(2)$.

47. If $f(x) = (x^2 + 2)(x^3 - 2x + 5)$, calculate $f'(1)$.

48. If $f(x) = (x + 1)(x + 2)(x - 5)$, find $f'(3)$.

49. Find the equation of the straight line tangent to $f(x) = (x^2 - 9)(x + 5)$ at $x = 1$.

50. Find the equation of the straight line tangent to $f(x) = 1/x$ at $x = 3$. Illustrate graphically.

51. Find the equation of the straight line tangent to $f(x) = 1/x^2$ at $x = 7$. Illustrate graphically.

52. Find the equation of the straight line tangent to

$$f(x) = \dfrac{x^2}{x - 3}$$

at $x = 4$.

53. Find the equation of the straight line tangent to

$$f(x) = \dfrac{(x^2 - 36)(x + 4)}{x^2 - 81}$$

at $x = 1$.

Applications

54. *Apple growing.* If an apple grower harvests his crop now, he will pick on the average 300 pounds per tree, and he will get $0.50 per pound for his apples. For each week that the grower waits before harvesting, the yield per tree will increase by 20 pounds, while the price will decrease by $0.02 per pound.
   a) Write the equation that gives total sales revenue, R, per tree as a function of x, the number of weeks that the grower waits before harvesting.
   b) Determine the formula for dR/dx.
   c) Evaluate dR/dx at $x = 3$ and interpret the result.

55. *Sales revenue.* The unit price, p (in dollars), of some product is changing with time, t (in months), in accordance with the equation

$$p = 10 + 2t$$

The demand, x, for the product is changing with time, t, in accordance with the equation

$$x = 20 + 0.2t^2$$

a) Write the equation for sales revenue, R, as a function of t.
b) Determine the formula for dR/dt.
c) Evaluate dR/dt at $t = 2$ and interpret the result.

Average cost. For each of the following cost functions,
a) Determine the formula for average cost per unit, $\overline{C}(X)$.
b) Determine the formula for $\overline{C}'(x)$.
c) Find $\overline{C}'(4)$, $\overline{C}'(5)$, and $\overline{C}'(6)$, and interpret the results.

56. $C(x) = 5x + 100$ **57.** $C(x) = 10x + 5\text{u}0$
58. $C(x) = -x^2 + 20x$ **59.** $C(x) = -x^2 + 30x$

60. *Production possibility curve.* The equation

$$y = \frac{500(x - 300)}{x - 320} \quad (0 \le x \le 300)$$

relates the number of units of products A and B that can be produced during a week. Here x and y denote the number of units produced of Products A and B, respectively.
a) Determine the formula for dy/dx.
b) Evaluate dy/dx at $x = 20$, $x = 30$, and $x = 50$, and interpret the results.

61. *Cost-benefit analysis.* The equation

$$y = \frac{30}{110 - x} \quad (0 \le x \le 100)$$

expresses the relationship between the cost, y (in millions of dollars), of removing $x\%$ of a pollutant from the atmosphere.
a) Determine the formula for dy/dx.
b) Evaluate dy/dx at $x = 60$, $x = 80$, and $x = 90$, and interpret the results.

62. *Bacteria population.* The equation

$$B(t) = 800\left(1 + \frac{6t}{90 + t^2}\right)$$

gives the number of bacteria, $B(t)$ (in millions), present in a culture at a given time, t (in weeks).
a) Determine the formula for $B'(t)$.
b) Compute $B'(2)$ and $B'(3)$, and interpret the results.

9-8 • THE CHAIN RULE

Different Variables

As we have seen, if $y = f(x)$, then its derivative is denoted by dy/dx. If letters other than y and x are dependent and independent variables, respectively, then the symbol dy/dx must be changed accordingly. Consider the function

$$z = t^3 - 8t^2 + 15t - 7$$

Since the dependent and independent variables are z and t, respectively, the derivative is denoted by dz/dt. Thus,

$$\frac{dz}{dt} = 3t^2 - 16t + 15$$

• **EXAMPLE 9-37** _____

Find the derivative of the function $w = r^4 - 8r^2 + 5$.

Solution

$dw/dr = 4r^3 - 16r$

• **EXAMPLE 9-38** _____

If $y = u^3$, then find its derivative.

Solution

$dy/du = 3u^2$

_____ •

We are now ready to discuss another useful rule for finding derivatives. It is called the **chain rule** and is stated here without proof.

Chain Rule

If $y = f(u)$ is a differentiable function of u and $u = g(x)$ is a differentiable function of x, then

$$\frac{dy}{dx} = \frac{dy}{du}\frac{du}{dx}$$

The chain rule states that if y is a function of u and u is a function of x, then the derivative of y with respect to x (i.e., dy/dx) equals the derivative of y with respect to u (i.e., dy/du) times the derivative of u with respect to x (i.e., du/dx).

As an example, consider the function

$$y = \underbrace{(6x^2 - 5)}_{u}{}^{10}$$

If we let $u = 6x^2 - 5$, then the function may be expressed as

$$y = f(u) = u^{10}$$
$$\uparrow\!\!\text{----- where } u = 6x^2 - 5$$

Thus, the derivative, dy/dx, is calculated by using the chain rule. Hence, we write

$$\frac{dy}{dx} = \frac{dy}{du}\frac{du}{dx}$$

$$y = u^{10}$$
$$\frac{dy}{du} = 10u^9$$

$$= 10u^9(12x)$$

$$u = 6x^2 - 5$$
$$\frac{du}{dx} = 12x$$

Replacing u by its equivalent expression, $6x^2 - 5$, we have

$$\frac{dy}{dx} = 10(6x^2 - 5)^9(12x)$$

$$= 120x(6x^2 - 5)^9$$

Applications

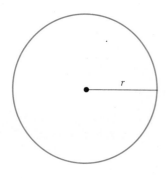

• **EXAMPLE 9-39** **Oil Spill.**

An oil tanker hits a reef and begins spilling oil over the ocean surface. The oil spill takes the form of a circle with the radius, r, (in feet) increasing as a function of time in accordance with the equation

$$r = 3t^2$$

where t is the time elapsed (in days) since the tanker began leaking oil. Given that the circumference of a circle is

$$C = 2\pi r$$

where r is its radius and $\pi \approx 3.1416$.

a) Find the formula for the instantaneous rate of change of the circumference with respect to time, dC/dt.

b) Compute dC/dt after 5 days (i.e., $t = 5$).

Solutions

a) Since C is a function of r and r is a function of t, then, by the chain rule,

$$\frac{dC}{dt} = \frac{dC}{dr}\frac{dr}{dt}$$

$$= (2\pi)\,(6t)$$

$$= 12\pi t$$

b)

$$\left.\frac{dC}{dt}\right|_{t=5} = 12\pi(5)$$

$$= 60\pi$$

$$\approx 188.5 \text{ feet/day}$$

Thus, 5 days after the tanker began leaking oil, the circumference of the oil slick is increasing at the rate of 188.5 feet/day.

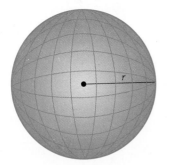

• **EXAMPLE 9-40** **Medical Science.** _____

The volume, V, of a sphere is given by

$$V = \frac{4}{3}\pi r^3$$

where r is the radius of the sphere. A tumor, having the shape of a sphere, is increasing in a manner such that its radius, r (in centimeters), is enlarging in accordance with the function

$$r = 0.008t^3$$

where t denotes elapsed time in months.

a) Determine the formula for the instantaneous rate of change of volume, V, with respect to time, t.

b) Determine the instantaneous rate of change of volume with respect to time at $t = 4$ months.

Solutions

a)   We want to determine dV/dt. Since V is a function of r such that $V = (4/3)\pi r^3$, we find

$$\frac{dV}{dr} = \frac{4}{3}\pi(3r^2)$$

$$= 4\pi r^2$$

Since r is a function of t such that $r = 0.008t^3$, we find

$$\frac{dr}{dt} = 0.024t^2$$

Using the chain rule, we write

$$\frac{dV}{dt} = \frac{dV}{dr}\frac{dr}{dt}$$

$$= (4\pi r^2)(0.024t^2)$$

$$= 0.096\pi r^2 t^2$$

Since $r = 0.008t^3$, we substitute $0.008t^3$ for r in the above expression for dV/dt to obtain an expression for dV/dt in terms of t. Hence,

$$\frac{dV}{dt} = 0.096\pi r^2 t^2$$

$$= 0.096\pi(0.008t^3)^2 t^2$$

$$= 0.000006144\pi t^8 = (6.144 \times 10^{-6})\pi t^8$$

b)

$$\frac{dV}{dt}\bigg|_{t=4} = (6.144 \times 10^{-6})\pi(4)^8$$

$$\approx 0.4027\pi \approx 1.27 \text{ cm}^3/\text{month}$$

Thus, at $t = 4$ months, the volume of the tumor is increasing at the rate of 1.27 cubic centimeters per month.

• **EXAMPLE 9-41   Cost.** _____

The total cost, C (in thousands of dollars), of producing x (in hundreds) units of some commodity is given by

$$C = 0.1x^3 + 9 \qquad (x \geq 0)$$

where x is related to time, t (in months), by the equation

$$x = 2t + 5 \qquad (t \geq 0)$$

Find the rate of change of cost with respect to time at $t = 4$.

Solution

We seek

$$\frac{dC}{dt}\bigg|_{t=4}$$

Since C is a function of x and x is a function of t, by the chain rule,

$$\frac{dC}{dt} = \frac{dC}{dx}\frac{dx}{dt}$$

Since $dC/dx = 0.3x^2$ and $dx/dt = 2$,

$$\frac{dC}{dt} = 0.3x^2(2)$$

$$= 0.6x^2$$

Substituting $x = 2t + 5$ into this result gives dc/dt in terms of t. Hence,

$$\frac{dC}{dt} = 0.6(2t + 5)^2$$

Evaluating this result at $t = 4$ gives

$$\frac{dC}{dt}\bigg|_{t\,=\,4} = 0.6[2(4) + 5]^2$$

$$= 0.6(13)^2 = 101.4$$

Thus, at $t = 4$, production cost is increasing at the rate of 101.4 thousand dollars per month.

General Power Rule

For functions of the form

$$y = u^n$$

where $u = f(x)$

the chain rule becomes

$$\frac{dy}{dx} = \frac{dy}{du}\frac{du}{dx}$$

$$= nu^{n-1}\frac{du}{dx}$$

This result is called the **general power rule,** which is formally stated in the following box.

> **General Power Rule**
>
> If $y = u^n$, where u is a differentiable function of x, then
>
> $$\frac{dy}{dx} = nu^{n-1}\frac{du}{dx}$$

Specifically, if

$$y = (x^6 - 8x)^{20}$$

where $u = x^6 - 8x$ and $n = 20$, we find

$$\frac{dy}{dx} = nu^{n-1}\frac{du}{dx}$$

$$= 20(x^6 - 8x)^{19}(6x^5 - 8)$$

• EXAMPLE 9-42 ─────────────

If $y = (x^5 - 9x^2)^{11}$, find dy/dx.

Solution

We write the above as

$$y = (x^5 - 9x^2)^{11}$$

$$\text{or}$$

$$y = u^{11}$$

↑ ── where $u = x^5 - 9x^2$

Using the general power rule,

$$\frac{dy}{dx} = \boxed{nu^{n-1}} \boxed{\frac{du}{dx}}$$

$$u = x^5 - 9x^2$$
$$\frac{du}{dx} = 5x^4 - 18x$$

$$= \boxed{11(x^5 - 9x^2)^{10}} \boxed{(5x^4 - 18x)}$$

• EXAMPLE 9-43 ─────────────

If $y = \sqrt{x^5 - 8}$, find dy/dx.

Solution

We rewrite the above as

$$y = (x^5 - 8)^{1/2}$$

$$\text{or}$$

$$y = u^{1/2}$$

↑ ── where $u = x^5 - 8$

Using the general power rule,

$$\frac{dy}{dx} = \boxed{nu^{n-1}} \boxed{\frac{du}{dx}}$$

$$u = x^5 - 8$$
$$\frac{du}{dx} = 5x^4$$

$$= \boxed{\frac{1}{2}(x^5 - 8)^{1/2 - 1}} \boxed{(5x^4)}$$

$$= \frac{5}{2}x^4(x^5 - 8)^{-1/2}$$

$$= \frac{5x^4}{2\sqrt{x^5 - 8}}$$

Sometimes we must use the chain rule together with the product or quotient rules. The following two examples illustrate such situations.

• EXAMPLE 9-44 ─────────────

If $y = (x^3 - 6)^5(2x + 9)^8$, find dy/dx.

Solution

Since we have a product of two functions, we must first use the product rule. Hence, we calculate

$$\frac{dy}{dx} = (\text{first})\begin{pmatrix}\text{derivative} \\ \text{of second}\end{pmatrix} + (\text{second})\begin{pmatrix}\text{derivative} \\ \text{of first}\end{pmatrix}$$

$$= (x^3 - 6)^5 \cdot 8(2x + 9)^7(2) + (2x + 9)^8 \cdot 5(x^3 - 6)^4(3x^2)$$

Note that the chain rule was used to find the "derivative of second" and the "derivative of first." When simplified, the preceding result becomes

$$\frac{dy}{dx} = 16(x^3 - 6)^5(2x + 9)^7 + 15x^2(2x + 9)^8(x^3 - 6)^4$$

$$= (x^3 - 6)^4(2x + 9)^7(46x^3 + 135x^2 - 96)$$

• **EXAMPLE 9-45** _____

If

$$y = \left(\frac{x^2 + 3}{x^5 + 4}\right)^{20}$$

find dy/dx.

Solution

Since $u = (x^2 + 3)/(x^5 + 4)$ and $n = 20$, then we have

$$\frac{dy}{dx} = nu^{n-1}\frac{du}{dx}$$

$$= 20\left(\frac{x^2 + 3}{x^5 + 4}\right)^{19}\left[\frac{(x^5 + 4)(2x) - (x^2 + 3)(5x^4)}{(x^5 + 4)^2}\right]$$

Note that du/dx is computed by the quotient rule. When simplified, this result becomes

$$\frac{dy}{dx} = 20\left(\frac{x^2 + 3}{x^5 + 4}\right)^{19}\left[\frac{(-3x^6 - 15x^4 + 8x)}{(x^5 + 4)^2}\right]$$

$$= \frac{20(x^2 + 3)^{19}(-3x^6 - 15x^4 + 8x)}{(x^5 + 4)^{21}}$$

Application

• **EXAMPLE 9-46**   **Compound Interest.**

Five thousand dollars is deposited in an account earning interest at the rate of $r\%$ compounded monthly. At the end of 6 years, the balance in the account is given by

$$S = 5000\left(1 + \frac{r}{1200}\right)^{72}$$

Find the instantaneous rate of change of S with respect to r for these rates: $r = 6\%$, 8%, and 10%.

Solutions

We seek dS/dr evaluated at the above rates, r. Using the general power rule, we let $u = 1 + (r/1200)$ and find

$$\frac{dS}{dr} = 5000 \cdot \overbrace{72\left(1 + \frac{r}{1200}\right)^{71}}^{nu^{n-1}} \overbrace{\left(\frac{1}{1200}\right)}^{\frac{du}{dr}}$$

$$= 300 \cdot \left(1 + \frac{r}{1200}\right)^{71}$$

For $r = 6$,

$$\frac{dS}{dr} = 300\left(1 + \frac{6}{1200}\right)^{71} \approx \$427.48$$

Thus, at a rate of 6% compounded monthly, the instantaneous rate of change of the account's balance is $427.48 per percentage point.

For $r = 8$,

$$\frac{dS}{dr} = 300\left(1 + \frac{8}{1200}\right)^{71} \approx \$480.85$$

Thus, at a rate of 8% compounded monthly, the instantaneous rate of change of the account's balance is $480.85 per percentage point.

For $r = 10$,

$$\frac{dS}{dr} = 300\left(1 + \frac{10}{1200}\right)^{71} \approx \$540.77$$

Thus, at a rate of 10% compounded monthly, the instantaneous rate of change of the account's balance is $540.77 per percentage point.

Exercises 9-8

1. If $z = t^5 - 4t^3 + 7t - 8$, find dz/dt.
2. If $h = w^3 - 4w^2 + 8w - 9$, find dh/dw.
3. If $y = u^5$, find dy/du.
4. If $u = x^2$, find du/dx.
5. If $y = 3u^6 - 8u^5 + 4u - 8$, find dy/du.
6. If $u = 8x^2 - 3x + 5$, find du/dx.
7. If $f(u) = -7u^3 - 8u^2 + 6$, find $f'(u)$.
8. If $g(t) = 8t^2 - 4t + 5$, find $g'(t)$.

Find the derivative of each of the following.

9. $y = (x^3 + 5)^{11}$
10. $y = (x^6 - 4x + 9)^{1/2}$
11. $y = (x^3 - 6x)^{-4}$
12. $f(x) = (x^3 + x^2 + 9x)^{-5}$
13. $f(x) = (x^4 - 9)^{15}$
14. $y = 1/\sqrt{x^3 - 8x}$
15. $y = 1/\sqrt[3]{(x^6 - 8x)^2}$
16. $f(x) = (x^6 - 9x^2)^{-2/5}$
17. $y = (x^3 - 4x^2 + 5)^{20}$
18. $y = 1/(x^4 - 8x^3 + 5)^{10}$

Find the derivative of each of the following.

19. $y = (x^3 - 4x)^{10}(x^2 + 5)$
20. $y = x(x^2 - 4x + 5)^4$
21. $y = \left(\dfrac{5x - 3}{8 - x^4}\right)^7$
22. $y = \left(\dfrac{2x + 1}{x^2 - 5x}\right)^9$
23. $y = \dfrac{(5x - 3)^7}{(8 - x^4)^7}$
24. $y = \dfrac{(2x + 1)^9}{(x^2 - 5x)^9}$
25. $y = [(5x - 3)(x^2 - 1)]^{10}$
26. $y = [(6x - 7)(x^3 - 2)]^8$
27. $y = (5x - 3)^{10}(x^2 - 1)^{10}$
28. $y = (6x - 7)^8(x^3 - 2)^8$
29. $y = (x^3 - 4x^2)^5(x^2 - 1)^3$
30. $y = (x^2 - 4x)^6(x^2 - 5)^4$
31. $y = (x^3 + 1)^5 + (x^2 - 2)^7$
32. $y = (x^4 + 8)^9 + (x^2 - 6)^3$
33. $y = (\sqrt{x} + 9)^5$
34. $y = (\sqrt{x} - 3)^8$

For each of the following, find dy/dx.

35. $y = x\sqrt{x^3 + 1}$
36. $y = x^4\sqrt{x^2 + 8x}$
37. $y = x^3/\sqrt{x + 1}$
38. $y = x^5/\sqrt{x^2 + 5}$

For each of the following, find $\dfrac{dy}{dx}\bigg|_{x = 1}$.

39. $y = 1/(x^3 + 4)$
40. $y = x^2\sqrt{x^3 + 1}$
41. $y = x/\sqrt{x^3 + 9}$
42. $y = \left(\dfrac{3x}{x - 6}\right)^3$

43. Find the equation of the straight line tangent to $f(x) = (x - 7)^5$ at $x = 3$.
44. Find the equation of the straight line tangent to $f(x) = 1/(x - 1)^2$ at $x = 3$.

Applications

45. *Cost.* The total cost, C, of the producing x units of some commodity is given by

$$C = x^3 + 9 \qquad (x \geq 0)$$

The number of units produced, x, is a function of the number of days, t, subsequent to the start of a production run. The variable x is related to t by the equation

$$x = 5t + 4 \qquad (t \geq 0)$$

a) Find the formula for the rate of change of cost with respect to time.
b) Evaluate the result of part a at $t = 6$ and interpret the result.

46. *Cost.* The total cost, C (in millions of dollars), of producing x (in thousands) units of some commodity is given by

$$C = 0.2x^3 + 10 \qquad (x \geq 0)$$

where x is related to time, t (in months), by the equation

$$x = 4t + 3 \qquad (t \geq 0)$$

Find the rate of change of production cost with respect to time at $t = 5$.

47. *Cost.* The total cost, C (in millions of dollars), of producing x units of some commodity is given by

$$C = 0.01x^3 + 8 \qquad (x \geq 0)$$

If production is increasing in accordance with the equation

$$x = 50t + 90$$

where t is the number of months since production of this commodity began, find the rate of change of cost with respect to time, t (in months), at a production level of 200 units.

48. *Revenue.* The revenue, R (in thousands of dollars), gained from selling x units of some product is given by

$$R = -4x^2 + 80x \qquad (0 \leq x \leq 20)$$

If sales are increasing in accordance with the equation

$$x = 30t + 20$$

where t is the number of months this product has been marketed, find the rate of change of revenue with respect to time, t (in months), at a sales level of 4 units.

49. *Compound interest.* Ten thousand dollars is deposited in an account earning interest at the rate of $r\%$ compounded quarterly. At the end of 7 years, the balance in the account is given by

$$S = 10{,}000 \left(1 + \frac{r}{400}\right)^{28}$$

a) Find the formula for the instantaneous rate of change of S with respect to r.
b) Find $\left.\dfrac{dS}{dr}\right|_{r\,=\,8}$ and interpret the result.
c) Find $\left.\dfrac{dS}{dr}\right|_{r\,=\,10}$ and interpret the result.

50. *Compound interest.* Fifteen thousand dollars is deposited into an account earning interest at the rate of r% compounded annually. At the end of 5 years, the balance in the account is given by

$$S = 15{,}000 \left(1 + \frac{r}{100}\right)^5$$

a) Find the formula for the instantaneous rate of change of S with respect to r.

b) Find $\dfrac{dS}{dr}\Big|_{r=6}$ and interpret the result.

c) Find $\dfrac{dS}{dr}\Big|_{r=10}$ and interpret the result.

51. *Annuity.* At the end of each year, $6000 is deposited into an account earning interest at the rate of r% compounded annually. At the end of 8 years, the balance in the account is given by

$$S = \left(\frac{600{,}000}{r}\right)\left[\left(1 + \frac{r}{100}\right)^8 - 1\right]$$

a) Find the formula for the instantaneous rate of change of S with respect to r.

b) Find $\dfrac{dS}{dr}\Big|_{r=8}$ and interpret the result.

c) Find $\dfrac{dS}{dr}\Big|_{r=10}$ and interpret the result.

52. *Annuity.* At the end of each quarter, $2000 is deposited into an account earning interest at the rate of r% compounded quarterly. At the end of 6 years, the balance in the account is given by

$$S = \left(\frac{800{,}000}{r}\right)\left[\left(1 + \frac{r}{400}\right)^{24} - 1\right]$$

a) Find the formula for the instantaneous rate of change of S with respect r.

b) Find $\dfrac{dS}{dr}\Big|_{r=8}$ and interpret the result.

c) Find $\dfrac{dS}{dr}\Big|_{r=10}$ and interpret the result.

CHAPTER 9 HIGHLIGHTS

• Concepts

Your ability to answer the following questions is one indicator of the depth of your mastery of this chapter's important concepts. Note that the questions are grouped under various topic headings. For any question that you cannot answer, refer to the appropriate section of the chapter indicated by the topic heading. Pay particular attention to the summary boxes within a section.

9-1 LIMITS

1. Explain the term *limit*.

2. If a given function has a limit at a value of x, then this implies that the left-hand limit equals the _____-_____ _____ at that value of x.

3. Is it possible for a function to have a limit at a value of x even though the function is not defined at that value of x?

4. State six limit properties and explain each.

5. As x approaches positive or negative infinity, expressions of the form k/x^n, where n is a positive real number and k is a constant, approach _____.

6. If a function, $f(x)$, approaches L as x approaches positive (or negative) infinity, then graphically the line $y = L$ is a(n) _____ _____.

9-2 CONTINUITY

7. Explain continuity from a graphical perspective.

8. Explain continuity in terms of limits.

9. Explain what it means for a function to be continuous over an interval.

10. State and explain four continuity properties.

11. For which values of x are polynomial functions continuous?

12. For which values of x are rational functions continuous?

9-3 AVERAGE RATE OF CHANGE

13. Write the expression for the average rate of change of a function, $f(x)$, over the interval from x to $x + \Delta x$. This expression is called the _____ _____.

14. Graphically, the average rate of change between two points of a function is the slope of the _____ _____ passing through the points.

9-4 THE DERIVATIVE

15. Use limits to write an expression for the derivative.

16. Graphically, a derivative is the _____ of the _____ line to the graph of a function at a point.

9-5 DIFFERENTIABILITY AND CONTINUITY

17. A function is differentiable at a point if its _____ exists at that _____.

18. Graphically, what does it mean for a function to be differentiable at a point?

19. If a function is continuous at a point, does this imply that the function is differentiable at the point?

20. If a function is differentiable at a point, does this imply that the function is continuous at the point?

21. If a function is not continuous at a point, does this imply that it is not differentiable at the point?

9-6 RULES FOR FINDING DERIVATIVES

State and explain each of the following derivative rules.

22. Constant function rule   **23.** Power rule

24. Constant multiplier rule   **25.** Sum or difference rule

26. Explain the terms *marginal cost* and *marginal revenue*.

9-7 THE PRODUCT AND QUOTIENT RULES

State and explain each of the following derivative rules.

27. Product rule   **28.** Quotient rule

9-8   THE CHAIN RULE

State and explain each of the following derivative rules.

29. Chain rule

30. General power rule

REVIEW EXERCISES

• Limits and Continuity

For Exercises 1–6, determine whether or not $\lim_{x \to 2} f(x)$ exists.

1. $f(x) = \dfrac{1}{x - 2}$

2. $f(x) = \dfrac{x^2 - 4}{x - 2}$

3. $f(x) = 4x + 8$

4. $f(x) = \begin{cases} 2x - 1 & \text{for } x \le 2 \\ x^2 & \text{for } x > 2 \end{cases}$

5. $f(x) = \dfrac{\sqrt{x} - \sqrt{2}}{x - 2}$

6. $f(x) = \begin{cases} x^2 + 5 & \text{for } x \ne 2 \\ 12 & \text{for } x = 2 \end{cases}$

7–12. For Exercises 1–6, state where the function is discontinuous.

13. *Compound interest.* One thousand dollars is deposited into a savings account for 2 years at 8% compounded semiannually. If interest is added at the end of each half-year,
   a) Find the account's balance for each half-year.
   b) Draw a graph of the account's balance versus time, t (in half-years).
   c) Where is the graph of part b discontinuous?

14. *Cost analysis.* A company makes machine parts. For one of its products, the variable cost is $40 per unit, and the fixed cost is $50,000 for the first 10,000 units produced. When the production level exceeds 10,000 units, the fixed cost increases by $8000.
   a) Define the cost function.
   b) Graph the cost function.
   c) Where is the cost function discontinuous?

• Average Rate of Change

For Exercises 15 and 16, determine the formula for the difference quotient.

15. $f(x) = x^2 - 3x + 5$

16. $f(x) = x^3 + 5x^2 - 2x + 6$

17–18. For Exercises 15 and 16, use the formula for the difference quotient to determine the average rate of change of y with respect to x over the interval from $x = 1$ to $x = 3$.

19. *Sales revenue.* The total sales revenue gained from producing x units of some product is given by

$$R(x) = -x^2 + 8000x \qquad (0 \le x \le 8000)$$

Determine the average rate of change of sales revenue with respect to x over the interval
   a) $1000 \le x \le 3000$.
   b) $1000 \le x \le 2000$.
   c) Interpret the result of part a.
   d) Interpret the result of part b.
   e) Give a graphical interpretation of the result of part a.
   f) Give a graphical interpretation of the result of part b.

• *Derivatives and Derivative Rules*

For Exercises 20–23, find

a) $f'(x)$ b) $f'(1)$ c) $f'(-2)$

20. $f(x) = x^2 - 6x - 5$ **21.** $f(x) = -5x^2 + 2x + 7$
22. $f(x) = x^3 - 3x^2 + 6x$ **23.** $f(x) = x^8 - 8x$

24. *Sales revenue.* Return to Exercise 19 and determine
     a) $R'(x)$ b) $R'(1000)$
     c) Interpret the result of part b.
     d) Give a graphical interpretation of the result of part b.

25. *Population growth.* The population, P, of a given city is related to time, t (in years), by the function

$$P(t) = 5000t^2 + 300,000$$

     where $t = 0$ denotes the year 19X0, $t = 1$ denotes the year 19X1, etc.
     a) Determine the formula for the instantaneous rate of change of population with respect to time.

     Determine the instantaneous rate of change of the population at each of the following values of t and interpret the results.
     b) $t = 4$ c) $t = 6$ d) $t = 9$

26. Find the equation of the tangent line to $y = -x^2 + 9x$ at each of the following values of x and illustrate the results graphically.
     a) $x = 2$ b) $x = 3$ c) $x = 6$

For Exercises 27–41, find dy/dx.

27. $y = (x^2 + 4x + 7)(x^3 + 3x^2 + 8)$
28. $y = (x^3 - 4x^2 + 3)(x^5 + 6x^4 + 2)$
29. $y = (x^4 - 6x + 1)^6$ **30.** $y = x^5 + 6x^3 - 8x$
31. $y = 1/(x^2 + 8x + 2)^9$ **32.** $y = (x^3 + 5x + 8)^7$
33. $y = (x^3 + x^2 + 4)^5(x^2 + 4x + 5)$

34. $y = \dfrac{x^3 + 2x^2 - 5x}{x^2 - 4x + 8}$ **35.** $y = \dfrac{x^4 + 5x^2 + 7}{x^3 - 6x + 8}$

36. $y = \dfrac{(x^2 - 5)^8}{x^2 + 36}$ **37.** $y = \dfrac{(x^4 + 4x + 7)^9}{x^3 - 4x + 2}$

38. $y = (x^5 - 7x)\left(\dfrac{x^4 + 8x}{x^2 + 6}\right)$ **39.** $y = (x^8 + 9)\left(\dfrac{x^2 - 9}{x^4 + 7}\right)^6$
40. $y = (x + 1/\sqrt{x})(x + 3)$ **41.** $y = [(x + 6)/(x - 5)]^8$

42. *Sales revenue.* The unit price, p (in dollars), of some product is changing with demand, x, in accordance with the equation

$$p = 300 + 50x$$

The demand, x, is changing with time, t (in days), in accordance with the equation

$$x = 400 + 0.5t^3$$

     a) Determine the formula for dR/dt.
     b) Evaluate dR/dt at $t = 6$ and interpret the result.

43. *Average cost.* The cost of producing x units of some product is given by

$$C(x) = 8x + 240$$

     a) Determine the formula for the average cost per unit $\overline{C}(x)$.
     b) Determine the formula for $\overline{C}'(x)$.
     c) Find $\overline{C}'(5)$, $\overline{C}'(20)$, and $\overline{C}'(50)$, and interpret the results.

44. *Compound interest.* Twenty thousand dollars is deposited into an account earning interest at the rate of r% compounded annually. At the end of 8 years, the balance in the account is given by

$$S = 20,000[1 + (r/100)]^8$$

   a) Find the formula for the instantaneous rate of change of S with respect to r.
   b) Evaluate the result of part a at $r = 7$ and interpret the result.
   c) Evaluate the result of part a at $r = 9$ and interpret the result.

45. *Annuity.* At the end of each year, \$9000 is deposited into an account earning interest at the rate of r% compounded annually. At the end of 6 years, the balance in the account is given by

$$S = (900,000/r)([(1 + (r/100)]^6 - 1)$$

   a) Find the formula for the instantaneous rate of change of S with respect to r.
   b) Evaluate the result of part a at $r = 8$ and interpret the result.
   c) Evaluate the result of part a at $r = 10$ and interpret the result.

• Differentiability and Continuity

For Exercises 46 and 47:

a) For which value(s) of x is $f(x)$ not continuous?
b) For which value(s) of x is $f(x)$ not differentiable?

46. $f(x) = 1/(x - 7)^3$ **47.** $f(x) = \sqrt{x - 5}$

For Exercises 48–50, for which value(s) of x is $f(x)$ not differentiable?

48. $f(x) = |x|$ **49.** $f(x) = x^{1/5}$ **50.** $f(x) = x^{4/5}$

Algebra Refresher

FACTORING

Difference of Two Squares

$$a^2 - b^2 = (a - b)(a + b)$$

Examples $x^2 - 36 = (x - 6)(x + 6)$ $x^2 - 7 = (x - \sqrt{7})(x + \sqrt{7})$

Worksheet

Fill in the blanks.

$x^2 - 25 = (\underline{})(\underline{})$ Answer: $(x - 5)(x + 5)$

$x^2 - 81 = (\underline{})(\underline{})$ Answer: $(x - 9)(x + 9)$

$x^2 - 19 = (\underline{})(\underline{})$ Answer: $(x - \sqrt{19})(x + \sqrt{19})$

Trinomials

$$x^2 + bx + c = (x + p)(x + q)$$

where

$$p + q = b$$
$$p \cdot q = c$$

Examples $x^2 + 5x + 6 = (x + 3)(x + 2)$ $x^2 - 2x - 15 = (x - 5)(x + 3)$

Worksheet

Fill in the blanks.

$x^2 + 5x - 6 = (\underline{})(\underline{})$ Answer: $(x + 6)(x - 1)$

$x^2 - 5x + 6 = (\underline{})(\underline{})$ Answer: $(x - 2)(x - 3)$

$x^2 - 4x - 21 = (\underline{})(\underline{})$ Answer: $(x - 7)(x + 3)$

$x^2 - 8x + 16 = (\underline{})(\underline{})$ Answer: $(x - 4)(x - 4)$

$x^2 + 6x + 9 = (\underline{})(\underline{})$ Answer: $(x + 3)(x + 3)$

10

CURVE
SKETCHING AND
OPTIMIZATION

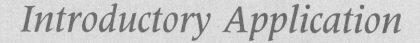

Introductory Application

Optimization: Quality Control and Profits

Sharp Industries produces table knives. Each knife costs $6 to produce and sells for $9. The quality control manager has determined from past data that out of x knives that are produced during any given day, the fraction defective for the day is given by $x^2/20{,}000{,}000$, where $100 \leq x \leq 1500$. Each defective knife costs the company an additional $20.

a) Determine the equation that gives daily profit, P, as a function of daily production volume, x.

b) Determine the maximum daily profit and the daily production volume that yields the maximum daily profit.

In this chapter, we discuss optimization procedures that enable us to solve problems such as the one above. The above problem is solved in Example 10-20.

10-1 • HIGHER-ORDER DERIVATIVES

The Second Derivative

The derivative of a function, $y = f(x)$, commonly denoted by $f'(x)$, dy/dx, y', or $D_x y$ is called a **first derivative.** The derivative of a first derivative is called the **second derivative** and is denoted by any of the following symbols:

$$f''(x) \qquad f^{(2)}(x) \qquad \frac{d^2 y}{dx^2} \qquad y'' \qquad y^{(2)}(x) \qquad D_x^2 y \qquad D_x^2[f(x)]$$

Thus, if

$$f(x) = x^4 - 8x^3 + 7x^2 - 15$$

the first derivative is

$$f'(x) = 4x^3 - 24x^2 + 14x$$

and the second derivative is

$$f''(x) = 12x^2 - 48x + 14$$

• **EXAMPLE 10-1** _____

If $f(x) = x^5 - 8x^4 + 7x^3 - 5$, find $f'(x)$, $f''(x)$, and $f''(1)$.

Solution

$$f'(x) = 5x^4 - 32x^3 + 21x^2$$

The derivative of $f'(x)$ is

$$f''(x) = 20x^3 - 96x^2 + 42x$$

Evaluating $f''(x)$ at $x = 1$ gives

$$f''(1) = 20(1)^3 - 96(1)^2 + 42(1) = -34$$

_____ •

The derivative of the second derivative is called the **third derivative** and is denoted by any of the following symbols:

$$f'''(x) \qquad f^{(3)}(x) \qquad \frac{d^3 y}{dx^3} \qquad y''' \qquad y^{(3)}(x) \qquad D_x^3 y \qquad D_x^3[f(x)]$$

Analogously, the derivative of the third derivative is called the fourth derivative, the derivative of the fourth derivative is called the fifth derivative, etc. In general, the *n*th **derivative** of a function $y = f(x)$ is denoted by any of the following symbols:

$$f^{(n)}(x) \qquad \frac{d^n y}{dx^n} \qquad y^{(n)} \qquad y^{(n)}(x) \qquad D_x^n y \qquad D_x^n[f(x)]$$

• **EXAMPLE 10-2** _____

If $y = x^4 - 2x^3 + 5x^2 - 3x + 4$, find dy/dx, d^2y/dx^2, d^3y/dx^3, and $\left.\dfrac{d^3 y}{dx^3}\right|_{x = 2}$.

Solution

$$\frac{dy}{dx} = 4x^3 - 6x^2 + 10x - 3$$

The derivative of dy/dx is

$$\frac{d^2y}{dx^2} = 12x^2 - 12x + 10$$

The derivative of d^2y/dx^2 is

$$\frac{d^3y}{dx^3} = 24x - 12$$

Evaluating d^3y/dx^3 at $x = 2$ gives

$$\frac{d^3y}{dx^3}\bigg|_{x=2} = 24(2) - 12 = 36$$

• **EXAMPLE 10-3** _____

If $f(x) = x^5 - 6x^4 + 3x^2 + 5$, find $f'(x), f''(x), f'''(x), f^{(4)}(x)$, and $f^{(4)}(3)$.

Solution

$$f'(x) = 5x^4 - 24x^3 + 6x$$

The derivative of $f'(x)$ is

$$f''(x) = 20x^3 - 72x^2 + 6$$

The derivative of $f''(x)$ is

$$f'''(x) = 60x^2 - 144x$$

The derivative of $f'''(x)$ is

$$f^{(4)}(x) = 120x - 144$$

Evaluating $f^{(4)}(x)$ at $x = 3$ gives

$$f^{(4)}(3) = 120(3) - 144 = 216$$

_____ •

Acceleration

A second derivative d^2y/dx^2 of a function $y = f(x)$ gives the instantaneous rate of change of the first derivative with respect to x. If $S = f(t)$, then d^2S/dt^2 gives the instantaneous rate of change of the first derivative with respect to t. Thus, if a ball moves in the path of a straight line and its distance, S (in feet), from its starting point after t seconds have elapsed is given by

$$S = -4t^2 + 36t \qquad (0 \le t \le 9)$$

then the formula for the ball's instantaneous speed (or velocity) is given by

$$\frac{dS}{dt} = -8t + 36$$

The ball's instantaneous speed (or velocity) at $t = 2$ is given by

$$\frac{dS}{dt}\bigg|_{t=2} = -8(2) + 36 = 20$$

Thus, at $t = 2$, the ball's instantaneous speed is 20 ft/sec.

The ball's instantaneous speed at $t = 3$ is given by

$$\frac{dS}{dt}\bigg|_{t = 3} = -8(3) + 36 = 12$$

Thus, at $t = 3$, the ball's speed is 12 ft/sec.

Note that the ball's instantaneous speed changes as t changes. The instantaneous rate of change of speed with respect to time is called **instantaneous acceleration** and is given in this case by

$$\frac{d^2S}{dt^2} = -8$$

Thus, the ball's instantaneous acceleration is -8 ft/sec^2 (i.e., -8 feet per second per second).

The concept of acceleration is most clearly explained by considering a person driving an automobile. If the speedometer reads 50 on the mph scale, then the car is moving at a speed of 50 mph. As long as the speedometer remains at 50 mph, the car is moving at a constant speed, and the acceleration (the rate of change of speed with respect to time) is 0. If the driver further depresses the gas pedal, the speedometer's reading increases beyond 50 mph, and the acceleration is greater than 0. If the driver releases pressure on the gas pedal, the acceleration is less than 0, and the speed decreases. Negative acceleration is called **deceleration.** Specifically, the *negative* acceleration, $d^2S/dt^2 = -8$, of the ball of the above illustrative example indicates that the ball's speed is *decreasing* at a rate of 8 feet per second per second.

Exercises 10-1

For each of the following, find $f'(x)$ and $f''(x)$.

1. $f(x) = x^3 - 4x^2 + 7x - 9$
2. $f(x) = x^4 - 7x^3 + 8x - 3$
3. $f(x) = x^5 - 8x^3 + 2x^2 + 4x + 1$
4. $f(x) = (x - 1)/(x + 6)$
5. $f(x) = (x^3 + 1)(x^2 - x + 4)$
6. $f(x) = (x^2 + 5)(x^3 - x + 1)$
7. $f(x) = (x + 1)^4(x - 2) + 6$

For each of the following, find dy/dx and d^2y/dx^2.

8. $y = x^4 - 8x^3 + 6x - 9$
9. $y = x^3 - 2x^2 + 8x - 3$
10. $y = x^8 - 10x^2 + 4x + 1$
11. $y = (x^4 + 6)/(x^3 - 7)$
12. $y = (x^2 + 5)(x^3 - x + 6)$
13. $y = (x - 4)^3(x - 7) + 8$

14. If $f(x) = x^3 - 4x^2 + 7x + 9$, find $f'(x), f''(x), f'(2)$, and $f''(4)$.
15. If $g(x) = (x^2 - 1)/(x - 5)$, find $g'(x), g''(x)$, and $g''(2)$.
16. If $y(x) = (x + 1)(x + 3)^2$, find $y'(x), y''(x)$, and $y''(2)$.
17. If $y = x^4 - 5x^3 + 6x^2 + 3x + 1$, find $\dfrac{dy}{dx}, \dfrac{dy}{dx}\bigg|_{x = 1}, \dfrac{d^2y}{dx^2}$, and $\dfrac{d^2y}{dx^2}\bigg|_{x = 1}$.
18. If $y = x^5 - 8x^4 + 6x^3 - 9x^2 + 4$, find $\dfrac{dy}{dx}, \dfrac{dy}{dx}\bigg|_{x = 2}, \dfrac{d^2y}{dx^2}$, and $\dfrac{d^2y}{dx^2}\bigg|_{x = 2}$.
19. If $f(x) = x^4 - 6x^3 + 8x^2 - 4x - 5$, find $f'(x), f''(x), f'(1)$, and $f''(3)$.
20. If $f(x) = (x^3 - 1)(x^2 + x - 4)$, find $f'(x), f'(2), f''(x)$, and $f''(2)$.

21. If $f(x) = x^6 - 8x^5 + 6x^4 - 2x^3 + x + 5$, find $f'(x)$, $f''(x)$, $f'''(x)$, $f^{(4)}(x)$, and $f^{(4)}(3)$.

22. If $f(x) = x^7 - 4x^6 + 3x^4 + 6x - 9$, find $f'(x)$, $f''(x)$, $f'''(x)$, $f^{(4)}(x)$, $f^{(5)}(x)$, and $f^{(5)}(1)$.

23. If $f(x) = x^4 - 6x^3 + 4x^2 - 8x + 1$, find $f'(x)$, $f''(x)$, $f'''(x)$, $f^{(4)}(x)$, $f^{(5)}(x)$, and $f^{(6)}(x)$.

24. *Projectile.* A ball moves in the path of a straight line. Its distance, S (in feet), from its starting point after t seconds have elapsed is given by

$$S = -4t^2 + 32t \qquad (0 \le t \le 8)$$

a) Find the ball's instantaneous speed at $t = 1$ and $t = 2$.
b) Find the ball's instantaneous acceleration at $t = 1$ and $t = 2$.

25. *Projectile.* A ball is projected vertically into the air. The function defined by

$$S = -16t^2 + 192t \qquad (0 \le t \le 12)$$

gives the height of the ball (in feet) above the ground at time t (in seconds).
a) Find the ball's instantaneous speed at $t = 2$, at $t = 3$, and at $t = 8$.
b) Find the ball's instantaneous acceleration at $t = 2$, at $t = 3$, and at $t = 8$.

10-2 • CRITICAL VALUES AND THE FIRST DERIVATIVE

Consider the graph in Figure 10-1. In this chapter, we will be concerned with identifying the x- and y-coordinates of points such as A and B. We first begin by identifying points of relative maxima and relative minima. Point A $(x_1, f(x_1))$ is an example of a **relative maximum** point because it is *higher* than any of its neighboring points on the graph of $f(x)$. Mathematically, this is expressed by saying that $f(x_1) > f(x)$ for all values of x near x_1. Point B $(x_2, f(x_2))$ in Figure 10-1 is an example of a **relative minimum** point because it is *lower* than any of its neighboring points on the graph of $f(x)$. Mathematically, this is expressed by saying that $f(x_2) < f(x)$ for all values of x near x_2. More precisely, a point $(x_1, f(x_1))$ is called a relative maximum point of the function $f(x)$ if $f(x_1) > f(x)$ for all x-values in some open interval containing x_1 and in the domain of f (see Figure 10-2).* A point $(x_2, f(x_2))$ is called a relative minimum point of the function $f(x)$ if $f(x_2) < f(x)$ for all x-values in some open interval containing x_2 and in the domain of f (see Figure 10-2).

Points of relative maxima and relative minima should be distinguished from points of absolute maxima and absolute minima. Referring to Figure 10-2, point A $(x_1, f(x_1))$ is a relative maximum point because it is higher than any of its neighboring points on the graph of $f(x)$. However, it is not the highest point on the graph of $f(x)$. Observe that point C $(b, f(b))$ is higher than point A. If we choose the domain of $f(x)$ to be the closed interval $a \le x \le b$, then point C is the highest point on the graph of $f(x)$.† Hence, its y-coordinate is called the **absolute maximum** value of $f(x)$. Similarly, observe that point B $(x_2, f(x_2))$ is a relative minimum point because it is lower than any of its neighboring points on the graph of $f(x)$. However, it is not the lowest point on the graph of the function. That dis-

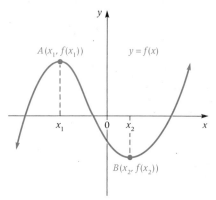

FIGURE 10-1

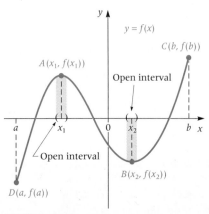

FIGURE 10-2

---

*Recall from the Algebra Review chapter that an open interval does not contain its endpoints.
†Recall from the Algebra Review chapter that a closed interval does contain its endpoints.

tinction is attributed to the point D $(a, f(a))$. Thus, the y-coordinate of point D $(a, f(a))$ is called the **absolute minimum** value of $f(x)$. Note that if the domain of $f(x)$ is the set of all real numbers, then there is neither an absolute maximum nor an absolute minimum since the function $f(x)$ extends downward indefinitely to the left and upward indefinitely to the right. Thus, we state the following.

SUMMARY

Relative Extrema

Relative Maximum

1. A point $(x_0, f(x_0))$ is a **relative maximum point** of a function $f(x)$ if $f(x_0) > f(x)$ for all x-values in some open interval containing x_0.
2. $f(x_0)$ is a **relative maximum value** (or, simply, *relative maximum*) of the function $f(x)$.
3. A relative maximum point is higher than any of its neighboring points on the graph of $f(x)$.

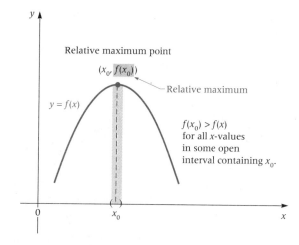

Other examples of relative maxima

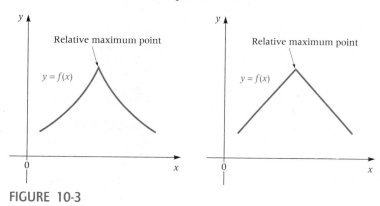

FIGURE 10-3

continues

SUMMARY—*Continued*

Relative Minimum

1. A point $(x_0, f(x_0))$ is a **relative minimum point** of a function $f(x)$ if $f(x_0) < f(x)$ for all x-values in some open interval containing x_0.
2. $f(x_0)$ is a **relative minimum value** (or, simply, *relative minimum*) of the function $f(x)$.
3. A relative minimum point is lower than any of its neighboring points on the graph of $f(x)$.

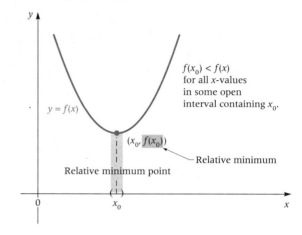

Other examples of relative minima

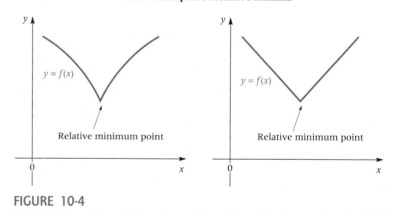

FIGURE 10-4

  SUMMARY

Absolute Extrema

Absolute Maximum

1. A point $(x_0, f(x_0))$ is an **absolute maximum point** of a function $f(x)$ if $f(x_0) \geq f(x)$ for all x-values over which $f(x)$ is defined. $f(x_0)$ is the **absolute maximum value** (or, simply, *absolute maximum*) of

continues

SUMMARY—*Continued*

the function $f(x)$. The absolute maximum, $f(x_0)$, is the largest value of the function, $f(x)$ for all x-values over which $f(x)$ is defined.

2. A function can have more than one absolute maximum point, but only one absolute maximum. If a function has more than one absolute maximum point, then all such points have the same value of $f(x)$ (i.e., the same y-value). Thus, there is no point on the graph of $f(x)$ that is higher than an absolute maximum point. Study Figure 10-5.

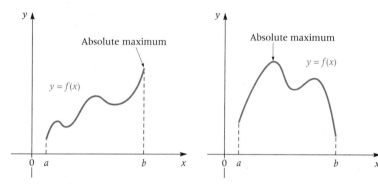

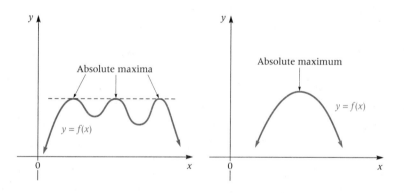

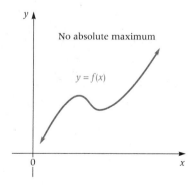

FIGURE 10-5

continues

SUMMARY—*Continued*

Absolute Minimum

1. A point $(x_0, f(x_0))$ is an **absolute minimum point** of a function $f(x)$ if $f(x_0) \leq f(x)$ for all x-values over which $f(x)$ is defined. $\boldsymbol{f(x_0)}$ is the **absolute minimum value** (or, simply, *absolute minimum*) of the function $f(x)$. The absolute minimum, $f(x_0)$, is the smallest value of the function $f(x)$ for all x-values over which $f(x)$ is defined.

2. A function can have more than one absolute minimum point, but only one absolute minimum. If a function has more than one absolute minimum point, then all such points have the same value of $f(x)$ (i.e., the same y-value). Thus, there is no point on the graph of $f(x)$ that is lower than an absolute minimum point. Study Figure 10-6.

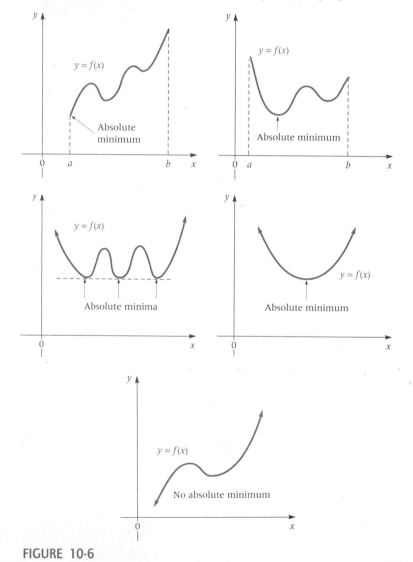

FIGURE 10-6

We also state the following.

Extreme Value Theorem

A continuous function defined on a closed interval will have both an absolute maximum and an absolute minimum at points in the interval.

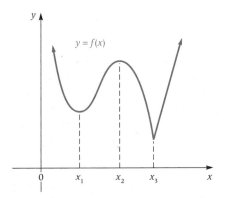

FIGURE 10-7

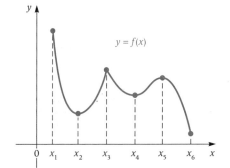

FIGURE 10-8

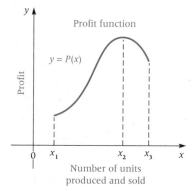

FIGURE 10-9

• **EXAMPLE 10-4** _____

Consider the graph in Figure 10-7.

a) Identify all relative maximum and minimum points and their respective relative maximum and minimum values.

b) Identify the absolute maximum and minimum points and their respective absolute maximum and minimum values.

Solutions

a) The relative maximum points are $(x_3, f(x_3))$ and $(x_5, f(x_5))$. Thus, $f(x_3)$ and $f(x_5)$ are relative maximum values of $f(x)$ or, simply, relative maxima. The relative minimum points are $(x_2, f(x_2))$ and $(x_4, f(x_4))$. Thus, $f(x_2)$ and $f(x_4)$ are relative minimum values of $f(x)$ or, simply, relative minima.

b) Here there is only one absolute maximum point, $(x_1, f(x_1))$. Thus, $f(x_1)$ is the absolute maximum value or, simply, absolute maximum of $f(x)$. Also, there is only one absolute minimum point, $(x_6, f(x_6))$. Thus, $f(x_6)$ is the absolute minimum value or, simply, absolute minimum of $f(x)$.

• **EXAMPLE 10-5** _____

Consider the graph in Figure 10-8.

a) Identify all relative extrema.

b) Identify all absolute extrema.

Solutions

a) $f(x_2)$ is a relative maximum; $f(x_1)$ and $f(x_3)$ are relative minima.

b) $f(x_3)$ is an absolute minimum. There is no absolute maximum as the graph of $f(x)$ continues upward indefinitely.

• **EXAMPLE 10-6** _____

Consider the graph of the profit function in Figure 10-9.

a) How many units should be produced and sold in order to maximize profit?

b) What is the maximum profit? Is this a relative maximum? Is this an absolute maximum?

Solutions

a) x_2 units should be produced and sold in order to maximize profit.

b) The maximum profit is given by $P(x_2)$. $P(x_2)$ is both a relative maximum and an absolute maximum.

_____ •

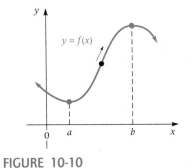

FIGURE 10-10

Increasing and Decreasing Functions

An important concept in graphing is identifying values of x for which a function $f(x)$ is increasing or decreasing. Consider the graph in Figure 10-10. If we place the point of a pencil on the graph of $f(x)$ at $x = a$ and move along the graph of $f(x)$ from $x = a$ to $x = b$, as indicated by the arrow above the black point in Figure 10-10, then our pencil will be moving uphill on the graph of $f(x)$. Thus, we say that $f(x)$ is increasing over the interval $a < x < b$. A more formal definition of an increasing function is given in the following box.

Increasing Function

Let x_1 and x_2 be any x-values in the interval $a < x < b$ such that $x_2 > x_1$ (see Figure 10-11). The function $f(x)$ is **increasing** over the interval $a < x < b$ if $f(x_2) > f(x_1)$.

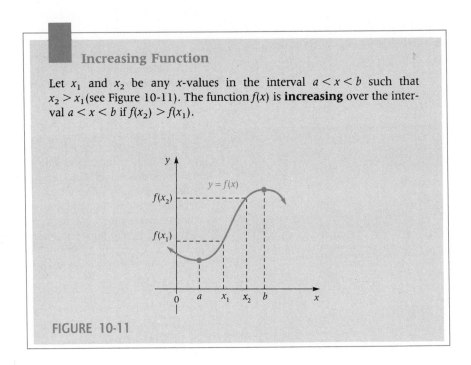

FIGURE 10-11

Consider the graph in Figure 10-12. If we move our pencil along the graph of $f(x)$ from $x = a$ to $x = b$, then our pencil will be moving downhill on the graph of $f(x)$. Thus, we say that $f(x)$ is decreasing over the interval $a < x < b$. A more formal definition of a decreasing function is given in the following box.

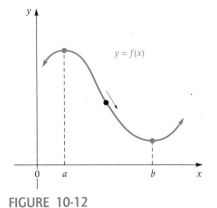

FIGURE 10-12

Decreasing Function

Let x_1 and x_2 be any x-values in the interval $a < x < b$ such that $x_2 > x_1$ (see Figure 10-13). The function $f(x)$ is **decreasing** over the interval $a < x < b$ if $f(x_2) < f(x_1)$.

continues

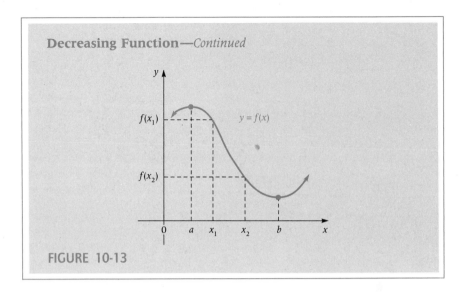

Decreasing Function—*Continued*

FIGURE 10-13

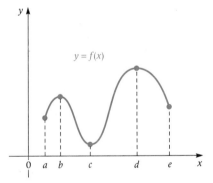

FIGURE 10-14

• **EXAMPLE 10-7**

Consider the graph in Figure 10-14.

a) State the interval(s) over which the function $f(x)$ is increasing.
b) State the interval(s) over which the function $f(x)$ is decreasing.
c) Identify all relative maxima and relative minima.
d) Identify the absolute maximum and absolute minimum values of $f(x)$.

Solutions

a) The function $f(x)$ is increasing over the intervals $a < x < b$ and $c < x < d$.
b) The function $f(x)$ is decreasing over the intervals $b < x < c$ and $d < x < e$.
c) $f(b)$ and $f(d)$ are relative maxima; $f(c)$ is a relative minimum.
d) The absolute maximum is $f(d)$; the absolute minimum is $f(c)$.

We will now be concerned mainly with graphing functions and with determining their relative maxima and relative minima. In this regard, we consider the graph of the function illustrated in Figure 10-15 on page 686. Observe that certain segments of the function are identified as either increasing or decreasing. Specifically, the function $f(x)$ is *increasing* as we move along its path from point *D* to point *A* and from point *B* to point *C*. Thus, the function is said to be increasing on each of the intervals $a < x < x_1$ and $x_2 < x < b$. Note that, within these intervals, any tangent line to the function has a *positive slope*. Since the slope of a tangent line is the derivative of the function at the point of tangency, we state the following.

Given that f(x) *is differentiable on the interval* a < x < b, *then* f(x) *is increasing on this interval if* f′(x) > 0 *for all values of* x *within* a < x < b.

Again referring to Figure 10-15 on page 686, observe that the function is *decreasing* as we move along its path from point *A* to point *B*. The function is said to be decreasing on the interval $x_1 < x < x_2$. Any tangent line to the function within this interval has a *negative slope*. Thus, we state the following.

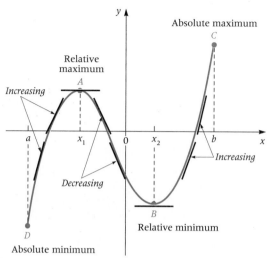

FIGURE 10-15

Given that f(x) *is differentiable on the interval* a < x < b, *then* f(x) *is decreasing on this interval if* f'(x) < 0 *for all values of* x *within* a < x < b.

Thus, for a given function, we can use the first derivative to determine where the function is increasing or decreasing, as summarized in the following box.

SUMMARY

First Derivative and Increasing and Decreasing Functions

Given a function $f(x)$ that is differentiable on some open interval, then

- If $f'(x) > 0$ for all values of x in the open interval, then $f(x)$ is **increasing** on the interval (see Figure 10-16).

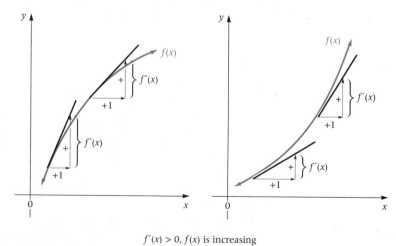

$f'(x) > 0$, $f(x)$ is increasing

FIGURE 10-16

continues

SUMMARY—*Continued*

- If $f'(x) < 0$ for all values of x in some open interval, then $f(x)$ is **decreasing** on the interval (see Figure 10-17).

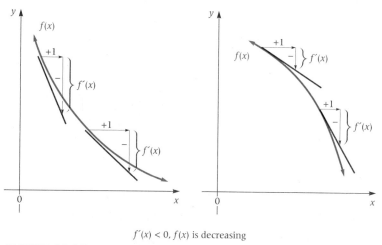

$f'(x) < 0$, $f(x)$ is decreasing

FIGURE 10-17

Once again observing Figure 10-15, note that at a point of relative maximum or relative minimum, the tangent line is *horizontal.* Hence, its *slope is 0.* Since the slope of a tangent line is the derivative of the function, then $f'(x) = 0$ for values of x where $f(x)$ has either relative maxima or minima. We now state the following.

If a function f(x) *has either a relative minimum or a relative maximum at* $x = x_0$ *and is differentiable at* $x = x_0$, *then*

$$f'(x_0) = 0$$

Thus, we can usually identify relative maxima and relative minima by finding the values of x for which $f'(x) = 0$. This assumes that $f(x)$ is differentiable at the points of relative maxima and minima. However, this is not always the case. An example of a function that is not differentiable at a relative minimum is $f(x) = x^{2/3}$. Observing its graph in Figure 10-18, note that the point $(0, 0)$ is a relative minimum point since it is lower than any of its neighboring points. However, since the graph of $f(x)$ comes to a sharp point at $x = 0$, then $f(x)$ is not differentiable there. Hence, $f'(0)$ does not exist. Therefore, in order to identify points of relative maxima and relative minima of a continuous function $f(x)$, we should follow the subsequent procedure.

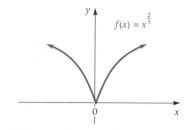

FIGURE 10-18

To Identify Candidates for Relative Extrema

Find $f'(x)$ and determine those values of x for which $f'(x) = 0$. Additionally, look for values of x at which $f'(x)$ does not exist.

Values of x at which either $f'(x) = 0$ or $f'(x)$ does not exist are called **critical values.** We summarize as follows.

> **SUMMARY**
>
> **Critical Values and Relative Extrema**
>
> 1. **Critical values** of x are those values of x at which either $f'(x) = 0$ or $f'(x)$ is undefined, and $f(x)$ is defined.
> 2. **Existence of Relative Extrema.** Given that $f(x)$ is continuous over some open interval, then relative maxima or minima, if they exist, occur at critical values of x.
>   *Note:* This does not mean that all critical values yield relative extrema. We should understand that a critical value may or may not yield relative extrema. In other words, critical values yield candidates for relative extrema.

• **EXAMPLE 10-8** _____

Find the critical values of $f(x) = 2x^3 - 3x^2 - 36x + 7$.

Solution

Here we calculate

$$f'(x) = 6x^2 - 6x - 36$$

Since we seek values of x for which $f'(x) = 0$, we set $f'(x) = 0$ and solve for x to obtain

$$6x^2 - 6x - 36 = 0$$
$$6(x^2 - x - 6) = 0$$
$$6(x - 3)(x + 2) = 0$$

Thus, $x = 3$ and $x = -2$ are critical values. Since there are no values of x at which $f'(x)$ does not exist, these are the only critical values. Computing the corresponding y-coordinates, we have

$$f(3) = 2(3)^3 - 3(3)^2 - 36(3) + 7 = -74$$
$$f(-2) = 2(-2)^3 - 3(-2)^2 - 36(-2) + 7 = 51$$

Hence, the points $(3, -74)$ and $(-2, 51)$ are candidates for relative maximum and minimum points.

• **EXAMPLE 10-9** _____

Find the critical values of $f(x) = x^{2/3}$.

Solution

Here we calculate

$$f'(x) = \frac{2}{3}x^{-1/3}$$
$$= \frac{2}{3} \cdot \frac{1}{x^{1/3}} = \frac{2}{3} \cdot \frac{1}{\sqrt[3]{x}}$$

A sign chart for $f'(x)$ is given in Table 10-1.

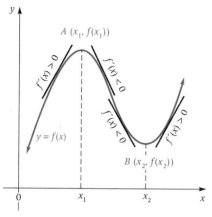

FIGURE 10-19

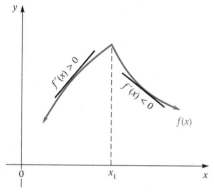

FIGURE 10-20

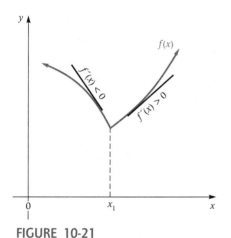

FIGURE 10-21

TABLE 10-1

Sign chart for $f'(x) = \dfrac{2}{3} \cdot \dfrac{1}{\sqrt[3]{x}}$		

$f'(x)$ — — — — — — — — — — — — — — — — — Undefined ↓ +

0 x

↑
critical
value
here

Note that there are no values of x for which $f'(x) = 0$. However, $f'(x)$ does not exist at $x = 0$. Thus, $x = 0$ is the only critical value. Computing the corresponding y-coordinate, we have

$$f(0) = 0^{2/3} = 0$$

Therefore, $(0, 0)$ is a candidate for a relative maximum or minimum point.

Recall, from Section 9-5, that the graph of $f(x) = x^{2/3}$ is as given in Figure 10-18.

First-Derivative Test

A critical value may or may not lead to a relative maximum or minimum point. In other words, not every critical value yields a relative maximum or minimum point. Thus, we need a test to determine whether a critical value yields either a relative maximum or a relative minimum, or neither. One such test is called the **first-derivative test** since it is based on the first derivative, $f'(x)$, of a function $f(x)$.

We will explain the first-derivative test by referring to the function in Figure 10-19. Observing the relative maximum point $A\ (x_1, f(x_1))$, note that the tangent line to the left of x_1 has a positive slope, whereas the tangent line to the right of x_1 has a negative slope. Thus, if x_1 is a critical value of $f(x)$, then x_1 yields a relative maximum if $f'(x) > 0$ for all nearby values of x to the left of x_1 and $f'(x) < 0$ for all nearby values of x to the right of x_1. This is true even if $f'(x_1)$ does not exist (see Figure 10-20). For a relative minimum, the reverse holds. Observing the relative minimum point B $(x_2, f(x_2))$ in Figure 10-19, note that the tangent line to the left of x_2 has a negative slope, whereas the tangent line to the right of x_2 has a positive slope. Thus, if x_2 is a critical value of $f(x)$, then x_2 yields a relative minimum if $f'(x) < 0$ for all nearby values of x to the left of x_2 and $f'(x) > 0$ for all nearby values of x to the right of x_2. This also is true even if $f'(x_2)$ does not exist, as illustrated in Figure 10-21. Thus, we now state the first-derivative test.

SUMMARY

First-Derivative Test for Relative Extrema

If x_0 is a critical value of $f(x)$ (in other words, $f'(x_0) = 0$ or $f'(x_0)$ is undefined) where $f(x_0)$ is defined, then

1. $f(x_0)$ is a **relative maximum** of $f(x)$ if $f'(x)$ is positive for all nearby values of x to the left of x_0 and $f'(x)$ is negative for all nearby values of x to the right of x_0 (see Figure 10-22).
2. $f(x_0)$ is a **relative minimum** of $f(x)$ if $f'(x)$ is negative for all nearby values of x to the left of x_0 and $f'(x)$ is positive for all nearby values of x to the right of x_0 (see Figure 10-23).

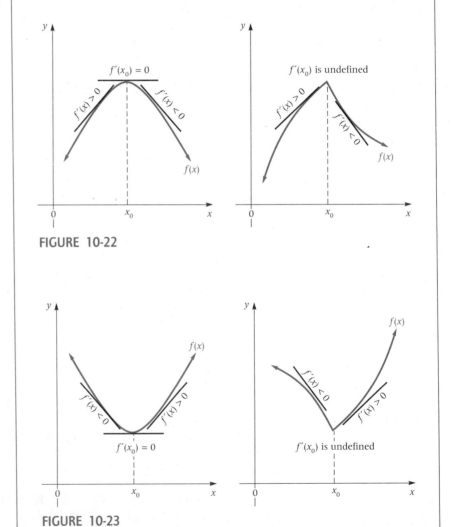

FIGURE 10-22

FIGURE 10-23

• EXAMPLE 10-10 _____

Find the relative maxima and minima of the function $f(x) = x^3 + 3x^2 - 72x + 9$.

Solution

First, we find

$$f'(x) = 3x^2 + 6x - 72$$

Setting $f'(x) = 0$ and solving for x yields

$$3x^2 + 6x - 72 = 0$$
$$3(x^2 + 2x - 24) = 0$$
$$3(x + 6)(x - 4) = 0$$

Thus, $x = -6$ and $x = 4$ are critical values. Since there are no values of x at which $f'(x)$ does not exist, these are the only critical values. We now apply the first-derivative test by analyzing the sign of $f'(x)$, as illustrated in Table 10-2.

Studying Table 10-2 on page 692, note that the sign of $3(x + 6)$ is the same as the sign of $(x + 6)$ since the *positive* constant multiplier, 3, does not change the sign of $(x + 6)$. Since $f'(x) > 0$ for all nearby values of x to the left of $x = -6$ and $f'(x) < 0$ for all nearby values of x to the right of $x = -6$, then, by the first-derivative test, a relative maximum exists at $x = -6$. Also, since $f'(x) < 0$ for all nearby values of x to the left of $x = 4$ and $f'(x) > 0$ for all nearby values of x to the right of $x = 4$, then, by the first derivative test, a relative minimum exists at $x = 4$.

Computing the y-coordinates corresponding to the relative maximum and minimum, we have

$$f(-6) = (-6)^3 + 3(-6)^2 - 72(-6) + 9 = 333 \qquad \text{Relative maximum}$$
$$f(4) = 4^3 + 3(4)^2 - 72(4) + 9 = -167 \qquad \text{Relative minimum}$$

Plotting the relative maximum and minimum points and the y-intercept on the rectangular coordinate system gives us the graph in Figure 10-24. Observe that it is not difficult to determine the general nature of the graph of $f(x)$, which appears in Figure 10-25, since $f(x)$ is increasing for those values of x at which $f'(x) > 0$ and decreasing for those values of x at which $f'(x) < 0$.

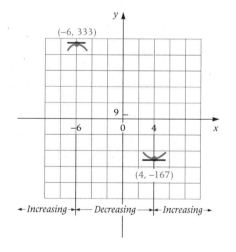

FIGURE 10-24

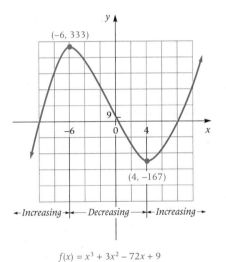

$$f(x) = x^3 + 3x^2 - 72x + 9$$

FIGURE 10-25

TABLE 10-2

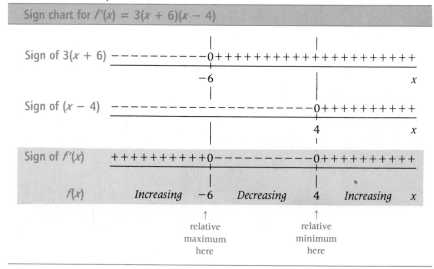

Remember that a sign change in $f'(x)$ indicates the occurrence of a relative extremum. The nature of the sign change indicates whether the relative extremum is either a maximum or a minimum.

• **EXAMPLE 10-11** _____

Find any relative maxima and minima of the function $f(x) = x^{2/3}$.

Solution

In Example 10-9, we calculated

$$f'(x) = \frac{2}{3} \cdot \frac{1}{x^{1/3}}$$

which yielded a critical value of $x = 0$. Applying the first-derivative test, we analyze the sign of $f'(x)$. Note that, as illustrated in Table 10-3, the sign of $f'(x)$ is the same as the sign of $x^{1/3} = \sqrt[3]{x}$. If $x > 0$, then $\sqrt[3]{x} > 0$, and, hence, $f'(x) > 0$. If $x < 0$, then $\sqrt[3]{x} < 0$, and, hence, $f'(x) < 0$. Since $f'(x) < 0$ for all nearby values of x to the left of $x = 0$ and $f'(x) > 0$ for all nearby values of x to the right of $x = 0$, then, by the first-derivative test, a relative minimum exists at $x = 0$. Note that $f(0) = 0^{2/3} = 0$.

TABLE 10-3

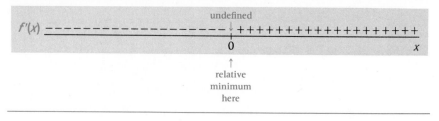

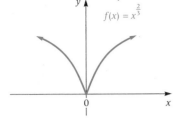

FIGURE 10-26

Although the preceding information does not enable us to sketch a graph of $f(x)$, its graph is included in Figure 10-26.

• **EXAMPLE 10-12 Sales Revenue.**

The sales revenue, R (in millions of dollars), gained from selling x (in thousands) units of a particular product is given by

$$R(x) = -x^3 - 6x^2 + 180x \qquad (0 \le x \le 10)$$

a) Graph the function $R(x)$ and determine the relative and absolute extrema.

b) How many units of this product should be produced and sold in order to maximize the sales revenue? What is the maximum sales revenue?

Solutions

a) We find

$$R'(x) = -3x^2 - 12x + 180$$

Setting $R'(x) = 0$ and solving for x yields

$$0 = -3x^2 - 12x + 180$$
$$0 = -3(x^2 + 4x - 60)$$
$$0 = -3(x - 6)(x + 10)$$

Thus, $x = 6$ and $x = -10$ are critical values. We rule out $x = -10$ since the function $R(x)$ is defined over the interval $0 \le x \le 10$. Since there are no values of x at which $R(x)$ does not exist, then $x = 6$ is the only relevant critical value. We now apply the first-derivative test by analyzing the sign of $R'(x)$ in Table 10-4. Although we include the sign chart for all values of x, we are concerned only with that portion over the interval $0 \le x \le 10$. Accordingly, we have shaded the corresponding portion in Table 10-4.

Note that the sign chart of Table 10-4 indicates the occurrence of a relative maximum at the critical value $x = 6$. Then we find the y-coordinate

TABLE 10-4

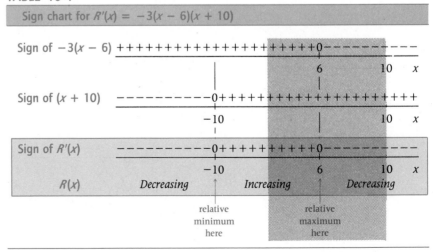

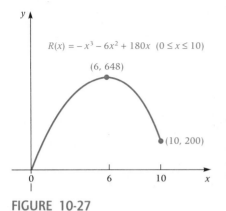

$R(x) = -x^3 - 6x^2 + 180x \quad (0 \le x \le 10)$

(6, 648)

(10, 200)

FIGURE 10-27

responding to $x = 6$ along with the y-coordinates of the endpoints of the interval $0 \le x \le 10$. Hence,

$$R(6) = -(6)^3 - 6(6)^2 + 180(6) = 648$$
$$R(0) = -(0)^3 - 6(0)^2 + 180(0) = 0$$
$$R(10) = -(10)^3 - 6(10)^2 + 180(10) = 200$$

The graph of $R(x)$ is sketched in Figure 10-27. Note that both a relative maximum and an absolute maximum occur at $x = 6$. An absolute minimum occurs at $x = 0$.

b) Thus, $x = 6$ thousand (remember that x is in thousands) units must be produced and sold in order to maximize sales revenue. The maximum sales revenue is given by the absolute maximum, $R(6) = 648$ million (remember that $R(x)$ is in millions) dollars.

Exercises 10-2

1. Consider the graph of Figure 10-28.
   a) State the interval(s) over which the function $f(x)$ is increasing.
   b) State the interval(s) over which the function $f(x)$ is decreasing.
   c) Identify all relative maxima and minima.
   d) Identify the absolute maximum and minimum values of $f(x)$.

2. Consider the graph of Figure 10-29.
   a) State the interval(s) over which $f(x)$ is increasing.
   b) State the interval(s) over which $f(x)$ is decreasing.
   c) Identify all relative maxima and minima.
   d) Identify the absolute maximum and minimum values of $f(x)$.

For each of the following sign charts, assume that the function $f(x)$ is continuous over the interval $(-\infty, \infty)$.
a) State the interval(s) over which the function $f(x)$ is increasing.
b) State the interval(s) over which the function $f(x)$ is decreasing.
c) State where relative maxima or minima occur.

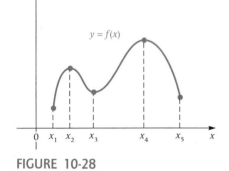

FIGURE 10-28

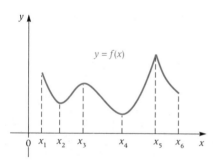

FIGURE 10-29

3. $f'(x)$ $--------------0+++++++++++0-----------$
                                      -2 2 x

4. $f'(x)$ $+++++++++++0-------------0++++++++++++$
                        -5 3 x

5. $f'(x)$ $++++++++++++0++++++++++++0-----------$
                        -4 5 x

6. $f'(x)$ $-----------0+++++++++++++0+++++++++++++$
                        -3 2 x

7. $f'(x)$ $-------0+++++++0++++++++0--------0+++++++$
                    -3 -1 2 4 x

8. $f'(x)$ $---------------0+++++++++++$ Undefined $\downarrow ------------$
                                  -2 1 x

9. $f'(x)$ $++++++++++++$ Undefined $\downarrow -------------0+++++++++++$
                                  -1 5 x

10. $f'(x)$ $------------$ Undefined $\downarrow ++++++++++++0-----------$
                                  -2 4 x

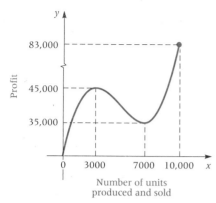

FIGURE 10-30

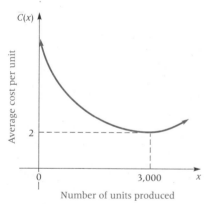

FIGURE 10-31

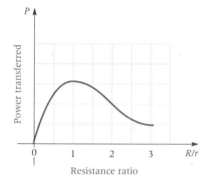

FIGURE 10-32

11. *Profit function.* Consider the graph of the profit function in Figure 10-30.
a) State the interval(s) over which profit is increasing.
b) State the interval(s) over which profit is decreasing.
c) Identify all relative extrema.
d) How many units should be produced and sold in order to maximize profit?
e) What is the maximum profit? Is this a relative maximum? Is this an absolute maximum?

12. *Physics: Power transfer.* When energy, such as electrical energy, is transferred from a source to a system (such as from a battery to an electrical system), the power, P, transferred to the system is a function of the ratio of the external resistance, R (the resistance of the system), to the internal resistance, r (the resistance of the source). Figure 10-31 gives a graph of this relationship.
a) What resistance ratio, R/r, yields the maximal power transfer? Is this a relative maximum? Is this an absolute maximum?
b) What relationship must exist between R and r in order for the maximal power transfer to occur?

13. *Average cost per unit.* Figure 10-32 gives a graph of the average cost per unit, $\overline{C}$, versus the number of units produced, x.
a) How many units should be produced in order to minimize the average cost per unit?
b) What is the minimum average cost per unit? Is this a relative minimum? Is this an absolute minimum?

For each of the following, use the first derivative to
a) Determine the interval(s) over which the function is increasing.
b) Determine the interval(s) over which the function is decreasing.
c) Determine any relative maxima and minima.

14. $y = x^2 + 2x - 15$ **15.** $y = 3x + 5$
16. $y = -2x + 8$ **17.** $y = -x^2 + 8x$
18. $y = 2x^3 + 15x^2 - 36x + 1$ **19.** $f(x) = 3x^4 - 4x^3 + 10$
20. $f(x) = 4x^3 - 72x^2 + 24x - 5$ **21.** $y = \sqrt{x^2 + 4}$
22. $y = \sqrt{x^2 + 9}$ **23.** $y = (x - 5)^3$
24. $y = \dfrac{x + 5}{x - 4}$ **25.** $y = \dfrac{x + 3}{x + 1}$

For each of the following, use the first derivative to
a) Determine the interval(s) over which the function is increasing.
b) Determine the interval(s) over which the function is decreasing.
c) Determine any relative maxima and minima.
d) Graph the function.

26. $y = x^2 + 8x + 5$ **27.** $y = -x^2 + 8x + 9$
28. $f(x) = -4x^2 + 32x + 19$ **29.** $y = x^3 - 6x^2$
30. $f(x) = 2x^3 + 3x^2 - 36x + 8$ **31.** $y = x^4 - 8x^2$
32. $f(x) = 3x^4 - 8x^3 + 20$ **33.** $y = x^4 + 5$

34. Find any relative maxima and minima of the function defined by $f(x) = x^{4/3}$. Use the first-derivative test.

35. Consider the function defined by

$$f(x) = x^3 + 6x^2 - 15x + 1 \qquad (-10 \le x \le 11)$$

Use the first-derivative test to find all relative maximum and relative minimum points. Also, determine the absolute maximum and minimum values of $f(x)$. Graph $f(x)$.

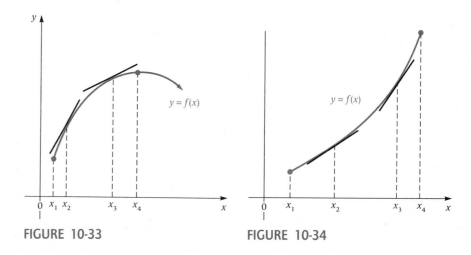

FIGURE 10-33   FIGURE 10-34

36. Consider the function defined by
$$f(x) = -x^3 - 9x^2 + 21x + 4 \qquad (-8 \le x \le 10)$$
Use the first-derivative test to find all relative maximum and relative minimum points. Also, determine the absolute maximum and minimum values of $f(x)$. Graph $f(x)$.

37. Use the first derivative to show that the x-coordinate of the vertex of a quadratic equation of the form $f(x) = ax^2 + bx + c$ is $-b/2a$.

38. Consider the graph in Figure 10-33.
   a) State the interval over which $f(x)$ is increasing.
   b) Observe the slopes of the tangent lines at $x = x_2$ and $x = x_3$. Is $f'(x_3) < f'(x_2)$? As one moves along the graph of $f(x)$ from $x = x_1$ to $x = x_4$, are the values of $f(x)$ increasing at an increasing rate, or are they increasing at a decreasing rate?

39. Consider the graph in Figure 10-34.
   a) State the interval over which $f(x)$ is increasing.
   b) Observe the slopes of the tangent lines at $x = x_2$ and $x = x_3$. Is $f'(x_3) > f'(x_2)$? As one moves along the graph of $f(x)$ from $x = x_1$ to $x = x_4$, are the values of $f(x)$ increasing at an increasing rate, or are they increasing at a decreasing rate?

Applications

40. *Projectile.* At the same instant a ball is projected into the air, a stopwatch is activated. The function
$$S(x) = -16x^2 + 96x \qquad (0 \le x \le 6)$$
gives the height (in feet) above the ground of the ball after x seconds have elapsed.
   a) State the interval(s) over which the height of the ball is increasing.
   b) State the interval(s) over which the height of the ball is decreasing.
   c) Identify all relative extrema.
   d) Graph the function, $S(x)$.
   e) When does the ball reach its maximum height? Is this a relative maximum? Is this an absolute maximum?
   f) What is the maximum height?

41. *Revenue function.* The sales revenue gained from selling x units of some product is given by

$$R(x) = -x^2 + 40x \qquad (0 \le x \le 40)$$

  a) State the interval(s) over which sales revenue is increasing.
  b) State the interval(s) over which sales revenue is decreasing.
  c) Identify all relative extrema.
  d) Graph the function, $R(x)$.
  e) What sales volume maximizes sales revenue? Is this a relative maximum? Is this an absolute maximum?
  f) What is the maximum sales revenue?

42. *Profit function.* The profit gained from producing and selling x units of some product is given by

$$P(x) = 3x - \frac{x^3}{1,000,000} \qquad (0 \le x \le 1500)$$

  a) State the interval(s) over which profit is increasing.
  b) State the interval(s) over which profit is decreasing.
  c) Identify any relative extrema.
  d) Graph the profit function.
  e) How many units should be produced and sold in order to maximize profit? Is this a relative maximum? Is this an absolute maximum?
  f) What is the maximum profit?

43. *Social science: Survey costs.* The total cost of surveying x respondents for a behavioral research study is given by

$$C(x) = 20(x - 100)^2 + 1000 \qquad (x \ge 90)$$

  a) State the interval(s) over which the function $C(x)$ is increasing.
  b) State the interval(s) over which the function $C(x)$ is decreasing.
  c) Graph the function, $C(x)$.
  d) How many respondents should be surveyed in order to minimize the total survey cost? Is this a relative minimum? Is this an absolute minimum?
  e) Find the minimum total survey cost.

44. *Learning.* An educational institution that specializes in teaching foreign languages to executives has determined that the length of time (in minutes) per word it takes a typical executive to learn x new words is given by

$$L(x) = 0.1(x - 10)^2 + 0.5 \qquad (0 \le x \le 20)$$

  a) State the interval(s) over which the function $L(x)$ is increasing.
  b) State the interval(s) over which the function $L(x)$ is decreasing.
  c) Graph the function, $L(x)$.
  d) How many words should be given to an executive to learn so that the learning time per word is minimized? Is this a relative minimum? Is this an absolute minimum?
  e) Find the minimum learning time per word.

10-3 • CONCAVITY AND THE SECOND DERIVATIVE

In Section 10-2, we discussed the first-derivative test for determining whether a critical value yields a relative maximum, a relative minimum, or

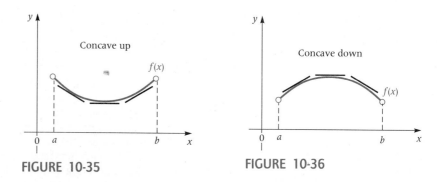

FIGURE 10-35   FIGURE 10-36

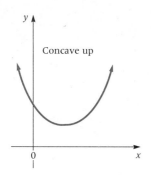

FIGURE 10-37

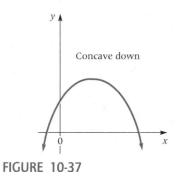

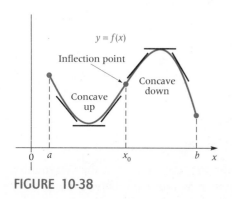

FIGURE 10-38

neither. Another test exists for making this determination, called the **second-derivative test.** In order to apply it, we must first consider the second derivative.

Graphical Interpretation of the Second Derivative

In order to discuss the graphical interpretation of the second derivative, we must define the terms *concave up* and *concave down* as they relate to functions. A function $f(x)$ is said to be **concave up** on an interval $a < x < b$ if each tangent line to the graph of $f(x)$ lies below the graph of $f(x)$ (see Figure 10-35). A function $f(x)$ is said to be **concave down** on an interval $a < x < b$ if each tangent line to the graph of $f(x)$ lies above its graph (see Figure 10-36). In Chapter 2, we classified the graphs of quadratic functions (parabolas) as either opening up or opening down. In terms of concavity, a parabola that opens up is said to be concave up, and a parabola that opens down is said to be concave down (see Figure 10-37).

We now consider the graph in Figure 10-38. Observe that $f(x)$ is concave up the interval $a < x < x_0$ and concave down on the interval $x_0 < x < b$. At $x = x_0$, the graph of $f(x)$ changes in concavity. Such a point, where a curve changes in concavity, is called an **inflection point.** Note that as we move along the concave-up portion of the curve from $(a, f(a))$ toward $(x_0, f(x_0))$, the slopes of the tangent lines are increasing. Thus, $f'(x)$ is increasing on the interval $a < x < x_0$. Since $f'(x)$ is increasing on the interval $a < x < x_0$, then its derivative $f''(x) > 0$. Analogously, as we move along the concave-down portion of the curve from $(x_0, f(x_0))$ to $(b, f(b))$, the slopes of the tangent lines are decreasing. Thus, $f'(x)$ is decreasing on the interval $x_0 < x < b$. Since $f'(x)$ is decreasing on the interval $x_0 < x < b$, then its derivative $f''(x) < 0$. At the inflection point, x_0, the second derivative $f''(x_0) = 0$. Therefore, as we move along a concave-up portion of the graph of a function, the first derivative is increasing, and, thus, the second derivative is positive. As we move along a concave-down portion, the first derivative is decreasing, and, thus, the second derivative is negative. At an inflection point, the first derivative is neither increasing nor decreasing, and, thus, the second derivative is often 0. However, this is not always the case (see Exercise 45 at the end of this section). A true test of the existence of an inflection point at $x = x_0$ is a change in sign of the second derivative at $x = x_0$. We summarize as follows.

SUMMARY

Second Derivative and Concavity

1. A function $f(x)$ is concave up at all values of x for which $f''(x) > 0$, as illustrated in Figure 10-39.
2. A function $f(x)$ is concave down at all values of x for which $f''(x) < 0$, as illustrated in Figure 10-40.
3. If $f''(x)$ changes sign at $x = x_0$, then an inflection point occurs at $x = x_0$ (see Figure 10-41).

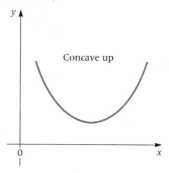

FIGURE 10-39

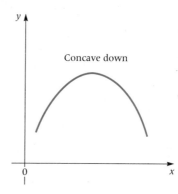

FIGURE 10-40

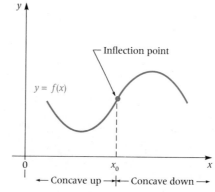

FIGURE 10-41

TABLE 10-5 **First and second derivatives and shape of graph**

Sign of $f'(x)$	Positive	Negative	Negative	Positive
Sign of $f''(x)$	Negative	Negative	Positive	Positive
Is $f(x)$ increasing or decreasing?	Increasing	Decreasing	Decreasing	Increasing
Concavity of $f(x)$	Concave down	Concave down	Concave up	Concave up
Shape of graph of $f(x)$	⌢	⌢	⌣	⌣

Table 10-5 summarizes the results of both first and second derivatives and the shape of the graph of the function.

• **EXAMPLE 10-13** _____

Use both first and second derivatives to graph
$$f(x) = x^4 - 6x^2 + 10$$
Identify all relative and absolute extrema and inflection points.

Solution

First-Derivative Analysis

First, we find
$$f'(x) = 4x^3 - 12x$$
$$= 4x(x^2 - 3)$$
$$= 4x(x - \sqrt{3})(x + \sqrt{3})$$

| Use difference of two squares. |

TABLE 10-6

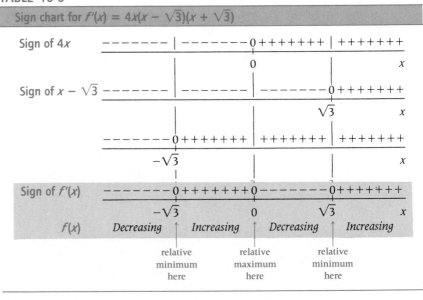

Setting $f'(x) = 0$ and solving for x gives critical values of

$$x = 0, x = \sqrt{3}, \text{ and } x = -\sqrt{3}$$

Since there are no values of x at which $f'(x)$ does not exist, these are the only critical values.

We now analyze the sign of $f'(x)$ to determine where $f(x)$ is increasing or decreasing and to determine points of relative extrema. A sign chart of $f'(x)$ is given in Table 10-6 on page 700. Note that relative minima occur at critical values $x = \pm\sqrt{3}$ and a relative maximum occurs at the critical value $x = 0$. We find the y-coordinates corresponding to the critical values. Hence,

$$f(0) = (0)^4 - 6(0)^2 + 10 = 10$$
$$f(-\sqrt{3}) = (-\sqrt{3})^4 - 6(-\sqrt{3})^2 + 10 = 1$$
$$f(\sqrt{3}) = (\sqrt{3})^4 - 6(\sqrt{3})^2 + 10 = 1$$

We begin to graph $f(x)$ in Figure 10-42 and include the above results.

Second-Derivative Analysis

We find

$$f''(x) = 12x^2 - 12$$
$$= 12(x^2 - 1)$$
$$= 12(x - 1)(x + 1)$$

and construct its sign chart in Table 10-7.

From Table 10-7, we learn that inflection points occur at $x = \pm 1$. Computing their y-coordinates, we obtain

$$f(-1) = (-1)^4 - 6(-1)^2 + 10 = 5$$
$$f(1) = (1)^4 - 6(1)^2 + 10 = 5$$

The results of the second-derivative analysis are summarized in Figure 10-43, and the graph of $f(x)$ is sketched.

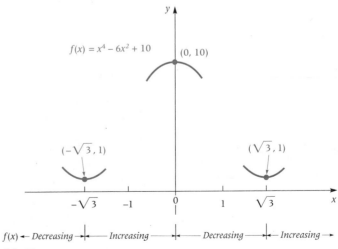

FIGURE 10-42

TABLE 10-7

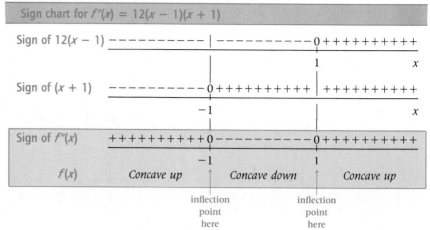

Sign chart for $f''(x) = 12(x - 1)(x + 1)$		

Sign of $12(x - 1)$ ---------- | ---------- 0 +++++++++
                                         1   x

Sign of $(x + 1)$ ---------- 0 +++++++++ | +++++++++
                        −1 x

Sign of $f''(x)$ +++++++++ 0 ---------- 0 +++++++++
                     −1   1

$f(x)$ *Concave up*   ↑ *Concave down* ↑ *Concave up*

                        inflection   inflection
                        point   point
                        here   here

Note: A sign change in $f''(x)$ indicates the occurrence of an inflection point.

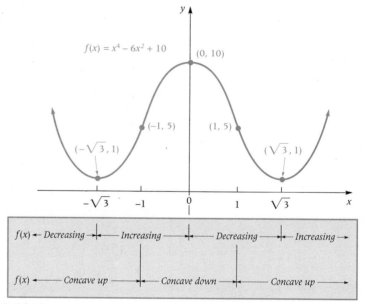

$f(x) = x^4 - 6x^2 + 10$

FIGURE 10-43

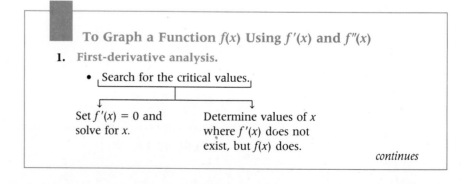

To Graph a Function $f(x)$ Using $f'(x)$ and $f''(x)$

1. **First-derivative analysis.**

   • Search for the critical values.

   Set $f'(x) = 0$ and solve for x.   Determine values of x where $f'(x)$ does not exist, but $f(x)$ does.

   continues

> **To Graph a Function $f(x)$ Using $f'(x)$ and $f''(x)$**—*Continued*
>
> - Draw a sign chart for $f'(x)$ This will indicate where $f(x)$ is increasing or decreasing and any relative extrema.
> - Find the y-coordinates of any relative extrema.
>
> **2. Second-derivative analysis.** Find $f''(x)$.
>
> - Draw a sign chart for $f''(x)$. This will indicate where $f(x)$ is concave up or down and any inflection points.
> - Find the y-coordinates of any inflection points.
>
> **3. Graph of $f(x)$.**
>
> - Summarize the results of steps 1 and 2 on a graph.
> - Plot the relative extrema and inflection points.
> - Plot the points of any x- and y-intercepts that are easily determined.
> - Sketch the graph of $f(x)$.

• **EXAMPLE 10-14   Cost Function.**

The ABC Container Company manufactures plastic bottles. Its cost function is defined by

$$C(x) = (x - 5)^3 + 1025$$

where x is the number (in millions) of bottles produced and $C(x)$ is the total cost (in thousands of dollars). Find all relative maxima and minima and inflection points of $C(x)$, and sketch its graph.

Solution

First-Derivative Analysis

$$C'(x) = 3(x - 5)^2$$

Critical value: $x = 5$

Sign chart for $C'(x) = 3(x - 5)^2$

Sign of $C'(x)$	$+++++++++++++++++++0+++++++++++++++++++$		
$C(x)$	Increasing	5	Increasing	x

Note that $C'(x)$ does not change sign at the critical value $x = 5$. This means that no relative extremum occurs at $x = 5$. However, since $C'(x) = 0$ at $x = 5$, the tangent line is horizontal there. This means that the graph of $C(x)$ is flat at $x = 5$.

Second-Derivative Analysis

$$C''(x) = 6(x - 5)$$

Sign chart for $C''(x) = 6(x - 5)$

Sign of $C''(x)$	$-----------------0+++++++++++++++++$		
$C(x)$	Concave down	5	Concave up	x

An inflection point occurs at $x = 5$. Hence, its y-coordinate is

$$C(5) = (5 - 5)^3 + 1025 = 1025$$

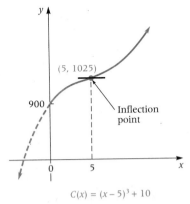

FIGURE 10-44

(5, 1025)

900

Inflection point

$C(x) = (x - 5)^3 + 10$

Graph of $C(x)$

The above results are summarized in Figure 10-44, and the graph of $C(x)$ is sketched. Assuming $x \geq 0$, our curve is drawn as a solid line in the first quadrant.

The shape of $C(x)$ is typical of nonlinear cost functions of some large companies. The marginal cost, $C'(x)$, is decreasing at values of x to the left of the inflection point since the company is making efficient use of its fixed costs. However, at values of x to the right of the inflection point, the marginal cost, $C'(x)$, is increasing since the company has reached a point—the inflection point—at which the variable cost begins to escalate.

Rational Functions

The next few examples involve rational functions. Recall that a function $f(x)$ is a rational function if it can be written as

$$f(x) = \frac{N(x)}{D(x)} \quad \begin{array}{l} \leftarrow \text{numerator function} \\ \leftarrow \text{denominator function} \end{array}$$

where $N(x)$ and $D(x)$ are polynomial functions. When graphing rational functions, we should be watchful for both vertical and horizontal asymptotes. Remember that vertical asymptotes occur at values of x where the denominator, $D(x)$, equals zero and the numerator does not. Thus, if a function has a vertical asymptote at a value of x, then the function is undefined at that x-value. Horizontal asymptotes, if they exist, are determined by evaluating $\lim_{x \to -\infty} f(x)$ and $\lim_{x \to \infty} f(x)$. We elaborate on the above in the succeeding boxes.

SUMMARY

Vertical Asymptotes

1. A rational function

$$f(x) = \frac{N(x)}{D(x)}$$

where $N(x)$ and $D(x)$ are polynomials, has a **vertical asymptote** at $x = a$ if and only if

$$\lim_{x \to a} f(x) = \infty \ (\text{or} -\infty)$$

This means that the values of $f(x)$ increase or decrease without bound as $x \to a$. Thus, the graph of $f(x)$ rises or falls without bound and gets closer and closer to the line $x = a$, the **vertical asymptote,** as illustrated in Figure 10-45.

continues

SUMMARY—*Continued*

Vertical asymptotes at $x = a$

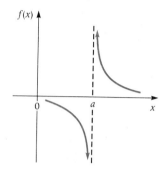
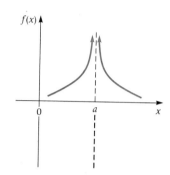

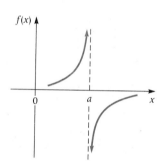
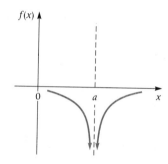

FIGURE 10-45

2. A rational function

$$f(x) = \frac{N(x)}{D(x)}$$

has vertical asymptotes at values of x where $D(x) = 0$ and $N(x) \neq 0$.

3. To find vertical asymptotes, we solve the equation

$$D(x) = 0$$

for x. This assumes that $N(x)$ and $D(x)$ have no common factors. In other words, if $D(a) = 0$, then $N(a) \neq 0$.

SUMMARY

Limits at Infinity and Horizontal Asymptotes

- A function $f(x)$ has a horizontal asymptote if and only if either

$$\lim_{x \to \infty} f(x) = L \qquad \text{or} \qquad \lim_{x \to -\infty} f(x) = M$$

where L and M are constants. Also, it might be the case that $L = M$.

- If $\lim_{x \to \infty} f(x) = L$, then the values of $f(x)$ approach the single num-

continues

SUMMARY—*Continued*

ber L as x gets larger and larger without bound. Thus, the graph of $f(x)$ approaches the horizontal line $y = L$ as $x \to \infty$. For such a case, the line $y = L$ is a **horizontal asymptote** of the function $f(x)$, as illustrated in Figure 10-46.

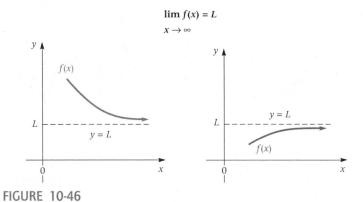

FIGURE 10-46

• If $\lim_{x \to -\infty} f(x) = M$, then the values of $f(x)$ approach the single number M as x gets more and more negative. Thus, the graph of $f(x)$ approaches the horizontal line $y = M$ as $x \to -\infty$. For such a case, the line $y = M$ is a **horizontal asymptote** of the function $f(x)$, as illustrated in Figure 10-47.

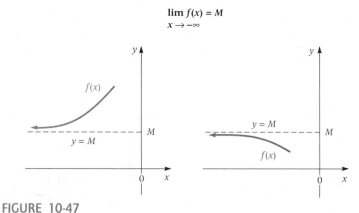

FIGURE 10-47

• If $L = M$, then the graph of $f(x)$ approaches the same horizontal asymptote as $x \to \infty$ and as $x \to -\infty$, as illustrated in Figure 10-48.

continues

SUMMARY—*Continued*

$$\lim_{x \to -\infty} f(x) = L \quad \text{and} \quad \lim_{x \to \infty} f(x) = L$$

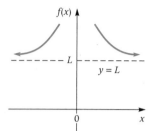

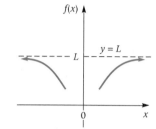

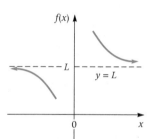

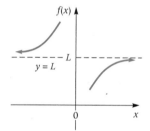

FIGURE 10-48

When evaluating limits, we note that if $n > 0$,

1. $\lim_{x \to \infty} \dfrac{1}{x^n} = 0$.

2. $\lim_{x \to -\infty} \dfrac{1}{x^n} = 0$ as long as x^n is defined for negative x-values.

• **EXAMPLE 10-15** _____

Sketch the graph of $f(x) = 2x + (32/x)$.

Solution

First-Derivative Analysis

$$f'(x) = 2 - 32x^{-2}$$
$$= 2 - \frac{32}{x^2}$$

Search for Critical Values

Note that $f'(x)$ is undefined at $x = 0$. Ordinarily, this would mean that $x = 0$ is a critical value. However, this is not the case here since $f(x)$ is undefined at $x = 0$. As a matter of fact, $f(x)$ has a vertical asymptote at $x = 0$.

Setting $f'(x) = 0$ and solving for x yields

$$0 = 2 - \frac{32}{x^2}$$

$$\frac{32}{x^2} = 2$$

$$2x^2 = 32$$

$$x^2 = 16$$

$$x = \pm 4 \qquad \text{Critical Values}$$

Draw a Sign Chart for $f'(x)$

We rewrite the equation for $f'(x)$ as follows:

$$f'(x) = 2\left(\frac{x^2}{x^2}\right) - \frac{32}{x^2}$$

$$= \frac{2x^2}{x^2} - \frac{32}{x^2}$$

$$= \frac{2x^2 - 32}{x^2} = \frac{2(x-4)(x+4)}{x^2}$$

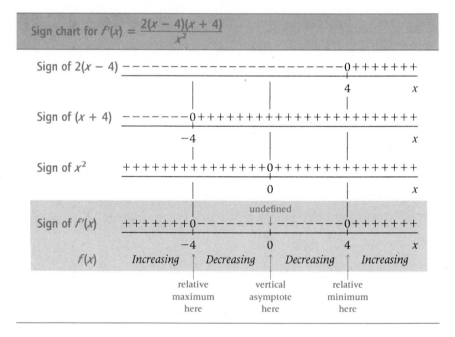

Find the y-coordinates of any relative extrema

$$f(-4) = 2(-4) + \frac{32}{-4} = -16$$

$$f(4) = 2(4) + \frac{32}{4} = 16$$

Second-Derivative Analysis

$$f''(x) = 64x^{-3} = \frac{64}{x^3}$$

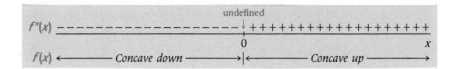

Sign chart for $f''(x) = \dfrac{64}{x^3}$

$f''(x)$ ‒‒‒‒‒‒‒‒‒‒‒‒‒‒‒‒‒‒‒‒↓++++++++++++++++++++

undefined

0

x

$f(x)$ ⟵‒‒‒‒‒ Concave down ‒‒‒‒→|←‒‒‒‒ Concave up ‒‒‒‒→

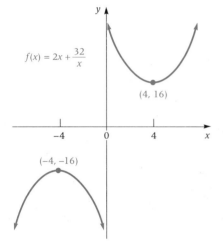

$f(x) = 2x + \dfrac{32}{x}$

(4, 16)

(−4, −16)

FIGURE 10-49

Vertical Asymptotes

Rewrite the equation for $f(x)$ as

$$f(x) = 2x\left(\frac{x}{x}\right) + \frac{32}{x} = \frac{2x^2 + 32}{x}$$

and note that at $x = 0$, the denominator is 0. Hence, as stated earlier, $f(x)$ has a vertical asymptote at $x = 0$.

Horizontal Asymptotes

$$\lim_{x \to \infty}\left(2x + \frac{32}{x}\right) = \lim_{x \to \infty}(2x) + \lim_{x \to \infty}\left(\frac{32}{x}\right)$$

$$= \infty + 0 = \infty$$

$$\lim_{x \to -\infty}\left(2x + \frac{32}{x}\right) = \lim_{x \to -\infty}(2x) + \lim_{x \to -\infty}\left(\frac{32}{x}\right)$$

$$= -\infty + 0 = -\infty$$

There are no horizontal asymptotes.

Graph of $f(x)$

The graph of $f(x)$ is sketched in Figure 10-49.

• EXAMPLE 10-16

Sketch the graph of

$$y = f(x) = \frac{x}{x^2 + 4}$$

Solution

First-Derivative Analysis

Using the quotient rule, we find

$$f'(x) = \frac{(x^2 + 4)(1) - x(2x)}{(x^2 + 4)^2}$$

$$= \frac{4 - x^2}{(x^2 + 4)^2}$$

$$= \frac{(2 - x)(2 + x)}{(x^2 + 4)^2}$$

Search for Critical Values

Setting $f'(x) = 0$ and solving for x gives critical values of $x = -2$ and $x = 2$. Since there are no values of x at which $f'(x)$ does not exist, these are the only critical values.

Draw a Sign Chart for $f'(x)$

We now analyze the sign of $f'(x)$ to determine where $f(x)$ is increasing or decreasing and to determine relative maximum and minimum points. These results are illustrated in Figure 10-50. Studying Figure 10-50, note that the sign of $f'(x)$ reveals the values of x for which $f(x)$ is increasing and decreasing. Also, by the first-derivative test, we determine the relative maximum and minimum points. Specifically, since $f'(x) < 0$ for nearby values of x to the left of $x = -2$ and $f'(x) > 0$ for nearby values of x to the right of $x = -2$, then, by the first-derivative test, a relative minimum point occurs at $x = -2$. Computing its y-coordinate, we obtain

$$f(-2) = \frac{-2}{(-2)^2 + 4} = -\frac{1}{4} \qquad \text{Relative Minimum}$$

and $(-2, -1/4)$ is a relative minimum point.

Also, since $f'(x) > 0$ for nearby values of x to the left of $x = 2$ and $f'(x) < 0$ for

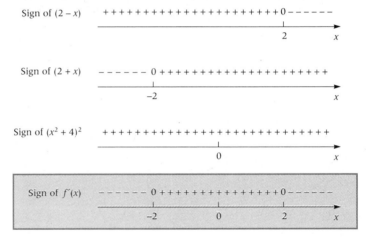

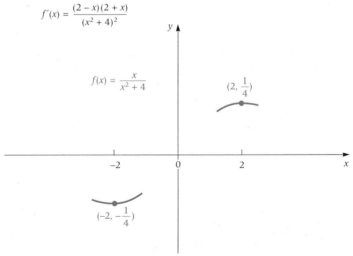

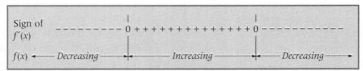

FIGURE 10-50

nearby values of x to the right of $x = 2$, then, by the first-derivative test, a relative maximum occurs at $x = 2$. Computing its y-coordinate, we obtain

$$f(2) = \frac{2}{(2)^2 + 4} = \frac{1}{4} \qquad \text{Relative Maximum}$$

and $(2, 1/4)$ is a relative maximum point.

Second-Derivative Analysis

We now analyze the second derivative to determine the concavity of $f(x)$. Computing the derivative of $f'(x)$, we obtain

$$f''(x) = \frac{(x^2 + 4)^2(-2x) - (-x^2 + 4)(2)(x^2 + 4)(2x)}{(x^2 + 4)^4}$$

$$= \frac{(x^2 + 4)(-2x)[(x^2 + 4) + (-2x^2 + 8)]}{(x^2 + 4)^{43}}$$

$$= \frac{2x(x^2 - 12)}{(x^2 + 4)^3}$$

$$= \frac{2x(x - \sqrt{12})(x + \sqrt{12})}{(x^2 + 4)^3} \quad\longleftarrow \boxed{\begin{array}{l}\text{Use difference of two squares:} \\ x^2 - 12 = (x - \sqrt{12})(x + \sqrt{12}).\end{array}}$$

The sign of $f''(x)$ appears in Figure 10-51. Since $f''(x) < 0$ for $x < -\sqrt{12}$ and for $0 < x < \sqrt{12}$, the graph of $f(x)$ is concave down over these intervals. Since $f''(x) > 0$ for $-\sqrt{12} < x < 0$ and for $x > \sqrt{12}$, the graph of $f(x)$ is concave up over these intervals. Since $f''(x)$ changes sign at $x = -\sqrt{12}$, $x = 0$, and $x = \sqrt{12}$, inflection points occur at these values of x. The y-coordinates of the inflection points are computed as follows:

$$f(-\sqrt{12}) = \frac{-\sqrt{12}}{(-\sqrt{12})^2 + 4} = \frac{-2\sqrt{3}}{16} = -\frac{\sqrt{3}}{8} \approx -0.22$$

$$f(\sqrt{12}) = \frac{\sqrt{12}}{(\sqrt{12})^2 + 4} = \frac{2\sqrt{3}}{16} = \frac{\sqrt{3}}{8} \approx 0.22$$

$$f(0) = 0$$

Thus, $(-\sqrt{12}, -0.22)$, $(\sqrt{12}, 0.22)$, and $(0, 0)$ are inflection points. Note that $(0, 0)$ is both the x-intercept and the y-intercept.

Vertical Asymptotes

Note that there are no vertical asymptotes since the denominator, $x^2 + 4$, does not equal 0 for any x-values.

Horizontal Asymptotes

Since $f(x)$ is a rational function, we examine its behavior as $x \rightarrow \infty$ and $x \rightarrow -\infty$ to find any horizontal asymptotes. Factoring out the highest-powered terms of both the numerator and the denominator of $f(x) = x/(x^2 + 4)$ gives

$$\frac{x}{x^2 + 4} = \frac{x(1)}{x^2\left(1 + \dfrac{4}{x^2}\right)}$$

$$= \frac{1}{x} \cdot \frac{1}{1 + \dfrac{4}{x^2}}$$

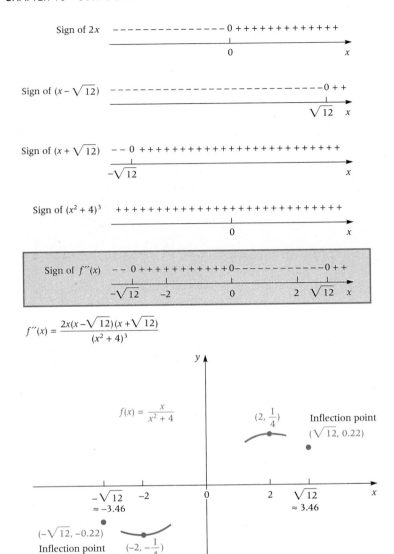

$$f''(x) = \frac{2x(x - \sqrt{12})(x + \sqrt{12})}{(x^2 + 4)^3}$$

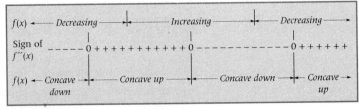

FIGURE 10-51

As $x \to \infty$, $4/x^2 \to 0$ and $1/x \to 0$ so that

$$\frac{1}{x} \cdot \frac{1}{1 + \dfrac{4}{x^2}} \to 0 \cdot 1 = 0$$

Hence, $\lim_{x \to \infty} f(x) = 0$, making $y = 0$ a horizontal asymptote. A similar manner of reasoning gives $\lim_{x \to -\infty} f(x) = 0$.

Graph of $f(x)$

The graph of $f(x)$ appears in Figure 10-52.

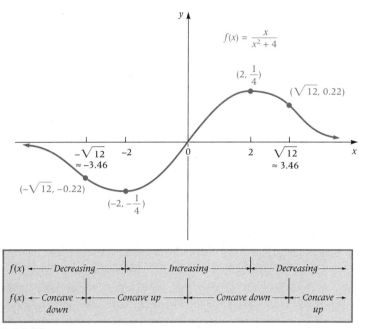

FIGURE 10-52

Exercises 10-3

1. Consider the graph of Figure 10-53.
   a) State the interval(s) over which the function $f(x)$ is concave up.
   b) State the interval(s) over which the function $f(x)$ is concave down.
   c) Identify any inflection points.
   d) Identify any relative extrema.
2. Consider the graph of Figure 10-54.
   a) State the interval(s) over which the function $f(x)$ is concave up.
   b) State the interval(s) over which the function $f(x)$ is concave down.
   c) Identify any inflection points.
   d) Identify any relative extrema.

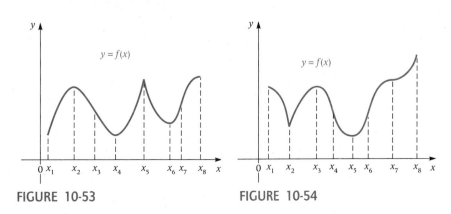

FIGURE 10-53   FIGURE 10-54

For each of the following sign charts, assume that the function $f(x)$ is continuous over the interval $(-\infty, \infty)$.

a) State the interval(s) over which the function $f(x)$ is concave up.
b) State the interval(s) over which the function $f(x)$ is concave down.
c) Identify any inflection points.

3. $f''(x)$ $++++++++++++0-------------0+++++++++++$
              -2 4 x

4. $f''(x)$ $-----------0+++++++++++0------------$
              -1 5 x

5. $f''(x)$ $+++++++++++++0-------------0+++++++++++$
              -3 3 x

6. $f''(x)$ $-----------0 +++++++++++ \downarrow$ undefined $-----------$
              -1 1 x

7. $f''(x)$ $+++++++++++$ undefined $\downarrow -----------0 +++++++++++$
              -1 2 x

8. $f''(x)$ $------------0++++++++++++0------------$
              -2 3 x

For each of the following, use both first and second derivatives to graph the function. Identify all relative and absolute extrema and inflection points.

9. $y = x^2 - 2x + 4$
10. $f(x) = x^3 + 6x^2 - 36x + 8$
11. $y = x^3 - 12x^2 - 27x - 1$
12. $f(x) = (1/3)x^3 - 4x + 8$
13. $f(x) = 5x^4 - 20x^3 + 7$
14. $f(x) = 5x^6 - 54x^5 + 60x^4 + 10$
15. $y = x^3 - 3x + 2$
16. $y = x^3 - 27x + 2$

17. $f(x) = (x - 5)^3$
18. $f(x) = (x - 6)^8$
19. $y = (x + 3)^{10} + 2$
20. $y = (x - 8)^5 + 2$
21. $y = (x + 2)(x - 5)^4 + 6$
22. $y = (x - 1)^3(x + 6) + 1$
23. $f(x) = (x - 4)^3(x + 2)^2$
24. $f(x) = x^3(x - 1)(x + 6)^4$
25. $y = x^3$
26. $f(x) = x^6$
27. $f(x) = x^{4/3}$
28. $f(x) = (x + 1)/x$

29. $y = \dfrac{-6}{x^2 + 2}$
30. $y = \dfrac{8}{x^2 + 1}$

31. $f(x) = \dfrac{x}{x^2 + 1}$
32. $y = \dfrac{x - 1}{x^2}$

33. $f(x) = \dfrac{800}{x} + 2x$
34. $y = \dfrac{x + 1}{x^2}$

35. $f(x) = \dfrac{(x - 3)^2}{x + 1}$
36. $f(x) = \dfrac{1}{x} - 3$

37. $f(x) = \dfrac{x^2(x - 2)}{(x - 1)^3}$
38. $y = \dfrac{1}{(x - 3)^2}$

39. $f(x) = \dfrac{20}{x} + x + 9$
40. $y = \dfrac{6}{x} + x + 5$

41. $f(x) = x^3 - 16x^2$ $(-5 \le x \le 6)$

42. $f(x) = -\dfrac{1}{100}x^3 + 16x$ $(-10 \le x \le 40)$

43. $f(x) = x^3 - 5x^2 + 7x - 3$ $(0 \le x \le 4)$
44. $f(x) = x^3 - 12x^2 + 45x - 50$ $(1 \le x \le 10)$

45. Given the function defined by $f(x) = x^{1/3}$:
   a) For which values of x is the graph of $f(x)$ concave up?
   b) For which values of x is the graph of $f(x)$ concave down?
   c) At which values of x does the graph of $f(x)$ change in concavity? Is $f''(x)$ defined there?
   d) Graph $f(x)$.

Applications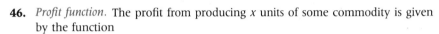

46. *Profit function.* The profit from producing x units of some commodity is given by the function

$$P(x) = -0.01x^3 + 1.20x^2 - 21x + 50{,}000 \qquad (10 \le x \le 80)$$

   a) Find any relative maxima, minima, and inflection points of $P(x)$, and sketch its graph.
   b) How many units must be sold in order to yield the maximum profit?
   c) What is the maximum profit? Is this an absolute maximum?

47. *Water pollution.* The amount of oxygen (measured in milligrams of oxygen per liter of water) in a pond x weeks after the dumping of organic waste is given by

$$f(x) = \frac{x^2 - x + 4}{x^2 + 4} \qquad (x \ge 0)$$

   a) Use both first- and second-derivative analyses to sketch the graph of $f(x)$.
   b) Determine the initial level of oxygen in the pond.
   c) For how many weeks after dumping organic waste is the oxygen level decreasing?
   d) How many weeks after dumping organic waste does the oxygen level begin to increase?
   e) What is the minimum oxygen level? When does it occur?
   f) What is the maximum oxygen level? When does it occur?
   g) After organic waste is dumped into the pond, does the amount of oxygen reach its initial level?

48. *Average cost per unit.* Given the cost function

$$C(x) = 5x + 1000 \qquad (x > 0)$$

where x is the number of units produced, the average cost per unit is given by

$$\overline{C}(x) = \frac{C(x)}{x}$$

$$= \frac{5x + 1000}{x} \qquad (x > 0)$$

   a) Use both first and second derivatives to graph the function, $\overline{C}(x)$.
   b) Identify any relative and absolute extrema.

49. *Average cost per unit.* Given the cost function

$$C(x) = x^2 - 4x + 64 \qquad (x > 0)$$

where x is the number of units produced, the average cost per unit is given by

$$\overline{C}(x) = \frac{C(x)}{x}$$

$$= \frac{x^2 - 4x + 64}{x} \qquad (x > 0)$$

   a) Use both first and second derivatives to graph the function, $\overline{C}(x)$.
   b) Identify any relative and absolute extrema.
   c) What production level minimizes the average cost per unit?
   d) What is the minimum average cost per unit?

50. *Learning.* A center for educational research has determined that the length of time (in minutes) it takes an average individual to learn x new words in a particular foreign language at a single study session is given by

$$L(x) = 0.1(x - 2)^3 + 8 \qquad (0 \le x \le 10)$$

a) Use both first and second derivatives to graph the function, $L(x)$.
b) Identify any relative and absolute extrema.
c) Identify any inflection points.
d) Graph the first derivative, $L'(x)$.
e) Identify any relative and absolute extrema of $L'(x)$.
f) How many new words should an average individual learn at a single study session in order to minimize $L'(x)$? Is this an absolute minimum value of $L'(x)$?

51. *Advertising and sales.* The sales revenue, R (in thousands of dollars), for a product is related to its advertising expenses, x (in thousands of dollars), by the equation

$$R(x) = -0.01x^3 + 6x^2 \qquad (0 \le x \le 500)$$

a) Use both first and second derivatives to graph the function, $R(x)$.
b) Identify any relative and absolute extrema.
c) Identify any inflection points.
d) Graph the first derivative, $R'(x)$.
e) Identify any relative and absolute extrema of $R'(x)$.
f) What level of advertising expenses maximizes $R'(x)$?

10-4 • OPTIMIZATION

In the previous two sections, we used the first and second derivatives to sketch graphs of functions. This enabled us to determine relative and absolute maximum and minimum values of functions.

In this section, we will be concerned with determining maximum or minimum values of functions without having to graph the functions. In other words, our goal will be to determine the maximum or minimum value of some quantity, Q, where $Q = f(x)$, and the value of x at which Q is either maximized or minimized. Our goal will not be to sketch the graph of $Q = f(x)$, although we will at times use graphical concepts to support conclusions regarding the optimality of our answers.

To find maximum and minimum values of functions without graphing the functions, we will first find critical values and then use a test to determine whether maxima, minima, or neither occurs at individual critical values. Up to this point in this text, the first-derivative test has been used to determine whether relative maxima, minima, or neither occurs at individual critical values.

Now we present another test, the second-derivative test, to determine the nature of relative extrema in certain situations. The advantage of the second-derivative test is that it is easier and faster to apply than the first-derivative test. However, the second-derivative test has limitations, and, therefore, the first-derivative test should be used if the second-derivative test fails or cannot be used.

SUMMARY

Second-Derivative Test for Relative Extrema

If $f(x)$ is a function and x_0 is a number such that $f'(x_0) = 0$, then

1. If $f''(x_0) < 0$, $f(x)$ has a relative maximum at $x = x_0$.
2. If $f''(x_0) > 0$, $f(x)$ has a relative minimum at $x = x_0$.
3. If $f''(x_0) = 0$, the test fails. In other words, the test gives no information regarding a relative maximum or relative minimum at $x = x_0$.

Notes:

1. This test applies only to critical values for which $f'(x) = 0$. It does not apply to critical values for which $f'(x)$ is undefined.
2. This test can fail. In other words, it can give no information regarding the nature of the relative extrema at x_0.
3. If either of the above occurs, use the first-derivative test.

We now give an example illustrating the use of the second-derivative test.

• **EXAMPLE 10-17** _____

Find the relative maximum and minimum values for

$$f(x) = x + \frac{9}{x}$$

Solution

First Derivative

$$f'(x) = 1 - \frac{9}{x^2}$$

$$0 = 1 - \frac{9}{x^2}$$

$$\frac{9}{x^2} = 1$$

$$x^2 = 9$$

$$x = \pm 3 \qquad \text{Critical Values}$$

Note that $x = 0$ is not a critical value despite the fact that $f'(0)$ is undefined. This is because $f(0)$ is undefined.

Second-Derivative Test

$$f''(x) = \frac{18}{x^3}$$

$$f''(-3) = \frac{18}{(-3)^3} < 0$$

critical value —↑

> By the second-derivative test, a relative maximum occurs at $x = -3$.

$$f''(3) = \frac{18}{(3)^3} > 0$$

critical value —↑

> By the second-derivative test, a relative minimum occurs at $x = 3$.

Find the relative extrema.

$$f(-3) = -3 + \frac{9}{-3} = -6 \qquad \text{Relative Maximum}$$

$$f(3) = 3 + \frac{9}{3} = 6 \qquad \text{Relative Minimum}$$

We now give an applied example illustrating the use of the second-derivative test.

• **EXAMPLE 10-18   Minimizing Average Cost Per Unit.** ——

The total cost of producing x units of some product is given by

$$C(x) = x^2 - 60x + 1600 \qquad (x > 0)$$

and the average cost per unit, when producing x units, is given by

$$\overline{C}(x) = \frac{C(x)}{x} \qquad (x > 0)$$

$$= \frac{x^2 - 60x + 1600}{x} \qquad (x > 0)$$

How many units should be produced in order to minimize the average cost per unit, $\overline{C}(x)$?

Solution

First Derivative

Using the quotient rule, we determine that

$$\overline{C}'(x) = \frac{x(2x - 60) - (x^2 - 60x + 1600)(1)}{x^2}$$

$$= \frac{x^2 - 1600}{x^2}$$

$$= \frac{(x - 40)(x + 40)}{x^2}$$

Critical Values

$x = 0$	$x = -40$	$x = 40$
↑	↑	↑
$\overline{C}'(0)$ is undefined. Rule out $x = 0$ because $\overline{C}(0)$ is undefined. Also, the restriction, $x > 0$, rules out $x = 0$.	$\overline{C}'(-40) = 0.$ Rule out $x = -40$ because of the restriction, $x > 0$.	$\overline{C}'(40) = 0.$ This is the only relevant critical value.

Second Derivative

We write the first derivative as

$$\overline{C}'(x) = \frac{x^2 - 1600}{x^2}$$

Using the quotient rule, we find

$$\overline{C}''(x) = \frac{x^2(2x) - (x^2 - 1600)(2x)}{(x^2)^2}$$

$$= \frac{3200x}{x^4} = \frac{3200}{x^3} \qquad \text{Second Derivative}$$

Second-Derivative Test

We evaluate the second-derivative at the critical value $x = 40$ to obtain

$$\overline{C}''(40) = \frac{3200}{(40)^3} = \frac{1}{20}$$

which is positive. Therefore, by the second-derivative test, a relative minimum exists at $x = 40$. The relative minimum is

$$\overline{C}(40) = \frac{(40)^2 - 60(40) + 1600}{40} = \$20 \text{ per unit}$$

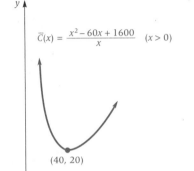

$$\overline{C}(x) = \frac{x^2 - 60x + 1600}{x} \quad (x > 0)$$

$(40, 20)$

FIGURE 10-55

Absolute Extrema

We have determined, in Example 10-18, that a relative minimum exists at $x = 40$. A much stronger result would be to determine that an absolute minimum occurs at $x = 40$. We do this by noting that $\overline{C}(x)$ is defined only for positive values of x (i.e., the restriction, $x > 0$). Next note that the second derivative

$$\overline{C}''(x) = \frac{3200}{x^3}$$

is positive for $x > 0$, and, therefore, the graph of $\overline{C}(x)$ is concave up over the interval $x > 0$. This implies that the graph of $\overline{C}(x)$ has the appearance of that of Figure 10-55 and then the relative minimum at the critical value $x = 40$ is an absolute minimum. Thus, the minimum average cost is \$20 per unit, and it occurs at a production level of $x = 40$ units.

Example 10-18 illustrates a special situation where a continuous function has only one critical value in some interval (the interval can be closed, open, half-closed, etc.). This case occurs so often in applications that we present a special second-derivative test for determining whether an absolute maximum, an absolute minimum, or neither occurs at the critical value.

SUMMARY

Second-Derivative Test for Absolute Extrema

When a function is continuous over some interval and *only one critical value* exists in the interval: Given that a function $f(x)$ is continuous over some interval, and x_0 is the only critical value interior to the interval, and $f'(x_0) = 0$, then

1. If $f''(x_0) < 0$, $f(x_0)$ is the **absolute maximum** value of $f(x)$ over the interval (see Figure 10-56).

continues

SUMMARY—*Continued*

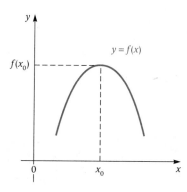

FIGURE 10-56

2. If $f''(x_0) > 0$, $f(x_0)$ is the **absolute minimum** value of $f(x)$ over the interval (see Figure 10-57).

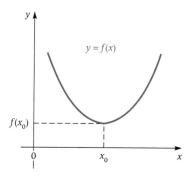

FIGURE 10-57

3. If $f''(x_0) = 0$, the test fails.

Since many optimization problems and applications involve the determination of absolute maximum and minimum values of functions defined over closed intervals, we now give a procedure for such situations.

 To Find Absolute Extrema

For Continuous Functions Defined on Closed Intervals.   To find the absolute extrema of a continuous function $f(x)$ on the closed interval $[a, b]$:

1. Find all critical values of $f(x)$ in $[a, b]$.
2. Evaluate $f(x)$ at the endpoints a and b and at the critical values found in step 1.

continues

To Find Absolute Extrema—*Continued*

3. Write the largest value found in step 2. This is the *absolute maximum* value of $f(x)$ on the interval $[a, b]$.
4. Write the smallest value found in step 2. This is the *absolute minimum* value of $f(x)$ on the interval $[a, b]$.

• **EXAMPLE 10-19**

Determine the absolute extrema for

$$f(x) = x^3 - 6x^2 - 36x + 10 \qquad (-3 \le x \le 9)$$

Solution

Critical Values

$$
\begin{aligned}
f'(x) &= 3x^2 - 12x - 36 \\
&= 3(x^2 - 4x - 12) \\
&= 3(x - 6)(x + 2)
\end{aligned}
$$

Setting $f'(x) = 0$ and solving for x gives

$$
\begin{array}{cc}
x - 6 = 0 & x + 2 = 0 \\
x = 6 & x = -2
\end{array}
$$

$\llcorner$ critical values $\lrcorner$

These are the only critical values since there are no values of x at which $f'(x)$ is undefined.

Evaluate f(x) *at Critical Values and at Endpoints*

$$f(6) = (6)^3 - 6(6)^2 - 36(6) + 10 = -206 \qquad \leftarrow \text{absolute}$$
critical value $\longrightarrow$ $\qquad$ minimum

$$f(-2) = (-2)^3 - 6(-2)^2 - 36(-2) + 10 = 50 \qquad \leftarrow \text{absolute}$$
critical value $\longrightarrow$ $\qquad$ maximum

$$f(-3) = (-3)^3 - 6(-3)^2 - 36(-3) + 10 = 37$$
endpoint $\longrightarrow$

$$f(9) = (9)^3 - 6(9)^2 - 36(9) + 10 = -71$$
endpoint $\longrightarrow$

Thus, the absolute maximum value of $f(x)$ is 50, and it occurs at $x = -2$; the absolute minimum value of $f(x)$ is -206, and it occurs at $x = 6$.

•

Since the remainder of this section entails solving applied optimization problems, we now present a procedure for solving such problems in Figure 10-58.

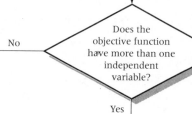

TO SOLVE OPTIMIZATION PROBLEMS

Objective function

Identify the quantity to be either maximized or minimized and the related variables. Write an equation for the quantity to be maximized or minimized. This equation is called the *objective function*.

Does the objective function have more than one independent variable?

No

Yes

Constraint equation

Reread the problem and search for an existing relationship between the independent variables. Write the equation that expresses such a relationship. This equation is called a *constraint equation*.

Solve and substitute

Solve the constraint equation for one independent variable in terms of the other. Substitute this result into the objective function. The objective function should now have only one independent variable.

Critical values

Find the critical values of the objective function.

Test for absolute extrema

1. If there is **only one critical value** in some interval, use the second-derivitive test for absolute extrema to test whether an absolute maximum or minimum occurs at the critical value.

2. If there is **more than one critical value** in some closed interval, evaluate the function at each critical value and at the endpoints to determine the absolute extrema.

3. If neither 1 nor 2 applies, then use both first and second derivatives to graph the function.

FIGURE 10-58

• EXAMPLE 10-20   **Quality Control and Profits.** ⸻

Sharp Industries produces table knives. Each knife costs $6 to produce and sells for $9. The quality control manager has determined from past data that out of x knives that are produced during any given day, the fraction defective for the day is given by $x^2/20{,}000{,}000$, where $100 \le x \le 1500$. Each defective knife costs the company an additional $20.

a) Determine the equation that gives daily profit, P, as a function of daily production volume, x.

b) Determine the maximum daily profit and the daily production volume that yields the maximum daily profit.

Solutions

Objective Function

a) A unit profit of $9 - $6 = $3 is made on each knife. The daily profit is given by

$$P = 3x - \text{(additional cost of the defective knives)}$$

The number of defective knives produced in a day is determined by multiplying the fraction defective and the daily production volume. Hence,

$$\begin{array}{l} \text{number of} \\ \text{defectives} \\ \text{(daily)} \end{array} = \left(\begin{array}{c}\text{fraction}\\\text{defective}\end{array}\right)\left(\begin{array}{c}\text{daily production}\\\text{volume}\end{array}\right)$$

$$= \left(\frac{x^2}{20{,}000{,}000}\right) x$$

$$= \frac{x^3}{20{,}000{,}000}$$

Since each defective costs the company an additional $20, then

$$\text{additional cost of the defective knives} = 20 \cdot \frac{x^3}{20{,}000{,}000} = \frac{x^3}{1{,}000{,}000}$$

Thus, the daily profit is given by

$$P(x) = 3x - \frac{x^3}{1{,}000{,}000} \qquad \text{Objective function} \qquad (100 \le x \le 1500)$$

Critical Values

$$P'(x) = 3 - \frac{3x^2}{1{,}000{,}000}$$

$$0 = 3 - \frac{3x^2}{1{,}000{,}000}$$

$$\frac{3x^2}{1{,}000{,}000} = 3$$

$$x^2 = \frac{3{,}000{,}000}{3} = 1{,}000{,}000$$

$$x = \pm 1000$$

We rule out $x = -1000$ because $100 \le x \le 1500$. Thus,

$$x = 1000 \text{ is the only critical value}$$

Test for Absolute Extrema

Second-Derivative Test

$$P''(x) = \frac{-6x}{1,000,000}$$

$$P''(1000) = \frac{-6(1000)}{1,000,000} < 0$$

By the second-derivative test for absolute extrema, the function $P(x)$ has an absolute maximum at $x = 1000$. Hence,

$$P(1000) = 3(1000) - \frac{(1000)^3}{1,000,000}$$

$$= 2000 \qquad \text{Absolute maximum}$$

Note: We could also have used the procedure for finding absolute extrema of continuous functions defined on closed intervals instead of the second-derivative test for absolute extrema.

• **EXAMPLE 10-21** **Apple Growing: Maximizing Revenue.**

From past experience, an apple grower knows that if the apples are harvested now, each tree will yield on the average 130 pounds, and the grower will sell the apples for $0.64 per pound. However, for each additional week that the grower waits before harvesting, the yield per tree will increase by 5 pounds, while the price per pound will decrease by $0.02. How many weeks should the grower wait before harvesting the apples in order to maximize the sales revenue per tree? What is the maximum sales revenue per tree?

Solution

Objective Function

Let $x =$ number of weeks the grower waits. The sales revenue per tree is given by

$$R = \left(\begin{array}{c}\text{number of pounds}\\ \text{per tree}\end{array}\right)\left(\begin{array}{c}\text{price per}\\ \text{pound}\end{array}\right)$$

$$R(x) = (130 + 5x)(0.64 - 0.02x)$$

Critical Values

Using the product rule, we find

$$R'(x) = (130 + 5x)(-0.02) + (0.64 - 0.02x)(5)$$
$$R'(x) = 0.60 - 0.20x$$
$$0 = 0.60 - 0.20x$$
$$x = 3 \qquad \text{Only critical value}$$

Test for Absolute Extrema

Second-Derivative Test

$$R''(x) = -0.20$$
$$R''(3) = -0.20 < 0$$

Therefore, by the second-derivative test for absolute extrema, the function $R(x)$ has an absolute maximum at $x = 3$.

$$R(3) = (130 + 5 \cdot 3)(0.64 - 0.02 \cdot 3)$$
$$= (145)(0.58)$$
$$= \$84.10 \quad \text{Absolute maximum}$$

Thus, the grower should wait 3 weeks before harvesting in order to attain the maximum sales revenue per tree of $84.10.

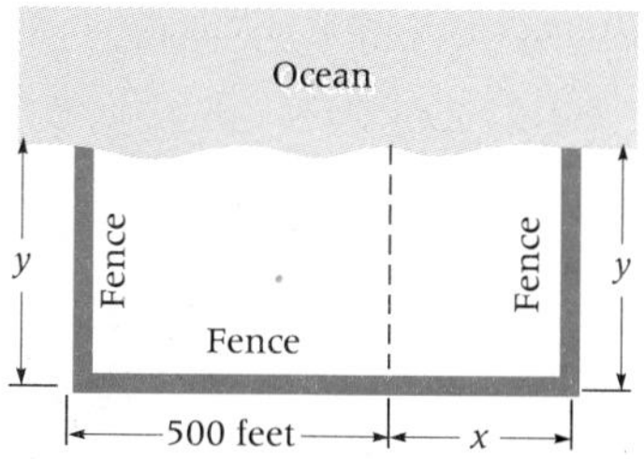

• **EXAMPLE 10-22** _____

The manager of an ocean resort wants to enclose a rectangular area of beach along the ocean. There must be at least 500 feet of frontage along the ocean, as illustrated in Figure 10-59. Find the dimensions that maximize the enclosed area if 2000 feet of fencing are available. Find the maximum area.

Solution

Objective Function

We wish to maximize the enclosed area, which is given by

$$A = (\text{length})(\text{width})$$
$$= (500 + x)\,y \qquad \boxed{\text{Two independent variables: } x \text{ and } y.}$$

Constraint Equation

$$\text{Length of fence} = 2000 \text{ feet}$$
$$y + (500 + x) + y = 2000$$
$$2y + 500 + x = 2000 \qquad \boxed{\text{Solve for one independent variable in terms of the other.}}$$
$$x = 1500 - 2y$$

Note: We could have solved for y in terms of x. However, we chose to solve for x in terms of y in order to avoid fractions. Substitute $1500 - 2y$ for x into the objective function.

Objective Function

$$A(y) = (500 + 1500 - 2y)y \qquad \boxed{\text{Note that } y \text{ is the independent variable}}$$
$$= (2000 - 2y)y$$
$$= 2000y - 2y^2 \qquad (y > 0)$$

Critical Values

$$A'(y) = 2000 - 4y$$
$$0 = 2000 - 4y$$
$$y = 500 \qquad \text{Only critical value}$$

Test for Absolute Extrema

Second-Derivative Test

$$A''(y) = -4$$
$$A''(500) = -4 < 0$$

Thus, by the second-derivative test for absolute extrema, the function $A(y)$ has an absolute maximum when $y = 500$ feet.

We determine x by substituting $y = 500$ into the constraint equation solved for x. Hence,

$$x = 1500 - 2y$$
$$= 1500 - 2(500) = 500 \text{ feet}$$

Ocean

Fence

Fence

Fence

y

y

500 feet

x

FIGURE 10-59

Thus, the dimensions of the enclosed area are

$$500 + x \text{ by } y$$
$$500 + 500 \text{ by } 500$$
$$1000 \text{ feet by } 500 \text{ feet}$$

The maximum area is given by

$$A = (\text{length})(\text{width})$$
$$= (1000)(500)$$
$$= 500,000 \text{ square feet}$$

Note: We could have determined the maximum area by evaluating $A(500)$.

• EXAMPLE 10-23   Minimizing Surface Area Cost. ───────

A company makes prefabricated steel buildings. One of its models is illustrated in Figure 10-60. The building must be 8 feet high and have a volume of 20,000 cubic feet. If the material for the sides costs $20 per square foot and the material for the roof costs $30 per square foot, determine the dimensions of the building that will minimize its cost. Also, determine the minimum cost. Do not consider the cost of the floor.

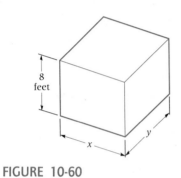

FIGURE 10-60

Solution

Objective Function

We want to minimize cost, which is given by

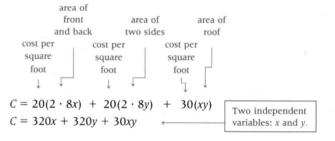

$$C = 20(2 \cdot 8x) + 20(2 \cdot 8y) + 30(xy)$$
$$C = 320x + 320y + 30xy \quad \longleftarrow \quad \boxed{\text{Two independent variables: } x \text{ and } y.}$$

Constraint Equation

$$\text{Volume} = 20,000 \text{ cubic feet}$$
$$8xy = 20,000$$
$$y = \frac{2500}{x} \quad \boxed{\text{Solve for one independent variable in terms of the other.}}$$

Substitute $2500/x$ for y into the objective function.

Objective Function

$$C = 320x + 320\left(\frac{2500}{x}\right) + 30x\left(\frac{2500}{x}\right)$$

$$C(x) = 320x + \frac{800,000}{x} + 75,000 \quad (x > 0)$$

Critical Values

$$C'(x) = 320 - \frac{800{,}000}{x^2}$$

$$0 = 320 - \frac{800{,}000}{x^2}$$

$$\frac{800{,}000}{x^2} = 320$$

$$x^2 = \frac{800{,}000}{320} = 2500$$

$$x = \pm\,50 \quad \longleftarrow \boxed{\begin{array}{l}\text{We disregard } x = -50 \text{ because}\\ \text{of the restriction, } x > 0.\end{array}}$$

$$x = 50 \quad \text{Only critical value}$$

We note that $C'(x)$ is undefined at $x = 0$. However, $x = 0$ is not a critical value since $C(0)$ is undefined.

Test for Absolute Extrema

Second-Derivative Test

$$C''(x) = \frac{1{,}600{,}000}{x^3}$$

$$C''(50) = \frac{1{,}600{,}000}{(50)^3} > 0$$

Thus, by the second-derivative test for absolute extrema, the function $C(x)$ has an absolute minimum when $x = 50$.

We determine y by substituting $x = 50$ into the secondary equation solved for y. Hence,

$$y = \frac{2500}{x}$$

$$= \frac{2500}{50} = 50 \text{ feet}$$

Thus, the base of the building should be 50 feet by 50 feet. The total cost is given by substituting $x = 50$ into the objective function to obtain

$$C(50) = 320(50) + \frac{800{,}000}{50} + 75{,}000$$

$$= \$107{,}000 \quad \textbf{Absolute minimum cost}$$

• EXAMPLE 10-24   Maximizing Profit.

A company manufactures a product used in the computer industry. The unit price, p (in thousands of dollars), and demand, x (in hundreds of units), are related by the equation

$$x = \frac{8100}{p^2} \quad (p > 0)$$

The cost, C (in thousands of dollars), of producing the items is given by

$$C(x) = 5x + 120 \quad (x > 0)$$

The company wishes to determine

a)   The demand level, x, for which profit is maximized.
b)   The unit price, p, for which profit is maximized.
c)   The maximum profit.

Solutions

Objective Function

a) Since we seek a value of x that maximizes profit, P, we must write profit in terms of x. If $P(x)$ = profit gained from selling x units and $R(x)$ = sales revenue gained from selling x units, then

$$P(x) = R(x) - C(x)$$

We must determine an equation for $R(x)$. Hence,

$$\text{sales revenue} = (\text{number of units sold})(\text{unit price})$$

or

$$R(x) = xp \qquad \overline{\underset{}{}} \text{ Constraint equation}$$

where x and p are related by the equation $x = 8100/p^2$. Solving for p gives $p = 90/\sqrt{x}$. Substituting this result for p into the formula for $R(x)$ gives

$$R(x) = x\left(\frac{90}{\sqrt{x}}\right)$$
$$= 90x^{1/2}$$

Hence,

$$P(x) = R(x) - C(x)$$
$$= 90x^{1/2} - (5x + 120)$$
$$= 90x^{1/2} - 5x - 120 \qquad \text{Objective function}$$

where P is in thousands of dollars and $x > 0$.

Critical Values

We now seek critical values of $P(x)$ by finding

$$P'(x) = 45x^{-1/2} - 5$$

Setting $P'(x) = 0$ and solving for x gives, successively,

$$0 = 45x^{-1/2} - 5$$
$$5 = \frac{45}{\sqrt{x}}$$
$$\sqrt{x} = 9$$
$$x = 81 \qquad \text{Only critical value}$$

Thus, $x = 81$ is a critical value. Since there are no positive values of x at which $P'(x)$ does not exist, this is the only critical value.

Test for Absolute Extrema

We now apply the second-derivative test to determine the nature of the critical value, $x = 81$. Hence, we differentiate $P'(x)$ to obtain

$$P''(x) = -22.5x^{-3/2}$$
$$= \frac{-22.5}{\sqrt{x^3}}$$

Since $P''(x) < 0$ at $x = 81$, then, by the second-derivative test for absolute extrema, an absolute maximum occurs at $x = 81$.

Thus, in order to maximize profit, the company should produce and sell 8100 units (remember that since x was defined in terms of hundreds of units, $x = 81$ means 81 hundred units).

b) The variables x and p are related by $x = 8100/p^2$, which, when solved for p, gives

$$p = \frac{90}{\sqrt{x}}$$

Substituting $x = 81$ into this equation gives

$$p = \frac{90}{\sqrt{81}} = 10$$

as the unit price at which profit is maximized. Since p is defined in terms of thousands of dollars, the company must charge $10,000 (i.e., $p = 10$ means $10,000) per 100 units for this product in order to maximize profit.

c) The maximum profit is $P(81)$. Since

$$P(x) = 90\sqrt{x} - 5x - 120$$

then

$$P(81) = 90\sqrt{81} - 5(81) - 120$$
$$= 285$$

Since P is given in terms of thousands of dollars, the *maximum profit* is $285,000.

•

In Example 10-24 we determined $P'(x)$ and set it equal to zero in order to maximize the profit, $P(x)$. Since

$$P(x) = R(x) - C(x)$$

where $R(x)$ and $C(x)$ denote sales revenue and cost, respectively, then differentiating both sides with respect to x gives

$$P'(x) = R'(x) - C'(x)$$

Setting $P'(x) = 0$ gives the equation

$$0 = R'(x) - C'(x)$$

or

$$R'(x) = C'(x)$$

Since $R'(x)$ gives marginal revenue and $C'(x)$ gives marginal cost, this equation implies that *profit is maximized when marginal revenue equals marginal cost*. Graphically, profit is maximized when the slope of the revenue graph equals the slope of the cost graph, as illustrated in Figure 10-61.

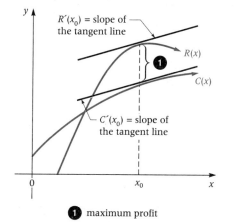

$R'(x_0) =$ slope of the tangent line

$R(x)$

1

$C(x)$

$C'(x_0) =$ slope of the tangent line

x_0

1 maximum profit

Profit is maximized when marginal revenue = marginal cost.

FIGURE 10-61

Exercises 10-4

Use the second-derivative test to find relative maxima and minima for each of the following.

1. $y = x^2 - 8x + 9$ **2.** $y = x^2 - 10x + 50$

3. $y = x^3 - 6x^2 + 7$ **4.** $y = x^3 - 12x^2 + 15$

5. $f(x) = x^3 - 3x + 5$ **6.** $f(x) = x^3 - 12x + 10$

7. $f(x) = 2x^3 + 3x^2 - 12x + 1$ **8.** $f(x) = x^3 - 3x^2 - 9x + 5$

9. $f(x) = x^3 - 3x^2 - 45x + 9$

10. $f(x) = 2x^3 - 9x^2 - 24x + 6$

11. $f(x) = x^4 - 8x^2 + 6$

12. $f(x) = x^4 - 18x^2 - 11$

13. $y = x + \dfrac{25}{x}$

14. $y = x + \dfrac{81}{x}$

15. $f(x) = x + \dfrac{27}{x^3}$

16. $f(x) = x + \dfrac{4}{x^2}$

Determine the absolute extrema for each of the following.

17. $f(x) = x^2 - 16x + 9$

18. $f(x) = x^2 - 10x + 4$

19. $f(x) = -x^2 + 8x + 3$

20. $f(x) = -x^2 + 10x + 6$

21. $f(x) = 4\sqrt{x} - x$

22. $f(x) = 8\sqrt{x} - x$

23. $f(x) = x^3 - 27x + 4 \quad (-4 \le x \le 4)$

24. $f(x) = x^3 - 48x + 9 \quad (-5 \le x \le 5)$

25. $f(x) = 9 + 5x + 125/x \quad (x > 0)$

26. $f(x) = 3 + 4x + 64/x \quad (x > 0)$

27. $f(x) = 2x + 54/x^3 \quad (x > 0)$

28. $f(x) = 6 + 3x + 12/x^2 \quad (x > 0)$

29. $f(x) = 5(x - 2)^3 \quad (0 \le x \le 4)$

30. $f(x) = 5(x + 1)^3 \quad (-3 \le x \le 0)$

31. $f(x) = (x - 1)(x - 4)^2 \quad (0 \le x \le 6)$

32. $f(x) = (x - 1)(x - 5)^3 \quad (0 \le x \le 7)$

General Word Problems

33. Find two numbers whose sum is 24 and whose product is as large as possible.

34. Find two numbers whose difference is 30 and whose product is as small as possible.

35. Find two numbers whose sum is 600 and whose sum of squares is as small as possible.

36. Find two numbers whose sum is 800 and whose sum of squares is as small as possible.

Applications

37. *Average cost.* The total cost of producing x units of some product is given by

$$C(x) = x^2 - 80x + 3600 \quad (x > 0)$$

How many units should be produced in order to minimize the average cost per unit?

38. *Energy costs.* The heating and cooling costs for a building with no insulation are \$853,333 per year. If x inches $(0 \le x \le 9)$ of insulation are added, the combined heating and cooling costs will be \$2,560,000/$(x + 3)$ dollars per year. If it costs \$200,000 for each inch (thickness) of insulation added, then the total energy cost (insulation cost + combined heating and cooling cost) for 5 years is given by

Insulation cost

Combined heating and cooling cost

$$C(x) = \overbrace{200{,}000x}^{} + 5\overbrace{\left(\dfrac{2{,}560{,}000}{x + 3}\right)}^{} \quad (0 \le x \le 9)$$

a) How many inches of insulation should be added in order to minimize the total energy costs over a 5-year period?

b) Using the result of part a, what are the savings over a 5-year period?

39. *Energy costs.* The heating and cooling costs for a building with no insulation are \$590,625 per year. If x inches $(0 \le x \le 10)$ of insulation are added, the

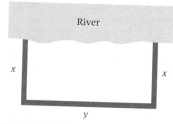

FIGURE 10-62

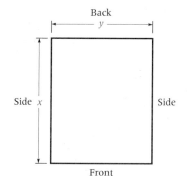

FIGURE 10-63

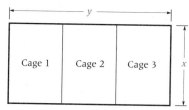

FIGURE 10-64

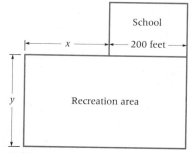

FIGURE 10-65

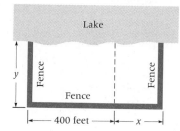

FIGURE 10-66

heating and cooling costs will be $2,362,500/(x + 4)$ dollars per year. If it costs $175,000 for each inch of insulation added,

    a) How many inches of insulation should be added in order to minimize the total energy costs over a 6-year period?

    b) Using the result of part (a), what are the savings over a 6-year period?

40. *Projectile.* A ball is projected vertically into the air. The function $S(t) = -16t^2 + 192t$ gives the height, S (in feet), above the ground of the ball at time, t (in seconds). When does the ball reach maximum height, and what is the maximum height?

41. *Area.* A park manager has 400 feet of fence to enclose a rectangular area alongside a river. No fence is needed along the river (see Figure 10-62). Use calculus to determine the dimensions x and y that maximize the enclosed area.

42. *Enclosure cost.* A city recreation department is planning to enclose a rectangular area of 125,000 square feet for a playground (see Figure 10-63). If the fence along the sides costs $10 per foot and the fence along the front and back costs $20 per foot, find the dimensions of the playground that minimize the fence cost.

43. *Enclosure.* A zoo manager wishes to enclose an area of 20,000 square feet into 3 cages of equal size, as illustrated in Figure 10-64. Find the dimensions x and y that minimize the length of fence used.

44. *Enclosure.* A park manager has 2000 feet of fence with which to enclose a rectangular area. Determine the dimensions of the rectangle that yield the maximum area.

45. *Enclosure.* Show that the maximum area enclosed by a rectangle with a fixed perimeter will always result in a square.

46. *Recreation area.* A school department wishes to enclose a recreation area adjacent to its high school, as illustrated in Figure 10-65. Find the dimensions that maximize the enclosed area if

    a) 3200 feet of fencing is available.

    b) 4800 feet of fencing is available.

47. *Enclosure.* A recreation manager wants to enclose a rectangular area of beach along a lake. There must be at least 400 feet of frontage along the lake, as illustrated in Figure 10-66. Find the dimensions that maximize the enclosed area if 1800 feet of fencing is available.

Profit. For each of the following, determine

a) The equation for profit, $P(x)$.

b) The number of units, x, for which profit is maximized.

c) The maximum profit.

48. $R(x) = -2x^2 + 400x; C(x) = 40x + 5000$

49. $R(x) = -4x^2 + 3200x; C(x) = 200x + 10,000$

50. $R(x) = 10x, C(x) = 0.01x^2 + 0.4x + 20$

51. $R(x) = 20x, C(x) = 0.01x^2 + 0.2x + 40$

Profit. For each of the following, assume that p denotes the unit price (in dollars) of some product and x denotes the demand for the product. Determine

a) The equation for revenue, $R(x)$.

b) The equation for profit, $P(x)$.

c) The demand level, x, for which profit is maximized.

d) The unit price, p, for which profit is maximized.

e) The maximum profit.

52. $p = -4x + 1600, C(x) = 40x + 3000$

53. $p = -5x + 3000, C(x) = 50x + 6000$

54. $p = -8x + 6400, C(x) = 60x + 8000$

55. $p = -2x + 2000, C(x) = 30x + 4000$

56. *Tax.* For Exercise 52, suppose a tax of $8 per unit produced is imposed on the producer. This modifies the cost equation so that

$$C(x) = \text{original cost} + \text{tax}$$
$$= 40x + 3000 + 8x$$
$$= 48x + 3000 \qquad \text{Modified cost equation}$$

a) Find the demand level, x, for which profit is maximized.
b) Find the unit price, p, for which profit is maximized.
c) How has the tax changed the price the producer charges for the product? (*Hint:* Compare the result of part b with that of Exercise 52(d).)
d) What portion of the tax is passed on to the consumer? (*Hint:* Use the result of part c.)

57. *Tax.* For Exercise 53, suppose a tax of $20 per unit produced is imposed on the producer. This modifies the cost equation so that

$$C(x) = \text{original cost} + \text{tax}$$
$$= 50x + 6000 + 20x$$
$$= 70x + 6000 \qquad \text{Modified cost equation}$$

a) Find the demand level, x, for which profit is maximized.
b) Find the unit price, p, for which profit is maximized.
c) How has the tax changed the price the producer charges for the product? (*Hint:* Compare the result of part b with that of Exercise 53(d).)
d) What portion of the tax is passed on to the consumer? (*Hint:* Use the result of part c.)

58. *Tax.* For Exercise 54, suppose a tax of $16 per unit produced is imposed on the producer.

a) Find the modified cost equation.
b) Find the demand level, x, for which profit is maximized.
c) Find the unit price, p, for which profit is maximized.
d) How has the tax changed the price the producer charges for the product? (*Hint:* Compare the result of part c with that of Exercise 54(d).
e) What portion of the tax is passed on to the consumer? (*Hint:* Use the result of part d.)

59. *Profit.* A company manufactures a product used in the computer industry. The unit price, p (in thousands of dollars), and the demand, x (in hundreds of units), are related by the equation

$$x = \frac{6400}{p^2} \qquad (p > 0)$$

The cost, C (in thousands of dollars), of producing the items is given by

$$C(x) = 8x + 50 \qquad (x > 0)$$

The company wishes to determine
a) The demand level, x, for which profit is maximized.
b) The unit price, p, for which profit is maximized.
c) The maximum profit.

60. *Quality control and profits.* Time Industries produces watches. Each watch costs $30 to produce and sells for $38. From past experience, it has been determined that out of x watches that are produced during any given day, the fraction defective for the day is given by $x^2/10{,}000{,}000$, where $0 \le x \le 2500$. Each defective watch costs the company an additional $15.

a) Determine the equation that gives daily profit, P, as a function of daily production volume, x.

b) Determine the maximum daily profit and the daily production volume that yields the maximum daily profit.

61. *Apple growing: Revenue per tree.* If an apple grower harvests her crop now, she will pick on the average 120 pounds per tree. She will get $0.48 per pound for the apples. From past experience, the grower knows that for each additional week she waits, the yield per tree will increase by about 10 pounds, while the price will decrease by about $0.03 per pound. Determine how many weeks the grower should wait in order to maximize sales revenue. What is the maximum sales revenue?

62. *Rental income.* An apartment building contains 100 apartments. If the rent is $300 per month, all apartments will be rented. However, for each additional $50 increase in the monthly rent, 5 additional apartments will become vacant.
a) Find the equation that gives the total monthly rental income, R, in terms of x, the number of $50 increases in monthly rent.
b) How many $50 increases in monthly rent will maximize the total monthly rental income?
c) Determine the maximum total monthly rental income.

63. *Continuing education income.* If an educational institution charges $1000 for a full-day workshop in time management, 40 managers usually enroll for the workshop. For each $50 decrease in the fee, 5 additional managers enroll for the workshop.
a) Determine the equation that gives workshop income as a function of the number of $50 decreases in the fee.
b) How many $50 decreases in the workshop fee will maximize the workshop income?
c) Determine the maximum workshop income.

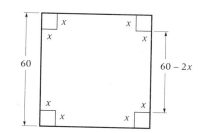

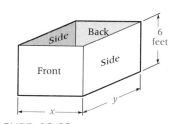

FIGURE 10-67

64. *Volume.* A company manufactures open boxes from square pieces of tin that are 60 inches on each side. The process involves cutting equal squares from the corners of each piece of tin and folding up the flaps to form sides, as illustrated in Figure 10-67.
a) What size square should be cut from each corner in order to maximize the volume of the box?
b) Determine the maximum volume.
c) Is the answer to part b an absolute maximum?

65. *Volume.* A company manufactures open boxes from square pieces of tin that are 18 inches on each side. The process involves cutting equal squares from the corners of each piece of tin and folding up the flaps to form sides. What size square should be cut from each corner in order to maximize the volume of the box?

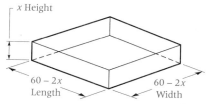

FIGURE 10-68

66. *Surface area.* A company manufactures the open trash bin illustrated in Figure 10-68. Each bin must be 6 feet high and have a volume of 294 cubic feet. Find the dimensions x and y of the base that minimize the total surface area of a bin. (*Note:* The total surface area is the sum of the areas of the sides and bottom).

67. *Material cost.* A company manufactures the open trash bin illustrated in Figure 10-69. Each bin must be 6 feet high and have a volume of 192 cubic feet. If the material for the front and back costs $5 per square foot, the material for the sides costs $10 per square foot, and the material for the bottom costs $20 per square foot, find the dimensions x and y of the base that minimize the total cost.

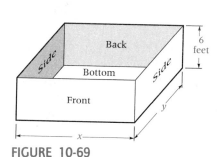

FIGURE 10-69

Maximum sustainable harvest. If a population (of living things such as whales, salmon, mink, etc.) of size P grows to $f(P)$ at the end of some unit of time, then, if $f(P) > P$, the amount

$$f(P) - P$$

could be *removed* or *harvested* from the population, and the population size would not fall below the initial population size, P. The function $f(P)$ reveals the growth pattern of the population and is thus called a **reproduction curve.** The quantity, $f(P) - P$, represents the amount harvested. We let H denote this quantity. Thus, H is a function of P and

$$H(P) = f(P) - P \qquad \text{Amount harvested}$$

We wish to determine the initial population size, P, which maximizes the amount harvested, $H(P)$. In other words, we want to determine the value of P that maximizes H. The maximum value of H is called the *maximum sustainable harvest*.

Determine the maximum sustainable harvest for each of the following reproduction curves, $f(P)$.

68. $f(P) = -0.05P^2 + 10P$
69. $f(P) = -0.01P^2 + 4P$
70. $f(P) = -0.02P^2 + 10P$, where P is measured in thousands
71. $f(P) = 60\sqrt{P}$, where P is measured in thousands
72. $f(P) = 20\sqrt{P}$, where P is measured in thousands
73. $f(P) = 1.10P$
74. $f(P) = 1.06P$

75. *Construction costs.* A construction company must lay a water line from point A on shore (see Figure 10-70) to point D on an island. The island is 9 miles offshore, as shown in Figure 10-70. It costs $600 per mile to run the water line along the shoreline and $800 per mile to run the water line underwater. At what point along the shoreline should the water line proceed under water in order to minimize the total construction cost?

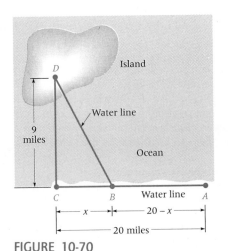

FIGURE 10-70

10-5 • MINIMIZING INVENTORY COST

A very important cost for many companies is that of financing and maintaining inventories. In this section, we develop a model for determining and minimizing total annual inventory cost. We begin with a discussion of the following typical situation.

A distributor of tires usually sells 100,000 tires per year. For each order for tires placed, it costs the distributor $20. Additionally, the cost of carrying 1 tire in inventory for a year is $4. The graph in Figure 10-71 illustrates the depletion of the distributor's inventory of tires over time, t. We assume that the annual demand is proportionally distributed throughout the year. In other words, if a work year consists of 50 weeks, then the weekly demand is $100,000/50 = 2000$ tires. Observing the graph of inventory level versus time in Figure 10-71, note that at $t = 0$, the initial inventory is Q tires. At $t = 1$ and $t = 2$, the inventory has reached a level of 0 tires. Thus, at $t = 1$ and $t = 2$, an order is placed for Q tires, and the inventory is immediately replenished.

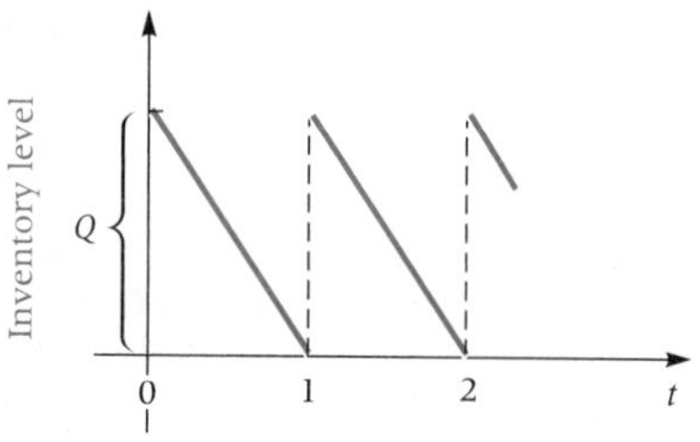

The distributor must find an answer to the following question:

Each time an order is placed for tires, how many tires (Q) should be ordered so that the total annual inventory cost is minimized?

FIGURE 10-71

Objective Function

The total annual inventory cost, C, is calculated by the following forula:

$$C = \text{ordering cost} + \text{carrying cost}$$

The **ordering cost** is calculated by multiplying the cost of placing an order by the number of orders placed in a year. Since 100,000 tires are usually ordered annually in quantities of Q tires per order, the number of orders per year is 100,000/Q. Thus, since the cost of placing each order is \$20, we have

$$\text{ordering cost} = 20\left(\frac{100,000}{Q}\right)$$

The **carrying cost** is calculated by multiplying the cost of carrying 1 unit in inventory for a year by the average number of units in inventory. The average inventory is $(0 + Q)/2 = Q/2$, since the inventory level varies from 0 to Q. Thus, since the cost of carrying 1 tire in inventory for a year is \$4, we obtain

$$\text{carrying cost} = 4\left(\frac{Q}{2}\right)$$

Therefore, the *total annual inventory cost* is calculated as

$$C(Q) = 20\left(\frac{100,000}{Q}\right) + 4\left(\frac{Q}{2}\right) \qquad \text{Objective function}$$

Simplifying, we obtain

$$C(Q) = \frac{2,000,000}{Q} + 2Q \qquad (Q > 0)$$

Critical Values

Since we must find the value of Q that minimizes $C(Q)$, we calculate $C'(Q)$, as follows:

$$C'(Q) = \frac{-2,000,000}{Q^2} + 2$$

A critical value is $Q = 0$. However, we exclude $Q = 0$ since it is not in the domain $Q > 0$. We set $C'(Q) = 0$ to obtain

$$0 = \frac{-2,000,000}{Q^2} + 2$$

Solving for Q^2 yields

$$Q^2 = 1,000,000$$
$$Q = \pm1000$$

We disregard the critical value $Q = -1000$ since it is outside the domain $Q > 0$. Thus, there is only one relevant critical value:

$$Q = 1000 \qquad \text{Only critical value}$$

Test for Absolute Extrema

Applying the second-derivative test to $Q = 1000$, we have

$$C''(Q) = \frac{4,000,000}{Q^3}$$

$$C''(1000) = \frac{4,000,000}{1000^3} = \frac{4}{1000} \quad \text{which is positive}$$

Therefore, by the second-derivative test for absolute extrema, an absolute minimum exists at $Q = 1000$.

Thus, in order to minimize the total annual inventory cost, the distributor should order tires in lots of 1000 tires. The minimum annual inventory cost is

$$C(1000) = \frac{2,000,000}{1000} + 2(1000)$$

$$= \$4000 \quad \text{Absolute minimum}$$

Graph of $C(Q)$

Since $C''(Q) > 0$ for all values of Q in the interval $Q > 0$, the cost function, $C(Q)$, is concave up over the interval $Q > 0$. This and the fact that $C'(1000) = 0$ imply that the graph of $C(Q)$ has the appearance of that shown in Figure 10-72.

We generalize as follows.

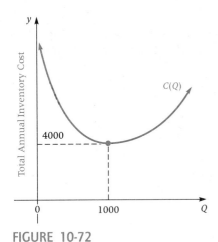

FIGURE 10-72

Total Inventory Cost

If

$\quad D$ = annual demand for a given product
$\quad K$ = cost of placing an order
$\quad H$ = cost of carrying (or holding) 1 unit of inventory for 1 year
$\quad Q$ = order size

the *total annual inventory cost* is given by

$$C(Q) = K\left(\frac{D}{Q}\right) + H\left(\frac{Q}{2}\right) \quad (Q > 0)$$

where

$\quad D/Q$ = number of orders placed per year at a cost of K dollars per order
$\quad Q/2$ = average number of units in inventory at a carrying (or holding) cost of H dollars per unit

The graph of $C(Q)$ has the appearance of that of Figure 10-73.

continues

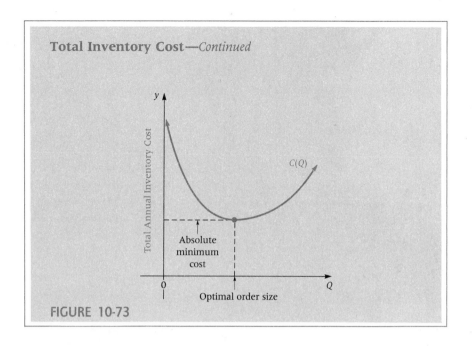

Total Inventory Cost—*Continued*

FIGURE 10-73

Unit Holding Cost

The holding cost, H, per unit of inventory includes financing costs (i.e., cost of capital) and other costs associated with holding inventory, such as insurance costs, taxes, breakage costs, etc. Often H is given as a percentage of the cost of 1 unit of inventory. For example, let's assume that each tire purchased by the distributor of the preceding discussion costs $20. If the distributor borrows money to buy tires at an annual rate of 19%, then the finance cost of each tire is $(0.19)(20) = \$3.80$ per year. If the annual insurance cost is $20,000, then the insurance cost per tire is $20,000/100,000 = \$0.20$ per tire. Thus, the breakdown of H, the annual holding cost per tire (assuming there are no other holding costs), is:

Finance cost	$3.80
Insurance cost	0.20
	$4.00

If we wish to express $H = \$4$ as a percentage of the cost per tire, then H is 20% (i.e., $4/20 = 0.20$) of the cost of each tire.

• EXAMPLE 10-25

One of many products sold by a discount store is a special model videocassette recorder (VCR). Each such VCR costs the store $200. The annual demand is 200,000 units. Ordering costs are $40 per order, and the annual holding cost per unit is 8% of the cost of a VCR.

a) Determine the equation for the total annual inventory cost.
b) Determine the order size that minimizes the total annual inventory cost.

c) Determine the minimum total annual inventory cost.

d) Determine the number of orders placed in a year for this particular VCR.

Solutions

a) The total annual inventory cost is given by

$$C(Q) = K\frac{D}{Q} + H\frac{Q}{2}$$

where

Q = order size

K = \$40 (cost of placing 1 order)

D = 200,000 (annual demand)

H = (0.08)(\$200) = \$16 (unit annual holding cost)

Thus

$$C(Q) = 40\left(\frac{200,000}{Q}\right) + 16\left(\frac{Q}{2}\right)$$

$$= \frac{8,000,000}{Q} + 8Q \quad (Q > 0)$$

b) Calculating $C'(Q)$ gives

$$C'(Q) = \frac{-8,000,000}{Q^2} + 8$$

A critical value is $Q = 0$, which we exclude because it is not in the domain $Q > 0$. Setting $C'(Q) = 0$ yields

$$0 = \frac{-8,000,000}{Q^2} + 8$$

Solving for Q^2 gives

$$Q^2 = 1,000,000$$

$$Q = \pm 1000$$

We disregard the critical value $Q = -1000$ since it is outside the domain $Q > 0$. Thus, there is only one relevant critical value:

$$Q = 1000 \qquad \text{Only critical value}$$

Applying the second-derivative test to $Q = 1000$, we have

$$C''(Q) = \frac{16,000,000}{Q^3}$$

$$C''(1000) = \frac{16,000,000}{1000^3}$$

$$= 0.016 \qquad \text{which is positive}$$

Therefore, by the second-derivative test for absolute extrema, an *absolute minimum* exists at $Q = 1000$.

Thus, in order to minimize the total annual inventory cost, the store should order this particular model of VCR in lots of 1000.

c) The *minimum annual inventory cost* is

$$C(1000) = \frac{8,000,000}{1000} + 8(1000)$$

$$= \$16,000$$

d) The *number of orders placed in a year* for this VCR is given by

$$\frac{D}{Q} = \frac{200{,}000}{1000}$$
$$= 200 \text{ orders}$$

Exercises 10-5

1. It costs a moped distributor $100 to place an order for Q mopeds. Also, it costs $20 per year to keep 1 moped in inventory. The distributor usually sells 25,000 mopeds annually.
   a) Find the formula for total inventory cost as a function of Q.
   b) What order size, Q, minimizes the total inventory cost?
2. A bicycle manufacturer finds that it costs $1500 to order Q bicycles. Also, it costs $3 per year to keep a bicycle in inventory. The manufacturer expects to sell 4,900,000 bicycles this year.
   a) Find the formula for total inventory cost as a function of Q.
   b) What production lot size, Q, minimizes the total inventory cost?
   c) What is the minimum total inventory cost?
3. A store sells 300,000 units of a particular model of color television. Each TV costs the store $500. Ordering costs are $60 per order, and the carrying cost per unit per year is 5% of the cost of the TV.
   a) Determine the equation for the total annual inventory cost.
   b) Determine the order size that minimizes the total annual inventory cost.
   c) Determine the minimum total annual inventory cost.
   d) Determine the number of orders placed in a year for this TV.
4. A computer store sells 400,000 units of a particular model home computer. Each computer costs the store $1000. Ordering costs are $80 per order, and annual holding costs per unit are 10% of the cost of a computer.
   a) Determine the equation for the total annual inventory cost.
   b) Determine the order size that minimizes the total annual inventory cost.
   c) Determine the minimum total annual inventory cost.
   d) Determine the total number of orders placed in a year for this computer.
5. A distributor of heating and cooling equipment sells 500,000 units of a particular model of air conditioner. Ordering costs are $100 per order. The annual finance charge for 500,000 units of this air conditioner is $7,000,000, and the annual insurance costs are $1,000,000. There are no other holding costs.
   a) Calculate the annual holding cost per air conditioner.
   b) Determine the equation for the total annual inventory cost.
   c) Determine the order size that minimizes the total annual inventory cost.
   d) Determine the minimum total annual inventory cost.
   e) Determine the number of orders placed in a year for this air conditioner.
6. Determine an equation for the value of Q that minimizes the total annual inventory cost

$$C(Q) = K\frac{D}{Q} + H\frac{Q}{2} \quad (Q > 0)$$

by following the steps.

Step 1 Find $C'(Q)$ by differentiating $C(Q)$ with respect to Q. Treat K, D, and H as positive constants.

Step 2 Set $C'(Q) = 0$, and solve for Q^2 and then Q. Call this minimizing value Q^*.

7. Verify that the equation for $Q*$ determined in Exercise 6 yields an absolute minimum for $C(Q)$ by following the steps:

Step 1   Find $C''(Q)$ by differentiating $C'(Q)$ with respect to Q. Treat K, D, and H as positive constants.

Step 2   Analyze the sign of $C''(Q)$.

EXTRA DIVIDENDS

• *The Production Lot Size Model—Medisoap, Inc.*

The inventory model in Section 10-5 assumed that items of inventory arrive in lots of size Q. However, there are real-life situations where items of inventory are supplied at a constant rate during a given time interval. This is characteristic of a production situation where a production run to manufacture a total of Q units is set up and the items are supplied to the inventory stockpile at a constant rate per time unit until the production run has been completed. The graph of inventory level versus time for such a situation appears in Figure 10-74.

We let

$$P = \text{annual production rate}$$

$$D = \text{annual demand rate}$$

where $P > D$, and note that these may be expressed in time units other than 1 year. If, for example, we wish to express P and D as daily rates, then we simply divide these annual rates by the number of work days in a year. The result is a daily production rate and a daily demand rate. Observing the graph in Figure 10-74, note that inventory is being produced (and supplied) at a rate, P (adjusted by a divisor for a daily, weekly, or monthly rate), and, simultaneously, is being sold at a rate, D (adjusted by a divisor for a daily, weekly, or monthly rate), during the production phase of the inventory cycle. This situation is illustrated in Figure 10-75. If P = production rate or rate of inflow of inventory into the stockpile and D = rate of outflow, then $P - D$ is the net rate of inflow of inventory into

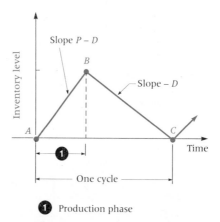

① Production phase

FIGURE 10-74

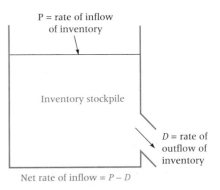

Production phase of inventory cycle

FIGURE 10-75

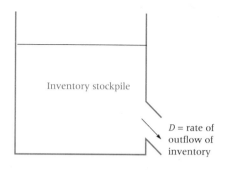

Inventory stockpile

D = rate of outflow of inventory

Post-production phase of inventory cycle

FIGURE 10-76

the stockpile during the production phase of the inventory cycle. As shown in Figure 10-74, $P - D$ is the slope of the line segment AB.

During the latter phase of the inventory cycle, no production is taking place; therefore, only the outflow of inventory at demand rate, D, is occurring. The slope, $-D$, of the line segment BC indicates that inventory is decreasing at an annual rate of D units. This is illustrated in Figure 10-76.

The **total annual inventory cost** associated with this production lot size inventory model is given by

$$C(Q) = K\frac{D}{Q} + H\left(\frac{P - D}{P}\right)\frac{Q}{2} \quad (Q > 0)$$

where

Q = number of units of inventory manufactured during a production run

D = annual demand rate

P = annual production rate

K = cost of setting up a production run

H = annual holding cost per unit of inventory

For this equation, the first component, $K(D/Q)$, gives the annual set-up cost for the production runs; the second component, $H[(P - D)/P](Q/2)$, gives the annual holding cost. Since K, D, H, and P are constants, *we seek a value of Q that minimizes the total annual inventory cost, C(Q).*

We now consider the following specific example. Medisoap, Inc., manufactures a special type of medicated soap. Medisoap can produce this soap at an annual rate of 480,000 cases. The annual demand is estimated to be 320,000 cases. It costs Medisoap $400 to set up a production run. The annual holding cost per case of soap is $12.

Exercises

1. Determine the equation defining the total annual inventory cost for Medisoap.
2. Determine the value of Q that minimizes the total annual inventory cost.
3. Determine the minimum total annual inventory cost.
4. Determine the annual set-up cost.
5. Determine the annual holding cost.
6. Determine an equation for the value of Q that minimizes the total annual inventory cost

$$C(Q) = K\frac{D}{Q} + H\left(\frac{P - D}{P}\right)\frac{Q}{2} \quad (Q > 0)$$

by following these steps.

Step 1 Find $C'(Q)$ by differentiating $C(Q)$ with respect to Q. Treat K, D, P, and H as positive constants.

Step 2 Set $C'(Q) = 0$, and solve for Q^2 and then Q. Call this minimizing value Q^*.

7. Verify that the equation for Q^* determined in Exercise 6 yields an absolute minimum for $C(Q)$ by following these steps.

Step 1 Find $C''(Q)$ by differentiating $C'(Q)$ with respect to Q. Treat K, D, P, and H as positive constants.

Step 2 Analyze the sign of $C''(Q)$.

CHAPTER 10 HIGHLIGHTS

• *Concepts*

Your ability to answer the following questions is one indicator of the depth of your mastery of this chapter's important concepts. Note that the questions are grouped under various topic headings. For any question that you cannot answer, refer to the appropriate section of the chapter indicated by the topic heading. Pay particular attention to the summary boxes within a section.

10-1 HIGHER-ORDER DERIVATIVES

1. How does one find a second derivative of a function?
2. How does one find a third derivative of a function?
3. If the distance, S, gained by a moving particle is given by a function, $S = f(t)$, where t denotes time, then
   a) Explain the term *velocity* and indicate how it is determined.
   b) Explain the term *acceleration* and indicate how it is found.

10-2 CRITICAL VALUES AND THE FIRST DERIVATIVE

4. Draw each of the following:
   a) A relative maximum point where the first derivative is 0
   b) A relative minimum point where the first derivative is 0
   c) A relative maximum point where the first derivative is undefined
   d) A relative minimum point where the first derivative is undefined
5. Draw two types of curve segments that are
   a) Increasing.   b) Decreasing.
6. a) If the first derivative of some function is positive over some interval, what does this indicate about the function over that interval?
   b) If the first derivative of some function is negative over some interval, what does this indicate about the function over that interval?
7. a) Define *critical values.*
   b) Do critical values always yield relative extrema?
   c) How do we determine whether or not a critical value yields a relative extremum?
   d) Can a relative extremum occur at a value of x that is not a critical value?
8. According to the first-derivative test for relative extrema,
   a) How do we determine whether or not a relative maximum occurs at a critical value?
   b) How do we determine whether or not a relative minimum occurs at a critical value?
9. a) State the difference between relative extrema and absolute extrema.
   b) Is it possible for a relative extremum to also be an absolute extremum? Draw graphs to support your answer.
   c) Is an absolute extremum always a relative extremum? Draw graphs to support your answer.

10-3 CONCAVITY AND THE SECOND DERIVATIVE

10. Draw a curve segment that is increasing and
a) Concave down.   b) Concave up.

11. Draw a curve segment that is decreasing and
a) Concave down.   b) Concave up.

12. a) If the second derivative of some function is positive over some interval, what does this indicate about the function over the interval?
b) If the second derivative of some function is negative over some interval, what does this indicate about the function over the interval?

13. a) What is an inflection point?
b) How do we determine the existence of an inflection point?

14. How do we determine the existence of vertical asymptotes?

15. Is a function defined at any of its vertical asymptotes?

16. How do we determine the existence of horizontal asymptotes?

10-4 OPTIMIZATION

17. Does the second-derivative test for relative extrema apply to
a) All critical values?
b) Critical values for which $f'(x) = 0$?
c) Critical values for which $f'(x)$ is undefined?

18. If $f(x)$ is a function and x_0 is a number such that $f'(x_0) = 0$, then, according to the second-derivative test for relative extrema,
a) If $f''(x_0) > 0$, what does this indicate?
b) If $f''(x_0) < 0$, what does this indicate?
c) If $f''(x_0) = 0$, what does this indicate?

19. If the second-derivative test for relative extrema fails, or if a critical value is such that $f'(x)$ is undefined, what test should be used to determine the existence or nonexistence of relative extrema?

20. Is the second-derivative test for relative extrema used to graph a function?

21. Is the second-derivative test for relative extrema used mainly to determine relative extrema without having to graph functions?

22. Can the second-derivative test for absolute extrema be used if two or more critical values exist in some interval of interest?

23. State the second-derivative test for absolute extrema.

24. State the procedure for finding absolute extrema of continuous functions defined on closed intervals.

10-5 MINIMIZING INVENTORY COST

25. State the two components that constitute total annual inventory cost. Give the formula for and explain each component.

REVIEW EXERCISES

• *Higher-Order Derivatives*

For Exercises 1-4, find
a) $f'(x)$ b) $f''(x)$ c) $f'(1)$ d) $f''(1)$

1. $f(x) = x^2 - 6x + 8$ **2.** $f(x) = x^4 - 2x^3 + 6x^2 + 9$
3. $f(x) = x^6 - 8x^4 + 7$ **4.** $f(x) = (x - 4)^2(x^2 + 6)$

5. *Projectile.* A ball moves in the path of a straight line. Its distance, S (in feet), from its starting point after t seconds have elapsed is given by

$$S(t) = -2t^2 + 80t \qquad (0 \le t \le 40)$$

a) Find the ball's instantaneous speed at $t = 5$ and $t = 10$.
b) Find the ball's instantaneous acceleration at $t = 5$ and $t = 10$.

• Critical Values and the First Derivative

For Exercises 6-9, use the first derivative to
a) Determine any critical values.
b) Determine the interval(s) over which the function is increasing.
c) Determine the interval(s) over which the function is decreasing.
d) Determine any relative maxima and minima.
e) Graph the function.

6. $f(x) = 2x^3 - 18x^2 + 30x + 5$
7. $f(x) = 2x^3 + 3x^2 - 60x + 8$
8. $f(x) = x^4 - 32x^2 + 10$
9. $f(x) = x^3 - 24x^2 + 6$

10. *Revenue function.* The sales revenue gained from selling x units of some product is given by

$$R(x) = -6x^2 + 600x \qquad (0 \le x \le 50)$$

a) State the interval(s) over which sales revenue is increasing.
b) State the interval(s) over which sales revenue is decreasing.
c) Identify all relative extrema.
d) Graph $R(x)$.
e) What sales volume maximizes sales revenue? Is this a relative maximum? Is this an absolute maximum?
f) What is the maximum sales revenue?

• Concavity and the Second Derivative

For Exercises 11-16, use both first and second derivatives to graph the function. Identify all relative and absolute extrema and inflection points.

11. $f(x) = 3x^4 - 8x^3 + 6x^2 + 2$
12. $f(x) = 3x^4 - 16x^3 + 24x^2 + 4$
13. $f(x) = x^{6/5}$
14. $f(x) = 1800/x + 2x$
15. $f(x) = 10/(x^2 + 4)$
16. $f(x) = (x + 8)/x$

17. *Average cost per unit.* Given the cost function

$$C(x) = x^2 - 8x + 100 \qquad (x > 0)$$

where x is the number of units produced,
a) Determine the formula for the average cost per unit.
b) Use both first and second derivatives to graph the average cost function.
c) Identify any relative and absolute extrema.
d) What production level minimizes the average cost per unit?
e) What is the minimum average cost per unit?

• Optimization

Use the second-derivative test to find relative extrema for Exercises 18-21.

18. $f(x) = x^2 - 10x + 8$
19. $f(x) = x^3 - 15x^2 + 48x + 4$
20. $f(x) = x^3 - 9x^2 - 48x + 12$
21. $f(x) = x + 100/x$

Determine the absolute extrema for Exercises 22-27.

22. $f(x) = x^2 - 20x + 5$
23. $f(x) = 3\sqrt{x} - x$
24. $f(x) = x^3 - 75x + 10 \qquad (-10 \le x \le 10)$
25. $f(x) = 7 + 3x + 48/x \qquad (x > 0)$

26. $f(x) = 6(x - 4)^3$ $(0 \le x \le 7)$
27. $f(x) = 8 + 2x + 128/x^3$ $(x > 0)$

Solve Exercises 28-34. Try to verify the existence of absolute extrema.

28. Find two numbers whose difference is 20 and whose product is as small as possible.

29. *Enclosure.* A person has 800 feet of fence to enclose a rectangular area. Use calculus to determine the dimensions that maximize the enclosed area.

30. *Enclosure.* A farmer must enclose a rectangular area of 40,000 square feet. Use calculus to determine the dimensions that minimize the length of fence used.

31. *Revenue.* A cable television company currently charges $20 per month for its service and has 5000 subscribers. Market surveys indicate that the number of subscribers will increase by 400 for each $1 decrease in the monthly rate.
    a) Determine the monthly rate that maximizes revenue.
    b) What is the maximum revenue?
    c) How many subscribers will produce the maximum revenue?

32. *Building cost.* A home improvement center is designing a greenhouse that is to have the shape of a box with a square base. The material for the floor costs $5 per square foot; the material for the roof and three sides is glass and costs $20 per square foot; the material for the fourth side is wood and costs $4 per square foot. If the greenhouse is to have a volume of 400 cubic feet, find the dimensions that minimize its cost.

33. *Enclosure.* A rectangular storage area containing 800 square feet is to be enclosed outside a shopping mall. Three sides are to consist of cedar fencing at a cost of $10 per foot; the fourth side is to consist of chain link fencing at a cost of $20 per foot. Find the dimensions that minimize the cost.

• *Minimizing Inventory Cost*

34. A distributor of cameras sells 600,000 cameras per year. The cost of placing an order for cameras is $5. The cost of holding 1 camera in inventory for 1 year is $6.
    a) Determine the equation for the total annual inventory cost, $C(Q)$.
    b) Each time the distributor places an order for cameras, how many should be ordered so that the total annual inventory cost is minimized?
    c) Determine the minimum total annual inventory cost.
    d) How many orders will be placed per year?

11

APPLICATIONS
OF THE
DERIVATIVE

Introductory Application

Elasticity of Demand

In earlier chapters of this text, we discussed demand functions and learned that, typically, as the unit price of some commodity increases, its demand decreases. Also, if the unit price decreases, the quantity demanded increases.

PROBLEM

Given the demand equation

$$q = \frac{p}{p - 5} \qquad (p > 5)$$

where q denotes the number of units demanded of some commodity at a unit price of p dollars, determine the effect upon demand of a 1% increase in the unit price.

SOLUTION

The answer to this problem involves the determination of a relationship between the percent change in demand and the percent change in unit price. In Section 11-3 of this chapter, we will discuss a ratio, called the elasticity of demand, which gives the relationship between the percent change in demand and the percent change in unit price for a commodity. The above problem is solved in Example 11-9.

11-1 • IMPLICIT DIFFERENTIATION

Up to this point, we have found derivatives of functions that were defined *explicitly in terms of x.* For example, the equation

$$y = f(x) = x^3 - 4x^2 + 5$$

defines y (or $f(x)$) explicitly in terms of x because y is written completely in terms of x and constants. If this equation were written as

$$y - x^3 + 4x^2 - 5 = 0$$

or

$$f(x) - x^3 + 4x^2 - 5 = 0$$

then y (or $f(x)$) is said to be defined implicitly in terms of x. Thus, if y is not written completely in terms of x and constants, then y is said to be defined **implicitly in terms of x.**

There are cases where y (or $f(x)$) cannot be defined explicitly in terms of x and also where it is difficult to do so. Consider the equation

$$xy^2 + x^2 + y = 2$$

It is difficult to solve this equation for y so that y is expressed explicitly in terms of x. Thus, we suppose that y (or $f(x)$) is defined implicitly in terms of x by the given equation and proceed as follows.

If we assume that y is a differentiable function of x—say, $y = f(x)$—then dy/dx is found by a method called **implicit differentiation.** To differentiate an expression such as

$$xy^2 + x^2 + y = 2$$

implicitly, we differentiate each side of the equation with respect to x, *term by term*, to obtain

$$\frac{d}{dx}(xy^2) + \frac{d}{dx}(x^2) + \frac{d}{dx}(y) = \frac{d}{dx}(2) \tag{1}$$

Since y is a differentiable function of x and xy^2 is a product, we must use the product rule to find $(d/dx)(xy^2)$. Hence

$$\frac{d}{dx}(xy^2) = x\frac{d}{dx}(y^2) + y^2\frac{d}{dx}(x)$$

$$= x \cdot 2y\frac{dy}{dx} + y^2(1)$$

Note that we used the general power rule to find

$$\frac{d}{dx}(y^2) = 2y\frac{dy}{dx}$$

Thus,

$$\frac{d}{dx}(xy^2) = 2xy\frac{dy}{dx} + y^2$$

and equation (1) becomes

$$2xy\frac{dy}{dx} + y^2 + 2x + \frac{dy}{dx} = 0$$

Combining terms with dy/dx gives

$$2xy\frac{dy}{dx} + \frac{dy}{dx} = -2x - y^2$$

Factoring out dy/dx, we have

$$(2xy + 1)\frac{dy}{dx} = -2x - y^2$$

Solving for dy/dx gives

$$\frac{dy}{dx} = \frac{-2x - y^2}{2xy + 1}$$

Note that dy/dx is expressed in terms of x and y.

• **EXAMPLE 11-1** ——————————————————————

For the equation $x^2 + y^2 = 16$:

a) Find the dy/dx by implicit differentiation.
b) Find the slope of the tangent line at $(3, \sqrt{7})$.

Solutions

a) Differentiating both sides with respect to x, term by term, gives

$$\frac{d}{dx}(x^2) + \frac{d}{dx}(y^2) = \frac{d}{dx}(16) \qquad (2)$$

Treating y as a function of x and using the general power rule,

$$\frac{d}{dx}(y^2) = 2y\frac{dy}{dx}$$

Thus, equation (2) becomes

$$2x + 2y\frac{dy}{dx} = 0$$

Solving for dy/dx yields

$$\frac{dy}{dx} = \frac{-2x}{2y} = \frac{-x}{y}$$

b) The circle* defined by $x^2 + y^2 = 16$ is graphed in Figure 11-1. Note that $(3, \sqrt{7})$ is a point on the circle since its coordinates satisfy the equation $x^2 + y^2 = 16$. To find the slope of the tangent line at $(3, \sqrt{7})$, we must evaluate dy/dx at $(3, \sqrt{7})$. Hence,

$$\frac{dy}{dx} = \frac{-x}{y}$$

$$\frac{dy}{dx}\bigg|_{(3, \sqrt{7})} = \frac{-3}{\sqrt{7}} \approx -1.13$$

Thus, the slope of the tangent line at $(3, \sqrt{7})$ is $-3/\sqrt{7}$, or approximately -1.13.

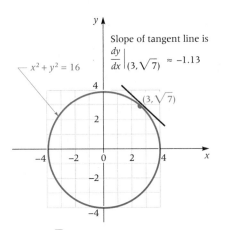

Slope of tangent line is

$$\frac{dy}{dx}\bigg|_{(3, \sqrt{7})} \approx -1.13$$

$(3, \sqrt{7})$ is a point on the circle since

$$x^2 + y^2 = 16$$

$$(3)^2 + (\sqrt{7})^2 = 16$$

FIGURE 11-1

——————————————————

*Equations of circles are discussed in Appendix B.

• **EXAMPLE 11-2**

For the equation $xy - 2y = 5$:

a) Find dy/dx by implicit differentiation.

b) Express y explicitly in terms of x, and find dy/dx.

c) Compare the results of parts a and b.

Solutions

a) Beginning with $xy - 2y = 5$, we differentiate both sides with respect to x, term by term, to obtain

$$\frac{d}{dx}(xy) - \frac{d}{dx}(2y) = \frac{d}{dx}(5)$$

Treating y as a function of x and using the appropriate differentiation rule, we obtain

$$x\frac{dy}{dx} + y - 2\frac{dy}{dx} = 0$$

Combining terms containing dy/dx gives

$$(x - 2)\frac{dy}{dx} = -y$$

Solving for dy/dx gives

$$\frac{dy}{dx} = \frac{-y}{x - 2}$$

b) $xy - 2y = 5$ can be written as $(x - 2)y = 5$. Solving for y explicitly yields

$$y = \frac{5}{x - 2}$$

Hence,

$$\frac{dy}{dx} = \frac{-5}{(x - 2)^2}$$

c) From part a, $dy/dx = -y/(x - 2)$. We solved the equation $xy - 2y = 5$ for y to obtain $y = 5/(x - 2)$. Substituting this result for y into the equation for dy/dx gives

$$\frac{dy}{dx} = \frac{-5/(x - 2)}{(x - 2)} = \frac{-5}{(x - 2)^2}$$

This answer is identical to that of part b.

dy/dx and *dx/dy*

If an equation defines y as a function of x, such as

$$y = 4x - 3$$

then the expression for the rate of change of y with respect to x is

$$\frac{dy}{dx} = 4$$

Suppose we wish to find an expression for the *instantaneous rate of change of x with respect to y, dx/dy*. We can solve the equation $y = 4x - 3$ for x to obtain

$$x = \frac{1}{4}y + 3$$

and differentiate with respect to y to obtain

$$\frac{dx}{dy} = \frac{1}{4}$$

Note that $dx/dy = 1/(dy/dx)$. Is this true in general? In other words, can we find dx/dy as the reciprocal of dy/dx without having to solve the equation for x and then differentiate with respect to y? The answer to both questions is yes, provided certain conditions hold. We will use implicit differentiation and the chain rule to show why.

Let $y = f(x)$ be an equation defining y as a function of x and $x = g(y)$ be its equivalent equation obtained by solving for x in terms of y. We begin with

$$y = f(x)$$

and differentiate both sides with respect to y to obtain

$$\frac{d}{dy}(y) = \frac{d}{dy}(f(x))$$

Since x is also a function of y, we apply the chain rule to obtain

$$\frac{d}{dy}(y) = \frac{d}{dx}(f(x))\frac{dx}{dy}$$

Since $(d/dy)(y) = 1$ and $(d/dx)(f(x)) = f'(x)$, the equation becomes

$$1 = f'(x)\frac{dx}{dy}$$

Solving for dx/dy yields

$$\frac{dx}{dy} = \frac{1}{f'(x)}$$

Since $f'(x) = dy/dx$, the equation becomes as follows.

$$\frac{dx}{dy} = \frac{1}{dy/dx}$$

provided dy/dx exists and $dy/dx \neq 0$.

• EXAMPLE 11-3

If $y = x^2 - 8x + 10$, then find dx/dy.

Solution

Since y is expressed in terms of x, we find dy/dx.

$$\frac{dy}{dx} = 2x - 8$$

Now

$$\frac{dx}{dy} = \frac{1}{dy/dx}$$

$$= \frac{1}{2x - 8} \qquad \text{provided that } x \neq 4$$

Exercises 11-1

Use implicit differentiation to find dy/dx for each of the following.

1. $xy^3 + x^4 + y = 8$ **2.** $x^2 + y^2 = 60$

3. $xy^5 + x^3 + y^4 = 10$ **4.** $x^3 + y^2 = 80$

5. $x^3 + y^6 = 8xy$ **6.** $\sqrt{x} + \sqrt{y} = 10$

7. $(x - y)(x^2 + y^2) = 9$ **8.** $x^2/4 + y^2/25 = 1$

9. $(x + y)^4 = x^2 + y^2$ **10.** $(x + y)(x + 3y) = 10$

For each of the following, find the slope of the tangent line to the curve at the indicated point.

11. $x^3 + xy^2 + y^4 = 21$, $(1, 2)$ **12.** $y^3 - x^2 + xy = 29$, $(2, 3)$

13. $x^2 - 3xy + 5y^2 = 15$, $(-2, 1)$ **14.** $3x + 4y^2 - y = 57$, $(-1, 4)$

15. $4x - 2y^2 + 5y = -7$, $(-1, 3)$ **16.** $x^3 - 2xy + y^2 = 4$, $(1, 3)$

17. For the equation $x^2 + y^2 = 64$:
  a) Find dy/dx by implicit differentiation.
  b) Find the slope of the tangent line at $(4, 4\sqrt{3})$.
  c) Find the equation of the tangent line of part b.
  d) Include a graphical interpretation of parts a through c.

18. For the equation $(x - 3)^2 + (y - 6)^2 = 25$:
  a) Find dy/dx by implicit differentiation.
  b) Find the slope of the tangent line at $(7, 9)$.
  c) Find the equation of the tangent line of part b.
  d) Include a graphical interpretation of parts a through c.

19. If $y = 6x + 10$, find dx/dy.

20. If $y = 3x^2 - 8x$, find dx/dy.

21. If $y = 4x^2 - 3x + 7$, find dx/dy.

22. If $y = 6x^2 - 2x + 1$, find dx/dy.

23. Given that $y = x^2 - 4x$,
  a) Find dx/dy.
  b) Evaluate dx/dy at $x = 3$.
  c) Interpret the result of part b as a rate of change.

24. Given that $y = -4x^2 + 36x$,
  a) Find dx/dy.
  b) Evaluate dx/dy at $x = 2$.
  c) Interpret the result of part b as a rate of change.

25. *Demand.* For some commodity, demand, q, and unit price, p, are related by

$$q = p^2 - 20p + 101 \qquad (0 < p \le 10)$$

  a) Find dp/dq.
  b) Evaluate dp/dq at $p = 7$.
  c) Interpret the result of part b as a rate of change.

26. *Demand.* For some commodity, demand, q, and unit price, p, are related by

$$q = p^2 - 40p + 405 \qquad (0 < p \le 20)$$

  a) Find dp/dq.
  b) Evaluate dp/dq at $p = 10$.
  c) Interpret the result of part b as a rate of change.

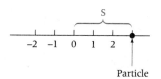

Physics: Velocity. A particle starts at point 0 and moves along a horizontal line, as illustrated to the left. The distance between the particle and its starting point, 0, after t seconds have elapsed is given by S. If S and t are related as follows, then, for each of the following, find a formula for the velocity, dS/dt.

27. $S^3 - 2St + 4t^3 - 2t = 0$ **28.** $S^2 - St + t^2 = 5$
29. $S^4 - 3St^2 + t^3 = 6$ **30.** $S^3 + 4St - t^2 = 9$

11-2

• RELATED RATES

In this section, we will encounter word problems—the solutions to which involve equations with variables that are implicit functions of time. Typically we will have to determine rates of change of such variables with respect to time. Since such variables will not usually be defined explicitly in terms of time, we will have to differentiate implicitly with respect to time to determine the rates of change.

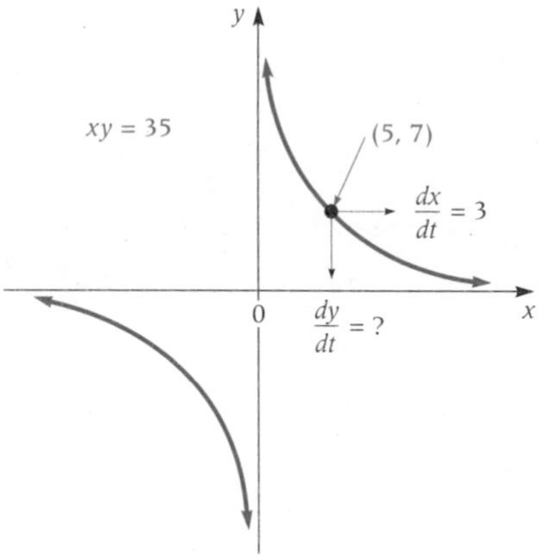

For example, suppose a point moves along the graph of

$$xy = 35$$

in such a manner that its x-coordinate is increasing at the rate of 3 units per second when the point is at $(5, 7)$(see Figure 11-2). Find the rate of change of the y-coordinate at that moment.

Here x and y are functions of time, t. We want to determine a formula for dy/dt. Since x and y are not defined explicitly in terms of t, we must implicitly differentiate each side of the equation $xy = 35$ with respect to t. This gives

$$\frac{d}{dt}(xy) = \frac{d}{dt}(35)$$

Since x and y are functions of t, we must use the product rule to differentiate the left-hand side. The derivative of 35, a constant, is 0. Hence, we have

$$\text{(first)}\begin{pmatrix}\text{derivative}\\\text{of second}\end{pmatrix} + \text{(second)}\begin{pmatrix}\text{derivative}\\\text{of first}\end{pmatrix} = 0$$

$$x\frac{dy}{dt} + y\frac{dx}{dt} = 0$$

Note that the derivatives dx/dt and dy/dt are related by the above equation. Hence, they are called **related rates.** Solving for dy/dt gives

$$x\frac{dy}{dt} = -y\frac{dx}{dt}$$

$$\frac{dy}{dt} = -\frac{y}{x} \cdot \frac{dx}{dt} \qquad \text{Formula for } dy/dt$$

Substituting 5 for x, 7 for y, and 3 for dx/dt gives

$$\frac{dy}{dt} = -\frac{7}{5}(3) = -4.2 \text{ units per second}$$

Thus, the y-coordinate is decreasing at a rate of 4.2 units per second.

• EXAMPLE 11-4

A 20-foot ladder is resting against a building, as illustrated in Figure 11-3. The bottom of the ladder is sliding away from the building at a rate of 3 feet per second.

FIGURE 11-2

$xy = 35$

$(5, 7)$

$\frac{dx}{dt} = 3$

$\frac{dy}{dt} = ?$

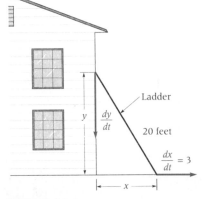

FIGURE 11-3

a) Use implicit differentiation to find a formula for dy/dt, the rate at which the top of the ladder is sliding downward.

b) How fast is the top of the ladder sliding downward when the bottom of the ladder is 12 feet away from the building?

Solutions

a) Observing Figure 11-3 and using the Pythagorean theorem, we obtain the equation

$$x^2 + y^2 = 20^2$$

Since x and y are changing as time elapses, then x and y are functions of time, t (in seconds). Since we want to determine a formula for dy/dt, we differentiate both sides of the above equation, term by term, with respect to t. This gives

$$\frac{d}{dt}(x^2) \;+\; \frac{d}{dt}(y^2) \;=\; \frac{d}{dt}(20^2)$$

$$2x\frac{dx}{dt} \;+\; 2y\frac{dy}{dt} = 0$$

Solving for dy/dt, we obtain

$$2y\frac{dy}{dt} = -2x\frac{dx}{dt}$$

$$\frac{dy}{dt} = \frac{-2x}{2y} \cdot \frac{dx}{dt}$$

$$= -\frac{x}{y} \cdot \frac{dx}{dt}$$

This expression gives dy/dt in terms of x, y, and dx/dt.

Since the ladder is sliding away from the wall (i.e., horizontally) at 3 feet per second, then

$$\frac{dx}{dt} = 3$$

Substituting this into the above formula for dy/dt gives

$$\frac{dy}{dt} = -\frac{x}{y}(3)$$

$$= -\frac{3x}{y}$$

This expression gives dy/dt in terms of x and y when $dx/dt = 3$.

b) When the ladder is 12 feet away from the building, then $x = 12$. Substituting into the equation

$$x^2 + y^2 = 20^2$$

gives

$$12^2 + y^2 = 20^2$$

or

$$144 + y^2 = 400$$
$$y^2 = 256$$
$$y = 16$$

Thus, when $x = 12$, $y = 16$. Substituting these results into the formula for dy/dt gives

$$\frac{dy}{dt} = -\frac{3x}{y}$$

$$= -\frac{3(12)}{16} = -2.25 \text{ feet per second}$$

Hence, the top of the ladder is sliding downward at a rate of 2.25 feet per second. The minus sign indicates that the top of the ladder is sliding *downward*.

• **EXAMPLE 11-5** _____

The unit price, p, of some product is related to the number of units sold, x, by the demand equation

$$p = 400 - \frac{x}{1000} \qquad \text{Demand equation}$$

The cost of producing x units of this product is given by

$$C(x) = 50x + 16{,}000 \qquad \text{Cost equation}$$

The number of units produced and sold, x, is increasing at a rate of 200 units per week. When the number of units produced and sold is 10,000, determine the instantaneous rate of change with respect to time, t (in weeks), of

a) Sales revenue. **b)** Cost. **c)** Profit.

Solutions

a) We determine the equation for sales revenue, R.

$$R = (\text{unit price})\binom{\text{number of}}{\text{units sold}}$$

$$= px$$

$$= \left(400 - \frac{x}{1000}\right)x$$

$$R = 400x - \frac{x^2}{1000} \qquad \text{Revenue equation}$$

Since x is changing as time, t, elapses, then R is changing as time elapses. We want to find dR/dt. Differentiating both sides of the revenue equation with respect to t gives

$$\frac{d}{dt}(R) = \frac{d}{dt}(400x) - \frac{d}{dt}\left(\frac{x^2}{1000}\right)$$

$$\frac{dR}{dt} = 400\frac{dx}{dt} - \frac{x}{500} \cdot \frac{dx}{dt}$$

$$= \left(400 - \frac{x}{500}\right)\frac{dx}{dt}$$

Since x is increasing at a rate of 200 units per week, $dx/dt = 200$. Substituting 200 for dx/dt and 10,000 for x, we obtain

$$\frac{dR}{dt} = \left(400 - \frac{10{,}000}{500}\right)(200) = \$76{,}000 \text{ per week}$$

Thus, sales revenue is increasing at a rate of $76,000 per week.

b) We want to find dC/dt where

$$C = 50x + 16{,}000$$

Since x changes with time, C also changes with time. Thus, to find dC/dt, we differentiate both sides of the cost equation with respect to t to obtain

$$\frac{d}{dt}(C) = \frac{d}{dt}(50x) + \frac{d}{dt}(16,000)$$

$$\frac{dC}{dt} = 50\frac{dx}{dt} + 0$$

$$= 50\frac{dx}{dt}$$

Substituting 200 for dx/dt gives

$$\frac{dC}{dt} = 50(200) = \$10,000 \text{ per week}$$

Thus, the cost is increasing at a rate of $10,000 per week

c) We want to find dP/dt where

$$P = R - C \qquad \text{Profit equation}$$

Since R and C change with time, then P changes with time. To find dP/dt, we differentiate both sides of the above profit equation with respect to time to obtain

$$\frac{dP}{dt} = \frac{dR}{dt} - \frac{dC}{dt}$$

from part a

from part b

$$\frac{dP}{dt} = \$76,000 - \$10,000 = \$66,000 \text{ per week}$$

Thus, profit is increasing at a rate of $66,000 per week.

We now state a procedure for solving related-rate problems.

To Solve Related-Rate Problems

1. Identify and list the variables involved. Draw a sketch, if possible.
2. Find an equation that relates the variables.
3. Identify and list the rates of change that are given and those that must be determined.
4. Differentiate the equation of step 2 implicitly with respect to time, t. Solve for the derivative that gives the desired rate of change.
5. Substitute in all given values.

• **EXAMPLE 11-6**

A metal cylinder, when heated, expands in such a manner that its radius, r, increases at a rate of 0.20 centimeter per minute and its height, h, increases at a rate of 0.15 centimeter per minute (see Figure 11-4). Determine the rate of change of the volume of the cylinder when its radius is 10 centimeters and its height is 25 centimeters.

Solution

Step 1 *Identify and list the variables.* r = radius, h = height, V = volume, and t = time in minutes.

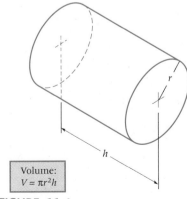

Volume:
$V = \pi r^2 h$

FIGURE 11-4

Step 2 *Write the equation.* The volume of a cylinder is given by

$$V = \pi r^2 h$$

where $\pi \approx 3.1416$.

Step 3 *Identify and list the rates of change.*

$$\frac{dr}{dt} = 0.20 \leftarrow \text{The radius is increasing at 0.20 centimeter per minute.}$$

$$\frac{dh}{dt} = 0.15 \leftarrow \text{The height is increasing at 0.15 centimeter perminute.}$$

$$\frac{dV}{dt} = ? \leftarrow \text{This must be determined.}$$

Step 4 *Differentiate implicitly.* As determined in step 2, the volume of a cylinder is given by

$$V = \pi r^2 h$$

Since r and h are changing with time, then V is also changing with time. We must find dV/dt.

Differentiating each side of the above equation with respect to t gives

$$\frac{d}{dt}(V) = \frac{d}{dt}(\pi r^2 h)$$

We must use the product rule to find the derivative of the right-hand side since r and h are functions of t. Hence,

$$\frac{dV}{dt} = (\text{first})\left(\begin{matrix}\text{derivative} \\ \text{of second}\end{matrix}\right) + (\text{second})\left(\begin{matrix}\text{derivative} \\ \text{of first}\end{matrix}\right)$$

$$\frac{dV}{dt} = \pi r^2 \frac{dh}{dt} + h \cdot 2\pi r \frac{dr}{dt}$$

$$= \pi r^2 \frac{dh}{dt} + 2\pi rh\frac{dr}{dt}$$

Step 5 *Substitute in the given values.* Since $dr/dt = 0.20$ and $dh/dt = 0.15$, we substitute these along with $r = 10$ and $h = 25$ into the above equation for dV/dt to obtain

$$\frac{dV}{dt} = \pi(10)^2(0.15) + 2\pi(10)(25)(0.20)$$

$$= 15\pi + 100\pi$$

$$= 115\pi$$

$$\approx 361.28 \text{ cubic centimeters per minute}$$

Thus, the volume of the cyclinder is increasing at approximately 361.28 cubic centimeters per minute.

• **EXAMPLE 11-7** _____

The cylinder in Example 11-6 is expanding in such a manner that its radius is increasing at 0.30 centimeter per minute and its height is increasing at a rate of 0.25 centimeter per minute. Determine the rate of change of the surface area of the cylinder when its radius is 10 centimeters and its height is 25 centimeters.

Solution

Step 1 *Identify and list the variables.* r = radius, h = height, S = surface area, and t = time.

Step 2 *Write the equation.* The surface area of a cylinder is given by

$$S = \underset{\substack{\uparrow \\ \text{area of top} \\ \text{and bottom}}}{2\pi r^2} + \underset{\substack{\uparrow \\ \text{area of} \\ \text{side}}}{2\pi rh}$$

Step 3 *Identify and list the rates of change.*

$$\frac{dr}{dt} = 0.30 \leftarrow \text{The radius is increasing at 0.30 centimeter per minute.}$$

$$\frac{dh}{dt} = 0.25 \leftarrow \text{The height is increasing at 0.25 centimeter per minute.}$$

$$\frac{dS}{dt} = ? \quad \leftarrow \text{This must be determined.}$$

Step 4 *Differentiate implicitly.* As determined in step 2, the surface area is given by

$$S = 2\pi r^2 + 2\pi rh$$

where *r* and *h* are changing with time. We must find *dS/dt*. Differentiating each side of the equation for *S* with respect to *t* gives

$$\frac{d}{dt}(S) = \boxed{\frac{d}{dt}(2\pi r^2)} + \boxed{\frac{d}{dt}(2\pi rh)}$$

Use the product rule.

$$\frac{dS}{dt} = \left(2\pi \cdot 2r\frac{dr}{dt}\right) + \overbrace{2\pi r\frac{dh}{dt} + \left(h \cdot 2\pi\frac{dr}{dt}\right)}$$

$$= (4\pi r + 2\pi h)\frac{dr}{dt} + 2\pi r\frac{dh}{dt}$$

$$= 2\pi(2r + h)\frac{dr}{dt} + 2\pi r\frac{dh}{dt}$$

Step 5 *Substitute in the given values.* Since *dr/dt* = 0.30 and *dh/dt* = 0.25, we substitute these along with *r* = 10 and *h* = 25 into the above equation for *dS/dt* to obtain

$$\frac{dS}{dt} = 2\pi(2 \cdot 10 + 25)(0.30) + 2\pi(10)(0.25)$$

$$= 27\pi + 5\pi$$

$$= 32\pi \approx 100.53 \text{ square centimeters per minute}$$

Thus, the surface area is increasing at the rate of approximately 100.53 square centimeters per minute.

• **EXAMPLE 11-8** _____

Rubbish is dumped into the container of Figure 11-5 at the rate of 20 cubic feet per day. Assuming that the rubbish is evenly distributed within the container, how fast is the depth of the rubbish increasing?

Solution

Step 1 *Identify and list the variables.* *h* = depth of rubbish and *t* = time in days.

Step 2 *Write the equation.* The volume of the rubbish is given by

$$V = (\text{length})(\text{width})(\text{height})$$

$$= (10)(8)h$$

$$= 80h$$

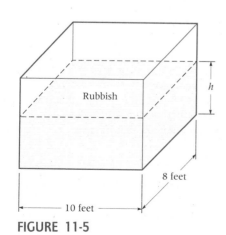

Rubbish

h

8 feet

10 feet

FIGURE 11-5

Step 3 *Identify and list the rates of change.*

$$\frac{dV}{dt} = 20 \;\leftarrow\; \text{Rubbish is dumped into the container at a rate}$$
$$\text{of 20 cubic feet per day.}$$

$$\frac{dh}{dt} = ? \;\leftarrow\; \text{This must be determined.}$$

Step 4 *Differentiate implicitly.* We differentiate with respect to t the formula for the volume of the rubbish, as shown below.

$$\frac{d}{dt}(V) = \frac{d}{dt}(80h)$$

$$\frac{dV}{dt} = 80\frac{dh}{dt}$$

Now we solve the above result for dh/dt to obtain

$$\frac{dh}{dt} = \frac{1}{80} \cdot \frac{dV}{dt}$$

Step 5 *Substitute in the given values.* We substitute 20 in place of dV/dt in the above equation to obtain

$$\frac{dh}{dt} = \frac{1}{80}(20) = 0.25 \text{ feet per day.}$$

Thus, the depth of the rubbish is increasing at a rate of 0.25 feet per day.

Exercises 11-2

For Exercises 1-12, assume x and y are functions of t. Determine the indicated rate, given the other information.

1. $y = 3x^2 + 4x$; $dx/dt = -1$, $x = 2$, $dy/dt = ?$
2. $y = 5x^2 - 7$; $dx/dt = 2$, $x = 3$, $dy/dt = ?$
3. $y = 4x^2 + 9$; $dy/dt = 4$, $x = 2$, $dx/dt = ?$
4. $y = 6x^3 - 1$; $dy/dt = 6$, $x = 1$, $dx/dt = ?$
5. $2y^2 + 3x = 8$; $dx/dt = 3$, $x = 2$, $y = 1$, $dy/dt = ?$
6. $x^2 + y^2 = 16$; $dy/dt = -3$, $x = 2$, $y = 2$, $dx/dt = ?$
7. $3x^2 + 2y^2 = 30$; $dx/dt = -2$, $x = 2$, $y = 3$, $dy/dt = ?$
8. $2y^3 + x^2 = 7$; $dy/dt = -1$, $x = 3$, $y = -1$, $dx/dt = ?$
9. $y^2 + xy = 6$; $dx/dt = 1$, $x = 5$, $y = 1$, $dy/dt = ?$
10. $x^2 - xy + 6 = 0$; $dy/dt = -4$, $x = 3$, $y = 5$, $dx/dt = ?$
11. $x^3 - xy + 4 = 0$; $dx/dt = -1$, $x = 2$, $y = 6$, $dy/dt = ?$
12. $y^3 + xy = 48$; $dy/dt = 2$, $x = 7$, $y = 3$, $dx/dt = ?$

13. A point moves on the graph of $xy = 8$ in such a manner that its y-coordinate is increasing at a rate of 2 units per second when the point is at $(2, 4)$. Find the rate of change of the x-coordinate at that moment.
14. A point moves on the graph of $4x^2 + 2y^2 = 18$ in such a manner that its x-coordinate is decreasing at a rate of 3 units per second when the point is at $(2, 1)$. Find the rate of change of the y-coordinate at that moment.

Applications

15. *Ladder.* A 25-foot ladder is resting against a building, as shown in Figure 11-6. The bottom of the ladder is sliding away from the building at a rate of 4 feet per second. Determine the rate at which the top of the ladder is sliding downward when the ladder is 20 feet from the building.

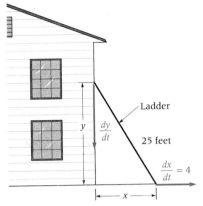

FIGURE 11-6

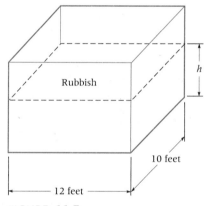

FIGURE 11-7

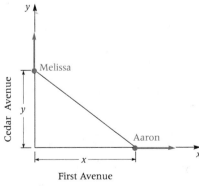

FIGURE 11-8

16. *Revenue, cost, profit.* The unit price, p, of some product is related to the number of units sold, x, by the demand equation

$$p = 200 - \frac{x}{1000}$$

The cost of producing x units of this product is given by

$$C = 40x + 12{,}000$$

The number of units produced and sold, x, is increasing at a rate of 300 units per week. When the number of units produced and sold is 20,000, determine the instantaneous rate of change with respect to time, t (in weeks), of
a) Sales revenue.　　b) Cost.　　c) Profit.

17. *Revenue, cost, profit.* Given are the following revenue, cost, and profit equations

$$R = 800x - \frac{x^2}{10}$$

$$C = 40x + 5000$$

$$P = R - C$$

where x denotes the number of units produced and sold. When production is at 2000 units and increasing at a rate of 100 units per month, determine the instantaneous rate of change with respect to time, t (in months), of
a) Sales revenue.　　b) Cost.　　c) Profit.

18. *Cylinder: Volume.* A metal cylinder is heated and expands so that its radius increases at a rate of 0.40 centimeter per minute and its height increases at a rate of 0.30 centimeter per minute. Determine the rate of change of the volume of the cylinder when its radius is 20 centimeters and its height is 40 centimeters.

19. *Cylinder: Surface area.* Determine the rate of change of the surface area of the cylinder in Exercise 18.

20. *Cylinder: Surface area.* The cylinder of Exercise 18 is heated and expands so that its radius is increasing at 0.35 centimeter per minute and its height is increasing at 0.25 centimeter per minute. Determine the rate of change of the surface area of the cylinder when its radius is 30 centimeters and its height is 50 centimeters.

21. *Rubbish Disposal.* Rubbish is dumped into the container of Figure 11-7 at the rate of 30 cubic feet per day. If the rubbish is evenly distributed within the container, how fast is the depth of the rubbish increasing?

22. *Jogging.* Two people, Melissa and Aaron, begin jogging at the intersection of First and Cedar Avenues (see Figure 11-8). Melissa jogs along Cedar Avenue at the rate of 350 yards per minute, while Aaron jogs along First Avenue at the rate of 300 yards per minute. How fast is the distance between them increasing
a) After 1 minute?　　　　　b) After 2 minutes?

23. *Radar speed check.* A state trooper, parked 40 feet away from Interstate 95 (see Figure 11-9 on page 762), uses radar to determine that the straight-line distance between himself and an oncoming vehicle is decreasing at the rate of 80 feet per second at the instant when the straight-line distance between both is 200 feet.
a) Determine the speed (in feet per second) of the oncoming car.
b) Using the facts that 5280 feet = 1 mile and 3600 seconds = 1 hour, convert the answer for part a to miles per hour.

24. *Baseball.* A batter hits a ball along the third-base line at a speed of 50 feet per second, as illustrated in Figure 11-10 on page 762. How fast is the distance between the ball and first base changing 1 second after the ball is hit?

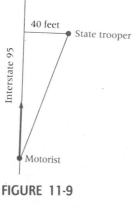

FIGURE 11-9

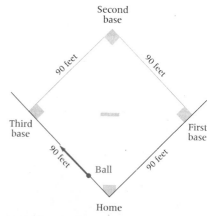

FIGURE 11-10

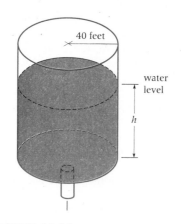

FIGURE 11-11

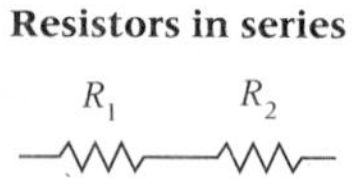

Resistors in series

R_1 R_2

FIGURE 11-12

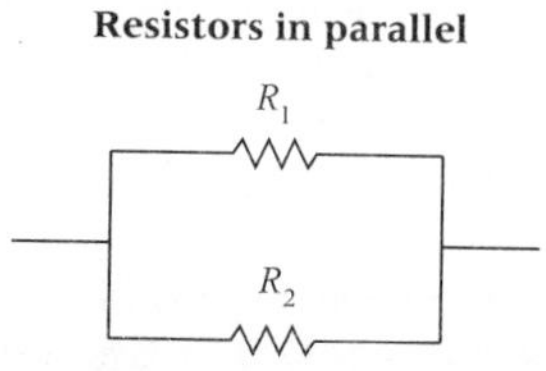

Resistors in parallel

R_1

R_2

FIGURE 11-13

25. *Sphere: Volume.* A spherical balloon is inflated so that its radius is increasing at the rate of 2 centimeters per minute. Determine the rate of change of volume when the radius is 20 centimeters. Use the fact that the volume of a sphere is given by

$$V = \frac{4}{3}\pi r^3$$

where r is the radius and $\pi \approx 3.1416$.

26. *Sphere: Surface area.* Use the fact that the surface area of a sphere is given by

$$S = 4\pi r^2$$

where r is the radius and $\pi \approx 3.1416$, to determine the rate of change of the surface area of the balloon of Exercise 25.

27. *Water usage.* A town stores its water in the cylindrical tank of Figure 11-11. During peak usage time, water flows out of the tank at a rate of 4000 cubic feet per hour. How fast is the depth of the water in the tank decreasing during peak usage time?

28. *Physics: Boyle's law.* According to Boyle's law, the volume, V, of an enclosed gas and the pressure, P, exerted on it are related by the equation

$$PV = k$$

where k is a constant. The above formula holds if the temperature of the gas remains constant. If the volume of the gas increases at a rate of 6 cubic inches per minute, determine the rate of change of pressure (in pounds per square inch per minute) when the volume is 500 cubic inches and the pressure is 25 pounds per square inch.

29. *Physics: Electricity.* If two resistances, R_1 and R_2 (measured in ohms), are connected in series, as illustrated in Figure 11-12, the combined resistance, R, is given by

$$R = R_1 + R_2$$

If R_1 and R_2 are increasing at 0.4 and 0.6 ohms per second, respectively, find the rate of change of the combined resistance, R.

30. *Physics: Electricity.* If two resistances, R_1 and R_2 (measured in ohms), are connected in parallel, as illustrated in Figure 11-13, the combined resistance, R, is given by

$$\frac{1}{R} = \frac{1}{R_1} + \frac{1}{R_2}$$

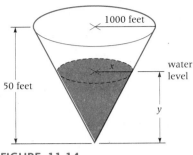

FIGURE 11-14

If R_1 and R_2 are increasing at 0.2 and 0.4 ohms per second, respectively, find the rate of change of the combined resistance when $R_1 = 150$ ohms and $R_2 = 200$ ohms.

31. *Reservoir.* A town's reservoir has the shape of the cone of Figure 11-14. If water is flowing into the reservoir at the rate of 200 cubic feet per minute, how fast is the depth of the water, y, changing when $y = 30$ feet? Use the fact that the volume of the portion of the cone that is filled with water is given by

$$V = \frac{1}{3}\pi x^2 y$$

where $\pi \approx 3.1416$. Also, you will need the relationship

$$\frac{x}{y} = \frac{1000}{50}$$

which is determined from similar triangles.

32. *Reservoir.* For the reservoir of Example 31, if, instead of water flowing into the reservoir, water is flowing out of the reservoir at the rate of 300 cubic feet per minute, how fast is the depth of the water, y, changing when $y = 40$ feet?

11-3 • ELASTICITY OF DEMAND

Frequently economists and managers wish to measure the responsiveness of consumers to changes in the price of a given commodity. This is accomplished by calculating a ratio, called the elasticity of demand, for the commodity. Elasticity of demand measures the sensitivity of demand to changes in price. Specifically, **elasticity of demand** is a ratio that compares the proportionate change in the quantity of a product demanded to the proportionate change in price. That is,

$$\text{elasticity of demand} = \frac{\%\ \text{change in quantity demanded}}{\%\ \text{change in price}}$$

To calculate elasticity of demand, we must be given an equation (defining a demand function) that relates the commodity's demand, q, with its unit price, p. Let $q = f(p)$* be a differentiable demand function, as illustrated in Figure 11-15. Observing the graph of Figure 11-15, if the unit price changes from p to $p + \Delta p$, then the demand changes from q to $q + \Delta q$. Thus, the percent change in quantity demanded is $(\Delta q/q)100$, the percent change in price is $(\Delta p/p)100$, and the elasticity of demand, E, is

$$E = \frac{\dfrac{\Delta q}{q}100}{\dfrac{\Delta p}{p}100}$$

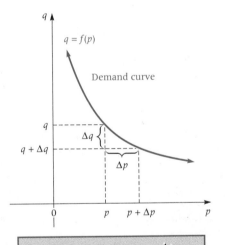

$$\begin{array}{c}\text{elasticity} \\ \text{of} \\ \text{demand}\end{array} = \frac{\%\ \text{change in } q}{\%\ \text{change in } p} = \frac{\dfrac{\Delta q}{q}\,100}{\dfrac{\Delta p}{p}\,100}$$

FIGURE 11-15

*When constructing supply and demand functions, economists consider quantity, q, to be dependent on price, p. However, when considering market mechanisms, p is defined as a function of q. In this section, we assume $q = f(p)$ unless otherwise specified.

The right-hand side of this equation can be rearranged as

$$E = \frac{p}{q} \cdot \frac{\Delta q}{\Delta p}$$

This formula is a measure of *arc elasticity of demand.* If the change in p is small (i.e., Δp is close to 0), then $\Delta q / \Delta p$ is approximated by dq/dp, and the limit of the arc elasticity as $\Delta p \to 0$ is

$$E = \frac{p}{q} \cdot \frac{dq}{dp}$$

This formula gives the *point elasticity of demand* at point (p, q).

In this text, we assume what is typical of most demand functions— that is, as the price of a commodity increases, its quantity demanded decreases. Thus, dq/dp is negative. This, plus the assumptions that $p > 0$ and $q > 0$, implies that elasticity of demand, as defined by $E = (p/q)(dq/dp)$, is negative.

SUMMARY

Point Elasticity of Demand
Given a demand function defined by an equation of the form $q = f(p)$, where q denotes demand and p denotes unit price, then the **point elasticity of demand** is given by

$$E = \frac{p}{q} \cdot \frac{dq}{dp}$$

This is interpreted as

$$E = \frac{\% \text{ change in quantity demanded}}{\% \text{ change in price}}$$

We note that elasticity, as given by the above formula, is negative.
We identify three cases:

1. If $|E| = 1$, then the percent change in demand equals the percent change in price. In this case, demand is said to have **unit elasticity.**
2. If $|E| > 1$, then the percent change in demand is greater than the percent change in price. In this case, demand is said to be **elastic.**
3. If $|E| < 1$, then the percent change in demand is less than the percent change in unit price. In this case, demand is said to be **inelastic.**

• **EXAMPLE 11-9** _____

The demand for a given commodity is given by

$$q = \frac{p}{p - 5} \quad (p > 5)$$

where p is the unit price.

a) Find the formula for point elasticity of demand.
b) Evaluate the formula in part a at $p = 7$.
c) Interpret the result of part b.

Solutions

a) First, we find dq/dp.

$$\frac{dq}{dp} = \frac{(p-5)(1) - (p)(1)}{(p-5)^2} = \frac{-5}{(p-5)^2}$$

Substituting this result for dq/dp and $p(p-5)$ for q into the formula

$$E = \frac{p}{q} \cdot \frac{dq}{dp}$$

yields

$$E = \left(\frac{p}{p/(p-5)}\right)\left(\frac{-5}{(p-5)^2}\right)$$
$$= \left(\frac{p(p-5)}{p}\right)\left(\frac{-5}{(p-5)^2}\right)$$
$$= \frac{-5}{p-5}$$

This result gives the formula for point elasticity of demand.

b) Substituting $p = 7$ into the formula

$$E = \frac{-5}{p-5}$$

gives

$$E = \frac{-5}{7-5}$$
$$= \frac{-5}{2} = -2.5 \qquad \text{Demand is elastic.}$$

c) Since

$$E = \frac{\% \text{ change in quantity demanded}}{\% \text{ change in price}}$$

the result, $E = -2.5$, means that if the price increases by 1% when $p = 7$, the quantity demanded will decrease by approximately 2.5%. Also, if the price decreases by 1% when $p = 7$, the quantity demanded will increase by approximately 2.5%.

• **EXAMPLE 11-10** ──────────────────────────

The demand (in pounds) for E-Z Chew peanuts is given by

$$q = -60p + 480 \qquad (0 < p < 7)$$

where p is the price (in dollars) of peanuts per pound.

a) Find the formula for point elasticity of demand.
b) Evaluate the formula of part a at $p = 3$.
c) Interpret the result of part b.
d) Determine the values of p for which demand is elastic.

Solutions

a) First, we find $dq/dp = -60$. Substituting this result for dq/dp and $-60p + 480$ for q into the formula

$$E = \frac{p}{q} \cdot \frac{dq}{dp}$$

yields

$$E = \left(\frac{p}{-60p + 480} \right)(-60)$$

$$= \frac{-60p}{-60(p - 8)}$$

$$= \frac{p}{p - 8}$$

This result gives the formula for point elasticity of demand.

b) Substituting $p = 3$ into the formula

$$E = \frac{p}{p - 8}$$

gives

$$E = \frac{3}{3 - 8}$$

$$= \frac{3}{-5} = -0.6$$

c) Since

$$E = \frac{\% \text{ change in quantity demanded}}{\% \text{ change in price}}$$

the result, $E = -0.6$, means that if the price increases by 1% when $p = 3$, the quantity demanded will decrease by approximately 0.6%. Also, if the price decreases by 1% when $p = 3$, the quantity demanded will increase by approximately 0.6%. Since $|E| < 1$, demand for E-Z Chew peanuts is inelastic.

d) Demand is elastic if $|E| > 1$. This plus the fact that $E < 0$ implies that $E < -1$. Hence,

$$\frac{p}{p - 8} < -1$$

To solve for p, we multiply both sides by $p - 8$. Note that $p - 8$ is negative since $0 < p < 7$. Thus, we must reverse the inequality when we multiply by $p - 8$. This gives

$$p > -1(p - 8)$$
$$p > -p + 8$$
$$2p > 8$$
$$p > 4$$

Thus, demand is elastic for values of p such that $p > 4$. However, since values of p were originally restricted to the interval $0 < p < 7$, then demand is elastic for values of p within the interval $4 < p < 7$.

⎯⎯⎯⎯⎯⎯⎯⎯⎯⎯⎯⎯⎯⎯⎯⎯⎯⎯⎯⎯⎯⎯⎯⎯⎯⎯⎯⎯⎯⎯⎯⎯ •

Elasticity and Marginal Revenue

A relationship between marginal revenue and point elasticity of demand is determined as follows. If q units are demanded at price p so that $p = f(q)$ where f is differentiable, then the total sales revenue is given by

$$R(q) = \text{(quantity demanded)(unit price)}$$

$$= q \cdot p$$

Since $p = f(q)$, the above becomes

$$R(q) = q \cdot f(q)$$

The equation for marginal revenue is obtained by differentiating this formula with respect to q. Using the product rule, we obtain

$$R'(q) = q \cdot f'(q) + f(q) \cdot 1$$

Substituting dp/dq for $f'(q)$ and p for $f(q)$ into this equation results in

$$R'(q) = q\frac{dp}{dq} + p$$

Factoring out p, we have

$$R'(q) = p\left(\frac{q}{p} \cdot \frac{dp}{dq} + 1\right)$$

Since $dp/dq = 1/(dq/dp)$, provided $dq/dp \neq 0$, the equation becomes

$$R'(q) = p\left(\frac{1}{\dfrac{p}{q} \cdot \dfrac{dq}{dp}} + 1\right)$$

Since $E = (p/q)(dq/dp)$, then this equation becomes

$$R'(q) = p\left(\frac{1}{E} + 1\right) \qquad \text{Marginal Revenue}$$

We assume what is typical of most demand functions—that $p > 0$ and $E < 0$. Thus,

1. If demand is elastic (in other words, $|E| > 1$), then $E < -1$, $(1/E + 1) > 0$, and marginal revenue is positive.
2. If demand is inelastic (in other words, $|E| < 1$), then $-1 < E < 0$, $(1/E + 1) < 0$, and marginal revenue is negative.

We summarize as follows.

SUMMARY

Elasticity and Marginal Revenue

Demand	Marginal Revenue
Elastic	Positive
Inelastic	Negative

Exercises 11-3

For each of the demand functions below, find the formula for point elasticity of demand.

1. $q = -3p + 90$
2. $q = -2p + 60$
3. $q = -p + 40$
4. $q = -p + 30$
5. $q = 3(p - 4)^2$
6. $q = 2(p - 5)^2$

7. $q = 40 - 10\sqrt{p}$

8. $q = 30 - 5\sqrt{p}$

9. $q = \sqrt{200 - p}$

10. $q = \sqrt{400 - p}$

11. $q = p/(p - 10)$

12. $q = p/(p - 20)$

13. Elasticity of demand for some commodity is given to be -1.5 at $p = 10$.
   a) Interpret this result.
   b) Is demand elastic or inelastic at $p = 10$?

14. Elasticity of demand for some product is given to be -0.70 at $p = 6$.
   a) Interpret this result.
   b) Is demand elastic or inelastic at $p = 6$?

15. Elasticity of demand for some commodity is given to be -0.80 at $p = 20$.
   a) Interpret this result.
   b) Is demand elastic or inelastic at $p = 20$?

16. Elasticity of demand for some commodity is given to be -1.3 at $p = 30$.
   a) Interpret this result.
   b) Is demand elastic or inelastic at $p = 30$?

17. The demand for bracelets is given by

$$q = -2p + 130 \qquad (0 < p < 65)$$

where p is the price per bracelet.
   a) Find the formula for point elasticity of demand.
   b) Evaluate the formula in part a at $p = 50$.
   c) Interpret the result of part b.

18. The demand for some commodity is given by

$$q = -3p + 15 \qquad (0 < p < 5)$$

where p is the unit price.
   a) Find the formula for point elasticity of demand.
   b) Evaluate the formula in part a at $p = 2$.
   c) Interpret the result of part b.

19. The demand for a given commodity is given by

$$q = \frac{p}{p - 8} \qquad (p > 8)$$

where p is the unit price.
   a) Find the formula for point elasticity of demand.
   b) Find the elasticity of demand at $p = 10$.
   c) Interpret the result of part b.

20. The demand for a product is given by

$$q = \sqrt{80 - p} \qquad (0 < p < 80)$$

where p is the unit price.
   a) Find the formula for point elasticity of demand.
   b) Find the elasticity of demand at $p = 16$.
   c) Interpret the result of part b.

21. The demand for a product is given by

$$q = 3(p - 10)^2 \qquad (0 < p < 10)$$

where p is the unit price.
   a) Find the formula for point elasticity of demand.
   b) Find the elasticity of demand at $p = 4$.
   c) Interpret the result of part b.

22. The demand for a given commodity is given by

$$q = 300 - 20\sqrt{p} \qquad (0 < p < 225)$$

where p is the unit price.

a) Find the formula for point elasticity of demand.
b) Find the elasticity of demand at $p = 100$.
c) Interpret the result of part b.
d) Find the elasticity of demand at $p = 49$.
e) Interpret the result of part d.
f) Find the elasticity of demand at $p = 121$.
g) Interpret the result of part f.

23. The demand for a given product is given by

$$q = \frac{10{,}000}{p} \qquad (p > 0)$$

where p is the unit price.
a) Find the formula for point elasticity of demand.
b) Interpret the result of part a.
c) For which values of p is demand elastic?
d) For which values of p is demand inelastic?

24. The demand for a given product is given by

$$q = \frac{c}{p} \qquad (p > 0)$$

where p is the unit price and c is a constant such that $c > 0$. Show that this demand equation has unit elasticity.

25. The demand for a product is given by

$$q = \sqrt{100 - p} \qquad (0 < p < 100)$$

where p is the unit price.
a) Find the formula for point elasticity of demand.
b) For which values of p is demand elastic?
c) For which values of p is demand inelastic?
d) For which value of p does demand have unit elasticity?

26. The demand for a product is given by

$$q = -4p + 100 \qquad (0 < p < 25)$$

where p is the unit price.
a) Find the formula for point elasticity of demand.
b) For which values of p is demand elastic?
c) For which values of p is demand inelastic?
d) For which values of p does demand have unit elasticity?

11-4 • DIFFERENTIALS

Up to this point, we have been using the symbol dy/dx to denote the derivative of y with respect to x. We now give meaning to the symbols dy and dx.

Consider a differentiable function $y = f(x)$ and its tangent line T at the point $P(x, f(x))$, as shown in Figure 11-16 on page 770. The vertical distance between the points $P(x, f(x))$ and $Q(x + \Delta x, f(x + \Delta x))$ is Δy. Since the slope of the tangent line T is $f'(x)$, then

$$\frac{dy}{\Delta x} = f'(x)$$

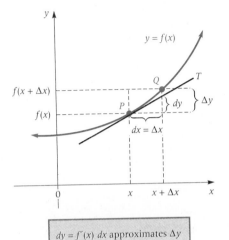

$dy = f'(x)\,dx$ approximates Δy

FIGURE 11-16

If we let $dx = \Delta x$, then

$$dy = f'(x)\,dx$$

Notice that dy is that portion of Δy shown in the figure. If dx is small (i.e., close to 0), then dy closely approximates the vertical distance Δy. For that reason, dy is called the *differential approximation to Δy* or, equivalently, the **differential of y**. Thus,

$$\Delta y \approx dy$$
$$f(x + \Delta x) - f(x) \approx dy$$

and

$$f(x + \Delta x) \approx f(x) + dy$$

The last equation above provides a useful approximation to $f(x + \Delta x)$ because it is usually easier to calculate the quantity $f(x) + dy$ than it is to calculate $f(x + \Delta x)$ for most nonlinear functions.

Differentials

If $y = f(x)$ defines a differentiable function of x, then

1. The differential of x, written dx, is an arbitrary real number (usually small).
2. The differential of y, written dy, is the product of $f'(x)$ and dx. In other words,

$$dy = f'(x)\,dx$$

dy approximates Δy, as illustrated in Figure 11-16.

The following two examples illustrate the computation of differentials.

• **EXAMPLES 11-11** ⎯⎯⎯⎯⎯⎯⎯⎯⎯⎯⎯⎯⎯⎯⎯⎯⎯⎯⎯

If $y = f(x) = x^3 - 5x^2 + 6x + 7$, find dy.

Solution

First, find $f'(x)$. Hence, $f'(x) = 3x^2 - 10x + 6$. Then

$$dy = f'(x)\,dx$$
$$= (3x^2 - 10x + 6)\,dx$$

• **EXAMPLE 11-12** ⎯⎯⎯⎯⎯⎯⎯⎯⎯⎯⎯⎯⎯⎯⎯⎯⎯⎯⎯

If $y = f(x) = x^2 + 5x - 6$,

a) Find dy.
b) Evaluate dy at $x = 3$ and $dx = 0.1$.

Solutions

a) We first find $f'(x) = 2x + 5$. Then

$$dy = f'(x)\,dx$$
$$= (2x + 5)\,dx$$

b) When $x = 3$ and $dx = 0.1$, then

$$dy = (2x + 5)dx$$
$$= [2(3) + 5](0.1)$$
$$= (11)(0.1) = 1.1$$

We now give examples using differentials as approximations.

• **EXAMPLE 11-13**

Approximate $\sqrt{36.12}$ by using differentials.

Solution

Let $f(x) = \sqrt{x}$. Then

$$f'(x) = \frac{1}{2}x^{-1/2} = \frac{1}{2\sqrt{x}}$$

and

$$dy = f'(x)dx$$
$$= \frac{1}{2\sqrt{x}}dx$$

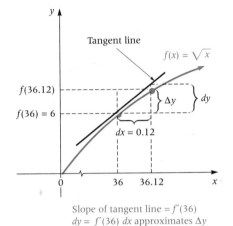

Slope of tangent line = $f'(36)$
$dy = f'(36) \, dx$ approximates Δy

FIGURE 11-17

Observing Figure 11-17, we evaluate dy at $x = 36$ and $dx = \Delta x = 0.12$ to obtain

$$dy = \frac{1}{2\sqrt{36}}(0.12)$$
$$= \frac{1}{(2)(6)}(0.12) = 0.01$$

Since

$$f(x + \Delta x) \approx f(x) + dy$$

then

$$f(36.12) \approx f(36) + dy$$
$$= 6 + 0.01 = 6.01 \qquad \text{Approximation}$$

The actual value of $\sqrt{36.12}$ to 5 decimal places is 6.00999.

• **EXAMPLE 11-14** **Profit.**

The profit, $P(x)$ (in millions of dollars), gained from producing x (in thousands) units of some product is given by

$$P(x) = -x^2 + 9x - 14 \qquad (2 \le x \le 7)$$

If the production level, x, changes from 3.5 to 3.75, use differentials to approximate the change in profit.

Solution

Since x changes from 3.5 to 3.75, then $dx = \Delta x = 3.75 - 3.5 = 0.25$. Thus, we seek to evaluate the differential dP when $x = 3.5$ and $dx = 0.25$. Hence, $P'(x) = -2x + 9$ and

$$dP = P'(x)dx$$
$$= (-2x + 9)dx$$

Evaluating dP at $x = 3.5$ and $dx = 0.25$ yields

$$dP = [-2(3.5) + 9](0.25)$$
$$= (2)(0.25) = 0.50$$

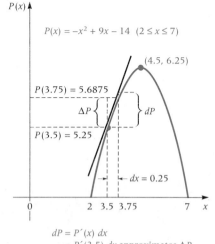

$P(x) = -x^2 + 9x - 14 \quad (2 \leq x \leq 7)$

$(4.5, 6.25)$

$P(3.75) = 5.6875$

ΔP $\Big\}$ $\Big\}$ dP

$P(3.5) = 5.25$

$\leftarrow dx = 0.25$

$dP = P'(x)\, dx$
$= P'(3.5)\, dx$ approximates ΔP

FIGURE 11-18

Thus, the approximate change in profit is 0.50 million dollars. Note that the actual change in profit is given by $P(3.75) - P(3.5) = 5.6875 - 5.25 = 0.4375$. A graphical interpretation appears in Figure 11-18.

• **EXAMPLE 11-15   Wind Power.** _____

According to Betz's Law, the available power in wind, P (in kilowatts), for a windmill with a rotor diameter of 20 feet is given by

$$P(x) = 0.000948x^3 \qquad (x \geq 0)$$

where x is the wind speed in miles per hour (mph). If the wind speed changes from 10 mph to 12 mph, approximate the change in power.

Solution

Since x changes from 10 mph to 12 mph, then $dx = \Delta x = 12 - 10 = 2$. Thus, we seek to evaluate the differential, dP, when $x = 10$ and $dx = 2$. Hence, $P'(x) = 0.002844x^2$ and

$$dP = P'(x)dx$$
$$= (0.002844x^2)dx$$

Evaluating dP at $x = 10$ and $dx = 2$ yields

$$dP = [0.002844(10^2)](2)$$
$$= (0.2844)(2) = 0.5688$$

Thus, the approximate change in power is 0.5688 kilowatts.

• **EXAMPLE 11-16   Cost.** _____

The cost, C (in millions of dollars), of producing x (in thousands) units of a product is given by

$$C(x) = 0.1x^2 + 10,000 \qquad (0 \leq x \leq 1000)$$

If the production level, x, changes from 500 to 501, find the approximate change in cost.

Solution

Since x changes from 500 to 501, then $dx = \Delta x = 501 - 500 = 1$. Thus, we seek to evaluate the differential, dC, when $x = 500$ and $dx = 1$. Hence, $C'(x) = 0.2x$ and

$$dC = C'(x)dx$$
$$= (0.2x)dx$$

evaluating dC at $x = 500$ and $dx = 1$ yields

$$dC = [0.2(500)](1)$$
$$= (100)(1) = 100$$

Thus, the approximate change in cost is 100 million dollars.

_____ •

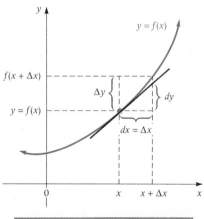

$y = f(x)$

$f(x + \Delta x)$

Δy $\Big\}$ $\Big\}$ dy

$y = f(x)$

$dx = \Delta x$

$x \qquad x + \Delta x$

Percent change in $y = \dfrac{\Delta y}{y}\,100 \approx \dfrac{dy}{y}\,100$

FIGURE 11-19

Consider the differentiable function $y = f(x)$ in Figure 11-19. When x changes by an amount Δx, the *percent change in y* is given by

$$\frac{\Delta y}{y}100$$

Using differentials, the *percent change in y* is approximated by

$$\frac{dy}{y}100$$

The following example illustrates the use of this concept.

• **EXAMPLE 11-17   Construction Cost.** _____

A 1-story building costs $1000 per square foot to construct. Thus, the cost of constructing a square 1-story building x feet on each side is given by

$$C(x) = 1000x^2 \qquad (x \geq 0)$$

a) Use differentials to approximate the percent change in cost if each side changes from 30 feet to 33 feet.

b) Use differentials to approximate the percent change in cost if each side increases by 5% from 30 feet.

Solutions

a) Since x changes from 30 to 33, then $dx = \Delta x = 33 - 30 = 3$. We first seek to evaluate dC/C when $x = 30$ and $dx = 3$. Since $dC = C'(x)dx$, we determine that $C'(x) = 2000x$ so that $dC = (2000x)dx$. Hence,

$$\frac{dC}{C} = \frac{2000x\,dx}{1000x^2}$$

$$= \frac{2dx}{x}$$

Evaluating dC/C at $x = 30$ and $dx = 3$ gives

$$\frac{dC}{C} = \frac{2(3)}{30} = 0.20$$

Thus, the approximate percent change in cost when $x = 30$ and $dx = 3$ is

$$\frac{dC}{C} \cdot 100 = (0.20)(100)$$

$$= 20\%$$

b) If x increases by 5% from 30 feet, then $dx = \Delta x = 0.05(30) = 1.5$. We seek to evaluate dC/C when $x = 30$ and $dx = 1.5$. From part a, we obtain

$$\frac{dC}{C} = \frac{2dx}{x}$$

Evaluating dC/C at $x = 30$ and $dx = 1.5$ gives

$$\frac{dC}{C} = \frac{2(1.5)}{30} = 0.10$$

Thus, the approximate percent change in cost when $x = 30$ and $dx = 1.5$ is

$$\frac{dC}{C} \cdot 100 = (0.10)(100)$$

$$= 10\%$$

_____   •

Exercises 11-4

Find dy for each of the following:

1. $y = x^3$

2. $y = x^2 - 8x + 9$

3. $y = f(x) = 8x^4 + 1$

4. $y = 1/x^3$

5. $y = 3x\sqrt{x}$

6. $y = f(x) = x^3(2x + 5)$

7. $y = 8(1 + 4/x)$

8. $y = \sqrt{x^4 + 9}$

9. $y = \sqrt[3]{x}$

10. $y = \sqrt[5]{x}$

11. If $y = x^2 - 6x + 5$, find dy and evaluate it at $x = 9$ and $dx = 0.5$.

12. If $y = f(x) = 0.4(x - 5)^3$, find dy and evaluate it at $x = 8$ and $dx = 0.7$.

13. If $y = f(x) = 1/(x - 9)^2$, find dy and evaluate it at $x = 3$ and $dx = 0.1$.
14. If $y = f(x) = \sqrt{x}$, find dy and evaluate it at $x = 25$ and $dx = 0.14$.
15. If $y = x^3 - 8x + 5$, find dy and evaluate it at $x = 4$ and $dx = 0.4$.
16. If $y = \sqrt{x^2 - 3x + 7}$, find dy and evaluate it at $x = 6$ and $dx = 0.8$.

Use differentials to approximate each of the following:

17. $\sqrt{81.68}$ 18. $\sqrt[3]{27.94}$ 19. $\sqrt{65}$
20. $\sqrt[4]{17}$ 21. $\sqrt[4]{15.8}$ 22. $\sqrt[5]{33}$

23. *Revenue.* The sales revenue, R (in millions of dollars), gained from selling x (in thousands) units of some product is given by

$$R(x) = -x^2 + 10x \qquad (0 \le x \le 5)$$

If x changes from 3.6 to 3.75, use differentials to approximate the change in sales revenue. Find the actual change in sales revenue.

24. *Revenue.* If the price of a widget is p dollars, the total sales revenue (in millions of dollars) gained from selling widgets is given by

$$R(p) = -200p^2 + 100p \qquad (0 \le p \le 0.50)$$

If the unit price, p, changes from \$0.15 to \$0.19, use differentials to approximate the change in sales revenue. Find the actual change in sales revenue.

25. *Demand.* The relation between unit price, p (in dollars), and demand, q (in millions of units), for gadgets is given by

$$p = 6/\sqrt{q} \qquad (q > 0)$$

If the demand, q, changes from 25 to 26, use differentials to approximate the change in unit price.

26. *Wind power.* The available power in wind, P (in kilowatts), for a windmill with a rotor diameter of 10 feet is given by

$$P(x) = 0.000237x^3 \qquad (x \ge 0)$$

where x is the wind speed in miles per hour (mph). If the wind speed changes from 12 mph to 13 mph, use differentials to approximate the change in power.

27. *Cost.* The cost, C (in millions of dollars), of producing x (in thousands) units of a product is given by

$$C(x) = 0.15x^2 + 7000 \qquad (0 \le x \le 500)$$

If the production level, x, changes from 200 to 201, find the approximate change in cost. Find the actual change in cost. Include a graphical interpretation.

28. *Average cost.* A company produces tires for trucks. The total cost, $C(x)$, of producing x tires is given by $C(x) = 50x + 30,000$. If

$$\overline{C} = \frac{\text{total cost}}{\text{number of tires produced}}$$

then $\overline{C}$ is the *average cost per tire.* The equation

$$\overline{C}(x) = \frac{C(x)}{x} \qquad (x > 0)$$

relates the average cost per tire, $\overline{C}$, with x, the number of tires produced. If the production level changes from 100 to 101, use differentials to approximate the change in average cost.

29. *Average cost.* The total cost of producing x units of some commodity is given by $C(x) = 100x + 50,000$.
   a) Find the equation for the average cost per unit, $\overline{C}(x)$.
   b) If the production level changes from 200 to 201, use differentials to approximate the change in average cost.

30. If $y = 0.6x^2 + 8$, use differentials to approximate the percent change in y as x changes from 6 to 6.2. Find the actual percent change in y. Include a graphical interpretation.

31. *Cost.* The cost, C(in dollars), of producing x units of some product is given by

$$C(x) = 0.25x^2 + 8000 \qquad (0 \le x \le 6000)$$

If the production level, x, changes from 40 to 41, use differentials to approximate the percent change in cost.

32. If $y = 0.8x^2 + 10$, use differentials to approximate the percent change in y when x increases by 8% from a value of 5.

33. *Construction cost.* A 1-story building costs $500 per square foot to construct. If x denotes the length of each side in feet, then

a) Use differentials to approximate the percent change in cost when each side changes from 20 feet to 22 feet.

b) Use differentials to approximate the percent change in cost when each side increases by 5% from 20 feet.

CHAPTER 11 HIGHLIGHTS

• *Concepts*

Your ability to answer the following questions is one indicator of the depth of your mastery of this chapter's important concepts. Note that the questions are grouped under various topic headings. For any question that you cannot answer, refer to the appropriate section of the chapter indicated by the topic heading. Pay particular attention to the summary boxes within a section.

11-1 IMPLICIT DIFFERENTIATION

1. What does it mean for a function to be defined implicitly in terms of x?

11-2 RELATED RATES

2. In a related-rate problem, each variable is assumed to be a function of _____.

3. State the procedure for solving related-rate problems.

11-3 ELASTICITY OF DEMAND

4. Elasticity of demand = (_____)/(_____).

5. Use the derivative to give the formula for elasticity of demand. Elasticity, as given by this formula, is always _____.

6. State and explain the three cases for elasticity of demand.

7. If demand is elastic, then marginal revenue is _____.

8. If demand is inelastic, then marginal revenue is _____.

11-4 DIFFERENTIALS

9. Give the formula for the differential of y, dy.

10. Give a graphical interpretation for the differential of y, dy.

11. Using differentials, give the formula for the percent change in y.

REVIEW EXERCISES

• *Implicit Differentiation*

Use implicit differentiation to find dy/dx for Exercises 1–4.

1. $xy^4 + x^3 + y = 3$ **2.** $x^2 + y^2 = 40$

3. $(x - y)(x + y^3) = 7$ **4.** $x + y = 30$

For Exercises 5 and 6, find the slope of the tangent line to the curve at the indicated point.

5. $x^2 + y^2 = 20$ $(4, 2)$ **6.** $x^4 + xy^3 + y^2 = 19$ $(2, 1)$

7. If $y = 8x^2 + 6x + 4$, find dx/dy.

• *Related Rates*

8. A point moves on the graph of $xy = 20$ in such a manner that its x-coordinate is increasing at a rate of 3 units per second when the point is at $(4, 5)$. Find the rate of change of the y-coordinate at that moment.

9. A point moves on the graph of $5x^2 + 3y^2 = 47$ in such a manner that its y-coordinate is increasing at a rate of 2 units per second when the point is at $(2, 3)$. Find the rate of change of the x-coordinate at that moment.

10. *Ladder.* A 30-foot ladder is resting against a building. The bottom of the ladder is sliding away from the building at a rate of 5 feet per second. Determine the rate at which the top of the ladder is sliding downward.

11. *Sphere: Volume.* A spherical balloon is inflated so that its radius is increasing at the rate of 1.5 centimeters per minute. Determine the rate of change of volume when the radius is 18 centimeters. Use the fact that the volume of a sphere is given by

$$V = \frac{4}{3}\pi r^3$$

where r is the radius and $\pi \approx 3.1416$.

• *Elasticity of Demand*

Exercises 12–15 each give a demand function. Find the formula for point elasticity of demand.

12. $q = -4p + 80$ **13.** $q = 4(p - 7)^2$

14. $q = 80 - 20p$ **15.** $q = p/(p - 30)$

16. The demand for a product is given by

$$q = -8p + 160 \qquad (0 < p < 20)$$

a) Find the formula for point elasticity of demand.
b) Evaluate the result of part a at $p = 10$.
c) Interpret the result of part b.

17. Elasticity of demand for some product is given to be -1.4 at $p = 20$.
a) Interpret this result.
b) Is demand elastic or inelastic at $p = 20$?

18. Elasticity of demand for some product is given to be -0.90 at $p = 50$.
a) Interpret this result.
b) Is demand elastic or inelastic at $p = 50$?

• *Differentials*

Find dy for Exercises 19-22.

19. $y = x^3 - 4x^2 + 5$ **20.** $y = x^2 + 4x - 8$

21. $y = 4x^2\sqrt{x}$ **22.** $y = \sqrt{x^2 + 20}$

23. If $y = x^2 + 2x + 3$, find dy and evaluate it at $x = 4$ and $dx = 0.05$.

24. *Cost.* The total cost, C (in dollars), of producing x units of some product is given by

$$C(x) = 0.40x^2 + 6000 \qquad (0 \le x \le 5000)$$

If the production level, x, changes from 100 to 101, use differentials to approximate the

a) Change in total cost.   b) Percent change in total cost.

25. *Revenue.* The sales revenue, R (in millions of dollars), gained from selling x (in thousands) units of some product is given by

$$R(x) = -x^2 + 40x \qquad (0 \le x \le 20)$$

If x changes from 10 to 10.5, use differentials to approximate the

a) Change in revenue.   b) Percent change in revenue.

12

DERIVATIVES OF
EXPONENTIAL
AND
LOGARITHMIC
FUNCTIONS

Introductory Application

Advertising Expenditures and Sales

A company's sales, $S(x)$ (in dollars), are related to advertising expenditures, x (in thousands of dollars), by the model

$$S(x) = 200{,}000 + 800{,}000 \ln x$$

If advertising expenditures are currently at 5 thousand dollars, determine the increase in sales resulting from spending an additional 1 thousand dollars on advertising.

This problem is solved in Example 12-21.

12-1

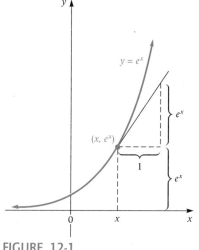

FIGURE 12-1

• DERIVATIVES OF EXPONENTIAL FUNCTIONS

In this section, we discuss rules for finding derivatives of exponential functions. Our first rule involves the exponential function $y = e^x$.

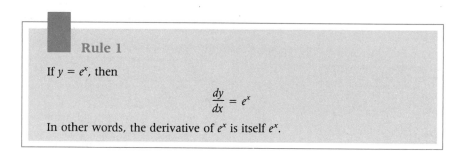

Rule 1

If $y = e^x$, then

$$\frac{dy}{dx} = e^x$$

In other words, the derivative of e^x is itself e^x.

The graphical implication, of course, is that the slope of the graph of $y = e^x$ at the point (x, e^x) is the height e^x, as shown in Figure 12-1.

An informal proof of rule 1 is as follows. If $y = f(x) = e^x$, then

$$\frac{dy}{dx} = f'(x)$$

$$= \lim_{\Delta x \to 0} \frac{f(x + \Delta x) - f(x)}{\Delta x}$$

$$= \lim_{\Delta x \to 0} \frac{e^{x + \Delta x} - e^x}{\Delta x}$$

$$= \lim_{\Delta x \to 0} \frac{e^x e^{\Delta x} - e^x}{\Delta x}$$

$$= \lim_{\Delta x \to 0} e^x \frac{e^{\Delta x} - 1}{\Delta x}$$

$$= e^x \lim_{\Delta x \to 0} \frac{e^{\Delta x} - 1}{\Delta x} \qquad \text{Limit property 3}$$

It is shown below that

$$\lim_{\Delta x \to 0} \frac{e^{\Delta x} - 1}{\Delta x} = 1$$

Thus, the resulting expression for dy/dx becomes

$$\frac{dy}{dx} = e^x \cdot 1 = e^x$$

To show that $\lim_{\Delta x \to 0} \frac{e^{\Delta x} - 1}{\Delta x} = 1$, we note that, by definition,

$$e = \lim_{x \to \infty} \left(1 + \frac{1}{x}\right)^x$$

This can be restated as

$$e = \lim_{x \to 0}(1 + x)^{1/x}$$

In terms of Δx,

$$e = \lim_{\Delta x \to 0}(1 + \Delta x)^{1/\Delta x}$$

so that for small values of Δx,

$$e \approx (1 + \Delta x)^{1/\Delta x}$$

and, therefore,

$$e^{\Delta x} \approx 1 + \Delta x$$

since

$$[(1 + \Delta x)^{1/\Delta x}]^{\Delta x} = (1 + \Delta x)^{\Delta x/\Delta x} = 1 + \Delta x$$

Substituting this result into the expression

$$\frac{e^{\Delta x} - 1}{\Delta x}$$

gives

$$\lim_{\Delta x \to 0} \frac{e^{\Delta x} - 1}{\Delta x} = 1$$

• **EXAMPLE 12-1** ─────────────────────────

If $y = 8e^x$, find dy/dx.

Solution

Using rule 1 and the constant multiplier rule, we have

$$\frac{dy}{dx} = 8\frac{d}{dx}(e^x) = 8e^x$$

• **EXAMPLE 12-2** ─────────────────────────

If $y = e^u$, find dy/du.

Solution

Using rule 1, we write

$$\frac{dy}{du} = e^u$$

─── •

We now consider exponential functions such as

$$y = e^{x^2 - 3x}$$

This function is of the form

$$y = e^u$$

where u is a function of x. The derivative of such a function is found by applying the chain rule to exponential functions. Recall that, according to the chain rule, if y is a function of u and u is a function of x, then

$$\frac{dy}{dx} = \frac{dy}{du} \cdot \frac{du}{dx}$$

Since $y = e^u$, then $dy/du = e^u$. Hence, we have

$$\frac{dy}{dx} = e^u \frac{du}{dx}$$

Thus, we have the following rule.

Rule 2

If $y = e^u$, where u is a differentiable function of x, then

$$\frac{dy}{dx} = e^u \frac{du}{dx}$$

Returning to the function

$$y = e^{x^2 - 3x}$$

with $u = x^2 - 3x$, its derivative is

$$\frac{dy}{dx} = e^u \frac{du}{dx}$$
$$= e^{x^2 - 3x}(2x - 3)$$

$$\boxed{\begin{array}{l} u = x^2 - 3x \\ \dfrac{du}{dx} = 2x - 3 \end{array}}$$

• EXAMPLE 12-3

If $y = e^{x^5 - 8x}$, find dy/dx.

Solution

Since $u = x^5 - 8x$, then $du/dx = 5x^4 - 8$. Hence, we obtain

$$\frac{dy}{dx} = e^u \frac{du}{dx}$$
$$= e^{x^5 - 8x}(5x^4 - 8)$$

• EXAMPLE 12-4

If $y = 7e^{5x}$, find dy/dx.

Solution

Since $u = 5x$, then $du/dx = 5$. Using rule 2 and the constant multiplier rule, we have

$$\frac{dy}{dx} = 7e^{5x}(5)$$
$$= 35e^{5x}$$

• **EXAMPLE 12-5**

If $f(t) = 800e^{-0.5t}$, find

a) $f'(t)$
b) $f'(6)$

Solutions

a) $f'(t) = 800e^{-0.5t}(-0.5)$
$= -400e^{-0.5t}$

b) $f'(6) = -400e^{-0.5(6)}$
$= -400e^{-3}$
$\approx -400(0.049787)$
≈ -19.91

Applications

• **EXAMPLE 12-6**

If \$1000 is invested for x years at 8% compounded continuously, then the total amount is given by $S(x) = 1000e^{0.08x}$.

a) Find $S'(x)$.
b) Find $S'(2)$ and interpret.
c) Find $S'(5)$ and interpret.
d) If, for each year beyond the fifth, interest is computed as simple interest instead of interest compounded continuously, find the total amount at the end of the tenth year. Compare this result with what the total amount should be under normal conditions.

Solutions

a) $S'(x) = 1000e^{0.08x}(0.08)$
$= 80e^{0.08x}$

b) $S'(2) = 80e^{0.08(2)}$
$= 80e^{0.16}$
$\approx 80(1.173511)$
$\approx \$93.88$

Thus, at the end of the second year, the total amount is instantaneously increasing by \$93.88 per year.

c) $S'(5) = 80e^{0.08(5)}$
$= 80e^{0.40}$
$\approx 80(1.491825)$
$\approx \$119.35$

Thus, at the end of the fifth year, the total amount is instantaneously increasing by \$119.35 per year.

d) If, for each year beyond the fifth, interest is computed as simple interest instead of interest compounded continuously, the total amount increases by the same constant amount for each year beyond the fifth. Then its graph is represented by the tangent line to $S(x)$ at $x = 5$ (see Figure 12-2). Since the slope of the tangent line is $S'(5) = 119.35$ and its point of tangency is $(5, S(5))$, or $(5, 1491.83)$, then according to the point-slope form

$$y - y_1 = m(x - x_1)$$

its equation is

$$y - 1491.83 = 119.35(x - 5)$$
$$y = 119.35x + 895.08$$

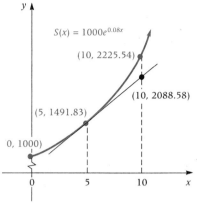

FIGURE 12-2

Thus, at the end of the tenth year ($x = 10$), the total amount is

$$y = 119.35(10) + 895.08$$
$$= \$2088.58$$

Note that under normal conditions of 8% compounded continuously, the total amount at the end of the tenth year is

$$S(10) = 1000e^{0.08(10)}$$
$$= 1000e^{0.80}$$
$$\approx 1000(2.225541)$$
$$\approx \$2225.54$$

These amounts are graphically illustrated in Figure 12-2.

• **EXAMPLE 12-7   Population Growth.** ⎯⎯⎯⎯⎯⎯⎯

The population, $P(t)$, of a city is related to time, t (in years), by the equation

$$P(t) = 60,000e^{0.08t}$$

where $t = 1$ denotes the end of year 19X1, $t = 2$ denotes the end of year 19X2, . . . , etc. Find the rate of change of the population

a) At $t = 5$.   **b)** At $t = 9$.

Solutions

First, we determine

$$P'(t) = 60,000e^{0.08t}(0.08)$$
$$= 4800e^{0.08t}$$

a) $P'(5) = 4800e^{0.08(5)}$
       $= 4800e^{0.40}$
       $\approx 4800(1.491825)$
       ≈ 7161

Thus, at $t = 5$ (the end of year 19X5), the city's population is growing at the rate of approximately 7161 people per year.

b) $P'(9) = 4800e^{0.08(9)}$
       $= 4800e^{0.72}$
       $\approx 4800(2.054433)$
       ≈ 9861

Thus, at $t = 9$ (the end of year 19X9), the city's population is growing at the rate of approximately 9861 people per year.

• **EXAMPLE 12-8   Market Penetration: Modified Exponential Model.** ⎯⎯⎯⎯⎯⎯⎯

In Section 3-1, we learned that the model

$$y = 98 - 90e^{-0.19x}$$

expresses the relationship between y, the percentage of the market penetrated by television sets, and x, the time in years, where $x = 0$ corresponds to the year 1950, . . . , and $x = 38$ corresponds to the year 1988.

a) Find dy/dx.
b) Evaluate dy/dx at $x = 1$ and interpret the result.
c) Evaluate dy/dx at $x = 5$ and interpret the result.
d) Evaluate dy/dx at $x = 20$ and interpret the result.

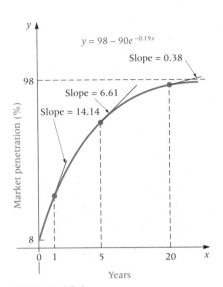

$y = 98 - 90e^{-0.19x}$

Slope = 0.38

Slope = 6.61

Slope = 14.14

98

Market penetration (%)

8

0 1   5   20   x

Years

FIGURE 12-3

Solutions

a) $\dfrac{dy}{dx} = (-90)e^{-0.19x}(-0.19) = 17.1e^{-0.19x}$

b) At $x = 1$,

$$\frac{dy}{dx} = 17.1e^{-0.19(1)} \approx 17.1(0.8270) \approx 14.14$$

Thus, at $x = 1$ (the year 1951), the percentage of the market penetrated by television sets was increasing at a rate of 14.14 percentage points per year.

c) At $x = 5$,

$$\frac{dy}{dx} = 17.1e^{-0.19(5)} = 17.1e^{-0.95} \approx 17.1(0.3867) \approx 6.61$$

Thus, at $x = 5$ (the year 1955), the percentage of the market penetrated by television sets was increasing at a rate of 6.61 percentage points per year.

d) At $x = 20$,

$$\frac{dy}{dx} = 17.1e^{-0.19(20)} = 17.1e^{-3.8} \approx 17.1(0.0223) \approx 0.38$$

Thus, at $x = 20$ (the year 1970), the percentage of the market penetrated by television sets was increasing at a rate of 0.38 percentage points per year.

Comparing the results of parts b, c, and d, note how the increase in market penetration declines with increasing time. This is illustrated graphically in Figure 12-3 by the slopes of the tangent lines at $x = 1$, 5, and 20.

Up to this point, we have calculated the derivatives of exponential functions having base e. The next rule tells us how to calculate derivatives of exponential functions with other bases. We consider functions with equations of the form $y = b^u$, where u is a function of x, $b > 0$, and $b \neq e$.

Rule 3

If $y = b^u$, where u is a differentiable function of x and $b > 0$, then

$$\frac{dy}{dx} = b^u \frac{du}{dx} \ln b$$

Note that if $b = e$, then rule 3 becomes rule 2. The proof of rule 3 appears below.

PROOF OF RULE 3

We make use of the fact stated in Section 3-2 that any positive number b can be expressed as $e^{\ln b}$. Hence,

$$
\begin{aligned}
y &= b^u \\
&= (e^{\ln b})^u \\
&= e^{u \ln b}
\end{aligned}
$$

Using rule 2 of this section, we find

$$\frac{dy}{dx} = e^{u \ln b} \frac{d}{dx}(u \ln b)$$

$$= e^{u \ln b} \frac{du}{dx} \ln b \qquad \text{Constant multiplier rule}$$

Replacing $e^{u \ln b}$ with b^u, this equation becomes

$$\frac{dy}{dx} = b^u \frac{du}{dx} \ln b$$

• **EXAMPLE 12-9** _____

If $y = 5^{x^7 - 4x}$, find dy/dx.

Solution

Note that $b = 5$, $u = x^7 - 4x$, and $du/dx = 7x^6 - 4$. Hence, we get

$$
\begin{aligned}
\frac{dy}{dx} &= b^u \frac{du}{dx} \ln b \\
&= 5^{x^7 - 4x}(7x^6 - 4) \ln 5 \\
&\approx 5^{x^7 - 4x}(7x^6 - 4)(1.609438)
\end{aligned}
$$

We now do a few examples involving the product and quotient rules.

• **EXAMPLE 12-10** _____

If $y = x^4 e^{3x}$, find dy/dx.

Solution

Using the product rule, we have

$$\frac{dy}{dx} = \text{(first)(derivative of second)} + \text{(second)(derivative of first)}$$

$$\frac{dy}{dx} = x^4 e^{3x}(3) + e^{3x}(4x^3)$$

$$= 3x^4 e^{3x} + 4x^3 e^{3x} \qquad \text{Simplifying}$$

$$= x^3 e^{3x}(3x + 4) \qquad \text{Factoring using the distributive law}$$

• **EXAMPLE 12-11** _____

If $y = \dfrac{e^{8x}}{x^5}$, find dy/dx.

Solution

Using the quotient rule, we have

$$\frac{dy}{dx} = \frac{(\text{denominator})\left(\begin{array}{c}\text{derivative}\\\text{of numerator}\end{array}\right) - (\text{numerator})\left(\begin{array}{c}\text{derivative}\\\text{of denominator}\end{array}\right)}{(\text{denominator})^2}$$

$$\frac{dy}{dx} = \frac{x^5 e^{8x}(8) - e^{8x}(5x^4)}{(x^5)^2}$$

$$= \frac{8x^5 e^{8x} - 5x^4 e^{8x}}{x^{10}} \qquad \text{Simplifying}$$

$$= \frac{x^4 e^{8x}(8x - 5)}{x^{10}} \qquad \text{Factoring using the distributive law}$$

$$= \frac{e^{8x}(8x - 5)}{x^6}$$

Exercises 12-1

Find the derivative of each of the following:

1. $y = e^{4x}$

2. $y = e^{-x}$

3. $y = 4e^{-2x}$

4. $y = -e^{-x}$

5. $f(x) = -2e^{-0.1x}$

6. $f(x) = e^x$

7. $y = e^{x^5 - 7x}$

8. $f(x) = 6e^{x^3 - 2x}$

9. $y = e^{2x - 5}$

10. $f(x) - 4e^{3x^2 + 4x}$

11. $y = 4^{x^2 - 3x}$

12. $f(x) = 2^{3x^2 - 5x}$

13. $y = 4^{-0.02x}$

14. $f(x) = -2(3^{-x})$

15. $y = (x^5 - 4x^2)e^{x^4 - 7x}$

16. $y = (x^3 - 2)e^{-x^2}$

17. $f(x) = (x^4 + 8x)e^{x^3 + 5x}$

18. $y = x^2 e^{x^5 + 6}$

19. $y = \dfrac{e^x + e^{-x}}{x}$

20. $y = \dfrac{3e^x - e^{-x}}{x}$

21. $y = \dfrac{e^x - e^{-x}}{x}$

22. $y = e^{\sqrt{4 - x^2}}$

23. $f(x) = \dfrac{e^{x^3 - 4x}}{x^2 - 3x}$

24. $f(x) = \dfrac{e^{x + 6}}{x + 6}$

25. $y = e^{\sqrt{25 - x^2}}$

26. $y = e^{-x^2}$

27. $y = e^{\sqrt{x}}$

28. $y = x^2 e^{-4x}$

29. $y = \dfrac{800}{1 + 40e^{-3x}}$

30. $y = \dfrac{60}{1 - 20e^{5x}}$

31. $y = \dfrac{1000}{5 - 80e^{-2x}}$

32. $y = \dfrac{70}{1 + 60e^{-2x}}$

33. $y = (4x + e^{-x})^2$

34. $y = (2x - e^x)^2$

35. $f(x) = \sqrt{x + e^{-x}}$

36. $f(x) = \sqrt{x - e^x}$

37. $y = \sqrt{x^2 + e^{-x^2}}$

38. $y = \sqrt{x^3 - e^{-x^2}}$

39. Find the equation of the straight line tangent to $f(x) = e^x$ at $x = 0$. Graph $f(x)$ and its tangent line.

40. Find the equation of the straight line tangent to $f(x) = e^{-x}$ at $x = 1$. Graph $f(x)$ and its tangent line.

Applications

41. *Continuous compounding.* If $10,000 is invested for x years at 10% compounded continuously, then the total amount is given by

$$S(x) = 10,000e^{0.10x}$$

a) Find $S'(x)$.
b) Find $S'(3)$ and interpret.
c) Find $S'(4)$ and interpret.
d) Find the rate of change of the total amount at $x = 5$.
e) If the total amount increases by the same amount for each year beyond the fifth, find the total amount at the end of the ninth year. Compare this with what the total amount should be under normal conditions.
f) Graphically illustrate part e.

42. *Continuous compounding.* If $50,000 is invested for x years at 9% compounded continuously, then the total amount is given by

$$S(x) = 50,000e^{0.09x}$$

a) Find $S'(x)$.
b) Find $S'(2)$ and interpret.
c) Find $S'(3)$ and interpret.
d) Find the rate of change of the total amount at $x = 4$.
e) If the total amount increases by the same amount for each year beyond the fourth, find the total amount at the end of the seventh year. Compare this with what the total amount should be under normal conditions.
f) Graphically illustrate part e.

43. *Employee growth.* The number of employees, $P(x)$, of a certain company is related to time, x (in years), by the exponential function defined by

$$P(x) = 1000e^{0.06x} \qquad (x \geq 0)$$

a) Find the rate of change of the number of employees at $x = 5$. Is the number of employees increasing or decreasing at this point?
b) Find the rate of change of the number of employees at $x = 10$. Is the number of employees increasing or decreasing at this point?
c) If the number of employees increases by a constant amount for each year beyond the tenth, find the number of employees at $x = 13$.
d) Graphically illustrate part c.

44. *Sales decay.* If a product is not advertised, then its monthly sales decay is in accordance with the equation

$$y(t) = 2000e^{-0.60t} \qquad (t \geq 0)$$

where $y(t)$ represents monthly sales at time t (in months).
a) Find $y'(t)$.
b) Find the rate of change of sales at $t = 1/2$.
c) How fast are sales decaying at $t = 2$?

45. *Learning curve.* The function defined by

$$N(x) = 50 - 50e^{-0.3x} \qquad (x \geq 0)$$

is a learning curve, where $N(x)$ represents the number of items produced by an assembly-line worker during the xth day after the training period. Is daily production increasing or decreasing at $x = 5$, and at what rate?

46. *Temperature.* The temperature of a heated cup of coffee, y, is related to the time elapsed, t (in minutes), by

$$y = 150e^{-0.02t} + 65 \quad (t \geq 0)$$

Is the temperature increasing or decreasing at $t = 5$, and at what rate?

47. *Market penetration: Modified exponential model.* The percentage of market penetration for a product x years after it has been introduced is given by

$$y = 90 - 82e^{-0.30x}$$

a) Find dy/dx.
b) Evaluate dy/dx at $x = 1$ and interpret the result.
c) Evaluate dy/dx at $x = 6$ and interpret the result.
d) Evaluate dy/dx at $x = 25$ and interpret the result.
e) Interpret the results of parts b, c, and d graphically.

48. *Radioactive decay.* A certain radioactive substance decays in accordance with the equation

$$f(t) = 4000e^{-0.60t} \quad (t > 0)$$

where $f(t)$ denotes the mass (in grams) at time t (in hours). Determine the rate of change of the substance's mass
a) At $t = 5$.
b) At $t = 10$.

49. *Population growth.* In a scientific experiment, a population of fruit flies grows in accordance with the equation

$$N(t) = 10{,}000e^{0.05t}$$

where $N(t)$ denotes the number of fruit flies present t days after the beginning of the experiment. Determine the rate of growth of the fruit flies
a) At $t = 10$.
b) At $t = 20$.

12-2 • DERIVATIVES OF LOGARITHMIC FUNCTIONS

We first consider the derivative of the logarithmic function

$$y = \ln x$$

When written in exponential form, the statement $y = \ln x$ is equivalent to

$$e^y = x$$

Taking the derivative of each side with respect to x and using the chain rule, we have

$$e^y \frac{dy}{dx} = 1$$

Solving for dy/dx, we obtain

$$\frac{dy}{dx} = \frac{1}{e^y}$$

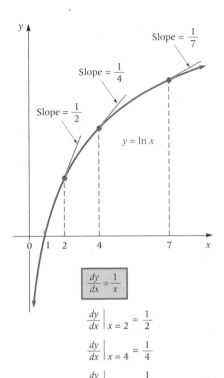

FIGURE 12-4

Since $e^y = x$, this expression becomes

$$\frac{dy}{dx} = \frac{1}{x}$$

We have just proven the following rule.

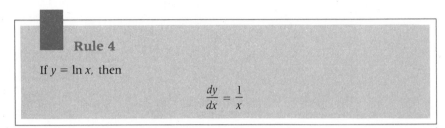

Rule 4

If $y = \ln x$, then

$$\frac{dy}{dx} = \frac{1}{x}$$

Using rule 4, we determine the slopes of tangent lines to the function $y = \ln x$, as illustrated in Figure 12-4.

• **EXAMPLE 12-12** _____

If $y = 5 \ln x$, find dy/dx.

Solution

Using rule 1 and the constant multiplier rule, we have

$$\frac{dy}{dx} = 5\frac{d}{dx}(\ln x)$$

$$= 5 \cdot \frac{1}{x} = \frac{5}{x}$$

• **EXAMPLE 12-13** _____

If $y = \ln u$, find dy/du.

Solution

Using rule 4, we have

$$\frac{dy}{du} = \frac{1}{u}$$

_____ •

By applying the chain rule, we can find the derivatives of functions of the form

$$y = \ln u$$

where u is a function of x. According to the chain rule, if y is a function of u and u is a function of x, then

$$\frac{dy}{dx} = \frac{dy}{du} \cdot \frac{du}{dx}$$

If $y = \ln u$, then $dy/du = 1/u$. Hence,

$$\frac{dy}{dx} = \frac{1}{u} \cdot \frac{du}{dx}$$

We now have the following rule.

Rule 5

If $y = \ln u$, where u is a differentiable function of x, then

$$\frac{dy}{dx} = \frac{1}{u} \cdot \frac{du}{dx}$$

• **EXAMPLE 12-14** ─────────────────────

If $y = \ln (x^3 - 5x^2 + 6)$, find dy/dx.

Solution

Let $u = x^3 - 5x^2 + 6$. Then $du/dx = 3x^2 - 10x$. Using rule 5, we have

$$\frac{dy}{dx} = \frac{1}{u} \cdot \frac{du}{dx}$$

$$= \frac{1}{x^3 - 5x^2 + 6}(3x^2 - 10x)$$

$$= \frac{3x^2 - 10x}{x^3 - 5x^2 + 6}$$

• **EXAMPLE 12-15** ─────────────────────

If $f(x) = e^{x^5 - 7} \ln (x^8 - 3x)$, find $f'(x)$.

Solution

We begin by using the product rule.

$$f'(x) = (\text{first})\binom{\text{derivative}}{\text{of second}} + (\text{second})\binom{\text{derivative}}{\text{of first}}$$

$$f'(x) = e^{x^5 - 7} \cdot \frac{8x^7 - 3}{x^8 - 3x} + \ln (x^8 - 3x) \cdot e^{x^5 - 7}(5x^4)$$

$$= \left[\frac{8x^7 - 3}{x^8 - 3x} + 5x^4 \ln (x^8 - 3x)\right]e^{x^5 - 7}$$

• **EXAMPLE 12-16** ─────────────────────

If $y = \sqrt{\ln (x^3 + 8)}$, find dy/dx.

Solution

Rewrite $y = \sqrt{\ln (x^3 + 8)}$ as

$$y = [\ln(x^3 + 8)]^{1/2}$$

and apply the general power rule to obtain

$$\frac{dy}{dx} = \frac{1}{2}[\ln(x^3 + 8)]^{-1/2} \cdot \left[\frac{3x^2}{x^3 + 8}\right]$$

$$nu^{n-1}\frac{du}{dx} \qquad \text{General power rule}$$

$$= \frac{1}{2\sqrt{\ln(x^3 + 8)}} \cdot \frac{3x^2}{x^3 + 8}$$

$$= \frac{3x^2}{2(x^3 + 8)\sqrt{\ln(x^3 + 8)}}$$

Rules 4 and 5 for finding the derivatives of logarithmic functions have applied only to those functions involving natural logarithms. The following rule applies to logarithmic functions with arbitrary bases—that is, to logarithmic functions with equations of the form $y = \log_b u$, where u is a function of x, $b > 0$, and $b \neq 1$.

Rule 6

If $y = \log_b u$, where u is a differentiable function of x, $b > 0$, and $b \neq 1$, then

$$\frac{dy}{dx} = \frac{1}{u \ln b} \cdot \frac{du}{dx}$$

The proof of this rule is given below. Note that if $b = e$, then rule 6 becomes rule 5.

PROOF OF RULE 6

When written in exponential form, the statement $y = \log_b u$ becomes

$$b^y = u$$

Taking the derivative of both sides with respect to x, we obtain

$$b^y \frac{dy}{dx} \ln b = \frac{du}{dx}$$

Solving for dy/dx yields

$$\frac{dy}{dx} = \frac{1}{b^y \ln b} \cdot \frac{du}{dx}$$

Since $b^y = u$, this equation becomes

$$\frac{dy}{dx} = \frac{1}{u \ln b} \cdot \frac{du}{dx}$$

• **EXAMPLE 12-17** _____

If $y = \log_{10}(x^6 - 9x^3)$, find dy/dx.

Solution

Since $b = 10$ and $u = x^6 - 9x^3$, then, using rule 6, we have

$$\frac{dy}{du} = \frac{1}{u \ln b} \cdot \frac{du}{dx}$$

$$= \frac{1}{(x^6 - 9x^3)\ln 10}(6x^5 - 27x^2)$$

$$\approx \frac{6x^5 - 27x^2}{2.302585(x^6 - 9x^3)}$$

• **EXAMPLE 12-18** _____

If $y = x^2 \ln x$, find dy/dx.

Solution

Using the product rule, we have

$$\frac{dy}{dx} = x^2(1/x) + (\ln x)(2x)$$

$$= x + 2x \ln x \qquad \text{Simplifying}$$

$$= x(1 + 2 \ln x) \qquad \text{Factoring using the distributive law}$$

• **EXAMPLE 12-19** _____

If $y = \sqrt[3]{\ln(4 + x^2)}$, find dy/dx.

Solution

First, rewrite the above as

$$y = [\ln(4 + x^2)]^{1/3}$$

and then use the general power rule (Section 9-8) with rule 5 to obtain

$$\frac{dy}{dx} = nu^{n-1}\frac{du}{dx}$$

$$\frac{dy}{dx} = \frac{1}{3}[\ln(4 + x^2)]^{-2/3}\left(\frac{2x}{4 + x^2}\right) \qquad \boxed{[\ln(4 + x^2)]^{-2/3} = \frac{1}{\sqrt[3]{[\ln(4 + x^2)]^2}}}$$

$$= \frac{2x}{3(4 + x^2)\sqrt[3]{[\ln(4 + x^2)]^2}}$$

Sometimes properties of logarithms are used to simplify differentiation. The next example illustrates such a situation.

• **EXAMPLE 12-20** _____

Use properties of logarithms to find dy/dx for

$$y = \ln \frac{(x^2 - 1)^3}{\sqrt{3 - 5x}}$$

Solution

Rewriting the above as

$$y = \ln \frac{(x^2 - 1)^3}{(3 - 5x)^{1/2}}$$

and using properties of logarithms on the right-hand side gives

$$y = \ln[(x^2 - 1)^3] - \ln[(3 - 5x)^{1/2}] \qquad \text{Logarithm of a quotient}$$
$$= 3 \ln(x^2 - 1) - (1/2)\ln(3 - 5x) \qquad \text{Logarithm of a power}$$

Now we find the derivative

$$\frac{dy}{dx} = 3\left(\frac{2x}{x^2 - 1}\right) - \frac{1}{2}\left(\frac{-5}{3 - 5x}\right)$$
$$= \frac{6x}{x^2 - 1} + \frac{5}{2}\left(\frac{1}{3 - 5x}\right)$$

Application

• **EXAMPLE 12-21** **Advertising Expenditures and Sales.**

A company's sales, $S(x)$ (in dollars), are related to advertising expenditures, x (in thousands of dollars), by the model.

$$S(x) = 200,000 + 800,000 \ln x$$

a) Determine the formula for the rate of change of S with respect to x.
b) Find $S'(5)$ and interpret.
c) Find $S'(20)$ and interpret.

Solutions

a) $S'(x) = 800,000\left(\dfrac{1}{x}\right) = \dfrac{800,000}{x}$

b) $S'(5) = 800,000/5 = 160,000$. This means that when advertising expenditures are 5 thousand dollars, an additional 1 thousand dollars spent on advertising results in $160,000 of additional sales.

c) $S'(20) = 800,000/20 = 40,000$. This means that when advertising expenditures are 20 thousand dollars, an additional 1 thousand dollars spent on advertising results in $40,000 of additional sales.

Comparing parts b and c, note that at higher levels of advertising expenditures, additional money spent on advertising results in less additional sales.

•

Exercises 12-2

Find the derivative of each of the following.

1. $y = 6 \ln x$
2. $y = -8 \ln x$
3. $y = \ln 3x$
4. $y = \ln 5x$
5. $f(x) = \ln(x^2 - 4x)$
6. $f(x) = -2 \ln(x^2 + 1)$
7. $f(x) = \ln(x^2 - 4x + 1)$
8. $f(x) = \ln(-x^6 + 3x)$
9. $y = x^4 + 3 \ln x$
10. $y = x^2 - 4 \ln x$

11. $f(x) = \dfrac{1}{x^3} - 7 \ln x$
12. $f(x) = \dfrac{1}{x^5} + 9 \ln x$
13. $y = 5\sqrt{x} - 3 \ln x$
14. $y = -8\sqrt{x} + 2 \ln x$

15. $y = x^3 \ln(x^2 + 5)$

16. $y = x^5 \ln(x^3 - 6)$

17. $y = \dfrac{\ln x^7}{x^9}$

18. $y = \dfrac{\ln x^8}{x^4}$

19. $y = (x^2 + 1)\ln(x^2 + 5)$

20. $y = (x^3 + 4)\ln(x^2 + 36)$

21. $y = \dfrac{x^2 + 6}{\ln(x^2 + 1)}$

22. $y = \dfrac{x^3 + 4}{\ln(x^2 + 25)}$

23. $y = [\ln(x^6 - 8x^3)]^{10}$

24. $y = [\ln(x^4 - 6x)]^8$

25. $y = \sqrt{\ln(x^3 + 7)}$

26. $y = \sqrt{\ln(x^6 + 5)}$

27. $y = \ln(\sqrt{x^3 + 7})$

28. $y = \ln(\sqrt{x^6 + 5})$

29. $y = \dfrac{e^x}{\ln x}$

30. $y = e^x \ln x$

31. $y = \dfrac{x^3 e^x}{\ln x}$

32. $y = \dfrac{x^2 e^{-x}}{\ln x}$

33. $f(x) = [\ln(x^3 - 2x)]e^{x^4 - 8}$

34. $f(x) = [\ln(x^5 - 7x)]e^{x^6 - 2}$

35. $y = \dfrac{\ln x^3}{\ln x^2}$

36. $y = \dfrac{\ln x^2}{\ln x^4}$

37. $y = \log_{10} 5x$

38. $y = \log_{10}(3x - 4)$

39. $y = \log_6(x^3 + 8x)$

40. $y = \log_3(2x^8 - 1)$

41. $y = \log_2(x^3 - 4x)$

42. $\log_4(x^5 - 2x^3)$

For Exercises 43–48, use properties of logarithms to find dy/dx.

43. $y = \ln \dfrac{x^5}{\sqrt{x^3 + 7}}$

44. $y = \ln \dfrac{x^2}{\sqrt[3]{x^4 - 9}}$

45. $y = \ln \dfrac{(x^3 + 7)^5}{\sqrt{4 - 5x}}$

46. $y = \ln \dfrac{(x^2 + 2)^3}{\sqrt{5 - 6x}}$

47. $y = \ln[(x^2 + 7)^4(x^6 - 5)^3]$

48. $y = \ln[(x^2 - 7)^5(x^3 + 8)^2]$

Applications

49. *Learning curve.* The function defined by

$$N(x) = 1000 \ln(0.5x)$$

is a learning curve, where $N(x)$ denotes the number of items produced by a new worker during the xth day following a training period.

a) Find the formula for the rate of change of N with respect to x.

b) Find $N'(4)$ and interpret.

c) Find $N'(8)$ and interpret.

50. *Advertising expenses.* A company's sales, $S(x)$ (in dollars), are related to advertising expenditures, x (in thousands of dollars), by the equation

$$S(x) = 300{,}000 + 500{,}000 \ln x$$

a) Determine the formula for the rate of change of S with respect to x.

b) Find $S'(10)$ and interpret.

c) Find $S'(15)$ and interpret.

51. *Cost.* The total cost of producing x units of some product is given by

$$C(x) = 9000 + 10 \ln(x + 1)$$

a) Find $C'(x)$.

b) Find $C'(10)$ and interpret.

c) Find $C'(20)$ and interpet.

52. *Continuous compounding.* The equation

$$t = \dfrac{\ln 2}{r}$$

gives the time, t (in years), it takes money to double at an interest rate of $r \cdot 100\%$ compounded continuously.
  a) Find dt/dr.
  b) Evaluate dt/dr at $r = 0.08$ and interpret the result.
  c) Evaluate dt/dr at $r = 0.10$ and interpret the result.
  d) Evaluate dt/dr at $r = 0.20$ and interpret the result.

53. *Continuous compounding.* The equation

$$t = \frac{\ln 3}{r}$$

gives the time, t (in years), it takes money to triple at an interest rate of $r \cdot 100\%$ compounded continuously.
  a) Find dt/dr.
  b) Evaluate dt/dr at $r = 0.08$ and interpret the result.
  c) Evaluate dt/dr at $r = 0.10$ and interpret the result.
  d) Evaluate dt/dr at $r = 0.20$ and interpret the result.
  e) Evaluate dt/dr at $r = 0.30$ and interpret the result.

CHAPTER 12 HIGHLIGHTS

• Concepts

Your ability to answer the following questions is one indicator of the depth of your mastery of this chapter's important concepts. Note that the questions are grouped under various topic headings. For any question that you cannot answer, refer to the appropriate section of the chapter indicated by the topic heading. Pay particular attention to the boxes within a section.

12-1   DERIVATIVES OF EXPONENTIAL FUNCTIONS

1. State the rule for finding the derivative of $y = e^x$.
2. State the rule for finding the derivative of $y = e^u$, where u is a differentiable function of x.
3. State the rule for finding the derivative of $y = b^u$, where u is a differentiable function of x and $b > 0$.

12-2   DERIVATIVES OF LOGARITHMIC FUNCTIONS

4. State the rule for finding the derivative of $y = \ln x$.
5. State the rule for finding the derivative of $y = \ln u$, where u is a differentiable function of x.
6. State the rule for finding the derivative of $y = \log_b u$, where u is a differentiable function of x, $b > 0$, and $b \neq 1$.

REVIEW EXERCISES

• Derivatives of Exponential Functions

For Exercises 1–14, find the derivative.

1. $y = e^{5x}$
2. $y = e^{-7x}$
3. $y = e^{8x+5}$
4. $y = 2^{3x+2}$
5. $y = (x^2 + 8x)e^{5x+9}$
6. $y = (x^4 - 7)e^{-x}$
7. $y = (4e^x - e^{-x})/x$
8. $y = [e^{x+8}]/(x - 4)$

9. $y = x^3 e^{6x}$

10. $y = e^{4\sqrt{x}}$

11. $y = 600/(1 + 20e^{5x})$

12. $y = 400/(1 + 10e^{-2x})$

13. $y = (8x + e^x)^2$

14. $y = (6x - e^{-4x})^{1/2}$

15. *Continuous compounding.* If \$40,000 is invested for x years at 8% compounded continuously, the total amount is given by

$$S(x) = 40,000e^{0.08x}$$

a) Find $S'(x)$.

b) Find $S'(3)$ and interpret.

c) Find $S'(6)$ and interpret.

16. *Continuous compounding.* If in Exercise 15, the total amount increases by the same amount for each year beyond the sixth, find the total amount at the end of the tenth year. Compare this with what the total amount should be under normal conditions, and illustrate graphically.

Market penetration. The percentage of market penetration for a product x years after it has been introduced is given by each of the functions of Exercises 17 and 18.

a) Find $f'(x)$.

b) Find $f'(3)$ and interpret.

c) Find $f'(8)$ and interpret.

17. $f(x) = 90 - 50e^{-0.60x}$

18. $f(x) = \dfrac{70}{1 + 300e^{-0.80x}}$

• *Derivatives of Logarithmic Functions*

For Exercises 19–30, find the derivative.

19. $y = -7 \ln x$

20. $y = \ln 9x$

21. $y = \ln(x^3 - 6x^2)$

22. $y = \ln(x^6 + 5x)$

23. $y = x^2 \ln(x^3 + 7x)$

24. $y = x^7 - 6 \ln x$

25. $y = [\ln(x^5 + 6x^2)]^8$

26. $y = \ln(x^7 - 6x^2)$

27. $y = e^{3x+5} \ln x$

28. $y = \log_5(x^2 + 6x)$

29. $y = [\ln(x^5 - 6x^2)]e^{8x}$

30. $y = [\ln x^7]e^{6x+5}$

31. *Cost.* The total cost of producing x units of some product is given by

$$C(x) = 20,000 + 40 \ln(x + 3)$$

a) Find $C'(x)$.

b) Find $C'(17)$ and interpret.

c) Find $C'(22)$ and interpret.

13

INTEGRATION

Introductory Application

Marginal Cost/Cost

Sometimes we are given a marginal cost equation, $C'(x)$, and must determine the cost equation, $C(x)$. Consider, for example, a firm that produces picture frames. At a production level of x frames, the marginal cost is

$$C'(x) = 4x + 5$$

Find the cost equation, $C(x)$, if the fixed cost is \$500.

In this chapter, we will discuss situations where we are given a derivative, $f(x)$, and must determine the equation of a function $F(x)$ such that $F'(x) = f(x)$. In other words, we must determine the equation of a function, given its derivative.

The above problem is solved in Example 13-10.

13-1 • ANTIDIFFERENTIATION

In Chapters 9 and 12, we discussed the calculations of derivatives $f'(x)$ of functions $f(x)$. The operation of calculating a derivative of a function is called **differentiation.** The result, $f'(x)$, is of course itself a function; it is called the derivative of the function $f(x)$. In this chapter, we will perform an operation that is the *reverse* of differentiation. It is called **antidifferentiation.** We will encounter problems in which we are given a function, $f(x)$, and must determine a function, $F(x)$, such that $F'(x) = f(x)$. Such a function $F(x)$ is called an antiderivative of $f(x)$.

Antiderivative

Given a function $f(x)$, $F(x)$ is an antiderivative of $f(x)$ if
$$F'(x) = f(x)$$

• **EXAMPLE 13-1**

Find an antiderivative of $f(x) = x^2$.

Solution

We seek a function $F(x)$ whose derivative is x^2. One such function is
$$F(x) = \frac{1}{3}x^3$$
since $F'(x) = x^2$. Another such function is
$$F(x) = \frac{1}{3}x^3 + 5$$
since $F'(x) = x^2$ because the derivative of a constant (in this case, 5) is 0. In fact, all antiderivatives of $f(x)$ are functions of the form
$$F(x) = \frac{1}{3}x^3 + c$$
where c is an arbitrary constant. The graph of all antiderivatives $F(x)$ is a family of curves, as illustrated in Figure 13-1.

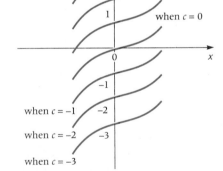

$F(x) = \frac{1}{3}x^3 + c$

when $c = 3$
when $c = 2$
when $c = 1$
when $c = 0$
when $c = -1$
when $c = -2$
when $c = -3$

FIGURE 13-1

• **EXAMPLE 13-2**

Find antiderivatives of $f(x) = e^x$.

Solution

We seek a function $f(x)$ whose derivative is e^x. Since e^x is its own derivative, then $F(x) = e^x$.

Also, if
$$F(x) = e^x + c$$
where c is an arbitrary constant, then
$$F'(x) = e^x$$
since the derivative of a constant is 0.

We now state the following.

If $F(x)$ and $G(x)$ are antiderivatives of a function $f(x)$, then

$$F(x) = G(x) + c$$

where c is a constant.

In other words, if a function $f(x)$ has two antiderivatives, $F(x)$ and $G(x)$, they differ by only a constant.

• **EXAMPLE 13-3**

Find antiderivatives of $f(x) = x^3$.

Solution

We seek all functions $F(x)$ such that $F'(x) = x^3$. One such function is

$$F(x) = \frac{1}{4}x^4$$

since $F'(x) = x^3$. In fact, all functions of the form

$$F(x) = \frac{1}{4}x^4 + c$$

where c is an arbitrary constant, represent the family of antiderivatives of $f(x) = x^3$ since $F'(x) = x^3$.

Note that in Examples 13-1 and 13-3, we have determined antiderivatives of functions of the form

$$f(x) = x^n \qquad (n \neq -1)$$

We now state a general rule for finding the antiderivatives of such functions.

Rule 13-1

If $n \neq -1$, the family of antiderivatives of functions of the form $f(x) = x^n$ is given by the set of all functions of the form

$$F(x) = \frac{x^{n+1}}{n+1} + c$$

where c is an arbitrary constant.

Note that if $F(x) = [1/(n+1)]x^{n+1} + c$, then $F'(x) = x^n$.

Indefinite Integrals

The family of antiderivatives of a function $f(x)$ is denoted by

$$\int f(x)\, dx$$

The symbol $\int$ is called an integral sign. The entire expression $\int f(x)\ dx$ is called the **indefinite integral** of $f(x)$. The process for finding $\int f(x)\ dx$ is called **indefinite integration.** The symbol dx indicates that we are integrating with respect to the variable x. Thus, rule 13-1 is restated as follows.

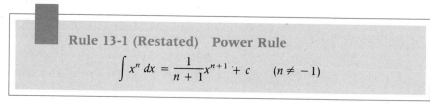

Rule 13-1 (Restated)   Power Rule

$$\int x^n\ dx = \frac{1}{n+1}x^{n+1} + c \qquad (n \neq -1)$$

• **EXAMPLE 13-4** _____

If $f(x) = \sqrt{x}$, find $\int f(x)\ dx$.

Solution

Since $f(x) = \sqrt{x} = x^{1/2}$, then, using rule 13-1 with $n = 1/2$, we have

$$\int x^{1/2}\ dx = \frac{1}{\frac{1}{2}+1}x^{1/2+1} + c$$

$$= \frac{2}{3}x^{3/2} + c$$

Note that the derivative of $\frac{2}{3}x^{3/2} + c$ is $x^{1/2}$.

_____ •

Note: Remember that we can always check an indefinite integral by taking its derivative.

• **EXAMPLE 13-5** _____

Determine $\int (1/x^2)\ dx$.

Solution

Since $1/x^2 = x^{-2}$, then, using rule 13-1 with $n = -2$, we have

$$\int x^{-2}\ dx = \frac{1}{-2+1}x^{-2+1} + c$$

$$= -x^{-1} + c$$

$$= -\frac{1}{x} + c$$

Observe that the derivative of $-x^{-1} + c$ is x^{-2}.

_____ •

Up to this point, we have used rule 13-1 to determine the antiderivatives, or indefinite integrals, of functions of the form $f(x) = x^n$, where $n \neq -1$. We now consider functions of the form

$$f(x) = kx^n \qquad (n \neq -1)$$

where k is a constant. Rule 13-2 provides a useful property of integrals that enables us to find the indefinite integrals of such functions.

Rule 13-2   Constant Multiplier Rule

$$\int kf(x)\, dx = k \int f(x)\, dx$$

Rule 13-2 states that the indefinite integral of a constant, k, times a function, $f(x)$, is equal to the constant, k, times the indefinite integral of the function, $f(x)$. This is the result of reversing the constant multiplier rule for derivatives. Specifically, we have

$$\int 5x^3\, dx = 5 \int x^3\, dx$$
$$= 5\left(\frac{1}{4}x^4 + c_1\right)$$

where c_1 is an arbitrary constant. Multiplying the expression inside the parentheses by 5, the result becomes $(5/4)x^4 + 5c_1$. Since c_1 is an arbitrary constant, then $5c_1$ is an arbitrary constant and may be written as c. Hence, we have

$$\int 5x^3\, dx = \frac{5}{4}x^4 + c$$

• **EXAMPLE 13-6** _____

Find $\int 8x\, dx$.

Solution

Using rules 13-2 and 13-1, we have

$$\int 8x\, dx = 8 \int x\, dx$$
$$= 8\left(\frac{1}{2}x^2 + c_1\right)$$
$$= \frac{8}{2}x^2 + 8c_1$$
$$= 4x^2 + 8c_1$$

Rewriting the arbitrary constant, $8c_1$, as c, we obtain

$$\int 8x\, dx = 4x^2 + c$$

• **EXAMPLE 13-7** _____

Find $\int 9\, dx$.

Solution

Since $9 = 9x^0$, we have

$$\int 9x^0 \, dx = 9 \int x^0 \, dx$$

$$= 9(x + c_1)$$
$$= 9x + 9c_1$$

Rewriting the arbitrary constant, $9c_1$, as c, we obtain

$$\int 9 \, dx = 9x + c$$

In general, since the derivative of $kx + c$ is k, where k is a nonzero constant and c is a constant, then we state the following special case of the constant multiplier rule.

Rule 13-3

In general, if k is a constant, then

$$\int k \, dx = kx + c$$

where c is an arbitrary constant.

Indefinite Integral of a Sum or Difference

Sometimes, we must determine the indefinite integral of a sum or difference, $f(x) \pm g(x)$, of two functions, $f(x)$ and $g(x)$. If we reverse the sum or difference rule for derivatives, we obtain Rule 13-4, which enables us to integrate a sum or difference of two functions.

Rule 13-4 Sum or Difference Rule

$$\int (f(x) \pm g(x)) \, dx = \int f(x) \, dx \pm \int g(x) \, dx$$

Rule 13-4 states that the indefinite integral of a sum or difference of two functions is the sum or difference of their individual integrals. For example,

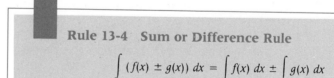

$$\int (5x^7 + 7x) \, dx = \int 5x^7 \, dx + \int 7x \, dx$$

$$= \left(\frac{5}{8}x^8 + c_1\right) + \left(\frac{7}{2}x^2 + c_2\right)$$

$$= \frac{5}{8}x^8 + \frac{7}{2}x^2 + c$$

For simplicity, the sum of the arbitrary constants, c_1 and c_2, is replaced by a single arbitrary constant, c.

Rule 13-4 may be extended to sums or differences that involve a finite number of three or more functions. Hence,

$$\int \left(9x^6 - \frac{1}{2}x^2 + 4 \right) dx = \int 9x^6 \, dx \quad - \quad \int \frac{1}{2}x^2 \, dx \quad + \quad \int 4 \, dx$$

$$= \frac{9}{7}x^7 - \frac{1}{6}x^3 + 4x + c$$

Note that it is not necessary to write the arbitrary constants associated with the individual indefinite integrals. Their sum is denoted by a single arbitrary constant, c.

• **EXAMPLE 13-8**

Determine $\int (3x^2 - x^{-5} - 7) \, dx$.

Solution

$$\int (3x^2 - x^{-5} - 7) \, dx = \int 3x^2 \, dx \; - \int x^{-5} \, dx \; - \int 7 \, dx$$

$$= \frac{3}{3}x^3 - \frac{1}{-4}x^{-4} - 7x + c$$

$$= x^3 + \frac{1}{4}x^{-4} - 7x + c$$

$$= x^3 + \frac{1}{4x^4} - 7x + c$$

Sometimes the independent variable is denoted by a letter other than x. Such a case is illustrated in Example 13-9.

• **EXAMPLE 13-9**

Find $\int (u^5 - 8u + 3) \, du$.

Solution

$$\int (u^5 - 8u + 3) \, du = \int u^5 \, du - \int 8u \, du + \int 3 \, du$$

$$= \frac{1}{6}u^6 - \frac{8}{2}u^2 + 3u + c$$

$$= \frac{1}{6}u^6 - 4u^2 + 3u + c$$

The next example illustrates a situation where we are given a marginal cost equation, $C'(x)$, and must integrate to determine the cost equation, $C(x)$.

Applications

• **EXAMPLE 13-10   Cost.**

A firm produces picture frames. At a production level of x frames, the marginal cost is

$$C'(x) = 4x + 5$$

Find the cost equation, $C(x)$, if the fixed cost is \$500.

Solution

Here we calculate

$$C(x) = \int C'(x)\, dx$$

$$= \int (4x + 5)\, dx$$

$$= 2x^2 + 5x + c$$

Since the fixed cost is \$500, then $C(0) = 500$. Hence,

$$500 = 2(0^2) + 5(0) + c$$

$$= c$$

Thus, we obtain

$$C(x) = 2x^2 + 5x + 500$$

• **EXAMPLE 13-11   Capital Formation.** _____

The value, V, of an investment fund changes over time, t (in years), at the rate

$$V'(t) = 18{,}000t^2$$

The amount in the fund at the end of the fourth year ($t = 4$) is \$1,134,000.

a) Find the equation defining V as a function of t.
b) Find the value of the fund at the end of the sixth year ($t = 6$).

Solutions

a) Here

$$V(t) = \int 18{,}000t^2\, dt$$

$$= 6000t^3 + c$$

The condition that $V(4) = 1{,}134{,}000$ allows us to solve for the arbitrary constant, c. Hence,

$$1{,}134{,}000 = 6000(4)^3 + c$$

$$= 384{,}000 + c$$

$$c = 750{,}000$$

Thus,

$$V(t) = 6000t^3 + 750{,}000$$

b) The value of the fund at the end of the sixth year is given by

$$V(6) = 6000(6)^3 + 750{,}000$$

$$= \$2{,}046{,}000$$

Indefinite Integrals of Exponential Functions

We have already stated that since e^x is its own derivative, then its family of antiderivatives is given by $e^x + c$, where c is an arbitrary constant. This means that

$$\int e^x \, dx = e^x + c$$

We also note that since the derivative of $(1/k)e^{kx}$, where k is a nonzero constant, is $(1/k)ke^{kx}$, which simplifies to e^{kx}, then

$$\int e^{kx} \, dx = \frac{1}{k}e^{kx} + c$$

Thus, we state the following.

Rule 13-5

If k is a constant,

a) $\int e^x \, dx = e^x + c$

b) $\int e^{kx} \, dx = \frac{1}{k}e^{kx} + c \qquad (k \neq 0)$

where c is the arbitrary constant of integration.

We now give some examples of the above rule.

• **EXAMPLE 13-12** _____

a) $\displaystyle \int 7e^x \, dx = 7 \int e^x \, dx = 7e^x + c$

      constant   rule
      multiplier   13-5 (a)
      rule

b) $\displaystyle \int e^{3x} \, dx = \frac{1}{3}e^{3x} + c$

      rule 13-5 (b)

c) $\displaystyle \int e^{-5t} \, dt = \frac{1}{-5}e^{-5t} + c = -\frac{1}{5}e^{-5t} + c$

      rule 13-5 (b)

d) $\displaystyle \int 4e^{(6/5)x} \, dx = 4\left(\frac{1}{6/5}e^{(6/5)x}\right) + c$

$$= 4\left(\frac{5}{6}\right)e^{(6/5)x} + c$$

$$= \frac{10}{3}e^{(6/5)x} + c$$

Indefinite Integrals Involving Logarithmic Functions

In Section 13-2, we learned that the derivative of $\ln x$ is $1/x$. We now show that the derivative of $\ln |x|$ is $1/x$ for $x \neq 0$ by considering two cases:

1. If $x > 0$, then $|x| = x$, so that

$$\frac{d}{dx}\left(\ln |x|\right) = \frac{d}{dx}\left(\ln x\right) = \frac{1}{x}$$

2. If $x < 0$, then $|x| = -x$, so that

$$\frac{d}{dx}\left(\ln |x|\right) = \frac{d}{dx}\left[\ln (-x)\right] = \frac{1}{-x}(-1) = \frac{1}{x}$$

Thus, Rule 13-6 holds.

Rule 13-6

$$\int x^{-1}\, dx = \int \frac{1}{x}\, dx = \ln |x| + c \qquad (x \neq 0)$$

We now provide some examples of the above rule.

• **EXAMPLE 13-13** _____

a)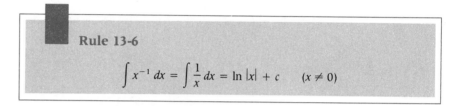
$$\int \frac{5}{x}\, dx = 5 \int \frac{1}{x}\, dx = 5 \ln |x| + c$$

constant
multiplier
rule

rule 13-6

b) $\displaystyle \int \left(\frac{8}{x} + e^{-3x}\right) dx = \int \frac{8}{x}\, dx + \int e^{-3x}\, dx$

sum or difference
rule

$$= 8 \ln |x| + \frac{1}{-3}e^{-3x} + c$$

$$= 8 \ln |x| - \frac{1}{3}e^{-3x} + c$$

c) $\displaystyle \int \left(\frac{7}{x} - \frac{6}{\sqrt{x}}\right) dx = \int \frac{7}{x}\, dx - \int 6x^{-1/2}\, dx$

sum or difference
rule

$$\frac{6}{\sqrt{x}} = \frac{6}{x^{1/2}} = 6x^{-1/2}$$

$$= 7 \ln |x| - 6\frac{x^{(-1/2)+1}}{-\frac{1}{2}+1} + c$$

$$= 7 \ln |x| - 6\left(\frac{2}{1}\right) x^{1/2} + c$$

$$= 7 \ln |x| - 12\sqrt{x} + c$$

d) For this part, we use algebra to simplify the expression before integrating.

$$\int \frac{e^x - 2x^2 - xe^x}{x^2 e^x}\, dx = \int \left(\frac{e^x}{x^2 e^x} - \frac{2x^2}{x^2 e^x} - \frac{xe^x}{x^{2\,1} e^x} \right) dx$$

$$= \int \left(\frac{1}{x^2} - \frac{2}{e^x} - \frac{1}{x} \right) dx$$

$$= \int \left(x^{-2} - 2e^{-x} - \frac{1}{x} \right) dx$$

$$= \frac{x^{-1}}{-1} - 2\left(\frac{1}{-1}\right)e^{-x} - \ln |x| + c$$

$$= -\frac{1}{x} + 2e^{-x} - \ln |x| + c$$

We now summarize the indefinite integral formulas of this section.

SUMMARY

Indefinite Integral Formulas

If k and c are constants:

1. $\displaystyle\int x^n\, dx = \frac{x^{n+1}}{n+1} + c \qquad (n \neq -1)$

2. $\displaystyle\int kf(x)\, dx = k \int f(x)\, dx$

3. $\displaystyle\int k\, dx = kx + c$

4. $\displaystyle\int [f(x) \pm g(x)]\, dx = \int f(x)\, dx \pm \int g(x)\, dx$

5. $\displaystyle\int e^x\, dx = e^x + c$

6. $\displaystyle\int e^{kx}\, dx = \frac{1}{k}e^{kx} + c$

7. $\displaystyle\int x^{-1}\, dx = \int \frac{1}{x}\, dx = \ln |x| + c$

Marginal Tax Rates

The **marginal tax rate** gives the amount of federal income tax due on each additional dollar of taxable income. Table 13-1 gives the marginal tax rates for married people filing jointly and qualifying widow-(er)s with taxable annual incomes not exceeding $155,320 for the 1989 tax year. We exclude the case where the annual taxable income exceeds $155,320 as this entails complications that we choose to avoid here.

TABLE 13-1

Taxable income		Marginal tax rate
over	**but not over**	
$0	$30,950	15%
$30,950	$74,850	28%
$74,850	$155,320	33%

We let

$$x = \text{taxable annual income in dollars}$$

$$T(x) = \text{amount of federal income tax (in dollars)}$$
$$\text{due for taxable income } x$$

$$T'(x) = \text{marginal tax rate for taxable income } x$$

Thus, the *marginal tax rate*, $T'(x)$, can be written as

$$T'(x) = \begin{cases} 0.15 & \text{if} & 0 < x \le 30{,}950 \\ 0.28 & \text{if } 30{,}950 < x \le 74{,}850 \\ 0.33 & \text{if } 74{,}850 < x \le 155{,}320 \end{cases}$$

The graph of $T'(x)$ is given in Figure 13-2. Note the existence of three tax brackets, depending on the amount of taxable income.

The *amount of federal income tax due* is given by the *tax function*

$$T(x) = \begin{cases} 0.15x & \text{if} & 0 < x \le 30{,}950 \\ 4642.50 + 0.28(x - 30{,}950) & \text{if } 30{,}950 < x \le 74{,}850 \\ 16{,}934.50 + 0.33(x - 74{,}850) & \text{if } 74{,}850 < x \le 155{,}320 \end{cases}$$

The graph of $T(x)$ is given in Figure 13-3. Again, note the existence of three tax brackets, depending on the amount of taxable income. The first $30,950 of annual income is taxed at 15%. Thus, for annual taxable income over $30,950, but not exceeding $74,850 (or, in other words, the second tax bracket), the tax on the first $30,950 is $0.15(30{,}950) = \$4642.50$; the amount over $30,950 is taxed at 28%. For annual taxable income over $74,850, but not exceeding $155,320 (or, in other words, the third tax bracket), the tax on the first $30,950 is $4642.50, the tax on the next $43,900 (i.e., $74{,}850 - \$30{,}950$) is $0.28(43{,}900) = \$12{,}292$. This amount, added to $4642.50, gives a sum of $16,934.50, which is the tax on the first $74,850 of annual taxable income. The amount of income over $74,850 is taxed at 33%.

Thus, for an annual taxable income of $40,000, the amount of federal income tax due is given by

$$T(40{,}000) = 4642.50 + 0.28(40{,}000 - 30{,}950)$$

This is the tax on the first $30,950 of taxable income at 15%.   This amount is taxed at 28%.

$$= 4642.50 + 0.28(9050)$$

$$= \$7176.50 \qquad \text{Federal Income Tax}$$

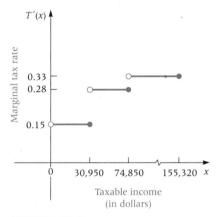

FIGURE 13-2

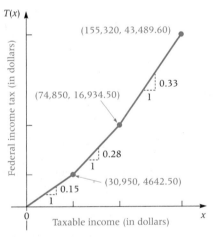

FIGURE 13-3

For an annual taxable income of $100,000, the amount of federal income tax due is given by

$$T(100,000) = 16{,}934.50 + 0.33(\underbrace{100{,}000 - 74{,}850})$$

This is the tax on the first $74,850. ↑ | This amount is taxed at 33%. ↑

$$= 16{,}934.50 + 0.33(25{,}150)$$
$$= \$25{,}234 \qquad \text{Federal Income Tax}$$

Exercises 13-1

For each of the following, verify that $F(x)$ is an antiderivative of $f(x)$.

1. $f(x) = 7x^6$, $F(x) = x^7$
2. $f(x) = 7x^6$, $F(x) = x^7 - 5$
3. $f(x) = x^2 - 8x + 5$, $F(x) = \frac{1}{3}x^3 - 4x^2 + 5x + 1$
4. $f(x) = \frac{1}{\sqrt[5]{x}}$, $F(x) = \frac{5}{4}\sqrt[5]{x^4} + 9$
5. $f(x) = e^{2x}$, $F(x) = \frac{1}{2}e^{2x}$
6. $f(x) = e^{-7x}$, $F(x) = -\frac{1}{7}e^{-7x}$
7. $f(x) = \frac{1}{x}$, $F(x) = \ln x$
8. $f(x) = \frac{3}{x}$, $F(x) = 3\ln x$

Find each of the indefinite integrals.

9. $\int x^{12}\, dx$
10. $\int 5\, dx$
11. $\int \frac{10}{\sqrt{x}}\, dx$
12. $\int \frac{dx}{x^3}$
13. $\int \sqrt[4]{x}\, dx$
14. $\int 20\sqrt{x}\, dx$
15. $\int \frac{1}{x^9}\, dx$
16. $\int x^{-1/6}\, dx$
17. $\int \sqrt[3]{x^2}\, dx$
18. $\int \frac{1}{\sqrt[7]{x}}\, dx$
19. $\int \frac{-4}{\sqrt[7]{x^2}}\, dx$
20. $\int \frac{1}{\sqrt[3]{x^5}}\, dx$
21. $\int \frac{-3}{\sqrt{x}}\, dx$
22. $\int \frac{8}{x^{1/3}}\, dx$
23. $\int \frac{1}{\sqrt[5]{x^2}}\, dx$
24. $\int e^x\, dx$
25. $\int e^{5x}\, dx$
26. $\int e^{-x}\, dx$
27. $\int e^{-4x}\, dx$
28. $\int 6e^{-2x}\, dx$
29. $\int 8e^{2x}\, dx$
30. $\int \frac{9}{x}\, dx$
31. $\int \frac{-4}{x}\, dx$
32. $\int \frac{600}{x}\, dx$
33. $\int \frac{300}{x}\, dx$

34. $\int \dfrac{1}{2x}\, dx$

35. $\int \dfrac{1}{5x}\, dx$

36. $\int \dfrac{1}{x^5}\, dx$

37. $\int \dfrac{1}{x^6}\, dx$

38. $\int \dfrac{6}{x^4}\, dx$

39. $\int \dfrac{8}{x^7}\, dx$

40. $\int (3x^2 - 8x + 5)\, dx$

41. $\int (4x^3 - 16)\, dx$

42. $\int (2x^7 - 6x^4 - 1)\, dx$

43. $\int (x^5 - 7x)\, dx$

44. $\int \left(5x^4 - \sqrt{x} + \dfrac{7}{\sqrt{x}}\right) dx$

45. $\int \left(x^3 - \dfrac{4}{x^2} + 6\right) dx$

46. $\int (u^4 - 6u^2 + 5)\, du$

47. $\int (t^3 - 2t^2)\, dt$

48. $\int (v^2 - 1)\, dv$

49. $\int (y^6 - 5y^4 + 1)\, dy$

50. $\int \left(t^6 - \dfrac{2}{t^2} + \dfrac{6}{\sqrt{t}}\right) dt$

51. $\int \left(4u^3 - \dfrac{8}{\sqrt{u}} + \dfrac{5}{u^2}\right) du$

52. $\int (5x^{-1} + e^{3x})\, dx$

53. $\int (7x^{-1} + e^{4x})\, dx$

54. $\int \left(\dfrac{3}{x} + e^{-2x}\right) dx$

55. $\int \left(\dfrac{9}{x} + e^{-x}\right) dx$

56. $\int \left(\dfrac{2}{x} - e^{6x}\right) dx$

57. $\int \left(\dfrac{4}{x} - e^{-5x}\right) dx$

58. $\int \left(\dfrac{3}{x^2} + \dfrac{1}{x}\right) dx$

59. $\int \left(\dfrac{4}{x^3} + \dfrac{2}{x}\right) dx$

60. $\int \left(\dfrac{5}{x^3} + e^{-2x}\right) dx$

61. $\int \left(\dfrac{6}{x^4} - e^{4x}\right) dx$

62. $\int (x^{-4} - e^{-x})\, dx$

63. $\int (x^{-2} + e^{-x})\, dx$

64. $\int (x^{-1} + x^{-3} + e^{-2x})\, dx$

65. $\int (x^{-1} - x^{-2} - e^x)\, dx$

Use algebra to rewrite each of the following so that the indefinite integral rules of this section can be applied, and then complete the integration.

66. $\int \dfrac{1 - x^5}{x^2}\, dx$

67. $\int \dfrac{x^6 - 4x}{x^3}\, dx$

68. $\int (3x + 2)^2\, dx$

69. $\int (x - 1)^2\, dx$

70. $\int \dfrac{4x - e^x}{xe^x}\, dx$

71. $\int \dfrac{e^x - x}{xe^x}\, dx$

72. $\int (x + 1)(x - 1)\, dx$

73. $\int (x + 2)(x - 2)\, dx$

74. $\int (x + 1)(x - 4)\, dx$

75. $\int (x - 3)(x + 2)\, dx$

76. $\int \dfrac{x^2 - 1}{x - 1}\, dx$

77. $\int \dfrac{x^2 - 4}{x + 2}\, dx$

Applications

78. *Cost.* The Safe Ride Company produces tires. At a production level of x tires, the marginal cost is

$$C'(x) = 8x + 2$$

Find the cost function, $C(x)$, if the fixed cost is $1000.

79. *Cost.* Given the marginal cost function

$$C'(x) = 6x^2 + 4x - 5$$

find the cost function, $C(x)$, if the fixed cost is $800.

80. *Cost.* Given the marginal cost function

$$C'(x) = 6x + 1$$

find the cost function, $C(x)$, if the total cost of producing 2 units is $900.

81. *Capital formation.* The value, V, of a mutual fund changes over time, t (in years), at the rate

$$V'(t) = 24{,}000t^2$$

The initial amount (i.e., at $t = 0$) in the fund is $1,000,000.
a) Find the equation defining V as a function of t.
b) Find the value of the mutual fund at the end of the fifth year (i.e., at $t = 5$).

82. *Marginal propensity to save.* The marginal propensity to save, $S'(x)$, is a function of a nation's income, x (in billions of dollars), as defined by the equation

$$S'(x) = 0.5 - 0.12x^{-1/2} \qquad (x > 0)$$

If $S = 0$ when $x = 81$, then
a) Find the equation defining total savings, $S(x)$.
b) Find the total savings at a national income of $144 billion.

Velocity/Distance. For each of the following, the velocity (or speed) of a moving particle after t seconds have elapsed is given by the formula for $v(t)$. Determine the formula for distance traveled, $S(t)$, after t seconds have elapsed if $S(0)$ is as given. Use the fact that $v(t) = S'(t)$.

83. $v(t) = 6t^2$, $S(0) = 2$
84. $v(t) = 3t$, $S(0) = 4$
85. $v(t) = 3t^2$, $S(0) = 6$

Acceleration/Velocity. For each of the following, the acceleration (or rate of change of velocity with respect to time) is given by the formula for $a(t)$. Determine the formula for velocity, $v(t)$, if $v(0)$ is as given. Use the fact that $a(t) = v'(t)$.

86. $a(t) = 2t$, $v(0) = 10$
87. $a(t) = 4t$, $v(0) = 30$
88. $a(t) = t^2 + 4$, $v(0) = 2$

89. *Biomedical: Wound healing.* The area, A (in square centimeters), of a wound that is healing is changing at a rate given by

$$\frac{dA}{dt} = -40t^{-3} \qquad (1 \leq t \leq 6)$$

where t is the time (in days) elapsed since the wound was inflicted.
a) Determine the formula for area, $A(t)$, if $A(1) = 19.5$.
b) Determine the area of the wound after 5 days.

90. *Population growth.* The growth rate of a city is given by

$$\frac{dP}{dt} = 10{,}000e^{0.10t} \qquad (0 \leq t \leq 10)$$

where $P(t)$ is the population t years after the city was chartered.
a) Determine the formula for $P(t)$ if $P(0) = 100,000$.
b) Determine the population 6 years after the city was chartered.

13-2   • THE DEFINITE INTEGRAL AND AREA UNDER A CURVE

In Section 13-1, we discussed indefinite integrals of functions $f(x)$. We will now consider the concept and the mechanics of computing a *definite integral*. A definite integral results in a numerical value. A definite integral of a function $f(x)$ is evaluated over an interval of x-values. The endpoints of this interval are called *limits of integration*. We now illustrate the concept of a definite integral by the following example.

Definite Integrals

Consider a firm producing some commodity. At a production level of x units, the marginal cost is

$$C'(x) = 6x + 8$$

The antiderivative of the marginal cost is

$$C(x) = \int (6x + 8)\, dx$$

$$= 3x^2 + 8x + c$$

If we are told that the fixed cost is $600, then we determine the arbitrary constant to be $c = 600$. Hence, the cost function is

$$C(x) = 3x^2 + 8x + 600$$

Suppose we wish to determine the *total net change* in cost if production rises from $x = 10$ to $x = 15$. This total net change in cost is determined by evaluating

$$C(15) - C(10)$$

Since

$$C(15) = 3(15^2) + 8(15) + 600 = \$1395$$

and

$$C(10) = 3(10^2) + 8(10) + 600 = \$980$$

the total net change in cost is

$$C(15) - C(10) = \$1395 - \$980$$

$$= \$415$$

Thus, as production changes from $x = 10$ to $x = 15$, the total cost increases by $415.

In general, if a and b are numbers and $F(x)$ is a function, then the quantity

$$F(b) - F(a)$$

is the **total net change** of $F(x)$ over the interval from $x = a$ to $x = b$. The quantity $F(b) - F(a)$ is often abbreviated by the symbol

$$F(x)\Big|_a^b$$

We now define a **definite integral.**

Definite Integral

Let a and b be numbers and $f(x)$ a continuous function with an antiderivative, $F(x)$. Then the **definite integral** of $f(x)$ from $x = a$ to $x = b$ is denoted and defined by

$$\int_a^b f(x)\, dx = F(x)\Big|_a^b = F(b) - F(a)$$

The numbers a and b are called **limits of integration.**

The definite integral $\int_a^b f(x)\, dx$ is the total change of the antiderivative, $F(x)$, over the interval from $x = a$ to $x = b$. It is assumed that $f(x)$ is continuous over the interval $a \leq x \leq b$.

• **EXAMPLE 13-14** _____

Find $\int_1^2 x^2\, dx$.

Solution

Here we write

$$\int_1^2 x^2\, dx = F(x)\Big|_1^2 = F(2) - F(1)$$

where

$$F(x) = \frac{1}{3}x^3 + c$$

Hence, we have

$$F(2) - F(1) = \left[\frac{1}{3}(2^3) + c\right] - \left[\frac{1}{3}(1^3) + c\right]$$
$$= \left(\frac{8}{3} + c\right) - \left(\frac{1}{3} + c\right)$$
$$= \frac{7}{3}$$

Notice that the definite integral does not depend on the choice of the arbitrary constant, c. Thus, we will choose $c = 0$ when computing definite integrals.

• **EXAMPLE 13-15** _____

Find $\int_{-1}^3 (8x^3 - 4x + 5)\, dx$.

Solution

$$\int_{-1}^{3} (8x^3 - 4x + 5)\, dx = \underbrace{2x^4 - 2x^2 + 5x}_{F(x)} \bigg|_{-1}^{3}$$

$$= F(3) - F(-1)$$
$$= [2(3^4) - 2(3^2) + 5(3)] - [2(-1)^4 - 2(-1)^2 + 5(-1)]$$
$$= (162 - 18 + 15) - (2 - 2 - 5)$$
$$= 164$$

• **EXAMPLE 13-16** _____

Find $\int_0^5 e^x\, dx$.

Solution

$$\int_0^5 e^x\, dx = \underbrace{e^x}_{F(x)} \bigg|_0^5 = F(5) - F(0)$$
$$= e^5 - e^0$$
$$\approx 148.41 - 1 = 147.41$$

• **EXAMPLE 13-17** _____

Find $\int_2^9 x^{-1}\, dx$.

Solution

$$\int_2^9 x^{-1}\, dx = \underbrace{\ln |x|}_{F(x)} \bigg|_2^9 = F(9) - F(2)$$
$$= \ln |9| - \ln |2|$$
$$\approx 2.1972 - 0.6931 = 1.5041$$

Definite integrals are used to find *areas under curves*. Since this is an important use of definite integrals, we now develop this topic.

Area Under a Curve

Suppose we had to compute the area bounded by the curve $f(x) = x^2$, the x-axis, and the vertical lines $x = 0$ and $x = 1$ (see Figure 13-4). We could obtain an approximation by arbitrarily dividing the interval $0 \leq x \leq 1$ into, say, four subintervals and then covering the shaded area with the four rectangles, as shown in Figure 13-5.

Observe that each rectangle has a width of 1/4 unit. Also, note that the height of each rectangle is given by the y-coordinate of the upper right-hand corner point (of the rectangle) on the graph of the function,

$$f(x) = x^2$$

Thus, the height of the first rectangle is

$$f\left(\frac{1}{4}\right) = \left(\frac{1}{4}\right)^2 = \frac{1}{16}$$

the height of the second rectangle is

$$f\left(\frac{1}{2}\right) = \left(\frac{1}{2}\right)^2 = \frac{1}{4}$$

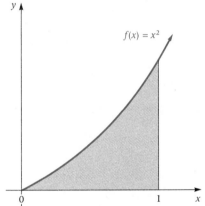

FIGURE 13-4

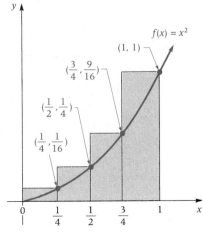

FIGURE 13-5

the height of the third rectangle is

$$f\left(\frac{3}{4}\right) = \left(\frac{3}{4}\right)^2 = \frac{9}{16}$$

and the height of the fourth rectangle is

$$f(1) = (1)^2 = 1$$

Since the area of each rectangle is the width times the height, the sum of the areas of the rectangles is

$$A_1 = \left[\frac{1}{4} \cdot f\left(\frac{1}{4}\right)\right] + \left[\frac{1}{4} \cdot f\left(\frac{1}{2}\right)\right] + \left[\frac{1}{4} \cdot f\left(\frac{3}{4}\right)\right] + \left[\frac{1}{4} \cdot f(1)\right]$$

$$= \left(\frac{1}{4} \cdot \frac{1}{16}\right) + \left(\frac{1}{4} \cdot \frac{1}{4}\right) + \left(\frac{1}{4} \cdot \frac{9}{16}\right) + \left(\frac{1}{4} \cdot 1\right)$$

$$= \frac{15}{32} \text{ square unit}$$

Of course, this approximation is greater than the actual area and is therefore called an *upper approximation*. Figure 13-6 illustrates the use of rectangles to obtain an approximation less than the actual area. Observing Figure 13-6, note that the sum of the areas of the rectangles is

$$A_2 = \left[\frac{1}{4} \cdot f\left(\frac{1}{4}\right)\right] + \left[\frac{1}{4} \cdot f\left(\frac{1}{2}\right)\right] + \left[\frac{1}{4} \cdot f\left(\frac{3}{4}\right)\right]$$

$$= \left(\frac{1}{4} \cdot \frac{1}{16}\right) + \left(\frac{1}{4} \cdot \frac{1}{4}\right) + \left(\frac{1}{4} \cdot \frac{9}{16}\right)$$

$$= \frac{7}{32} \text{ square unit}$$

Since A_2 is less than the actual area, it is called a *lower approximation*. The actual area, A, lies somewhere between A_1 and A_2. Hence,

$$\frac{7}{32} < A < \frac{15}{32}$$

Riemann Sum

A more accurate approximation of this area, A, in Figure 13-4 is obtained by dividing the interval $0 \leq x \leq 1$ into a greater number of subintervals and summing the areas of the respective rectangles. In Figure 13-7, we divide the interval $0 \leq x \leq 1$ into n subintervals, each of length $1/n$. Again, the height of each rectangle is given by the y-coordinate of the upper right-hand corner point (of the rectangle) on the graph of the function.

$$f(x) = x^2$$

Thus, the height of the first rectangle is

$$f\left(\frac{1}{n}\right) = \left(\frac{1}{n}\right)^2 = \frac{1^2}{n^2}$$

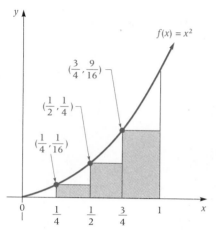

FIGURE 13-6

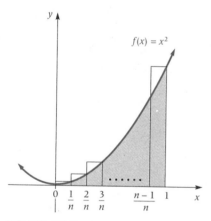

FIGURE 13-7

the height of the second rectangle is

$$f\left(\frac{2}{n}\right) = \left(\frac{2}{n}\right)^2 = \frac{2^2}{n^2}$$

and the height of the nth rectangle is

$$f\left(\frac{n}{n}\right) = \left(\frac{n}{n}\right)^2 = \frac{n^2}{n^2}$$

Since the area of each rectangle is the width times the height, the sum of the areas of the respective rectangles is

$$S = \left[\frac{1}{n} \cdot f\left(\frac{1}{n}\right)\right] + \left[\frac{1}{n} \cdot f\left(\frac{2}{n}\right)\right] + \ldots + \left[\frac{1}{n} \cdot f\left(\frac{n}{n}\right)\right]$$

$$= \left(\frac{1}{n} \cdot \frac{1^2}{n^2}\right) + \left(\frac{1}{n} \cdot \frac{2^2}{n^2}\right) + \ldots + \left(\frac{1}{n} \cdot \frac{n^2}{n^2}\right)$$

$$= \frac{1}{n^3}(1^2 + 2^2 + \ldots + n^2)$$

It can be verified that

$$1^2 + 2^2 + \ldots + n^2 = \frac{n(n + 1)(2n + 1)}{6}$$

Substituting this result into the preceding equation for S yields

$$S = \frac{1}{n^3}\left[\frac{n(n + 1)(2n + 1)}{6}\right]$$

$$= \frac{(n + 1)(2n + 1)}{6n^2}$$

$$= \frac{2n^2 + 3n + 1}{6n^2}$$

$$= \frac{2n^2}{6n^2} + \frac{3n}{6n^2} + \frac{1}{6n^2}$$

$$= \frac{1}{3} + \frac{1}{2n} + \frac{1}{6n^2}$$

The sum, S, is called a **Riemann sum.** The Riemann sum, S, approximates the shaded area of Figure 13-7. The actual area is obtained by letting the number of rectangles increase without bound (i.e., let $n \to \infty$). Hence, as $n \to \infty$, $1/2n \to 0$, $1/6n^2 \to 0$, and $S \to 1/3$. Thus, the area, A, equals 1/3 square unit.

In summary, if $f(x)$ is a non-negative continuous function over the interval $a \leq x \leq b$, then the area, A, between $f(x)$ and the x-axis from $x = a$ to $x = b$ may be approximated by the sum of areas of rectangles, as illustrated in Figure 13-8.

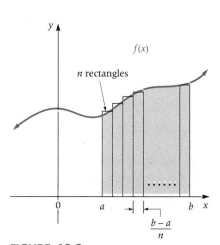

FIGURE 13-8

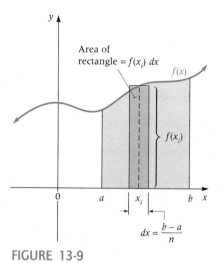

Area of
rectangle = $f(x_i)\,dx$

FIGURE 13-9

Each rectangle is constructed as follows:

1. The interval $a \leq x \leq b$ is divided into n subintervals, each of width $dx = (b - a)/n$.
2. The height of the ith rectangle is $f(x_i)$, where x_i may be any point in the ith subinterval (see Figure 13-9).

Thus, the area between $f(x)$ and the x-axis from $x = a$ to $x = b$ is approximated by the Riemann sum,

$$S = f(x_1)\,dx + f(x_2)\,dx + \ldots + f(x_n)\,dx$$

As $n \to \infty$, the Riemann sum approaches the area, A.

Fundamental Theorem of Calculus

We now state a result that relates area under a curve to the antiderivative. This result is called the **fundamental theorem of calculus.** An informal argument for the theorem appears later in this section.

SUMMARY

Fundamental Theorem of Calculus

Let $f(x)$ be defined and continuous over the interval $a \leq x \leq b$. Let $F(x)$ be an antiderivative of $f(x)$. Then the limit of every possible Riemann sum equals

$$\int_a^b f(x)\,dx = F(b) - F(a)$$

The fundamental theorem of calculus allows us to compute the area under the graph of a continuous non-negative function $f(x)$ over the interval $a \leq x \leq b$ by $\int_a^b f(x)\,dx = F(b) - F(a)$, where $F(x)$ is an antiderivative of $f(x)$ (see Figure 13-10). We note that the restriction that $f(x)$ be non-negative is needed only when the fundamental theorem is used to find area. However, later in this section, we will learn how to apply the fundamental theorem to find area when $f(x)$ is negative over some interval. We summarize as follows.

SUMMARY

Area Under a Curve

If $f(x) \geq 0$ over the interval $a \leq x \leq b$, the area bounded by the graph of $f(x)$ and the x-axis over the interval $a \leq x \leq b$, as illustrated in Figure 13-10, is given by

$$\int_a^b f(x)\,dx = F(b) - F(a)$$

continues

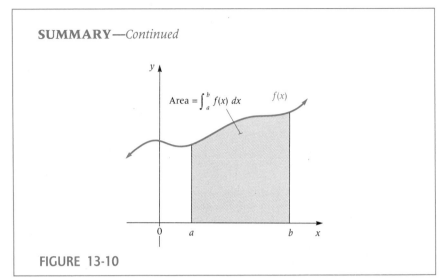

Area $= \int_a^b f(x)\,dx$ $f(x)$

FIGURE 13-10

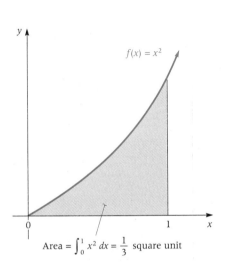

$f(x) = x^2$

Area $= \int_0^1 x^2\,dx = \frac{1}{3}$ square unit

FIGURE 13-11

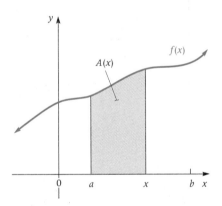

$A(x)$ $f(x)$

FIGURE 13-12

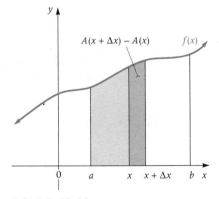

$A(x + \Delta x) - A(x)$ $f(x)$

FIGURE 13-13

Thus, for our illustrative example, the actual area between $f(x) = x^2$ and the x-axis from $x = 0$ to $x = 1$ is given by

$$\int_0^1 x^2\,dx = \underbrace{\frac{1}{3}x^3}_{F(x)} \bigg|_0^1$$

$$= F(1) - F(0)$$

$$= \frac{1}{3} - 0$$

$$= \frac{1}{3} \text{ square unit}$$

This result is illustrated in Figure 13-11.

Before proceeding with more examples, we now present an informal argument for the fundamental theorem of calculus.

Let $A(x)$ be a function that represents the area between $f(x)$ and the x-axis (see Figure 13-12) from a to x, where x is any number within the interval $a \leq x \leq b$. Note that $A(a) = 0$ and $A(b)$ represents the area over the entire interval $a \leq x \leq b$. If Δx is a small positive number, then $A(x + \Delta x) - A(x)$ is the area of the darker shaded region of Figure 13-13. This darker shaded region is approximately a rectangle with height $f(x)$, width Δx, and area $\Delta x \cdot f(x)$. Hence, we may write

$$A(x + \Delta x) - A(x) \approx \Delta x \cdot f(x)$$

where the approximation gets better as Δx approaches 0. Dividing this expression by Δx, we obtain

$$\frac{A(x + \Delta x) - A(x)}{\Delta x} \approx f(x)$$

Since the approximation becomes better as Δx approaches 0, the quotient, $[A(x + \Delta x) - A(x)]/\Delta x$, approaches $f(x)$. From the definition of a derivative, we know that the quotient, $[A(x + \Delta x) - A(x)]/\Delta x$, approaches $A'(x) = f(x)$. Since x is any number within the interval $a \leq x \leq b$, then $A(x)$ is an antiderivative of $f(x)$. Thus, if $F(x)$ is any other antiderivative of $f(x)$, we have

$$A(x) = F(x) + c$$

Since $A(a) = 0$, then $A(a) = F(a) + c = 0$ and

$$c = -F(a)$$

Substituting this into $A(x) = F(x) + c$ gives us

$$A(x) = F(x) - F(a)$$

Hence,

$$A(b) = F(b) - F(a)$$
$$= \int_a^b f(x)\, dx$$

Note that the fundamental theorem requires that the function $f(x)$ be non-negative over the interval $a \leq x \leq b$. If $f(x)$ is *negative* over the interval $a \leq x \leq b$, the definite integral, $\int_a^b f(x)\, dx$, results in a value that is the negative of the area between $f(x)$ and the x-axis from $x = a$ to $x = b$. In such a case, the area between the x-axis and the curve is the absolute value of the definite integral, $\int_a^b f(x)\, dx$. This is illustrated in Example 13-19.

We now state the following properties of definite integrals.

SUMMARY

Properties of Definite Integrals

1. $\displaystyle\int_a^a f(x)\, dx = 0$

2. $\displaystyle\int_a^b f(x)\, dx = -\int_b^a f(x)\, dx$

3. $\displaystyle\int_a^b k \cdot f(x)\, dx = k\int_a^b f(x)\, dx$ (k is a constant)

4. $\displaystyle\int_a^b [f(x) \pm g(x)]\, dx = \int_a^b f(x)\, dx \pm \int_a^b g(x)\, dx$

5. $\displaystyle\int_a^b f(x)\, dx = \int_a^c f(x)\, dx + \int_c^b f(x)\, dx$

We verify properties 1 and 2 and explain property 5, while noting that properties 3 and 4 parallel the constant multiplier and the sum or difference rules for indefinite integrals. If $F'(x) = f(x)$, then

1. $\displaystyle\int_a^a f(x)\, dx = F(a) - F(a) = 0$

2. $\displaystyle\int_a^b f(x)\, dx = F(b) - F(a), \int_b^a f(x)\, dx = F(a) - F(b)$

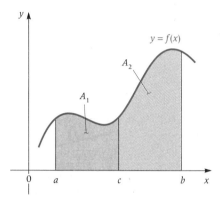

FIGURE 13-14

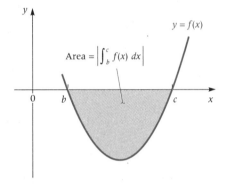

FIGURE 13-15

Since $F(b) - F(a) = -[F(a) - F(b)]$, then

$$\int_a^b f(x)\ dx = -\int_b^a f(x)\ dx$$

3. For $f(x) > 0$ and $a < c < b$, this property indicates that the area from $x = a$ to $x = b$ equals the sum of the component areas, A_1 and A_2 (see Figure 13-14). This allows us to split the interval over which a definite integral is evaluated. Although this property makes most sense when c lies within the interval $a < x < b$, it holds for any value of c for which both $f(x)$ and $F(x)$ are defined.

Areas Below the x-Axis

If $f(x) < 0$ over some interval $b < x < c$, the corresponding area between the graph of $f(x)$ and the x-axis lies below the x-axis (see Figure 13-15). The definite integral $\int_b^c f(x)\ dx$ results in a value that is the negative of the area, so the absolute value of such a definite integral gives the area, as indicated in Figure 13-15.

The following box provides a procedure for determining areas that lie above and below the x-axis.

SUMMARY

Areas Above and Below the x-Axis

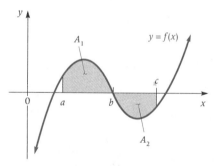

FIGURE 13-16

For a situation where the indicated area lies above and below the x-axis, as illustrated in Figure 13-16, the total area, A, is determined by finding the separate areas, A_1 and A_2, and summing the results. Hence,

$$A = A_1 + A_2$$

where

$$A_1 = \int_a^b f(x)\ dx \qquad \text{and} \qquad A_2 = \left| \int_b^c f(x)\ dx \right|$$

In the following box, we state a procedure that should be followed when finding areas.

To Find Areas

1. Graph the function.
2. Find any x-intercepts.
3. Shade the area to be found.
4. Note whether the shaded area contains any regions that lie below the x-axis as well as above the x-axis.
5. Evaluate the appropriate definite integrals.

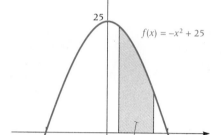

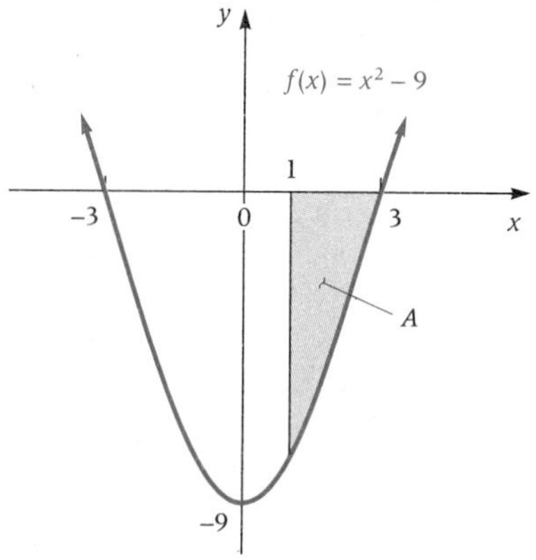

Area = $\int_1^4 (-x^2 + 25)\,dx = 54$ square units

FIGURE 13-17

• EXAMPLE 13-18

Find the area between the x-axis and the curve $f(x) = -x^2 + 25$ from $x = 1$ to $x = 4$.

Solution

A sketch of $f(x)$ and the indicated area appears in Figure 13-17. The shaded area is computed by the definite integral

$$\int_1^4 (-x^2 + 25)\,dx = \underbrace{-\frac{1}{3}x^3 + 25x}_{F(x)}\Big|_1^4$$
$$= F(4) - F(1)$$
$$= \left[-\frac{1}{3}(4^3) + 25(4)\right] - \left[-\frac{1}{3}(1^3) + 25(1)\right]$$
$$= \frac{236}{3} - \frac{74}{3}$$
$$= \frac{162}{3}$$
$$= 54 \text{ square units}$$

FIGURE 13-18

• EXAMPLE 13-19

Find the area between the x-axis and the curve $f(x) = x^2 - 9$ from $x = 1$ to $x = 3$.

Solution

A sketch of $f(x)$ and the indicated area appears in Figure 13-18. Observe that $f(x) \le 0$ over the interval $1 \le x \le 3$, and, thus, the shaded area appears below the x-axis. To determine the area, A, we begin by computing the definite integral as follows:

$$\int_1^3 (x^2 - 9)\,dx = \underbrace{\frac{1}{3}x^3 - 9x}_{F(x)}\Big|_1^3$$
$$= F(3) - F(1)$$
$$= \left[\frac{1}{3}(3^3) - 9(3)\right] - \left[\frac{1}{3}(1^3) - 9(1)\right]$$
$$= -18 - \left(-8\frac{2}{3}\right)$$
$$= -9\frac{1}{3}$$

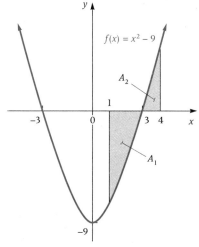

$f(x) = x^2 - 9$

A_2

A_1

FIGURE 13-19

The definite integral results in a negative number because the area is located below the x-axis. Thus,

$$A = \left| -9\frac{1}{3} \right| = 9\frac{1}{3} \text{ square units}$$

•

Example 13-20 illustrates a situation where some of the desired area is above the x-axis and some is below the x-axis.

• **EXAMPLE 13-20** ⎯⎯⎯⎯⎯⎯⎯⎯⎯⎯⎯⎯⎯⎯⎯⎯

Find the area between the x-axis and the curve $f(x) = x^2 - 9$ from $x = 1$ to $x = 4$.

Solution

A sketch of $f(x)$ and the indicated area appears in Figure 13-19. Observe that $f(x) \leq 0$ over the interval $1 \leq x \leq 3$ and $f(x) \geq 0$ over the interval $3 \leq x \leq 4$. Thus, part of the area appears below the x-axis, and part appears above the x-axis. Each part must be determined separately. Since A_1, the area below, was determined in Example 13-19, we now compute A_2 as follows:

$$A_2 = \int_3^4 (x^2 - 9)\, dx = \underbrace{\frac{1}{3}x^3 - 9x}_{F(x)} \Bigg|_3^4$$

$$= F(4) - F(3)$$

$$= \left[\frac{1}{3}(4^3) - 9(4) \right] - \left[\frac{1}{3}(3^3) - 9(3) \right]$$

$$= \left(\frac{64}{3} - 36 \right) - (-18)$$

$$= 3\frac{1}{3} \text{ square units}$$

Thus, the total area is

$$A = A_1 + A_2$$

$$= 9\frac{1}{3} + 3\frac{1}{3}$$

$$= 12\frac{2}{3} \text{ square units}$$

Application

• **EXAMPLE 13-21   Velocity/Distance.**

The velocity (or speed), v (in feet per second), of a moving particle after t seconds have elapsed is given by

$$v(t) = 3t^2 + 2t \qquad (t \geq 0)$$

Determine the distance traveled by the particle from the end of the third second to the end of the sixth second or, in other words, over the interval $3 \leq t \leq 6$.

Solution

We first sketch a graph of the function in Figure 13-20 and shade the area over the indicated interval.

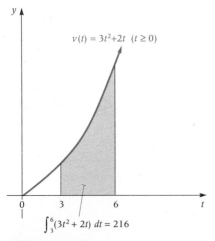

FIGURE 13-20

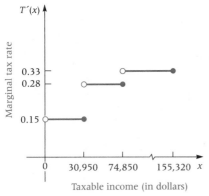

FIGURE 13-21

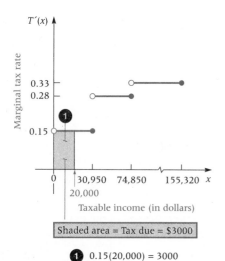

Shaded area = Tax due = $3000

① 0.15(20,000) = 3000

FIGURE 13-22

Since $v(t) = S'(t)$, where $S(t)$ denotes the distance traveled after t seconds have elapsed, then the distance traveled during the time interval $3 \leq t \leq 6$ is given by

$$\int_3^6 S'(t)\ dt = \int_3^6 v(t)\ dt$$

$$= \int_3^6 (3t^2 + 2t)\ dt$$

$$= (t^3 + t^2)\Big|_3^6$$

$$= (6^3 + 6^2) - (3^3 + 3^2)$$

$$= 216\ \text{feet}$$

Marginal Tax Rates

As we learned in the preceding section, the marginal tax rate gives the amount of federal income tax due on each additional dollar of taxable income. For married people filing jointly and qualifying widow(er)s with taxable incomes not exceeding $155,320 during the 1989 tax year, the marginal tax rate, $T'(x)$, is given by the function

$$T'(x) = \begin{cases} 0.15 & \text{if} \qquad\quad 0 < x \leq 30{,}950 \\ 0.28 & \text{if } 30{,}950 < x \leq 74{,}850 \\ 0.33 & \text{if } 74{,}850 < x \leq 155{,}320 \end{cases}$$

where x denotes annual taxable income in dollars.

The graph of $T'(x)$ is given in Figure 13-21. Note that

the area under the graph of T'(x) *gives the amount of federal income tax due.*

Thus, for taxable income of $20,000, the amount of federal income tax due is given by the area over the interval $0 < x \leq 20{,}000$ (see Figure 13-22), which can be determined by the definite integral

$$\int_0^{20{,}000} T'(x)\ dx = \int_0^{20{,}000} 0.15\ dx$$

$$= 0.15x\ \Big|_0^{20{,}000}$$

$$= 0.15(20{,}000) - 0.15(0)$$

$$= \$3000$$

This is illustrated in Figure 13-22, where the area is determined by multiplying the length and width of the rectangle. Note that the definite integral agrees with the result of Figure 13-22.

For taxable income of $40,000, the amount of federal income tax due

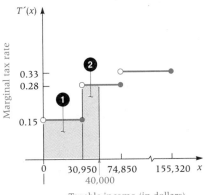

total shaded area = tax due = $7176.50

1 $0.15(30,950) = 4642.50$

2 $0.28(40,000 - 30,950) = 2534.00$

$4642.50 + 2534.00 = 7176.50$

FIGURE 13-23

is given by the area over the interval $0 < x \le 40,000$ (see Figure 13-23). This area can be determined by the definite integral

$$\int_0^{40,000} T'(x)\, dx$$

Since $T'(x)$ is piecewise defined by different formulas on either side of the discontinuity at $x = 30,950$, the above definite integral is evaluated as the sum of the definite integrals given below.

$$\int_0^{30,950} 0.15\, dx + \int_{30,950}^{40,000} 0.28\, dx$$

Note that we have split the interval $0 < x \le 40,000$ at the point of discontinuity, $x = 30,950$. In general, this is permissible for a function $f(x)$ defined over some interval if $|f(x)| < M$ (where M is a constant) for all values of x in the interval, and if $f(x)$ has at most a finite number of discontinuities over the interval.

Evaluating each definite integral gives the following results:

$$\int_0^{30,950} 0.15\, dx = 0.15x \Big|_0^{30,950}$$

$$= 0.15(30,950) - 0.15(0)$$

$$= 4642.50$$

$$\int_{30,950}^{40,000} 0.28\, dx = 0.28x \Big|_{30,950}^{40,000}$$

$$= 0.28(40,000) - 0.28(30,950)$$

$$= 0.28(40,000 - 30,950)$$

$$= 2534$$

Thus,

$$\int_0^{40,000} T'(x)\, dx = 4642.50 + 2534 = \$7176.50 \qquad \text{Tax Due}$$

This is illustrated in Figure 13-23, where the area of each rectangle is determined by multiplying its length and width. Note that the definite integral agrees with the result of Figure 13-23.

Exercises 13-2

Evaluate each of the following.

1. $\displaystyle\int_1^3 4x^3\, dx$

2. $\displaystyle\int_2^5 \frac{-6}{x^2}\, dx$

3. $\displaystyle\int_0^1 (4x + 1)\, dx$

4. $\displaystyle\int_{-2}^4 (8x^3 - 6x^2 + 2)\, dx$

5. $\displaystyle\int_1^4 \frac{4}{x^3}\, dx$

6. $\displaystyle\int_1^{27} 5\sqrt[3]{x}\, dx$

7. $\displaystyle\int_1^5 \frac{10}{x}\, dx$

8. $\displaystyle\int_2^4 \frac{8}{x}\, dx$

9. $\displaystyle\int_0^3 e^x \, dx$ **10.** $\displaystyle\int_1^{10} e^{-x} \, dx$

11. $\displaystyle\int_0^2 e^{-2x} \, dx$ **12.** $\displaystyle\int_0^1 e^{-4x} \, dx$

Area Approximation

Find both lower and upper approximations of the area bounded by the x-axis and the curve $f(x) = -x^2 + 4$ from $x = 0$ to $x = 1$ by dividing the interval $0 \le x \le 1$ into the following.

13. 4 subintervals
14. 10 subintervals

Find both lower and upper approximations of the area bounded by the x-axis and the curve $f(x) = 2x^2$ from $x = 1$ to $x = 2$ by dividing the interval $1 \le x \le 2$ into the following.

15. 5 subintervals
16. 10 subintervals

Riemann Sum

17. Using the formula

$$1 + 2 + \ldots + n = \frac{n(n + 1)}{2}$$

in conjunction with a Riemann sum as developed in this section, find the area bounded by the x-axis and the graph of $f(x) = x$ from $x = 0$ to $x = 1$. Check your answer by using $F(1) - F(0)$.

18. Using the formula

$$1^3 + 2^3 + \ldots + n^3 = \left[\frac{n(n + 1)}{2}\right]^2$$

in conjunction with a Riemann sum as developed in this section, find the area bounded by the x-axis and the graph of $f(x) = x^3$ over the interval $0 \le x \le 1$. Check your answer by using $F(1) - F(0)$.

19. Find the area between the curve $f(x) = 3x^2$ and the x-axis from $x = 0$ to $x = 1$ by using
  a) The Riemann sum as developed in this section.
  b) The definite integral.

Definite Integral Versus Area Approximation

20. Use the definite integral to determine the area bounded by the x-axis and the curve $f(x) = -x^2 + 4$ from $x = 0$ to $x = 1$. Compare your answer with those in Exercises 13 and 14.

21. Use the definite integral to determine the area bounded by the x-axis and the curve $f(x) = 2x^2$ from $x = 1$ to $x = 2$. Compare your answer with those in Exercises 15 and 16.

Definite Integrals and Areas

22. Find the area between the x-axis and the curve $f(x) = 3x^2 + 5$ from $x = 2$ to $x = 5$. Graph the curve and shade the desired area.

23. Find the area between the x-axis and the curve $y = x^3$ from $x = 0$ to $x = 4$. Graph the curve and shade the desired area.

24. Find the area between the x-axis and the curve $f(x) = -3x^2 + 24x$ from $x = 0$ to $x = 8$. Graph the curve and shade the desired area.

25. Find the area between the x-axis and the curve $f(x) = 1/x^2$ from $x = 1$ to $x = 3$. Graph the curve and shade the desired area.

26. Find the area between the x-axis and the curve $y = 2x + 6$ from $x = 0$ to $x = 2$. Graph the curve and shade the desired area.

27. Find the area between the x-axis and the curve $y = -2x + 8$ from $x = 0$ to $x = 3$. Graph the curve and shade the desired area.

28. Find the area between the x-axis and the curve $y = -x$ from $x = -2$ to $x = 0$. Graph the curve and shade the desired area.

29. Find the area between the x-axis and the curve $y = -2x$ from $x = -3$ to $x = -1$. Graph the curve and shade the desired area.

30. Find the area between the x-axis and the curve $y = -x^2 + 16$ from $x = 0$ to $x = 4$. Graph the curve and shade the desired area.

31. Find the area between the x-axis and the curve $y = -x^2 + 25$ from $x = 0$ to $x = 5$. Graph the curve and shade the desired area.

32. Find the area between the x-axis and the curve $y = -4x^2 + 32x$ from $x = 0$ to $x = 8$. Graph the curve and shade the desired area.

33. Find the area between the x-axis and the curve $y = -5x^2 + 20x$ from $x = 0$ to $x = 4$. Graph the curve and shade the desired area.

34. Find the area between the x-axis and the curve $y = x^2 - 4x + 5$ from $x = 0$ to $x = 2$. Graph the curve and shade the desired area.

35. Find the area between the x-axis and the curve $y = x^2 - 6x + 12$ from $x = 0$ to $x = 4$. Graph the curve and shade the desired area.

36. Find the area between the x-axis and the curve $y = x^2 - 10x + 30$ from $x = 1$ to $x = 2$. Graph the curve and shade the desired area.

37. Find the area between the x-axis and the curve $y = x^2 - 2x + 8$ from $x = -3$ to $x = 3$. Graph the curve and shade the desired area.

38. Find the area between the x-axis and the curve $y = e^x$ from $x = 0$ to $x = 2$. Graph the curve and shade the desired area.

39. Find the area between the x-axis and the curve $y = e^{-x}$ from $x = 0$ to $x = -3$. Graph the curve and shade the desired area.

40. Find the area between the x-axis and the curve $y = e^{-x}$ from $x = 0$ to $x = 3$. Graph the curve and shade the desired area.

41. Find the area between the x-axis and the curve $y = e^x$ from $x = -1$ to $x = 1$. Graph the curve and shade the desired area.

42. Find the area between the x-axis and the curve $y = 1/x$ from $x = 1$ to $x = 4$. Graph the curve and shade the desired area.

43. Find the area between the x-axis and the curve $y = 1/x$ from $x = 1$ to $x = 5$. Graph the curve and shade the desired area.

44. Find the area between the x-axis and the curve $y = 1/x^2$ from $x = 1$ to $x = 2$. Graph the curve and shade the desired area.

45. Find the area between the x-axis and the curve $y = 1/x^4$ from $x = 2$ to $x = 4$. Graph the curve and shade the desired area.

46. Find the area between the x-axis and the curve $y = x^4$ from $x = -2$ to $x = 2$. Graph the curve and shade the desired area.

47. Find the area between the x-axis and the curve $y = x^5$ from $x = 0$ to $x = 1$. Graph the curve and shade the desired area.

Areas Above and Below the x-Axis

For each of the following, find the area bounded by the x-axis and the function over the indicated interval. Graph the function and shade the desired area.

48. $y = x^2 - 9,\ 0 \le x \le 6$ **49.** $y = x^2 - 4,\ 0 \le x \le 3$
50. $y = x,\ -2 \le x \le 2$ **51.** $y = -x,\ -4 \le x \le 4$
52. $y = -x^2 + 1,\ 0 \le x \le 3$ **53.** $y = -x^2 + 4,\ 0 \le x \le 3$
54. $y = 4x - 12,\ 0 \le x \le 4$ **55.** $y = -2x + 6,\ 0 \le x \le 6$
56. $y = x^3,\ -1 \le x \le 1$ **57.** $y = -x^3,\ -2 \le x \le 4$
58. $y = x^2 - 4x - 5,\ 3 \le x \le 6$ **59.** $y = x^2 - x - 2,\ 0 \le x \le 3$
60. $y = -1 + 1/x,\ 0.5 \le x \le 4$ **61.** $y = -1 + 4/x,\ 1 \le x \le 6$
62. $y = -1 + 4/x^2,\ 1 \le x \le 4$ **63.** $y = -1 + 9/x^2,\ 1 \le x \le 6$
64. $y = 3x^2 - 27,\ 0 \le x \le 4$ **65.** $y = -3x^2 + 12,\ 0 \le x \le 6$

Applications

Marginal cost/Cost. For each marginal cost function, $C'(x)$, where x denotes the number of units produced, determine the total change in cost over the interval $a \le x \le b$ by using the definite integral

$$\int_a^b C'(x)\ dx = C(b) - C(a)$$

66. $C'(x) = 10x + 50,\ 5 \le x \le 10$
67. $C'(x) = 20x + 100,\ 10 \le x \le 20$
68. $C'(x) = 30x + 600,\ 20 \le x \le 30$

Marginal revenue/Revenue. For each marginal revenue function, $R'(x)$, where x denotes the number of units sold, determine the total change in revenue over the interval $a \le x \le b$ by using the formula

$$\int_a^b R'(x)\ dx = R(b) - R(a)$$

69. $R'(x) = -2x + 100,\ 10 \le x \le 30$
70. $R'(x) = -4x + 800,\ 20 \le x \le 50$
71. $R'(x) = -8x + 400,\ 5 \le x \le 40$

Velocity/Distance. Each of the following functions gives the velocity (or speed), v (in feet per second), of a moving particle after t seconds have elapsed. Find the distance traveled by the particle over the indicated interval.

72. $v(t) = 3t^2 + 4t,\ 0 \le t \le 3$ **73.** $v(t) = 6t^2 + 5t,\ 0 \le t \le 6$
74. $v(t) = 4t^3,\ 1 \le t \le 2$ **75.** $v(t) = 6t^5,\ 0 \le t \le 1$

76. *Oil leak.* Oil is leaking from a tanker at the rate of

$$L'(t) = 50t + 20$$

gallons per hour, where t denotes elapsed time (in hours) since the leak began.
a) Find the total number of gallons that have leaked during the first hour (or, in other words, during the time interval $0 \le t \le 1$).
b) Find the total number of gallons that have leaked during the first 2 hours.
c) Find the total number of gallons that have leaked during the third hour (or, in other words, during the time interval $2 \le t \le 3$).

77. *Natural gas leak.* A truck carrying natural gas gets stuck at a low underpass and leaks natural gas at the rate of

$$L'(t) = 10t + 20$$

cubic feet per minute, where t denotes time (in minutes) elapsed since the gas first began leaking.
a) Find the total amount of natural gas that has leaked during the first 5 minutes.

  b) Find the total amount of gas that has leaked during the first 10 minutes.
  c) Find the total amount of gas that has leaked during the fifth minute (i.e., $4 \leq t \leq 5$).
  d) Find the total amount of gas that has leaked during the sixth minute.

78. *Timber depletion.* In a given geographic area, timber is being depleted at the rate of

$$D'(t) = 2000e^t$$

trees per year, where t denotes time in years, with $t = 0$ denoting the present year.
  a) How many trees will be cut down during the first year?
  b) How many trees will be cut down during the second year?
  c) How many trees will be cut down during the third year?

79. *Marketing.* The weekly rate of increase in sales of a new product is given by

$$S'(t) = 100 - 100e^{-0.20t}$$

where t denotes the number of weeks since the beginning of an advertising campaign for the product. Determine the total sales during
  a) The first 5 weeks.   b) The first 10 weeks.

80. *Population growth.* The population, P, of a state is growing at an annual rate given by

$$P'(t) = 4000e^{0.10t}$$

where t denotes the time elapsed (in years) since the end of last year. Find the total increase in population during the next
  a) 2 years.   b) 4 years.   c) 6 years.   d) 10 years.

81. *Job growth.* For a given state, the annual rate of increase of jobs is given by

$$J'(t) = 100e^{-0.05t}$$

where t denotes the time elapsed (in years) since the end of last year. Find the total increase in jobs during the next
  a) 2 years.   b) 3 years.   c) 5 years.   d) 10 years.

Marketing tax rates. For single tax filers with annual taxable incomes not exceeding $93,130 during the 1989 tax year, the federal marginal tax rate, $T'(x)$, is given by the function

$$T'(x) = \begin{cases} 0.15 & \text{if} \quad 0 < x \leq 18{,}550 \\ 0.28 & \text{if } 18{,}550 < x \leq 44{,}900 \\ 0.33 & \text{if } 44{,}900 < x \leq 93{,}130 \end{cases}$$

Find the appropriate area under the graph of $T'(x)$ by integration in order to determine the amount of federal income tax due on the following taxable incomes.

82. $14,000	**83.** $18,400	**84.** $19,000
85. $30,000	**86.** $43,000	**87.** $50,000
88. $60,000	**89.** $80,000	**90.** $90,000

13-3 • AREA BETWEEN TWO CURVES

Sometimes we must determine the area between the graphs of two continuous functions, $f(x)$ and $g(x)$, over an interval, $a \leq x \leq b$, as

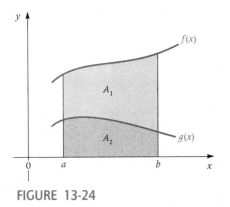

FIGURE 13-24

illustrated by the shaded area A_1 of Figure 13-24. The shaded area A_1 is determined by noting the following:

1. The area A_2 is the area between the graph of $g(x)$ and the x-axis over the interval $a \leq x \leq b$. Therefore, it is determined by the definite integral given below.

$$A_2 = \int_a^b g(x)\, dx$$

2. The area $A_1 + A_2$ is the area between the x-axis and the graph of $f(x)$ over the interval $a \leq x \leq b$. Therefore, it is determined by the definite integral given below.

$$A_1 + A_2 = \int_a^b f(x)\, dx$$

3. This implies that

$$A_1 = \int_a^b f(x)\, dx - \int_a^b g(x)\, dx$$

$$= \int_a^b [f(x) - g(x)]\, dx$$

where $f(x) \geq g(x)$ over the interval $a \leq x \leq b$. This formula holds even if $f(x)$ or $g(x)$ is negative for values of x in the interval $a \leq x \leq b$.

We summarize as follows.

SUMMARY

Area Between Two Curves

The area between the graphs of two continuous functions, f and g, over an interval, $a \leq x \leq b$, where $f(x) \geq g(x)$ (as illustrated in Figure 13-25), is given by the definite integral

$$\int_a^b [f(x) - g(x)]\, dx$$

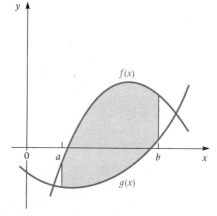

FIGURE 13-25

• EXAMPLE 13-22 _____

Find the area between $f(x) = x + 6$ and $g(x) = x^2$ from $x = 1$ to $x = 2$.

Solution

A sketch of both functions appears in Figure 13-26. We must determine the x-coordinates of both intersection points of the functions. Setting

$$f(x) = g(x)$$

we have

$$x + 6 = x^2$$

Solving for x yields

$$0 = x^2 - x - 6$$
$$0 = (x - 3)(x + 2)$$
$$x - 3 = 0 \qquad x + 2 = 0$$
$$x = 3 \qquad\quad x = -2$$

The area included between the two curves from $x = 1$ to $x = 2$ is shaded in Figure 13-27. This area is determined by the definite integral

$$\int_1^2 [f(x) - g(x)]\, dx$$

where

$$f(x) - g(x) = x + 6 - x^2$$
$$= -x^2 + x + 6$$

Thus, we have

$$\int_1^2 [f(x) - g(x)]\, dx = \int_1^2 (-x^2 + x + 6)\, dx$$

$$= \underbrace{-\frac{1}{3}x^3 + \frac{1}{2}x^2 + 6x}_{F(x)} \Bigg|_1^2$$

$$= F(2) - F(1)$$

$$= \frac{34}{3} - \frac{37}{6}$$

$$= \frac{31}{6} \text{ square units}$$

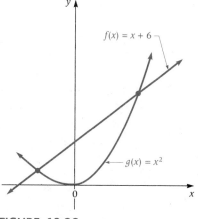

FIGURE 13-26

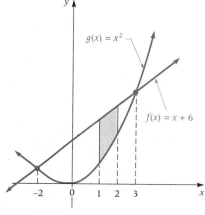

FIGURE 13-27

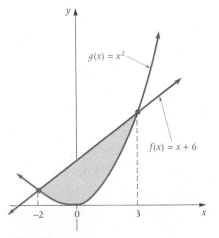

FIGURE 13-28

• **EXAMPLE 13-23** _____

Find the total area bounded by the graphs of $f(x) = x + 6$ and $g(x) = x^2$ in Example 13-22.

Solution

We seek the shaded area in Figure 13-28. This area is determined by the definite integral

$$\int_{-2}^{3} [f(x) - g(x)] \, dx = \int_{-2}^{3} (-x^2 + x + 6) \, dx$$

$$= \underbrace{-\frac{1}{3}x^3 + \frac{1}{2}x^2 + 6x}_{F(x)} \Bigg|_{-2}^{3}$$

$$= F(3) - F(-2)$$

$$= \frac{27}{2} - \left(-\frac{22}{3}\right)$$

$$= \frac{125}{6} \text{ square units}$$

• **EXAMPLE 13-24** _____

Find the area included between the graphs of the functions $f(x) = x + 6$ and $g(x) = x^2$ in Examples 13-22 and 13-23 from $x = -2$ to $x = 4$.

Solution

We seek the shaded area in Figure 13-29. Observing Figure 13-29, note that for the area between $x = 3$ and $x = 4$, $g(x) \geq f(x)$. Thus, we must determine area A_2 separately by the definite integral

$$\int_{3}^{4} [g(x) - f(x)] \, dx$$

Since

$$g(x) - f(x) = x^2 - (x + 6)$$
$$= x^2 - x - 6$$

then we have

$$\int_{3}^{4} [g(x) - f(x)] \, dx = \int_{3}^{4} (x^2 - x - 6) \, dx$$

$$= \underbrace{\frac{1}{3}x^3 - \frac{1}{2}x^2 - 6x}_{F(x)} \Bigg|_{3}^{4}$$

$$= F(4) - F(3)$$

$$= -\frac{32}{3} - \left(-\frac{27}{2}\right)$$

$$= -\frac{64}{6} + \frac{81}{6}$$

$$= \frac{17}{6} \text{ square units}$$

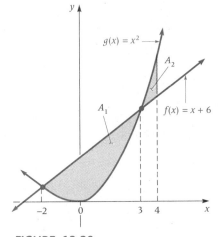

FIGURE 13-29

Since area A_1 was determined in Example 13-23, the total area, A, is

$$A = A_1 + A_2$$

$$= \frac{125}{6} + \frac{17}{6}$$

$$= \frac{71}{3} \text{ square units}$$

EXAMPLE 13-25

Find the area between the graphs of $f(x) = 2x + 8$ and $g(x) = -3x^2$ from $x = -1$ to $x = 2$.

Solution

A sketch of both functions is given in Figure 13-30. Since the graphs of Figure 13-30 indicate that the curves do not intersect, we do not have to determine intersection points. The area to be determined is shaded in Figure 13-30 and is given by the definite integral

$$\int_{-1}^{2} [f(x) - g(x)] \, dx$$

where

$$f(x) - g(x) = 2x + 8 - (-3x^2)$$
$$= 3x^2 + 2x + 8$$

Thus,

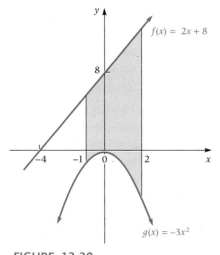

$$\int_{-1}^{2} [f(x) - g(x)] \, dx = \int_{-1}^{2} [3x^2 + 2x + 8] \, dx$$

$$= x^3 + x^2 + 8x \Big|_{-1}^{2}$$

$$= F(2) - F(-1)$$

$$= [2^3 + 2^2 + 8(2)] - [(-1)^3 + (-1)^2 + 8(-1)]$$

$$= [28] - [-8] = 36 \text{ square units}$$

FIGURE 13-30

Application

Consumers' and Producers' Surpluses

Suppose a product has the supply function $p = S(q)$ and the demand function $p = D(q)$, as illustrated in Figure 13-31 on page 836. Assume that p denotes the unit price (in dollars) of this product and q denotes the number of units supplied or demanded. Thus, the supply function, $p = S(q)$, gives the unit price at which suppliers are willing to produce q units of this product; the demand function, $p = D(q)$, gives the unit price at which consumers are willing to buy q units of this product. Note that, at the equilibrium point, supply = demand = q_E units and the unit price stabilizes at p_E dollars.

However, when the market is at equilibrium, there are still some consumers who would have paid a unit price higher than the equilibrium price, p_E. Since these consumers would have paid a unit price p, where $p > p_E$, then the area under the demand curve, but above the horizontal line, $p = p_E$, represents the increase in unit price times demand, or the ad-

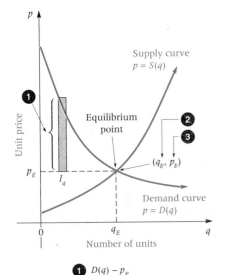

FIGURE 13-31

ditional revenue that would have been paid by these consumers (see Figure 13-31). Since the market is at equilibrium, this additional revenue is not paid by consumers; thus, it is the total amount of money saved by consumers as a result of the market being at equilibrium and is called the **consumers' surplus.** Since the consumers' surplus (denoted CS) is represented by the area under the demand curve, but above the horizontal line, $p = p_E$, over the interval $0 \le q \le q_E$, as illustrated in Figure 13-32, it is determined by the definite integral

$$\text{CS} = \int_0^{q_E} [D(q) - p_E]\, dq$$

Also, there are producers who are willing to supply this product at prices lower than its equilibrium price, p_E. Since these producers would have received a unit price p, where $p < p_E$, then the area between the supply curve and the horizontal axis [the gray area of Figure 13-33] represents the amount of revenue that would have been received by these producers. However, since the market is at equilibrium, then producers will sell q_E units at a unit price of p_E dollars to receive total revenue of $p_E q_E$ dollars. This total revenue is represented by the area of the rectangle (colored area + gray area) of Figure 13-33(a). Thus, the area between the horizontal line, $p = p_E$, and the supply curve [the colored area of Figure 13-33(a)] represents the additional revenue gained by producers as a result of the market being at equilibrium. This additional revenue is called the **producers' surplus** and is denoted PS. The producers' surplus is determined by the definite integral

$$\text{PS} = \int_0^{q_E} [p_E - S(q)]\, dq$$

as is illustrated in Figure 13-33(b).

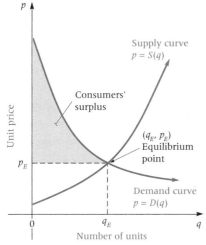

FIGURE 13-32

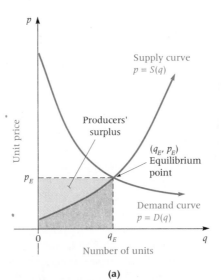

(a)

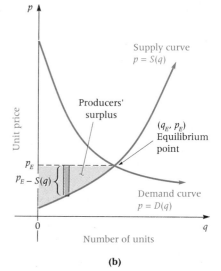

(b)

FIGURE 13-33

We summarize as follows.

SUMMARY

Consumers' and Producers' Surpluses

Given a demand function, $p = D(q)$, and a supply function, $p = S(q)$, where p denotes the unit price and q denotes the number of units supplied or demanded of some product (see Figure 13-34), then

1. The consumers' surplus is given by

$$CS = \int_0^{q_E} [D(q) - p_E] \, dq$$

2. The producers' surplus is given by

$$PS = \int_0^{q_E} [P_E - S(q)] \, dq$$

3. The corresponding areas are given in Figure 13-34.

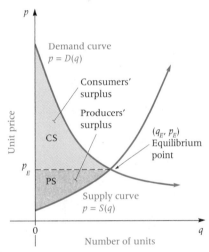

FIGURE 13-34

• **EXAMPLE 13-26**

Given the demand function

$$p = (q - 10)^2 \qquad (0 \le q \le 10)$$

and the supply function

$$p = q^2 \qquad (0 \le q \le 10)$$

where p denotes the unit price in dollars and q denotes the number of units of some product, find the consumers' and producers' surpluses.

Solution

We first graph both functions and indicate the areas to be found as CS and PS in Figure 13-35.

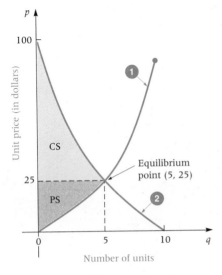

① $p = q^2$ $(0 \leq q \leq 10)$

② $p = (q - 10)^2$ $(0 \leq q \leq 10)$

FIGURE 13-35

Next we find the equilibrium point by equating the values of p given by the supply and demand functions. Hence,

$$(q - 10)^2 = q^2$$
$$q^2 - 20q + 100 = q^2$$
$$-20q = -100$$
$$q = 5 \qquad \text{Equilibrium quantity}$$

We find the equilibrium price by evaluating either

$$p = S(5) = 5^2 = 25$$

$$\text{or} \qquad \qquad \text{Equilibrium price}$$

$$p = D(5) = (5 - 10)^2 = 25$$

The coordinates of the equilibrium point are indicated in Figure 13-35.

The consumers' surplus is determined as follows:

$$\begin{aligned}
\text{CS} &= \int_0^5 [D(q) - p_E]\, dq \\[2mm]
&= \int_0^5 [(q - 10)^2 - 25]\, dq \\[2mm]
&= \int_0^5 [(q^2 - 20q + 100) - 25]\, dq \\[2mm]
&= \int_0^5 (q^2 - 20q + 75)\, dq \\[2mm]
&= \left(\frac{1}{3} q^3 - 10q^2 + 75q \right) \Big|_0^5 \\[2mm]
&= \left[\frac{1}{3}(5^3) - 10(5^2) + 75(5) \right] - 0 \\[2mm]
&= \frac{500}{3} = 166.67
\end{aligned}$$

Thus, the consumers' surplus is $166.67.

The producers' surplus is determined below.

$$\begin{aligned}
\text{PS} &= \int_0^5 [p_E - S(q)]\, dq \\[2mm]
&= \int_0^5 (25 - q^2)\, dq \\[2mm]
&= \left(25q - \frac{1}{3} q^3 \right) \Big|_0^5 \\[2mm]
&= \left[25(5) - \frac{1}{3}(5^3) \right] - 0 \\[2mm]
&= \frac{250}{3} = 83.33
\end{aligned}$$

Thus, the producers' surplus is $83.33.

Exercises 13-3

For each of the following, graph the functions and find the area between the graphs of the functions over the indicated interval.

1. $f(x) = 2x + 20, g(x) = x^2 + 5; 1 \le x \le 3$
2. $f(x) = x, g(x) = x^3; 0 \le x \le 1$
3. $f(x) = x^2, g(x) = x^3; 0 \le x \le 1$
4. $f(x) = 2x^2 + 4, g(x) = x^2 + 3; 0 \le x \le 3$
5. $y = 3x^2 + 5, y = x^2 + 5; 0 \le x \le 2$
6. $y = x, y = x^4; 0 \le x \le 1$
7. $f(x) = x, g(x) = x^5; 0 \le x \le 1$
8. $f(x) = \sqrt{x}, g(x) = x; 0 \le x \le 4$
9. $f(x) = 2x + 5, g(x) = 1; 0 \le x \le 3$
10. $f(x) = 2x + 8, g(x) = 3; 0 \le x \le 4$
11. $y = -x + 4, y = 3/x; 1 \le x \le 3$
12. $y = -x + 6, y = 8/x; 2 \le x \le 4$
13. $f(x) = -x + 5, g(x) = 6/x; 2 \le x \le 3$
14. $f(x) = -x + 10, g(x) = 24/x; 4 \le x \le 6$
15. $f(x) = e^x, g(x) = 1; 0 \le x \le 2$
16. $f(x) = e^{-x}, g(x) = 1; 0 \le x \le 4$
17. $y = -x, y = x; 0 \le x \le 2$
18. $y = -x, y = x; -2 \le x \le 0$
19. $y = x^4, y = x^3; 0 \le x \le 1$
20. $y = x, y = 1/x; -2 \le x \le -1$
21. $y = e^x, y = e^{-x}; 0 \le x \le 1$
22. $f(x) = -x^2 + 8, g(x) = 2x; 0 \le x \le 2$
23. $f(x) = -x^2 + 6, g(x) = x; -3 \le x \le 2$
24. $f(x) = -x^2 + 10, g(x) = 3x; -5 \le x \le 2$
25. $y = x + 1, y = 2; 0 \le x \le 4$
26. $y = x + 3, y = 5; 0 \le x \le 6$
27. $f(x) = x, g(x) = x^2; 0 \le x \le 3$
28. $f(x) = x^3, g(x) = x^2; 0 \le x \le 6$
29. $f(x) = x, g(x) = x^3; -1 \le x \le 4$
30. $y = \sqrt{x}, y = x; 0 \le x \le 4$
31. $y = -x^2 + 5, y = 1; -2 \le x \le 6$
32. $y = -x^2 + 12, y = 3; -3 \le x \le 6$
33. $f(x) = e^x, g(x) = e^{-x}; -2 \le x \le 3$
34. $f(x) = -x + 4, g(x) = 3/x; 1 \le x \le 4$
35. $f(x) = -x + 6, g(x) = 8/x; 2 \le x \le 6$

Consumers' and producers' surpluses. Find the consumers' and producers' surpluses for each of the following.

36. $p = D(q) = -0.5q + 8, p = S(q) = 2q + 0.5$
37. $p = D(q) = -0.5q + 20, p = S(q) = q + 8$
38. $p = D(q) = (q - 20)^2, p = S(q) = q^2 + 40$
39. $p = D(q) = (q - 30)^2, p = S(q) = q^2 + 300$
40. $p = D(q) = -2q + 80, p = S(q) = 3q + 5$
41. $p = D(q) = (q - 40)^2, p = S(q) = q^2 + 640$

Marginal analysis. For a given product, a company's sales revenue changes with time at a rate of $R'(t)$ dollars per month and its cost changes with time at the rate of $C'(t)$ dollars per month. Then the total profit (for the product) accumulated during the time interval $a \le t \le b$, as illustrated in Figure 13-36, is given by

$$\int_a^b [R'(t) - C'(t)]\, dt$$

where t is given in months. For each of the following, determine the total profit accumulated during the indicated time interval.

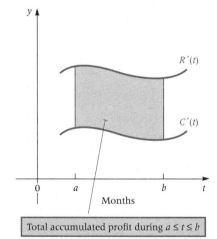

Total accumulated profit during $a \le t \le b$

FIGURE 13-36

42. $R'(t) = 50t^2 + 10$, $C'(t) = t + 5$; $0 \le t \le 10$
43. $R'(t) = 20t + 5$, $C'(t) = 4t + 2$; $2 \le t \le 6$
44. $R'(t) = -t^2 + 1600$, $C'(t) = 10$; $0 \le t \le 20$
45. $R'(t) = 1000e^t + 1000$, $C'(t) = 2t + 4$; $0 \le t \le 8$

13-4 • INTEGRATION BY SUBSTITUTION

Up to this point, we have been finding indefinite integrals of functions consisting of sums of terms of the form

$$kx^n, \ e^{kx}, \text{ and } \frac{1}{x}$$

where k and n are constants and $n \ne -1$. In this section, we will learn a technique that will enable us to find indefinite integrals of a greater variety of functions. The technique will involve the **substitution** principle. Since the substitution principle involves writing expressions for differentials, we briefly review this procedure.

Differentials

If $u = f(x)$ defines a differentiable function of x and dx is any real number, then, as discussed in Section 11-4, the quantity

$$du = f'(x) \, dx$$

is called the **differential of u.** Thus, if

$$u = f(x) = x^3$$

then

$$du = f'(x) \, dx$$
$$= 3x^2 \, dx$$

Differentials have a special meaning, as was discussed in Section 11-4. However, here we will need to determine only the formula for du, given some equation $u = f(x)$.

• **EXAMPLE 13-27** _____

If $u = x^6$, find the differential du.

Solution

Since $u = f(x) = x^6$, then $f'(x) = 6x^5$. Hence,

$$du = f'(x) \, dx$$
$$= 6x^5 \, dx$$

• **EXAMPLE 13-28** _____

If $u = x^4 - 8x^2 + 16$, find du.

Solution

Since $u = f(x) = x^4 - 8x^2 + 16$, then $f'(x) = 4x^3 - 16x$. Hence,

$$du = f'(x)\, dx$$
$$= (4x^3 - 16x)\, dx$$

In rule 13-1 of Section 13-1, we saw that

$$\int x^n\, dx = \frac{1}{n+1}x^{n+1} + c \qquad (n \neq -1)$$

This rule may be restated in terms of the variable u. If x is replaced by u and dx by du, then we have rule 13-7.

Rule 13-7

$$\int u^n\, du = \frac{1}{n+1}u^{n+1} + c \qquad (n \neq -1)$$

Rule 13-7 will be used in conjunction with the substitution principle to integrate the functions in this section.

We now consider the problem of finding

$$\int (x^3 - 4)^7\, 3x^2\, dx$$

In order to determine this indefinite integral, we will restate the problem in an equivalent, but simpler, form by substituting the variable u in place of $x^3 - 4$ and then making appropriate symbolic changes. Hence, we let

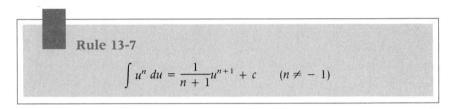

Then we have

Substitution

Thus, the indefinite integral

$$\int \underbrace{(x^3 - 4)}_{u}^7\, \underbrace{3x^2\, dx}_{du}$$

becomes simply

$$\int u^7\, du$$

This result is integrated by using rule 13-7. Hence, we obtain

$$\int u^7\, du = \frac{1}{8}u^8 + c$$

Since the solution

$$\frac{1}{8}u^8 + c$$

is written in terms of u, we must rewrite it in terms of x. Since

$$u = x^3 - 4$$

replacing u with $x^3 - 4$ in the solution yields

$$\frac{1}{8}(x^3 - 4)^8 + c$$

Hence, we have

$$\int (x^3 - 4)^7 \, 3x^2 \, dx = \frac{1}{8}(x^3 - 4)^8 + c$$

the validity of which can be verified by differentiation as given below.
Check:

$$\frac{d}{dx}\left[\frac{1}{8}(x^3 - 4)^8 + c\right] = \frac{1}{8} \cdot 8(x^3 - 4)^7(3x^2) + 0$$

$$= (x^3 - 4)^7(3x^2)$$

• **EXAMPLE 13-29** _____

Find $\int (x^5 - 6)^9 \, 5x^4 \, dx$.

Solution

Let $u = x^5 - 6$. Then

$$du = 5x^4 \, dx \left.\right\} \text{Substitution}$$

Hence,

$$\int \underbrace{(x^5 - 6)^9}_{u} \, \underbrace{5x^4 \, dx}_{du} = \int u^9 \, du$$

$$= \frac{1}{10}u^{10} + c$$

Replacing u with $x^5 - 6$ gives

$$\int (x^5 - 6)^9 \, 5x^4 \, dx = \frac{1}{10}(x^5 - 6)^{10} + c$$

_____ •

We now consider a problem in which du does not appear explicitly in the function to be integrated. Consider the indefinite integral

$$\int (x^3 - 7)^5 \, x^2 \, dx$$

If $u = x^3 - 7$, then

$$du = 3x^2 \, dx \left.\right\} \text{Substitution}$$

In order to rewrite the integral in terms of u, the $x^2\ dx$ term must equal du.

$$\int (x^3 - 7)^5\ x^2\ dx = \int u^5\ \underline{\ ?\ }$$

Since $du = 3x^2\ dx$, we must multiply $x^2\ dx$ by 3 and compensate by multiplying the integral by 1/3 to obtain

$$\frac{1}{3} \int \underbrace{(x^3 - 7)^5}_{u}\ \underbrace{3x^2\ dx}_{du}$$

Our multiplying $x^2\ dx$ by 3 and the integral by 1/3 is allowed by rule 13-2 of Section 13-1, which states that the integral of a constant times a function is equal to the constant times the integral of the function. It must be noted that this works only for a *constant multiplier*. It does not apply to variables. Also, if the x^2 term was not present in the original problem, we could not have used the substitution technique. Example 13-32 illustrates such a situation in greater detail. Thus, in our example,

$$\frac{1}{3} \int \underbrace{(x^3 - 7)^5}_{u}\ \underbrace{3x^2\ dx}_{du} = \frac{1}{3} \int u^5\ du$$

$$= \frac{1}{3} \cdot \frac{1}{6} u^6 + c$$

$$= \frac{1}{18}(x^3 - 7)^6 + c$$

• **EXAMPLE 13-30** _____

Find

$$\int \frac{x^4\ dx}{\sqrt{x^5 - 9}}$$

Solution

We write

$$\int \frac{x^4\ dx}{\sqrt{x^5 - 9}} = \int (x^5 - 9)^{-1/2}\ x^4\ dx$$

Letting $u = x^5 - 9$ gives us

$$du = 5x^4\ dx$$

Hence, we obtain

$$\int (x^5 - 9)^{-1/2}\ x^4\ dx = \frac{1}{5} \int \underbrace{(x^5 - 9)^{-1/2}}_{u}\ \underbrace{5x^4\ dx}_{du}$$

$$= \frac{1}{5} \int u^{-1/2}\ du$$

$$= \frac{1}{5} \cdot \frac{1}{1/2} u^{1/2} + c$$

$$= \frac{2}{5}(x^5 - 9)^{1/2} + c$$

• **EXAMPLE 13-31** _____

Find $\int (2x^3 - 5)^{11} \, 5x^2 \, dx$.

Solution

Letting $u = 2x^3 - 5$ gives us

$$du = 6x^2 \, dx$$

Hence, we obtain

$$\int (2x^3 - 5)^{11} \, 5x^2 \, dx = \frac{5}{6} \int \underbrace{(2x^3 - 5)^{11}}_{u} \cdot \underbrace{\frac{6}{5} \cdot 5x^2 \, dx}_{du}$$
Multiply $5x^2 \, dx$ by 6/5 to obtain du.

$$= \frac{5}{6} \int u^{11} \, du$$
Multiply the integral by 5/6, the reciprocal of 6/5.

$$= \frac{5}{6} \cdot \frac{1}{12} u^{12} + c$$

$$= \frac{5}{72} (2x^3 - 5)^{12} + c$$

We now give an example where du cannot be formed.

• **EXAMPLE 13-32** _____

Find

$$\int \frac{x^3 \, dx}{(x^5 + 6)^4}$$

Solution

We rewrite the above integral as

$$\int (x^5 + 6)^{-4} x^3 \, dx$$

and let $u = x^5 + 6$. This gives

$$du = 5x^4 \, dx$$

Hence, we have

$$\int \underbrace{(x^5 + 6)^{-4}}_{u} \underbrace{x^3 \, dx}_{?} = \int u^{-4} \underline{\quad ? \quad}$$

$$du = 5x^4 \, dx$$

Although we would like to multiply $x^3 \, dx$ by $5x$ to give $5x^4 \, dx$, as shown below,

$$\frac{1}{5x} \int \underbrace{(x^5 + 6)}_{u}^{-4} \underbrace{5x \cdot x^3 \, dx}_{du}$$

we cannot do this because $5x$ is not a constant. Thus, this integral cannot be evaluated by the substitution rules presented in this text. As of now, we have no way to evaluate this integral.

Definite Integrals: Substitution Method

When evaluating a definite integral using the substitution method, either of two computational procedures can be used. One procedure involves writing the antiderivative in terms of x and evaluating the definite integral using the original limits of integration. A second procedure is to write the antiderivative in terms of the substitution variable u, change the original limits (given in terms of x) to corresponding values of u, and then evaluate the definite integral (written in terms of u) using the new limits (written as values of u). Accordingly, this procedure is called **change of limits.** The next two examples illustrate both procedures to evaluate the same definite integral.

• **EXAMPLE 13-33** _____

Evaluate

$$\int_1^3 (9 - x^2)^4 x \, dx$$

using the original limits of integration.

Solution

Letting $u = 9 - x^2$ gives

$$du = -2x \, dx \quad \Big\} \text{ Substitution}$$

so that

$$\int_1^3 (9 - x^2)^4 x \, dx = \frac{1}{-2} \int_1^3 \underbrace{(9 - x^2)^4}_{u} \underbrace{(-2)x \, dx}_{du}$$

$$= \frac{1}{-2} \cdot \frac{1}{5}(9 - x^2)^5 \Big|_1^3 \quad \begin{array}{l}\text{Write antiderivative in terms of } x.\\ \text{Use original limits of integration.}\end{array}$$

$$= -\frac{1}{10}[(9 - 3^2)^5 - (9 - 1^2)^5]$$

$$= -\frac{1}{10}[(0)^5 - (8)^5] = 3276.8$$

• **EXAMPLE 13-34** _____

Evaluate

$$\int_1^3 (9 - x^2)^4 x \, dx$$

by using the change of limits procedure.

Solution

Letting $u = 9 - x^2$ gives

$$du = -2x \, dx \quad \Big\} \text{ Substitution}$$

Change Limits

Lower limit: When $x = 1$, $u = 9 - x^2 = 9 - 1^2 = 8$.
Upper limit: When $x = 3$, $u = 9 - x^2 = 9 - 3^2 = 0$.

Note that the upper limit is smaller than the lower limit. This sometimes happens with the change of limits procedure. Do not change the order of the limits and proceed with the integration in the usual manner.

Make the substitution, write the antiderivative in terms of u, and use the new limits. Hence,

$$\int_1^3 (9 - x^2)^4 x \, dx = \frac{1}{-2}\int_1^3 \underbrace{(9 - x^2)^4}_{u}\underbrace{(-2)x \, dx}_{du}$$

$$= -\frac{1}{2}\int_8^0 u^4 \, du \qquad \text{Use the new limits.}$$

$$= -\frac{1}{2} \cdot \frac{1}{5}u^5 \Big|_8^0 \qquad \text{Write the antiderivative in terms of } u.$$

$$= -\frac{1}{10}[0^5 - 8^5] = 3276.8 \qquad \text{Use the new limits.}$$

Note that this answer agrees with that of the previous example.

Exercises 13-4

Determine each of the following.

1. $\displaystyle\int (x^3 - 7)^{10}3x^2 \, dx$

2. $\displaystyle\int (x^2 - 3)^4 2x \, dx$

3. $\displaystyle\int (x^3 - 4x)^5(3x^2 - 4) \, dx$

4. $\displaystyle\int (5x + 6)^{12}5 \, dx$

5. $\displaystyle\int (x^4 - 8)^9 x^3 \, dx$

6. $\displaystyle\int (2x^5 - 7)^6 x^4 \, dx$

7. $\displaystyle\int (x - 3)^9 \, dx$

8. $\displaystyle\int (x^3 - 4)^{1/2}x^2 \, dx$

9. $\displaystyle\int (x^4 + 6)^5 5x^3 \, dx$

10. $\displaystyle\int (x^4 - 8x + 5)^7(2x^3 - 4) \, dx$

11. $\displaystyle\int (x^6 + 9)^{10}2x^5 \, dx$

12. $\displaystyle\int (4x^3 - 1)^{11}5x^2 \, dx$

13. $\displaystyle\int \frac{x^2}{(x^3 - 5)^{10}}dx$

14. $\displaystyle\int \sqrt{(4x^2 + 5)}\,x \, dx$

15. $\displaystyle\int \frac{x^3}{\sqrt{x^4 - 6}}dx$

16. $\displaystyle\int \sqrt[3]{(x^3 - 9)^4}x^2 \, dx$

17. $\displaystyle\int \frac{dx}{(3x - 5)^4}$

18. $\displaystyle\int \frac{5x^2 \, dx}{\sqrt[5]{(x^3 - 9)^2}}$

Evaluate each of the following:

19. $\displaystyle\int_2^4 (\sqrt{x^2 + 9})x \, dx$

20. $\displaystyle\int_1^2 (x^4 - 3)^3 x^3 \, dx$

21. $\displaystyle\int_3^5 \frac{x \, dx}{(x^2 - 5)^2}$

22. $\displaystyle\int_0^1 (x^2 + 2x)^3(x + 1) \, dx$

23. Find the area between the x-axis and the curve $f(x) = (x - 5)^3$ from $x = 5$ to $x = 7$. Sketch $f(x)$ and shade the desired area.

24. Find the area between the x-axis and the curve $f(x) = (x + 4)^3$ from $x = -4$ to $x = 0$. Sketch $f(x)$ and shade the desired area.

25. Find the area between the x-axis and the curve $y = 1/(x - 6)^2$ from $x = 0$ to $x = 5$. Sketch the function and shade the desired area.

26. Find the area between the x-axis and the function $f(x) = 1/(x - 5)^3$ from $x = 6$ to $x = 8$. Sketch $f(x)$ and shade the desired area.

27. Consider the indefinite integral

$$\int (x^3 - 5)^{10} x\ dx$$

Why can't this indefinite integral be determined by the techniques of this section? [Of course, this indefinite integral can be determined by using the time-consuming process of expanding $(x^3 - 5)^{10}$.]

Applications

28. *Revenue flow.* If the rate of flow of revenue into a mutual fund is given by

$$R'(t) = 50t + 20t\sqrt{1 + t^2}$$

where t is given in months, find the total revenue obtained during the first 2 years.

29. *Oil leak.* An oil tanker is leaking crude oil at the rate of $B'(t)$ barrels per hour, where t is the number of hours since the leak began. If

$$B'(t) = 200t + 50$$

how many barrels of oil will have leaked into the water during the first 2 days?

30. *Population growth.* Executive Realty Corporation has recently completed a new development called Hidden Valley Estates. The population of Hidden Valley Estates has been growing at the rate of $P'(t)$ individuals per month, where t is the number of months elapsed since December 31 of the past year. If

$$P'(t) = 100 + 18t$$

find the total increase in population during the first three-quarters of the present year.

31. *Profit.* The rate of change of the annual profit of a firm is given by

$$P'(x) = 500{,}000x + 100{,}000$$

where x denotes the number of years after December 31 of a particular year. Find the equation for $P(x)$, given the initial condition that $P(2) = 1{,}000{,}000$.

32. *Cash reserves.* The rate of change of the cash reserves of a scholarship fund is given by

$$C'(x) = \frac{x}{(x^2 + 4)^2}$$

where x denotes time (in years) since the inception of the fund and $C'(x)$ is given in millions of dollars. Find the equation for $C(x)$ if the fund had 8.2 million dollars one year after its inception.

13-5 • INTEGRALS INVOLVING EXPONENTIAL AND LOGARITHMIC FUNCTIONS

In Chapter 12, we used the chain rule to derive the following rule for differentiating exponential functions: If $y = e^u$, where u is a function of x, then

$$\frac{dy}{dx} = e^u \frac{du}{dx}$$

We use this rule to find the derivative of the exponential function

$$y = e^{x^3 + 7}$$

Hence,

$$\frac{dy}{dx} = e^{x^3 + 7}(3x^2)$$

Since integration is the reverse process of differentiation, the integral of a derivative results in the original function. Thus, for the above example,

$$\int e^{x^3 + 7}(3x^2)\, dx = e^{x^3 + 7} + c$$

where c is an arbitrary constant. Note the form of the above integral. Specifically, if we let

$$\left. \begin{array}{l} u = x^3 + 7 \\[2ex] du = 3x^2\, dx \end{array} \right\} \text{Substitution}$$

then

and the integrand (the expression following the integral sign) is of the form

$$e^u\, du$$

as is illustrated below.

$$\int \overbrace{e^{x^3+7}}^{u}\ \overbrace{3x^2\, dx}^{du} = \overbrace{e^{x^3+7}}^{u} + c$$

The above discussion suggests the following rule.

Rule 13-8

If $u = f(x)$ and $du = f'(x)\, dx$, then

$$\int e^u\, du = e^u + c$$

Note that this rule is a restatement of the formula (from Section 13-1)

$$\int e^x \, dx = e^x + c$$

with $u = f(x)$ replacing x and $du = f'(x) \, dx$ replacing dx.

Rule 13-8 may be used in conjunction with the substitution principle to integrate exponential functions with base e. Consider

$$\int e^{x^8 - 5} x^7 \, dx$$

If we let $u = x^8 - 5$, then

$$du = 8x^7 \, dx \quad \Big\} \text{ Substitution}$$

Thus, we obtain

$$\int e^{x^8 - 5} x^7 \, dx = \frac{1}{8} \int e^{\overbrace{x^8 - 5}^{u}} \underbrace{8x^7 \, dx}_{du}$$

$$= \frac{1}{8} \int e^u \, du$$

$$= \frac{1}{8} e^u + c$$

$$= \frac{1}{8} e^{x^8 - 5} + c$$

Check by finding the derivative:

$$\frac{d}{dx}\left(\frac{1}{8} e^{x^8 - 5} + c\right) = \frac{1}{8} e^{x^8 - 5} (8x^7) + c = e^{x^8 - 5}(x^7)$$

• EXAMPLE 13-35

Find $\int e^{x^3 - 6} 2x^2 \, dx$.

Solution

Let $u = x^3 - 6$. Then

$$du = 3x^2 \, dx \quad \Big\} \text{ Substitution}$$

Thus, we have

$$\int e^{x^3 - 6} 2x^2 \, dx = \frac{2}{3} \int e^{\overbrace{x^3 - 6}^{u}} \underbrace{\frac{3}{2} \, 2x^2 \, dx}_{du} \qquad \text{Multiply the integrand by 3/2 to form } du.$$

$$= \frac{2}{3} \int e^u \, du \qquad \text{Multiply the integral by the reciprocal of } 3/2, \, 2/3.$$

$$= \frac{2}{3} e^u + c$$

$$= \frac{2}{3} e^{x^3 - 6} + c$$

In Section 13-1, we stated the formula

$$\int \frac{dx}{x} = \ln |x| + c$$

Using reasoning similar to that employed to develop rule 13-8 for exponential functions, we state the following rule.

Rule 13-9

If $u = f(x)$ and $du = f'(x)\, dx$, then

$$\int \frac{du}{u} = \ln |u| + c$$

Rule 13-9 may be used in conjunction with the substitution principle to integrate functions that may be expressed in the form du/u. Consider, for instance,

$$\int \frac{x\, dx}{x^2 - 1}$$

If we let $u = x^2 - 1$, then

$$du = 2x\, dx \left.\right\} \text{Substitution}$$

Hence, we have

$$\int \frac{x\, dx}{x^2 - 1} = \frac{1}{2} \int \frac{\overbrace{2x\, dx}^{du}}{\underbrace{x^2 - 1}_{u}}$$

$$= \frac{1}{2} \int \frac{du}{u}$$

$$= \frac{1}{2} \ln |u| + c$$

$$= \frac{1}{2} \ln |x^2 - 1| + c$$

• **EXAMPLE 13-36**

Find

$$\int \frac{x^6\, dx}{x^7 + 15}$$

Solution

Let $u = x^7 + 15$. Then

$$du = 7x^6\, dx \left.\right\} \text{Substitution}$$

Hence, we find

$$\int \frac{x^6 \, dx}{x^7 + 15} = \frac{1}{7} \int \overbrace{\frac{7x^6 \, dx}{\underbrace{x^7 + 15}_{u}}}^{du}$$

$$= \frac{1}{7} \int \frac{du}{u}$$

$$= \frac{1}{7} \ln |u| + c$$

$$= \frac{1}{7} \ln |x^7 + 15| + c$$

• **EXAMPLE 13-37   Revenue Flow.**

The rate of flow of revenue (in dollars) into a firm is given by

$$R'(t) = \frac{10,000,000}{5 + t} \qquad (t \geq 0)$$

where t is time (in years). Determine the total revenue flowing in during the time interval $4 \leq t \leq 20$.

Solution

We first graph $R'(t)$ in Figure 13-37. The shaded area denotes the total revenue flow that must be determined. We seek

$$\int_4^{20} R'(t) \, dt = R(20) - R(4)$$

Hence,

$$\int_4^{20} R'(t) \, dt = \int_4^{20} \frac{10,000,000}{5 + t} \, dt \qquad \begin{array}{l} \text{Substitution} \\ u = 5 + t \\ du = dt \end{array}$$

$$= \underbrace{10,000,000 \ln |5 + t|}_{R(t)} \Big|_4^{20}$$

$$= R(20) - R(4)$$

$$= 10,000,000 \ln |5 + 20| - 10,000,000 \ln |5 + 4|$$

$$= 10,000,000(\ln 25 - \ln 9)$$

$$= 10,000,000(\ln 25/9) \qquad \text{Property of logarithms}$$

$$\approx 10,000,000(1.0216512) = \$10,216,512 \qquad \text{Total revenue flow}$$

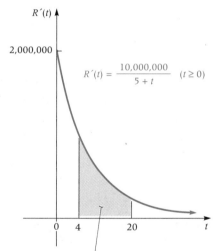

$R'(t)$

2,000,000

$R'(t) = \dfrac{10,000,000}{5 + t} \qquad (t \geq 0)$

0   4   20 t

Total revenue flow during $4 \leq t \leq 20$

FIGURE 13-37

Exercises 13-5

Determine each of the following:

1. $\int e^x \, dx$

2. $\int e^{-x} \, dx$

3. $\int e^{4x} \, dx$

4. $\int_0^1 e^{-3x} \, dx$

5. $\int e^{x/2}\,dx$ **6.** $\int 6e^{-0.3x}\,dx$

7. $\int e^{x^3-5}x^2\,dx$ **8.** $\int \dfrac{x\,dx}{e^{x^2}}$

9. $\int x^3 e^{x^4+6}\,dx$ **10.** $\int x e^{x^2+1}\,dx$

11. $\int (x+1)e^{x^2+2x}\,dx$ **12.** $\int e^{5x-2}\,dx$

13. $\int \dfrac{5\,dx}{x}$ **14.** $\int \dfrac{dx}{x+1}$

15. $\int \dfrac{x}{x^2+1}\,dx$ **16.** $\int \dfrac{x^3\,dx}{x^4-1}$

17. $\int \dfrac{6x^2\,dx}{x^3+4}$ **18.** $\int \dfrac{5x\,dx}{x^2-4}$

19. $\int \dfrac{-x\,dx}{5x^2-6}$ **20.** $\int \dfrac{-4x^2}{x^3+5}\,dx$

Evaluate each of the following.

21. $\int_0^4 e^x\,dx$ **22.** $\int_0^2 x e^{x^2/2}\,dx$

23. $\int_0^1 x e^{-x^2}\,dx$ **24.** $\int_0^1 (t+1)e^{t^2+2}\,dt$

25. $\int_1^4 (1/x)\,dx$ **26.** $\int_2^6 (8/x)\,dx$

27. $\int_1^6 (-6/x)\,dx$ **28.** $\int_1^5 (-4/t)\,dt$

Determine each of the following.

29. $\int \dfrac{(\ln x)^2}{x}\,dx$ **30.** $\int \dfrac{\ln 4x}{x}\,dx$

31. $\int \dfrac{(\ln 3x)^4}{x}\,dx$ **32.** $\int \dfrac{e^x\,dx}{5+e^x}$

33. $\int \dfrac{x-2}{x^2-4x+1}\,dx$ **34.** $\int \dfrac{x-4}{x^2-8x+5}\,dx$

35. $\int \dfrac{1}{x\ln x}\,dx$ **36.** $\int \dfrac{1}{x(\ln x)^3}\,dx$

37. $\int \dfrac{1}{x\ln x^2}\,dx$ **38.** $\int \dfrac{4}{x\ln x^2}\,dx$

39. Find the area bounded by the x-axis and $f(x) = e^{-2x}$ from $x = 0$ to $x = 1$. Sketch $f(x)$ and shade the desired area.

40. Find the area bounded by the x-axis and the curve $f(x) = 1/(x-2)$ from $x = 3$ to $x = 6$. Sketch $f(x)$ and shade the desired area.

41. Find the area bounded by the x-axis and $f(x) = 1/(x-9)$ from $x = 1$ to $x = 4$. Sketch $f(x)$ and shade the desired area.

Applications

42. *Revenue flow.* If the rate of flow of revenue into a firm is given by

$$R'(t) = \frac{10,000,000}{t+5}$$

where t is measured in years, find the total revenue obtained during the interval $0 \le t \le 4$.

43. *Revenue flow.* If the rate of flow of revenue into a firm is given by

$$R'(t) = 100t + 10e^{-t}$$

where t is measured in years, find the total revenue obtained during the interval $1 \le t \le 10$.

44. *Drug reaction.* After a certain cancer-inducing drug is injected into a mouse, cancer cells increase at the rate of $D'(t)$ cells per day, where t is the number of days following the drug injection. If

$$D'(t) = 100e^{5t}$$

find the total increase in cancer cells during the first 2 days following the drug injection.

45. *Bacteria growth.* The rate of growth of a population of bacteria is given by

$$B'(x) = \frac{10,000}{5x + 1}$$

where x denotes time in days. Find the equation for $B(x)$, given that $B(2) = 9000$.

46. *Cash reserves.* The rate of change of the cash reserves of an emergency fund is given by

$$C'(x) = xe^{x^2}$$

where x denotes time in years since the fund's inception and $C'(x)$ is given in thousands of dollars. Find the equation for $C(x)$ if the fund's value was 30 thousand dollars 2 years after its inception.

13-6   • INTEGRATION BY PARTS

Try to determine the indefinite integral

$$\int xe^x \, dx$$

If we attempt to use the substitution principle, we let $u = x$; then $du = dx$, and we realize that $\int xe^x \, dx$ cannot be expressed in the form $\int e^u \, du$ since $x \, dx$ does not equal and cannot be modified (by multiplication by a constant) to equal du. This problem cannot be integrated by any of the substitution techniques discussed up to this point.

A useful technique to solve the above problem is integration by parts. The integration by parts technique involves application of the formula below.

SUMMARY

Integration by Parts

If u and v are differentiable functions of x, then

$$\int u \, dv = uv - \int v \, du$$

The above formula is derived from the product rule for differentiation as follows: Let u and v be differentiable functions of x. Then, by the product rule,

$$\frac{d}{dx}(uv) = u\frac{dv}{dx} + v\frac{du}{dx}$$

Integrating both sides with respect to x gives

$$\int \frac{d}{dx}(uv)\, dx = \int u\frac{dv}{dx}\, dx + \int v\frac{du}{dx}\, dx$$

Since the integral of the derivative of uv is uv, the left-hand side of the above formula becomes uv, so that the formula is rewritten as

$$uv = \int u\, dv + \int v\, du$$

Solving the above equation for $\int u\, dv$ gives

$$\int u\, dv = uv - \int v\, du$$

The arbitrary constant is included when $\int v\, du$ is determined.

To apply integration by parts to evaluate the indefinite integral

$$\int xe^x\, dx$$

we must express the integral in the form

$$\int u\, dv$$

Also, we must determine u and dv so that $\int v\, du$ can be easily determined by one of our known integration techniques. Note that if

$$u = x \quad \text{and} \quad dv = e^x\, dx$$

then

$$du = dx \quad \text{and} \quad v = \int e^x\, dx$$
$$= e^x$$

> Omit the constant of integration here. Include it when $\int v\, du$ is determined.

Thus, applying the integration by parts formula, we have

$$\int u\, dv = uv - \int v\, du$$

or

$$\int x\, e^x\, dx = xe^x - \int e^x\, dx$$

Note that $\int e^x \, dx$ is easily determined to be $e^x + c$. Thus, our final answer is

$$\int xe^x \, dx = xe^x - e^x + c$$

The integration by parts technique depends on the proper choice of u and dv. To illustrate this point, we attempt the above problem with a different choice of u and dv.

Wrong Choice of u and dv.   Let

$$u = e^x \quad \text{and} \quad dv = x \, dx$$

then

$$du = e^x \, dx \quad \text{and} \quad v = \int x \, dx$$

$$= \frac{1}{2}x^2$$

so that

$$\int u \, dv = uv - \int v \, du$$

becomes

$$\int e^x x \, dx = e^x \left[(1/2)x^2 \right] - \int (1/2)x^2 e^x \, dx$$

Note that the integral $\int (1/2)x^2 e^x \, dx$ is more complex than the original integral $\int xe^x \, dx$ and, thus, cannot be determined by any of the substitution techniques discussed up to this point. This indicates a wrong choice of u and dv.

Arbitrary Constant of Integration

When using the integration by parts formula,

$$\int u \, dv = uv - \int v \, du$$

v is determined by integrating dv. At this point, we omit the arbitrary constant of integration and include it at the end of the procedure when we evaluate $\int v \, du$. This simplifies the integration by parts process. Its legitimacy is shown by replacing v with $v + c$ (where c is an arbitrary constant) in the integration by parts formula to obtain the result

$$\int u \, dv = u(v + c) - \int (v + c) \, du$$

$$= uv + uc - \int v \, du - \int c \, du$$

$$= uv + uc - \int v \, du - cu$$

Since $uc = cu$, the above equation reduces to the integration by parts formula

$$\int u\ dv = uv - \int v\ du$$

We now provide another example of the application of integration by parts.

• **EXAMPLE 13-38** _____

Evaluate $\int x\sqrt{x - 2}\ dx$.

Solution

Let

$$u = x \quad \text{and} \quad dv = \sqrt{x - 2}\ dx.$$

Then

$$du = dx \quad \text{and} \quad v = \int (x - 2)^{1/2}\ dx$$
$$= \frac{2}{3}(x - 2)^{3/2}$$

Applying the integration by parts formula, we have

$$\int u\ dv = uv - \int v\ du$$

or

$$\int \underbrace{x}_{u}\ \underbrace{\sqrt{x - 2}\ dx}_{dv} = x\frac{2}{3}(x - 2)^{3/2} - \int \frac{2}{3}(x - 2)^{3/2}\ dx$$
$$= \frac{2}{3}x(x - 2)^{3/2} - \frac{4}{15}(x - 2)^{5/2} + c$$

SUMMARY

Guidelines for Choosing u and dv

1. Make certain that dv can be integrated.
2. Make certain that the integral $\int v\ du$ either can be integrated or is of a simpler form than the original integral, $\int u\ dv$.

• **EXAMPLE 13-39** _____

Evaluate $\int x \ln x\ dx$.

Solution

Let

$$u = \ln x \quad \text{and} \quad dv = x\ dx$$

Then

$$du = \frac{1}{x} dx \quad \text{and} \quad v = \int x \, dx$$

$$= \frac{1}{2}x^2$$

Applying the integration by parts formula, we have

$$\int u \, dv = uv - \int v \, du$$

or

$$\int \underbrace{(\ln x)}_{u} \underbrace{x \, dx}_{dv} = \underbrace{(\ln x)}_{u} \underbrace{\frac{1}{2}x^2}_{v} - \int \underbrace{\frac{1}{2}x^2}_{v} \underbrace{\frac{1}{x} dx}_{du}$$

$$= \frac{1}{2}x^2 \ln x - \int \frac{1}{2}x \, dx$$

$$= \frac{1}{2}x^2 \ln x - \frac{1}{4}x^2 + c$$

• **EXAMPLE 13-40**

Evaluate

$$\int \frac{xe^x}{(x+1)^2} dx$$

Solution

Remember that we must choose u and dv so that $\int v \, du$ is evaluated by one of our known integration techniques. Let

$$u = xe^x \quad \text{and} \quad dv = \frac{1}{(x+1)^2} dx$$

Then

$$du = (xe^x + e^x) \, dx \quad \text{and} \quad v = \int \frac{1}{(x+1)^2} dx$$

$$= (x+1)e^x \, dx \qquad \qquad = -\frac{1}{x+1}$$

Using the integration by parts formula, we have

$$\int u \, dv = uv - \int v \, du$$

or

$$\int \frac{xe^x}{(x+1)^2} dx = \underbrace{xe^x}_{u} \underbrace{\left(-\frac{1}{x+1}\right)}_{v} - \int \underbrace{-\frac{1}{x+1}}_{v} \underbrace{(x+1)e^x \, dx}_{du}$$

$$= -\frac{xe^x}{x+1} + \int e^x \, dx$$

Since $\int e^x \, dx = e^x + c$, the above becomes

$$\int \frac{xe^x}{(x+1)^2} dx = -\frac{xe^x}{x+1} + e^x + c$$

Sometimes we must use the integration by parts formula repeatedly in a given problem. The next example illustrates such a case.

• **EXAMPLE 13-41** _____

Evaluate $\int x^2 e^x \, dx$.

Solution

Let

$$u = x^2 \quad \text{and} \quad dv = e^x \, dx$$

Then

$$du = 2x \, dx \quad \text{and} \quad v = \int e^x \, dx$$
$$= e^x$$

Using the integration by parts formula, we have

$$\int u \, dv = uv - \int v \, du$$

or

$$\int \underbrace{x^2}_{u} \underbrace{e^x \, dx}_{dv} = \underbrace{x^2}_{u} \underbrace{e^x}_{v} - \int \underbrace{2x}_{} \underbrace{e^x}_{v} \underbrace{dx}_{du} \tag{1}$$

Note that $\int 2xe^x \, dx$ is of a form simpler than the original integral. Thus, we apply the integration by parts formula again to evaluate $\int 2xe^x \, dx$. Letting

$$u = 2x \quad \text{and} \quad dv = e^x \, dx$$

then

$$du = 2 \, dx \quad \text{and} \quad v = \int e^x \, dx$$
$$= e^x$$

Again, using the integration by parts formula, we have

$$\int u \, dv = uv - \int v \, du$$

or

$$\int 2xe^x \, dx = \underbrace{2xe^x}_{u \quad v} - \int \underbrace{e^x}_{v} \underbrace{2 \, dx}_{du}$$
$$= 2xe^x - \int 2e^x \, dx$$

Substituting this result into equation (1), we have

$$\int x^2 e^x \, dx = x^2 e^x - \left(2xe^x - \int 2e^x \, dx \right)$$
$$= x^2 e^x - 2xe^x + \int 2e^x \, dx$$
$$= x^2 e^x - 2xe^x + 2e^x + c$$
$$= (x^2 - 2x + 2)e^x + c$$

Application

• **EXAMPLE 13-42** **Marginal Cost/Cost.**

The marginal cost (in dollars per unit) for some product is given by

$$C'(x) = \ln x \qquad (x > 1)$$

where x denotes the number of units produced. Find the increase in total cost as the number of units produced changes from $x = 5$ to $x = 10$.

Solution

As discussed in Section 13-2, we seek the value of the definite integral,

$$\int_5^{10} C'(x)\ dx = \int_5^{10} \ln x\ dx$$

We first evaluate the corresponding indefinite integral by letting

$$u = \ln x \qquad \text{and} \qquad dv = dx$$

Then

$$du = \frac{1}{x}\ dx \qquad \text{and} \qquad v = \int dx$$
$$= x$$

Using the integration by parts formula, we have

$$\int u\ dv = uv - \int v\ du$$

$$C(x) = x \ln x - \int x \cdot \frac{1}{x}\ dx = x \ln x - \int dx$$
$$= x \ln x - x + c$$

Hence,

$$\int_5^{10} \ln x\ dx = (x \ln x - x)\ \Big|_5^{10}$$
$$= C(10) - C(5)$$
$$= (10 \ln 10 - 10) - (5 \ln 5 - 5)$$
$$= 10 \ln 10 - 5 \ln 5 - 5$$
$$\approx 10(2.3026) - 5(1.6094) - 5$$
$$\approx \$9.98 \qquad \text{Increase in total cost}$$

We now summarize correct choices of u and dv for some of the most common integral forms evaluated by integration by parts.

SUMMARY

Common Integral Forms and Correct Choices of u and dv

Assume that n, k, a, and b are constants.

1. For integrals of the form $\int x^n e^{kx}\ dx$, let $u = x^n$ and $dv = e^{kx}\ dx$. (See Example 13-41 and the illustrative example on page 854.

continues

SUMMARY—*Continued*

2. For integrals of the form $\int x^n (\ln x)^k\, dx$, let $u = (\ln x)^k$ and $dv = x^n\, dx$. (See Example 13-39.)

3. For integrals of the form $\int x(ax + b)^n\, dx$, let $u = x$ and $dv = (ax + b)^n\, dx$. (See Example 13-38.)

Exercises 13-6

Use integration by parts to find each of the following integrals.

1. $\int xe^{3x}\, dx$

2. $\int x\sqrt{x + 5}\, dx$

3. $\int \dfrac{x}{\sqrt{x - 3}}\, dx$

4. $\int xe^{-5x}\, dx$

5. $\int \dfrac{x}{e^x}\, dx$

6. $\int \ln x\, dx$

7. $\int \dfrac{x}{(x - 4)^3}\, dx$

8. $\int x(x + 6)^4\, dx$

9. $\int \dfrac{x}{e^{4x}}\, dx$

10. $\int x^2 \ln x\, dx$

11. $\int x^3 \ln x\, dx$

12. $\int \dfrac{xe^{3x}}{(3x + 1)^2}\, dx$

13. $\int x(x - 9)^5\, dx$

14. $\int x\sqrt{x - 6}\, dx$

15. $\int \dfrac{x}{(6 + 5x)^2}\, dx$

16. $\int \dfrac{x + 2}{e^x}\, dx$

17. $\int \dfrac{x}{\sqrt{5 + 3x}}\, dx$

18. $\int \dfrac{\ln x}{x^4}\, dx$

19. $\int 3x\sqrt{3x + 7}\, dx$

20. $\int x(e^x - 1)\, dx$

21. $\int x \ln 9x\, dx$

22. $\int 5x(5x - 1)^3\, dx$

23. $\int x^3 e^x\, dx$

24. $\int x^4 e^x\, dx$

25. Referring to Exercises 23 and 24 above, verify the formula

$$\int x^n e^x\, dx = x^n e^x - n \int x^{n-1} e^x\, dx$$

where n is a positive integer.

26. Use the integration by parts formula twice to evaluate $\int x^2(x + 7)^{10}\, dx$.

Use integration by parts for Exercises 27–29.

27. $\int (\ln x)^2\, dx$

28. $\int (\ln x)^3\, dx$

29. Verify the formula

$$\int (\ln x)^n \, dx = x(\ln x)^n - n \int (\ln x)^{n-1} \, dx$$

where n is a positive integer.

30. Determine the area bounded by the x-axis and the curve $f(x) = \ln x$ from $x = 1$ to $x = 3$.

31. Determine the area bounded by the x-axis and the curve $f(x) = xe^x$ from $x = 0$ to $x = 2$.

32. Determine the area bounded by the x-axis and the curve $f(x) = x \ln x$ from $x = 1$ to $x = 3$.

33. Determine the area bounded by the x-axis and the curve $f(x) = x^3 e^{x^2}$ from $x = 0$ to $x = 1$.

For Exercises 34–39, some require integration by parts, while others require techniques discussed in this chapter. Find each of the following.

34. $\int 2x^3 e^{x^3} \, dx$ **35.** $\int x^2 e^x \, dx$ **36.** $\int 2xe^x \, dx$

37. $\int \frac{1}{x+6} \, dx$ **38.** $\int \frac{x}{x+6} \, dx$ **39.** $\int \frac{x}{2x+9} \, dx$

Applications

40. *Revenue.* For a given product, a company's sales revenue changes with time at a rate of $R'(t)$ dollars per month, where t is given in months. Find the total sales revenue accumulated during the time interval $0 \le t \le 1$ if

$$R'(t) = 10{,}000te^t$$

41. *Profit.* For a given product, a company's profit changes at a rate given by

$$P'(t) = 2000te^{0.2t}$$

where t is given in months. Find the total profit accumulated during the first 6 months.

42. *Population growth.* The population of a town grows at a rate given by

$$P'(t) = 200te^{2t}$$

where t is in years. Find the total accumulated population growth during the first 4 years.

43. *Medical research.* After a certain experimental drug is injected into a mouse infected with cancer, cancer cells decrease at the rate of $D'(t)$ cells per day, where t is the number of days following the drug injection. If

$$D'(t) = 10{,}000te^{-t}$$

find the total accumulated decrease in cancer cells during the first 2 days following the drug injection.

44. *Marginal cost/Cost.* Find the total cost equation, $C(x)$, if the marginal cost function is given by

$$C'(x) = 10 \ln x \qquad (x > 1)$$

where x denotes the number of units produced and $C(1) = 20$.

45. *Marginal revenue/Revenue.* Find the sales revenue equation, $R(x)$, if the marginal revenue function is given by

$$R'(x) = x^3(\ln x) \qquad (x > 1)$$

where x denotes the number of units sold and $R(1) = 80$.

13-7 • USING TABLES OF INTEGRALS

In Sections 13-4 and 13-5, we integrated functions by using the substitution principle in conjunction with the formulas

$$\int u^n \, du = \frac{1}{n+1} u^{n+1} + c \qquad (n \neq -1)$$

$$\int e^u \, du = e^u + c$$

$$\int \frac{du}{u} = \ln |u| + c$$

These formulas allow us to integrate a variety of functions. However, the functions are limited to those that can be expressed in one of these forms. There are many functions that must be integrated by other methods.

Table 9 of Appendix C lists additional integral forms. Such a table is called a **table of integrals.** A more complete table of integrals appears in *CRC Standard Mathematical Tables.** Table 13-2 is an abridged version of a table of integrals. We now illustrate how a table of integrals is used.

TABLE 13-2   **Table of integrals (Abridged)**

1. $\int \dfrac{du}{\sqrt{a^2 + u^2}} = \ln |u + \sqrt{a^2 + u^2}| + c$

2. $\int \dfrac{du}{a^2 - u^2} = \dfrac{1}{2a} \ln \left| \dfrac{a+u}{a-u} \right| + c$

3. $\int u^n e^u \, du = u^n e^u - n \int u^{n-1} e^u \, du$

4. $\int \dfrac{du}{u^2(a + bu)} = -\dfrac{1}{au} + \dfrac{b}{a^2} \ln \left| \dfrac{a + bu}{u} \right| + c$

• **EXAMPLE 13-43** _____

Find

$$\int \frac{dx}{\sqrt{36 + x^2}}$$

Solution

Scanning the integral forms in Table 13-2, note that this integral is of the form

$$\int \frac{du}{\sqrt{a^2 + u^2}} = \ln |u + \sqrt{a^2 + u^2}| + c$$

with $a^2 = 36$, $u = x$, and $du = dx$. Substituting 36 for a^2, x for u, and dx for du into this form, we have

$$\int \frac{dx}{\sqrt{36 + x^2}} = \ln |x + \sqrt{36 + x^2}| + c$$

_____ •

_____

*CRC Standard Mathematical Tables. 27th ed. Boca Raton, Fl.: CRC Press, 1984.

• **EXAMPLE 13-44** _____

Find

$$\int \frac{dx}{x^2(3 - 5x)}$$

Solution

Scanning the integral forms of Table 13-2, we see that this integral is of the form

$$\int \frac{du}{u^2(a + bu)} = -\frac{1}{au} + \frac{b}{a^2} \ln \left| \frac{a + bu}{u} \right| + c$$

with $a = 3$, $b = -5$, $u = x$, and $du = dx$. Substituting 3 for a, -5 for b, x for u, and dx for du into this form, we obtain

$$\int \frac{dx}{x^2(3 - 5x)} = -\frac{1}{3x} + \frac{-5}{3^2} \ln \left| \frac{3 - 5x}{x} \right| + c$$
$$\qquad\quad {\uparrow}\;\; {\uparrow} \atop {a}\;\; {b}$$

$$= -\frac{1}{3x} - \frac{5}{9} \ln \left| \frac{3 - 5x}{x} \right| + c$$

• **EXAMPLE 13-45** _____

Find $\int x^2 e^x\, dx$.

Solution

Scanning the integral forms in Table 13-2, we determine this integral to be of the form

$$\int u^n e^u\, du = u^n e^u - n \int u^{n-1} e^u\, du$$

with $n = 2$, $u = x$, and $du = dx$. Substituting 2 for n, x for u, and dx for du into this form yields

$$\int x^2 e^x\, dx = x^2 e^x - 2 \int x e^x\, dx$$

In this case, we see that the initial solution actually contains an indefinite integral that must be evaluated. Examining its nature, we see that we can use the same form to evaluate $\int x e^x\, dx$. This time $n = 1$. Hence,

$$\int x e^x\, dx = x e^x - \int e^x\, dx$$
$$= x e^x - e^x + c_1$$

Combining the two results, we see that

$$\int x^2 e^x\, dx = x^2 e^x - 2 \int x e^x\, dx$$
$$= x^2 e^x - 2(x e^x - e^x + c_1)$$
$$= x^2 e^x - 2x e^x + 2e^x - 2c_1$$
$$= x^2 e^x - 2x e^x + 2e^x + c$$

where $-2c_1 = c$ is an arbitrary constant.

Application

• **EXAMPLE 13-46**   **Velocity/Distance.**

The velocity, v (in feet per second), of a moving particle is given by

$$v(t) = \frac{1}{t(5 - t)} \qquad (1 \le t \le 4)$$

where t denotes the time (in seconds) elapsed. Find the distance traveled by the particle during the time interval $1 \le t \le 4$.

Solution

Since $v(t) = S'(t)$, where $S(t)$ denotes distance (in feet), we seek the value of the definite integral

$$\int_1^4 v(t) \, dt = \int_1^4 \frac{1}{t(5 - t)} \, dt$$

Scanning the integral forms of Table 9 in Appendix c, we see that this integral is of the form

$$\int \frac{du}{u(a + bu)} = -\frac{1}{a} \ln \left| \frac{a + bu}{u} \right| + c$$

with $u = t$, $du = dt$, $a = 5$, and $b = -1$. Using the above form,

$$\int_1^4 \frac{1}{t(5 - t)} \, dt = -\frac{1}{5} \ln \left| \frac{5 - t}{t} \right| \Big|_1^4$$

$$= (-1/5) \left[\ln | (5 - 4)/4 | - \ln | (5 - 1)/1 | \right]$$

$$= (-1/5) (\ln | 1/4 | - \ln | 4 |)$$

$$= (-1/5)(\ln 1 - \ln 4 - \ln 4) \qquad \text{Property of logs}$$

$$= (-1/5)(0 - 2 \ln 4) \qquad \ln 1 = 0$$

$$= (-1/5)(-\ln 4^2) \qquad \text{Property of logs}$$

$$\approx (1/5)(2.7726)$$

$$\approx 0.55 \text{ feet} \qquad \text{Distance traveled}$$

Exercises 13-7

Using Table 13-2 find each of the following:

1. $\displaystyle\int \frac{dx}{\sqrt{81 + x^2}}$

2. $\displaystyle\int \frac{dx}{\sqrt{x^2 + 64}}$

3. $\displaystyle\int_0^8 \frac{dx}{\sqrt{x^2 + 36}}$

4. $\displaystyle\int \frac{dx}{4 - x^2}$

5. $\displaystyle\int \frac{-7 \, dx}{81 - x^2}$

6. $\displaystyle\int \frac{dx}{x^2(5 + 3x)}$

7. $\displaystyle\int \frac{3 \, dx}{x^2(4 - 7x)}$

8. $\displaystyle\int x^2 e^{5x} \, dx$

9. $\displaystyle\int_0^1 x^3 e^x \, dx$

10. $\displaystyle\int_0^2 \frac{dx}{\sqrt{x^2 + 25}}$

Using Table 9 of Appendix C, find each of the following:

11. $\displaystyle\int \ln 5x \, dx$

12. $\displaystyle\int \ln(3x - 1) \, dx$

13. $\displaystyle\int \frac{dx}{x\sqrt{5 - 2x}}$

14. $\displaystyle\int \frac{dx}{x\sqrt{2 + 6x}}$

15. $\displaystyle\int \frac{dx}{\sqrt{x^2 - 100}}$

16. $\displaystyle\int \frac{dx}{x^2 - 64}$

17. $\displaystyle\int \frac{dx}{x\sqrt{25 - x^2}}$

18. $\displaystyle\int \frac{dx}{x\sqrt{x^2 + 4}}$

19. $\displaystyle\int (36 - x^2)^{-3/2} \, dx$

20. $\displaystyle\int_0^7 \frac{dx}{(x^2 + 49)^{3/2}}$

21. $\displaystyle\int (\ln x)^2 \, dx$

22. $\displaystyle\int (\ln x)^3 \, dx$

23. $\displaystyle\int x^2 \ln x \, dx$

24. $\displaystyle\int x^3 \ln x \, dx$

25. $\displaystyle\int (x^2 + 25)^{-3/2} \, dx$

26. $\displaystyle\int (16 - x^2)^{-3/2} \, dx$

27. $\displaystyle\int (x + 1) \ln(x + 1) \, dx$

28. $\displaystyle\int (x + 1)^2 \ln(x + 1) \, dx$

29. $\displaystyle\int \frac{4}{x(3 + 7x)} \, dx$

30. $\displaystyle\int \frac{6}{x\sqrt{4 - x^2}} \, dx$

Applications

31. *Velocity/Distance.* The velocity, v (in feet per minute), of a moving particle is given by

$$v(t) = \frac{1}{64 - t^2} \qquad (0 \le t \le 6)$$

where t denotes time (in minutes) elapsed. Find the total distance traveled by the particle over the time interval $0 \le t \le 6$.

32. *Marginal profit/Profit.* The marginal profit (in dollars per unit) for some product is given by

$$P'(x) = \frac{1}{x^2 - 100} \qquad (x > 10)$$

where x denotes the number of units produced and sold. Find the increase in profit as the number of units produced and sold changes from $x = 11$ to $x = 15$.

Water pollution. Raw sewage discharged into a bay is accumulating at the rate of $R'(t)$ gallons per hour, where t denotes the time (in hours) elapsed. For Exercises 33 and 34, find the total amount of sewage accumulated during the time interval $0 \le t \le 10$.

33. $R'(t) = \dfrac{200}{\sqrt{t^2 + 1}} \qquad (t \ge 0)$

34. $R'(t) = 500 \left(1 - \dfrac{1}{\sqrt{t^2 + 1}} \right) \qquad (t \ge 0)$

CHAPTER 13 HIGHLIGHTS

• *Concepts*

Your ability to answer the following questions is one indicator of the depth of your mastery of this chapter's important concepts. Note that the questions are grouped under various topic headings. For any question that you cannot answer, refer to the appropriate section of the chapter indicated by the topic heading. Pay particular attention to the boxes within a section.

13-1 ANTIDIFFERENTIATION

1. If $F(x)$ is an antiderivative of $f(x)$, then $F'(x) =$ _____.
2. If a function has two antiderivatives, they differ by only a(n) _____.
3. State and explain each of the following rules:
   a) Power rule
   b) Constant multiplier rule
   c) Sum or difference rule

4. $\int k\, dx =$ _____
5. $\int e^x\, dx =$ _____
6. $\int e^{kx}\, dx =$ _____
7. $\int x^{-1}\, dx =$ _____

8. Explain the term *marginal tax rate*.

13-2 THE DEFINITE INTEGRAL AND AREA UNDER A CURVE

9. Explain each of the following terms: definite integral, limits of integration, Riemann sum.
10. Explain the fundamental theorem of calculus.
11. Give the procedure for finding areas.
12. Explain how to find an area where a portion of the area lies above the x-axis and a portion lies below the x-axis.

13-3 AREA BETWEEN TWO CURVES

13. Explain, using graphs, how to find the area between two curves.
14. Explain the term *consumers' surplus,* and indicate how it is determined.
15. Explain the term *producers' surplus,* and indicate how it is determined.

13-4 INTEGRATION BY SUBSTITUTION

16. State the rule for determining $\int u^n\, du$. Explain the quantity du.

13-5 INTEGRALS INVOLVING EXPONENTIAL AND LOGARITHMIC FUNCTIONS

17. State the rule for determining $\int e^u\, du$. Explain the quantity du.
18. State the rule for determining $\int du/u$. Explain the quantity du.

13-6 INTEGRATION BY PARTS

19. State the formula for integration by parts.

13-7 USING TABLES OF INTEGRALS

20. Explain the term *tables of integrals*.

REVIEW EXERCISES

• *Antidifferentiation*

Find the indefinite integral for Exercises 1–16.

1. $\int x^4\,dx$ **2.** $\int dx/x^2$ **3.** $\int (20/x)\,dx$ **4.** $\int e^x\,dx$

5. $\int e^{-x}\,dx$ **6.** $\int (7/x)\,dx$ **7.** $\int 7\,dx$ **8.** $\int x\,dx$

9. $\int (5x^4 + 6x^2 - 8x + 4)\,dx$ **10.** $\int (x^3 - 2x + 7)\,dx$

11. $\int (4x^{-1} + e^{6x})\,dx$ **12.** $\int (x^{-1} - x^{-4} - e^{-x})\,dx$

13. $\int [(4 - x^6)/x^2]\,dx$ **14.** $\int [(8x - e^x)/xe^x]\,dx$

15. $\int (x - 5)(x + 5)\,dx$ **16.** $\int [(x^2 - 9)/(x + 3)]\,dx$

17. *Marginal cost.* The marginal cost for some product is given by

$$C'(x) = 9x^2 + 4x - 1$$

where x is the production level. Find the cost function, $C(x)$, if the fixed cost is $5000.

18. *Velocity/Distance.* The velocity, v, of a moving particle after t seconds have elapsed is given by

$$v(t) = 9t^2$$

Determine the formula for the distance traveled, $S(t)$, by the particle after t seconds have elapsed if $S(0) = 5$.

• *The Definite Integral and Area*

Evaluate Exercises 19–24.

19. $\int_1^4 (8x + 2)\,dx$ **20.** $\int_1^3 (6x^2 - 2x + 4)\,dx$

21. $\int_2^5 (20/x)\,dx$ **22.** $\int_0^1 e^x\,dx$

23. $\int_1^4 (40/\sqrt{x})\,dx$ **24.** $\int_0^2 e^{-4x}\,dx$

Area. For Exercises 25–29, find the area between the x-axis and the graph of $f(x)$ over the indicated interval. Include a graph and shade the desired area.

25. $f(x) = -x^2 + 36$ from $x = 0$ to $x = 6$
26. $f(x) = -x^2 + 16$ from $x = -4$ to $x = 4$
27. $f(x) = x^4 + 10$ from $x = 0$ to $x = 2$
28. $f(x) = -2x^2 + 6x$ from $x = 0$ to $x = 8$
29. $f(x) = x^2 - 4$ from $x = 0$ to $x = 4$
30. Find the area between two curves, $f(x) = x^2$ and $g(x) = 4x$, from $x = 1$ to $x = 2$. Graph both functions and shade the desired area.
31. Find the area between two curves, $f(x) = -x^2 + 16$ and $g(x) = x^2 - 16$, from $x = -4$ to $x = 4$. Graph both functions and shade the desired area.

Consumers' and producers' surpluses. Find the consumers' and producers' surpluses for Exercises 32 and 33.

32. $p = D(q) = (q - 10)^2, p = S(q) = q^2 + 20$
33. $p = D(q) = -4q + 56, p = S(q) = 2q + 8$

● *Integration by Substitution*

Determine Exercises 34–43.

34. $\int (x^2 + 8)^6 x \, dx$

35. $\int (x^4 + 6x)^5 (4x^3 + 6) \, dx$

36. $\int e^{x+4} \, dx$

37. $\int e^{x^2+6} x \, dx$

38. $\int x^2 \sqrt{x^3 + 9} \, dx$

39. $\int [x/(x^2 + 4)] \, dx$

40. $\int [x^2/(x^3 + 6)^7] \, dx$

41. $\int [(\ln 5x)^3/x] \, dx$

42. $\int [e^x/(7 + e^x)] \, dx$

43. $\int (x^2 + 10x - 7)^6 (x + 5) \, dx$

● *Integration by Parts*

Use integration by parts to determine Exercises 44–47.

44. $\int xe^{8x} \, dx$

45. $\int x\sqrt{x - 8} \, dx$

46. $\int x \ln 4x \, dx$

47. $\int [x/(8 + 5x)] \, dx$

● *Tables of Integrals*

Use Table 9 of Appendix C to determine Exercises 48–55.

48. $\int \dfrac{1}{\sqrt{x^2 + 25}} \, dx$

49. $\int \dfrac{1}{7 - x} \, dx$

50. $\int \ln (4x + 5) \, dx$

51. $\int \dfrac{1}{x\sqrt{7 - 2x}} \, dx$

52. $\int \dfrac{1}{\sqrt{x^2 - 36}} \, dx$

53. $\int (x^2 + 16)^{-3/2} \, dx$

54. $\int (x + 3) \ln (x + 3) \, dx$

55. $\int x^2 e^{8x} \, dx$

Applications

56. *Revenue.* The rate of flow of revenue (in dollars) into a firm is given by

$$R'(t) = 200t + 50e^{-t}$$

where t is given in years. Find the total revenue gained during the interval $0 \le t \le 5$.

57. *Population growth.* The population of a given community has been growing at the rate of $P'(t)$ individuals per month, where t is the number of months elapsed since December 31 of the past year. If

$$P'(t) = 0.25te^t$$

find the total increase in the population during the first 8 months of this year.

14

FURTHER TOPICS
OF INTEGRATION

Introductory Application

Probability: Interarrival Time

The interarrival time, x (i.e., the time between two successive arrivals), of customers at a particular bank is exponentially distributed, with $k = 10$. Find the probability that the interarrival time is between 0.1 and 0.5 minute.

In this chapter, we will learn that an exponentially distributed random variable has a density function typified by the graph of Figure 14-A. Furthermore, the above probability is given by the shaded area under the graph of the density function in Figure 14-A. This problem is solved in Example 14-11.

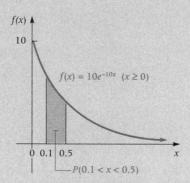

FIGURE 14-A

14-1 • CONTINUOUS MONEY FLOW

In previous sections of this text, we have encountered situations where money flowed into a firm's treasury at a rate of $R'(t)$ dollars, where t denotes time. In this section, we will consider such problems under the added assumption that the money flow, once received, earns interest that is compounded continuously at a nominal rate, r. In order to simplify our notation, we will use $f(x)$, instead of $R'(t)$, to denote the rate of money flow. Also, we assume that x denotes time in years; therefore, $f(x)$ denotes an annual rate of money flow, and r denotes an annual rate at which interest is compounded continuously.

There are many business situations (as when chain stores, large manufacturing operations, or toll roads and bridges receive revenues) where the flow of revenue is most accurately approximated by a continuous flow of money into a fund. An analogy can be drawn between a liquid flowing into a container and money flowing into a fund, as illustrated in Figure 14-1. Again, $f(x)$ denotes the rate of money flow (in dollars per year).

We now review the case where the continuous money flow does not earn interest.

Total Money Flow

If money flows into a fund at a rate, $f(x)$, during a time interval, $0 \le x \le t$, then the total amount of money accumulated is given by

$$\int_0^t f(x)\ dx$$

This is the area under the graph of $f(x)$, as shown in Figure 14-1.

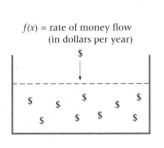

$f(x)$ = rate of money flow
(in dollars per year)

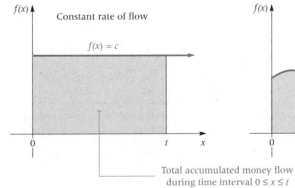

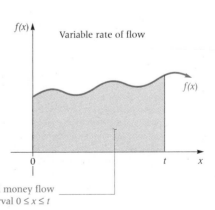

Total accumulated money flow
during time interval $0 \le x \le t$

FIGURE 14-1

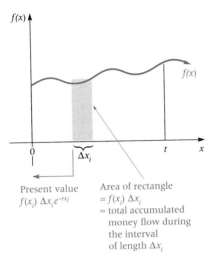

Present value
$f(x_i) \Delta x_i e^{-rx_i}$

Area of rectangle
$= f(x_i) \Delta x_i$
$\approx$ total accumulated
money flow during
the interval
of length Δx_i

FIGURE 14-2

Interest-Earning Money Flows

We now consider the case where the continuous money flow earns interest. We will develop formulas for the present and future values of such money flows. We first begin with present value by considering the graph of Figure 14-2. Note that the area of the rectangle at $x = x_i$, $f(x_i) \Delta x_i$, approximates the total (accumulated) money flow during the time interval of length Δx_i. The present value of this incremental accumulated money flow is given by

$$f(x_i) \ \Delta x_i e^{-rx_i}$$

where r is the annual interest rate compounded continuously. The sum of all such incremental present values, where Δx_i gets smaller and smaller (or, equivalently, as the number of such rectangles increases without bound), results in the definite integral given below.

$$\text{Present value} = \int_0^t f(x) \ e^{-rx} \ dx$$

We note that the **present value** is the single-sum equivalent at time $x = 0$ of the total money flow including interest earned at an annual rate, r, compounded continuously during the time interval.

The **future value** of the continuous money flow is the total accumulated money flow plus interest earned during the time interval. The future value is determined by multiplying the present value by e^{rt}. Thus, the future value is given by the definite integral below.

$$\text{Future value} = e^{rt} \int_0^t f(x) \ e^{-rx} \ dx$$

or

$$\text{Future value} = e^{rt}(\text{present value})$$

We summarize these results below.

Present and Future Values

If money flows into a fund at a rate of $f(x)$ dollars per year (where x denotes time in years) and is compounded continuously at an annual interest rate, r, during the time interval $0 \leq x \leq t$, then

1. The present value of the money flow is given by

$$\text{present value} = \int_0^t f(x) \ e^{-rx} \ dx$$

continues

Present and Future Values—*Continued*

2. The future value, which is the total accumulated money flow including interest, is given by

$$\text{future value} = e^{rt} \int_0^t f(x)\, e^{-rx}\, dx$$

or

$$\text{future value} = e^{rt}(\text{present value})$$

The interpretation of these results is illustrated in Figure 14-3.

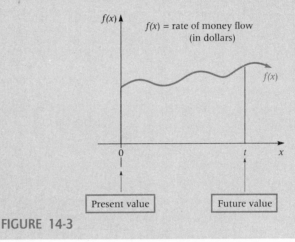

FIGURE 14-3

• **EXAMPLE 14-1** _____

Revenues from a manufacturing operation flow continuously into a firm's treasury at the rate of $f(x)$ dollars per year where

$$f(x) = 60{,}000$$

and x denotes time in years.

a) Find the total money flow at the end of 5 years (or, in other words, over the time interval $0 \le x \le 5$).

b) If the money flow, over the time interval $0 \le x \le 5$, is compounded continuously at 6%, find its present value.

c) If the money flow, over the time interval $0 \le x \le 5$, is compounded continuously at 6%, find its future value.

Solutions

a) The *total money flow (without interest)* is given by

$$\int_0^5 f(x)\, dx = \int_0^5 60{,}000\, dx$$

$$= 60{,}000x \Big|_0^5$$

$$= 60{,}000(5) - 60{,}000(0)$$

$$= \$300{,}000 \qquad \text{Total Money Flow}$$

b) The *present value*, at 6% compounded continuously, of the money flow is given by

$$\text{present value} = \int_0^5 f(x) \, e^{-rx} \, dx$$

$$= \int_0^5 60{,}000 e^{-0.06x} \, dx$$

$$= \frac{60{,}000}{-0.06} \int_0^5 \overbrace{e^{-0.06x}}^{u} \underbrace{(-0.06) \, dx}_{du}$$

$$= -1{,}000{,}000 e^{-0.06x} \Big|_0^5$$

$$= -1{,}000{,}000(e^{-0.06(5)} - e^{-0.06(0)})$$

$$= -1{,}000{,}000(e^{-0.30} - 1)$$

$$\approx -1{,}000{,}000(0.740818 - 1)$$

$$= \$259{,}182 \qquad \text{Present Value}$$

c) The *future value*, at 6% compounded continuously, of the money flow is given by

$$\text{future value} = e^{rt} \int_0^t f(x) \, e^{-rx} \, dx$$

$$= e^{rt}(\text{present value})$$

$$= e^{0.06(5)}(259{,}182)$$

$$= e^{0.30}(259{,}182) = \$349{,}859 \qquad \text{Future Value}$$

This is the total amount of money flow including interest into the firm's treasury after 5 years.

• **EXAMPLE 14-2** _____

Revenues flow into a fund at the rate of $f(x)$ dollars per year, where

$$f(x) = 8000x$$

and x denotes time in years.

a) Find the total money flow (no interest) at the end of 4 years.
b) If the money flow, over the time interval $0 \leq x \leq 4$, is compounded continuously at 10%, find its present value.
c) If the money flow, over the time interval $0 \leq x \leq 4$, is compounded continuously at 10%, find its future value.

Solutions

a) The *total money flow* is given by

$$\int_0^4 8000x \, dx = 4000x^2 \Big|_0^4$$

$$= 4000(4^2) - 4000(0^2)$$

$$= \$64{,}000$$

b) The *present value*, at 10% compounded continuously, is given by

$$\text{present value} = \int_0^4 f(x) \, e^{-rx} \, dx$$

$$= \int_0^4 8000x e^{-0.10x} \, dx$$

This integral may be evaluated either by using formula 7 of our table of integrals (see Table 9 in Appendix C) or by integrating by parts. This form is

$$\int ue^u \, du = e^u(u - 1) + c$$

We must find $\int 8000xe^{-0.10x} \, dx$ by using this form. Using the substitution principle, we let $u = -0.10x$. Then $du = -0.10 \, dx$, and the integral becomes

$$\frac{8000}{(-0.10)^2} \int \underbrace{(-0.10)x}_{u} \overbrace{e^{-0.10x}}^{u} \underbrace{(-0.10) \, dx}_{du} = 800{,}000 \int ue^u \, du$$

$$= 800{,}000e^u(u - 1) + c$$

We must multiply by -0.10 twice, once for du and then for u.

Replacing u with $-0.10x$ gives the result below.

$$= 800{,}000e^{-0.10x}(-0.10x - 1)$$

Hence,

$$\int_0^4 8000xe^{-0.10x} \, dx = \underbrace{800{,}000e^{-0.10x}(-0.10x - 1)}_{F(x)} \Big|_0^4$$

$$= F(4) - F(0)$$
$$= 800{,}000[e^{-0.40}(-1.40) - e^0(-1)]$$
$$\approx 800{,}000(-0.938448 + 1)$$
$$\approx \$49{,}241.55 \quad \text{Present Value}$$

c) The *future value*, at 10% compounded continuously, is given by

$$\text{future value} = e^{rt} \int_0^t f(x) \, e^{-rx} \, dx$$

$$= e^{rt}(\text{present value})$$
$$\approx e^{0.10(4)}(49{,}241.55)$$
$$\approx \$73{,}459.76 \quad \text{Future Value}$$

This is the total money flow including interest over 4 years.

Exercises 14-1

For Exercises 1–16, assume revenues flow into a fund at the rate of $f(x)$ dollars per year, where x denotes time in years.
a) Find the total money flow (no interest) at the end of 5 years.
b) If the money flow, over the time interval $0 \le x \le 5$, is compounded continuously at 9%, find its present value.
c) If the money flow, over the time interval $0 \le x \le 5$, is compounded continuously at 9%, find its future value.

1. $f(x) = 2000$ **2.** $f(x) = 3000$
3. $f(x) = 60{,}000$ **4.** $f(x) = 40{,}000$
5. $f(x) = 6000x$ **6.** $f(x) = 4000x$
7. $f(x) = 0.8x$ **8.** $f(x) = 0.6x$

9. $f(x) = 3000e^{0.05x}$ **10.** $f(x) = 20,000e^{-0.10x}$
11. $f(x) = 40,000e^{-0.04x}$ **12.** $f(x) = 8000e^{0.02x}$
13. $f(x) = 0.20x + 1000$ **14.** $f(x) = 0.60x + 1200$
15. $f(x) = 2500 - 250x$ **16.** $f(x) = 10,000 - 100x$

17. *Sales revenue.* Sales revenue flows continuously into the treasury of a super-market at the rate of $f(x)$ dollars per year ($x =$ time in years), where $f(x) = 10,000$ during the time interval $0 \le x \le 7$.
   a) Find the total money flow (no interest) at the end of 7 years.
   b) If the money flow, over the time interval $0 \le x \le 7$, is compounded continuously at 10%, find its present value.
   c) If the money flow, over the time interval $0 \le x \le 7$, is compounded continuously at 10%, find its future value.

18. *Toll road revenue.* Money from toll roads in a given state flows into the state treasury at the rate of $f(x)$ dollars per year ($x =$ time in years), where $f(x) = 9,500,000x$ during the time interval $0 \le x \le 5$.
   a) Find the total money flow (no interest) at the end of 5 years.
   b) If the money flow, over the time interval $0 \le x \le 5$, is compounded continuously at 8%, find its present value.
   c) If the money flow, over the time interval $0 \le x \le 5$, is compounded continuously at 8%, find its future value.

19. *Sales revenue.* Sales revenue flows continuously into the treasury of a retail store outlet at the rate of $f(x)$ dollars per year ($x =$ time in years), where $f(x) = 10,000,000x$ during the time interval $0 \le x \le 4$.
   a) Find the total money flow (no interest) at the end of 4 years.
   b) If the money flow, over the time interval $0 \le x \le 4$, is compounded continuously at 12%, find its present value.
   c) If the money flow, over the time interval $0 \le x \le 4$, is compounded continuously at 12%, find its future value.

20. *Mutual fund revenue.* Revenue flows continuously into a mutual fund at the rate of $f(x)$ dollars per year ($x =$ time in years), where $f(x) = 10,000,000x^2$ during the time interval $0 \le x \le 6$.
   a) Find the total money flow (no interest) at the end of 6 years.
   b) If the money flow, over the time interval $0 \le x \le 6$, is compounded continuously at 10%, find its present value.
   c) If the money flow, over the time interval $0 \le x \le 6$, is compounded continuously at 10%, find its future value.

14-2 • IMPROPER INTEGRALS

Suppose we wish to compute the area between the x-axis and the curve $f(x) = e^x$ *over the interval* $-\infty < x \le 0$ [see Figure 14-4 (a)]. Studying Figure 14-4 (a), note that the shaded region has no bound as $x \to -\infty$. Since the shaded region has no bound as $x \to -\infty$, we begin to compute its area by finding

$$\int_a^0 e^x \, dx$$

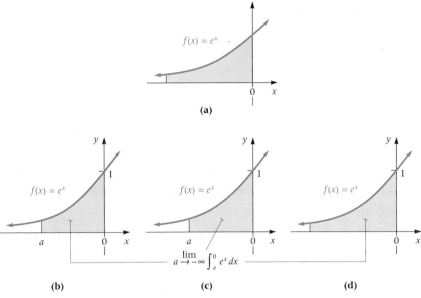

FIGURE 14-4

where a is a real number, as illustrated in Figure 14-4 (b). Hence,

$$\int_a^0 e^x \, dx = e^x \Big|_a^0$$

$$= e^0 - e^a$$

$$= 1 - e^a$$

As $a \to -\infty$, then the definite integral $\int_a^0 e^x \, dx$ becomes

$$\lim_{a \to -\infty} \int_a^0 e^x \, dx = \lim_{a \to -\infty} (1 - e^a)$$

$$= 1 - 0$$

$$= 1$$

as illustrated by the graphs in Figure 14-4(b), (c), and (d). Since $\lim_{a \to -\infty} \int_a^0 e^x \, dx = 1$, then the shaded area in Figure 14-4 (a) is 1. The fact that

$$\int_a^0 e^x \, dx \text{ approaches 1 as } a \to -\infty$$

is written as

$$\int_{-\infty}^0 e^x \, dx = 1$$

An integral such as $\int_{-\infty}^0 e^x \, dx$ where either one or both limits of integration are infinite is called an **improper integral.** Since the definite integral $\int_a^0 e^x \, dx$ approaches a *finite number* as $a \to -\infty$, then the improper integral $\int_{-\infty}^0 e^x \, dx$ is said to be *convergent.* If this were not the case, then the improper integral would be said to be *divergent.*

We define three types of improper integrals.

Improper Integrals

If the function $f(x)$ is continuous over the indicated intervals, and if the indicated limits exist, then

1. $\displaystyle\int_a^\infty f(x)\,dx = \lim_{b\to\infty}\int_a^b f(x)\,dx$,

2. $\displaystyle\int_{-\infty}^b f(x)\,dx = \lim_{a\to-\infty}\int_a^b f(x)\,dx$, and

3. $\displaystyle\int_{-\infty}^\infty f(x)\,dx = \int_{-\infty}^c f(x)\,dx + \int_c^\infty f(x)\,dx$,

where a, b, and c are real numbers.

Note: If the right-hand-side expressions exist, then the improper integrals are said to be **convergent.** If the right-hand-side expressions do not exist, then the improper integrals are said to be **divergent.**

• **EXAMPLE 14-3**

Find the area between the x-axis and the curve $f(x) = 1/x$ over the interval $1 \le x < \infty$, as illustrated in Figure 14-5.

Solution

We seek to evaluate the improper integral

$$\int_1^\infty \frac{1}{x}\,dx$$

by letting $b > 1$ denote a real number and computing the definite integral $\int_1^b (1/x)\,dx$. Hence,

$$\int_1^b \frac{1}{x}\,dx = \ln|x|\,\Big|_1^b$$
$$= \ln|b| - \ln|1|$$
$$= \ln|b| - 0$$
$$= \ln|b|$$

Now, as $b\to\infty$, $\ln|b|\to\infty$, and the definite integral $\int_1^b (1/x)\,dx$ does not approach a finite number. Thus, the improper integral $\int_1^\infty (1/x)\,dx$ is divergent, and the shaded area in Figure 14-5 is infinite.

• **EXAMPLE 14-4**

Determine whether the improper integral

$$\int_2^\infty \frac{1}{x^2}\,dx$$

is convergent or divergent.

Solution

We let $b > 2$ denote a real number and compute the definite integral

$$\int_2^b \frac{1}{x^2}\,dx$$

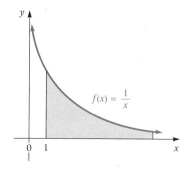

$f(x) = \dfrac{1}{x}$

FIGURE 14-5

Hence,

$$\int_2^b \frac{1}{x^2}\, dx = \int_2^b x^{-2}\, dx$$

$$= -\frac{1}{x}\bigg|_2^b$$

$$= -\frac{1}{b} - \left(-\frac{1}{2}\right)$$

$$= -\frac{1}{b} + \frac{1}{2}$$

Now, as $b \to \infty$, $-1/b \to 0$, so that

$$\int_2^b \frac{1}{x^2}\, dx \to 0 + \frac{1}{2} = \frac{1}{2}$$

Since the definite integral $\int_2^b (1/x^2)\, dx$ approaches 1/2 as $b \to \infty$, then the improper integral $\int_2^\infty (1/x^2)\, dx = 1/2$ and thus is convergent.

Present Value of a Perpetual Flow

In certain situations (e.g., where interest from a perpetual bond or income from an indestructible asset such as land is earned), a continuous stream of money flows forever (i.e., perpetually). We will now show how to find the present value of such a perpetual flow. If a continuous stream of money flows perpetually into a fund at a rate of $f(x)$ dollars per year (x = time in years) during the time interval $0 \le x < \infty$, and if this money flow is compounded continuously at an annual interest rate of r, then its present value at $x = 0$ is given by the improper integral

$$\int_0^\infty f(x)\, e^{-rx}\, dx$$

• **EXAMPLE 14-5** _____

Income from a piece of land flows continuously into a trust fund at a constant rate of $f(x)$ = \$600,000 per year (x = time in years) and is compounded continuously at 10%. If this flow continues forever (i.e., $0 \le x < \infty$), find its present value.

Solution

The present value at $x = 0$ is given by

$$\int_0^\infty 600{,}000 e^{-0.10x}\, dx$$

We must evaluate the definite integral $\int_0^b 600{,}000 e^{-0.10x}\, dx$. We let $b > 0$ denote a real number and compute the definite integral $\int_0^b 600{,}000 e^{-0.10x}\, dx$. Hence.

$$\int_0^b 600{,}000 e^{-0.10x}\, dx = -6{,}000{,}000 e^{-0.10x}\bigg|_0^b$$

$$= -6{,}000{,}000 e^{-0.10b} - (-6{,}000{,}000 e^0)$$

$$= -6{,}000{,}000 e^{-0.10b} + 6{,}000{,}000$$

Now, as $b \to \infty$, $e^{-0.10b} \to 0$, so that

$$\int_0^b 600{,}000 e^{-0.10x}\, dx \to 0 + 6{,}000{,}000 = 6{,}000{,}000$$

Thus, the improper integral

$$\int_0^\infty 600,000e^{-0.10x}\,dx = 6,000,000$$

and the present value is $6,000,000. Thus, $6,000,000 invested now at 10% compounded continuously will provide for payments at the rate of $600,000 per year forever.

• **EXAMPLE 14-6   Radioactive Waste.** _____

The rate (in tons per year) at which radioactive waste is being released into the atmosphere is given by

$$f(t) = 2000e^{-0.05t} \qquad (t \ge 0)$$

where t denotes time in years. If this flow of radioactive waste continues indefinitely, find the total amount released.

Solution

The *total amount released* is given by the improper integral

$$\int_0^\infty 2000e^{-0.05t}\,dt = \lim_{b \to \infty} \int_0^b 2000e^{-0.05t}\,dt$$

We must evaluate the definite integral

$$\int_0^b 2000e^{-0.05t}\,dt = \frac{2000}{-0.05}e^{-0.05t}\Big|_0^b$$

$$= -40,000e^{-0.05b} - (-40,000e^{-0.05(0)})$$

$$= -40,000e^{-0.05b} + 40,000$$

Now, as $b \to \infty$, $e^{-0.05b} \to 0$, so that

$$\int_0^b 2000e^{-0.05t}\,dt \to 0 + 40,000 = 40,000$$

Thus, the improper integral

$$\int_0^\infty 2000e^{-0.05t}\,dt = 40,000 \qquad \text{Total amount (in tons) of radioactive waste released}$$

Exercises 14-2

Evaluate whichever of the following improper integrals converge.

1. $\int_1^\infty \dfrac{dx}{x^2}$

2. $\int_1^\infty \dfrac{dx}{x^4}$

3. $\int_6^\infty \dfrac{dx}{x}$

4. $\int_2^\infty \dfrac{dx}{x^3}$

5. $\int_3^\infty \dfrac{dx}{x+1}$

6. $\int_1^\infty \dfrac{dx}{2x+5}$

7. $\int_0^\infty e^{-2x}\,dx$

8. $\int_0^\infty e^{-4x}\,dx$

9. $\int_0^\infty xe^{-x}\,dx$

10. $\int_0^\infty xe^{-2x}\,dx$

11. $\int_{-\infty}^0 e^{2x}\,dx$

12. $\int_{-\infty}^0 e^x\,dx$

13. $\int_4^\infty x^{-1/2}\,dx$

14. $\int_8^\infty x^{-1/3}\,dx$

15. $\int_1^\infty \dfrac{dx}{(x+2)^2}$

16. $\int_0^\infty \dfrac{dx}{(x+4)^3}$

17. $\int_0^\infty xe^{-x^2}\,dx$

18. $\int_1^\infty x^2\,dx$

19. $\int_{-\infty}^{\infty} xe^{-x^2} dx$

20. $\int_{2}^{\infty} \frac{\ln x}{x} dx$

21. $\int_{1}^{\infty} \frac{dx}{\sqrt{x+6}}$

22. $\int_{8}^{\infty} \frac{dx}{\sqrt{x-7}}$

23. $\int_{0}^{\infty} x^3 dx$

24. $\int_{1}^{\infty} \frac{(2x+4)}{x^2+4x} dx$

Area

25. Find the area between the x-axis and the curve $y = e^{-x}$ over the interval $0 \le x < \infty$. Sketch the function and shade the desired area.

26. Find the area between the x-axis and the curve $f(x) = 1/(x-3)^2$ over the interval $10 \le x < \infty$. Sketch the function and shade the desired area.

27. Find the area between the x-axis and the curve $f(x) = 1/(x-3)^2$ over the interval $4 \le x < \infty$. Sketch the function and shade the desired area.

28. Find the area between the x-axis and the curve $f(x) = 1/(x-1)^3$ over the interval $2 \le x < \infty$. Sketch the function and shade the desired area.

29. Find the area between the x-axis and the curve $f(x) = 1/(x-1)^3$ over the interval $3 \le x < \infty$. Sketch the function and shade the desired area.

30. Find the area between the x-axis and the curve $y = e^{x}$ over the interval $-\infty < x \le 0$. Sketch the function and shade the desired area.

Applications

31. *Perpetual flow.* A perpetual bond yields a continuous flow of interest at a constant rate of $f(x) = \$40,000$ per year (x = time in years). If this perpetual flow is compounded continuously at 9%, find its present value.

32. *Perpetual flow.* A piece of land yields a continuous flow of revenue at a constant rate of $800,000 per year. If this perpetual flow is compounded continuously at 12%, find its present value.

33. *Perpetual flow: Endowment fund.* A college wishes to establish an endowment fund to provide for annual scholarships in the amount of $20,000. If the fund is to be invested at 10% compounded continuously, how much should be solicited from donors for this fund now?

34. *Perpetual flow: Endowment fund.* A donor wishes to establish an endowment fund to provide a hospital with annual $50,000 research grants. If the fund is to be invested at 9% compounded continuously, how much should the donor provide to set up the fund?

35. *Radioactive waste.* The rate at which radioactive waste is being released into the atmosphere is given by

$$f(t) = 8000e^{-0.04t} \qquad (t \ge 0)$$

where t denotes time in years. If this flow of radioactive waste continues indefinitely, find the total amount released.

36. *Radioactive waste.* The rate at which radioactive waste is being released into the atmosphere is given by

$$f(t) = 6000e^{-0.03t} \qquad (t \ge 0)$$

where t denotes time in years. If this flow continues indefinitely, find the total amount released.

37. *Water pollution.* In a given area, toxic chemicals from a nearby dump are seeping into the groundwater at a rate of

$$f(t) = \frac{600}{(1+t)^3} \qquad (t \ge 0)$$

gallons per year, where t denotes time in years. If this seepage continues indefinitely, find the total amount of seepage.

14-3

TABLE 14-1   Box full of numbers

1	(20%)
3	(50%)
5	(15%)
8	(10%)
10	(5%)

TABLE 14-2

x	P(x)
1	.20
3	.50
5	.15
8	.10
10	.05
	1.00

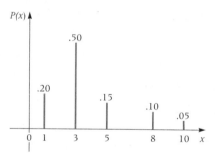

FIGURE 14-6

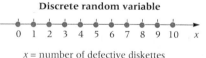

x = number of defective diskettes obtained in a box of diskettes

(a)

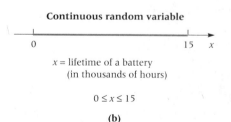

x = lifetime of a battery (in thousands of hours)

$0 \le x \le 15$

(b)

FIGURE 14-7

• PROBABILITY DISTRIBUTIONS

Frequently, in business and industry, chance events take the form of numerical outcomes. The numerical outcomes are denoted by a letter—say, x—which is called a **random variable.** We now discuss this concept in detail.

Consider a simple type of gambling machine—a box full of numbers (see Table 14-1). Observing Table 14-1, note that the box contains the numbers 1, 3, 5, 8, and 10. Specifically, in the proportions shown, 20% of all the numbers in the box are 1s, 50% are 3s, 15% are 5s, 10% are 8s, and 5% are 10s.

A chance experiment consists of selecting 1 number from the box. The number selected may be taken to a cashier who will pay the player a dollar amount equal to the number. Observing the percentages in Table 14-1, it is obvious that the player has a 20% probability of winning $1, a 50% probability of winning $3, a 15% probability of winning $5, a 10% probability of winning $8, and a 5% probability of winning $10.

Since the outcomes of this chance experiment are numerical values, they may be listed in tabular form, as shown in Table 14-2. Observing Table 14-2, note that the numerical values 1, 3, 5, 8, and 10 are denoted by a letter—in this case, x. Since the values of x are chance outcomes, x is called a **random variable.** Observe that the probability of occurrence of each x-value is listed in the "P(x)" column (i.e., the "probability of x" column). Such a display of values of random variables and their corresponding probabilities is called a **probability distribution.** As shown in Table 14-2, the sum of the probabilities of a probability distribution is 1. Figure 14-6 graphically illustrates this probability distribution. Since the random variable, x, takes on a finite number of values, it is called a **discrete random variable,** and its probability distribution is termed a **discrete probability distribution.** If a random variable can take on all possible values within an interval of numbers, it is termed a **continuous random variable,** and its probability distribution is called a **continuous probability distribution.**

An example of a discrete random variable is given by the number of defective diskettes obtained in a box of 10 diskettes, as is illustrated in Figure 14-7(a). The lifetime (in thousands of hours) of a battery is an example of a continuous random variable, as is illustrated in Figure 14-7(b).

We now give an example illustrating an application of a discrete random variable.

• EXAMPLE 14-7

The manager of Howie's Hamburger Stand has kept a record of daily demand for hamburgers during the past 400 days. For example, on precisely 20 of the 400 days, there was a demand for x = 100 hamburgers. The complete results are shown in Table 14-3. Such a display of data is called a **frequency (f) distribution.**

a) Convert this frequency distribution into a probability distribution by expressing the frequency of occurrence as a percentage for each x-value.

TABLE 14-3

x (Demand)	f (# days)
100	20
110	80
120	200
130	80
140	20
	400

TABLE 14-4

x	P(x)
100	.05 ←20/400
110	.20 ←80/400
120	.50 ←200/400
130	.20 ←80/400
140	.05 ←20/400
	1.00

TABLE 14-5

x	P(x)
1	.25
3	.25
5	.25
7	.25
	1.00

b) Find the probability that daily demand is 130 hamburgers.

c) Find the probability that daily demand is at most 130 hamburgers.

d) How many hamburgers should be kept on hand in order to satisfy daily demand 95% of the time?

Solutions

a) Dividing each frequency value by the total frequency, 400, we have the probability distribution in Table 14-4.

b) Observing Table 14-4, we note that the probability that daily demand is 130 hamburgers is .20. This is expressed symbolically as

$$P(x = 130) = P(130) = .20$$

c) The probability that daily demand is at most 130 is

$$P(x \leq 130) = P(130) + P(120) + P(110) + P(100)$$
$$= .20 + .50 + .20 + .05$$
$$= .95$$

d) Since there is a 95% probability (see part c) that daily demand will be at most 130 hamburgers, then 130 hamburgers should be kept on hand in order to satisfy demand 95% of the time.

Uniform Distributions

Consider for a moment a box of numbers whose distribution is given by the discrete probability distribution in Table 14-5. A graph of this probability distribution appears in Figure 14-8. If a chance experiment consists of selecting 1 number from the box, the chance outcomes of 1, 3, 5, and 7 have equal probabilities of occurring. Thus, we say that the random variable, x, is *uniformly distributed.*

Now consider a uniformly distributed random variable, x, having possible values within the interval $1 \leq x \leq 7$. Since x is a continuous random variable, it takes on an infinite number of possible values. Thus, we can no longer list all possible individual values of x and their probabilities as we do with a discrete random variable. Instead, we use a graph to illustrate the distribution of the random variable, x, over the interval $1 \leq x \leq 7$. Since the random variable, x, is uniformly distributed over the interval $1 \leq x \leq 7$, the graph of its probability distribution takes on a *constant value* over the interval $1 \leq x \leq 7$, as illustrated in Figure 14-9.

With a probability distribution of a continuous random variable, the

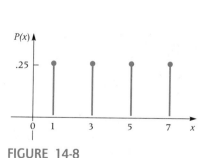

FIGURE 14-8

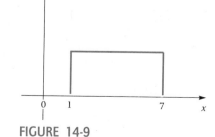

FIGURE 14-9

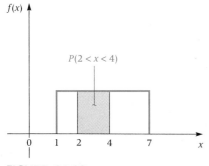

FIGURE 14-10

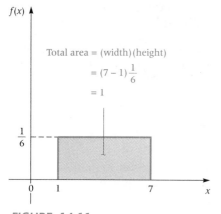

FIGURE 14-11

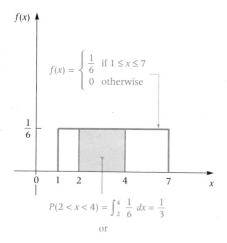

$P(2 < x < 4) = \int_2^4 \frac{1}{6}\, dx = \frac{1}{3}$

or

$P(2 < x < 4) = (\text{width})(\text{height})$

$= (4 - 2)\left(\frac{1}{6}\right)$

$= \frac{1}{3}$

FIGURE 14-12

area between its graph and the *x*-axis measures *probability*. Thus, if a chance experiment consists of selecting a number from the interval $1 \le x \le 7$ in Figure 14-9, the probability that the selected number lies between 2 and 4, or, in other words,

$$P(2 < x < 4)$$

is represented by the shaded area in Figure 14-10. Since the random variable, *x*, represents all values within the interval $1 \le x \le 7$, then $P(1 \le x \le 7) = 1$. Therefore, the total area between the graph of the probability distribution and the *x*-axis over the interval $1 \le x \le 7$ equals 1, and the height of the graph is 1/6 (see Figure 14-11) since the enclosed area is a rectangle. Hence,

$$P(2 < x < 4) = (\text{width})(\text{height})$$

$$= (4 - 2)\left(\frac{1}{6}\right)$$

$$= \frac{1}{3}$$

Note that with a continuous random variable, we determine the probability that the random variable has a value within a specified interval. Such a probability is given by the area between the graph of the probability distribution and the *x*-axis *over the specified interval.* We do not attempt to determine the probability that a random variable takes on an individual value since the area above an individual value is zero. Thus, if a continuous random variable, *x*, is defined over some interval that includes the real numbers *a* and *b*, where $a < b$, then $P(x = a) = 0$, $P(x = b) = 0$, and $P(a < x < b) = P(a \le x \le b)$. As an example, for the uniformly distributed random variable in Figure 14-10, $P(2 < x < 4) = P(2 \le x \le 4) = 1/3$.

A continuous probability distribution is usually described by a function, called its **probability density function.** The probability density function for the preceding uniform distribution is given by

$$f(x) = \begin{cases} \dfrac{1}{6} & \text{if } 1 \le x \le 7 \\ 0 & \text{otherwise} \end{cases}$$

Thus, since the probability is represented by the area under the graph (see Figure 14-12), the probability $P(2 < x < 4)$ can also be determined by the definite integral

$$\int_2^4 f(x)\, dx = \int_2^4 \frac{1}{6}\, dx$$

$$= \frac{1}{6}x \bigg|_2^4$$

$$= \frac{1}{6}(4) - \frac{1}{6}(2)$$

$$= \frac{1}{3}$$

We summarize as follows.

SUMMARY

Uniform Distribution

If a random variable, x, is **uniformly distributed** over the interval $a \leq x \leq b$, its probability density function is given by

$$f(x) = \begin{cases} \dfrac{1}{b-a} & \text{for } a \leq x \leq b \\ 0 & \text{otherwise} \end{cases}$$

The graph of $f(x)$ appears in Figure 14-13. Observe that the base of the rectangle has length $b - a$, while the height is $1/(b-a)$, so that the enclosed area is $(b-a)[1/(b-a)] = 1$.

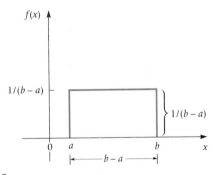

FIGURE 14-13

• **EXAMPLE 14-8   Waiting Time.** _____

The time (in minutes) a customer waits at a department store's counter is a uniformly distributed random variable, x, having possible values within the interval $0 \leq x \leq 5$. Find the probability that an arriving customer will wait at most 4 minutes.

Solution

We seek $P(0 \leq x \leq 4)$. This probability is represented by the shaded area in Figure 14-14. Since the shaded area is rectangular, the probability may be determined by the product $4(1/5)$. Hence,

$$P(0 \leq x \leq 4) = 4\left(\frac{1}{5}\right)$$
$$= .8$$

Using the definite integral to find the shaded area yields the same result. Therefore,

$$P(0 \leq x \leq 4) = \int_0^4 \frac{1}{5}\,dx = \frac{1}{5}x \, \bigg|_0^4$$

$$= \frac{1}{5}(4) - \frac{1}{5}(0)$$

$$= .8 \qquad \text{Probability of a customer waiting at most 4 minutes}$$

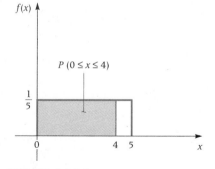

FIGURE 14-14

We now summarize the concept of probability density functions.

SUMMARY

Probability Density Function

Let x be a continuous random variable. A function $f(x)$ is a probability density function over some interval a $\leq x \leq$ b if

1. $f(x) \geq 0$ for $a \leq x \leq b$.
2. The area under the graph of the density function over the interval $[a, b]$ equals 1. In other words,

$$\int_a^b f(x) \, dx = 1$$

as illustrated in Figure 14-15.

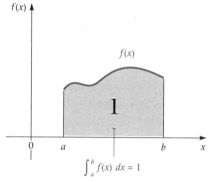

FIGURE 14-15

3. If $[c, d]$ is a subinterval of $[a, b]$, then

$$P(c \leq x \leq d) = \int_c^d f(x) \, dx$$

as illustrated in Figure 14-16.

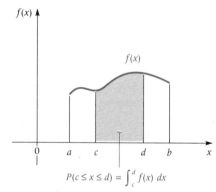

FIGURE 14-16

Note: The above holds if the interval $[a, b]$ is replaced with $(-\infty, b]$, $[a, \infty)$, or $(-\infty, \infty)$.

• **EXAMPLE 14-9**   **Product Lifetime.** ——————————

The length of life (in years) of a certain brand of battery is a continuous random variable with density function

$$f(x) = \frac{10}{3x^2} \quad (2 \leq x \leq 5)$$

a)   Verify that the area under the graph of $f(x)$ over the interval [2, 5] equals 1.

b)   Find the probability that a battery of this brand will last between 3 and 4 years.

c)   Find the probability that a battery of this brand will last at most 4 years.

d)   Find the probability that a battery of this brand will last at least 4 years.

Solutions

a)
$$\int_2^5 \frac{10}{3x^2}\,dx = \int_2^5 \frac{10}{3}x^{-2}\,dx$$

$$= \frac{10}{3}\frac{x^{-1}}{-1}\Big|_2^5$$

$$= -\frac{10}{3x}\Big|_2^5$$

$$= -\frac{10}{3(5)} - \left[-\frac{10}{3(2)}\right]$$

$$= -\frac{10}{15} + \frac{10}{6}$$

$$= -\frac{20}{30} + \frac{50}{30} = 1$$

b)   The probability that a battery of this brand will last anywhere from 3 to 4 years is

$$P(3 \leq x \leq 4) = \int_3^4 \frac{10}{3x^2}\,dx$$

$$= -\frac{10}{3x}\Big|_3^4$$

$$= -\frac{10}{3(4)} - \left[-\frac{10}{3(3)}\right]$$

$$= \frac{5}{18} \approx .28$$

This is illustrated in Figure 14-17.

c)   The probability that a battery of this brand will last at most 4 years is

$$P(2 \leq x \leq 4) = \int_2^4 \frac{10}{3x^2}\,dx$$

$$= -\frac{10}{3x}\Big|_2^4$$

$$= -\frac{10}{3(4)} - \left[-\frac{10}{3(2)}\right]$$

$$= -\frac{10}{12} + \frac{10}{6}$$

$$= \frac{5}{6} \approx .83$$

This is illustrated in Figure 14-18.

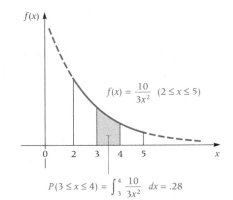

$$P(3 \leq x \leq 4) = \int_3^4 \frac{10}{3x^2}\,dx = .28$$

FIGURE 14-17

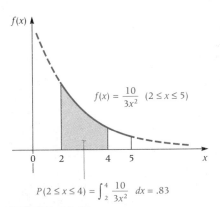

$$P(2 \leq x \leq 4) = \int_2^4 \frac{10}{3x^2}\,dx = .83$$

FIGURE 14-18

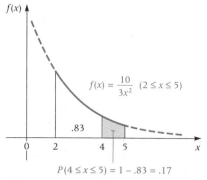

$$f(x) = \frac{10}{3x^2} \quad (2 \leq x \leq 5)$$

.83

$$P(4 \leq x \leq 5) = 1 - .83 = .17$$

FIGURE 14-19

d) The probability that a battery of this brand will last at least 4 years is $P(4 \leq x \leq 5)$, which is illustrated in Figure 14-19. Since this area is the complement of the area corresponding to $P(2 \leq x \leq 4)$, which was determined in part c, we easily determine

$$P(4 \leq x \leq 5) = 1 - P(2 \leq x \leq 4)$$

$$= 1 - \frac{5}{6}$$

$$= \frac{1}{6} \approx .17$$

We note that this same result could have been determined by the definite integral

$$\int_4^5 \frac{10}{3x^2}\, dx = \frac{1}{6} \approx .17$$

We now discuss another probability distribution called the exponential distribution.

> ### SUMMARY
>
> **Exponential Distribution**
>
> If a random variable, x, is distributed in accordance with the density function
>
> $$f(x) = \begin{cases} ke^{-kx} & \text{if } x \geq 0 \\ 0 & \text{otherwise} \end{cases}$$
>
> where the constant $k > 0$, then x is said to be **exponentially distributed.** A graph of the exponential density function appears in Figure 14-20.
>
>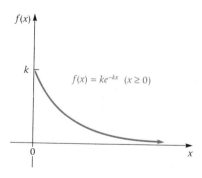
>
> $$f(x) = ke^{-kx} \quad (x \geq 0)$$
>
> **FIGURE 14-20**

• **EXAMPLE 14-10**

Show that the total area between the exponential density function and the x-axis is 1.

Solution

We must show that the improper integral

$$\int_0^\infty k e^{-kx}\, dx$$

with constant $k > 0$, converges to 1. Hence, we let $b > 0$ denote a real number and compute the definite integral

$$\int_0^b k e^{-kx}\, dx = -e^{-kx}\ \bigg|_0^b$$

$$= -e^{-kb} - (-e^{-k(0)})$$

$$= -e^{-kb} - (-1)$$

$$= -e^{-kb} + 1$$

Since $-e^{-kb} \to 0$ as $b \to \infty$, then

$$\int_0^b k e^{-kx}\, dx \to 0 + 1 = 1$$

and thus the total area equals 1.

• EXAMPLE 14-11   Interarrival Time.

The interarrival time, x (i.e., the time between two successive arrivals), of customers at a particular bank is exponentially distributed, with $k = 10$. Find the probability that the interarrival time is between 0.1 and 0.5 minute.

Solution

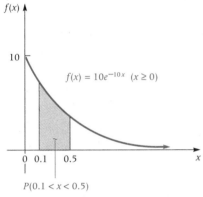

$f(x) = 10e^{-10x}$ ($x \geq 0$)

$P(0.1 < x < 0.5)$

FIGURE 14-21

We seek the shaded area in Figure 14-21. Thus, we have

$$P(0.1 < x < 0.5) = \int_{0.1}^{0.5} 10 e^{-10x}\, dx$$

$$= -e^{-10x}\ \bigg|_{0.1}^{0.5}$$

$$= -e^{-10(0.5)} - (-e^{-10(0.1)})$$

$$= -e^{-5} + e^{-1}$$

$$\approx -.006738 + .367879$$

$$\approx .3611 \qquad \text{Probability that the interarrival}$$
$$\text{time is between 0.1 and 0.5 minute}$$

Exercises 14-3

1. *Waiting time.* A customer's waiting time, x (in minutes), is a random variable that is uniformly distributed over the interval $0 \leq x \leq 20$. If a customer arrives at this restaurant, find the probability that he or she must wait
   a) At least 12 minutes.
   b) Less than 5 minutes.
   c) Between 5 and 10 minutes.

2. *Product life.* The length of life (in years) of a certain brand of battery is a random variable, x, distributed in accordance with the probability density function

$$f(x) = \begin{cases} -6x^2 + 6x & \text{if } 0 \leq x \leq 1 \\ 0 & \text{otherwise} \end{cases}$$

a) Sketch $f(x)$ and verify that $\int_0^1 f(x)\, dx = 1$.
b) Find the probability that a battery lasts longer than 3/4 year.
c) Find $P(0 \le x \le 0.2)$.
d) If the batteries are unconditionally guaranteed for 2 months, what percentage will be returned?

3. A random variable, x, is uniformly distributed over the interval $2 \le x \le 7$.
   a) Determine its probability density function, $f(x)$.
   b) Find $P(2 \le x \le 3)$.
   c) Find $P(4 \le x \le 6)$.

4. A random variable, x, is distributed in accordance with a probability density function of the form $f(x) = kx$ (where k is a constant) over the interval $0 \le x \le 4$.
   a) Determine k.
   b) Sketch $f(x)$.
   c) Calculate $P(0 \le x \le 2)$.
   d) Calculate $P(3 \le x \le 4)$.
   e) Calculate $P(1 \le x \le 2)$.

5. *Interarrival time.* The interarrival times (in minutes) of incoming calls at a certain switchboard are exponentially distributed, with $k = 5$. Find the probability that the time between two successive arrivals is
   a) Less than 0.1 minute.
   b) Between 0.2 and 0.6 minute.
   c) Longer than 0.4 minute.

6. *Interarrival time.* At a certain self-service gas station, the interarrival times (in minutes) are exponentially distributed, with $k = 0.5$. Find the probability that the interarrival time is
   a) Less than 0.6 minute.
   b) Between 0.2 and 0.8 minute.
   c) Longer than 1 minute.

7. A random variable, x, is exponentially distributed, with $k = 2$. Find each of the following.
   a) $P(0.5 \le x \le 1)$
   b) $P(0 \le x \le 1.5)$
   c) $P(x \ge 3)$

8. *Reliability.* Let the random variable, x, represent the length of life of some mechanical component with probability density function $f(x)$. If t is a given length of time, then

$$P(x > t) = \int_t^\infty f(x)\, dx$$

Since this integral represents the probability that the component's lifetime exceeds t units of time (see Figure 14-22), it is called the **reliability function** and is denoted by $R(t)$. Hence,

$$R(t) = P(x > t) = \int_t^\infty f(x)\, dx$$

a) Find $R(t)$ for an exponential density function, with $k = 0.8$.
b) Find $R(1)$ and interpret.
c) Find $R(5)$ and interpret.

9. *Reliability.* The length of life (in years) of circuitry in a certain brand of calculator is exponentially distributed, with $k = 0.5$.
   a) Find the reliability function, $R(t)$.
   b) Find $R(1)$ and interpret.
   c) Find $R(4)$ and interpret.

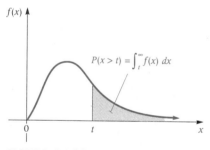

$$P(x > t) = \int_t^\infty f(x)\, dx$$

FIGURE 14-22

14-4

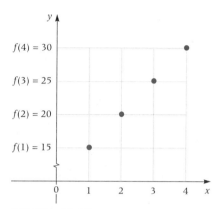

FIGURE 14-23

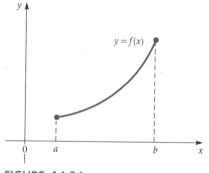

FIGURE 14-24

• APPLICATIONS: AVERAGE VALUE AND VOLUME

Average Value of a Function

Consider a firm that produces either 1, 2, 3, or 4 units of some commodity. If the variable cost per unit is $5 and the fixed cost is $10, then the cost function is defined by

$$f(x) = 5x + 10$$

with domain consisting of the x-values given in Table 14-6. A graph of the cost function, $f(x)$, appears in Figure 14-23. The **average value,** Av, of the function is determined by summing the y-coordinates of $f(x)$ and dividing this result by the number of points. Hence,

$$Av = \frac{f(1) + f(2) + f(3) + f(4)}{4}$$

$$= \frac{15 + 20 + 25 + 30}{4}$$

$$= 22.5$$

Thus, the average cost is $22.50.

In general, given a function $f(x)$ with domain consisting of the x-values $x_1, x_2, \ldots, x_n$, the average value, Av, of $f(x)$ is given by

$$Av = \frac{f(x_1) + f(x_2) + \ldots + f(x_n)}{n}$$

If $f(x)$ is a continuous function defined over the interval $a \le x \le b$ (see Figure 14-24), its average value cannot be computed by the above formula since the domain $a \le x \le b$ contains infinitely many values. The average value of such a continuous function is determined by the formula

$$\frac{1}{b - a} \int_a^b f(x)\, dx$$

An explanation of this formula for determining the average value of a continuous function, $f(x)$, defined over the interval $a \le x \le b$ is presented in the succeeding paragraph.

Divide the interval $a \le x \le b$ into n subintervals, each of length $(b - a)/n$, and choose n x-values, $x_1, x_2, \ldots, x_n$, such that x_1 is in the first subinterval, x_2 is in the second subinterval, . . . , and x_n is in the nth sub-

TABLE 14-6

x	y	$y = f(x) = 5x + 10$
1	15	$f(1) = 5(1) + 10 = 15$
2	20	$f(2) = 5(2) + 10 = 20$
3	25	$f(3) = 5(3) + 10 = 25$
4	30	$f(4) = 5(4) + 10 = 30$

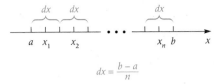

$$dx = \frac{b-a}{n}$$

FIGURE 14-25

interval, as illustrated in Figure 14-25. The average value of $f(x)$ over these n particular x-values is

$$\frac{f(x_1) + f(x_2) + \ldots + f(x_n)}{n}$$

This can be rewritten as

$$\left[f(x_1) \cdot \frac{1}{n}\right] + \left[f(x_2) \cdot \frac{1}{n}\right] + \ldots + \left[f(x_n) \cdot \frac{1}{n}\right]$$

Multiplying the above by $(b - a)/(b - a)$ gives

$$\frac{1}{b-a}\left[f(x_1) \cdot \frac{b-a}{n} + f(x_2) \cdot \frac{b-a}{n} + \ldots + f(x_n) \cdot \frac{b-a}{n}\right]$$

If we let $dx = (b - a)/n$, this becomes

$$\frac{1}{b-a}\left[f(x_1)\ dx + f(x_2)\ dx + \ldots + f(x_n)\ dx\right]$$

As the number of x-values becomes arbitrarily large, or, in other words, as $n \to \infty$, then

$$f(x_1)\ dx + f(x_2)\ dx + \ldots + f(x_n)\ dx$$

becomes the definite integral

$$\int_a^b f(x)\ dx$$

and the average value of $f(x)$ over the interval $a \le x \le b$ becomes

$$\frac{1}{b-a}\int_a^b f(x)\ dx$$

We summarize the following.

Average Value of a Function

The average value of a continuous function, $f(x)$, over the interval $[a, b]$ is given by

$$\frac{1}{b-a}\int_a^b f(x)\ dx$$

• **EXAMPLE 14-12**

Find the average value of $f(x) = 3x^2$ over the interval $1 \le x \le 3$.

Solution

A graph of $f(x)$ appears in Figure 14-26. Since

$$\text{average value} = \frac{1}{b-a}\int_a^b f(x)\ dx$$

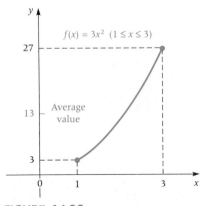

FIGURE 14-26

then for the function in Figure 14-26, $a = 1$, $b = 3$, and $f(x) = 3x^2$. Hence,

$$\text{average value} = \frac{1}{3 - 1} \int_1^3 3x^2 \, dx$$

$$= \frac{1}{2} x^3 \Big|_1^3$$

$$= \frac{1}{2}(3^3) - \frac{1}{2}(1^3)$$

$$= \frac{27}{2} - \frac{1}{2}$$

$$= 13$$

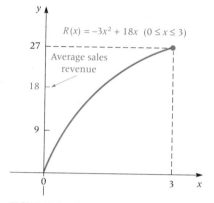

$R(x) = -3x^2 + 18x \quad (0 \le x \le 3)$

Average sales revenue

FIGURE 14-27

• EXAMPLE 14-13

The function $R(x) = -3x^2 + 18x$ represents the sales revenue (in millions of dollars) received from selling x (in thousands) units of some item. If $0 \le x \le 3$, then find the average sales revenue.

Solution

A graph of $R(x)$ appears in Figure 14-27. The average sales revenue is the average value of $R(x)$ over the interval $0 \le x \le 3$. Thus,

$$\text{average sales revenue} = \frac{1}{3 - 0} \int_0^3 R(x) \, dx$$

$$= \frac{1}{3} \int_0^3 (-3x^2 + 18x) \, dx$$

$$= \frac{1}{3}(-x^3 + 9x^2) \Big|_0^3$$

$$= \frac{1}{3}\left[-(3^3) + 9(3^2) \right] - \frac{1}{3}(0)$$

$$= 18 - 0 = 18$$

Thus, the average sales revenue is \$18 million when sales are between 0 and 3 thousand units.

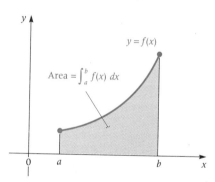

$y = f(x)$

$\text{Area} = \int_a^b f(x) \, dx$

FIGURE 14-28

Geometric Interpretation

Consider the function $f(x)$ in Figure 14-28 and the shaded area from $x = a$ to $x = b$. Suppose we want to determine the height, H, of the rectangle in Figure 14-29 having the same area as that shaded under $f(x)$ in Figure 14-28. Since

$$\text{area of rectangle} = \text{area under curve}$$

then

$$H(b - a) = \int_a^b f(x) \, dx$$

Solving for H, we have

$$H = \frac{1}{b - a} \int_a^b f(x) \, dx$$

Note that H equals the *average value of the function* $f(x)$ over the interval $a \le x \le b$.

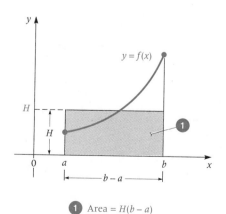

$y = f(x)$

① Area = $H(b - a)$

FIGURE 14-29

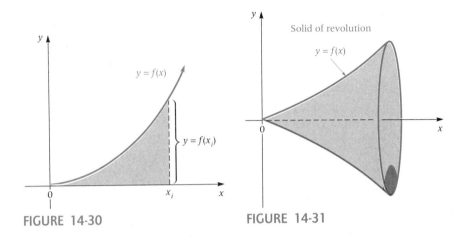

FIGURE 14-30

FIGURE 14-31

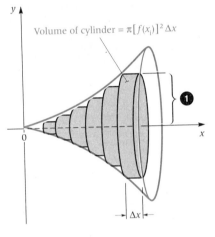

Volume of cylinder = $\pi[f(x_i)]^2 \Delta x$

1

Δx

1 $y = f(x)$: radius

FIGURE 14-32

Volume of a Solid of Revolution

Consider a function defined by

$$y = f(x)$$

with a graph as illustrated in Figure 14-30. If we rotate the graph of $y = f(x)$ and the shaded area of Figure 14-30 about rhe x-axis, the result is the three-dimensional solid of Figure 14-31. A solid formed by such a rotation of the graph of $y = f(x)$ is called a **solid of revolution.**

We now discuss the determination of the *volume* of a solid of revolution. The volume of a solid of revolution is approximated by the sum of volumes of cylinders, each of height Δx, as illustrated in Figure 14-32. We note that height is measured along the x-axis since the cylinder is on its side.

The volume of each of the approximating cylinders is given by

$$\text{volume} = \pi \, (\text{radius})^2(\text{height})$$
$$= \pi \, [f(x_i)]^2 \, \Delta x$$

Volume of a cylinder

Thus, the volume, V, of the solid of revolution is approximated by the sum of all such cylinders as given below.

$$V = \pi[f(x_1)]^2 \, \Delta x + \pi[f(x_2)]^2 \, \Delta x + \ldots + \pi[(f(x_n)]^2 \, \Delta x$$

As the number of approximating cylinders approaches infinity, the height (or thickness) of each such cylinder approaches 0, and the actual volume is given by the definite integral

$$\int_a^b \pi[f(x)]^2 \, dx$$

We summarize as follows.

Volume of a Solid of Revolution

The volume, V, of a solid of revolution formed by rotating about the x-axis the region between the graph of $y = f(x)$ and the x-axis from $x = a$ to $x = b$ (see Figure 14-33) is given by

$$V = \int_a^b \pi [f(x)]^2 \, dx$$

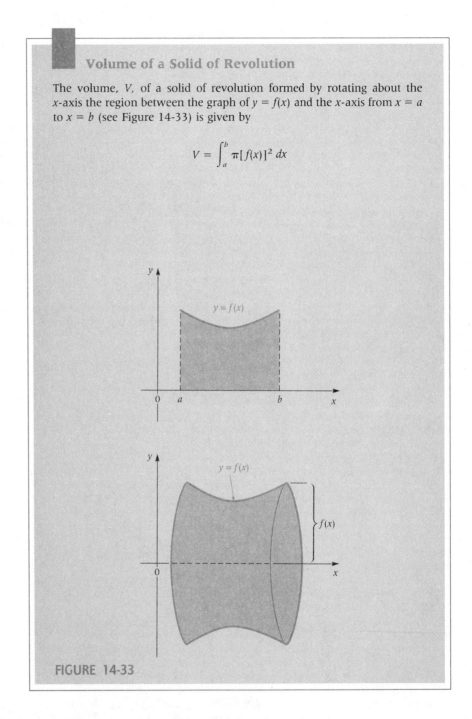

FIGURE 14-33

• **EXAMPLE 14-14** _____

Find the volume of the solid of revolution formed by rotating about the x-axis the region between the graph of $y = \sqrt{x}$ and the x-axis from $x = 0$ to $x = 2$.

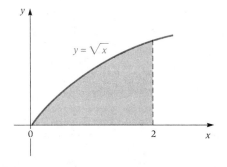

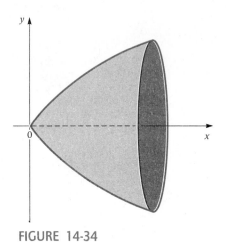

FIGURE 14-34

Solution

We first graph the function $y = \sqrt{x}$, shade the region, and draw the solid of revolution in Figure 14-34. The volume, V, is given by

$$V = \int_0^2 \pi [f(x)]^2 \, dx$$

$$= \int_0^2 \pi (\sqrt{x})^2 \, dx$$

$$= \int_0^2 \pi x \, dx$$

$$= \left. \frac{\pi x^2}{2} \right|_0^2$$

$$= \frac{\pi (2)^2}{2} - \frac{\pi (0)^2}{2}$$

$$= 2\pi \approx 6.28 \qquad \text{Volume}$$

• **EXAMPLE 14-15** _____

Find the volume of the solid of revolution formed by rotating about the x-axis the region between the graph of $y = x^2$ and the x-axis from $x = 1$ to $x = 4$.

Solution

We first graph $y = x^2$, shade the region, and draw the solid of revolution in Figure 14-35.

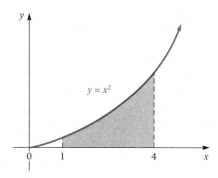

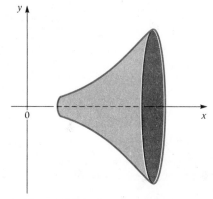

FIGURE 14-35

The volume, V, is given by

$$V = \int_1^4 \pi[f(x)]^2 \, dx$$

$$= \int_1^4 \pi(x^2)^2 \, dx$$

$$= \int_1^4 \pi x^4 \, dx$$

$$= \frac{\pi x^5}{5}\Big|_1^4$$

$$= \frac{\pi(4)^5}{5} - \frac{\pi(1)^5}{5}$$

$$= \frac{1023\pi}{5} \approx 642.44 \qquad \text{Volume}$$

Exercises 14-4

Average Value

Find the average value of each function over the indicated interval.

1. $f(x) = -3x + 15$, $0 \leq x \leq 5$
2. $f(x) = x^2$, $1 \leq x \leq 4$
3. $f(x) = \sqrt{x}$, $1 \leq x \leq 4$
4. $f(x) = 1/x$, $1 \leq x \leq 3$
5. $f(x) = -3x^2 + 6$, $0 \leq x \leq 1$
6. $f(x) = e^x$, $0 \leq x \leq 1$
7. Find the average value of the function $f(x) = -2x + 10$ over the interval $0 \leq x \leq 5$. Graph $f(x)$ and illustrate the geometric interpretation of its average value.
8. Find the average value of the function $f(x) = -3x^2 + 27$ over the interval $0 \leq x \leq 3$. Graph $f(x)$ and illustrate the geometric interpretation of its average value.

Applications

9. *Revenue.* The sales revenue gained from selling x units of some commodity is given by

$$R(x) = -5x^2 + 40$$

   If $0 \leq x \leq 2$, then find the average sales revenue. Graph $R(x)$ and illustrate the geometric interpretation of its average value.
10. *Population.* The population of a certain town is related to time, t (in years), by the exponential function defined by

$$P(t) = 1000e^{0.05t}$$

   Note that $t = 0$ corresponds to the year 19X0, $t = 1$ corresponds to the year 19X1, etc. Find the average population over the interval $0 \leq t \leq 10$.
11. *Temperature.* The temperature, y, of a heated cup of coffee is related to the time, t (in minutes), elapsed by the exponential function defined by

$$y = 150e^{-0.02t} \qquad (t \geq 0)$$

   Find the average temperature during the first 5 minutes (i.e., $0 \leq t \leq 5$).
12. *Radioactive decay.* A certain radioactive substance decays in accordance with the function defined by

$$y(t) = 2000e^{-0.06t} \qquad (t \geq 0)$$

   where $y(t)$ is the mass (in grams) at time t (in hours). Find the average mass of the radioactive substance during the first 3 hours.

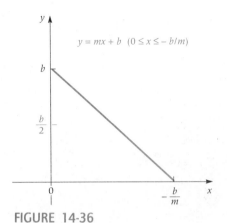

$y = mx + b \quad (0 \le x \le -b/m)$

FIGURE 14-36

13. *Compound amount.* A sum of $10,000 is deposited in a bank that pays interest at the rate of 8% compounded continuously. Find the average value of this bank account over the next 5 years.

14. *Average inventory.* An oil company stores its home heating oil in large tanks, each with a capacity of 100,000 gallons. After a tank has been filled, its level of inventory (oil) is related to the time (in days) elapsed since filling by the function defined by

$$I(t) = -5t + 100 \qquad (t \ge 0)$$

where $I(t)$ is the amount of oil (in thousands of gallons) in the tank t days after filling.
a) Graph $I(t)$.
b) Find the number of days before the tank is empty.
c) Find the average level of inventory during the time interval determined by part b.

15. Show that the average value of the linear function $y = mx + b$ in Figure 14-36 over the interval $0 \le x \le -b/m$ is $b/2$.

Volume

For each of the following, find the volume of the solid of revolution formed by rotating about the x-axis the region between the graph of the given function and the x-axis over the indicated interval. Illustrate graphically.

16. $y = 2x$ from $x = 0$ to $x = 1$
17. $y = -4x + 8$ from $x = 0$ to $x = 2$
18. $y = 3x^2$ from $x = 1$ to $x = 2$
19. $y = -6x^2 + 6$ from $x = 0$ to $x = 1$
20. $y = e^x$ from $x = 1$ to $x = 3$
21. $y = e^{-x}$ from $x = 0$ to $x = 1$
22. $y = 1/x$ from $x = 1$ to $x = 2$
23. $y = \sqrt{x}$ from $x = 1$ to $x = 4$
24. *Sphere.* $y = \sqrt{1 - x^2}$ from $x = -1$ to $x = 1$
25. *Sphere.* $y = \sqrt{4 - x^2}$ from $x = -2$ to $x = 2$
26. *Sphere.* $y = \sqrt{9 - x^2}$ from $x = -3$ to $x = 3$
27. *Sphere.* $y = \sqrt{16 - x^2}$ from $x = -4$ to $x = 4$

CHAPTER 14 HIGHLIGHTS

• Concepts

Your ability to answer the following questions is one indicator of the depth of your mastery of this chapter's concepts. Note that the questions are grouped under various topic headings. For any question that you cannot answer, refer to the appropriate section of the chapter indicated by the topic heading. Pay particular attention to the boxes within a section.

14-1 CONTINUOUS MONEY FLOW

1. State and explain the formula for total money flow.
2. State and explain the formulas for present and future values of continuous money flows.

14-2   IMPROPER INTEGRALS

   3. Give the three types of improper integrals. Explain the terms *convergent* and *divergent*.

   4. State and explain the formula for the present value of a perpetual flow.

14-3   PROBABILITY DISTRIBUTIONS

   5. Explain each of the following terms: discrete random variable, continuous random variable.

   6. Give the formula for the density function of the uniform distribution, and draw its graph.

   7. State and explain three properties of probability density functions.

   8. Give the formula for the density function of the exponential distribution, and draw its graph.

14-4   APPLICATIONS: AVERAGE VALUE AND VOLUME

   9. Give the formula for the average value of a function, and explain its geometric interpretation.

   10. State and explain the formula for a volume of a solid of revolution.

REVIEW EXERCISES

• *Continuous Money Flow*

For Exercises 1–4, assume revenues flow into a fund at the rate of $f(x)$ dollars per year, where x denotes time in years.

a)   Find the total money flow (no interest) at the end of 4 years.

b)   If the money flow, over the time interval $0 < x < 4$, is compounded continuously at 8%, find its present value.

c)   If the money flow, over the time interval $0 < x < 4$, is compounded continuously at 8%, find its future value.

   1. $f(x) = 5000$ **2.** $f(x) = 2000x$
   3. $f(x) = 2000e^{0.10x}$ **4.** $f(x) = 4000 - 40x$

• *Improper Integrals*

Evaluate whichever of the following improper integrals converge.

   5. $\int_1^\infty (1/x)\, dx$ **6.** $\int_1^\infty (1/x^2)\, dx$

   7. $\int_0^\infty e^{-x}\, dx$ **8.** $\int_9^\infty x^{-1/2}\, dx$

   9. $\int_1^\infty [1/(x + 4)^2]\, dx$ **10.** $\int_0^\infty [1/(x + 9)^3]\, dx$

   11. *Perpetual flow: Endowment fund.* A college wishes to establish an endowment fund to provide \$100,000 annually. If the fund is to be invested at 8% compounded continuously, how much should be provided now to set up the fund?

• *Probability Distributions*

   12. *Uniform distribution.* A random variable, x, is uniformly distributed over the interval $4 < x < 9$.

a) Graph its density function.

b) Determine $P(4 < x < 7)$ and shade the corresponding area on the graph.

13. *Uniform distribution.* At a given bus stop, a bus going to a certain destination appears every 20 minutes. The time (in minutes) a bus rider spends waiting at this bus stop is a random variable uniformly distributed over the interval $0 < x < 20$. If a bus rider arrives at this bus stop, find the probability that she (he) must wait

a) At least 15 minutes.
b) At most 12 minutes.
c) Between 5 and 17 minutes.
d) Between 6 and 15 minutes.

14. *Exponential distribution.* A random variable x is exponentially distributed, with $k = 0.25$. Graph the density function and find

a) $P(0 < x < 2)$
b) $P(1 < x < 3)$
c) $P(x > 2)$
d) $P(x > 1)$

15. *Service time: Exponential distribution.* The time (in minutes) it takes to change an automobile's oil at a service center is exponentially distributed, with $k = 0.10$. Find the probability that an oil change takes

a) At most 5 minutes.
b) At most 12 minutes.
c) At least 8 minutes.
d) At least 10 minutes.

16. Given the probability distribution with density function

$$f(x) = 4 - 8x \quad (0 \le x \le 0.5)$$

a) Graph $f(x)$.
b) Verify that the total area is 1.
c) Find $P(0 < x < 0.3)$.
d) Find $P(0 < x < 0.4)$.

• Average Value of a Function

For Exercises 17 and 18, find the average value of the function over the indicated interval.

17. $f(x) = -5x + 20, 0 \le x \le 4$
18. $f(x) = -x^2 + 25, -5 \le x \le 5$

19. *Revenue.* The sales revenue gained from selling x units of some product is given by

$$R(x) = -6x^2 + 240x$$

If $0 \le x \le 20$, find the average sales revenue.

20. *Compound amount.* A sum of $40,000 is deposited in a bank that pays interest at 9% compounded continuously. Find the average value of this bank account

a) Over the next 3 years.
b) Over the next 6 years.

• Volume

For Exercises 21–23, find the volume of the solid of revolution formed by rotating about the x-axis the region between the graph of the given function and the x-axis over the indicated interval. Illustrate graphically.

21. $y = 6x^2$ from $x = 0$ to $x = 4$
22. $y = 1/x^2$ from $x = 1$ to $x = 3$
23. $y = -x^2 + 4$ from $x = 0$ to $x = 2$
24. *Sphere.* $y = \sqrt{25 - x^2}$ from $x = -5$ to $x = 5$

15

FUNCTIONS OF SEVERAL VARIABLES

Introductory Application

Cost, Revenue, and Profit Functions: Two Products

A firm manufactures two competing brands of a given product. Let p_1 and p_2 be the case selling prices (in dollars) of brands 1 and 2, respectively. If x_1 cases of brand 1 and x_2 cases of brand 2 are demanded by the market, then the relationships between the unit (case) selling prices and the demands for the competing brands are given by the equations

$$x_1 = 80 - 2p_1 + p_2$$
$$x_2 = 30 + p_1 - p_2$$

If \$40 and \$30 are the unit case costs of brands 1 and 2, respectively, determine the case selling prices, p_1 and p_2, that maximize total profit, $P(p_1, p_2)$.

This problem is solved in Example 15-24.

15-1

• FUNCTIONS OF SEVERAL VARIABLES

A function such as

$$y = f(x) = x^3 + \frac{4}{x} + 17$$

has dependent variable y and independent variable x. Since there is only one independent variable, $f(x)$ is called a **function of one variable.** If a function has two independent variables—say, x and y—it is called a **function of two variables** and is usually denoted by $f(x, y)$. If a function has three independent variables—say, x, y, and w—it is called a **function of three variables** and may be denoted by $f(x, y, w)$. In general, functions of more than one variable are called **multivariate functions.**

As a specific example, we consider a company producing metal tanks. It has been determined that the daily production cost, z, is dependent on the daily number of tanks produced, x, and the daily number of person-hours used, y. These quantities are related by the multivariate function

$$z = f(x, y) = x^2 - 8x + y^2 - 12y + 1500$$

If, during a given day, the company produced $x = 2$ tanks and used $y = 5$ person-hours of labor, then the daily production cost is

$$z = f(2, 5) = 2^2 - 8(2) + 5^2 - 12(5) + 1500 = \$1453$$

A function of two variables, $z = f(x, y)$, associates a single value of z with each ordered pair of real numbers, (x, y). The set of all such ordered pairs (x, y) is the **domain** of f, and the set of all such possible values of z is called the **range** of f. If the domain of a function of two variables, $z = f(x, y)$, is not specified, then it is the set of all ordered pairs (x, y) for which the function is defined.

• EXAMPLE 15-1

Consider the function defined by

$$z = f(x, y) = \frac{x^2 + y^2 + 8}{(x - 4)(y + 3)}$$

a) Compute $f(2, 5)$.
b) Specify the domain of f.

Solutions

a) $f(2, 5) = \dfrac{(2)^2 + (5)^2 + 8}{(2 - 4)(5 + 3)}$

$= \dfrac{37}{-16} = -\dfrac{37}{16}$

Hence, the function f associates $-37/16$ with the ordered pair $(2, 5)$.

b) Since the domain of f is not specified, it is the set of all ordered pairs (x, y) for which f is defined. The function f is defined for all ordered pairs (x, y) such that $x \neq 4$ and $y \neq -3$.

• **EXAMPLE 15-2**   **Wind Power.** _____

According to Betz's Law, the available power in wind, P (in kilowatts), for a windmill with a rotor diameter of D feet and wind speed of V miles per hour (mph) is given by

$$P(D, V) = 0.0000023694D^2V^3$$

If the wind speed is 20 mph, find the power produced by a windmill with a rotor diameter of 10 feet.

Solution

Our answer is given by $P(10, 20)$. Hence,

$$P(10, 20) = 0.0000023694(10^2)(20^3)$$
$$= 1.8955 \text{ kilowatts}$$

_____ •

The concepts of the preceding paragraphs of this section can be generalized to functions of n variables, where n is a positive integer. Specifically, if, with each ordered n-tuple of real numbers $(x_1, x_2, \ldots, x_n)$, the equation $z = f(x_1, x_2, \ldots, x_n)$ associates a unique value of z, then f is called a function of $x_1, x_2, \ldots,$ and x_n. The set of all such ordered n-tuples is the *domain* of f, and the set of all such values of z is called the *range* of f. If the domain of a function of n variables is not specified, then it is the set of all ordered n-tuples $(x_1, x_2, \ldots, x_n)$ for which f is defined.

• **EXAMPLE 15-3** _____

Given

$$z = f(x_1, x_2, x_3) = \frac{x_1^2 - 4x_1x_3 + x_2^3 + 8}{(x_1 - 4)(x_3 + 6)}$$

a)   Compute $f(2, 3, 1)$.
b)   Specify the domain of f.

Solutions

a) $f(2, 3, 1) = \dfrac{(2)^2 - 4(2)(1) + (3)^3 + 8}{(2 - 4)(1 + 6)}$

$= \dfrac{31}{-14} = -\dfrac{31}{14}$

The function f associates $-31/14$ with the ordered triple $(2, 3, 1)$.

b)   Since the domain of f is not specified, it is the set of all ordered triples of real numbers (x_1, x_2, x_3) for which f is defined. The function f is defined for all ordered triples (x_1, x_2, x_3) such that $x_1 \neq 4$ and $x_3 \neq -6$.

_____ •

Revenue Function: Several Products

The sales revenue gained from selling n products is given by

$$R = x_1p_1 + x_2p_2 + \ldots + x_np_n$$

where

$x_i = $ the number of units sold of the ith product

$p_i = $ unit price of the ith product

• **EXAMPLE 15-4**   **Revenue Function: Two Products.** _____

Find the equation defining the revenue function, $R(p_1, p_2)$, where the numbers of units sold and the unit prices are related by the equations

$$x_1 = 60 - 2p_1 + p_2$$
$$x_2 = 20 + p_1 - 2p_2$$

Solution

The revenue is given by the equation

$$R = x_1 p_1 + x_2 p_2$$

Substituting the above equations for x_1 and x_2 into the above equation gives

$$R(p_1, p_2) = \overbrace{(60 - 2p_1 + p_2)}^{x_1} p_1 + \overbrace{(20 + p_1 - 2p_2)}^{x_2} p_2$$
$$= -2p_1^2 - 2p_2^2 + 2p_1 p_2 + 60p_1 + 20p_2$$

Note that the revenue function, $R(p_1, p_2)$, gives revenue in terms of the unit prices of the products.

Sales revenue can also be given in terms of x_1 and x_2, as we show in Example 15-5.

• **EXAMPLE 15-5**   **Revenue Function: Two Products.** _____

Find the equation defining the revenue function, $R(x_1, x_2)$, where the numbers of units sold and the unit prices are related by the equations

$$p_1 = 59 - 4x_1 - 3x_2$$
$$p_2 = 78 - 3x_1 - 6x_2$$

Note that prices are given in terms of number of units sold.

Solution

The revenue is given by the equation

$$R = x_1 p_1 + x_2 p_2$$

Substituting the equations for p_1 and p_2 into the above equation for revenue gives

$$R(x_1, x_2) = x_1 \overbrace{(59 - 4x_1 - 3x_2)}^{p_1} + x_2 \overbrace{(78 - 3x_1 - 6x_2)}^{p_2}$$
$$= -4x_1^2 - 6x_2^2 - 6x_1 x_2 + 59x_1 + 78x_2$$

Note that the revenue function, $R(x_1, x_2)$, gives revenue in terms of the numbers of units sold of both products.

Cobb-Douglas Production Function

Economists frequently use a model that gives production as a function of labor and capital. One such model is the *Cobb-Douglas production function*, which is given by

$$f(x, y) = Cx^a y^{1-a}$$

where C and a are constants with $0 < a < 1$, $x = $ number of units of labor, and $y = $ number of units of capital.

We now consider the following examples.

• **EXAMPLE 15-6** _____

For some company, the number of units produced when using x units of labor and y units of capital is given by the production function

$$f(x, y) = 80x^{1/4}y^{3/4}$$

Find the number of units produced when 625 units of labor and 81 units of capital are used.

Solution

$$f(625, 81) = 80(625)^{1/4}(81)^{3/4}$$
$$= 80(5)(27) = 10{,}800 \qquad \text{Production}$$

• **EXAMPLE 15-7** _____

Show, in general, for the Cobb-Douglas production function that the doubling of both labor and capital results in the doubling of production.

Solution

We begin with the equation

$$f(x, y) = Cx^a y^{1-a}$$

and replace x with $2x$ and y with $2y$ to obtain

$$f(2x, 2y) = C(2x)^a(2y)^{1-a}$$
$$= C(2)^a x^a (2)^{1-a} y^{1-a}$$
$$= (2)^a (2)^{1-a} \, Cx^a y^{1-a}$$
$$= 2Cx^a y^{1-a} \;\leftarrow$$

$$= 2 \; \boxed{f(x, y)}$$

> Production with doubled labor and capital

> Production before doubling labor and capital

Graphs of Functions of Two Variables

A function of two variables is graphed in a **three-dimensional coordinate system.** Such a system consists of three mutually perpendicular real number lines intersecting at the origin of each line, as illustrated in Figure 15-1. The two horizontal number lines are called the x-axis and the y-axis; the vertical number line is called the z-axis. Each point in a three-dimensional coordinate system is denoted by an ordered triple of real numbers (x, y, z), which locates its position relative to the three axes. The origin is denoted by the ordered triple $(0, 0, 0)$. For example, looking at Figure 15-1, the ordered triple $(2, 1, 5)$ is associated with the point that is plotted as follows:

1. Starting at the origin, move 2 units in the positive direction along the x-axis.

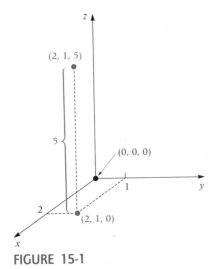

FIGURE 15-1

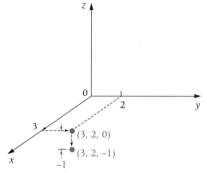

FIGURE 15-2

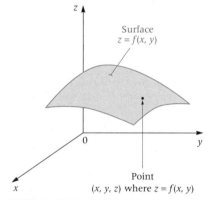

FIGURE 15-3

2. Then move 1 unit horizontally in the positive direction parallel to the y-axis.

3. Last, move 5 units vertically in the positive direction parallel to the z-axis.

• **EXAMPLE 15-8** ⎯⎯⎯⎯⎯⎯⎯⎯⎯⎯⎯⎯⎯⎯⎯⎯⎯⎯

Plot the point given by $(3, 2, -1)$ in the three-dimensional coordinate system.

Solution

Observing Figure 15-2, we begin at the origin, move 3 units in the positive direction along the x-axis, then 2 units horizontally in the positive direction parallel to the y-axis, and, finally, 1 unit vertically in the negative direction parallel to the z-axis.

⎯⎯⎯⎯⎯⎯⎯⎯⎯⎯⎯⎯⎯⎯⎯⎯⎯⎯⎯⎯⎯ •

The graph of a function of two variables

$$z = f(x, y)$$

consists of a set of points (x, y, z) such that the variables are related by the equation $z = f(x, y)$. In general, the set of such points constitutes a surface in three-dimensional space, as is illustrated in Figure 15-3.

Figure 15-4 on page 908 gives the graphs of some specific functions of two variables.

The plane of Figure 15-4(a) consists of all points (x, y, z) such that $x = x_0$, where x_0 is a constant; the plane of Figure 15-4(b) consists of all points (x, y, z) such that $y = y_0$, where y_0 is a constant.

The plane of Figure 15-4(c) consists of all points (x, y, z) such that $2x + 4y + z = 12$. The x-intercept is determined by setting both y and z equal to 0 and solving the resulting equation for x; the y-intercept is determined by setting both x and z equal to zero and solving the resulting equation for y; the z-intercept is determined by setting both x and y equal to zero and solving the resulting equation for z. The xz-trace is the intersection of the plane with the xz-plane; its equation is determined by setting $y = 0$ in the original equation. Thus, the xz-trace is the straight line $2x + z = 12$. The xy- and yz-traces are defined and obtained in a similar manner.

The plane of Figure 15-4(d) consists of all points (x, y, z) such that $5x + 3y = 30$. The surface of Figure 15-4(e) consists of all points (x, y, z) such that $z = x^2$. Note that the xz-trace of this surface is the parabola $z = x^2$.

The surface of Figure 15-4(f) consists of all points (x, y, z) such that $z = x^2 + y^2$. Here the xz-trace (set $y = 0$) is the parabola $z = x^2$, and the yz-trace (set $x = 0$) is the parabola $z = y^2$.

The surface of Figure 15-4(g) consists of all points (x, y, z) such that $z = y^2 - x^2$. The yz-trace (set $x = 0$) is the parabola $z = y^2$, and the xz-trace (set $y = 0$) is the parabola $z = -x^2$.

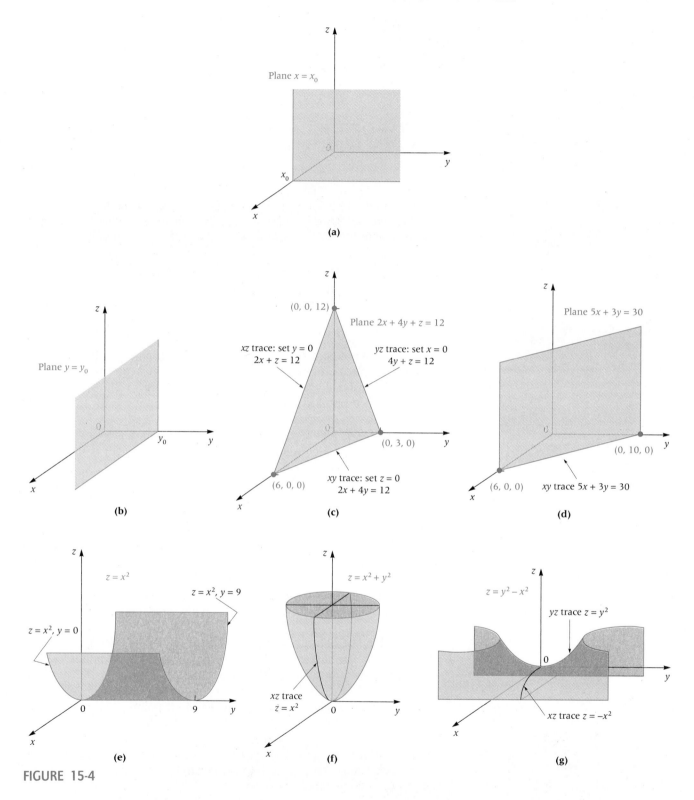

FIGURE 15-4

Exercises 15-1

1. If $f(x, y) = 3x^2 - 4y + 6xy + y^2 + 5$, then compute each of the following:
   a) $f(0, 1)$ b) $f(2, 5)$ c) $f(1, 0)$
2. If $f(x, y) = 3x^4 - 2xy + y^2 - 8x + 1$, then compute each of the following:
   a) $f(1, 3)$ b) $f(-2, 1)$ c) $f(0, -1)$
3. If $z = x^3 - y^4/4$, then find the value of z associated with $x = 2$ and $y = 1$.
4. If $H = P^2 - 5PT^2 - 4/T$, then find the value of H associated with $P = 3$ and $T = 2$.
5. If $z = f(x_1, x_2, x_3) = x_1^2 - 4x_1x_3 + x_3^2 + x_2x_3$, then
   a) z is a function of how many variables?
   b) Compute $f(2, 1, -3)$.
   c) Compute $f(-2, -1, 4)$.
6. If $K = f(H, T, P) = H^2 - 3TP + HP^3 + 5$, then
   a) K is a function of how many variables?
   b) Compute $f(4, -2, 3)$
   c) Compute $f(-3, -1, 5)$.
7. If $g(x_1, x_2, x_3, x_4) = x_1^2 + x_2x_3 + x_3^2x_4^3 + 5$, then
   a) g is a function of how many variables?
   b) Compute $g(1, -1, 2, -3)$.
   c) Compute $g(-1, 0, -3, 4)$.
8. If $f(x, y) = (3x^2 - 2xy + 5y)/(x - 2)(x + 4)$, then specify the domain of f.
9. If $g(x, y) = 4x^2 + 5x^3/y + 8/(x - 2)$, then specify the domain of g.
10. If $f(x_1 x_2, x_3) = (x_1^2 + 5x_2x_3)/(x_2 - 4)$, then specify the domain of f.
11. If $f(x, y) = (x^3 - 4xy + y^2)/\sqrt{x - 3}$, then specify the domain of f.
12. If $f(x, y) = (x^2 + 4xy + 6y)/\sqrt{x^2 - 25}$, then specify the domain of f.
13. If $f(x, y) = \ln(x/y)$, then specify the domain of f.

Plot each of the following points in a three-dimensional coordinate system.

14. $(5, 3, 9)$ 15. $(-1, 5, 2)$ 16. $(2, -3, -5)$
17. $(3, 2, -4)$ 18. $(4, 6, 9)$ 19. $(-2, 1, 8)$

Applications

20. *Revenue Function: Two products.*
    a) Find the equation defining the revenue function, $R(p_1, p_2)$, where the numbers of units sold and the unit prices are related by the equations

    $$x_1 = 80 - p_1 - 2p_2$$
    $$x_2 = 25 + 2p_1 - p_2$$

    b) Find the revenue if the unit prices of the first and second products are $5 and $8, respectively.

21. *Revenue function: Two products.*
    a) Find the equation defining the revenue function, $R(x_1, x_2)$, where the numbers of units sold and the unit prices are related by the equations

    $$p_1 = 90 - 4x_1 - 3x_2$$
    $$p_2 = 60 - 2x_1 - 5x_2$$

    b) Find the revenue gained from selling 3 and 5 units of products 1 and 2, respectively.

22. *Cobb-Douglas production function.* For some firm, the number of units produced when using x units of labor and y units of capital is given by the production function

$$f(x, y) = 100x^{1/5}y^{4/5}$$

Find the number of units produced when 243 units of labor and 32 units of capital are used.

23. *Cost Function: Two products.* The total cost (in thousands of dollars) of producing x thousand units of product 1 and y thousand units of product 2 is given by

$$C(x, y) = x^2 + 4y^2 - 2xy + 8x + 6y + 3$$

Find the total cost of producing 3 thousand units of product 1 and 5 thousand units of product 2.

24. *Revenue, cost, profit functions: Two products.* Consider the following revenue and cost functions for x and y units of products 1 and 2, respectively.

$$R(x, y) = -20x^2 - 10y^2 + 200x + 100y + 400xy + 800$$
$$C(x, y) = 10x + 5y + 100$$

a) Using the formula

$$\text{profit} = \text{revenue} - \text{cost}$$

find the equation defining the profit function.

b) Find the profit from selling 10 and 20 units of products 1 and 2, respectively.

25. *Optimum level of energy conservation.* The effectiveness of insulation in resisting heat loss is expressed by a number called its **R-value.** Fiberglass batts of insulation that are 3½ inches thick typically have an R-value of 11. Fiberglass batts of insulation that are 6 inches thick have an R-value of 19. A formula for determining the optimum R-value needed for insulating a building is

$$F(e, i, c) = \sqrt{\frac{1 + e}{c(1 + i)}}$$

where e is the fuel price growth rate (compounded annually), i is the current rate at which money earns interest (compounded annually), and c is the cost (in dollars) per square foot of insulation per unit of R.

a) If fuel prices are increasing at 15% per year (i.e., $e = 0.15$) and money currently earns interest at 10% per year (i.e., $i = 0.10$), compute the optimum R-value for insulation that costs \$0.03 per square foot per unit of R.

b) If fuel prices are increasing at 10% per year (i.e., $e = 0.10$) and money currently earns interest at 12% per year (i.e., $i = 0.12$), compute the optimum R-value for insulation that costs \$0.03 per square foot per unit of R.

15-2   • PARTIAL DERIVATIVES

Recall the company producing metal tanks in Section 15-1. It has been determined that the daily production cost, z, is dependent on the daily number of tanks produced, x, and the daily number of person-hours used, y. These quantities are related by the multivariate function

$$z = f(x, y) = x^2 - 8x + y^2 - 12y + 1500$$

We now consider finding the *instantaneous rate of change of z with respect to* x (i.e., the instantaneous rate of change of cost with respect to the number of tanks produced). This is expressed by finding the derivative of z with respect to x. However, since $z = f(x, y)$ has two independent variables, the derivative of z with respect to one of the independent variables is called a **partial derivative,** or simply a **partial.** Specifically, the derivative of z with respect to x is called the **partial derivative of z with respect to x** and is denoted by any of the following:

$$\frac{\partial z}{\partial x} \qquad f_x(x, y) \qquad f_x$$

The partial derivative of z with respect to x is found by treating x as a variable and the remaining independent variables (in this example, y) as constants and applying the differentiation rules of Chapter 9. Thus, if

$$z = f(x, y) = \boxed{x^2} - 8\,\boxed{x} + y^2 - 12y + 1500 \qquad \text{Color screen indicates the variable.}$$

then

$$f_x(x, y) = 2x - 8$$

Similarly, the *instantaneous rate of change of z with respect to* y is expressed by the **partial derivative of z with respect to y** and is denoted by any of the following:

$$\frac{\partial z}{\partial y} \qquad f_y(x, y) \qquad f_y$$

The partial derivative of z with respect to y is found by treating y as a variable and the remaining independent variables (in this example, x) as constants. Hence, if

$$z = f(x, y) = x^2 - 8x + \boxed{y^2} - 12\,\boxed{y} + 1500 \qquad \text{Color screen indicates the variable.}$$

then

$$f_y(x, y) = 2y - 12$$

If we wish to evaluate $\partial z / \partial x$ at $x = 6$ and $y = 10$, this is denoted by any of the following notations.

$$\frac{\partial z}{\partial x}\bigg|_{\substack{x = 6 \\ y = 10}} \qquad \frac{\partial z}{\partial x}\bigg|_{(6, 10)} \qquad f_x(6, 10)$$

Since $\partial z / \partial x$ or $f_x(x, y)$ is given by

$$f_x(x, y) = 2x - 8$$

then

$$\frac{\partial z}{\partial x}\bigg|_{(6, 10)} \qquad \text{or} \qquad f_x(6, 10)$$

is given by

$$f_x(6, 10) = 2(6) - 8$$
$$= 4$$

Thus, when $x = 6$ tanks are being produced daily and $y = 10$ person-hours are being used daily, the *instantaneous rate of change of cost with respect to the number of tanks produced* (i.e., the *marginal cost*) is $4. In other words, assuming the number of person-hours used daily does not change, an additional tank costs approximately $4.

Analogously, if we wish to evaluate $\partial z/\partial y$ at $x = 6$ and $y = 10$, this is denoted by any of the following notations:

$$\left.\frac{\partial z}{\partial y}\right| \begin{array}{l} x = 6 \\ y = 10 \end{array} \qquad \left.\frac{\partial z}{\partial y}\right|(6, 10) \qquad f_y(6, 10)$$

Since $\partial z/\partial y$ or $f_y(x, y)$ is given by

$$f_y(x, y) = 2y - 12$$

then

$$\left.\frac{\partial z}{\partial y}\right|(6, 10) \qquad \text{or} \qquad f_y(6, 10)$$

is given by

$$f_y(6, 10) = 2(10) - 12$$
$$= 8$$

Thus, when $x = 6$ tanks are being produced daily and $y = 10$ person-hours are being used daily, an additional person-hour costs approximately $8. This assumes the number of tanks produced daily remains fixed.

We summarize as follows.

Partial Derivatives

If $z = f(x, y)$, then

1. The **partial derivative of z with respect to x** is

    $$f_x = \frac{\partial z}{\partial x} = \text{instantaneous rate of change of } z \text{ with respect to } x$$

    assuming that y is held constant. To find f_x, use the derivative rules (i.e., the power rule, product rule, quotient rule, etc.) of Chapters 9 and 12, while treating y as a constant.

2. The **partial derivative of z with respect to y** is

    $$f_y = \frac{\partial z}{\partial y} = \text{instantaneous rate of change of } z \text{ with respect to } y$$

    assuming that x is held constant. To find f_y, use the derivative rules (i.e., the power rule, product rule, quotient rule, etc.) of Chapters 9 and 12, while treating x as a constant.

• **EXAMPLE 15-9** _____

If $z = f(x, y) = 3x^2 + 4x^2y^3 - 6x + 8y - 9$, then find each of the following:

a) f_x **b)** $f_x(1, 2)$ **c)** f_y **d)** $f_y(2, -1)$

Solutions

a) We find f_x from

$$f(x, y) = 3\;\boxed{x^2}\; + 4\;\boxed{x^2}\;y^3 - 6\;\boxed{x}\; + 8y - 9 \qquad \text{Color screens indicate the variable.}$$

by using the power rule, treating x as a variable and y as a constant. Hence,

$$f_x(x, y) = 6x + 8xy^3 - 6$$

> Note that for the term $4x^2y^3$, $4y^3$ is treated as the constant coefficient of x^2. Thus, the derivative with respect to x is $4y^3(2x) = 8xy^3$.

b) $f_x(1, 2) = 6(1) + 8(1)(2)^3 - 6$
       $= 64$

c) We find f_y from

$$f(x, y) = 3x^2 + 4x^2\;\boxed{y^3}\; - 6x + 8\;\boxed{y}\; - 9 \qquad \text{Color screens indicate the variable.}$$

by using the power rule, treating y as a variable and x as a constant. Hence,

$$f_y(x, y) = 12x^2y^2 + 8$$

> Note that for the term $4x^2y^3$, $4x^2$ is treated as the constant coefficient of y^3. Thus, the derivative with respect to y is $4x^2(3y^2) = 12x^2y^2$.

d) $f_y(2, -1) = 12(2)^2(-1)^2 + 8$
       $= 56$

_____ •

Graphical Interpretation of Partial Derivatives

Up to this point, we have discussed the computation and application of partial derivatives. We now focus on the graphical interpretation of partial derivatives.

Consider a function of two variables defined by

$$z = f(x, y)$$

and assume its graph is the surface in Figure 15-5. Since $\partial z/\partial x$ or $f_x(x, y)$ is the instantaneous rate of change of z with respect to x, while y is held constant, then $\partial z/\partial x$ or $f_x(x, y)$ is formally defined as

$$f_x(x, y) = \lim_{\Delta x \to 0} \frac{f(x + \Delta x, y) - f(x, y)}{\Delta x} \qquad \text{Formal definition of } f_x$$

If we evaluate $f_x(x, y)$ at $x = x_0$ and $y = y_0$, where x_0 and y_0 are constant real numbers, then $f_x(x_0, y_0)$ gives the slope of the straight line tangent to the curve $z = f(x, y_0)$ on the graph of $f(x)$ at (x_0, y_0, z_0), where $z_0 = f(x_0, y_0)$, as illustrated in Figure 15-5. The curve $z = f(x, y_0)$ is the intersection of the plane $y = y_0$ and the surface $z = f(x, y)$, as shown in Figure 15-5.

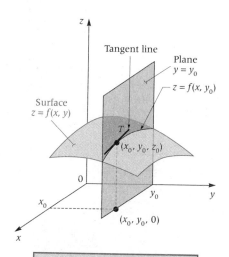

$f_x(x_0, y_0) = $ slope of tangent line, T

FIGURE 15-5

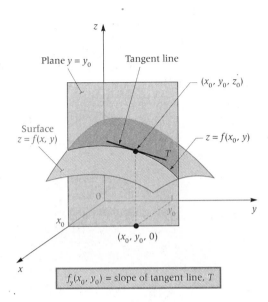

FIGURE 15-6

Analagously, $\partial z/\partial y$ or $f_y(x, y)$ is defined as

$$f_y(x, y) = \lim_{\Delta y \to 0} \frac{f(x, y + \Delta y) - f(x, y)}{\Delta y}$$ Formal definition of f_y

If we evaluate $f_y(x, y)$ at $x = x_0$ and $y = y_0$, where x_0 and y_0 are constant real numbers, then $f_y(x_0, y_0)$ gives the slope of the straight line tangent to the curve $z = f(x_0, y)$ on the graph of $f(x, y)$ at (x_0, y_0, z_0), where $z_0 = f(x_0, y_0)$, as illustrated in Figure 15-6. The curve $z = f(x_0, y)$ is the intersection of the plane $x = x_0$ and the surface $z = f(x, y)$, as shown in Figure 15-6.

We now give more examples of partial derivatives.

• EXAMPLE 15-10

If $f(x, y) = \ln (x^2 + y^2)$, find

a) f_x **b)** f_y

Solutions

Using the rule that the derivative of $\ln u$ is $1/u$ times the derivative of u, we let $u = x^2 + y^2$ and obtain the following:

a) $f_x(x, y) = \underset{\frac{1}{u}}{\underbrace{\frac{1}{x^2 + y^2}}} \ \underset{\frac{\partial u}{\partial x}}{\underbrace{(2x)}} = \frac{2x}{x^2 + y^2}$

b) $f_y(x, y) = \underset{\frac{1}{u}}{\underbrace{\frac{1}{x^2 + y^2}}} \ \underset{\frac{\partial u}{\partial y}}{\underbrace{(2y)}} = \frac{2y}{x^2 + y^2}$

• EXAMPLE 15-11

If $f(x, y) = e^{x^2 + y^3}$, find each of the following:

a) f_x **b)** f_y

Solutions

Using the rule that the derivative of e^u is e^u times the derivative of u, we let $u = x^2 + y^3$ and obtain the following:

a) $f_x(x, y) = \underset{e^u}{\boxed{e^{x^2+y}}} \; \underset{\frac{\partial u}{\partial x}}{\boxed{(2x)}} = 2xe^{x^2+y^3}$

b) $f_y(x, y) = \underset{e^u}{\boxed{e^{x^2+y^3}}} \; \underset{\frac{\partial u}{\partial y}}{\boxed{(3y^2)}} = 3y^2e^{x^2+y^3}$

• **EXAMPLE 15-12** _____

If $f(x, y) = (x^2 + y^4)e^{x^3+y^2}$, find each of the following:

a) f_x **b)** f_y

Since the function $f(x, y)$ is a product of two functions, we must use the product rule. Also, within the product rule, we must use the rule that the derivative of e^u is e^u times the derivative of u. Of course, all derivatives are partial derivatives.

a)

(first) $\begin{pmatrix}\text{partial derivative}\\ \text{of second}\end{pmatrix}$ + (second) $\begin{pmatrix}\text{partial derivative}\\ \text{of first}\end{pmatrix}$

$f_x(x, y) = (x^2 + y^4)\; \underset{e^u}{\boxed{e^{x^3+y^2}}} \; \underset{\frac{\partial u}{\partial x}}{\boxed{(3x^2)}} + e^{x^3+y^2}(2x)$ Partial derivatives with respect to x

$= [(x^2 + y^4)(3x^2) + 2x]e^{x^3+y^2}$

$= (3x^4 + 3x^2y^4 + 2x)e^{x^3+y^2}$

b)

(first) $\begin{pmatrix}\text{partial derivative}\\ \text{of second}\end{pmatrix}$ + (second) $\begin{pmatrix}\text{partial derivative}\\ \text{of first}\end{pmatrix}$

$f_y(x, y) = (x^2 + y^4)\; \underset{e^u}{\boxed{e^{x^3+y^2}}} \; \underset{\frac{\partial u}{\partial y}}{\boxed{(2y)}} + e^{x^3+y^2}(4y^3)$ Partial derivatives with respect to y

$= [(x^2 + y^4)(2y) + 4y^3]e^{x^3+y^2}$

$= (2x^2y + 2y^5 + 4y^3)e^{x^3+y^2}$

Application

• **EXAMPLE 15-13**

The revenue, z, derived from selling x calculators and y adding machines is given by the function

$$z = f(x, y) = -x^2 + 8x - 2y^2 + 6y + 2xy + 50$$

a) At a sales level of $x = 4$ calculators and $y = 3$ adding machines, find the marginal revenue resulting from the sale of 1 additional calculator.

b) At a sales level of $x = 4$ calculators and $y = 3$ adding machines, find the marginal revenue resulting from the sale of 1 additional adding machine.

Solutions

a) Since the marginal revenue resulting from the sale of 1 additional calculator is defined as the instantaneous rate of change of z with respect to x, we calculate f_x by treating x as a variable and y as a constant. We thus obtain

$$f_x(x, y) = -2x + 8 + 2y$$
$$f_x(4, 3) = -2(4) + 8 + 2(3) = 6 \qquad \text{Marginal Revenue}$$

Therefore, at $x = 4$ and $y = 3$, sales revenue is increasing at the rate of approximately \$6 per calculator sold. Hence, the *marginal revenue* is \$6.

b) Since the marginal revenue resulting from the sale of 1 additional adding machine is defined as the instantaneous rate of change of z with respect to y, we calculate f_y by treating y as a variable and x as a constant. Here we get

$$f_y(x, y) = -4y + 6 + 2x$$
$$f_y(4, 3) = -4(3) + 6 + 2(4) = 2 \qquad \text{Marginal Revenue}$$

Thus, at $x = 4$ and $y = 3$, sales revenue is increasing at the rate of approximately \$2 per adding machine. Hence, the *marginal revenue* is \$2.

Cobb-Douglas Production Function

As stated in Section 15-1 economists frequently use a model that gives production as a function of labor and capital. One such model is the Cobb-Douglas production function, which is given by

$$f(x, y) = Cx^a y^{1-a}$$

where C is a positive constant and $0 < a < 1$. Here $f(x, y)$ denotes the number of units produced using x units of labor and y units of capital. The partial derivatives are interpreted below.

$$f_x = \text{marginal productivity of labor}$$
$$f_y = \text{marginal productivity of capital}$$

We now consider the following example.

• **EXAMPLE 15-14** _____

For some firm, the number of units produced when using x units of labor and y units of capital is given by the production function

$$f(x, y) = 80x^{1/4}y^{3/4}$$

a) Find the equations for both marginal productivities.
b) Evaluate and interpret the results of part a when 625 units of labor and 81 units of capital are used.

Solutions

a) Equations for marginal productivities:

$$f_x(x, y) = 80\left(\frac{1}{4}\right)x^{-3/4}y^{3/4} = 20x^{-3/4}y^{3/4} \qquad \text{Labor}$$

$$f_y(x, y) = 80x^{1/4}\left(\frac{3}{4}\right)y^{-1/4} = 60x^{1/4}y^{-1/4} \qquad \text{Capital}$$

b)
$$f_x(625, 81) = 20(625)^{-3/4}(81)^{3/4}$$
$$= 20\left(\frac{1}{125}\right)(27) = 4.32 \qquad \text{Marginal Productivity of Labor}$$

Thus, when 625 units of labor and 81 units of capital are used, 1 more unit of labor results in approximately 4.32 more units of production.

$$f_y(625, 81) = 60(625)^{1/4}(81)^{-1/4}$$
$$= 60(5)\left(\frac{1}{3}\right) = 100 \qquad \text{Marginal Productivity of Capital}$$

Thus, when 625 units of labor and 81 units of capital are used, 1 more unit of capital results in approximately 100 more units of production.

•

Second Partial Derivatives

The partial derivative of a partial derivative is called a **second partial derivative,** or simply a **second partial.** Specifically, if $z = f(x, y)$, then there are four second partials:

1. The partial derivative of $\partial z/\partial x$ with respect to x, or

$$\frac{\partial}{\partial x}\left(\frac{\partial z}{\partial x}\right)$$

| Take the first partial with respect to x. Then take the partial of that result again with respect to x. |

This is denoted by any of the following:

$$\frac{\partial^2 z}{\partial x^2} \qquad f_{xx}(x, y) \qquad f_{xx}$$

2. The partial derivative of $\partial z/\partial y$ with respect to y, or

$$\frac{\partial}{\partial y}\left(\frac{\partial z}{\partial y}\right)$$

| Take the first partial with respect to y. Then take the partial of that result again with respect to y. |

This is denoted by any of the following:

$$\frac{\partial^2 z}{\partial y^2} \qquad f_{yy}(x, y) \qquad f_{yy}$$

3. The partial derivative of $\partial z/\partial y$ with respect to x, or

$$\frac{\partial}{\partial x}\left(\frac{\partial z}{\partial y}\right)$$

| Take the first partial with respect to y. Then take the partial of that result with respect to x. |

This is denoted by any of the following:

$$\frac{\partial^2 z}{\partial x \partial y} \qquad f_{yx}(x, y) \qquad f_{yx}$$

4. The partial derivative of $\partial z/\partial x$ with respect to y, or

$$\frac{\partial}{\partial y}\left(\frac{\partial z}{\partial x}\right)$$

| Take the first partial with respect to x. Then take the partial of that result with respect to y. |

This is denoted by any of the following:

$$\frac{\partial^2 z}{\partial y \partial x} \qquad f_{xy}(x, y) \qquad f_{xy}$$

Therefore, if

$$z = f(x, y) = x^5 - y^4 + 3x^2y^6 + 18$$

then

$$f_x = 5x^4 + 6xy^6$$

The derivative of f_x with respect to x is f_{xx}. Thus, treating x as a variable and y as a constant, we differentiate f_x with respect to x to obtain

$$f_{xx} = 20x^3 + 6y^6$$

The derivative of f_x with respect to y is f_{xy}. Returning to f_x, we treat y as a variable and x as a constant and differentiate f_x with respect to y to obtain

$$f_{xy} = 36xy^5$$

Returning to $z = f(x, y) = x^5 - y^4 + 3x^2y^6 + 18$, we calculate

$$f_y = -4y^3 + 18x^2y^5$$

The derivative of f_y with respect to y is f_{yy}. Treating x as a constant and y as a variable, we differentiate f_y with respect to y to obtain

$$f_{yy} = -12y^2 + 90x^2y^4$$

The derivative of f_y with respect to x is f_{yx}. Returning to f_y, we treat x as a variable and y as a constant and differentiate f_y with respect to x to obtain

$$f_{yx} = 36xy^5$$

Observe that $f_{xy} = f_{yx}$. This is always true if f_x, f_y, f_{xy}, and f_{yx} are all continuous. In this text, $f_{xy} = f_{yx}$ for all functions $z = f(x, y)$.

• **EXAMPLE 15-15** _____

If $z = f(x, y) = 3x^2 + 4y^5 - 8x^3y^6 + 15$, calculate each of the following:

a) f_x b) f_{xx} c) $f_{xx}(1, 0)$ d) f_{xy}
e) f_y f) f_{yy} g) f_{yx} h) $f_{yx}(-1, 1)$

Solutions

a) $f_x = 6x - 24x^2y^6$
b) $f_{xx} = 6 - 48xy^6$
c) $f_{xx}(1, 0) = 6 - 48(1)(0)^6 = 6$
d) $f_{xy} = -144x^2y^5$
e) $f_y = 20y^4 - 48x^3y^5$
f) $f_{yy} = 80y^3 - 240x^3y^4$
g) $f_{yx} = -144x^2y^5$
h) $f_{yx}(-1, 1) = -144(-1)^2(1)^5 = -144$

_____ •

Exercises 15-2

1. If $f(x, y) = 3x^2 + 4y^3 + 6xy - x^2y^3 + 5$, find each of the following:
   a) f_x b) f_y c) $f_x(1, -1)$ d) $f_y(2, 1)$

2. If $f(x, y) = 4x^2 - 2y^4 + 6x^2y^2 - xy + 3$, find each of the following:
   a) f_x b) f_y c) $f_x(-1, 2)$ d) $f_y(0, 2)$

3. If $z = x^3 + y^5 - 8xy + 2x^3y^2 + 11$, find each of the following:
   a) $\dfrac{\partial z}{\partial x}$ b) $\dfrac{\partial z}{\partial y}$

4. $f_x(x, y) = 5x^2 + 8y^4 - 2x^3y^6 + 7xy + 9$, find each of the following:
   a) $f_x(x, y)$ b) $f_y(x, y)$
   c) $f_x(1, 2)$ d) $f_y(0, 3)$

5. If $f(x, y) = 8x^3 - 2y^2 - 7x^5y^8 + 8xy^2 + y + 6$, find each of the following:
   a) $f_x(x, y)$ b) $f_y(x, y)$
   c) $f_x(1, 2)$ d) $f_y(1, 2)$

6. If $s = x^3 + 4y^2 + y^4 - xy + x^3y^2 + 18$, find each of the following:
   a) $\dfrac{\partial s}{\partial x}$ b) $\dfrac{\partial s}{\partial y}$

7. If $z = 4x^6 - 8x^3 - 7x + 6xy + 8y + x^3y^5$, find each of the following:
   a) $\dfrac{\partial z}{\partial x}$ b) $\dfrac{\partial z}{\partial y}$ c) $\dfrac{\partial^2 z}{\partial x^2}$
   d) $\dfrac{\partial^2 z}{\partial y^2}$ e) $\dfrac{\partial^2 z}{\partial x \partial y}$ f) $\dfrac{\partial^2 z}{\partial y \partial x}$

8. If $f(x, y) = 4x^2 - 8y^3 + 6x^5y^2 + 4x + 6y + 9$, find each of the following:
   a) $f_x(x, y)$ b) $f_y(x, y)$
   c) $f_x(2, 1)$ d) $f_y(0, 2)$
   e) $f_{xx}(x, y)$ f) $f_{yy}(x, y)$
   g) $f_{xx}(2, 1)$ h) $f_{yy}(1, 0)$
   i) $f_{xy}(x, y)$ j) $f_{yx}(x, y)$
   k) $f_{xy}(2, 3)$ l) $f_{yx}(2, 3)$

9. If $f(x, y) = 1000 - x^3 - y^2 + 4x^3y^6 + 8y$, find each of the following:
   a) f_x b) f_y c) f_{xx} d) f_{yy}
   e) f_{xy} f) f_{yx} g) $f_x(2, -1)$ h) $f_{yy}(1, 3)$

10. If $f(x, y) = \ln(x^3 + y^2)$, find each of the following:
   a) f_x b) f_y c) f_{xx} d) f_{yy}

11. If $z = x^3 e^{x^2 + y^2}$, find each of the following:
   a) $\dfrac{\partial z}{\partial x}$ b) $\dfrac{\partial z}{\partial y}$

12. If $z = \dfrac{x^3 + 4xy^2}{2x - 3y}$, find each of the following:
   a) $\dfrac{\partial z}{\partial x}$ b) $\dfrac{\partial z}{\partial y}$

13. If $f(x, y) = (x^3 + y^2)e^{2x + 3y + 5}$, find each of the following:
   a) $f_x(x, y)$ b) $f_y(x, y)$ c) $f_x(0, 1)$

14. If $f(x, y) = (x^2 + 2y^5) \cdot \ln(x^2 + 2y + y^3)$, find each of the following:
   a) f_x b) f_y c) $f_x(1, 0)$ d) $f_y(1, 0)$

Applications

15. *Cost.* The cost of producing x washers and y dryers is given by

$$C(x, y) = 40x + 200y + 10xy + 300$$

Presently, 50 washers and 90 dryers are being produced. Find the marginal cost of producing

a) 1 more washer.   b) 1 more dryer.

16. *Revenue.* The revenue derived from selling x toasters and y broilers is given by

$$R(x, y) = 2x^2 + y^2 + 4x + 5y + 1000$$

At present, the retailer is selling 30 toasters and 50 broilers. Which of these two product lines should be expanded in order to yield the greater increase in revenue?

17. *Profit.* The annual profit of a certain hotel is given by

$$P(x, y) = 100x^2 + 4y^2 + 2x + 5y + 100{,}000$$

where x is the number of rooms available for rent and y is the monthly advertising expenditures. Presently, the hotel has 90 rooms available and is spending \$1000 per month on advertising.

a) If an additional room is constructed in an unfinished area, how will this affect annual profits?

b) If an additional dollar is spent on monthly advertising expenditures, how will this affect annual profit?

18. *Competitive pricing.* Two brands of ice cream, Farmer's Delight and Mellow Creme, are competing for the same market. The demands (in cases) for Farmer's Delight and Mellow Creme are represented by D_f and D_m, respectively. If x is the price of one case of Farmer's Delight and y is the price of one case of Mellow Creme, then

$$D_f = 5000 - 50x + 25y - 2xy$$
$$D_m = 6000 + 30x - 20y - xy$$

In economics, these two products are said to be competitive at those values of x and y for which

$$\frac{\partial D_f}{\partial y} > 0 \quad \text{and} \quad \frac{\partial D_m}{\partial x} > 0$$

Find those prices at which these two products are competitive.

15-3 • RELATIVE MAXIMA AND MINIMA (FUNCTIONS OF TWO VARIABLES)

Relative maxima and minima of multivariate functions are defined in a manner similar to that used for single variable functions. The graphs in Figure 15-7 illustrate relative maximum and minimum points of multivariate functions. Notice that the point labeled "Relative minimum" is lower than any of its neighboring points and that the point labeled "Relative maximum" is higher than any of its neighboring points.

Specifically, a function $z = f(x, y)$ is said to have a *relative maximum* at the point (x_0, y_0) if $f(x_0, y_0) \geq f(x, y)$ for all points (x, y) neighboring (x_0, y_0). A function $z = f(x, y)$ is said to have a *relative minimum* at the point (x_0, y_0) if $f(x_0, y_0) \leq f(x, y)$ for all points (x, y) neighboring (x_0, y_0).

To determine relative maxima and relative minima of functions of two variables, we use the first-derivative rule for functions of two variables.

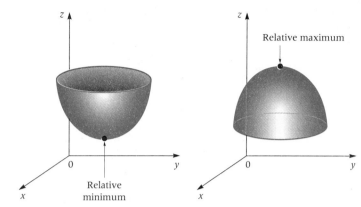

FIGURE 15-7

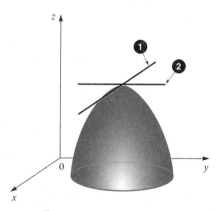

1. $f_x = 0$: slope of tangent line

2. $f_y = 0$: slope of tangent line

FIGURE 15-8

> **First-Derivative Rule for Functions of Two Variables**
>
> If the function $z = f(x, y)$ has either a relative maximum or a relative minimum at a point (x_0, y_0), and if $f_x(x_0, y_0)$ and $f_y(x_0, y_0)$ exist, then
>
> $$f_x(x_0, y_0) = 0$$
> $$f_y(x_0, y_0) = 0$$

This rule states that if a function $z = f(x, y)$ has either a relative maximum or a relative minimum at a point (x_0, y_0) and if both partial derivatives $\partial z/\partial x$ and $\partial z/\partial y$ exist at (x_0, y_0), then it is necessary that both partial derivatives, when evaluated at $x = x_0$ and $y = y_0$, to be equal to 0. This is because at a relative maximum or minimum located at (x_0, y_0), the slope, $f_x(x_0, y_0)$, of the tangent line parallel to the xz-plane is 0 and the slope, $f_y(x_0, y_0)$, of the tangent line parallel to the yz-plane is 0 as is illustrated in Figure 15-8. Such a point (x_0, y_0), at which both partial derivatives $\partial z/\partial x$ and $\partial z/\partial y$ equal 0, is called a critical point of the function $z = f(x, y)$.

Thus, to determine relative maxima and relative minima of functions of two variables, we first search for critical points. A point (x_0, y_0) is called a critical point of $z = f(x, y)$ if

$$f_x(x_0, y_0) = 0 \quad \text{and} \quad f_y(x_0, y_0) = 0$$

Critical points yield candidates for relative maxima/minima.

• **EXAMPLE 15-16** _____

Find the critical points of the function

$$z = f(x, y) = x^2 - 8x + y^2 - 12y + 1500$$

Solution

We must compute f_x and f_y, set them equal to 0, and solve for x and y. Computing f_x and f_y gives

$$f_x = 2x - 8 \quad \text{and} \quad f_y = 2y - 12$$

Setting f_x and f_y equal to 0 and solving for x and y yields

$$0 = 2x - 8 \qquad 0 = 2y - 12$$
$$x = 4 \qquad y = 6$$

Thus, the point $(x_0, y_0) = (4, 6)$ is the only critical point of the function $z = f(x, y)$.

• EXAMPLE 15-17

Find the critical points of

$$z = f(x, y) = x^2 + 2xy + 1.5y^2 - 16x + y + 1000$$

Solution

We must compute f_x and f_y, set them equal to 0, and solve for x and y. Computing f_x and f_y gives

$$f_x = 2x + 2y - 16$$
$$f_y = 2x + 3y + 1$$

Setting f_x and f_y equal to 0 gives the linear system

$$0 = 2x + 2y - 16$$
$$0 = 2x + 3y + 1$$

Solving this linear system, we obtain $x = 25$ and $y = -17$. Thus, $(25, -17)$ is the only critical point of the function $z = f(x, y)$.

• EXAMPLE 15-18

Find the critical points of

$$z = f(x, y) = x^3 + x^2y + 2x - 4y + 8$$

Solution

We must compute f_x and f_y, set them equal to 0, and solve for x and y. Computing f_x and f_y gives

$$f_x = 3x^2 + 2xy + 2$$
$$f_y = x^2 - 4$$

Setting f_x and f_y equal to 0 gives the equations

$$3x^2 + 2xy + 2 = 0$$
$$x^2 - 4 = 0$$

Since this set of equations does not constitute a linear system, we attempt to solve one of the equations for one of its unknowns and substitute the result(s) into the other equation to solve for the remaining unknown.

Solving the second equation, $x^2 - 4 = 0$, gives $x = \pm 2$. Solving the first equation, $3x^2 + 2xy + 2 = 0$, for y gives

$$y = \frac{-3x^2 - 2}{2x}$$

Substituting $x = 2$ into this equation gives

$$y = \frac{-3(2)^2 - 2}{2(2)}$$
$$= \frac{-14}{4} = -\frac{7}{2}$$

Thus, $(2, -7/2)$ is a critical point. Substituting $x = -2$ into the equation for y gives

$$y = \frac{-3(-2)^2 - 2}{2(-2)}$$

$$= \frac{-14}{-4} = \frac{7}{2}$$

Thus, $(-2, 7/2)$ is another critical point.

As previously stated in this section, we first search for critical points when attempting to determine relative maxima and relative minima of functions of two variables. However, a critical point may or may not yield either a relative maximum or a relative minimum. Recall that this is also the case with functions of one variable. Just as we have a second-derivative test for functions of one variable, we also have a similar test to identify the relative maxima and minima of functions of two variables. This test is stated as follows.

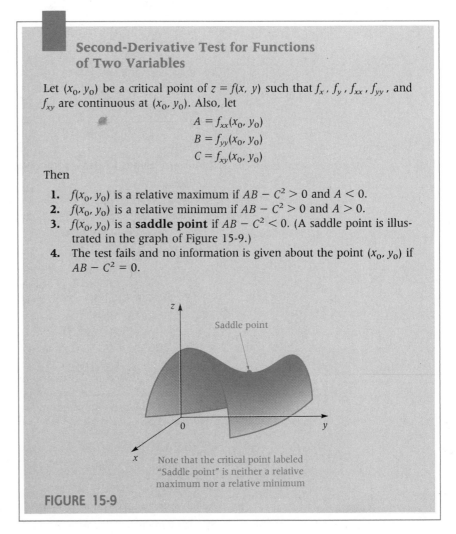

Second-Derivative Test for Functions of Two Variables

Let (x_0, y_0) be a critical point of $z = f(x, y)$ such that f_x, f_y, f_{xx}, f_{yy}, and f_{xy} are continuous at (x_0, y_0). Also, let

$$A = f_{xx}(x_0, y_0)$$
$$B = f_{yy}(x_0, y_0)$$
$$C = f_{xy}(x_0, y_0)$$

Then

1. $f(x_0, y_0)$ is a relative maximum if $AB - C^2 > 0$ and $A < 0$.
2. $f(x_0, y_0)$ is a relative minimum if $AB - C^2 > 0$ and $A > 0$.
3. $f(x_0, y_0)$ is a **saddle point** if $AB - C^2 < 0$. (A saddle point is illustrated in the graph of Figure 15-9.)
4. The test fails and no information is given about the point (x_0, y_0) if $AB - C^2 = 0$.

Saddle point

0

z

x

y

Note that the critical point labeled "Saddle point" is neither a relative maximum nor a relative minimum

FIGURE 15-9

The subsequent examples in this section illustrate the use of this test.

• **EXAMPLE 15-19** _____

Find any relative maxima and minima of the function

$$z = f(x, y) = x^2 - 8x + y^2 - 12y + 1500$$

Solution

First, we find the critical points. Computing f_x and f_y gives

$$f_x = 2x - 8$$
$$f_y = 2y - 12$$

Setting f_x and f_y equal to 0 and solving for x and y gives $x = 4$ and $y = 6$. Hence, (4, 6) is the only critical point.

We now apply the second-derivative test for functions of two variables. Computing f_{xx}, f_{yy}, and f_{xy} gives

$$f_{xx}(x, y) = 2 \qquad f_{yy}(x, y) = 2 \qquad f_{xy}(x, y) = 0$$

Evaluating each of these at the critical point (4, 6) gives

$$A = f_{xx}(4, 6) = 2$$
$$B = f_{yy}(4, 6) = 2$$
$$C = f_{xy}(4, 6) = 0$$
$$AB - C^2 = 2(2) - 0^2 = 4$$

Since $AB - C^2 > 0$ and $A > 0$, then, according to the second-derivative test, a relative minimum occurs at (4, 6). Thus, the relative minimum value of z is

$$z = f(4, 6) = (4)^2 - 8(4) + 6^2 - 12(6) + 1500 = 1448 \qquad \text{Relative Minimum}$$

At this point, we state a procedure for finding relative maximum and minimum values for functions of two variables.

To Find Relative Extrema for Functions of Two Variables

1. Search for critical points.
   - Find the first-order partials f_x and f_y.
   - Set the first-order partials equal to zero, and solve for x and y.
   - Determine all possible ordered pairs (x, y) that satisfy both equations
     $$f_x(x, y) = 0 \qquad \text{and} \qquad f_y(x, y) = 0$$
   These are the critical points.
2. Apply the second-derivative test for functions of two variables.
   - Compute the second-order partials f_{xx}, f_{yy}, and f_{xy}.
   - Evaluate the second-order partials at each critical point.
   - Apply the second-derivative test to each critical point.

• **EXAMPLE 15-20** _____

Consider the function

$$z = f(x, y) = -x^2 + 8x - 2y^2 + 6y + 2xy + 50$$

where z is the sales revenue derived from selling x calculators and y adding machines.

a) How many calculators and adding machines should be sold in order to maximize sales revenue?

b) What is the maximum sales revenue?

Solutions

Critical Points

a) We first calculate f_x and f_y, as follows:

$$f_x = -2x + 8 + 2y$$
$$f_y = -4y + 6 + 2x$$

Setting f_x and f_y equal to 0, we have

$$0 = -2x + 8 + 2y$$
$$0 = -4y + 6 + 2x$$

Solving this linear system for x and y, we obtain $x = 11$ and $y = 7$. Thus, the only critical point is $(11, 7)$.

Second-Derivative Test

We calculate

$$f_{xx} = -2 \qquad f_{yy} = -4 \qquad f_{xy} = 2$$

Since the critical point is $(11, 7)$, then

$$A = f_{xx}(11, 7) = -2$$
$$B = f_{yy}(11, 7) = -4$$
$$C = f_{xy}(11, 7) = 2$$
$$AB - C^2 = -2(-4) - 2^2 = 4$$

Since $AB - C^2 > 0$ and $A < 0$, then, according to the second-derivative test, a relative maximum occurs at $(11, 7)$. Thus, in order to maximize revenue, $x = 11$ calculators and $y = 7$ adding machines must be sold.

b) The maximum sales revenue is

$$z = f(11, 7) = -(11)^2 + 8(11) - 2(7)^2 + 6(7) + 2(11)(7) + 50$$
$$= \$115 \qquad \text{Relative maximum}$$

• EXAMPLE 15-21

Find any relative maxima and minima of the function

$$f(x, y) = 3x^2 - x^3 + 12y^2 - 8y^3 + 60$$

Solution

Critical Points

$$f_x = 6x - 3x^2 = 0 \qquad f_y = 24y - 24y^2 = 0$$
$$= 3x(2 - x) = 0 \qquad = 24y(1 - y) = 0$$
$$x = 0 \quad x = 2 \qquad y = 0 \quad y = 1$$

Possible ordered pairs (or critical points)

			Verify that $f_x = 0$ and $f_y = 0$	
$x = 0$	$y = 0$	$(0, 0)$	$f_x(0, 0) = 0$	$f_y(0, 0) = 0$
	$y = 1$	$(0, 1)$	$f_x(0, 1) = 0$	$f_y(0, 1) = 0$
$x = 2$	$y = 0$	$(2, 0)$	$f_x(2, 0) = 0$	$f_y(2, 0) = 0$
	$y = 1$	$(2, 1)$	$f_x(2, 1) = 0$	$f_y(2, 1) = 0$

↑
critical points

Since all of the above ordered pairs satisfy both equations, $f_x = 0$ and $f_y = 0$, then they are critical points, as indicated above.

Second-Derivative Test

Second-order partials:

$$f_{xx}(x, y) = 6 - 6x \qquad f_{yy}(x, y) = 24 - 48y \qquad f_{xy}(x, y) = 0$$

Apply the second-derivative test to each critical point.

Critical Point (0, 0)

$$A = f_{xx}(0, 0) = 6 \qquad B = f_{yy}(0, 0) = 24 \qquad C = f_{xy}(0, 0) = 0$$
$$AB - C^2 = (6)(24) - 0^2 = 144$$

Since $A > 0$ and $AB - C^2 > 0$, then, by the second-derivative test for functions of two variables, a relative minimum occurs at $(0, 0)$. Hence,

$$f(0, 0) = 3(0)^2 - (0)^3 + 12(0)^2 - 8(0)^3 + 60 = 60 \qquad \text{Relative minimum}$$

Critical Point (0, 1)

$$A = f_{xx}(0, 1) = 6 \qquad B = f_{yy}(0, 1) = -24 \qquad C = f_{xy}(0, 1) = 0$$
$$AB - C^2 = (6)(-24) - 0^2 = -144$$

Since $AB - C^2 < 0$, a saddle point occurs at $(0, 1)$.

Critical Point (2, 0)

$$A = f_{xx}(2, 0) = -6 \qquad B = f_{yy}(2, 0) = 24 \qquad C = f_{xy}(2, 0) = 0$$
$$AB - C^2 = (-6)(24) - 0^2 = -144$$

Since $AB - C^2 < 0$, a saddle point occurs at $(2, 0)$.

Critical Point (2, 1)

$$A = f_{xx}(2, 1) = -6 \qquad B = f_{yy}(2, 1) = -24 \qquad C = f_{xy}(2, 1) = 0$$
$$AB - C^2 = (-6)(-24) - 0^2 = 144$$

Since $A < 0$ and $AB - C^2 > 0$, a relative maximum occurs at $(2, 1)$. Hence,

$$f(2, 1) = 3(2)^2 - (2)^3 + 12(1)^2 - 8(1)^3 + 60 = 68 \qquad \text{Relative maximum}$$

• EXAMPLE 15-22

Find any relative maxima and minima of the function

$$z = f(x, y) = -x^3 - y^2 + 4xy + 6$$

Solution

Critical Points

First, we find the critical points. Computing f_x and f_y gives

$$f_x = -3x^2 + 4y$$
$$f_y = -2y + 4x$$

Setting f_x and f_y equal to 0, we have

$$-3x^2 + 4y = 0$$
$$-2y + 4x = 0$$

Since this set of equations does not constitute a linear system, we attempt to solve one of the equations for one of its unknowns and substitute the result into the other equation to solve for the remaining unknown.

Solving the second equation, $-2y + 4x = 0$, for y, we obtain

$$y = 2x$$

Substituting this result into the first equation, $-3x^2 + 4y = 0$, gives

$$-3x^2 + 4(2x) = 0$$

or

$$-3x^2 + 8x = 0$$

Solving this equation for x gives

$$x = 0 \quad \text{or} \quad x = \frac{8}{3}$$

Substituting these results into the second equation, $y = 2x$, gives the following results:

- If $x = 0$, then $y = 2(0) = 0$ and $(0, 0)$ is a critical point.
- If $x = 8/3$, then $y = 2(8/3) = 16/3$ and $(8/3, 16/3)$ is a critical point.

Thus, $(0, 0)$ and $(8/3, 16/3)$ are the critical points.

Second-Derivative Test

We now apply the second-derivative test for functions of two variables. Computing f_{xx}, f_{yy}, and f_{xy} gives

$$f_{xx}(x, y) = -6x$$
$$f_{yy}(x, y) = -2$$
$$f_{xy}(x, y) = 4$$

Evaluating each of these at the critical point $(0, 0)$ gives

$$A = f_{xx}(0, 0) = 0$$
$$B = f_{yy}(0, 0) = -2$$
$$C = f_{xy}(0, 0) = 4$$
$$AB - C^2 = 0(-2) - 4^2 = -16$$

Since $AB - C^2 < 0$, then, according to the second-derivative test of this section, a saddle point occurs at $(0, 0)$.

Applying the second-derivative test to the critical point $(8/3, 16/3)$ gives

$$A = f_{xx}(8/3, 16/3) = -6(8/3) = -16$$
$$B = f_{yy}(8/3, 16/3) = -2$$
$$C = f_{xy}(8/3, 16/3) = 4$$
$$AB - C^2 = (-16)(-2) - 4^2 = 16$$

Since $AB - C^2 > 0$ and $A < 0$, then, by the second-derivative test, a relative maximum occurs at $(8/3, 16/3)$. The relative maximum value of z is

$$z = f\left(\frac{8}{3}, \frac{16}{3}\right) = -\left(\frac{8}{3}\right)^3 - \left(\frac{16}{3}\right)^2 + 4\left(\frac{8}{3}\right)\left(\frac{16}{3}\right) + 6$$

$$= \frac{418}{27} \approx 15.48 \qquad \text{Relative maximum}$$

Applications

• EXAMPLE 15-23   Cost, Revenue, Profit.

Meditech, Inc., produces two products used in the dental industry. Each thousand units of product 1 sells for $100, and each thousand units of product 2 sells for $80. Meditech's analysts have determined that if x thousand units of product 1 and y thousand units of product 2 are produced, the total production cost is given by

$$C(x, y) = 10x^2 + 5y^2 - 10xy - 20x + 5y + 12$$

a) Determine the equation for total sales revenue, $R(x, y)$.
b) Determine the equation for total profit, $P(x, y)$.
c) Determine the number of units of each product that should be produced in order to maximize total profit.

Solutions

a) The total sales revenue is given by

$$R(x, y) = 100x + 80y$$

b) The total profit is given by

$$
\begin{aligned}
P(x, y) &= R(x, y) - C(x, y) \\
&= 100x + 80y - (10x^2 + 5y^2 - 10xy - 20x + 5y + 12) \\
&= -10x^2 - 5y^2 + 10xy + 120x + 75y - 12
\end{aligned}
$$

c) Computing P_x and P_y, we have

$$
\begin{aligned}
P_x &= -20x + 10y + 120 \\
P_y &= -10y + 10x + 75
\end{aligned}
$$

Setting P_x and P_y equal to 0 and solving for x and y yields the critical point, $(19.5, 27)$. Computing P_{xx}, P_{yy}, and P_{xy} and applying the second-derivative test for functions of two variables gives

$$
\begin{aligned}
P_{xx}(x, y) &= -20 \\
P_{yy}(x, y) &= -10 \\
P_{xy}(x, y) &= 10
\end{aligned}
$$

Hence,

$$
\begin{aligned}
A &= P_{xx}(19.5, 27) = -20 \\
B &= P_{yy}(19.5, 27) = -10 \\
C &= P_{xy}(19.5, 27) = 10 \\
AB - C^2 &= (-20)(-10) - (-10)^2 = 100
\end{aligned}
$$

Since $AB - C^2 > 0$ and $A < 0$, then, by the second-derivative test, a relative maximum occurs at $(19.5, 27)$. Thus, 19.5 thousand units of product 1 and 27 thousand units of product 2 should be produced in order to maximize total profit. The maximum profit is

$$
\begin{aligned}
P(19.5, 27) &= -10(19.5)^2 - 5(27)^2 + 10(19.5)(27) + 120(19.5) + 75(27) - 12 \\
&= \$2170.50 \qquad \text{Relative maximum}
\end{aligned}
$$

• EXAMPLE 15-24   Cost, Revenue, Profit.

A firm manufactures two competing brands of a given product. Let p_1 and p_2 be the case selling prices (in dollars) of brands 1 and 2, respectively. If x_1 cases of brand 1 and x_2 cases of brand 2 are demanded by the market, then the relationship between the unit (case) prices and the demands for the competing brands are given by the equations

$$
\begin{aligned}
x_1 &= 80 - 2p_1 + p_2 \\
x_2 &= 30 + p_1 - p_2
\end{aligned}
$$

a) Determine the equation for total sales revenue, $R(p_1, p_2)$.
b) If \$40 and \$30 are the unit case costs of brands 1 and 2, respectively, determine the total cost, $C(p_1, p_2)$.
c) Determine the equation for total profit, $P(p_1, p_2)$.
d) Determine the case selling prices, p_1 and p_2, that maximize total profit, $P(p_1, p_2)$.

Solutions

a) Since sales revenue for each brand is *price* $\times$ *quantity*, then the total sales revenue is

$$R = p_1 x_1 + p_2 x_2$$

Since we want $R(p_1, p_2)$, we substitute $80 - 2p_1 + p_2$ for x_1 and $30 + p_1 - p_2$ for x_2 to obtain

$$R(p_1, p_2) = p_1(80 - 2p_1 + p_2) + p_2(30 + \cdot p_1 - p_2)$$
$$= -2p_1^2 - p_2^2 + 2p_1 p_2 + 80p_1 + 30p_2$$

b) Multiplying each case cost by the respective demand gives the total cost

$$C = 40x_1 + 30x_2$$

Since we want $C(p_1, p_2)$, we substitute $80 - 2p_1 + p_2$ for x_1 and $30 + p_1 - p_2$ for x_2 to obtain

$$C(p_1, p_2) = 40(80 - 2p_1 + p_2) + 30(30 + p_1 - p_2)$$
$$= -50p_1 + 10p_2 + 4100$$

c) The total profit is given by

$$P(p_1, p_2) = R(p_1, p_2) - C(p_1, p_2)$$
$$= (-2p_1^2 - p_2^2 + 2p_1 p_2 + 80p_1 + 30p_2) - (-50p_1 + 10p_2 + 4100)$$
$$= -2p_1^2 - p_2^2 + 2p_1 p_2 + 130p_1 + 20p_2 - 4100$$

d) Computing the partial derivatives P_{p1} and P_{p2} gives

$$P_{p1} = -4p_1 + 2p_2 + 130$$
$$P_{p2} = -2p_2 + 2p_1 + 20$$

Setting the above partial derivatives equal to 0 and solving for p_1 and p_2 yields the approximate critical point, $(75, 85)$. Computing the second partials and applying the second-derivative test for functions of two variables gives

$$P_{p1p1}(p_1, p_2) = -16$$
$$P_{p2p2}(p_1, p_2) = -2$$
$$P_{p1p2}(p_1, p_2) = 2$$

Hence,

$$A = P_{p1p1}(75, 85) = -16$$
$$B = P_{p2p2}(75, 85) = -2$$
$$C = P_{p1p2}(75, 85) = 2$$
$$AB - C^2 = (-16)(-2) - 2^2 = 28$$

Since $AB - C^2 > 0$ and $A < 0$, then, by the second-derivative test, a relative maximum occurs at $(75, 85)$. Thus, brand 1 should be priced at \$75 per case, and brand 2 should be priced at \$85 per case in order to maximize total profit. The maximum profit is

$$P(75, 85) = -2(75)^2 - (85)^2 + 2(75)(85)$$
$$+ 130(75) + 20(85) - 4100$$
$$= \$1625 \quad \text{Relative maximum}$$

Exercises 15-3

Find any critical points for each of the following:

1. $z = x^2 + 3y^2 - 10x + 48y + 86$

2. $f(x, y) = -2x^2 - 3y^2 + 20x - 30y + 90$

3. $f(x, y) = -x^2 - y^2 + 4x + 8y + xy + 56$
4. $f(x, y) = x^2 + 2y^2 - 10x - 12y + 2xy + 7$
5. $z = 3x^2 + 2y^2 + 24x - 36y + 50$
6. $f(x, y) = -x^2 - 3y^2 + 10x + 54y + 80$
7. $f(x, y) = -x^2 - 5y^2 + 30x + 20y + 3xy + 8$
8. $f(x, y) = 5x^2 + 4y^2 + 6xy + 10x - 64y - 67$
9. $f(x, y) = 2x^3 + x^2y + 5x - 36y + 90$
10. $z = -2x^3 - y^2 + 10xy + 60$
11. $z = -x^2 + y^3 - 12y + 8x + 80$
12. $f(x, y) = x^2 - 2x^3 + 5y^2 - 10y^3 + 65$

Find any relative maxima or relative minima of each of the following:

13. $z = x^2 + 2y^2 - 8x - 20y + 18$
14. $f(x, y) = 2x^2 + y^2 - 28x - 20y + 80$
15. $f(x, y) = 9x - 50y + x^2 + 5y^2 + 100$
16. $z = 40x + 160y - 2x^2 - 4y^2 + 1000$
17. $f(x, y) = 1000 + 80x + 100y - 2x^2 - y^2$
18. $f(x, y) = 4x^2 + 2y^2 + 3xy - 70x - 55y + 1000$
19. $z = 3x^2 + 4y^2 + 2xy - 30x - 32y + 50$
20. $f(x, y) = 4x^2 + 5y^2 + 5xy - 73x - 80y + 6$
21. $z = 200 - 2x^2 - 6y^2 + 2xy + 32x + 28y$
22. $f(x, y) = 80 + 3xy + 42x - 16y - 3x^2 - 2y^2$
23. $z = f(x, y) = 2x^3 + x^2y + 8x - 25y + 800$
24. $f(x, y) = -x^3 - 2y^2 + 30xy + 50$
25. $z = f(x, y) = -x^2 + y^3 - 24y + 10x + 95$
26. $f(x, y) = 2x^2 - x^3 + 4y^2 - 12y^3 + 850$

27. Show that the function defined by
$$f(x, y) = 500 + x^2 - 2y^2 - 18x + 16y$$
has neither a relative maximum nor a relative minimum. Additionally, show that $f(x, y)$ has a saddle point, and find it.

28. Show that the function defined by
$$z = x^2 + 2y^2 + 3xy - 40x - 55y + 100$$
has a saddle point, and find it. Does the function have any relative maxima or minima?

Applications

29. *Profit.* The profit of a company is given by
$$P(x, y) = 1,000,000 + 1600x + 2000y - 4x^2 - 2y^2$$
where x is the unit labor cost and y is the unit raw material cost.
a) Find the unit labor cost and unit raw material cost that maximizes profit.
b) Find the maximum profit.

30. *Cost.* The manager of Freddy's Frogurt Stand has determined that the cost of producing x gallons of strawberry frogurt and y gallons of blueberry frogurt is given by
$$C(x, y) = 2x^2 + 3y^2 + 2xy - 800x - 1400y + 185,000$$
a) How many gallons of each flavor should be produced in order to minimize cost?
b) Find the minimum cost.

31. *Production output.* The weekly output of a firm is given by
$$z(x, y) = 1000x + 1600y + 2xy - 5x^2 - 2y^2$$
where x is the number of hours of labor and y is the number of units of raw material used weekly.

a) How many hours of labor and how many units of raw material should be used weekly in order to maximize output?

b) Find the maximum output.

32. *Cost, revenue, profit.* A firm produces two products, which are used in the automobile industry. Each thousand units of product 1 sells for $200, and each thousand units of product 2 sells for $295. If x thousand units of product 1 are produced and y thousand units of product 2 are produced, the total production cost is given by

$$C(x, y) = 5x^2 + 10y^2 + 5xy - 10x + 15y + 10$$

a) Determine the equation for total sales revenue, $R(x, y)$.

b) Determine the equation for total profit, $P(x, y)$.

c) Determine the number of units of each product that should be produced in order to maximize total profit.

33. *Revenue.* A large bottling company produces two competing brands of soda, Crystal Club and Mineral Club. The demands (in cases) for Crystal Club and Mineral Club are given by x_1 and x_2, respectively. If p_1 is the price for 1 case of Crystal Club and p_2 is the price for 1 case of Mineral Club, then

$$x_1 = 200 - 20p_1 + p_2$$
$$x_2 = 300 - 15p_2 + 2p_1$$

a) Determine the equation for total sales revenue, $R(p_1, p_2)$.

b) How should each brand be priced in order to maximize sales revenue, $R(p_1, p_2)$?

c) Determine the maximum sales revenue.

d) Find the demand for each brand at the optimal prices.

34. *Cost, revenue, profit.* A company manufactures two competing brands of a given product. Let p_1 and p_2 be the case prices (in dollars) of brands 1 and 2, respectively. If x_1 cases of brand 1 and x_2 cases of brand 2 are demanded by the marketplace, then the relationships between unit prices and demands for both competing brands are given by the equations

$$x_1 = 100 - 5p_1 + p_2$$
$$x_2 = 50 + p_1 - p_2$$

a) Determine the equation for total sales revenue, $R(p_1, p_2)$.

b) If $20 and $30 are the unit case costs of brands 1 and 2, respectively, determine the total cost, $C(p_1, p_2)$.

c) Determine the equation for total profit, $P(p_1, p_2)$.

d) Determine the case prices, p_1 and p_2, that maximize total profit, $P(p_1, p_2)$.

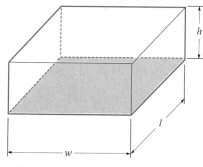

FIGURE 15-10

35. *Surface area.* A company manufactures boxes such as the one shown in Figure 15-10. If each such box must have a volume of 200 cubic inches, determine the dimensions of the box that minimize its surface area (i.e., surface area = area of four sides + area of top + area of bottom).

36. *Production cost.* A company manufactures boxes such as the one shown in Figure 15-10. Each side costs $5 per square inch to manufacture, and the top and bottom cost $8 per square inch to manufacture. If each box is to have a volume of 200 cubic inches, determine the dimensions that minimize its production cost.

37. *Heating and cooling costs.* A building is to be built in the shape of a rectangular box such as that shown in Figure 15-10. The building is to have a volume of 10,000 cubic feet. The combined annual heating and cooling costs are $10 per square foot for the top of the building (i.e., the roof) and $4 per square foot for the sides. Determine the dimensions of the building that will minimize the combined annual heating and cooling costs.

15-4

• APPLICATION: THE METHOD OF LEAST SQUARES

TABLE 15-1

x Annual advertising expense ($ millions)	y Annual sales ($ millions)
1	14
2	19
4	30
5	33

Table 15-1 gives annual advertising expenses and corresponding annual sales from a sample of 4 years' data for a corporation. The firm's management wishes to determine a mathematical relationship between annual advertising expense, x, and annual sales, y. The given data points (x, y) are plotted in Figure 15-11. Studying this figure, notice that the data points approximately follow the path of a straight line. Although the points do not necessarily lie on the straight line in Figure 15-11, their trend appears to be linear. Thus, the firm's analyst decides to *fit a straight line* to the set of data points. In other words, the analyst wishes to determine the equation $y = mx + b$ of the straight line that *best fits* the set of data points. The equation

$$y = mx + b$$

provides a mathematical model that describes the relationship between annual advertising expense, x, and annual sales, y. Thus, the analyst's problem reduces to finding the slope m and y-intercept b of the straight line $y = mx + b$ that *best fits* the set of data points.

We must understand what the phrase "best fits" might mean as we try to fit a straight line to a set of data points. Although we have discussed this term in previous Extra Dividends at the end of chapters 1 and 2, we again explain it by focusing on the given data point (4, 30) and the point directly below on the straight line, $y = mx + b$, in Figure 15-12. Note that the point on the straight line, $y = mx + b$, directly below (4, 30) has x-coordinate 4 and y-coordinate $m(4) + b$ or $4m + b$. Hence, its ordered pair is $(4, 4m + b)$. The extent to which the straight line, $y = mx + b$, does not fit

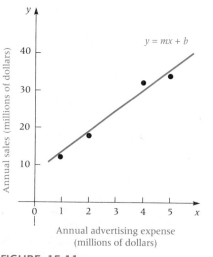

FIGURE 15-11

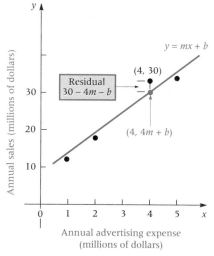

FIGURE 15-12

the data point (4, 30) could be expressed by the vertical distance between (4, 30) and (4, 4m + b). This vertical distance is called a **residual** and is given by the expression

$$30 - (4m + b)$$

or

$$30 - 4m - b$$

Since this quantity will be negative for points below the line, we determine and use its square

$$(30 - 4m - b)^2$$

Figure 15-13 shows the expressions of such vertical distances, or residuals, and their squares for all of the observed data points. The *best-fitting* straight line is defined as the one that *minimizes the sum of the squares* of the residuals. Since the sum of the squares is a measure of the extent to which the straight line does not pass through the given data points, it is called **sum of squares error** and is denoted by S. Hence,

$$S = (14 - m - b)^2 + (19 - 2m - b)^2 + (30 - 4m - b)^2 + (33 - 5m - b)^2$$

We must determine the slope m and y-intercept b (of the straight line, $y = mx + b$) that *minimize the sum of squares error*. The procedure is called

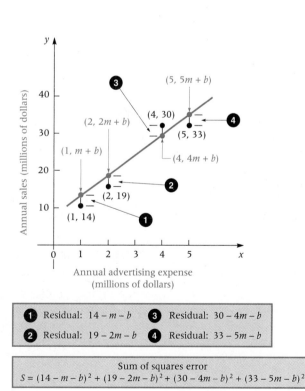

| ● 1 | Residual: $14 - m - b$ | ● 3 | Residual: $30 - 4m - b$ |
| ● 2 | Residual: $19 - 2m - b$ | ● 4 | Residual: $33 - 5m - b$ |

Sum of squares error
$$S = (14 - m - b)^2 + (19 - 2m - b)^2 + (30 - 4m - b)^2 + (33 - 5m - b)^2$$

FIGURE 15-13

the **method of least squares.** Note that S is a function of two variables, m and b. To find the values of m and b that minimize S, we determine the partial derivatives with respect to m and b, set them equal to 0, and solve for m and b. Computing $\partial S/\partial m$ and $\partial S/\partial b$ gives

$$\frac{\partial S}{\partial m} = 2(14 - m - b)(-1) + 2(19 - 2m - b)(-2) \\ + 2(30 - 4m - b)(-4) + 2(33 - 5m - b)(-5)$$

$$\frac{\partial S}{\partial b} = 2(14 - m - b)(-1) + 2(19 - 2m - b)(-1) \\ + 2(30 - 4m - b)(-1) + 2(33 - 5m - b)(-1)$$

Setting $\partial S/\partial m$ and $\partial S/\partial b$ equal to 0 and simplifying yields the linear system

$$92m + 24b = 674$$
$$24m + 8b = 192$$

Solving for m and b gives the critical point $(m, b) = (4.9, 9.3)$.

Computing the second partials and applying the second-derivative test for functions of two variables gives

$$S_{mm}(m, b) = 92 \qquad S_{bb}(m, b) = 8 \qquad S_{mb}(m, b) = 24$$

Hence,

$$A = S_{mm}(4.9, 9.3) = 92$$
$$B = S_{bb}(4.9, 9.3) = 8$$
$$C = S_{mb}(4.9, 9.3) = 24$$
$$AB - C^2 = (92)(8) - 24^2 = 160$$

Since $AB - C^2 > 0$ and $A > 0$, then, by the second-derivative test, a relative minimum value of S occurs at $(4.9, 9.3)$.

Thus, the equation of the best-fitting straight line (i.e., the straight line that minimizes the sum of squares error) is

$$y = 4.9x + 9.3 \qquad \text{Regression line}$$

This best-fitting line to a set of data points is called the **least-squares line** or the **regression line,** as indicated above.

Using the Regression Line As a Predictor

The regression line is used to predict y-values corresponding to given x-values. For example, we can predict the annual sales corresponding to the annual advertising expenditure of 3 million dollars by substituting $x = 3$ into the equation of the regression line. Hence,

$$y = 4.9(3) + 9.3$$
$$= 24 \qquad \text{24 million dollars of annual sales} \\ \text{correspond to annual advertising} \\ \text{expenditures of 3 million dollars.}$$

General Case

It can be shown, in general, that the slope m and the y-intercept b of the least squares or regression line for a set of n data points, (x_1, y_1), (x_2, y_2), . . . , (x_n, y_n), satisfy the linear system

$$nb + \left(\sum_{i=1}^{n} x_i\right) m = \sum_{i=1}^{n} y_i$$

$$\left(\sum_{i=1}^{n} x_i\right) b + \left(\sum_{i=1}^{n} x_i^2\right) m = \sum_{i=1}^{n} x_i y_i$$

where

$$\sum_{i=1}^{n} x_i = x_1 + x_2 + \ldots + x_n$$

$$\sum_{i=1}^{n} y_i = y_1 + y_2 + \ldots + y_n$$

$$\sum_{i=1}^{n} x_i^2 = x_1^2 + x_2^2 + \ldots + x_n^2$$

$$\sum_{i=1}^{n} x_i y_i = x_1 y_1 + x_2 y_2 + \ldots + x_n y_n$$

Note that if we divide the first equation by n, we obtain

$$b + \underbrace{\frac{\sum_{i=1}^{n} x_i}{n}}_{\bar{x}} m = \underbrace{\frac{\sum_{i=1}^{n} y_i}{n}}_{\bar{y}}$$

Since

$$\bar{x} = \frac{\sum_{i=1}^{n} x_i}{n} \qquad \text{Average of the } x\text{-values}$$

$$\bar{y} = \frac{\sum_{i=1}^{n} y_i}{n} \qquad \text{Average of the } y\text{-values}$$

then the above equation can be rewritten as

$$b + \bar{x}m = \bar{y}$$

or

$$\bar{y} = m\bar{x} + b$$

The last equation implies that the regression line always passes through the point $(\bar{x}, \bar{y})$.

Alternate Formulas for m and b

The equations in the color screen on page 935 can be rewritten to give the following formulas for the slope m and the y-intercept b.

$$m = \frac{\displaystyle\sum_{i=1}^{n} x_i y_i - n\bar{x}\bar{y}}{\displaystyle\sum_{i=1}^{n} x_i^2 - n\bar{x}^2} \qquad \text{Slope}$$

$$b = \bar{y} - m\bar{x} \qquad \text{y-Intercept}$$

These enable us to obtain m and b expeditiously without having to solve a linear system. We summarize as follows.

SUMMARY

Method of Least Squares

Given data points

x	y	(x, y)
x_1	y_1	(x_1, y_1)
x_2	y_2	(x_2, y_2)
$\vdots$	$\vdots$	$\vdots$
x_n	y_n	(x_n, y_n)

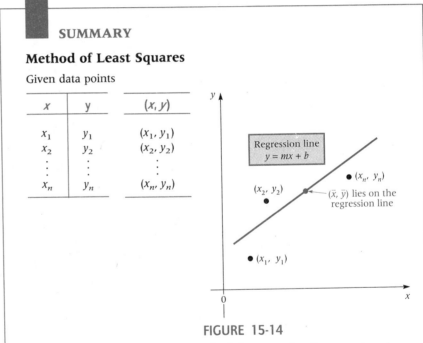

FIGURE 15-14

the **slope** m and the **y-intercept** b of the regression line are given by the formulas

$$m = \frac{\displaystyle\sum_{i=1}^{n} x_i y_i - n\bar{x}\bar{y}}{\displaystyle\sum_{i=1}^{n} x_i^2 - n\bar{x}^2}$$

$$b = \bar{y} - m\bar{x}$$

continues

SUMMARY—*Continued*

where

$$\bar{x} = \frac{\displaystyle\sum_{i=1}^{n} x_i}{n} \qquad \text{Average of } x\text{-values}$$

$$\bar{y} = \frac{\displaystyle\sum_{i=1}^{n} y_i}{n} \qquad \text{Average of } y\text{-values}$$

$$\sum_{i=1}^{n} x_i y_i = x_1 y_1 + x_2 y_2 + \ldots + x_n y_n$$

$$\sum_{i=1}^{n} x_i^2 = x_1^2 + x_2^2 + \ldots + x_n^2$$

Applications

Investment Risk Measurement

Table 15-2 gives annual percent changes of net asset values of Fidelity Magellan Fund versus those of the overall stock market as measured by the Standard & Poors 500 Composite Index (S&P 500).

PROBLEM

We want to determine the linear relationship between the performance of Fidelity Magellan Fund and that of the overall market. This relationship is given by the regression line

$$y = mx + b$$

SOLUTION

Using the least squares method as outlined in the box on page 936, our computations appear in Table 15-3. Note that we multiply each x-value by

TABLE 15-2 Annual Percent Changes

		1984	1985	1986	1987	1988
x	S&P 500	6.2	31.3	18.1	4.7	16.2
y	Fidelity Magellan	2.0	43.2	23.7	1.0	22.8

TABLE 15-3

x_i	y_i	$x_i y_i$	x_i^2
6.2	2.0	12.40	38.44
31.3	43.2	1352.16	979.69
18.1	23.7	428.97	327.61
4.7	1.0	4.70	22.09
16.2	22.8	369.36	262.44
76.5	92.7	2167.59	1630.27

its corresponding y-value to obtain the entries of the $x_i y_i$ column. Also, we square each x-value to obtain the entries of the x_i^2 column.

$$\bar{x} = \frac{\sum_{i=1}^{n} x_i}{n} = \frac{76.5}{5} = 15.3 \qquad \text{Average of } x\text{-values}$$

$$\bar{y} = \frac{\sum_{i=1}^{n} y_i}{n} = \frac{92.7}{5} = 18.54 \qquad \text{Average of } y\text{-values}$$

$$m = \frac{\sum_{i=1}^{n} x_i y_i - n\bar{x}\bar{y}}{\sum_{i=1}^{n} x_i^2 - n\bar{x}^2} = \frac{2167.59 - 5(15.3)(18.54)}{1630.27 - 5(15.3)^2} \approx \frac{749.28}{459.82} \approx 1.63$$

$$b = \bar{y} - m\bar{x} = 18.54 - 1.63(15.3) = -6.40$$

Thus, the regression equation is

$$y = 1.63x - 6.40$$

Slope and Risk

When the performance of a mutual fund or stock (as measured in percent changes) is related to the overall market, as in this example, the slope of the regression line is, in most financial publications, denoted by β (read "beta") and is interpreted in the following box.

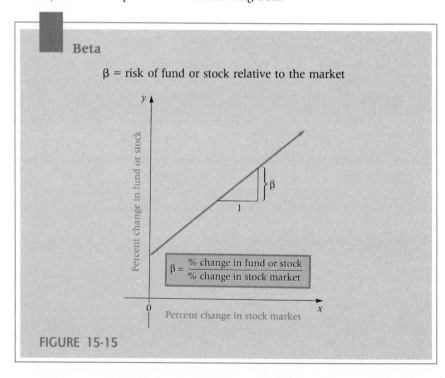

Beta

β = risk of fund or stock relative to the market

$$\beta = \frac{\% \text{ change in fund or stock}}{\% \text{ change in stock market}}$$

Percent change in fund or stock (y-axis)

Percent change in stock market (x-axis)

FIGURE 15-15

Thus Fidelity Magellan Fund's beta, $\beta = 1.63$, means that if the overall stock market, as measured by the S&P 500, goes up 1 percentage point, then Fidelity Magellan Fund can be expected to go up by 1.63 percentage points. Also, if the overall market goes down 1 percentage point, then Fidelity Magellan Fund can be expected to go down by 1.63 percentage points.

Time Series

Farm Population

Table 15-4 gives U.S. farm population as a percentage of total U.S. population for the years 1958 through 1984. A set of data, such as that of Table 15-4, that relates some quantity versus time is called a **time series.**

TABLE 15-4   U.S. farm population as a percentage of total U.S. population

Year	x	y	Year	x	y	Year	x	y	Year	x	y
1958	1	9.8	1965	8	6.4	1972	15	4.6	1979	22	2.8
1959	2	9.3	1966	9	5.9	1973	16	4.5	1980	23	2.7
1960	3	8.7	1967	10	5.5	1974	17	4.3	1981	24	2.5
1961	4	8.1	1968	11	5.2	1975	18	4.1	1982	25	2.4
1962	5	7.7	1969	12	5.1	1976	19	3.8	1983	26	2.5
1963	6	7.1	1970	13	4.7	1977	20	2.8	1984	27	2.4
1964	7	6.7	1971	14	4.5	1978	21	2.9			

x = coded years
y = U.S. farm population as a percentage of total U.S. population

We use the MINITAB statistical software package to plot the y-values versus the x-values. The results appear in Figure 15-16. A graph, such as that of Figure 15-16, that relates some quantity versus time is called a **time series plot.**

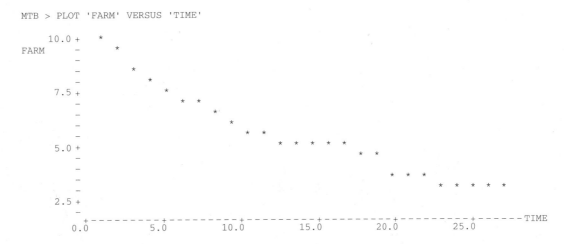

This graph was drawn using the MINITAB statistical software package.

FIGURE 15-16

PROBLEM

We want to fit a straight line to the set of data points of Figure 15-16. In other words, we want to determine the equation of the regression line

$$y = mx + b$$

for this set of data.

COMPUTER SOLUTION

We use a computer software package to find the equation of the regression line. The results are given below. Also, a graph of the regression line fit to the data is given in Figure 15-17.

Regression Line

$$y = -0.275x + 8.93$$

Sum of Squares Error

7.17

Studying the computer solution, note that the slope of the regression line indicates that during the indicated time period, the U.S. farm population as a percentage of the total U.S. population is decreasing at the rate of 0.275 percentage points per year. Also, note that we have given the sum of squares error (i.e., the sum of the squares of the residuals) below the regression line. The reason for this will be apparent when we study the next example.

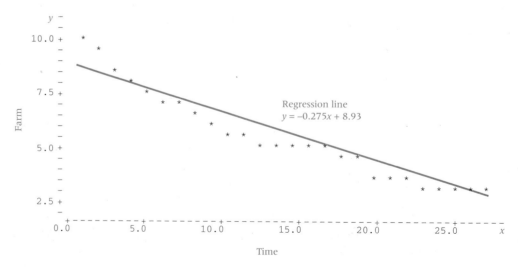

This graph was drawn using the MINITAB statistical software package. The regression line and annotations have been added.

FIGURE 15-17

Nonlinear Regression

Farm Population

Here we continue our analysis of the farm population data given in Table 15-4 and Figure 15-16. Studying the time series plot of Figure 15-16, note that the way that the data trail off at around the coded year $x = 13$ suggests a nonlinear pattern, perhaps an exponential pattern, to the data. This suggests that we try an *exponential model*

PROBLEM

Fit the exponential model

$$y = ab^x$$

to the farm population data of Table 15-4.

COMPUTER SOLUTION

The exponential model

$$y = ab^x \qquad \text{Exponential form}$$

can be written in logarithmic form by taking the natural logarithm (or, for that matter, the common logarithm) of each side to obtain

$$\ln y = \ln ab^x$$
$$= \ln a + \ln b^x$$
$$= \ln a + x \ln b$$
$$= \ln a + (\ln b)x \qquad \text{Logarithmic form}$$

Thus, the exponential form, $y = ab^x$, is restated in the equivalent logarithmic form, $\ln y = \ln a + (\ln b)x$. Note that the logarithmic equation

$$\ln y = \ln a + (\ln b)x \qquad \ln y \text{ and } x \text{ are linearly related}$$

expresses a linear relationship between $\ln y$ and x, where $\ln b$ is the slope and $\ln a$ is the y-intercept. This means that we can fit an exponential model to a set of data points by finding the equation of the regression line relating $\ln y$-values and x-values. Thus, we use a calculator or computer to find the natural logarithms (or, if we prefer, common logarithms) of the y-values of our data. Then we use a computer software package to find the regression line relating the $\ln y$-values and x-values. The results are given in Table 15-5, along with the data and $\ln y$-values.

Studying the results of Table 15-5, note that the sum of squares error (i.e., the sum of the squares of the residuals) is 1.4451 as compared to 7.17 for the linear model of the previous example. The smaller sum of squares error for the exponential model suggests that the exponential model fits the data better than the linear model does.

TABLE 15-5

x	y	$\ln y$
1	9.8	2.28238
2	9.3	2.23001
3	8.7	2.16332
4	8.1	2.09186
5	7.7	2.04122
6	7.1	1.96009
7	6.7	1.90211
8	6.4	1.85630
9	5.9	1.77495
10	5.5	1.70475
11	5.2	1.64866
12	5.1	1.62924
13	4.7	1.54756
14	4.5	1.50408
15	4.6	1.52606
16	4.5	1.50408
17	4.3	1.45862
18	4.1	1.41099
19	3.8	1.33500
20	2.8	1.02962
21	2.9	1.06471
22	2.8	1.02962
23	2.7	0.99325
24	2.5	0.91629
25	2.4	0.87547
26	2.5	0.91629
27	2.4	0.87547

Regression Line

$\ln y = 2.31 - 0.0561x$

$\ln y = \ln a + (\ln b)x$

Sum of Squares Error

1.4451

WRITING THE MODEL IN EXPONENTIAL

Studying the regression line of Table 15-5, note that

$$\ln a = 2.31 \quad \text{and} \quad \ln b = -0.0561$$

Rewriting the above in exponential form gives

$$a = e^{2.31} \qquad\qquad b = e^{-0.0561}$$
$$= 10.07$$

Thus, the equivalent exponential form

$$y = ab^x$$

is given by

$$y = 10.07e^{-0.0561x}$$

Its graph is given in Figure 15-18.

Using the concepts of continuous compounding and exponential functions discussed in Chapters 3, and 4, the exponent, -0.0561, indicates that the U.S. farm population as a percentage of total U.S. population is decreasing at an annual rate of approximately 5.61% compounded continuously. As we learned in Chapter 4, this translates into the effective annual rate given below.

Effective Annual Rate

$$e^{-0.0561} - 1 = -0.0546$$
$$= 5.46\% \text{ decrease per year}$$

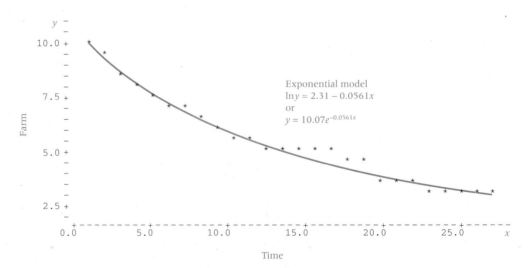

This graph was drawn using the MINITAB statistical software package. The regression line and annotations have been added.

FIGURE 15-18

Quadratic Models

Up to this point in this section, we have presented numerous applications of the least squares method of fitting regression lines to sets of data. We have indicated how to fit linear models and exponential models to data.

We wish to note that the least squares method is used to fit *quadratic models* of the form

$$y = ax^2 + bx + c$$

to sets of data. Graphically, these result in the fitting of a parabola to a set of data points. Here the least squares method is used to find the coefficients a, b, and c of the best-fitting parabola to a set of data points. Specifically, the sum of squares error, S, is a function of a, b, and c. Thus, the coefficients a, b, and c are determined by taking the partial derivatives of S with respect to a, b, and c, respectively; setting them equal to zero; and solving for a, b, and c. In other words, the coefficients a, b, and c are solutions to the linear system

$$S_a(a, b, c) = 0 \qquad S_b(a, b, c) = 0 \qquad S_c(a, b, c) = 0$$

Since such computations are usually long and tedious, we will use a computer software package to fit parabolas to sets of data in the homework exercises.

Multiple Linear Regression Models

Also, the least squares method is used to relate y-values to more than one independent variable. Specifically, if a set of data relates y-values to x_1-values and x_2-values, then a linear relationship between y and a joint combination of x_1 and x_2 is given by the equation

$$y = a + b_1x_1 + b_2x_2$$

Such a model is called a *multiple linear regression model*

Exercises 15-4

For each of the following:
a) Find the equation of the linear regression line.
b) Graph the data and the regression line on the same set of axes.
c) Compute the residuals.
d) Compute the sum of squares error.

1.

x	y
2	8
3	10
2	7
5	15

2.

x	y
3	7
2	5
4	10
3	6

3.

x	y
4	8
2	5
8	14
6	9

4.

x	y
5	7
3	4
9	15
7	10

5.

x	y
1	4
2	6
3	7
4	10
5	13

6.

x	y
−2	3
−1	7
0	11
1	15
2	19

7.

x	y
−2	2
−1	4
0	7
1	10
2	12

8.

x	y
−3	5
−1	9
1	12
3	14

A computer was used to fit a linear regression line to each set of data below. Computer results, including residuals, are given next to each set of data. For each of the following:

a) Use the equation of the regression line to estimate y at $x = 3.5$.

b) Compute the sum of squares error.

9.

x	y	Residuals
2	7	1.6890
4	9	−0.8841
6	13	−1.4573
8	16	−3.0305
9	25	3.6829

The regression equation is
$y = 0.74 + 2.29x$.

10.

x	y	Residuals
1	9	1.6520
3	13	−0.6912
4	16	−0.8627
7	24	−2.3775
9	35	2.2794

The regression equation is
$y = 4.18 + 3.17x$.

11.

x	y	Residuals
2	6	1.1340
3	9	0.3093
7	19	−4.9897
8	28	0.1856
9	35	3.3608

The regression equation is
$y = -2.78 + 3.82x$.

12.

x	y	Residuals
2	9	0.3494
4	19	−0.7108
5	27	2.1084
8	38	−2.4337
9	47	1.3855

The regression equation is
$y = -1.01 + 5.18x$.

Goodness-of-Fit. A computer was used to fit both an exponential and a quadratic model to each set of data below. The results, including the sum of squares error for each model, are given for each set of data. Therefore, for each of the following:

a) State which model best fits the set of data.
b) Write the exponential model in the form $y = ab^x$.
c) Use the exponential model to estimate y at $x = 4.5$.
d) Use the quadratic model to estimate y at $x = 4.5$.

13.

x	y
1	10
3	50
4	90
6	185
2	20

Exponential Model
$\ln y = 1.89 + 0.593x$

Sum of Squares Error
2684.9

Quadratic Model
$y = 4.71x^2 + 2.76x + 0.05$

Sum of Squares Error
40

14.

x	y
1	3
2	5
3	10
4	18
5	30

Exponential Model
$\ln y = 0.495 + 0.589x$

Sum of Squares Error
2.0482

Quadratic Model
$y = 1.64x^2 - 3.16x + 4.60$

Sum of Squares Error
0.11

Applications

Accounting: Cost Segregation

In an Extra Dividends section following Chapter 1, we used a method called the high-low point method to fit a straight line to a set of cost data. The equation of the resulting straight line was used to segregate the fixed and variable portions of cost as follows:

1. The y-intercept of the straight line estimates the fixed cost.
2. The slope of the straight line estimates the variable cost per unit.

For each of the exercises below, we will use the linear regression line to segregate the fixed and variable portions of cost. Specifically, for Exercises 15 and 16, we have used a computer to fit a linear regression line to the data.

15. *Electric power costs.* The data below give electric power costs associated with various hours of operation for some firm.

x Hours	y Cost (\$)
5800	7000
5000	6500
5600	6700
5900	7400

Regression Line
$y = 0.841x + 2211$

a) State the fixed cost.
b) State the variable cost per hour.

16. *The following cost data appeared on a past Uniform CPA Examination.* Labor hours and production costs for 4 representative months of a given year are as follows:

Month	Labor hours	Total production costs ($)
September	2500	20,000
October	3500	25,000
November	4500	30,000
December	3500	25,000

Regression Line
$y = 5x + 7500$

a) State the fixed monthly production cost.
b) State the variable production cost per hour.

Investment Risk Measurement

The data below give annual percent changes of the net asset values of various mutual funds versus those of the overall market as measured by the Standard & Poors 500 Composite Index (S&P 500).

Annual percent changes

		1984	1985	1986	1987	1988
x	S&P 500	6.2	31.3	18.1	4.7	16.2
y	Mutual Shares	14.5	26.6	17.0	6.4	30.8
y	20th Century Vista	−16.3	29.5	26.3	6.0	2.4
y	Neuberger Manhattan	6.9	37.2	17.0	0.4	18.3
y	Nicholas Fund	10.0	29.6	11.7	−0.8	18.0

We used a computer to find the equation of the linear regression line relating each fund's performance versus that of the overall stock market as measured by the S&P 500. The results are given below. For each of the following, state the fund's beta and give its interpretation.

17. Mutual Shares
Regression line: $y = 0.655x + 9.04$
18. 20th Century Vista
Regression line: $y = 1.38x − 11.5$
19. Neuberger Manhattan
Regression line: $y = 1.29x − 3.75$
20. Nicholas Fund
Regression line: $y = 0.957x − 0.94$

Time Series

21. *Gross National Product (GNP).* The data below give the GNP (in billions of dollars) for the United States for the years indicated.

Year	1955	1956	1957	1958	1959	1960	1961
GNP	405.9	428.2	451.0	456.8	495.8	515.3	533.8
Year	1962	1963	1964	1965	1966	1967	1968
GNP	574.6	606.9	649.8	705.1	772.0	816.4	892.7
Year	1969	1970	1971	1972	1973	1974	1975
GNP	963.9	1015.5	1102.7	1212.8	1359.3	1472.8	1598.4
Year	1976	1977	1978	1979	1980	1981	1982
GNP	1782.8	1990.5	2249.7	2508.3	2732.0	3052.6	3166.0
Year	1983	1984	1985	1986			
GNP	3405.7	3765.0	3998.1	4208.5			

A computer was used to fit the exponential moded to the GNP data with coded x-values such that $x = 1$ corresponds to 1955, $x = 2$ to 1956, etc., and y denotes GNP. The result is given below.

Regression line: $\ln y = 5.77 + 0.0785x$

a) Write the equation of the regression line in the form $y = ab^x$.
b) At what annual rate (i.e., compounded annually) has GNP been increasing during this time interval?
c) Using this model, forecast GNP for the years 1987, 1988, and 1989.

22. *Imports.* The data below give U.S. imports (in billions of dollars) for the indicated years.

Year	1967	1968	1969	1970	1971	1972
Imports	42.1	49.3	54.7	60.5	66.1	78.2
Year	1973	1974	1975	1976	1977	1978
Imports	97.3	135.2	130.3	158.9	189.7	223.4
Year	1979	1980	1981	1982	1983	1984
Imports	272.5	318.9	348.9	335.6	358.7	441.4
Year	1985	1986				
Imports	448.6	478.7				

A computer was used to fit the exponential model to the data with coded x-values such that $x = 1$ corresponds to the year 1967, $x = 2$ to 1968, etc., and y denotes imports. The result is given below.

Regression line: $\ln y = 3.64 + 0.138x$

a) Write the equation of the regression line in the form $y = ab^x$.
b) At what annual rate (i.e., compounded annually) have imports been increasing during this time interval?
c) Using this model, forecast U.S. imports for the years 1987, 1988, and 1989.

23. *Exports.* The data below give U.S. exports (in billions of dollars) for the indicated years.

Year	1976	1977	1978	1979	1980	1981
Exports	177.7	191.6	227.5	291.2	351.0	382.8
Year	1982	1983	1984	1985	1986	
Exports	361.9	352.5	382.7	369.8	373.0	

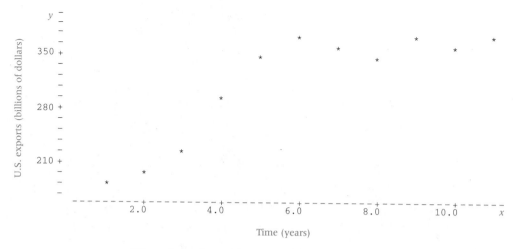

This graph was drawn using the MINITAB statistical software package. The regression line and annotations have been added.

FIGURE 15-19

A computer was used to fit both linear and quadratic models to the data with coded x-values such that $x = 1$ corresponds to the year 1976, $x = 2$ to 1977, etc., and y denotes exports. A time series plot of the data prepared using the Minitab statistical software package is given in Figure 15-19. Also, the computer results are given below.

Linear Model	Quadratic Model
$y = 20.8x + 190$	$y = -3.60x^2 + 64x + 96.3$
Sum of Squares Error	*Sum of Squares Error*
15,143	4031

a) State which model better fits the data.

b) Use the linear model to forecast U.S. exports for the years 1987, 1988, and 1989.

c) Figure 15-20 on page 949 gives a Minitab plot of the fitted quadratic model. According to this graph, are U.S. exports increasing, decreasing, or leveling off?

d) Use the quadratic model to forecast U.S. exports for the years 1987, 1988, and 1989.

24. *Systolic blood pressure.* A person's systolic blood pressure (SBP) is recorded weekly, with the following results:

Week	1	2	3	4	5	6	7	8	9
SBP	125	128	130	129	135	138	140	146	145

a) Find the equation of the linear regression line for this time series data.

b) How is this person's blood pressure changing with time?

c) Using the linear model of part a, forecast blood pressure for the tenth week.

25. *Education.* The data below relate undergraduate grade point average (GPA) with starting salary (in thousands of dollars) for a sample of recent graduates of a small liberal arts college.

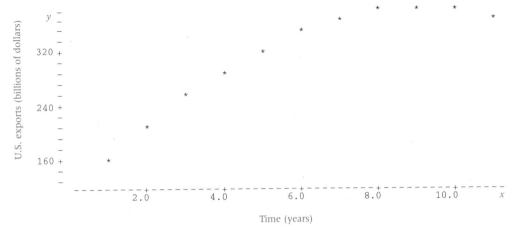

This graph was drawn using the MINITAB statistical software package. The regression line and annotations have been added.

FIGURE 15-20

x GPA	2.5	3.0	2.4	3.5	2.1	2.6
y Starting salary	15.5	19.7	15.2	22.8	14.6	15.8

a) Find the equation of the linear regression line.
b) According to the linear model of part a, state the effect of GPA on starting salary.
c) Estimate the starting salary for a GPA of 2.9.

26. *Medical science.* The data below relate serum cholesterol level (in milligrams/100 milliters) with age for a sample of adult males.

x Age	20	35	27	40	49	55
y Cholesterol	210	279	230	190	252	287

a) Find the equation of the regression line.
b) According to these data, state the effect of age on cholesterol level.
c) Estimate the cholesterol level of a 30-year-old male.

Multiple Linear Regression

27. *Agriculture.* The multiple linear regression model

$$y = 630.4 - 7.8x_1 + 4.3x_2$$

gives the relationship among y, x_1, and x_2, where

y = yield of some crop (in millions of bushels)

x_1 = average temperature (in degrees Fahrenheit) during the growing season

x_2 = average percentage of sunshine during the growing season

a) If x_2 is held constant and x_1 increases by 1 degree Fahrenheit, what effect will this have on crop yield?
b) If x_1 is held constant and x_2 increases by 1 percentage point, what effect will this have on crop yield?

28. *Education.* The multiple linear regression model

$$y = -0.86 + 0.00025x_1 + 0.00513x_2$$

gives the relationship among y, x_1, and x_2, where

$$y = \text{first-year GPA}$$
$$x_1 = \text{SAT mathematics score}$$
$$x_2 = \text{SAT verbal score}$$

for a sample of freshmen students at a college. According to the multiple linear regression model:

a) State the effect on GPA of a 100-point increase in the SAT mathematics score, assuming the SAT verbal score remains constant.

b) State the effect on GPA of a 100-point increase in the SAT verbal score, assuming the SAT mathematics score remains constant.

15-5 • LAGRANGE MULTIPLIERS

Sometimes we must optimize a function $z = f(x, y)$, where x and y are constrained. As an example, consider a factory that burns two types of fuel: BF108 and BF109. The number of tons of pollutant exhausted by the factory in a year is given by

$$z = f(x, y) = x^2 + 2y^2 - xy - 279{,}990$$

where x is the amount (in thousands of gallons) of BF108 fuel used annually and y is the amount (in thousands of gallons) of BF109 fuel used annually. The factory uses a combined amount of 800 thousand gallons of fuel annually. We seek to determine how many thousands of gallons of each type fuel should be burned annually in order to minimize the amount of pollutant exhausted.

Since the factory uses a combined amount of 800 thousand gallons of fuel annually, then

$$x + y = 800$$

Mathematically, our problem is to

Minimize $f(x, y) = x^2 + 2y^2 - xy - 279{,}990$
subject to the constraint $g(x, y) = x + y = 800$

Such a problem may be solved by the method of *Lagrange multipliers.*, A graphical interpretation of this constrained optimization problem is given in Figure 15-21.

In general, the method of Lagrange multipliers is used to solve the following type of problem.

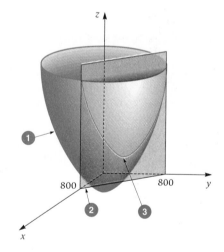

① Surface: $z = x^2 + 2y^2 - xy - 279{,}900$

② Constraint: $x + y = 800$

③ Constrained minimum

Note: The constrained minimum occurs at the lowest point on the curve where the surface intersects with the constraint (plane).

FIGURE 15-21

Maximize (or minimize) $z = f(x, y)$
subject to $g(x, y) = c$
where c is a constant.

To use the method of LaGrange multipliers, we define a new function

$$F(x, y, \lambda) = f(x, y) + \lambda(c - g(x, y))$$

where λ is called the **Lagrange multiplier** and the function F is called the **lagrangian function.** Studying the lagrangian function, F, note that since $g(x, y) = c$, then $c - g(x, y) = 0$, and the value of F will equal that of the original function, f. The following is proven in more advanced texts.

The relative maxima (or minima) of the function $z = f(x, y)$ subject to the constraint $g(x, y) = c$ will be among those points (x_0, y_0) such that (x_0, y_0, λ_0) is a critical point of the lagrangian function, F.

Thus, by finding the values of x, y, and λ that maximize (or minimize) F, we also find the values of x and y that maximize (or minimize) $f(x, y)$ subject to the constraint equation $g(x, y) = c$.

Returning to our problem, we find

$$F(x, y, \lambda) = f(x, y) + \lambda(c - g(x, y))$$
$$= x^2 + 2y^2 - xy - 279{,}900 + \lambda(800 - x - y)$$

We now find the critical values of F.

Calculating F_x, F_y, F_λ, we have

$$F_x = 2x - y - \lambda$$
$$F_y = 4y - x - \lambda$$
$$F_\lambda = 800 - x - y$$

Setting these equal to 0 yields

$$2x - y - \lambda = 0$$
$$4y - x - \lambda = 0$$
$$800 - x - y = 0$$

Solving the first two equations for λ, we have

$$\lambda = 2x - y$$
$$\lambda = 4y - x$$

Equating these two expressions for λ yields

$$2x - y = 4y - x$$
$$-5y = -3x$$
$$y = \frac{3}{5}x$$

Substituting $(3/5)x$ for y into the third equation

$$800 - x - y = 0$$

yields

$$800 - x - \frac{3}{5}x = 0$$

Solving for x, we obtain

$$x = 500$$

Substituting $x = 500$ into

$$y = \frac{3}{5}x$$

we have

$$y = \frac{3}{5}(500)$$

$$= 300$$

We now substitute $x = 500$ and $y = 300$ into either of the equations for λ. Arbitrarily choosing the equation

$$\lambda = 2x - y$$

we obtain

$$\lambda = 2(500) - 300$$

$$= 700$$

Thus, the function F has a *critical point*

$$x = 500 \qquad y = 300 \qquad \lambda = 700$$

Second Order Conditions

We must now determine whether either a relative maximum of F or a relative minimum of F exists at the critical point in question. To determine the behavior of F (and also f subject to the constraint) at a critical point, we define the matrix

$$H = \begin{bmatrix} 0 & g_x & g_y \\ g_x & f_{xx} & f_{xy} \\ g_y & f_{yx} & f_{yy} \end{bmatrix}$$

The matrix H is called a **bordered Hessian matrix** and must be evaluated at the critical point. The determinant* of H (denoted $|H|$) indicates whether either a relative maximum or a relative minimum exists at the critical point in accordance with the rule stated here.

———————————————

*The evaluation of determinants is presented in Appendix B.

Second-Order Conditions

Given critical values $x = x_0$, $y = y_0$, and $\lambda = \lambda_0$ for the lagrangian function, F, $|H|$ is evaluated at the critical values.

If $|H| > 0$, a relative maximum exists.

If $|H| < 0$, a relative minimum exists.

Returning to our example, we compute the elements of H and evaluate them at the critical values of F.

$$g(x, y) = x + y, g_x = 1, g_x(500, 300) = 1$$
$$g_y = 1, g_y(500, 300) = 1$$
$$f(x, y) = x^2 + 2y^2 - xy - 279{,}990$$
$$f_x = 2x - y, f_x(500, 300) = 2(500) - 300 = 700$$
$$f_y = 4y - x, f_y(500, 300) = 4(300) - 500 = 700$$
$$f_{xx} = 2, \quad f_{xx}(500, 300) = 2, \quad f_{yy} = 4, \quad f_{yy}(500, 300) = 4$$
$$f_{xy} = -1, f_{xy}(500, 300) = -1, f_{yx} = -1, f_{yx}(500, 300) = -1$$

Thus, H evaluated at the critical values is

$$H = \begin{bmatrix} 0 & 1 & 1 \\ 1 & 2 & -1 \\ 1 & -1 & 4 \end{bmatrix}$$

and $|H| = -8$. Since $|H| < 0$, a relative minimum exists at the critical values $x = 500$, $y = 300$, and $\lambda = 700$. Also, the minimal value of f (i.e., the minimal number of tons of exhausted pollutant) subject to the constraint is given by

$$f(500, 300) = (500)^2 + 2(300)^2 - 500(300) - 279{,}990$$
$$= 10$$

Interpretation of λ

If $x = x_0$, $y = y_0$ and $\lambda = \lambda_0$ are the optimal solution values to the constrained optimization problem

Maximize (or minimize) $z = f(x, y)$ subject to $g(x, y) = c$

then it can be shown that

$$\frac{dz}{dc} = \lambda_0$$

where dz/dc is evaluated at the optimal solution values.

In other words, λ_0 is the rate of change of z with respect to c and thus measures the sensitivity of the optimal value of f to a change in c.

Returning to our original example, recall that $\lambda_0 = 700$. Since $dz/dc = \lambda_0 = 700$, then each unit increase in c (i.e., each additional thousand gallons of fuel used) increases the optimal amount of pollutant exhausted by approximately 700 tons.

We now summarize the method of Lagrange multipliers.

SUMMARY

Method of LaGrange Multipliers

To solve the problem

$$\text{Maximize (or minimize) } z = f(x, y)$$
$$\text{subject to } g(x, y) = c$$
$$\text{where } c \text{ is a constant}$$

1. Determine the lagrangian function

$$F(x, y, \lambda) = f(x, y) + \lambda(c - g(x, y))$$

   where λ is the lagrangian multiplier.

2. Search for the critical points.
   - Find the first-order partials F_x, F_y, and F_λ.
   - Set the first-order partials equal to zero and solve for x, y, and λ.
   - Determine all possible ordered triples (x, y, λ) that satisfy all three equations:

   $$F_x(x, y, \lambda) = 0 \qquad F_y(x, y, \lambda) = 0 \qquad F_\lambda(x, y, \lambda) = 0$$

   These are the critical points of F.

3. Apply the second-order conditions.
   - Compute g_x, g_y, f_{xx}, f_{yy}, f_{xy}, and f_{yx}.
   - Evaluate the above at each critical point, and form the bordered Hessian matrix, H, for each critical point.
   - Evaluate the determinant of each bordered Hessian matrix, H (there will be a bordered Hessian matrix, H, for each critical point), and apply the second-order conditions to each such H as follows.

   Second-Order Conditions

   If $|H| > 0$, a relative maximum exists
   If $|H| < 0$, a relative minimum exists

• **EXAMPLE 15-25** _____

Maximize (or minimize) $f(x, y) = -x^2 + 4xy - y^2 + 10$ subject to $x + 2y = 9$.

Solution

Determine the Lagrangian Function

$$F(x, y, \lambda) = f(x, y) + \lambda(c - g(x, y))$$
$$= -x^2 + 4xy - y^2 + 10 + \lambda(9 - x - 2y)$$

Search for the Critical Points

We find the first-order partials and set them equal to 0. Hence,

$$F_x = -2x + 4y - \lambda = 0$$
$$F_y = 4x - 2y - 2\lambda = 0$$
$$F_\lambda = 9 - x - 2y = 0$$

Solving the first two equations for λ, we have

$$\lambda = -2x + 4y$$
$$\lambda = 2x - y$$

Equating these two, we have

$$-2x + 4y = 2x - y$$
$$y = \frac{4}{5}x$$

Substituting $(4/5)x$ for y in the third equation, $9 - x - 2y = 0$, yields

$$9 - x - \frac{8}{5}x = 0$$

Solving for x, we obtain

$$x = \frac{45}{13}$$

Since $y = (4/5)x$, then $y = (4/5)(45/13) = 36/13$. We now substitute $x = 45/13$ and $y = 36/13$ into either equation containing λ. Arbitrarily choosing

$$\lambda = 2x - y$$

we obtain

$$\lambda = 2\left(\frac{45}{13}\right) - \frac{36}{13}$$
$$= \frac{54}{13}$$

Thus, the function F has a critical point at

$$x = \frac{45}{13} \qquad y = \frac{36}{13} \qquad \lambda = \frac{54}{13}$$

Apply the Second-Order Conditions

We must determine whether either a relative maximum or a relative minimum exists at the critical point by determining the bordered Hessian matrix

$$H = \begin{bmatrix} 0 & g_x & g_y \\ g_x & f_{xx} & f_{xy} \\ g_y & f_{yx} & f_{yy} \end{bmatrix}$$

We first compute the elements of H and evaluate them at the critical values of F. Hence,

$$g(x, y) = x + 2y, g_x = 1, g_x(45/13, 36/13) = 1$$
$$g_y = 2, g_y(45/13, 36/13) = 2$$

$$f(x, y) = -x^2 + 4xy - y^2 + 10$$
$$f_x = -2x + 4y, f_x(45/13, 36/13) = -2(45/13) + 4(36/13) = 54/13$$
$$f_y = 4x - 2y, f_y(45/13, 36/13) = 4(45/13) - 2(36/13) = 108/13$$
$$f_{xx} = -2, f_{xx}(45/13, 36/13) = -2, f_{yy} = -2, f_{yy}(45/13, 36/13) = -2$$
$$f_{xy} = 4, f_{xy}(45/13, 36/13) = 4, f_{yx} = 4, f_{yx}(45/13, 36/13) = 4$$

Thus, H evaluated at the critical values is

$$H = \begin{bmatrix} 0 & 1 & 2 \\ 1 & -2 & 4 \\ 2 & 4 & -2 \end{bmatrix}$$

and $|H| = 26$. Since $|H| > 0$, a *relative maximum* exists at the critical values $x = 45/13$, $y = 36/13$, and $\lambda = 54/13$. Also, the maximum value of f subject to the constraint is given by

$$f(45/13, 36/13) = -(45/13)^2 + 4(45/13)(36/13) - (35/13)^2 + 10$$
$$= 373/13 \approx 28.69$$

• EXAMPLE 15-26

Interpret the lagrangian multiplier, λ, for Example 15-25.

Solution

Since $dz/dc = \lambda_0 = 54/13$, then each unit increase in c (where $c = 9$) increases the optimal value of f by approximately $54/13$ units.

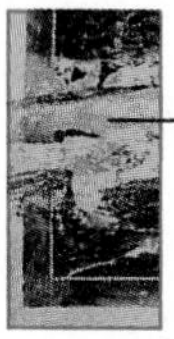

Applications

• EXAMPLE 15-27 **Sawmill: Maximizing Cross-Sectional Area of a Beam.**

A sawmill receives logs with a cross-sectional diameter of $\sqrt{2}$ (approximately 1.414) feet. A rectangular beam is cut from each such log, as illustrated in Figure 15-22. Determine the cross-sectional dimensions that result in a beam with maximal cross-sectional area.

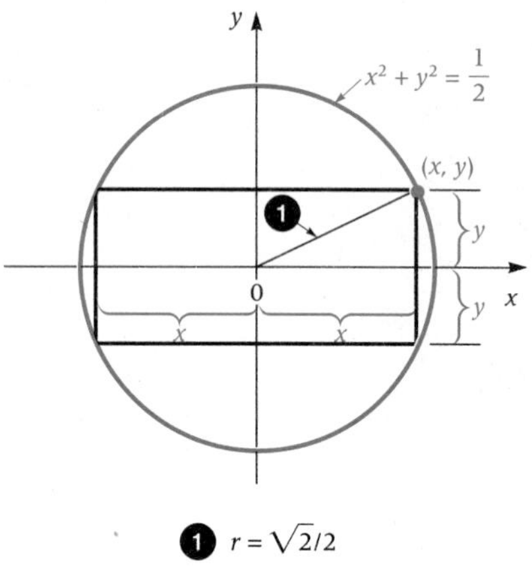

Solution

In terms of Figure 15-22, the cross-sectional rectangular dimensions are $2x$ by $2y$. Thus, the cross-sectional area, which we seek to maximize, is $(2x)(2y) = 4xy$. Therefore, our problem is stated mathematically below.

$$\text{Maximize } z = f(x, y) = 4xy$$
$$\text{subject to } \underbrace{x^2 + y^2}_{g(x,\ y)} = 1/2$$

Determine the Lagrangian Function

$$F(x, y, \lambda) = f(x, y) + \lambda(c - g(x, y))$$
$$= 4xy + \lambda(1/2 - x^2 - y^2)$$

Search for Critical Points

We find the first-order partials and set them equal to 0. Hence,

$$F_x = 4y - 2\lambda x = 0$$
$$F_y = 4y - 2\lambda y = 0$$
$$F_\lambda = \frac{1}{2} - x^2 - y^2 = 0$$

Solving the first equation for λ gives $\lambda = 2y/x$. Solving the second equation for λ gives $\lambda = 2x/y$. Setting both expressions for λ equal to each other gives

$$\frac{2y}{x} = \frac{2x}{y} \quad \text{or} \quad y^2 = x^2$$
$$y = \pm x$$

FIGURE 15-22

(1) $r = \sqrt{2}/2$

$x^2 + y^2 = \dfrac{1}{2}$

(x, y)

Substituting $y = \pm x$ into the third equation

$$\frac{1}{2} - x^2 - y^2 = 0$$

gives

$$\frac{1}{2} - x^2 - (\pm x)^2 = 0$$

$$-2x^2 = -\frac{1}{2}$$

$$x^2 = \frac{1}{4}$$

$$x = \pm \frac{1}{2}$$

Due to the symmetry of the problem, as seen in Figure 15-22, we need to consider only positive x- and y-values. In other words, the Lagrange multiplier method has given us all four corner points of the cross-sectional area of the beam, as shown in Figure 15-22. We only need one corner point in order to determine the cross-sectional dimensions. Thus, we substitute $x = 1/2$ and $y = 1/2$ into either equation for λ. Arbitrarily choosing the equation

$$\lambda = \frac{2y}{x}$$

we get

$$\lambda = \frac{2(1/2)}{(1/2)} = 2$$

Thus, the function F has a *critical point* at

$$x = 1/2 \qquad y = 1/2 \qquad \lambda = 2$$

Apply the Second-Order Conditions
We determine the following and evaluate at the critical values of F.

$$g_x(x, y) = 2x \qquad g_x(1/2, 1/2) = 2(1/2) = 1$$
$$g_y(x, y) = 2y \qquad g_y(1/2, 1/2) = 2(1/2) = 1$$
$$f_x = 4y \qquad f_{xx}(x, y) = 0 \qquad f_{xx}(1/2, 1/2) = 0$$
$$f_y = 4x \qquad f_{yy}(x, y) = 0 \qquad f_{yy}(1/2, 1/2) = 0$$
$$f_{xy}(x, y) = 4 \qquad f_{xy}(1/2, 1/2) = 4$$
$$f_{yx}(x, y) = 4 \qquad f_{yx}(1/2, 1/2) = 4$$

The bordered Hessian matrix, H, for our critical point is

$$H = \begin{bmatrix} 0 & 1 & 1 \\ 1 & 0 & 4 \\ 1 & 4 & 0 \end{bmatrix}$$

and its determinant is $|H| = 8$, which is positive. Therefore, by the second-order conditions, a *relative maximum* occurs at the critical values $x = 1/2$, $y = 1/2$, and $\lambda = 2$. Thus, the *maximal cross-sectional area* of the beam is given by

$$f(1/2, 1/2) = 4(1/2)(1/2) = 1 \text{ square foot}$$

• **EXAMPLE 15-28** _____

Interpret the Lagrange multiplier for Example 15-27.

Solution

$$\lambda_0 = \frac{dz}{dc} = \frac{2}{1} \begin{array}{l} \leftarrow \text{change in cross-sectional area} \\ \leftarrow \text{change in radius squared} \end{array}$$

Thus, for each 1-foot increase in the square of the radius of a log, the maximal cross-sectional area, 1, increases by approximately 2 square feet.

_____ •

Exercises 15-5

1. Maximize (or minimize)
$$f(x, y) = x^2 - 4xy + y^2 + 200$$
subject to the constraint
$$2x + y = 26$$

2. Maximize (or minimize)
$$f(x, y) = x^2 + 6xy + y^2$$
subject to the constraint
$$x + y = 10$$

3. Maximize (or minimize)
$$f(x, y) = x^2 + 6xy + 2y^2$$
subject to $4x + y = 18$.

4. Maximize (or minimize)
$$f(x, y) = x^2 + 4xy + y$$
subject to $x + y = 12$.

5. Maximize (or minimize)
$$f(x, y) = x^2 + 2xy + y^2 - 3x - 5y$$
subject to $x + y = 18$.

6. Maximize (or minimize)
$$f(x, y) = -y^2 + xy + x$$
subject to $2x + y = 19$.

7. Maximize (or minimize)
$$f(x, y) = x^2 - 5xy + 2y^2$$
subject to $3x + y = 20$.

Lagrange multiplier. Interpret the Lagrange multiplier λ for each of the indicated exercises.

8. Exercise 1	**9.** Exercise 2	**10.** Exercise 3
11. Exercise 4	**12.** Exercise 6	**13.** Exercise 7

Applications

14. *Profit.* A farmer's profit per square foot of cropland is given by
$$P(x, y) = -x^2 - 5y^2 + 10xy + 4x + 2y - 1100$$

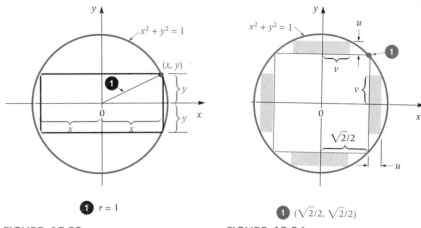

① $r = 1$

FIGURE 15-23

① $(\sqrt{2}/2, \sqrt{2}/2)$

FIGURE 15-24

where x is the amount spent on labor per square foot and y is the amount spent on fertilizer per square foot of cropland. If the farmer spends a total of $31.90 per square foot of cropland for labor and fertilizer, then how many dollars per square foot should be allocated to labor and fertilizer in order to maximize the profit per square foot?

15. *Cost.* The total cost of producing x units of product A and y units of product B is given by

$$C(x, y) = x^2 + 4y^2 - 5xy + 2000$$

If a combined total of 40 units is produced daily, then how many units of each product should be produced daily in order to minimize the total cost?

16. *Sawmill: Maximizing cross-sectional area of a beam.* sawmill receives logs with a cross-sectional diameter of 2 feet. A rectangular beam is cut from each such log, as illustrated in Figure 15-23. Determine the cross-sectional dimensions that result in a beam with maximal cross-sectional area.

17. *Sawmill: Maximizing the use of scrap lumber.* After the beam of Exercise 16 is cut from the log, the remaining scrap lumber is to be used to cut smaller beams, as illustrated in Figure 15-24. Determine the dimensions of the smaller beams that maximize the combined cross-sectional area of the 4 smaller beams.

18. *Cobb-Douglas production function.* For some firm, the number of units produced when using x units of labor and y units of capital is given by the production function

$$z = f(x, y) = 100x^{3/5}y^{2/5}$$

Each unit of labor costs $600, and each unit of capital costs $200. The firm has $700,000 budgeted for combined labor and capital costs.
a) Write the constraint for the combined labor and capital costs.
b) Determine the number of units of labor and capital required to maximize production subject to the constraint of part a.
c) Determine the maximum number of units produced.

19. *Volume.* A box with a square base (see Figure 15-25) is constructed such that the material for the sides costs $1 per square foot and the material for the base costs $3 per square foot. There is no top as the box is open. If each such box is to cost $60, then find its dimensions so that the volume is maximized.

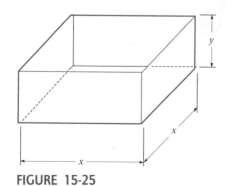

FIGURE 15-25

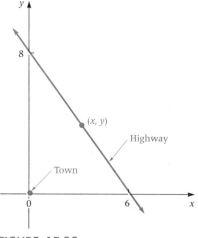

FIGURE 15-26

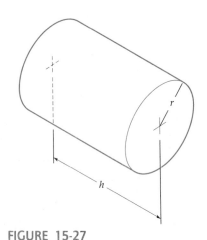

FIGURE 15-27

20. *Cost.* A rubbish container is in the form of a box (as illustrated in Figure 15-25 on page 959) with a square base. It is to cost $14,400. If the material for the sides costs $100 per square foot and the base and top cost $150 per square foot, find the dimensions that maximize its volume.

21. *Emergency facility location.* An emergency facility is to be built somewhere along the highway in Figure 15-26. Since the facility is to service both highway travelers and town residents, at what point on the highway should it be built in order to minimize its distance from the town located at (0, 0)? Assume x and y are in miles.

22. *Cylinder.* A cylindrical container (see Figure 15-27) must have a surface area 54π square feet. What dimensions r and h maximize its volume? What is the maximum volume? Use the facts that the volume of a cylinder is given by $\pi r^2 h$ and that the surface area is given by $2\pi rh + 2\pi r^2$.

23. *Cost.* A 1-product company has 2 plants. The cost of producing x units at plant A is given by the cost function

$$C(x) = 80 + x^2/8$$

The cost of producing y units at plant B is given by the cost function

$$C(y) = 100 + y^2/4$$

The total cost of producing x units at plant A and y units at plant B is given by the cost function

$$C(x, y) = C(x) + C(y)$$

If a total of $x + y = 9000$ units is to be made, then how many units should be produced at each plant in order to minimize the total production cost?

Lagrange multiplier. Interpret the Lagrange multiplier λ for each of the indicated exercises.

24. Exercise 14	25. Exercise 15	26. Exercise 16
27. Exercise 17	28. Exercise 18	29. Exercise 19
30. Exercise 20	31. Exercise 21	32. Exercise 22
33. Exercise 23		

EXTRA DIVIDENDS

• *Back-Order Inventory Model—BFI, Inc.*

The distributor of plumbing supplies, BFI, Inc., allows back orders to be taken when demand exceeds the available supply of inventory. This results in the imposition of a stockout cost (or penalty cost) on the average number of back orders. If

D = annual demand (in units) for a given inventory product

K = cost of placing an order

H = annual carrying cost per unit

B = annual stockout cost (or back-order cost) per unit

Q = number of units ordered per order

S = maximum number of back orders allowed

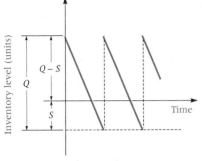

FIGURE 15-28

then the total annual inventory cost in such situations is given by

$$C(Q, S) = K\frac{D}{Q} + H\frac{(Q - S)^2}{2Q} + B\frac{S^2}{2Q}$$

Figure 15-28 illustrates a graph of inventory level versus time for such an inventory model.

Using the optimization methods of Section 15-3, it can be determined that the values of Q and S that minimize the total annual inventory cost, C, are given by

$$Q^* = \sqrt{\frac{2DK}{H}\left(\frac{H + B}{B}\right)}$$

$$S^* = Q^*\left(\frac{H}{H + B}\right)$$

One of BFI's products, the BFI307, has an annual demand of 1200, an ordering cost of $5.00 per order, an annual carrying cost of $1.15 per unit, and an annual stockout cost of $2.40 per unit.

Exercises

1. Determine the equation defining the total annual inventory cost.
2. Determine the values of Q and S that minimize the total annual inventory cost.
3. What is the minimum total annual inventory cost?
4. How many back orders are allowed?
5. Every time an order is placed for the BFI307, how many are ordered? After back orders have been set aside, how many are available for sale?

EXTRA DIVIDENDS

• *Using a Response Surface to Increase Industrial Productivity*

Pfichem, Inc., produces a chemical (PFI 707) that is used to clean circuits of computers. The yield (z) in kilograms of the chemical process used to produce PFI 707 is dependent on the *temperature* in degrees Celsius at which the process is run and the *process time* in minutes that the chemical process is allowed to react. The plant manager wants to determine the optimum combination of temperature and process time in order to maximize the yield (z). After running the process at various combinations of temperature and process time, and after analyzing the results, the manager has determined that the process yield (z) is near optimum when the temperature is kept within the interval 100°C to 120°C and the process time is kept within the interval 50 min to 60 min.

To facilitate computational efficiency, these temperature levels are expressed in terms of the coded variable x_1, where $x_1 = -1$ denotes 100°C and $x_1 = 1$ denotes 120°C. Specifically, if C denotes the temperature in degrees Celsius, the equation relating the coded variable x_1 and C is given by

$$x_1 = \frac{C - 110}{10} \qquad (100 \le C \le 120)$$

Similarly, the process time is expressed in terms of the coded variable x_2 such that $x_2 = -1$ denotes 50 minute and $x_2 = 1$ denotes 60 minutes. Specifically, if T denotes the process time in minutes, the equation relating x_2 and T is given by

$$x_2 = \frac{T - 55}{5} \qquad (50 \le T \le 60)$$

The graph of the region denoting feasible near-optimum combinations of temperature and process time appears in Figure 15-29.

The plant manager runs the process repeatedly at each combination of temperature and process time indicated by the colored points of Figure 15-29 and records the corresponding yields, z. Since the values of z indicate how the process yield responds to different combinations of temperature and process time, z is called a **response variable.** The method of least squares is used to fit a model that expresses the relationship between the process yield, z, and the coded variables, x_1 and x_2. This model is given by the equation

$$z = 50 + 1.6x_1 - 1.4x_2 + 2x_1x_2 - 3x_1^2 - 2x_2^2$$

where $-1 \le x_1 \le 1$ and $-1 \le x_2 \le 1$. The graph of this equation over the region $-1 \le x_1 \le 1$ and $-1 \le x_2 \le 1$ is the surface sketched in Figure 15-30. Since a point on this surface is denoted by an ordered triple (x_1, x_2, z), where z is the response variable, the surface of Figure 15-30 is called a **response surface.**

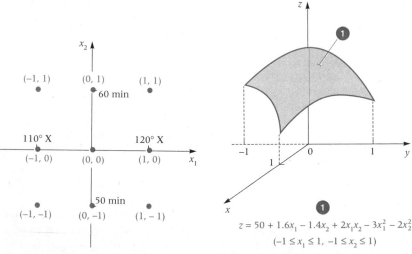

FIGURE 15-29   FIGURE 15-30

Exercises

1. Determine the values of x_1 and x_2 that maximize the process yield, z.
2. Determine the maximum process yield.
3. Determine the optimum combination of temperature in degrees Celsius and process time in minutes in order to maximize the yield, z.

CHAPTER 15 HIGHLIGHTS

• *Concepts*

Your ability to answer the following questions is one indicator of the depth of your mastery of this chapter's important concepts. Note that the questions are grouped under various topic headings. For any question that you cannot answer, refer to the appropriate section of the chapter indicated by the topic heading. Pay particular attention to the summary boxes within a section.

15-1 FUNCTIONS OF SEVERAL VARIABLES

1. Explain each of the following terms: function of two variables, function of three variables, multivariate functions.
2. Draw a three-dimensional coordinate system, and explain how an ordered triple (x, y, z) is plotted.

15-2 PARTIAL DERIVATIVES

3. Given a function $z = f(x, y)$, explain each of the following and indicate how it is determined:
   a) Partial derivative of z with respect to x
   b) Partial derivative of z with respect to y
4. What is a second partial derivative?
5. State the four types of second partials.

15-3 RELATIVE MAXIMA AND MINIMA (FUNCTIONS OF TWO VARIABLES)

6. What is a critical point?
7. If a function $z = f(x, y)$ has relative maxima/minima, do they occur at critical points?
8. Does a critical point always result in a relative extremum?
9. According to the second-derivative test for functions of two variables:
   a) State the conditions for a relative maximum.
   b) State the conditions for a relative minimum.
   c) State the conditions for a saddle point and explain this term.
   d) State the condition for the test failing.
10. Give the procedure for finding relative extrema for functions of two variables.

15-4 APPLICATION: THE METHOD OF LEAST SQUARES

11. What does the method of least squares provide?
12. Give the formulas for determining the slope and y-intercept of a regression line. Explain the components.
13. With regard to investment risk measurement, explain the term *beta*.

14. How does one fit an exponential model to a set of data using the method of least squares?
15. State the three coefficients that must be determined when fitting a quadratic model to a set of data.
16. What is a multiple linear regression model?

15-5 **LAGRANGE MULTIPLIERS**

17. Describe the type of problem solved by the method of Lagrange multipliers.
18. Outline the method of Lagrange multipliers.
19. Interpret the Lagrange multiplier.

REVIEW EXERCISES

• *Functions of Two Variables*

1. If $f(x, y) = 2x^2 + 7xy^3 - 6y^4 + 9$, compute each of the following:
   a) $f(1, -1)$ b) $f(-1, 0)$ c) $f(2, 1)$ d) $f(0, -2)$
2. If $f(x, y) = (5x^2 + 6y^2 + 9xy)/(x^2 - 4)$, specify the domain of f.
3. If $f(x, y) = (x^3 + 6xy^2 + 7x - 6)/(x - 4)$, specify the domain of f.

For Exercises 4–6, plot the point in a three-dimensional coordinate system.

4. $(2, 4, 7)$ 5. $(3, -1, 5)$ 6. $(-2, 1, 6)$

• *Partial Derivatives*

7. If $f(x, y) = 2x^2 + 6xy - 8y^4 + 5x + 9$, find each of the following:
   a) $f_x(x, y)$ b) $f_y(x, y)$ c) $f_x(1, 0)$ d) $f_y(-1, 2)$
8. If $g(x, y) = x^4 - 6y^2 - 8x^2y^4 + 9y + 7$, find each of the following:
   a) $g_x(x, y)$ b) $g_y(x, y)$ c) $g_x(-2, 1)$ d) $g_y(1, 2)$
9. If $f(x, y) = x^5 e^{x+y}$, find each of the following:
   a) $f_x(x, y)$ b) $f_y(x, y)$ c) $f_x(1, 0)$ d) $f_y(1, 2)$
10. If $f(x, y) = y^5 \ln (x^3 + 6y^4)$, find each of the following:
    a) $f_x(x, y)$ b) $f_y(x, y)$ c) $f_x(-2, 1)$ d) $f_y(1, -2)$
11. *Cost.* The cost of producing x units of product 1 and y units of product 2 is given by

$$C(x, y) = 80x + 50y + 40xy + 500$$

If 30 units of product 1 and 40 units of product 2 are currently being produced, find the marginal cost of producing an additional unit of
    a) Product 1.   b) Product 2.

• *Second-Order Partial Derivatives*

For Exercises 12–15, find each of the following:

a) f_x b) f_{xx} c) f_y d) f_{yy} e) f_{xy} f) f_{yx}
g) $f_{xx}(-1, 3)$ h) $f_{yy}(1, -2)$ i) $f_{xy}(1, 0)$

12. $f(x, y) = x^3 + 4y^2 - 6xy^5 + 9$ 13. $f(x, y) = x^4 e^{x+y}$
14. $f(x, y) = x^5 \ln (x^3 + y^4)$ 15. $f(x, y) = (x^3 + y^5)^4$

• *Relative Extrema*

Find any relative extrema for Exercises 16–19.

16. $f(x, y) = x^2 + y^2 + 6xy + 27x + 21y + 90$
17. $f(x, y) = -x^2 - 2y^2 + 8xy + 32x + 12y + 60$

18. $f(x, y) = 4x^2 - 12x^3 + 6y^2 - 8y^3 + 80$

19. $f(x, y) = -2x^3 - 8y^2 + 24xy + 12$

20. Show that the function defined by

$$f(x, y) = x^2 - 4y^2 - 20x + 24y + 800$$

has no relative extrema. Additionally, show that $f(x, y)$ has a saddle point, and find it.

21. *Sales revenue.* The sales revenue gained from selling x and y units of products A and B, respectively, is given by

$$R(x, y) = -10x^2 - 16y^2 + 48x + 36y$$

Determine the number of units of products A and B that should be sold in order to maximize the sales revenue. Find the maximum sales revenue.

22. *Profit.* A profit function is defined by

$$P(x, y) = -4x^2 - 3y^2 + 54x + 96y - 2xy - 10$$

where x and y denote the sales of gadgets and widgets, respectively. Determine the number of gadgets and widgets that must be sold in order to maximize profit. Find the maximum profit.

23. *Revenue.* A company produces two competing products: A and B. The numbers of units demanded of products A and B are denoted by x_1 and x_2, respectively, and are related to the unit prices, p_1 and p_2, of products A and B, respectively, as given by the following equations:

$$x_1 = 400 - 12p_1 + 14p_2$$
$$x_2 = 600 - 15p_2 + 6p_1$$

a) Determine the equation for total sales revenue, $R(p_1, p_2)$.

b) How should each product be priced in order to maximize the total sales revenue, $R(p_1, p_2)$?

c) Determine the maximum sales revenue.

d) Find the demand for each product at the optimal prices.

• The Method of Least Squares

For Exercises 24–26:

a) Find the equation of the linear regression line.

b) Graph the data and the regression line on the same set of axes.

c) Compute the residuals.

d) Compute the sum of squares error.

e) Use the regression line to predict y at $x = 5$.

24.

x	y
1	4
3	10
2	7
6	19

25.

x	y
4	9
8	20
3	8
9	23

26.

x	y
2	7
8	30
7	25
3	8

27. *Investment risk.* The relationship between the percent change of XYZ Mutual Fund and that of the S&P 500 is given by the least squares line

$$y = 1.90x - 1.05$$

Interpret the slope.

28. *Exponential model.* Fit the exponential model to the data points $(1, 3)$, $(2, 17)$, and $(3, 68)$. Write the answer in both logarithmic and exponential forms. Use the model to predict y at $x = 2.5$.

29. *Exponential model.* Fit the exponential model to the data points $(1, 130)$, $(2, 30)$ and $(3, 4)$. Write the answer in both logarithmic and exponential forms. Use the model to predict y at $x = 1.5$.

• *Lagrange Multipliers*

For Exercises 30–32, use the method of Lagrange multipliers.

30. Maximize (or minimize) $f(x, y) = x^2 - 10xy + 2y^2 + 200$ subject to $x + y = 52$.

31. Maximize (or minimize) $f(x, y) = x^2 + 8xy + y^2 + 600$ subject to $x + 2y = 66$.

32. Maximize (or minimize) $f(x, y) = x^2 + 6xy + 4y + 900$ subject to $x + y = 24$.

Interpret the Lagrange multiplier, λ, for each of the indicated exercises.

33. Exercise 30   34. Exercise 31   35. Exercise 32

36. *Cost.* The total cost of producing x units of product A and y units of product B is given by

$$C(x, y) = x^2 + 3y^2 - 4xy + 6000$$

If a combined total of 800 units is to be produced weekly, then how many units of each product should be produced weekly in order to minimize the total cost? Find the minimum cost. Interpret the Lagrange multiplier.

37. *Container cost.* A company produces a container in the shape of a box with a square base. The cost per square foot for the top and bottom is $5. The cost per square foot for the sides is $10. If the container is to cost $480, find the dimensions that maximize its volume. Interpret the Lagrange multiplier.

APPENDIXES

Appendix A
Proofs of Derivative Rules

- ## POWER RULE

If $f(x) = x^n$, where n is a real number, then
$$f'(x) = nx^{n-1}$$

We will prove the power rule for positive integers n only. Proofs for real numbers n are found in any standard calculus text. To prove the power rule, we must review the binomial theorem for expansion of binomials. The following formulas illustrate equivalent expressions for $(a + b)^n$ for positive integers n:

If $n = 2$, then $(a + b)^2 = a^2 + 2ab + b^2$

If $n = 3$, then $(a + b)^3 = a^3 + 3a^2b + 3ab^2 + b^3$

If $n = 4$, then $(a + b)^4 = a^4 + 4a^3b + 6a^2b^2 + 4ab^3 + b^4$

If $n = 5$, then $(a + b)^5 = a^5 + 5a^4b + 10a^3b^2 + 10a^2b^3 + 5ab^4 + b^5$

The **binomial theorem** provides the following general formula for $(a + b)^n$:

$$(a + b)^n = \binom{n}{0}a^n + \binom{n}{1}a^{n-1}b + \binom{n}{2}a^{n-2}b^2 + \ldots + \binom{n}{n-1}ab^{n-1} + \binom{n}{n}b^n$$

Note that the combinations $\binom{n}{0}$, $\binom{n}{1}$, $\binom{n}{2}$, . . . , $\binom{n}{n-1}$, and $\binom{n}{n}$ are evaluated as follows:

$$\binom{n}{0} = \frac{n!}{0!n!} = 1$$

$$\binom{n}{1} = \frac{n!}{1!(n-1)!} = n$$

$$\binom{n}{2} = \frac{n!}{2!(n-2)!} = \frac{n(n-1)(n-2)!}{2!(n-2)!} = \frac{n(n-1)}{2}$$

.

.

.

$$\binom{n}{n-1} = \frac{n!}{(n-1)!1!} = \frac{n(n-1)!}{(n-1)!1!} = n$$

$$\binom{n}{n} = \frac{n!}{n!0!} = 1$$

Thus, the binomial theorem may be rewritten as

$$(a+b)^n = a^n + na^{n-1}b + \frac{n(n-1)}{2}a^{n-2}b^2 + \ldots + nab^{n-1} + b^n$$

Returning to the power rule, we now use the binomial theorem to compute

$$f(x + \Delta x) = (x + \Delta x)^n$$

$$= x^n + nx^{n-1}(\Delta x) + \frac{n(n-1)}{2}x^{n-2}(\Delta x)^2 + \ldots + nx(\Delta x)^{n-1} + (\Delta x)^n$$

For our purpose, it is only necessary to notice that

$$f(x + \Delta x) = (x + \Delta x)^n$$

$$= x^n + nx^{n-1}(\Delta x) + (\Delta x)^2 \text{ (a sum of products of powers of } x \text{ and } \Delta x)$$

Thus, the derivative of $f(x) = x^n$ is

$$f'(x) = \lim_{\Delta x \to 0} \frac{f(x + \Delta x) - f(x)}{\Delta x}$$

$$= \lim_{\Delta x \to 0} \frac{x^n + nx^{n-1}\Delta x + \Delta x^2(\text{a sum of products of powers of } x \text{ and } \Delta x) - x^n}{\Delta x}$$

$$= \lim_{\Delta x \to 0} \frac{nx^{n-1}\Delta x + \Delta x^2(\text{a sum of products of powers of } x \text{ and } \Delta x)}{\Delta x}$$

$$= \lim_{\Delta x \to 0} [nx^{n-1} + \Delta x (\text{a sum of products of powers of } x \text{ and } \Delta x)]$$

$$= nx^{n-1}$$

Hence, $f'(x) = nx^{n-1}$.

• **PRODUCT RULE**

If $y = f(x)s(x)$, where $f(x)$ and $s(x)$ are differentiable functions at x, then

$$\frac{dy}{dx} = f(x)s'(x) + s(x)f'(x)$$

$$\frac{dy}{dx} = \lim_{\Delta x \to 0} \frac{f(x + \Delta x)s(x + \Delta x) - f(x)s(x)}{\Delta x}$$

Adding and subtracting $f(x + \Delta x)s(x)$ to the numerator yields

$$\frac{dy}{dx} = \lim_{\Delta x \to 0} \frac{f(x + \Delta x)s(x + \Delta x) - f(x + \Delta x)s(x) + f(x + \Delta x)s(x) - f(x)s(x)}{\Delta x}$$

$$= \lim_{\Delta x \to 0} \left[f(x + \Delta x) \frac{s(x + \Delta x) - s(x)}{\Delta x} + s(x) \frac{f(x + \Delta x) - f(x)}{\Delta x} \right]$$

By limit property 2 of Section 9-1, this result becomes

$$\frac{dy}{dx} = \lim_{\Delta x \to 0} \left[f(x + \Delta x) \frac{s(x + \Delta x) - s(x)}{\Delta x} \right] + \lim_{\Delta x \to 0} \left[s(x) \frac{f(x + \Delta x) - f(x)}{\Delta x} \right]$$

By limit property 5 of Section 9-1, this becomes

$$\frac{dy}{dx} = \lim_{\Delta x \to 0} f(x + \Delta x) \lim_{\Delta x \to 0} \frac{s(x + \Delta x) - s(x)}{\Delta x} + \lim_{\Delta x \to 0} s(x) \lim_{\Delta x \to 0} \frac{f(x + \Delta x) - f(x)}{\Delta x}$$

Since $f(x)$ is differentiable at x, $f(x)$ is continuous at x, and so $\lim_{\Delta x \to 0} f(x + \Delta x) = f(x)$. Then the preceding expression becomes

$$\frac{dy}{dx} = f(x)s'(x) + s(x)f'(x)$$

• **QUOTIENT RULE**

If $y = n(x)/d(x)$, where $n(x)$ and $d(x)$ are differentiable functions at x and $d(x) \neq 0$, then

$$\frac{dy}{dx} = \frac{d(x)n'(x) - n(x)d'(x)}{[d(x)]^2}$$

By definition,

$$\frac{dy}{dx} = \lim_{\Delta x \to 0} \frac{\dfrac{n(x + \Delta x)}{d(x + \Delta x)} - \dfrac{n(x)}{d(x)}}{\Delta x}$$

If we multiply the first term of the numerator by $d(x)/d(x)$ and the second term by $d(x + \Delta x)/d(x + \Delta x)$, we have

$$\frac{dy}{dx} = \lim_{\Delta x \to 0} \frac{\dfrac{n(x + \Delta x)d(x) - d(x + \Delta x)n(x)}{d(x + \Delta x)d(x)}}{\Delta x}$$

$$= \lim_{\Delta x \to 0} \frac{n(x + \Delta x)d(x) - d(x + \Delta x)n(x)}{\Delta x\, d(x + \Delta x)d(x)}$$

Adding and subtracting $n(x)d(x)$ to the numerator yields

$$\frac{dy}{dx} = \lim_{\Delta x \to 0} \frac{n(x + \Delta x)d(x) - n(x)d(x) + n(x)d(x) - d(x + \Delta x)n(x)}{\Delta x\, d(x + \Delta x)d(x)}$$

$$= \lim_{\Delta x \to 0} \frac{d(x)\dfrac{n(x + \Delta x) - n(x)}{\Delta x} - n(x)\dfrac{d(x + \Delta x) - d(x)}{\Delta x}}{d(x + \Delta x)d(x)}$$

By limit properties 2, 5, and 6 of Section 9-1, this expression becomes

$$\frac{dy}{dx} = \frac{\displaystyle\lim_{\Delta x \to 0} d(x) \lim_{\Delta x \to 0}\frac{n(x + \Delta x) - n(x)}{\Delta x} - \lim_{\Delta x \to 0} n(x) \lim_{\Delta x \to 0}\frac{d(x + \Delta x) - d(x)}{\Delta x}}{\displaystyle\lim_{\Delta x \to 0} d(x + \Delta x) \lim_{\Delta x \to 0} d(x)}$$

Since $d(x)$ is differentiable at x, it is continuous at x, and so $\lim_{\Delta x \to 0} d(x + \Delta x) = d(x)$. Hence, the preceding expression becomes

$$\frac{dy}{dx} = \frac{d(x)n'(x) - n(x)d'(x)}{[d(x)]^2}$$

Appendix B
Special Topics

- ### DERIVATION OF THE QUADRATIC FORMULA

On page 79 of Section 2-2, we stated the quadratic formula for solutions, if any exist, to quadratic equations of the form

$$ax^2 + bx + c = 0 \qquad (a \neq 0)$$

The quadratic formula is derived by beginning with the above equation and dividing both sides by a to obtain

$$x^2 + \frac{b}{a}x + \frac{c}{a} = 0$$

Subtracting c/a from both sides gives

$$x^2 + \frac{b}{a}x = -\frac{c}{a}$$

Adding $(b/2a)^2$ or, equivalently, $b^2/4a^2$ to both sides gives a perfect square for the left-hand side as given below.

$$x^2 + \frac{b}{a}x + \left(\frac{b}{2a}\right)^2 = \frac{b^2}{4a^2} - \frac{c}{a}$$

The left-hand side can be expressed in factored form as indicated below

$$\left(x + \frac{b}{2a}\right)^2 = \frac{b^2}{4a^2} - \frac{c}{a}\left(\frac{4a}{4a}\right)$$

and the (c/a) term is multiplied by $4a/4a$ to give a common denominator. Combining the right-hand-side terms gives

$$\left(x + \frac{b}{2a}\right)^2 = \frac{b^2 - 4ac}{4a^2}$$

Solving the resulting formula for x, we begin by taking the square root of each side to obtain

$$x + \frac{b}{2a} = \pm \sqrt{\frac{b^2 - 4ac}{4a^2}}$$

A-7

Using a property of square roots on the right-hand side, the above becomes

$$x + \frac{b}{2a} = \pm \frac{\sqrt{b^2 - 4ac}}{\sqrt{4a^2}}$$

$$= \pm \frac{\sqrt{b^2 - 4ac}}{2a}$$

Adding $-b/2a$ to both sides results in

$$x = -\frac{b}{2a} \pm \frac{\sqrt{b^2 - 4ac}}{2a}$$

$$= \frac{-b \pm \sqrt{b^2 - 4ac}}{2a}$$

Note that

1. There is one real solution if $b^2 - 4ac = 0$. That solution is $-b/2a$.
2. There are no real solutions if $b^2 - 4ac < 0$. This is because the square root of a negative number does not exist.
3. There are two real solutions if $b^2 - 4ac > 0$:

$$x = \frac{-b + \sqrt{b^2 - 4ac}}{2a} \qquad x = \frac{-b - \sqrt{b^2 - 4ac}}{2a}$$

• DISTANCE; THE EQUATION OF A CIRCLE

Sometimes we must find the distance between two points on the rectangular coordinate system. The distance between the two points, (x_1, y_1) and (x_2, y_2), in Figure B-1 is denoted by d. Observe that the vertical dis-

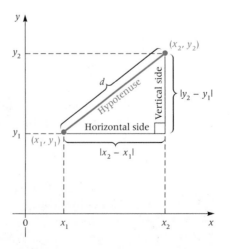

FIGURE B-1

tance between the two points is $|y_2 - y_1|$ and the horizontal distance between the two points is $|x_2 - x_1|$. Also, the vertical distance, $|y_2 - y_1|$, is the length of the vertical side of the right triangle, and the horizontal distance, $|x_2 - x_1|$, the length of the horizontal side of the right triangle. The length of the hypotenuse is the distance, d, between the two points, (x_1, y_1) and (x_2, y_2). According to the Pythagorean theorem,

$$d^2 = (\text{horizontal distance})^2 + (\text{vertical distance})^2$$
$$= |x_2 - x_1|^2 + |y_2 - y_1|^2$$
$$= (x_2 - x_1)^2 + (y_2 - y_1)^2$$

Hence,

$$d = \sqrt{(x_2 - x_1)^2 + (y_2 - y_1)^2} \qquad \text{Distance Formula}$$

Since this formula gives the distance between two points, (x_1, y_1) and (x_2, y_2), in the plane, it is called the **distance formula.**

• EXAMPLE B-1

Find the distance between $(1, -2)$ and $(4, 5)$ in Figure B-2.

Solution

Let $(x_1, y_1) = (1, -2)$ and $(x_2, y_2) = (4, 5)$. Then the distance, d, between the points is

$$d = \sqrt{(x_2 - x_1)^2 + (y_2 - y_1)^2}$$
$$= \sqrt{(4 - 1)^2 + [5 - (-2)]^2}$$
$$= \sqrt{3^2 + 7^2}$$
$$= \sqrt{58} \approx 7.62$$

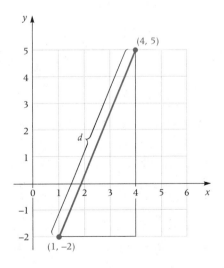

FIGURE B-2

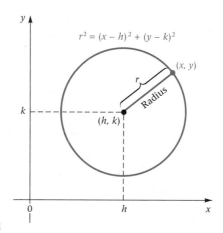

FIGURE B-3

Consider the circle of radius, r, with center at (h, k), as shown in Figure B-3. The circle consists of all points (x, y) that are at distance r from (h, k). Using the distance formula, the distance between a point (x, y) on the circle and the center, (h, k), is given by

$$r = \sqrt{(x - h)^2 + (y - k)^2}$$

Squaring both sides, we have the equation of a circle of radius r and center at (h, k).

$$r^2 = (x - h)^2 + (y - k)^2 \qquad \text{Equation of a circle}$$

Thus, any point (x, y) on the circle satisfies this equation.

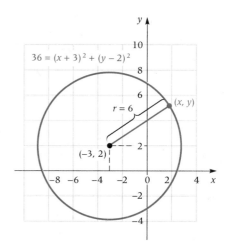

FIGURE B-4

• EXAMPLE B-2

Find the equation of a circle of radius 6 with center at $(-3, 2)$.

Solution

The equation of a circle of radius r and center (h, k) is $r^2 = (x - h)^2 + (y - k)^2$. Since $(h, k) = (-3, 2)$ and $r = 6$, this equation becomes $6^2 = [x - (-3)]^2 + (y - 2)^2$. Thus, the equation of the circle is $36 = (x + 3)^2 + (y - 2)^2$. The circle appears in Figure B-4 on page A-10.

Exercises

Find the distance between the following points.

1. $(4, 6)$ and $(7, 10)$ **2.** $(-1, 2)$ and $(8, 5)$
3. $(3, 0)$ and $(4, 2)$ **4.** $(-2, 8)$ and $(-1, -3)$
5. $(5, 3)$ and $(5, 7)$ **6.** $(1, 4)$ and $(8, 4)$
7. $(8, 2)$ and $(6, 9)$ **8.** $(-6, 2)$ and $(-6, -5)$
9. Find y so that the distance between the origin and the point $(4, y)$ is 6.
10. Find x so that the distance between the origin and the point $(x, 3)$ is 4.
11. Find y so that the distance between $(3, 1)$ and $(7, y)$ is 5.

Find the equation of each of the following circles.

12. Center at $(4, 6)$ and radius is 8
13. Center at $(-2, 5)$ and radius is 3
14. Center at $(4, 0)$ and radius is 6
15. Center at $(0, 3)$ and radius is 5

Graph each of the following:

16. $(x - 2)^2 + (y - 5)^2 = 81$ **17.** $x^2 + y^2 = 36$
18. $(x + 9)^2 + (y - 1)^2 = 64$ **19.** $x^2 + (y - 1)^2 = 25$

Answers

1. $d = \sqrt{(7 - 4)^2 + (10 - 6)^2} = \sqrt{3^2 + 4^2} = \sqrt{25} = 5$
2. $d = \sqrt{[8 - (-1)]^2 + (5 - 2)^2} = \sqrt{9^2 + 3^2} = \sqrt{90} \approx 9.49$
3. $d = \sqrt{(4 - 3)^2 + (2 - 0)^2} = \sqrt{1^2 + 2^2} = \sqrt{5} \approx 2.24$
4. $d = \sqrt{[-1 - (-2)]^2 + (-3 - 8)^2} = \sqrt{1^2 + (-11)^2} = \sqrt{122} \approx 11.05$
5. $d = \sqrt{(5 - 5)^2 + (7 - 3)^2} = \sqrt{0^2 + 4^2} = \sqrt{16} = 4$
6. $d = \sqrt{(8 - 1)^2 + (4 - 4)^2} = \sqrt{7^2 + 0^2} = \sqrt{49} = 7$
7. $d = \sqrt{(6 - 8)^2 + (9 - 2)^2} = \sqrt{(-2)^2 + 7^2} = \sqrt{53} \approx 7.28$
8. $d = \sqrt{[-6 - (-6)]^2 + (-5 - 2)^2} = \sqrt{0^2 + (-7)^2} = \sqrt{49} = 7$
9. $6 = \sqrt{(4 - 0)^2 + (y - 0)^2} = \sqrt{4^2 + y^2} = \sqrt{16 + y^2}$, so $36 = 6^2 = (\sqrt{16 + y^2})^2$ $= 16 + y^2$. Therefore, $y^2 = 36 - 16 = 20$, and so $y = \pm\sqrt{20} \approx \pm 4.47$.
10. $4 = \sqrt{(x - 0)^2 + (3 - 0)^2} = \sqrt{x^2 + 3^2} = \sqrt{x^2 + 9}$, so $16 = 4^2 = (\sqrt{x^2 + 9})^2$ $= x^2 + 9$. Therefore, $x^2 = 16 - 9 = 7$, and so $x = \pm \sqrt{7} \approx \pm 2.65$.
11. $5 = \sqrt{(7 - 3)^2 + (y - 1)^2} = \sqrt{4^2 + (y - 1)^2} = \sqrt{16 + (y - 1)^2}$, so $25 = 5^2$ $= [\sqrt{16 + (y - 1)^2}]^2 = 16 + (y - 1)^2$. Therefore, $(y - 1)^2 = 25 - 16 = 9$, and so $y - 1 = \pm 3$. Thus, $y = 3 + 1 = 4$, or $y = -3 + 1 = -2$.
12. $(x - 4)^2 + (y - 6)^2 = 8^2$, or $(x - 4)^2 + (y - 6)^2 = 64$
13. $[x - (-2]^2 + (y - 5)^2 = 3^2$, or $(x + 2)^2 + (y - 5)^2 = 9$

14. $(x - 4)^2 + (y - 0)^2 = 6^2$, or $(x - 4)^2 + y^2 = 36$
15. $(x - 0)^2 + (y - 3)^2 = 5^2$, or $x^2 + (y - 3)^2 = 25$
16. $(x - 2)^2 + (y - 5)^2 = 81$

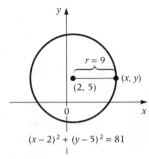

17. $x^2 + y^2 = 36$

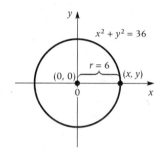

18. $(x + 9)^2 + (y - 1)^2 = 64$

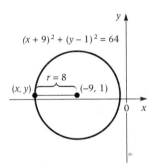

19. $x^2 + (y - 1)^2 = 25$

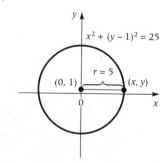

• DETERMINANTS

A **determinant** is a number associated with a square matrix. Given a 2×2 matrix

$$A = \begin{bmatrix} a_{11} & a_{12} \\ a_{21} & a_{22} \end{bmatrix}$$

its determinant is denoted by either of the following:

$$|A| \qquad \begin{vmatrix} a_{11} & a_{12} \\ a_{21} & a_{22} \end{vmatrix}$$

The determinant of A is defined as follows:

$$|A| = \begin{vmatrix} a_{11} & a_{12} \\ a_{21} & a_{22} \end{vmatrix} = a_{11}a_{22} - a_{12}a_{21}$$

Thus, if

$$A = \begin{bmatrix} 4 & 3 \\ 8 & 7 \end{bmatrix}$$

its determinant is

$$|A| = \begin{vmatrix} 4 & 3 \\ 8 & 7 \end{vmatrix} = (4)(7) = (3)(8) = 4$$

• EXAMPLE B-3

Find $\begin{vmatrix} -8 & 5 \\ 4 & 6 \end{vmatrix}$.

Solution

$$\begin{vmatrix} -8 & 5 \\ 4 & 6 \end{vmatrix} = (-8)(6) - (5)(4) = -68$$

• EXAMPLE B-4

If

$$A = \begin{bmatrix} -4 & 3 \\ -2 & -1 \end{bmatrix}$$

find the determinant of A.

Solution

$$|A| = (-4)(-1) - (3)(-2) = 10$$

Finding the determinant of a square matrix of a dimension greater than 2×2 is more complicated than in the 2×2 case. In order to find the determinant of a square matrix of dimension greater than 2×2, we must understand the following concept.

Minor of an Element

Each element a_{ij} of a square matrix of dimension $n \times n$ has an associated square matrix of dimension $(n - 1) \times (n - 1)$, which is determined by blocking out the row and column of element a_{ij}. The determinant of the associated $(n - 1) \times (n - 1)$ matrix is called the **minor** of element a_{ij}.

For example, consider the general 3×3 matrix

$$A = \begin{bmatrix} a_{11} & a_{12} & a_{13} \\ a_{21} & a_{22} & a_{23} \\ a_{31} & a_{32} & a_{33} \end{bmatrix}$$

To find the minor of element a_{12}, we block out the row and column of a_{12} as shown here.

$$\begin{bmatrix} a_{11} & a_{12} & a_{13} \\ a_{21} & a_{22} & a_{23} \\ a_{31} & a_{32} & a_{33} \end{bmatrix}$$

The remaining 2×2 matrix is

$$\begin{bmatrix} a_{21} & a_{23} \\ a_{31} & a_{33} \end{bmatrix}$$

Its determinant

$$\begin{vmatrix} a_{21} & a_{23} \\ a_{31} & a_{33} \end{vmatrix} = a_{21}a_{33} - a_{23}a_{31}$$

is the *minor of a_{12}*.

• **EXAMPLE B-5** _____

Find the minor of -2 (located in row 2 and column 2) of matrix B.

$$B = \begin{bmatrix} 1 & 0 & 5 \\ 4 & -2 & -3 \\ 6 & -1 & 8 \end{bmatrix}$$

Solution

We first block out the row and column of -2 as shown below.

$$\begin{bmatrix} 1 & 0 & 5 \\ 4 & -2 & -3 \\ 6 & -1 & 8 \end{bmatrix}$$

The remaining 2×2 matrix is

$$\begin{bmatrix} 1 & 5 \\ 6 & 8 \end{bmatrix}$$

Its determinant,

$$\begin{vmatrix} 1 & 5 \\ 6 & 8 \end{vmatrix} = (1)(8) - (5)(6) = -22$$

is the minor of -2.

Now that we know how to find the minor of an element a_{ij} of a square matrix, we must also understand the following concept.

Cofactor of an Element

Each element a_{ij} of a square matrix has an associated number called the **cofactor** of a_{ij}. The cofactor of an element a_{ij} is determined by the following procedure:

Step 1   Find the *minor* of element a_{ij}.

Step 2   Multiply the minor by $(-1)^{i+j}$, where i is the row number of element a_{ij} and j is the column number of a_{ij}.

We illustrate by finding the cofactor of an element of the matrix

$$M = \begin{bmatrix} 2 & -3 & 3 \\ -6 & 2 & -4 \\ 7 & 2 & -5 \end{bmatrix}$$

Let's find the cofactor of -6, which is located in row 2 and column 1 of matrix M. We first find the *minor of* -6 by blocking out its row and column as shown here

and then finding the determinant of the resulting matrix. Hence,

$$\begin{vmatrix} -3 & 3 \\ 2 & -5 \end{vmatrix} = (-3)(-5) - (3)(2) = 9$$

is the minor of -6. Multiplying 9, the minor of -6, by

$$(-1)^{i+j}$$

where i is the row number of -6 and j is its column number, gives

$$(-1)^{2+1}(9) = -1(9) = -9$$

Thus, -9 is the cofactor of -6.

The minor and cofactor of each element of column 3 of matrix M are given in Table B-1.

TABLE B-1

Element	Minor	Cofactor
Element 3 located in row 1 and column 3 of M	$\begin{vmatrix} -6 & 2 \\ 7 & 2 \end{vmatrix} = -26$	$(-1)^{1+3}(-26) = -26$
Element -4 located in row 2 and column 3 of M	$\begin{vmatrix} 2 & -3 \\ 7 & 2 \end{vmatrix} = 25$	$(-1)^{2+3}(25) = -25$
Element -5 located in row 3 and column 3 of M	$\begin{vmatrix} 2 & -3 \\ -6 & 2 \end{vmatrix} = -14$	$(-1)^{3+3}(-14) = -14$

Now that we know how to determine the cofactor of an element of a square matrix, we are ready to learn how to find the determinant of a square matrix of dimension higher than 2×2. The procedure is as follows.

To Find the Determinant of an $n \times n$ Matrix ($n > 2$)

Step 1 Choose either a row or a column of the original matrix.

Step 2 Multiply each element of this chosen row (or column) by its respective cofactor.

Step 3 Add the products obtained in step 2. The result is the determinant of the matrix.

• **EXAMPLE B-6** _____

Find the determinant of matrix M where

$$M = \begin{bmatrix} 2 & -3 & 3 \\ -6 & 2 & -4 \\ 7 & 2 & -5 \end{bmatrix}$$

Solution

Since the cofactors of the elements in column 3 are given in Table B-1 of this section, we choose column 3 of matrix M. Multiplying each element in column 3 by its respective cofactor and adding the products gives

$$\begin{aligned} |M| &= 3(-26) + (-4)(-25) + (-5)(-14) \\ &= -78 + 100 + 70 \\ &= 92 \end{aligned}$$

• **EXAMPLE B-7** _____

Find the determinant of matrix M of the previous example by choosing row 2.

Solution

The cofactors of -6, 2, and -4 are -9, -31, and -25, respectively. Multiplying each element of row 2 by its respective cofactor and adding the products gives

$$|M| = (-6)(-9) + 2(-31) + (-4)(-25)$$
$$= 54 - 62 + 100$$
$$= 92$$

Note that $|M| = 92$ regardless of the row or column with which we choose to find the determinant of M.

In general, the determinant of a given square matrix is the same number regardless of the row or column chosen.

• **EXAMPLE B-8**

Find $|A|$ if

$$A = \begin{bmatrix} 1 & 0 & -1 & 4 \\ 0 & 3 & 2 & -4 \\ 2 & 0 & -1 & 0 \\ 5 & 0 & 0 & 0 \end{bmatrix}$$

Solution

Choosing column 2, we determine the cofactor of 3 to be

$$(-1)^{2+2} \begin{vmatrix} 1 & -1 & 4 \\ 2 & -1 & 0 \\ 5 & 0 & 0 \end{vmatrix}$$

We need not determine the cofactors of the 0s since the product of a 0 and its cofactor is 0. We determine that

$$\begin{vmatrix} 1 & -1 & 4 \\ 2 & -1 & 0 \\ 5 & 0 & 0 \end{vmatrix} = 20$$

and, thus, the cofactor of 3 is

$$(-1)^{2+2}(20) = 20$$

Hence,

$$|A| = 3(20) = 60$$

Exercises

1. Find $|D|$ if

$$D = \begin{bmatrix} 2 & -1 & 3 \\ 3 & 2 & -4 \\ 4 & 2 & -5 \end{bmatrix}$$

2. Find $|C|$ if

$$C = \begin{bmatrix} 5 & 3 & 2 \\ 8 & -1 & 4 \\ 1 & 2 & -3 \end{bmatrix}$$

3. Find $|H|$ if

$$H = \begin{bmatrix} 5 & 0 & 4 \\ 3 & 2 & -1 \\ -8 & -5 & 7 \end{bmatrix}$$

4. Find $|K|$ if

$$K = \begin{bmatrix} 0 & -1 & 5 \\ 2 & -3 & -4 \\ 0 & 4 & 7 \end{bmatrix}$$

5. Find $|N|$ if

$$N = \begin{bmatrix} 4 & 0 & 3 & 1 \\ -1 & 0 & 2 & -3 \\ 3 & 5 & 1 & -2 \\ -4 & 0 & -3 & 1 \end{bmatrix}$$

Answers

1. $|D| = -9$
2. $|C| = 93$
3. $|H| = 49$
4. $|K| = 54$
5. $|N| = -110$

Appendix C
Tables

TABLE 1 Common logarithms

x	0	1	2	3	4	5	6	7	8	9
1.0	0.0000	0.0043	0.0086	0.0128	0.0170	0.0212	0.0253	0.0294	0.0334	0.0374
1.1	0.0414	0.0453	0.0492	0.0531	0.0569	0.0607	0.0645	0.0682	0.0719	0.0755
1.2	0.0792	0.0828	0.0864	0.0899	0.0934	0.0969	0.1004	0.1038	0.1072	0.1106
1.3	0.1139	0.1173	0.1206	0.1239	0.1271	0.1303	0.1335	0.1367	0.1399	0.1430
1.4	0.1461	0.1492	0.1523	0.1553	0.1584	0.1614	0.1644	0.1673	0.1703	0.1732
1.5	0.1761	0.1790	0.1818	0.1847	0.1875	0.1903	0.1931	0.1959	0.1987	0.2014
1.6	0.2041	0.2068	0.2095	0.2122	0.2148	0.2175	0.2201	0.2227	0.2253	0.2279
1.7	0.2304	0.2330	0.2355	0.2380	0.2405	0.2430	0.2455	0.2480	0.2504	0.2529
1.8	0.2553	0.2577	0.2601	0.2625	0.2648	0.2672	0.2695	0.2718	0.2742	0.2765
1.9	0.2788	0.2810	0.2833	0.2856	0.2878	0.2900	0.2923	0.2945	0.2967	0.2989
2.0	0.3010	0.3032	0.3054	0.3075	0.3096	0.3118	0.3139	0.3160	0.3181	0.3201
2.1	0.3222	0.3243	0.3263	0.3284	0.3304	0.3324	0.3345	0.3365	0.3385	0.3404
2.2	0.3424	0.3444	0.3464	0.3483	0.3502	0.3522	0.3541	0.3560	0.3579	0.3598
2.3	0.3617	0.3636	0.3655	0.3674	0.3692	0.3711	0.3729	0.3747	0.3766	0.3784
2.4	0.3802	0.3820	0.3838	0.3856	0.3874	0.3892	0.3909	0.3927	0.3945	0.3962
2.5	0.3979	0.3997	0.4014	0.4031	0.4048	0.4065	0.4082	0.4099	0.4116	0.4133
2.6	0.4150	0.4166	0.4183	0.4200	0.4216	0.4232	0.4249	0.4265	0.4281	0.4298
2.7	0.4314	0.4330	0.4346	0.4362	0.4378	0.4393	0.4409	0.4425	0.4440	0.4456
2.8	0.4472	0.4487	0.4502	0.4518	0.4533	0.4548	0.4564	0.4579	0.4594	0.4609
2.9	0.4624	0.4639	0.4654	0.4669	0.4683	0.4698	0.4713	0.4728	0.4742	0.4757
3.0	0.4771	0.4786	0.4800	0.4814	0.4829	0.4843	0.4857	0.4871	0.4886	0.4900
3.1	0.4914	0.4928	0.4942	0.4955	0.4969	0.4983	0.4997	0.5011	0.5024	0.5038
3.2	0.5052	0.5065	0.5079	0.5092	0.5105	0.5119	0.5132	0.5145	0.5159	0.5172
3.3	0.5185	0.5198	0.5211	0.5224	0.5237	0.5250	0.5263	0.5276	0.5289	0.5302
3.4	0.5315	0.5328	0.5340	0.5353	0.5366	0.5378	0.5391	0.5403	0.5416	0.5428
3.5	0.5441	0.5453	0.5465	0.5478	0.5490	0.5502	0.5515	0.5527	0.5539	0.5551
3.6	0.5563	0.5575	0.5587	0.5599	0.5611	0.5623	0.5635	0.5647	0.5658	0.5670
3.7	0.5682	0.5694	0.5705	0.5717	0.5729	0.5740	0.5752	0.5763	0.5775	0.5786
3.8	0.5798	0.5809	0.5821	0.5832	0.5843	0.5855	0.5866	0.5877	0.5888	0.5899
3.9	0.5911	0.5922	0.5933	0.5944	0.5955	0.5966	0.5977	0.5988	0.5999	0.6010
4.0	0.6021	0.6031	0.6042	0.6053	0.6064	0.6075	0.6085	0.6096	0.6107	0.6117
4.1	0.6128	0.6138	0.6149	0.6160	0.6170	0.6180	0.6191	0.6201	0.6212	0.6222
4.2	0.6232	0.6243	0.6253	0.6263	0.6274	0.6284	0.6294	0.6304	0.6314	0.6325

continues

TABLE 1 **Common logarithms** *(continued)*

x	0	1	2	3	4	5	6	7	8	9
4.3	0.6335	0.6345	0.6355	0.6365	0.6375	0.6385	0.6395	0.6405	0.6415	0.6425
4.4	0.6435	0.6444	0.6454	0.6464	0.6474	0.6484	0.6493	0.6503	0.6513	0.6522
4.5	0.6532	0.6542	0.6551	0.6561	0.6571	0.6580	0.6590	0.6599	0.6609	0.6618
4.6	0.6628	0.6637	0.6646	0.6656	0.6665	0.6675	0.6684	0.6693	0.6702	0.6712
4.7	0.6721	0.6730	0.6739	0.6749	0.6758	0.6767	0.6776	0.6785	0.6794	0.6803
4.8	0.6812	0.6821	0.6830	0.6839	0.6848	0.6857	0.6866	0.6875	0.6884	0.6893
4.9	0.6902	0.6911	0.6920	0.6928	0.6937	0.6946	0.6955	0.6964	0.6972	0.6981
5.0	0.6990	0.6998	0.7007	0.7016	0.7024	0.7033	0.7042	0.7050	0.7059	0.7067
5.1	0.7076	0.7084	0.7093	0.7101	0.7110	0.7118	0.7126	0.7135	0.7143	0.7152
5.2	0.7160	0.7168	0.7177	0.7185	0.7193	7.7202	0.7210	0.7218	0.7226	0.7235
5.3	0.7243	0.7251	0.7259	0.7267	0.7275	0.7284	0.7292	0.7300	0.7308	0.7316
5.4	0.7324	0.7332	0.7340	0.7348	0.7356	0.7364	0.7372	0.7380	0.7388	0.7396
5.5	0.7404	0.7412	0.7419	0.7427	0.7435	0.7443	0.7451	0.7459	0.7466	0.7474
5.6	0.7482	0.7490	0.7497	0.7505	0.7513	0.7520	0.7528	0.7536	0.7543	0.7551
5.7	0.7559	0.7566	0.7574	0.7582	0.7589	0.7597	0.7604	0.7612	0.7619	0.7627
5.8	0.7634	0.7642	0.7649	0.7657	0.7664	0.7672	0.7679	0.7686	0.7694	0.7701
5.9	0.7709	0.7716	0.7723	0.7731	0.7738	0.7745	0.7752	0.7760	0.7767	0.7774
6.0	0.7782	0.7789	0.7796	0.7803	0.7810	0.7818	0.7825	0.7832	0.7839	0.7846
6.1	0.7853	0.7860	0.7868	0.7875	0.7882	0.7889	0.7896	0.7903	0.7910	0.7917
6.2	0.7924	0.7931	0.7938	0.7945	0.7952	0.7959	0.7966	0.7973	0.7980	0.7987
6.3	0.7993	0.8000	0.8007	0.8014	0.8021	0.8028	0.8035	0.8041	0.8048	0.8055
6.4	0.8062	0.8069	0.8075	0.8082	0.8089	0.8096	0.8102	0.8109	0.8116	0.8122
6.5	0.8129	0.8136	0.8142	0.8149	0.8156	0.8162	0.8169	0.8176	0.8182	0.8189
6.6	0.8195	0.8202	0.8209	0.8215	0.8222	0.8228	0.8235	0.8241	0.8248	0.8254
6.7	0.8261	0.8267	0.8274	0.8280	0.8287	0.8293	0.8299	0.8306	0.8312	0.8319
6.8	0.8325	0.8331	0.8338	0.8344	0.8351	0.8357	0.8363	0.8370	0.8376	0.8382
6.9	0.8388	0.8395	0.8401	0.8407	0.8414	0.8420	0.8426	0.8432	0.8439	0.8445
7.0	0.8451	0.8457	0.8463	0.8470	0.8476	0.8482	0.8488	0.8494	0.8500	0.8506
7.1	0.8513	0.8519	0.8525	0.8531	0.8537	0.8543	0.8549	0.8555	0.8561	0.8567
7.2	0.8573	0.8579	0.8585	0.8591	0.8597	0.8603	0.8609	0.8615	0.8621	0.8627
7.3	0.8633	0.8639	0.8645	0.8651	0.8657	0.8663	0.8669	0.8675	0.8681	0.8686
7.4	0.8692	0.8698	0.8704	0.8710	0.8716	0.8722	0.8727	0.8733	0.8739	0.8745
7.5	0.8751	0.8756	0.8762	0.8768	0.8774	0.8779	0.8785	0.8791	0.8797	0.8802
7.6	0.8808	0.8814	0.8820	0.8825	0.8831	0.8837	0.8842	0.8848	0.8854	0.8859
7.7	0.8865	0.8871	0.8876	0.8882	0.8887	0.8893	0.8899	0.8904	0.8910	0.8915
7.8	0.8921	0.8927	0.8932	0.8938	0.8943	0.8949	0.8954	0.8960	0.8965	0.8971
7.9	0.8976	0.8982	0.8987	0.8993	0.8998	0.9004	0.9009	0.9015	0.9020	0.9025
8.0	0.9031	0.9036	0.9042	0.9047	0.9053	0.9058	0.9063	0.9069	0.9074	0.9079
8.1	0.9085	0.9090	0.9096	0.9101	0.9106	0.9112	0.9117	0.9122	0.9128	0.9133
8.2	0.9138	0.9143	0.9149	0.9154	0.9159	0.9165	0.9170	0.9175	0.9180	0.9186
8.3	0.9191	0.9196	0.9201	0.9206	0.9212	0.9217	0.9222	0.9227	0.9232	0.9238
8.4	0.9243	0.9248	0.9253	0.9258	0.9263	0.9269	0.9274	0.9279	0.9284	0.9289
8.5	0.9294	0.9299	0.9304	0.9309	0.9315	0.9320	0.9325	0.9330	0.9335	0.9340
8.6	0.9345	0.9350	0.9355	0.9360	0.9365	0.9370	0.9375	0.9380	0.9385	0.9390
8.7	0.9395	0.9400	0.9405	0.9410	0.9415	0.9420	0.9425	0.9430	0.9435	0.9440
8.8	0.9445	0.9450	0.9455	0.9460	0.9465	0.9469	0.9474	0.9479	0.9484	0.9489
8.9	0.9494	0.9499	0.9504	0.9509	0.9513	0.9518	0.9523	0.9528	0.9533	0.9538
9.0	0.9542	0.9547	0.9552	0.9557	0.9562	0.9566	0.9571	0.9576	0.9581	0.9586
9.1	0.9590	0.9595	0.9600	0.9605	0.9609	0.9614	0.9619	0.9624	0.9628	0.9633

continues

TABLE 1 Common logarithms *(continued)*

x	0	1	2	3	4	5	6	7	8	9
9.2	0.9638	0.9643	0.9647	0.9652	0.9657	0.9661	0.9666	0.9671	0.9675	0.9680
9.3	0.9685	0.9689	0.9694	0.9699	0.9703	0.9708	0.9713	0.9717	0.9722	0.9727
9.4	0.9731	0.9736	0.9741	0.9745	0.9750	0.9754	0.9759	0.9764	0.9768	0.9773
9.5	0.9777	0.9782	0.9786	0.9791	0.9795	0.9800	0.9805	0.9809	0.9814	0.9818
9.6	0.9823	0.9827	0.9832	0.9836	0.9841	0.9845	0.9850	0.9854	0.9859	0.9863
9.7	0.9868	0.9872	0.9877	0.9881	0.9886	0.9890	0.9894	0.9899	0.9903	0.9908
9.8	0.9912	0.9917	0.9921	0.9926	0.9930	0.9934	0.9939	0.9943	0.9948	0.9952
9.9	0.9956	0.9961	0.9965	0.9969	0.9974	0.9978	0.9983	0.9987	0.9991	0.9996

TABLE 2 Natural logarithms

x	ln x	x	ln x	x	ln x
0.1	−2.302585	3.5	1.252763	6.9	1.931521
0.2	−1.609438	3.6	1.280934	7.0	1.945910
0.3	−1.203973	3.7	1.308333	7.1	1.960095
0.4	−0.916291	3.8	1.335001	7.2	1.974081
0.5	−0.693147	3.9	1.360977	7.3	1.987874
0.6	−0.510826	4.0	1.386294	7.4	2.001480
0.7	−0.356675	4.1	1.410987	7.5	2.014903
0.8	−0.223144	4.2	1.435085	7.6	2.028148
0.9	−0.105361	4.3	1.458615	7.7	2.041220
1.0	0.000000	4.4	1.481605	7.8	2.054124
1.1	0.095310	4.5	1.504077	7.9	2.066863
1.2	0.182322	4.6	1.526056	8.0	2.079442
1.3	0.262364	4.7	1.547563	8.1	2.091864
1.4	0.336472	4.8	1.568616	8.2	2.104134
1.5	0.405465	4.9	1.589235	8.3	2.116256
1.6	0.470004	5.0	1.609438	8.4	2.128232
1.7	0.530628	5.1	1.629241	8.5	2.140066
1.8	0.587787	5.2	1.648659	8.6	2.151762
1.9	0.641854	5.3	1.667707	8.7	2.163323
2.0	0.693147	5.4	1.686399	8.8	2.174752
2.1	0.741937	5.5	1.704748	8.9	2.186051
2.2	0.788457	5.6	1.722767	9.0	2.197225
2.3	0.832909	5.7	1.740466	9.1	2.208274
2.4	0.875469	5.8	1.757858	9.2	2.219203
2.5	0.916291	5.9	1.774952	9.3	2.230014
2.6	0.955511	6.0	1.791759	9.4	2.240710
2.7	0.993252	6.1	1.808289	9.5	2.251292
2.8	1.029619	6.2	1.824549	9.6	2.261763
2.9	1.064711	6.3	1.840550	9.7	2.272126
3.0	1.098612	6.4	1.856298	9.8	2.282382
3.1	1.131402	6.5	1.871802	9.9	2.292535
3.2	1.163151	6.6	1.887070	10.0	2.302585
3.3	1.193922	6.7	1.902108	11.0	2.397895
3.4	1.223775	6.8	1.916923	12.0	2.484907

continues

TABLE 2 **Natural logarithms** *(continued)*

x	ln x	x	ln x	x	ln x
13.0	2.564949	25.0	3.218876	65.0	4.174387
14.0	2.639057	30.0	3.401197	70.0	4.248495
15.0	2.708050	35.0	3.555348	75.0	4.317488
16.0	2.772589	40.0	3.688879	80.0	4.382027
17.0	2.833213	45.0	3.806662	85.0	4.442651
18.0	2.890372	50.0	3.912023	90.0	4.499810
19.0	2.944439	55.0	4.007333	95.0	4.553877
20.0	2.995732	60.0	4.094345	100.0	4.605170

TABLE 3 **Exponential functions**

x	e^x	e^{-x}	x	e^x	e^{-x}
0.00	1.000000	1.000000	1.40	4.055200	0.246597
0.01	1.010050	0.990050	1.50	4.481689	0.223130
0.02	1.020201	0.980199	1.60	4.953032	0.201897
0.03	1.030455	0.970446	1.70	5.473947	0.182684
0.04	1.040811	0.960789	1.80	6.049647	0.165299
0.05	1.051271	0.951229	1.90	6.685894	0.149569
0.06	1.061837	0.941765	2.00	7.389056	0.135335
0.07	1.072508	0.932394	2.10	8.166170	0.122456
0.08	1.083287	0.923116	2.20	9.025013	0.110803
0.09	1.094174	0.913931	2.30	9.974182	0.100259
0.10	1.105171	0.904837	2.40	11.023176	0.090718
0.11	1.116278	0.895834	2.50	12.182494	0.082085
0.12	1.127497	0.886920	2.60	13.463738	0.074274
0.13	1.138828	0.878095	2.70	14.879732	0.067206
0.14	1.150274	0.869358	2.80	16.444647	0.060810
0.15	1.161834	0.860708	2.90	18.174145	0.055023
0.16	1.173511	0.852144	3.00	20.085537	0.049787
0.17	1.185305	0.843665	3.50	33.115452	0.030197
0.18	1.197217	0.835270	4.00	54.598150	0.018316
0.19	1.209250	0.826959	4.50	90.017131	0.011109
0.20	1.221403	0.818731	5.00	148.413159	0.006738
0.30	1.349859	0.740818	5.50	244.691932	0.004087
0.40	1.491825	0.670320	6.00	403.428793	0.002479
0.50	1.648721	0.606531	6.50	665.141633	0.001503
0.60	1.822119	0.548812	7.00	1096.633158	0.000912
0.70	2.013753	0.496585	7.50	1808.042414	0.000553
0.80	2.225541	0.449329	8.00	2980.957987	0.000335
0.90	2.459603	0.406570	8.50	4914.768840	0.000203
1.00	2.718282	0.367879	9.00	8103.083928	0.000123
1.10	3.004166	0.332871	9.50	13359.726830	0.000075
1.20	3.320117	0.301194	10.00	22026.465795	0.000045
1.30	3.669297	0.272532			

TABLE 4 Compound amount $(1 + i)^n$

n	½%	¾%	1%	1¼%	1½%	1¾%	2%
1	1.005000	1.007500	1.010000	1.012500	1.015000	1.017500	1.020000
2	1.010025	1.015056	1.020100	1.025156	1.030225	1.035306	1.040400
3	1.015075	1.022669	1.030301	1.037971	1.045678	1.053424	1.061208
4	1.020151	1.030339	1.040604	1.050945	1.061364	1.071859	1.082432
5	1.025251	1.038067	1.051010	1.064082	1.077284	1.090617	1.104081
6	1.030378	1.045852	1.061520	1.077383	1.093443	1.109702	1.126162
7	1.035529	1.053696	1.072135	1.090850	1.109845	1.129122	1.148686
8	1.040707	1.061599	1.082857	1.104486	1.126493	1.148882	1.171659
9	1.045911	1.069561	1.093685	1.118292	1.143390	1.168987	1.195093
10	1.051140	1.077583	1.104622	1.132271	1.160541	1.189444	1.218994
11	1.056396	1.085664	1.115668	1.146424	1.177949	1.210260	1.243374
12	1.061678	1.093807	1.126825	1.160755	1.195618	1.231439	1.268242
13	1.066986	1.102010	1.138093	1.175264	1.213552	1.252990	1.293607
14	1.072321	1.110276	1.149474	1.189955	1.231756	1.274917	1.319479
15	1.077683	1.118603	1.160969	1.204829	1.250232	1.297228	1.345868
16	1.083071	1.126992	1.172579	1.219890	1.268986	1.319929	1.372786
17	1.088487	1.135445	1.184304	1.235138	1.288020	1.343028	1.400241
18	1.093929	1.143960	1.196147	1.250577	1.307341	1.366531	1.428246
19	1.099399	1.152540	1.208109	1.266210	1.326951	1.390445	1.456811
20	1.104896	1.161184	1.220190	1.282037	1.346855	1.414778	1.485947
21	1.110420	1.169893	1.232392	1.298063	1.367058	1.439537	1.515666
22	1.115972	1.178667	1.244716	1.314288	1.387564	1.464729	1.545980
23	1.121552	1.187507	1.257163	1.330717	1.408377	1.490361	1.576899
24	1.127160	1.196414	1.269735	1.347351	1.429503	1.516443	1.608437
25	1.132796	1.205387	1.282432	1.364193	1.450945	1.542981	1.640606
26	1.138460	1.214427	1.295256	1.381245	1.472710	1.569983	1.673418
27	1.144152	1.223535	1.308209	1.398511	1.494800	1.597457	1.706886
28	1.149873	1.232712	1.321291	1.415992	1.517222	1.625413	1.741024
29	1.155622	1.241957	1.334504	1.433692	1.539981	1.653858	1.775845
30	1.161400	1.251272	1.347849	1.451613	1.563080	1.682800	1.811362
31	1.167207	1.260656	1.361327	1.469759	1.586526	1.712249	1.847589
32	1.173043	1.270111	1.374941	1.488131	1.610324	1.742213	1.884541
33	1.178908	1.279637	1.388690	1.506732	1.634479	1.772702	1.922231
34	1.184803	1.289234	1.402577	1.525566	1.658996	1.803725	1.960676
35	1.190727	1.298904	1.416603	1.544636	1.683881	1.835290	1.999890
36	1.196681	1.308645	1.430769	1.563944	1.709140	1.867407	2.039887
37	1.202664	1.318460	1.445076	1.583493	1.734777	1.900087	2.080685
38	1.208677	1.328349	1.459527	1.603287	1.760798	1.933338	2.122299
39	1.214721	1.338311	1.474123	1.623328	1.787210	1.967172	2.164745
40	1.220794	1.348349	1.488864	1.643619	1.814018	2.001597	2.208040
41	1.226898	1.358461	1.503752	1.664165	1.841229	2.036625	2.252200
42	1.233033	1.368650	1.518790	1.684967	1.868847	2.072266	2.297244
43	1.239198	1.378915	1.533978	1.706029	1.896880	2.108531	2.343189
44	1.245394	1.389256	1.549318	1.727354	1.925333	2.145430	2.390053
45	1.251621	1.399676	1.564811	1.748946	1.954213	2.182975	2.437854
46	1.257879	1.410173	1.580459	1.770808	1.983526	2.221177	2.486611
47	1.264168	1.420750	1.596263	1.792943	2.013279	2.260048	2.536344
48	1.270489	1.431405	1.612226	1.815355	2.043478	2.299599	2.587070
49	1.276842	1.442141	1.628348	1.838047	2.074130	2.339842	2.638812

continues

TABLE 4 Compound amount $(1 + i)^n$ *(continued)*

n	½%	¾%	1%	1¼%	1½%	1¾%	2%
50	1.283226	1.452957	1.644632	1.861022	2.105242	2.380789	2.691588
51	1.289642	1.463854	1.661078	1.884285	2.136821	2.422453	2.745420
52	1.296090	1.474833	1.677689	1.907839	2.168873	2.464846	2.800328
53	1.302571	1.485894	1.694466	1.931687	2.201406	2.507980	2.856335
54	1.309083	1.497038	1.711410	1.955833	2.234428	2.551870	2.913461
55	1.315629	1.508266	1.728525	1.980281	2.267944	2.596528	2.971731
56	1.322207	1.519578	1.745810	2.005034	2.301963	2.641967	3.031165
57	1.328818	1.530975	1.763268	2.030097	2.336493	2.688202	3.091789
58	1.335462	1.542457	1.780901	2.055473	2.371540	2.735245	3.153624
59	1.342139	1.554026	1.798710	2.081167	2.407113	2.783112	3.216697
60	1.348850	1.565681	1.816697	2.107181	2.443220	2.831816	3.281031
61	1.355594	1.577424	1.834864	2.133521	2.479868	2.881373	3.346651
62	1.362372	1.589254	1.853212	2.160190	2.517066	2.931797	3.413584
63	1.369184	1.601174	1.871744	2.187193	2.554822	2.983104	3.481856
64	1.376030	1.613183	1.890462	2.214532	2.593144	3.035308	3.551493
65	1.382910	1.625281	1.909366	2.242214	2.632042	3.088426	3.622523
66	1.389825	1.637471	1.928460	2.270242	2.671522	3.142473	3.694974
67	1.396774	1.649752	1.947745	2.298620	2.711595	3.197466	3.768873
68	1.403758	1.662125	1.967222	2.327353	2.752269	3.253422	3.844251
69	1.410777	1.674591	1.986894	2.356444	2.793553	3.310357	3.921136
70	1.417831	1.687151	2.006763	2.385900	2.835456	3.368288	3.999558
71	1.424920	1.699804	2.026831	2.415724	2.877988	3.427233	4.079549
72	1.432044	1.712553	2.047099	2.445920	2.921158	3.487210	4.161140
73	1.439204	1.725397	2.067570	2.476494	2.964975	3.548236	4.244363
74	1.446401	1.738337	2.088246	2.507450	3.009450	3.610330	4.329250
75	1.453633	1.751375	2.109128	2.538794	3.054592	3.673511	4.415835
76	1.460901	1.764510	2.130220	2.570529	3.100411	3.737797	4.504152
77	1.468205	1.777744	2.151522	2.602660	3.146917	3.803209	4.594235
78	1.475546	1.791077	2.173037	2.635193	3.194120	3.869765	4.686120
79	1.482924	1.804510	2.194768	2.668133	3.242032	3.937486	4.779842
80	1.490339	1.818044	2.216715	2.701485	3.290663	4.006392	4.875439
81	1.497790	1.831679	2.238882	2.735254	3.340023	4.076504	4.972948
82	1.505279	1.845417	2.261271	2.769444	3.390123	4.147843	5.072407
83	1.512806	1.859258	2.283884	2.804062	3.440975	4.220430	5.173855
84	1.520370	1.873202	2.306723	2.839113	3.492590	4.294287	5.277332
85	1.527971	1.887251	2.329790	2.874602	3.544978	4.369437	5.382879
86	1.535611	1.901405	2.353088	2.910534	3.598153	4.445903	5.490536
87	1.543289	1.915666	2.376619	2.946916	3.652125	4.523706	5.600347
88	1.551006	1.930033	2.400385	2.983753	3.706907	4.602871	5.712354
89	1.558761	1.944509	2.424389	3.021049	3.762511	4.683421	5.826601
90	1.566555	1.959092	2.448633	3.058813	3.818949	4.765381	5.943133
91	1.574387	1.973786	2.473119	3.097048	3.876233	4.848775	6.061996
92	1.582259	1.988589	2.497850	3.135761	3.934376	4.933629	6.183236
93	1.590171	2.003503	2.522829	3.174958	3.993392	5.019967	6.306900
94	1.598122	2.018530	2.548057	3.214645	4.053293	5.107816	6.433038
95	1.606112	2.033669	2.573538	3.254828	4.114092	5.197203	6.561699
96	1.614143	2.048921	2.599273	3.295513	4.175804	5.288154	6.692933
97	1.622213	2.064288	2.625266	3.336707	4.238441	5.380697	6.826792
98	1.630324	2.079770	2.651518	3.378416	4.302017	5.474859	6.963328
99	1.638476	2.095369	2.678033	3.420646	4.366547	5.570669	7.102594
100	1.646668	2.111084	2.704814	3.463404	4.432046	5.668156	7.244646

TABLE 4   Compound amount $(1 + i)^n$

n	3%	4%	5%	6%	7%	8%	9%
1	1.030000	1.040000	1.050000	1.060000	1.070000	1.080000	1.090000
2	1.060900	1.081600	1.102500	1.123600	1.144900	1.166400	1.188100
3	1.092727	1.124864	1.157625	1.191016	1.225043	1.259712	1.295029
4	1.125509	1.169859	1.215506	1.262477	1.310796	1.360489	1.411582
5	1.159274	1.216653	1.276282	1.338226	1.402552	1.469328	1.538624
6	1.194052	1.265319	1.340096	1.418519	1.500730	1.586874	1.677100
7	1.229874	1.315932	1.407100	1.503630	1.605781	1.713824	1.828039
8	1.266770	1.368569	1.477455	1.593848	1.718186	1.850930	1.992563
9	1.304773	1.423312	1.551328	1.689479	1.838459	1.999005	2.171893
10	1.343916	1.480244	1.628895	1.790848	1.967151	2.158925	2.367364
11	1.384234	1.539454	1.710339	1.898299	2.104852	2.331639	2.580426
12	1.425761	1.601032	1.795856	2.012196	2.252192	2.518170	2.812665
13	1.468534	1.665074	1.885649	2.132928	2.409845	2.719624	3.065805
14	1.512590	1.731676	1.979932	2.260904	2.578534	2.937194	3.341727
15	1.557967	1.800944	2.078928	2.396558	2.759032	3.172169	3.642482
16	1.604706	1.872981	2.182875	2.540352	2.952164	3.425943	3.970306
17	1.652848	1.947900	2.292018	2.692773	3.158815	3.700018	4.327633
18	1.702433	2.025817	2.406619	2.854339	3.379932	3.996019	4.717120
19	1.753506	2.106849	2.526950	3.025600	3.616528	4.315701	5.141661
20	1.806111	2.191123	2.653298	3.207135	3.869684	4.660957	5.604411
21	1.860295	2.278768	2.785963	3.399564	4.140562	5.033834	6.108808
22	1.916103	2.369919	2.925261	3.603537	4.430402	5.436540	6.658600
23	1.973587	2.464716	3.071524	3.819750	4.740530	5.871464	7.257874
24	2.032794	2.563304	3.225100	4.048935	5.072367	6.341181	7.911083
25	2.093778	2.665836	3.386355	4.291871	5.427433	6.848475	8.623081
26	2.156591	2.772470	3.555673	4.549383	5.807353	7.396353	9.399158
27	2.221289	2.883369	3.733456	4.822346	6.213868	7.988061	10.245082
28	2.287928	2.998703	3.920129	5.111687	6.648838	8.627106	11.167140
29	2.356566	3.118651	4.116136	5.418388	7.114257	9.317275	12.172182
30	2.427262	3.243398	4.321942	5.743491	7.612255	10.062657	13.267678
31	2.500080	3.373133	4.538039	6.088101	8.145113	10.867669	14.461770
32	2.575083	3.508059	4.764941	6.453387	8.715271	11.737083	15.763329
33	2.652335	3.648381	5.003189	6.840590	9.325340	12.676050	17.182028
34	2.731905	3.794316	5.253348	7.251025	9.978114	13.690134	18.728411
35	2.813862	3.946089	5.516015	7.686087	10.676581	14.785344	20.413968
36	2.898278	4.103933	5.791816	8.147252	11.423942	15.968172	22.251225
37	2.985227	4.268090	6.081407	8.636087	12.223618	17.245626	24.253835
38	3.074783	4.438813	6.385477	9.154252	13.079271	18.625276	26.436680
39	3.167027	4.616366	6.704751	9.703507	13.994820	20.115298	28.815982
40	3.262038	4.801021	7.039989	10.285718	14.974458	21.724521	31.409420
41	3.359899	4.993061	7.391988	10.902861	16.022670	23.462483	34.236268
42	3.460696	5.192784	7.761588	11.557033	17.144257	25.339482	37.317532
43	3.564517	5.400495	8.149667	12.250455	18.344355	27.366640	40.676110
44	3.671452	5.616515	8.557150	12.985482	19.628460	29.555972	44.336960
45	3.781596	5.841176	8.985008	13.764611	21.002452	31.920449	48.327286
46	3.895044	6.074823	9.434258	14.590487	22.472623	34.474085	52.676742
47	4.011895	6.317816	9.905971	15.465917	24.045707	37.232012	57.417649
48	4.132252	6.570528	10.401270	16.393872	25.728907	40.210573	62.585237
49	4.256219	6.833349	10.921333	17.377504	27.529930	43.427419	68.217908

continues

TABLE 4 **Compound amount $(1 + i)^n$** *(continued)*

n	3%	4%	5%	6%	7%	8%	9%
50	4.383906	7.106683	11.467400	18.420154	29.457025	46.901613	74.357520
51	4.515423	7.390951	12.040770	19.525364	31.519017	50.653742	81.049697
52	4.650886	7.686589	12.642808	20.696885	33.725348	54.706041	88.344170
53	4.790412	7.994052	13.274949	21.938698	36.086122	59.082524	96.295145
54	4.934125	8.313814	13.938696	23.255020	38.612151	63.809126	104.961708
55	5.082149	8.646367	14.635631	24.650322	41.315001	68.913856	114.408262
56	5.234613	8.992222	15.367412	26.129341	44.207052	74.426965	124.705005
57	5.391651	9.351910	16.135783	27.697101	47.301545	80.381122	135.928456
58	5.553401	9.725987	16.942572	29.358927	50.612653	86.811612	148.162017
59	5.720003	10.115026	17.789701	31.120463	54.155539	93.756540	161.496598
60	5.891603	10.519627	18.679186	32.987691	57.946427	101.257064	176.031292
61	6.068351	10.940413	19.613145	34.966952	62.002677	109.357629	191.874108
62	6.250402	11.378029	20.593802	37.064969	66.342864	118.106239	209.142778
63	6.437914	11.833150	21.623493	39.288868	70.986865	127.554738	227.965628
64	6.631051	12.306476	22.704667	41.646200	75.955945	137.759117	248.482535
65	6.829983	12.798735	23.839901	44.144972	81.272861	148.779847	270.845963
66	7.034882	13.310685	25.031896	46.793670	86.961962	160.682234	295.222099
67	7.245929	13.843112	26.283490	49.601290	93.049299	173.536813	321.792088
68	7.463307	14.396836	27.597665	52.577368	99.562750	187.419758	350.753376
69	7.687206	14.972710	28.977548	55.732010	106.532142	202.413339	382.321180
70	7.917822	15.571618	30.426426	59.075930	113.989392	218.606406	416.730086
71	8.155357	16.194483	31.947747	62.620486	121.968650	236.094918	454.235794
72	8.400017	16.842262	33.545134	66.377715	130.506455	254.982512	495.117015
73	8.652018	17.515953	35.222391	70.360378	139.641907	275.381113	539.677547
74	8.911578	18.216591	36.983510	74.582001	149.416840	297.411602	588.248526
75	9.178926	18.945255	38.832686	79.056921	159.876019	321.204530	641.190893
76	9.454293	19.703065	40.774320	83.800336	171.067341	346.900892	698.898074
77	9.737922	20.491187	42.813036	88.828356	183.042055	374.652964	761.798900
78	10.030060	21.310835	44.953688	94.158058	195.854998	404.625201	830.360801
79	10.330962	22.163268	47.201372	99.807541	209.564848	436.995217	905.093274
80	10.640891	23.049799	49.561441	105.795993	224.234388	471.954834	986.551668
81	10.960117	23.971791	52.039513	112.143753	239.930795	509.711221	1075.341318
82	11.288921	24.930663	54.641489	118.872378	256.725950	550.488119	1172.122037
83	11.627588	25.927889	57.373563	126.004721	274.696767	594.527168	1277.613020
84	11.976416	26.965005	60.242241	133.565004	293.925541	642.089342	1392.598192
85	12.335709	28.043605	63.254353	141.578904	314.500328	693.456489	1517.932029
86	12.705780	29.165349	66.417071	150.073639	336.515351	748.933008	1654.545912
87	13.086953	30.331963	69.737925	159.078057	360.071426	808.847649	1803.455044
88	13.479562	31.545242	73.224821	168.622741	385.276426	873.555461	1965.765998
89	13.883949	32.807051	76.886062	178.740105	412.245776	943.439897	2142.684938
90	14.300467	34.119333	80.730365	189.464511	441.102980	1018.915089	2335.526582
91	14.729481	35.484107	84.766883	200.832382	471.980188	1100.428296	2545.723975
92	15.171366	36.903471	89.005227	212.882325	505.018802	1188.462560	2774.839132
93	15.626507	38.379610	93.455489	225.655264	540.370118	1283.539565	3024.574654
94	16.095302	39.914794	98.128263	239.194580	578.196026	1386.222730	3296.786373
95	16.578161	41.511386	103.034676	253.546255	618.669748	1497.120549	3593.497147
96	17.075506	43.171841	108.186410	268.759030	661.976630	1616.890192	3916.911890
97	17.587771	44.898715	113.595731	284.884572	708.314994	1746.241408	4269.433960
98	18.115404	46.694664	119.275517	301.977646	757.897044	1885.940720	4653.683016
99	18.658866	48.562450	125.239293	320.096305	810.949837	2036.815978	5072.514488
100	19.218632	50.504948	131.501258	339.302084	867.716326	2199.761256	5529.040792

TABLE 4 **Compound amount** $(1 + i)^n$

n	10%	11%	12%	13%	14%	15%	16%
1	1.100000	1.110000	1.120000	1.130000	1.140000	1.150000	1.16000
2	1.210000	1.232100	1.254400	1.276900	1.299600	1.322500	1.34560
3	1.331000	1.367631	1.404928	1.442897	1.481544	1.520875	1.56090
4	1.464100	1.518070	1.573519	1.630474	1.688960	1.749006	1.81064
5	1.610510	1.685058	1.762342	1.842435	1.925415	2.011357	2.10034
6	1.771561	1.870415	1.973823	2.081952	2.194973	2.313061	2.43640
7	1.948717	2.076160	2.210681	2.352605	2.502269	2.660020	2.82622
8	2.143589	2.304538	2.475963	2.658444	2.852586	3.059023	3.27841
9	2.357948	2.558037	2.773079	3.004042	3.251949	3.517876	3.80296
10	2.593742	2.839421	3.105848	3.394567	3.707221	4.045558	4.41144
11	2.853117	3.151757	3.478550	3.835861	4.226232	4.652391	5.11726
12	3.138428	3.498451	3.895976	4.334523	4.817905	5.350250	5.93603
13	3.452271	3.883280	4.363493	4.898011	5.492411	6.152788	6.88579
14	3.797498	4.310441	4.887112	5.534753	6.261349	7.075706	7.98752
15	4.177248	4.784589	5.473566	6.254270	7.137938	8.137062	9.26552
16	4.594973	5.310894	6.130394	7.067326	8.137249	9.357621	10.74800
17	5.054470	5.895093	6.866041	7.986078	9.276464	10.761264	12.46768
18	5.559917	6.543553	7.689966	9.024268	10.575169	12.375454	14.46251
19	6.115909	7.263344	8.612762	10.197423	12.055693	14.231772	16.77652
20	6.727500	8.062312	9.646293	11.523088	13.743490	16.366537	19.46076
21	7.400250	8.949166	10.803848	13.021089	15.667578	18.821518	22.57448
22	8.140275	9.933574	12.100310	14.713831	17.861039	21.644746	26.18640
23	8.954302	11.026267	13.552347	16.626629	20.361585	24.891458	30.37622
24	9.849733	12.239157	15.178629	18.788091	23.212207	28.625176	35.23642
25	10.834706	13.585464	17.000064	21.230542	26.461916	32.918953	40.87424
26	11.918177	15.079865	19.040072	23.990513	30.166584	37.856796	47.41412
27	13.109994	16.738650	21.324881	27.109279	34.389906	43.535315	55.00038
28	14.420994	18.579901	23.883866	30.633486	39.204493	50.065612	63.80044
29	15.863093	20.623691	26.749930	34.615839	44.693122	57.575454	74.00851
30	17.449402	22.892297	29.959922	39.115898	50.950159	66.211772	85.84988
31	19.194342	25.410449	33.555113	44.200965	58.083181	76.143538	99.58586
32	21.113777	28.205599	37.581726	49.947090	66.214826	87.565068	115.51959
33	23.225154	31.308214	42.091533	56.440212	75.484902	100.699829	134.00273
34	25.547670	34.752118	47.142517	63.777439	86.052788	115.804803	155.44317
35	28.102437	38.574851	52.799620	72.068506	98.100178	133.175523	180.31407
36	30.912681	42.818085	59.135574	81.437412	111.834203	153.151852	209.16432
37	34.003949	47.528074	66.231843	92.024276	127.490992	176.124630	242.63062
38	37.404343	52.756162	74.179664	103.987432	145.339731	202.543324	281.45151
39	41.144778	58.559340	83.081224	117.505798	165.687293	232.924823	326.48376
40	45.259256	65.000867	93.050970	132.781552	188.883514	267.863546	378.72116
41	49.785181	72.150963	104.217087	150.043153	215.327206	308.043078	439.31654
42	54.763699	80.087569	116.723137	169.548763	245.473015	354.249540	509.60719
43	60.240069	88.897201	130.729914	191.590103	279.839237	407.386971	591.14434
44	66.264076	98.675893	146.417503	216.496816	319.016730	468.495017	685.72744
45	72.890484	109.530242	163.987604	244.641402	363.679072	538.769269	795.44383
46	80.179532	121.578568	183.666116	276.444784	414.594142	619.584659	922.71484
47	88.197485	134.952211	205.706050	312.382606	472.637322	712.522358	1070.34921
48	97.017234	149.796954	230.390776	352.992345	538.806547	819.400712	1241.60509
49	106.718957	166.274619	258.037669	398.881350	614.239464	942.310819	1440.26190
50	117.390853	184.564827	289.002190	450.735925	700.232988	1083.657442	1670.70380

TABLE 5 **Present value** $(1 + i)^{-n}$

n	½%	¾%	1%	1¼%	1½%	1¾%	2%
1	0.995025	0.992556	0.990099	0.987654	0.985222	0.982801	0.980392
2	0.990075	0.985167	0.980296	0.975461	0.970662	0.965898	0.961169
3	0.985149	0.977833	0.970590	0.963418	0.956317	0.949285	0.942322
4	0.980248	0.970554	0.960980	0.951524	0.942184	0.932959	0.923845
5	0.975371	0.963329	0.951466	0.939777	0.928260	0.916913	0.905731
6	0.970518	0.956158	0.942045	0.928175	0.914542	0.901143	0.887971
7	0.965690	0.949040	0.932718	0.916716	0.901027	0.885644	0.870560
8	0.960885	0.941975	0.923483	0.905398	0.887711	0.870412	0.853490
9	0.956105	0.934963	0.914340	0.894221	0.874592	0.855441	0.836755
10	0.951348	0.928003	0.905287	0.883181	0.861667	0.840729	0.820348
11	0.946615	0.921095	0.896324	0.872277	0.848933	0.826269	0.804263
12	0.941905	0.914238	0.887449	0.861509	0.836387	0.812058	0.788493
13	0.937219	0.907432	0.878663	0.850873	0.824027	0.798091	0.773033
14	0.932556	0.900677	0.869963	0.840368	0.811849	0.784365	0.757875
15	0.927917	0.893973	0.861349	0.829993	0.799852	0.770875	0.743015
16	0.923300	0.887318	0.852821	0.819746	0.788031	0.757616	0.728446
17	0.918707	0.880712	0.844377	0.809626	0.776385	0.744586	0.714163
18	0.914136	0.874156	0.836017	0.799631	0.764912	0.731780	0.700159
19	0.909588	0.867649	0.827740	0.789759	0.753607	0.719194	0.686431
20	0.905063	0.861190	0.819544	0.780009	0.742470	0.706825	0.672971
21	0.900560	0.854779	0.811430	0.770379	0.731498	0.694668	0.659776
22	0.896080	0.848416	0.803396	0.760868	0.720688	0.682720	0.646839
23	0.891622	0.842100	0.795442	0.751475	0.710037	0.670978	0.634156
24	0.887186	0.835831	0.787566	0.742197	0.699544	0.659438	0.621721
25	0.882772	0.829609	0.779768	0.733034	0.689206	0.648096	0.609531
26	0.878380	0.823434	0.772048	0.723984	0.679021	0.636950	0.597579
27	0.874010	0.817304	0.764404	0.715046	0.668986	0.625995	0.585862
28	0.869662	0.811220	0.756836	0.706219	0.659099	0.615228	0.574375
29	0.865335	0.805181	0.749342	0.697500	0.649359	0.604647	0.563112
30	0.861030	0.799187	0.741923	0.688889	0.639762	0.594248	0.552071
31	0.856746	0.793238	0.734577	0.680384	0.630308	0.584027	0.541246
32	0.852484	0.787333	0.727304	0.671984	0.620993	0.573982	0.530633
33	0.848242	0.781472	0.720103	0.663688	0.611816	0.564111	0.520229
34	0.844022	0.775654	0.712973	0.655494	0.602774	0.554408	0.510028
35	0.839823	0.769880	0.705914	0.647402	0.593866	0.544873	0.500028
36	0.835645	0.764149	0.698925	0.639409	0.585090	0.535502	0.490223
37	0.831487	0.758461	0.692005	0.631515	0.576443	0.526292	0.480611
38	0.827351	0.752814	0.685153	0.623719	0.567924	0.517240	0.471187
39	0.823235	0.747210	0.678370	0.616019	0.559531	0.508344	0.461948
40	0.819139	0.741648	0.671653	0.608413	0.551262	0.499601	0.452890
41	0.815064	0.736127	0.665003	0.600902	0.543116	0.491008	0.444010
42	0.811009	0.730647	0.658419	0.593484	0.535089	0.482563	0.435304
43	0.806974	0.725208	0.651900	0.586157	0.527182	0.474264	0.426769
44	0.802959	0.719810	0.645445	0.578920	0.519391	0.466107	0.418401
45	0.798964	0.714451	0.639055	0.571773	0.511715	0.458090	0.410197
46	0.794989	0.709133	0.632728	0.564714	0.504153	0.450212	0.402154
47	0.791034	0.703854	0.626463	0.557742	0.496702	0.442469	0.394268
48	0.787098	0.698614	0.620260	0.550856	0.489362	0.434858	0.386538
49	0.783128	0.693414	0.614199	0.544056	0.482130	0.427379	0.378958
50	0.779286	0.688252	0.608039	0.537339	0.475005	0.420029	0.371528

continues

TABLE 5 **Present value $(1 + i)^{-n}$** *(continued)*

n	½%	¾%	1%	1¼%	1½%	1¾%	2%
51	0.775409	0.683128	0.602019	0.530705	0.467985	0.412805	0.364243
52	0.771551	0.678043	0.596058	0.524153	0.461069	0.405705	0.357101
53	0.767713	0.672995	0.590156	0.517682	0.454255	0.398727	0.350099
54	0.763893	0.667986	0.584313	0.511291	0.447542	0.391869	0.343234
55	0.760093	0.663013	0.578528	0.504979	0.440928	0.385130	0.336504
56	0.756311	0.658077	0.572800	0.498745	0.434412	0.378506	0.329906
57	0.7ɔ2548	0.653178	0.567129	0.492587	0.427992	0.371996	0.323437
58	0.748804	0.648316	0.561514	0.486506	0.421667	0.365598	0.317095
59	0.745079	0.643490	0.555954	0.480500	0.415435	0.359310	0.310878
60	0.741372	0.638700	0.550450	0.474568	0.409296	0.353130	0.304782
61	0.737684	0.633945	0.545000	0.468709	0.403247	0.347057	0.298806
62	0.734014	0.629226	0.539604	0.462922	0.397288	0.341088	0.292947
63	0.730362	0.624542	0.534261	0.457207	0.391417	0.335221	0.287203
64	0.726728	0.619893	0.528971	0.451563	0.385632	0.329456	0.281572
65	0.723113	0.615278	0.523734	0.445988	0.379933	0.323790	0.276051
66	0.719515	0.610698	0.518548	0.440482	0.374318	0.318221	0.270638
67	0.715935	0.606152	0.513414	0.435044	0.368787	0.312748	0.265331
68	0.712374	0.601639	0.508331	0.429673	0.363337	0.307369	0.260129
69	0.708829	0.597161	0.503298	0.424368	0.357967	0.302082	0.255028
70	0.705303	0.592715	0.498315	0.419129	0.352677	0.296887	0.250028
71	0.701794	0.588303	0.493381	0.413955	0.347465	0.291781	0.245125
72	0.698302	0.583924	0.488496	0.408844	0.342330	0.286762	0.240319
73	0.694828	0.579577	0.483659	0.403797	0.337271	0.281830	0.235607
74	0.691371	0.575262	0.478871	0.398811	0.332287	0.276983	0.230987
75	0.687932	0.570980	0.474129	0.393888	0.327376	0.272219	0.226458
76	0.684509	0.566730	0.469435	0.389025	0.322538	0.267537	0.222017
77	0.681104	0.562511	0.464787	0.384222	0.317771	0.262936	0.217664
78	0.677715	0.558323	0.460185	0.379479	0.313075	0.258414	0.213396
79	0.674343	0.554167	0.455629	0.374794	0.308448	0.253969	0.209212
80	0.670988	0.550042	0.451118	0.370167	0.303890	0.249601	0.205110
81	0.667650	0.545947	0.446651	0.365597	0.299399	0.245308	0.201088
82	0.664329	0.541883	0.442229	0.361083	0.294975	0.241089	0.197145
83	0.661023	0.537849	0.437851	0.356625	0.290615	0.236943	0.193279
84	0.657735	0.533845	0.433515	0.352223	0.286321	0.232868	0.189490
85	0.654462	0.529871	0.429223	0.347874	0.282089	0.228862	0.185774
86	0.651206	0.525927	0.424974	0.343580	0.277920	0.224926	0.182132
87	0.647967	0.522012	0.420766	0.339338	0.273813	0.221058	0.178560
88	0.644743	0.518126	0.416600	0.335148	0.269767	0.217256	0.175059
89	0.641535	0.514269	0.412475	0.331011	0.265780	0.213519	0.171627
90	0.638344	0.510440	0.408391	0.326924	0.261852	0.209847	0.168261
91	0.635168	0.506641	0.404348	0.322888	0.257982	0.206238	0.164962
92	0.632008	0.502869	0.400344	0.318902	0.254170	0.202691	0.161728
93	0.628863	0.499126	0.396380	0.314965	0.250414	0.199204	0.158556
94	0.625735	0.495410	0.392456	0.311076	0.246713	0.195778	0.155448
95	0.622622	0.491722	0.388570	0.307236	0.243067	0.192411	0.152400
96	0.619524	0.488062	0.384723	0.303443	0.239475	0.189102	0.149411
97	0.616442	0.484428	0.380914	0.299697	0.235936	0.185850	0.146482
98	0.613375	0.480822	0.377142	0.295997	0.232449	0.182653	0.143609
99	0.610323	0.477243	0.373408	0.292342	0.229014	0.179512	0.140794
100	0.607287	0.473690	0.369711	0.288733	0.225629	0.176424	0.138033

TABLE 5   Present value $(1 + i)^{-n}$

n	3%	4%	5%	6%	7%	8%	9%
1	0.970874	0.961538	0.952381	0.943396	0.934579	0.925926	0.917431
2	0.942596	0.924556	0.907029	0.889996	0.873439	0.857339	0.841680
3	0.915142	0.888996	0.863838	0.839619	0.816298	0.793832	0.772183
4	0.888487	0.854804	0.822702	0.792094	0.762895	0.735030	0.708425
5	0.862609	0.821927	0.783526	0.747258	0.712986	0.680583	0.649931
6	0.837484	0.790315	0.746215	0.704961	0.666342	0.630170	0.596267
7	0.813092	0.759918	0.710681	0.665057	0.622750	0.583490	0.547034
8	0.789409	0.730690	0.676839	0.627412	0.582009	0.540269	0.501866
9	0.766417	0.702587	0.644609	0.591898	0.543934	0.500249	0.460428
10	0.744094	0.675564	0.613913	0.558395	0.508349	0.463193	0.422411
11	0.722421	0.649581	0.584679	0.526788	0.475093	0.428883	0.387533
12	0.701380	0.624597	0.556837	0.496969	0.444012	0.397114	0.355535
13	0.680951	0.600574	0.530321	0.468839	0.414964	0.367698	0.326179
14	0.661118	0.577475	0.505068	0.442301	0.387817	0.340461	0.299246
15	0.641862	0.555265	0.481017	0.417265	0.362446	0.315242	0.274538
16	0.623167	0.533908	0.458112	0.393646	0.338735	0.291890	0.251870
17	0.605016	0.513373	0.436297	0.371364	0.316574	0.270269	0.231073
18	0.587395	0.493628	0.415521	0.350344	0.295864	0.250249	0.211994
19	0.570286	0.474642	0.395734	0.330513	0.276508	0.231712	0.194490
20	0.553676	0.456387	0.376889	0.311805	0.258419	0.214548	0.178431
21	0.537549	0.438834	0.358942	0.294155	0.241513	0.198656	0.163698
22	0.521893	0.421955	0.341850	0.277505	0.225713	0.183941	0.150182
23	0.506692	0.405726	0.325571	0.261797	0.210947	0.170315	0.137781
24	0.491934	0.390121	0.310068	0.246979	0.197147	0.157699	0.126405
25	0.477606	0.375117	0.295303	0.232999	0.184249	0.146018	0.115968
26	0.463695	0.360689	0.281241	0.219810	0.172195	0.135202	0.106393
27	0.450189	0.346817	0.267848	0.207368	0.160930	0.125187	0.097608
28	0.437077	0.333477	0.255094	0.195630	0.150402	0.115914	0.089548
29	0.424346	0.320651	0.242946	0.184557	0.140563	0.107328	0.082155
30	0.411987	0.308319	0.231377	0.174110	0.131367	0.099377	0.075371
31	0.399987	0.296460	0.220359	0.164255	0.122773	0.092016	0.069148
32	0.388337	0.285058	0.209866	0.154957	0.114741	0.085200	0.063438
33	0.377026	0.274094	0.199873	0.146186	0.107235	0.078889	0.058200
34	0.366045	0.263552	0.190355	0.137912	0.100219	0.073045	0.053395
35	0.355383	0.253415	0.181290	0.130105	0.093663	0.067635	0.048986
36	0.345032	0.243669	0.172657	0.122741	0.087535	0.062625	0.044941
37	0.334983	0.234297	0.164436	0.115793	0.081809	0.057986	0.041231
38	0.325226	0.225285	0.156605	0.109239	0.076457	0.053690	0.037826
39	0.315754	0.216621	0.149148	0.103056	0.071455	0.049713	0.034703
40	0.306557	0.208289	0.142046	0.097222	0.066780	0.046031	0.031838
41	0.297628	0.200278	0.135282	0.091719	0.062412	0.042621	0.029209
42	0.288959	0.192575	0.128840	0.086527	0.058329	0.039464	0.026797
43	0.280543	0.185168	0.122704	0.081630	0.054513	0.036541	0.024584
44	0.272372	0.178046	0.116861	0.077009	0.050946	0.033834	0.022555
45	0.264439	0.171198	0.111297	0.072650	0.047613	0.031328	0.020692
46	0.256737	0.164614	0.105997	0.068538	0.044499	0.029007	0.018984
47	0.249259	0.158283	0.100949	0.064658	0.041587	0.026859	0.017416
48	0.241999	0.152195	0.096142	0.060998	0.038867	0.024869	0.015978
49	0.234950	0.146341	0.091564	0.057546	0.036324	0.023027	0.014659
50	0.228107	0.140713	0.087204	0.054288	0.033948	0.021321	0.013449

continues

TABLE 5   **Present value** $(1 + i)^{-n}$ *(continued)*

n	3%	4%	5%	6%	7%	8%	9%
51	0.221463	0.135301	0.083051	0.051215	0.031727	0.019742	0.012338
52	0.215013	0.130097	0.079096	0.048316	0.029651	0.018280	0.011319
53	0.208750	0.125093	0.075330	0.045582	0.027711	0.016925	0.010385
54	0.202670	0.120282	0.071743	0.043001	0.025899	0.015672	0.009527
55	0.196767	0.115656	0.068326	0.040567	0.024204	0.014511	0.008741
56	0.191036	0.111207	0.065073	0.038271	0.022621	0.013436	0.008019
57	0.185472	0.106930	0.061974	0.036105	0.021141	0.012441	0.007357
58	0.180070	0.102817	0.059023	0.034061	0.019758	0.011519	0.006749
59	0.174825	0.098863	0.056212	0.032133	0.018465	0.010666	0.006192
60	0.169733	0.095060	0.053536	0.030314	0.017257	0.009876	0.005681
61	0.164789	0.091404	0.050986	0.028598	0.016128	0.009144	0.005212
62	0.159990	0.087889	0.048558	0.026980	0.015073	0.008467	0.004781
63	0.155330	0.084508	0.046246	0.025453	0.014087	0.007840	0.004387
64	0.150806	0.081258	0.044044	0.024012	0.013166	0.007259	0.004024
65	0.146413	0.078133	0.041946	0.022653	0.012304	0.006721	0.003692
66	0.142149	0.075128	0.039949	0.021370	0.011499	0.006223	0.003387
67	0.138009	0.072238	0.038047	0.020161	0.010747	0.005762	0.003108
68	0.133989	0.069460	0.036235	0.019020	0.010044	0.005336	0.002851
69	0.130086	0.066788	0.034509	0.017943	0.009387	0.004940	0.002616
70	0.126297	0.064219	0.032866	0.016927	0.008773	0.004574	0.002400
71	0.122619	0.061749	0.031301	0.015969	0.008199	0.004236	0.002201
72	0.119047	0.059374	0.029811	0.015065	0.007662	0.003922	0.002020
73	0.115580	0.057091	0.028391	0.014213	0.007161	0.003631	0.001853
74	0.112214	0.054895	0.027039	0.013408	0.006693	0.003362	0.001700
75	0.108945	0.052784	0.025752	0.012649	0.006255	0.003113	0.001560
76	0.105772	0.050754	0.024525	0.011933	0.005846	0.002883	0.001431
77	0.102691	0.048801	0.023357	0.011258	0.005463	0.002669	0.001313
78	0.099700	0.046924	0.022245	0.010620	0.005106	0.002471	0.001204
79	0.096796	0.045120	0.021186	0.010019	0.004772	0.002288	0.001105
80	0.093977	0.043384	0.020177	0.009452	0.004460	0.002119	0.001014
81	0.091240	0.041716	0.019216	0.008917	0.004168	0.001962	0.000930
82	0.088582	0.040111	0.018301	0.008412	0.003895	0.001817	0.000853
83	0.086002	0.038569	0.017430	0.007936	0.003640	0.001682	0.000783
84	0.083497	0.037085	0.016600	0.007487	0.003402	0.001557	0.000718
85	0.081065	0.035659	0.015809	0.007063	0.003180	0.001442	0.000659
86	0.078704	0.034287	0.015056	0.006663	0.002972	0.001335	0.000604
87	0.076412	0.032969	0.014339	0.006286	0.002777	0.001236	0.000554
88	0.074186	0.031701	0.013657	0.005930	0.002596	0.001145	0.000509
89	0.072026	0.030481	0.013006	0.005595	0.002426	0.001060	0.000467
90	0.069928	0.029309	0.012387	0.005278	0.002267	0.000981	0.000428
91	0.067891	0.028182	0.011797	0.004979	0.002119	0.000909	0.000393
92	0.065914	0.027098	0.011235	0.004697	0.001980	0.000841	0.000360
93	0.063994	0.026056	0.010700	0.004432	0.001851	0.000779	0.000331
94	0.062130	0.025053	0.010191	0.004181	0.001730	0.000721	0.000303
95	0.060320	0.024090	0.009705	0.003944	0.001616	0.000668	0.000278
96	0.058563	0.023163	0.009243	0.003721	0.001511	0.000618	0.000255
97	0.056858	0.022272	0.008803	0.003510	0.001412	0.000573	0.000234
98	0.055202	0.021416	0.008384	0.003312	0.001319	0.000530	0.000215
99	0.053594	0.020592	0.007985	0.003124	0.001233	0.000491	0.000197
100	0.052033	0.019800	0.007604	0.002947	0.001152	0.000455	0.000181

TABLE 5 **Present value** $(1 + i)^{-n}$

n	10%	11%	12%	13%	14%	15%	16%
1	0.909091	0.900901	0.892857	0.884956	0.877193	0.869565	0.862069
2	0.826446	0.811622	0.797194	0.783147	0.769468	0.756144	0.743163
3	0.751315	0.731191	0.711780	0.693050	0.674972	0.657516	0.640658
4	0.683013	0.658731	0.635518	0.613319	0.592080	0.571753	0.552291
5	0.620921	0.593451	0.567427	0.542760	0.519369	0.497177	0.476113
6	0.564474	0.534641	0.506631	0.480319	0.455587	0.432328	0.410442
7	0.513158	0.481658	0.452349	0.425061	0.399637	0.375937	0.353830
8	0.466507	0.433926	0.403883	0.376160	0.350559	0.326902	0.305025
9	0.424098	0.390925	0.360610	0.332885	0.307508	0.284262	0.262953
10	0.385543	0.352184	0.321973	0.294588	0.269744	0.247185	0.226684
11	0.350494	0.317283	0.287476	0.260698	0.236617	0.214943	0.195417
12	0.318631	0.285841	0.256675	0.230706	0.207559	0.186907	0.168463
13	0.289664	0.257514	0.229174	0.204165	0.182069	0.162528	0.145227
14	0.263331	0.231995	0.204620	0.180677	0.159710	0.141329	0.125195
15	0.239392	0.209004	0.182696	0.159891	0.140096	0.122894	0.107927
16	0.217629	0.188292	0.163122	0.141496	0.122892	0.106865	0.093041
17	0.197845	0.169633	0.145644	0.125218	0.107800	0.092926	0.080207
18	0.179859	0.152822	0.130040	0.110812	0.094561	0.080805	0.069144
19	0.163508	0.137678	0.116107	0.098064	0.082948	0.070265	0.059607
20	0.148644	0.124034	0.103667	0.086782	0.072762	0.061100	0.051385
21	0.135131	0.111742	0.092560	0.076798	0.063826	0.053131	0.044298
22	0.122846	0.100669	0.082643	0.067963	0.055988	0.046201	0.038188
23	0.111678	0.090693	0.073788	0.060144	0.049112	0.040174	0.032920
24	0.101526	0.081705	0.065882	0.053225	0.043081	0.034934	0.028380
25	0.092296	0.073608	0.058823	0.047102	0.037790	0.030378	0.024465
26	0.083905	0.066314	0.052521	0.041683	0.033149	0.26415	0.021091
27	0.076278	0.059742	0.046894	0.036888	0.029078	0.022970	0.018182
28	0.069343	0.053822	0.041869	0.032644	0.025507	0.019974	0.015674
29	0.063039	0.048488	0.037383	0.028889	0.022375	0.017369	0.013512
30	0.057309	0.043683	0.033378	0.025565	0.019627	0.015103	0.011648
31	0.052099	0.039354	0.029802	0.022624	0.017217	0.013133	0.010042
32	0.047362	0.035454	0.026609	0.020021	0.015102	0.011420	0.008657
33	0.043057	0.031940	0.023758	0.017718	0.013248	0.009931	0.007463
34	0.039143	0.028775	0.021212	0.015680	0.011621	0.008635	0.006433
35	0.035584	0.025924	0.018940	0.013876	0.010194	0.007509	0.005546
36	0.032349	0.023355	0.016910	0.012279	0.008942	0.006529	0.004781
37	0.029408	0.021040	0.015098	0.010867	0.007844	0.005678	0.004121
38	0.026735	0.018955	0.013481	0.009617	0.006880	0.004937	0.003553
39	0.024304	0.017077	0.012036	0.008510	0.006035	0.004293	0.003063
40	0.022095	0.015384	0.010747	0.007531	0.005294	0.003733	0.002640
41	0.020086	0.013860	0.009595	0.006665	0.004644	0.003246	0.002276
42	0.018260	0.012486	0.008567	0.005898	0.004074	0.002823	0.001962
43	0.016600	0.011249	0.007649	0.005219	0.003573	0.002455	0.001692
44	0.015091	0.010134	0.006830	0.004619	0.003135	0.002134	0.001458
45	0.013719	0.009130	0.006098	0.004088	0.002750	0.001856	0.001257
46	0.012472	0.008225	0.005445	0.003617	0.002412	0.001614	0.001084
47	0.011338	0.007410	0.004861	0.003201	0.002116	0.001403	0.000934
48	0.010307	0.006676	0.004340	0.002833	0.001856	0.001220	0.000805
49	0.009370	0.006014	0.003875	0.002507	0.001628	0.001061	0.000694
50	0.008519	0.005418	0.003460	0.002219	0.001428	0.000923	0.000599

TABLE 6   Amount of an annuity $s_{\overline{n}|i} = \dfrac{(1 + i)^n - 1}{i}$

n	½%	¾%	1%	1¼%	1½%	1¾%	2%
1	1.000000	1.000000	1.000000	1.000000	1.000000	1.000000	1.000000
2	2.005000	2.007500	2.010000	2.012500	2.015000	2.017500	2.020000
3	3.015025	3.022556	3.030100	3.037656	3.045225	3.052806	0.060400
4	4.030100	4.045225	4.060401	4.075627	4.090903	4.106230	4.121608
5	5.050251	5.075565	5.101005	5.126572	5.152267	5.178089	5.204040
6	6.075502	6.113631	6.152015	6.190654	6.229551	6.268706	6.308121
7	7.105879	7.159484	7.213535	7.268038	7.322994	7.378408	7.434283
8	8.141409	8.213180	8.285671	8.358888	8.432839	8.507530	8.582969
9	9.182116	9.274779	9.368527	9.463374	9.559332	9.656412	9.754628
10	10.228026	10.344339	10.462213	10.581666	10.702722	10.825399	10.949721
11	11.279167	11.421922	11.566835	11.713937	11.863262	12.014844	12.168715
12	12.335562	12.507586	12.682503	12.860361	13.041211	13.225104	13.412090
13	13.397240	13.601393	13.809328	14.021116	14.236830	14.456543	14.680332
14	14.464226	14.703404	14.947421	15.196380	15.450382	15.709533	15.973938
15	15.536548	15.813679	16.096896	16.386335	16.682138	16.984449	17.293417
16	16.614230	16.932282	17.257864	17.591164	17.932370	18.281677	18.639285
17	17.697301	18.059274	18.430443	18.811053	19.201355	19.601607	20.012071
18	18.785788	19.194718	19.614748	20.046192	20.489376	20.944635	21.412312
19	19.879717	20.338679	20.810895	21.296769	21.796716	22.311166	22.840559
20	20.979115	21.491219	22.019004	22.562979	23.123667	23.701611	24.297370
21	22.084011	22.652403	23.239194	23.845016	24.470522	25.116389	25.783317
22	23.194431	23.822296	24.471586	25.143078	25.837580	26.555926	27.298984
23	24.310403	25.000963	25.716302	26.457367	27.225144	28.020655	28.844963
24	25.431955	26.188471	26.973465	27.788084	28.633521	29.511016	30.421862
25	26.559115	27.384884	28.243200	29.135435	30.063024	31.027459	32.030300
26	27.691911	28.590271	29.525631	30.499628	31.513969	32.570440	33.670906
27	28.830370	29.804698	30.820888	31.880873	32.986678	34.140422	35.344324
28	29.974522	31.028233	32.129097	33.279384	34.481479	35.737880	37.051210
29	31.124395	32.260945	33.450388	34.695377	35.998701	37.363293	38.792235
30	32.280017	33.502902	34.784892	36.129069	37.538681	39.017150	40.568079
31	33.441417	34.754174	36.132740	37.580682	39.101762	40.699950	42.379441
32	34.608624	36.014830	37.494068	39.050441	40.688288	42.412200	44.227030
33	35.781667	37.284941	38.869009	40.538571	42.298612	44.154413	46.111570
34	36.960575	38.564578	40.257699	42.045303	43.933092	45.927115	48.033802
35	38.145378	39.853813	41.660276	43.570870	45.592088	47.730840	49.994478
36	39.336105	41.152716	43.076878	45.115505	47.275969	49.566129	51.994367
37	40.532785	42.461361	44.507647	46.679449	48.985109	51.433537	54.034255
38	41.735449	43.779822	45.952724	48.262942	50.719885	53.333624	56.114940
39	42.944127	45.108170	47.412251	49.866229	52.480684	55.266962	58.237238
40	44.158847	46.446482	48.886373	51.489557	54.267894	57.234134	60.401983
41	45.379642	47.794830	50.375237	53.133177	56.081912	59.235731	62.610023
42	46.606540	49.153291	51.878989	54.797341	57.923141	61.272357	64.862223
43	47.839572	50.521941	53.397779	56.482308	59.791988	63.344623	67.159468
44	49.078770	51.900856	54.931757	58.188337	61.688868	65.453154	69.502657
45	50.324164	53.290112	56.481075	59.915691	63.614201	67.598584	71.892710
46	51.575785	54.689788	58.045885	61.664637	65.568414	69.781559	74.330564
47	52.833664	56.099961	59.626344	63.435445	67.551940	72.002736	76.817176

continues

TABLE 6 **Amount of an annuity** $s_{\overline{n}|i} = \dfrac{(1+i)^n - 1}{i}$ *(continued)*

n	½%	¾%	1%	1¼%	1½%	1¾%	2%
48	54.097832	57.520711	61.222608	65.228388	69.565219	74.262784	79.353519
49	55.368321	58.952116	62.834834	67.043743	71.608698	76.562383	81.940490
50	56.645163	60.394257	64.463182	68.881790	73.682828	78.902225	84.579401
51	57.928389	61.847214	66.107814	70.742812	75.788070	81.283014	87.270989
52	59.218031	63.311068	67.768892	72.627097	77.924892	83.705466	90.016409
53	60.514121	64.785901	69.446581	74.534936	80.093765	86.170312	92.816737
54	61.816692	66.271796	71.141047	76.466623	82.295171	88.678292	95.673072
55	63.125775	67.768834	72.852457	78.422456	84.529599	91.230163	98.586534
56	64.441404	69.277100	74.580982	80.402736	86.797543	93.826690	101.558264
57	65.763611	70.796679	76.326792	82.407771	89.099506	96.468658	104.589430
58	67.092429	72.327654	78.090060	84.437868	91.435999	99.156859	107.681218
59	68.427891	73.870111	79.870960	86.493341	93.807539	101.892104	110.834843
60	69.770031	75.424137	81.669670	88.574508	96.214652	104.675216	114.051539
61	71.118881	76.989818	83.486367	90.681689	98.657871	107.507032	117.332570
62	72.474475	78.567242	85.321280	92.815210	101.137740	110.388405	120.679222
63	73.836847	80.156496	87.174443	94.975400	103.654806	113.320202	124.092806
64	75.206032	81.757670	89.046187	97.162593	106.209628	116.303306	127.574662
65	76.582062	83.370852	90.936649	99.377125	108.802772	119.338614	131.126155
66	77.964972	84.996134	92.846015	101.619339	111.434814	122.427039	134.748679
67	79.354797	86.633605	94.774475	103.889581	114.106336	125.659513	138.443652
68	80.751571	88.283357	96.722220	106.188201	116.817931	128.766979	142.212525
69	82.155329	89.945482	98.689442	108.515553	119.570200	132.020401	146.056776
70	83.566105	91.620073	100.676337	110.871998	122.363753	135.330758	149.977911
71	84.983936	93.307223	102.683100	113.257898	125.199209	138.699047	153.977469
72	86.408856	95.007028	104.709931	115.673621	128.077197	142.126280	158.057019
73	87.840900	96.719580	106.757031	118.119542	130.998355	145.613490	162.218159
74	89.280104	98.444977	108.824601	120.596036	133.963331	149.161726	166.462522
75	90.726505	100.183314	110.912847	123.103486	136.972781	152.772056	170.791773
76	92.180138	101.934689	113.021975	125.642280	140.027372	156.445567	175.207608
77	93.641038	103.699199	115.152195	128.212809	143.127783	160.183364	179.711760
78	95.109243	105.476943	117.303717	130.815469	146.274700	163.986573	184.305996
79	95.584790	107.268021	119.476754	133.450662	149.468820	167.856338	188.992115
80	98.067714	109.072531	121.671522	136.118795	152.710852	171.793824	193.771958
81	99.558052	110.890575	123.888237	138.820280	156.001515	175.800216	198.647397
82	101.055842	112.722254	126.127119	141.555534	159.341538	179.876720	203.620345
83	102.561122	114.567671	128.388390	144.324978	162.731661	184.024563	208.692752
84	104.073927	116.426928	130.672274	147.129040	166.172636	188.244992	213.866607
85	105.594297	118.300130	132.978997	149.968153	169.665226	192.539280	219.143939
86	107.122268	120.187381	135.308787	152.842755	173.210204	196.908717	224.526818
87	108.657880	122.088787	137.661875	155.753289	176.808357	201.354620	230.017354
88	110.201169	124.004453	140.038494	158.700206	180.460482	205.878326	235.617701
89	111.752175	125.934486	142.438879	161.683958	184.167390	210.481196	241.330055
90	113.310936	127.878995	144.863267	164.705008	187.929900	215.164617	247.156656
91	114.877490	129.838087	147.311900	167.763820	191.748849	219.929998	253.099789
92	116.451878	131.811873	149.785019	170.860868	195.625082	224.778773	259.161785
93	118.034137	133.800462	152.282869	173.996629	199.559458	229.712401	265.345021
94	119.624308	135.803965	154.805698	177.171587	203.552850	234.732369	271.651921

continues

TABLE 6 Amount of an annuity $s_{\overline{n}|i} = \dfrac{(1 + i)^n - 1}{i}$ (continued)

n	1/2%	3/4%	1%	1 1/4%	1 1/2%	1 3/4%	2%
95	121.222430	137.822495	157.353755	180.386232	207.606142	239.840185	278.084960
96	122.828542	139.856164	159.927293	183.641059	211.720235	245.037388	284.646659
97	124.442684	141.905085	162.526565	186.936573	215.896038	250.325542	291.339592
98	126.064898	143.969373	165.151831	190.273280	220.134479	255.706239	298.166384
99	127.695222	146.049143	167.803349	193.651696	224.436496	261.181099	305.129712
100	129.333698	148.144512	170.481383	197.072342	228.803043	266.751768	312.232306

TABLE 6 Amount of an annuity $s_{\overline{n}|i} = \dfrac{(1 + i)^n - 1}{i}$

n	3%	4%	5%	6%	7%	8%	9%
1	1.000000	1.000000	1.000000	1.000000	1.000000	1.000000	1.000000
2	2.030000	2.040000	2.050000	2.060000	2.070000	2.080000	2.090000
3	3.090900	3.121600	3.152500	3.183600	3.214900	3.246400	3.278100
4	4.183627	4.246464	4.310125	4.374616	4.439943	4.506112	4.573129
5	5.309136	5.416323	5.525631	5.637093	5.750739	5.866601	5.984711
6	6.468410	6.632975	6.801913	6.975319	7.153291	7.335929	7.523335
7	7.662462	7.898294	8.142008	8.393838	8.654021	8.922803	9.200435
8	8.892336	9.214226	9.549109	9.897468	10.259803	10.636628	11.028474
9	10.159106	10.582795	11.026564	11.491316	11.977989	12.487558	13.021036
10	11.463879	12.006107	12.577893	13.180795	13.816448	14.486562	15.192930
11	12.807796	13.486351	14.206787	14.971643	15.783599	16.645487	17.560293
12	14.192030	15.025805	15.917127	16.869941	17.888451	18.977126	20.140720
13	15.617790	16.626838	17.712983	18.882138	20.140643	21.495297	22.953385
14	17.086324	18.291911	19.598632	21.015066	22.550488	24.214920	26.019189
15	18.598914	20.023588	21.578564	23.275970	25.129022	27.152114	29.360916
16	20.156881	21.824531	23.657492	25.672528	27.888054	30.324483	33.003399
17	21.761588	23.697512	25.840366	28.212880	30.840217	33.750226	36.973705
18	23.414435	25.645413	28.132385	30.905653	33.999033	37.450244	41.301338
19	25.116868	27.671229	30.539004	33.759992	37.378965	41.446263	46.018458
20	26.870374	29.778079	33.065954	36.785591	40.995492	45.761964	51.160120
21	28.676486	31.969202	35.719252	39.992727	44.865177	50.422921	56.764530
22	30.536780	34.247970	38.505214	43.392290	49.005739	55.456755	62.873338
23	32.452884	36.617889	41.430475	46.995828	53.436141	60.893296	69.531939
24	34.426470	39.082604	44.501999	50.815577	58.176671	66.764759	76.789813
25	36.459264	41.645908	47.727099	54.864512	63.249038	73.105940	84.700896
26	38.553042	44.311745	51.113454	59.156383	68.676470	79.954415	93.323977
27	40.709634	47.084214	54.669126	63.705766	74.483823	87.350768	102.723135
28	42.930923	49.967583	58.402583	68.528112	80.697691	95.338830	112.968217
29	45.218850	52.966286	62.322712	73.639798	87.346529	103.965936	124.135356
30	47.575416	56.084938	66.438848	79.058186	94.460786	113.283211	136.307539
31	50.002678	59.328335	70.760790	84.801677	102.073041	123.345868	149.575217
32	52.502759	62.701469	75.298829	80.889778	110.218154	134.213537	164.036987
33	55.077841	66.209527	80.063771	97.343165	118.933425	145.950620	179.800315
34	57.530177	69.857909	85.066959	104.183755	128.258765	158.626670	196.982344
35	60.462082	73.652225	90.320307	111.434780	138.236878	172.316804	215.710755

continues

TABLE 6 Amount of an annuity $s_{\overline{n}|i} = \dfrac{(1 + i)^n - 1}{i}$ *(continued)*

n	3%	4%	5%	6%	7%	8%	9%
36	63.275944	77.598314	95.836323	119.120867	148.913460	187.102148	236.124723
37	66.174223	81.702246	101.628139	127.268119	160.337402	203.070320	258.375948
38	69.159449	85.970336	107.709546	135.904206	172.561020	220.315945	282.629783
39	72.234233	90.409150	114.095023	145.058458	185.640292	238.941221	309.066463
40	75.401260	95.025516	120.799774	154.761966	199.635112	259.056519	337.882445
41	78.663298	99.826536	127.839763	165.047684	214.609570	280.781040	369.291865
42	82.023196	104.819598	135.231751	175.950545	230.632240	304.243523	403.528133
43	85.483892	110.012382	142.993339	187.507577	247.776496	329.583005	440.845665
44	89.048409	115.412877	151.143006	199.758032	266.120851	356.949646	481.521775
45	92.719861	121.029392	159.700156	212.743514	285.749311	386.505617	525.858734
46	96.501457	126.870568	168.685164	226.508125	306.751763	418.426067	574.186021
47	100.396501	132.945390	178.119422	241.098612	329.224386	452.900152	626.862762
48	104.408396	139.263206	188.025393	256.564529	353.270093	490.132164	684.280411
49	108.540648	145.833734	198.426663	272.958401	378.999000	530.342737	746.865648
50	112.796867	152.667084	209.347996	290.335905	406.528929	573.770156	815.083556

TABLE 6 Amount of an annuity $s_{\overline{n}|i} = \dfrac{(1 + i)^n - 1}{i}$

n	10%	11%	12%	13%	14%	15%
1	1.000000	1.000000	1.000000	1.000000	1.000000	1.000000
2	2.100000	2.110000	2.120000	2.130000	2.140000	2.150000
3	3.310000	3.342100	3.374400	3.406900	3.439600	3.472500
4	4.641000	4.709731	4.779328	4.849797	4.921144	4.993375
5	6.105100	6.227801	6.352847	6.480271	6.610104	6.742381
6	7.715610	7.912860	8.115189	8.322706	8.535519	8.753738
7	9.487171	9.732274	10.089012	10.404658	10.730491	11.066799
8	11.435888	11.859434	12.299693	12.757263	13.232760	13.726819
9	13.579477	14.163972	14.775656	15.415707	16.805347	16.785842
10	15.937425	16.722009	17.548735	18.419749	19.337295	20.303718
11	18.531167	19.561430	20.654583	21.814317	23.044516	24.349276
12	21.384284	22.713187	24.133133	25.650178	27.270749	29.001667
13	24.522712	26.211638	28.029109	29.984701	32.088654	34.351917
14	27.974983	30.094918	32.392602	34.882712	37.581065	40.504705
15	31.772482	34.405359	37.279715	40.417464	43.842414	47.580411
16	35.949730	39.189948	42.753280	46.671735	50.980352	55.717472
17	40.544703	44.500843	48.883674	53.739060	59.117601	65.075093
18	45.599173	50.395936	55.749715	61.725138	68.394066	75.836357
19	51.159090	56.939488	63.439681	70.749406	78.969235	88.211811
20	57.274999	64.202832	72.052442	80.946829	91.024928	102.443583
21	64.002499	72.265144	81.698736	92.469917	104.768418	118.810120
22	71.402749	81.214309	92.502584	105.491006	120.435996	137.631638
23	79.543024	91.147884	104.602894	120.204837	138.297035	159.276384
24	88.497327	102.174151	118.155241	136.831465	158.658620	184.167841
25	98.347059	114.413307	133.333870	155.619556	181.870827	212.793017

continues

TABLE 6   Amount of an annuity $s_{\overline{n}|i} = \dfrac{(1 + i)^n - 1}{i}$ (continued)

n	10%	11%	12%	13%	14%	15%
26	109.181765	127.998771	150.333934	176.850098	208.332743	245.711970
27	121.099942	143.078636	169.374007	200.840611	238.499327	283.568766
28	134.209936	159.817286	190.698887	227.949890	272.889233	327.104080
29	148.630930	178.397187	214.582754	258.583376	312.093725	377.169693
30	164.494023	199.020878	241.332684	293.199215	356.786847	434.745146
31	181.943425	221.913174	271.292606	332.315113	407.737006	500.956918
32	201.137767	247.323624	304.847719	376.516078	465.820186	577.100456
33	222.251544	275.529222	342.429446	426.463168	532.035012	664.665524
34	245.476699	306.837437	384.520979	482.903380	607.519914	765.365353
35	271.024368	341.589555	431.663496	546.680819	693.572702	881.170156
36	299.126805	380.164406	484.463116	618.749325	791.672881	1014.345680
37	330.039486	422.982490	543.598690	700.186738	903.507084	1167.497532
38	364.043434	470.510564	609.830533	792.211014	1030.998076	1343.622161
39	401.447778	523.266726	684.010197	896.198445	1176.337806	1546.165485
40	442.592556	581.826066	767.091420	1013.704243	1342.025099	1779.090308
41	487.851811	646.826934	860.142391	1146.485795	1530.908613	2046.953854
42	537.636992	718.977896	964.359478	1296.528948	1746.235819	2354.996933
43	592.400692	799.065465	1081.082615	1466.077712	1991.708833	2709.246473
44	652.640761	887.962666	1211.812529	1657.667814	2271.548070	3116.633443
45	718.904837	986.638559	1358.230032	1874.164630	2590.564800	3585.128460
46	791.795321	1096.168801	1522.217636	2118.806032	2954.243872	4123.897729
47	871.974853	1217.747369	1705.883752	2395.250816	3368.838014	4743.482388
48	960.172338	1352.699580	1911.589803	2707.633422	3841.475336	5456.004746
49	1057.189572	1502.496533	2141.980579	3060.625767	4380.281883	6275.405458
50	1163.908529	1668.771152	2400.018249	3459.507117	4994.521346	7217.716277

TABLE 7   Present value of an annuity $a_{\overline{n}|i} = \dfrac{1 - (1 + i)^{-n}}{i}$

n	½%	¾%	1%	1¼%	1½%	1¾%	2%
1	0.995025	0.992556	0.990099	0.987654	0.985222	0.982801	0.980392
2	1.985099	1.977723	1.970395	1.963115	1.955883	1.948699	1.941561
3	2.970248	2.955556	2.940985	2.926534	2.912200	2.897984	2.883883
4	3.950496	3.926110	3.901966	3.878058	3.854385	3.830943	3.807729
5	4.925866	4.889440	4.853431	4.817835	4.782645	4.747855	4.713460
6	5.896384	5.845598	5.795476	5.746010	5.697187	5.688998	5.601431
7	6.862074	6.794638	6.728195	6.662726	6.598214	6.534641	6.471991
8	7.822959	7.736613	7.651678	7.568124	7.485925	7.405053	7.325481
9	8.779064	8.671576	8.566018	8.462345	8.360517	8.260494	8.162237
10	9.730412	9.599580	9.471305	9.345526	9.222185	9.101223	8.982585
11	10.677027	10.520675	10.367628	10.217803	10.071118	9.927492	9.786848
12	11.618932	11.434913	11.255077	11.079312	10.907505	10.739550	10.575341
13	12.556151	12.342345	12.133740	11.930185	11.731532	11.537641	11.348374
14	13.488708	13.243022	13.003703	12.770553	12.543382	12.322006	12.106249
15	14.416625	14.136995	13.865053	13.600546	13.343233	13.092880	12.849264
16	15.339925	15.024313	14.717874	14.420292	14.131264	13.850497	13.577709

continues

TABLE 7 Present value of an annuity $a_{\overline{n}|i} = \dfrac{1 - (1 + i)^{-n}}{i}$ *(continued)*

n	½%	¾%	1%	1¼%	1½%	1¾%	2%
17	16.258632	15.905025	15.562251	15.229918	14.907649	14.595083	14.291872
18	17.172768	16.779181	16.398269	16.029549	15.672561	15.326863	14.992031
19	18.082356	17.646830	17.226008	16.819308	16.426168	16.046057	15.678462
20	18.987419	18.508020	18.045553	17.599316	17.168639	16.752881	16.351433
21	19.887979	19.362799	18.856983	18.369695	17.900137	17.447549	17.011209
22	20.784059	20.211215	19.660379	19.130563	18.620824	18.130269	17.658048
23	21.675681	21.053315	20.455821	19.882037	19.330861	18.801248	18.292204
24	22.562866	21.889146	21.243387	20.624235	20.030405	19.460686	18.913926
25	23.445638	22.718755	22.023156	21.357269	20.719611	20.108782	19.523456
26	24.324018	23.542189	22.795204	22.081253	21.398632	20.745732	20.121036
27	25.198028	24.359493	23.559608	22.796299	22.067617	21.371726	20.706898
28	26.067689	25.170713	24.316443	23.502518	22.726717	21.986955	21.281272
29	26.933024	25.975893	25.065785	24.200018	23.376076	22.591602	21.844385
30	27.794054	26.775080	25.807708	24.888906	24.015838	23.185849	22.396456
31	28.650800	27.568318	26.542285	25.569290	24.646146	23.769877	22.937702
32	29.503284	28.355650	27.269589	26.241274	25.267139	24.343859	23.468335
33	30.351526	29.137122	27.989693	26.904962	25.878954	24.907970	23.988564
34	31.195548	29.912776	28.702666	27.560456	26.481728	25.462378	24.498592
35	32.035371	30.682656	29.408580	28.207858	27.075595	26.007251	24.998619
36	32.871016	31.446805	30.107505	28.847267	27.660684	26.542753	25.488842
37	33.702504	32.205266	30.799510	29.478783	28.237127	27.069045	25.969453
38	34.529854	32.958080	31.484663	30.102501	28.805052	27.586285	26.440641
39	35.353089	33.705290	32.163033	30.718520	29.364583	28.094629	26.902589
40	36.172228	34.446938	32.834686	31.326933	29.915845	28.594230	27.355479
41	36.987291	35.183065	33.499689	31.927835	30.458961	29.085238	27.799489
42	37.798300	35.913713	34.158108	32.521319	30.994050	29.567801	28.234794
43	38.605274	36.638921	34.810008	33.017475	31.521232	30.042065	28.661562
44	39.408232	37.358730	35.455454	33.686395	32.040622	30.508172	29.079963
45	40.207196	38.073181	36.094508	34.258168	32.552337	30.966263	29.490160
46	41.002185	38.782314	36.727236	34.822882	33.056490	31.416474	29.892314
47	41.793219	39.486168	37.353699	35.380624	33.553192	31.858943	30.286582
48	42.580318	40.184782	37.973959	35.931481	34.042554	32.293801	30.673120
49	43.363500	40.878195	38.588079	36.475537	34.524683	32.721181	31.052078
50	44.142786	41.566447	39.196118	37.012876	34.999688	33.141209	31.423606
51	44.918195	42.249575	39.798136	37.543581	35.467673	33.554014	31.787849
52	45.689747	42.927618	40.394194	38.067734	35.928742	33.959719	32.144950
53	46.457459	43.600614	40.984351	38.585417	36.382997	34.358446	32.495049
54	47.221353	44.268599	41.568664	39.096708	36.830539	34.750316	32.838283
55	47.981445	44.931612	42.147192	39.601687	37.271467	35.135445	33.174788
56	48.737757	45.589689	42.719992	40.100431	37.705879	35.513951	33.504694
57	49.490305	46.242868	43.287121	40.593019	38.133871	35.885947	33.828131
58	50.239109	46.891184	43.848635	41.079524	38.555538	36.251545	34.145226
59	50.984189	47.534674	44.404589	41.560024	38.970973	36.610855	34.456104
60	51.725561	48.173374	44.955038	42.034592	39.380269	36.963986	34.760887
61	52.463245	48.807319	45.500038	42.503301	39.783516	37.311042	35.059693
62	53.197258	49.436545	46.039642	42.966223	40.180804	37.652130	35.352640
63	53.927620	50.061086	46.573903	43.423430	40.572221	37.987351	35.639843
64	54.654348	50.680979	47.102874	43.874992	40.957853	38.316807	35.921415

continues

TABLE 7 Present value of an annuity $a_{\overline{n}|i} = \dfrac{1 - (1 + i)^{-n}}{i}$ *(continued)*

n	½%	¾%	1%	1¼%	1½%	1¾%	2%
65	55.377461	51.296257	47.626608	44.320980	41.337786	38.640597	36.197466
66	56.096976	51.906955	48.145156	44.761462	41.712105	38.958817	36.468103
67	56.812912	52.513107	48.658571	45.196506	42.080891	39.271565	36.733435
68	57.525285	53.114746	49.166901	45.626178	42.444228	39.578934	36.993564
69	58.234115	53.711907	49.670199	46.050547	42.802195	39.881016	37.248592
70	58.939418	54.304622	50.168514	46.469676	43.154872	40.177903	37.498619
71	59.641212	54.892925	50.661895	46.883630	43.502337	40.469683	37.743744
72	60.339514	55.476849	51.150391	47.292474	43.844667	40.756445	37.984063
73	61.034342	56.056426	51.634051	47.696271	44.181938	41.038276	38.219670
74	61.725714	56.631688	52.112922	48.095082	44.514224	41.315259	38.450657
75	62.413645	57.202668	52.587051	48.488970	44.841600	41.587478	38.677114
76	63.098155	57.769397	53.056486	48.877995	45.164138	41.855015	38.899132
77	63.779258	58.331908	53.521274	49.262218	45.481910	42.117951	39.116796
78	64.456973	58.890231	53.981459	49.641696	45.794985	42.376364	39.330192
79	65.131317	59.444398	54.437088	50.016490	46.103433	42.630334	39.539404
80	65.802305	59.994440	54.888206	50.386657	46.407323	42.879935	39.744514
81	66.469956	60.540387	55.334858	50.752254	46.706723	43.125243	39.945602
82	67.134284	61.082270	55.777087	51.113337	47.001697	43.366332	40.142747
83	67.795308	61.620119	56.214937	51.469963	47.292313	43.603275	40.336026
84	68.453042	62.153965	56.648453	51.822185	47.578633	43.836142	40.525516
85	69.107505	62.683836	57.077676	52.170060	47.860722	44.065005	40.711290
86	69.758711	63.209763	57.502650	52.513639	48.138643	44.289931	40.893422
87	70.406678	63.731774	57.923415	52.852977	48.412456	44.510989	41.071982
88	71.051421	64.249900	58.340015	53.188125	48.682222	44.728244	41.247041
89	71.692956	64.764169	58.752490	53.519136	48.948002	44.941764	41.418668
90	72.331300	65.274609	59.160881	53.846060	49.209855	45.151610	41.586929
91	72.966467	65.781250	59.565229	54.168948	49.467837	45.357848	41.751891
92	73.598475	66.284119	59.965573	54.487850	49.722007	45.560539	41.913619
93	74.227338	66.783245	60.361954	54.802815	49.972421	45.759743	42.072175
94	74.853073	67.278655	60.754410	55.113892	50.219134	45.955521	42.227623
95	75.475694	67.770377	61.142980	55.421127	50.462201	46.147933	42.380023
96	76.095218	68.258439	61.527703	55.724570	50.701675	46.337035	42.529434
97	76.711660	68.742867	61.908617	56.024267	50.937611	46.522884	42.675916
98	77.325035	69.223689	62.285759	56.320264	51.170060	46.705537	42.819525
99	77.935358	69.700932	62.659168	56.612606	51.399074	46.885049	42.960319
100	78.542645	70.174623	63.028879	56.901339	51.624704	47.061473	43.098352

TABLE 7 Present value of an annuity $a_{\overline{n}|i} = \dfrac{1 - (1 + i)^{-n}}{i}$

n	3%	4%	5%	6%	7%	8%	9%
1	0.970874	0.961538	0.952381	0.943396	0.934579	0.925926	0.917431
2	1.913470	1.886095	1.859410	1.833393	1.808018	1.783265	1.759111
3	2.828611	2.775091	2.723248	2.673012	2.624316	2.577097	2.531295
4	3.717098	3.629895	3.545951	3.465106	3.387211	3.312127	3.239720

continues

TABLE 7 **Present value of an annuity** $a_{\overline{n}|i} = \dfrac{1 - (1 + i)^{-n}}{i}$ *(continued)*

n	3%	4%	5%	6%	7%	8%	9%
5	4.579707	4.451822	4.329477	4.212364	4.100197	3.992710	3.889651
6	5.417191	5.242137	5.075692	4.917324	4.766540	4.622880	4.485919
7	6.230283	6.002055	5.786373	5.582381	5.389289	5.206370	5.032953
8	7.019692	6.732745	6.463213	6.209794	5.971299	5.746639	5.534819
9	7.786109	7.435332	7.107822	6.801692	6.515232	6.246888	5.995247
10	8.530203	8.110896	7.721735	7.360087	7.023582	6.710081	6.417658
11	9.252624	8.760477	8.306414	7.886875	7.498674	7.138964	6.805191
12	9.954004	9.385074	8.863252	8.383844	7.942686	7.536078	7.160725
13	10.634955	9.985648	9.393573	8.852683	8.357651	7.903776	7.486904
14	11.296073	10.563123	9.898641	9.294984	8.745468	8.244237	7.786150
15	11.937935	11.118387	10.379658	9.712249	9.107914	8.559479	8.060688
16	12.561102	11.652296	10.837770	10.105895	9.446649	8.851369	8.312558
17	13.166118	12.165669	11.274066	10.477260	9.763223	9.121638	8.543631
18	13.753513	12.659297	11.689587	10.827603	10.059087	9.371887	8.755625
19	14.323799	13.133939	12.085321	11.158116	10.335595	9.603599	8.950115
20	14.877475	13.590326	12.462210	11.469921	10.594014	9.818147	9.128546
21	15.415024	14.029160	12.821153	11.764077	10.835527	10.016803	9.292244
22	15.936917	14.451115	13.163003	12.041582	11.061240	10.200744	9.442425
23	16.443608	14.856842	13.488574	12.303379	11.272187	10.371059	9.580207
24	16.935542	15.246963	13.798642	12.550358	11.469334	10.528758	9.706612
25	17.413148	15.622080	14.093945	12.783356	11.653583	10.674776	9.822580
26	17.876842	15.982769	14.375185	13.003166	11.825779	10.809978	9.928972
27	18.327031	16.329586	14.643034	13.210534	11.986709	10.935165	10.026580
28	18.764108	16.663063	14.898127	13.406164	12.137111	11.051078	10.116128
29	19.188455	16.983715	15.141074	13.590721	12.277674	11.158406	10.198283
30	19.600441	17.292033	15.372451	13.764831	12.409041	11.257783	10.273654
31	20.000428	17.588494	15.592811	13.929086	12.531814	11.349799	10.342802
32	20.388766	17.873551	15.802677	14.084043	12.646555	11.434999	10.406240
33	20.765792	18.147646	16.002549	14.230230	12.753790	11.513888	10.464441
34	21.131837	18.411198	16.192904	14.368141	12.854009	11.586934	10.517835
35	21.487220	18.664613	16.374194	14.498246	12.947672	11.654568	10.566821
36	21.832252	18.908282	16.546852	14.620987	13.035208	11.717193	10.611763
37	22.167235	19.142579	16.711287	14.736780	13.117017	11.775179	10.652993
38	22.492462	19.367864	16.867893	14.846019	13.193473	11.828869	10.690820
39	22.808215	19.584485	17.017041	14.949075	13.264928	11.878582	10.725523
40	23.114772	19.792774	17.159086	15.046297	13.331709	11.924613	10.757360
41	23.412400	19.993052	17.294368	15.138016	13.394120	11.967235	10.786569
42	23.701359	20.185627	17.423208	15.224543	13.452449	12.006699	10.813366
43	23.981902	20.370795	17.545912	15.306173	13.506962	12.043240	10.837950
44	24.254274	20.548841	17.662773	15.383182	13.557908	12.077074	10.860505
45	24.518713	20.720040	17.774070	15.455832	13.605522	12.108402	10.881197
46	24.775449	20.884654	17.880066	15.524370	13.650020	12.137409	10.900181
47	25.024708	21.042936	17.981016	15.589028	13.691608	12.164267	10.917597
48	25.266707	21.195131	18.077158	15.650027	13.730474	12.189136	10.933575
49	25.501657	21.341472	18.168722	15.707572	13.766799	12.212163	10.948234
50	25.729764	21.482185	18.255925	15.761861	13.800746	12.233485	10.961683
51	25.951227	21.617485	18.338977	15.813076	13.832473	12.253227	10.974021

continues

TABLE 7 Present value of an annuity $a_{\overline{n}|i} = \dfrac{1 - (1 + i)^{-n}}{i}$ (continued)

n	3%	4%	5%	6%	7%	8%	9%
52	26.166240	21.747582	18.418073	15.861393	13.862124	12.271506	10.985340
53	26.374990	21.872675	18.493403	15.906974	13.889836	12.288432	10.995725
54	26.577660	21.992957	18.565146	15.949976	13.915735	12.304103	11.005252
55	26.774428	22.108612	18.633472	15.990543	13.939939	12.318614	11.013993
56	26.965464	22.219819	18.698545	16.028814	13.962560	12.332050	11.022012
57	27.150936	22.326749	18.760519	16.064919	13.983701	12.344491	11.029369
58	27.331005	22.429567	18.819542	16.098980	14.003458	12.356010	11.036118
59	27.505831	22.528430	18.875754	16.131113	14.021924	12.366676	11.042310
60	27.675564	22.623490	18.929290	16.161428	14.039181	12.376552	11.047991
61	27.840353	22.714894	18.980276	16.190026	14.055309	12.385696	11.053203
62	28.000343	22.802783	19.028834	16.217006	14.070383	12.394163	11.057984
63	28.155673	22.887291	19.075080	16.242458	14.084470	12.402003	11.062371
64	28.306478	22.968549	19.119124	16.266470	14.097635	12.409262	11.066395
65	28.452892	23.046682	19.161070	16.289123	14.109940	12.415983	11.070087
66	28.595040	23.121810	19.201019	16.310493	14.121439	12.422207	11.073475
67	28.733049	23.194048	19.239066	16.330654	14.132186	12.427969	11.076582
68	28.867038	23.263507	19.275301	16.349673	14.142230	12.433305	11.079433
69	28.997124	23.330296	19.309810	16.367617	14.151617	12.438245	11.082049
70	29.123421	23.394515	19.342677	16.384544	14.160389	12.442820	11.084449
71	29.246040	23.456264	19.373978	16.400513	14.168588	12.447055	11.086650
72	29.365088	23.515639	19.403788	16.415578	14.176251	12.450977	11.088670
73	29.480667	23.572730	19.432179	16.429791	14.183412	12.454608	11.090523
74	29.592881	23.627625	19.459218	16.443199	14.190104	12.457971	11.092223
75	29.701826	23.680408	19.484970	16.455848	14.196359	12.461084	11.093782
76	19.807598	23.731162	19.509495	16.467781	14.202205	12.463967	11.095213
77	29.910290	23.779963	19.532853	16.479039	14.207668	12.466636	11.096526
78	30.009990	23.826888	19.555098	16.489659	14.212774	12.469107	11.097730
79	30.106786	23.872008	19.576284	16.499679	14.217546	12.471396	11.098835
80	30.200763	23.915392	19.596460	16.509131	14.222005	12.473514	11.099849
81	30.292003	23.957108	19.615677	16.518048	14.226173	12.475476	11.100778
82	30.380586	23.997219	19.633978	16.526460	14.230069	12.477293	11.101632
83	30.466588	24.035787	19.651407	16.534396	14.233709	12.478975	11.102414
84	30.550086	24.072872	19.668007	16.541883	14.237111	12.480532	11.103132
85	30.631151	24.108531	19.683816	16.548947	14.240291	12.481974	11.103791
86	30.709855	24.142818	19.698873	16.555610	14.243262	12.483310	11.104396
87	30.786267	24.175787	19.713212	16.561896	14.246040	12.484546	11.104950
88	30.860454	24.207487	19.726869	16.567827	14.248635	12.485691	11.105459
89	30.932479	24.237969	19.739875	16.573421	14.251061	12.486751	11.105926
90	31.002407	24.267278	19.752262	16.578699	14.253328	12.487732	11.106354
91	31.070298	24.295459	19.764059	16.583679	14.255447	12.488641	11.106746
92	31.136212	24.322557	19.775294	16.588376	14.257427	12.489482	11.107107
93	31.200206	24.348612	19.785994	16.592808	14.259277	12.490261	11.107437
94	31.262336	24.373666	19.796185	19.596988	14.261007	12.490983	11.107741
95	31.322656	23.397756	19.805891	16.600932	14.262623	12.491651	11.108019
96	31.381219	24.420919	19.815134	16.604653	14.264134	12.492269	11.108274
97	31.438077	24.443191	19.823937	16.608163	14.265546	12.492842	11.108509
98	31.493279	24.464607	19.832321	16.611475	14.266865	12.493372	11.108724
99	31.546872	24.485199	19.840306	16.614599	14.268098	12.493863	11.108921
100	31.598905	24.504999	19.847910	16.617546	14.269251	12.494318	11.109102

TABLE 7 Present value of an annuity $a_{\overline{n}|i} = \dfrac{1 - (1 + i)^{-n}}{i}$

n	10%	11%	12%	13%	14%	15%	16%
1	0.909091	0.900901	0.892857	0.884956	0.877193	0.869565	0.862069
2	1.735537	1.712523	1.690051	1.668102	1.646661	1.625709	1.605232
3	2.486852	2.443715	2.401831	2.361153	2.321632	2.283225	2.245890
4	3.169865	3.102446	3.037349	2.974471	2.913712	2.854978	2.798181
5	3.790787	3.695897	3.604776	3.517231	3.433081	3.352155	3.274294
6	4.355261	4.230538	4.111407	3.997550	3.888668	3.784483	3.684736
7	4.868419	4.712196	4.563757	4.422610	4.288305	4.160420	4.038565
8	5.334926	5.146123	4.967640	4.798770	4.638864	4.487322	4.343591
9	5.759024	5.537048	5.328250	5.131655	4.946372	4.771584	4.606544
10	6.144567	5.889232	5.650223	5.426243	5.216116	5.018769	4.833227
11	6.495061	6.206515	5.937699	5.686941	5.452733	5.233712	5.028644
12	6.813692	6.492356	6.194374	5.917647	5.660292	5.420619	5.197107
13	7.103356	6.749870	6.423548	6.121812	5.842362	5.583147	5.342334
14	7.366687	6.981865	6.628168	6.302488	6.002072	5.724476	5.467529
15	7.606080	7.190870	6.810864	6.462379	6.142168	5.847370	5.575456
16	7.823709	7.379162	6.973986	6.603875	6.265060	5.954235	5.668497
17	8.021553	7.548794	7.119630	6.729093	6.372859	6.047161	5.748704
18	8.201412	7.701617	7.249670	6.839905	6.467420	6.127966	5.817848
19	8.364920	7.839294	7.365777	6.937969	6.550369	6.198231	5.877455
20	8.513564	7.963328	7.469444	7.024752	6.623131	6.259331	5.928841
21	8.648694	8.075070	7.562003	7.101550	6.686957	6.312462	5.973139
22	8.771540	8.175739	7.644646	7.169513	6.742944	6.358663	6.011326
23	8.883218	8.266432	7.718434	7.229658	6.792056	6.398837	6.044147
24	8.984744	8.348137	7.784316	7.282883	6.835137	6.433771	6.072627
25	9.077040	8.421745	7.843139	7.329985	6.872927	6.464149	6.097092
26	9.160945	8.488058	7.895660	7.371668	6.906077	6.490564	6.118183
27	9.237223	8.547800	7.942554	7.408556	6.935155	6.513534	6.136364
28	9.306567	8.601622	7.984423	7.441200	6.960662	6.533508	6.152038
29	9.369606	8.650110	8.021806	7.470088	6.983037	6.550877	6.165550
30	9.426914	8.693793	8.055184	7.495653	7.002664	6.565980	6.177198
31	9.479013	8.733146	8.084986	7.518277	7.019881	6.579113	6.187240
32	9.526376	8.768600	8.111594	7.538299	7.034983	6.590533	6.195897
33	9.569432	8.800541	8.135352	7.556016	7.048231	6.600463	6.203359
34	9.608575	8.829316	8.156564	7.571696	7.059852	6.609099	6.209792
35	9.644159	8.855240	8.175504	7.585572	7.070045	6.616607	6.215338
36	9.676508	8.878594	8.192414	7.597851	7.078987	6.623137	6.220119
37	9.705917	8.899635	8.207513	7.608718	7.086831	6.628815	6.224241
38	9.732651	8.918590	8.220993	7.618334	7.093711	6.633752	6.227794
39	9.756956	8.935666	8.233030	7.626844	7.099747	6.638045	6.230857
40	9.779051	8.951051	8.243777	7.634376	7.105041	6.641778	6.233497
41	9.799137	8.964911	8.253372	7.641040	7.109685	6.645025	6.235773
42	9.817397	8.977397	8.261939	7.646938	7.113759	6.647848	6.237736
43	9.833998	8.988646	8.269589	7.652158	7.117332	6.650302	6.239427
44	9.849089	8.998780	8.276418	7.656777	7.120467	6.652437	6.240886
45	9.862808	9.007910	8.282516	7.660864	7.123217	6.654293	6.242143
46	9.875280	9.016135	8.287961	7.664482	7.125629	6.655907	6.243227
47	9.886618	9.023545	8.292822	7.667683	7.127744	6.657310	6.244161
48	9.896926	9.030221	8.297163	7.670516	7.129600	6.658531	6.244966
49	9.906296	9.036235	8.301038	7.673023	7.131228	6.659592	6.245661
50	9.914814	9.041653	8.304498	7.675242	7.132656	6.660515	6.246259

TABLE 8   Standard normal curve areas

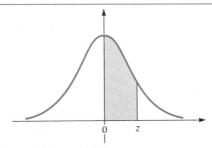

z	.00	.01	.02	.03	.04	.05	.06	.07	.08	.09
0.0	0.0000	0.0040	0.0080	0.0120	0.0160	0.0199	0.0239	0.0279	0.0319	0.0359
0.1	0.0398	0.0438	0.0478	0.0517	0.0557	0.0596	0.0636	0.0675	0.0714	0.0753
0.2	0.0793	0.0832	0.0871	0.0910	0.0948	0.0987	0.1026	0.1064	0.1103	0.1141
0.3	0.1179	0.1217	0.1255	0.1293	0.1331	0.1368	0.1406	0.1443	0.1480	0.1517
0.4	0.1554	0.1591	0.1628	0.1664	0.1700	0.1736	0.1772	0.1808	0.1844	0.1879
0.5	0.1915	0.1950	0.1985	0.2019	0.2054	0.2088	0.2123	0.2157	0.2190	0.2224
0.6	0.2257	0.2291	0.2324	0.2357	0.2389	0.2422	0.2454	0.2486	0.2517	0.2549
0.7	0.2580	0.2611	0.2642	0.2673	0.2704	0.2734	0.2764	0.2794	0.2823	0.2852
0.8	0.2881	0.2910	0.2939	0.2967	0.2995	0.3023	0.3051	0.3078	0.3106	0.3133
0.9	0.3159	0.3186	0.3212	0.3238	0.3264	0.3289	0.3315	0.3340	0.3365	0.3389
1.0	0.3413	0.3438	0.3461	0.3485	0.3508	0.3531	0.3554	0.3577	0.3599	0.3621
1.1	0.3643	0.3665	0.3686	0.3708	0.3729	0.3749	0.3770	0.3790	0.3810	0.3830
1.2	0.3849	0.3869	0.3888	0.3907	0.3925	0.3944	0.3962	0.3980	0.3997	0.4015
1.3	0.4032	0.4049	0.4066	0.4082	0.4099	0.4115	0.4131	0.4147	0.4162	0.4177
1.4	0.4192	0.4207	0.4222	0.4236	0.4251	0.4265	0.4279	0.4292	0.4306	0.4319
1.5	0.4332	0.4345	0.4357	0.4370	0.4382	0.4394	0.4406	0.4418	0.4429	0.4441
1.6	0.4452	0.4463	0.4474	0.4484	0.4495	0.4505	0.4515	0.4525	0.4535	0.4545
1.7	0.4554	0.4564	0.4573	0.4582	0.4591	0.4599	0.4608	0.4616	0.4625	0.4633
1.8	0.4641	0.4649	0.4656	0.4664	0.4671	0.4678	0.4686	0.4693	0.4699	0.4706
1.9	0.4713	0.4719	0.4726	0.4732	0.4738	0.4744	0.4750	0.4756	0.4761	0.4767
2.0	0.4772	0.4778	0.4783	0.4788	0.4793	0.4798	0.4803	0.4808	0.4812	0.4817
2.1	0.4821	0.4826	0.4830	0.4834	0.4838	0.4842	0.4846	0.4850	0.4854	0.4857
2.2	0.4861	0.4864	0.4868	0.4871	0.4875	0.4878	0.4881	0.4884	0.4887	0.4890
2.3	0.4893	0.4896	0.4898	0.4901	0.4904	0.4906	0.4909	0.4911	0.4913	0.4916
2.4	0.4918	0.4920	0.4922	0.4925	0.4927	0.4929	0.4931	0.4932	0.4934	0.4936
2.5	0.4938	0.4940	0.4941	0.4943	0.4945	0.4946	0.4948	0.4949	0.4951	0.4952
2.6	0.4953	0.4955	0.4956	0.4957	0.4959	0.4960	0.4961	0.4962	0.4963	0.4964
2.7	0.4965	0.4966	0.4967	0.4968	0.4969	0.4970	0.4971	0.4972	0.4973	0.4974
2.8	0.4974	0.4975	0.4976	0.4977	0.4977	0.4978	0.4979	0.4979	0.4980	0.4981
2.9	0.4981	0.4982	0.4982	0.4983	0.4984	0.4984	0.4985	0.4985	0.4986	0.4986
3.0	0.4987	0.4987	0.4987	0.4988	0.4988	0.4989	0.4989	0.4989	0.4990	0.4990

TABLE 9   A brief table of integrals

1. $\int u^n \, du = \dfrac{1}{n+1} u^{n+1} + c \qquad (n \neq -1)$

2. $\int e^u \, du = e^u + c$

continues

TABLE 9   **A brief table of integrals** *(continued)*

3. $\displaystyle\int \frac{du}{u} = \ln|u| + c$

4. $\displaystyle\int u\,dv = uv - \int v\,du$

5. $\displaystyle\int \frac{du}{\sqrt{a^2 + u^2}} = \ln\left|u + \sqrt{a^2 + u^2}\right| + c$

6. $\displaystyle\int \frac{du}{a^2 - u^2} = \frac{1}{2a}\ln\left|\frac{a + u}{a - u}\right| + c$

7. $\displaystyle\int ue^u\,du = e^u(u - 1) + c$

8. $\displaystyle\int u^n e^u\,du = u^n e^u - n\int u^{n-1}e^u\,du$

9. $\displaystyle\int \frac{du}{u^2(a + bu)} = -\frac{1}{au} + \frac{b}{a^2}\ln\left|\frac{a + bu}{u}\right| + c$

10. $\displaystyle\int \ln u\,du = u\ln|u| - u + c$

11. $\displaystyle\int (\ln u)^n\,du = u(\ln u)^n - n\int (\ln u)^{n-1}\,du \qquad (n \neq -1)$

12. $\displaystyle\int u^n \ln u\,du = u^{n+1}\left[\frac{\ln u}{n + 1} - \frac{1}{(n + 1)^2}\right] + c \qquad (n \neq -1)$

13. $\displaystyle\int \frac{du}{\sqrt{u^2 - a^2}} = \ln\left|u + \sqrt{u^2 - a^2}\right| + c$

14. $\displaystyle\int \frac{du}{u^2 - a^2} = \frac{1}{2a}\ln\left|\frac{u - a}{u + a}\right| + c$

15. $\displaystyle\int \frac{du}{u\sqrt{a^2 - u^2}} = -\frac{1}{a}\ln\left|\frac{a + \sqrt{a^2 + u^2}}{u}\right| + c$

16. $\displaystyle\int \frac{du}{u\sqrt{a^2 + u^2}} = -\frac{1}{a}\ln\left|\frac{a + \sqrt{a^2 + u^2}}{u}\right| + c$

17. $\displaystyle\int \frac{du}{u\sqrt{a + bu}} = \frac{1}{\sqrt{a}}\ln\left|\frac{\sqrt{a + bu} - \sqrt{a}}{\sqrt{a + bu} + \sqrt{a}}\right| + c \qquad (a > 0)$

18. $\displaystyle\int \frac{\sqrt{a^2 - u^2}}{u}\,du = -\sqrt{a^2 - u^2} - a\ln\left|\frac{a + \sqrt{a^2 - u^2}}{u}\right| + c$

19. $\displaystyle\int \frac{du}{u^2\sqrt{a^2 - u^2}} = -\frac{\sqrt{a^2 - u^2}}{a^2 u} + c$

20. $\displaystyle\int \frac{du}{(a^2 - u^2)^{3/2}} = \frac{u}{a^2\sqrt{a^2 - u^2}} + c$

21. $\displaystyle\int \frac{u\,du}{(a + bu)^2} = \frac{1}{b^2}\left[\frac{a}{a + bu} + \ln|a + bu|\right] + c$

22. $\displaystyle\int \sqrt{a^2 + u^2}\,du = \frac{u}{2}\sqrt{a^2 + u^2} + \frac{a^2}{2}\ln\left|u + \sqrt{a^2 + u^2}\right| + c$

23. $\displaystyle\int \frac{du}{(a^2 + u^2)^{3/2}} = \frac{u}{a^2\sqrt{a^2 + u^2}} + c$

24. $\displaystyle\int \frac{du}{u(a + bu)} = -\frac{1}{a}\ln\left|\frac{a + bu}{u}\right| + c$

Answers to Selected Exercises

• CHAPTER R

SECTION R-1

1. True **3.** False **5.** True **7.** True **9.** True **11.** False
13. True **15.** True **17.** True **19.** False **21.** True
23. True **25.** True **27.** False
29. (number line: closed dots at -5 and -1)
31. (number line: open dots at -4 and -2)
33. (number line: open dot at -3, closed dot at 2)
35. (number line: closed dot at 5)
37. (number line: ray left from -3)
39. (number line: open dot at -2)
41. (number line: open dot at 2, ray right)
43. (number line: open dot at 2, ray left)
45. Closed **47.** Open **49.** Closed
51. (number line: closed dots at 3 and 9)
53. (number line: closed dot at -4, ray left)
55. (number line: open dot at 6, ray left)
57. (number line: open dot at 4, closed dot at 9)
59. 0 **61.** 1 **63.** 2 **65.** 15 **67.** 20 **69.** 4 **71.** 9
73. 6 **75.** 13 **77.** 6 (segment: $\leftarrow 6 \rightarrow$ from 5 to 11)

79. 5 (segment: $\leftarrow 5 \rightarrow$ from -9 to -4)

SECTION R-2

1. $x = 6$ **3.** $x = 9$ **5.** $x = 12$ **7.** $x = 8$ **9.** $y = 10$

11. $\left(-\infty, 5\frac{1}{2}\right]$ (number line: closed dot at $5\frac{1}{2}$, ray left)

13. $\left(-\infty, 7\frac{1}{2}\right)$ (number line: open dot at $7\frac{1}{2}$, ray left)

15. $\left(-\infty, 10\frac{1}{3}\right]$ (number line: closed dot at $10\frac{1}{3}$, ray left)

17. $(-\infty, 3]$ (number line: closed dot at 3, ray left)

19. $[11, \infty)$ (number line: closed dot at 11, ray right)

SECTION R-3

1. 9 **3.** 25 **5.** $4^6 = 4096$ **7.** $\dfrac{1}{16}$ **9.** 64

11. $5^7 = 78{,}125$ **13.** $\dfrac{9}{25}$ **15.** $\dfrac{1}{64}$ **17.** $\dfrac{1}{8}$ **19.** 4 **21.** 7

23. $8^5 = 32{,}768$ **25.** 343 **27.** 36 **29.** 1
31. $7^5 = 16{,}807$ **33.** 5^{-6} **35.** $(-5)^{-3}$ **37.** x^{-8}
39. $4^{9/2} = 2^9$ **41.** $2^{1/5}$ **43.** $9^{4/7}$ **45.** $5^{7/3}$ **47.** $5^{-3/2}$
49. $x^{-5/2}$ **51.** $x^{-2/3}$ **53.** $9x^2$ **55.** $125x^3y^3$

57. $2 \cdot 9 = 18$ **59.** $\dfrac{5^3}{6^3} = \dfrac{125}{216}$ **61.** $\dfrac{x^5}{3^5} = \dfrac{x^5}{243}$ **63.** $\dfrac{x^2}{25}$

65. $\dfrac{-8}{x^3}$ **67.** $2^{12} = 4096$ **69.** $\dfrac{1}{3}$ **71.** 4.96×10^2

73. 8×10^9 **75.** 8×10^{-7} **77.** 5.6×10^{-1}
79. 3.57×10^{-3}

SECTION R-4

1. $3x + 12$ **3.** $-2x - 12$ **5.** $9x + 27$
7. $-4x^2 + 12x - 28$ **9.** $5x^4 - 20x^3 + 20x^2 + 25x$
11. $3x^6y^3 - 15x^2y^5 + 18x^3y^4$ **13.** $5(x + 4)$ **15.** $3(x - 9)$
17. $6(x - 5)$ **19.** $3x(x - 9)$ **21.** $-6x(x - 8)$
23. $7x(x + 4)$ **25.** $3xy^2(xy^2 + 2)$ **27.** $-5x^3y^6(x - 4y)$
29. $3x^2y^3(y^3 + 3x^3 + 2xy)$ **31.** $P(1 + rt)$ **33.** $P(1 + i)$
35. $x(ax - b)$ **37.** $P(1 + i)^3$ **39.** $3x(2x - 3)$
41. $(x + 3)(2x - y)$ **43.** $x(x - 2)(5y + 8x)$

SECTION R-5

1. $x^2 + x - 6$ **3.** $x^2 + 6x + 5$ **5.** $x^2 - 15x + 56$
7. $3x^2 + 2x - 5$ **9.** $8x^2 - 2x - 21$ **11.** $21x^2 + x - 2$

13. $x^2 - 9$ **15.** $x^2 - 81$ **17.** $9x^2 - 4$ **19.** $x^2 - 4x + 4$
21. $x^2 + 10x + 25$ **23.** $4x^2 - 12x + 9$

SECTION R-6

1. $(x + 9)(x - 2)$ **3.** $(x + 5)(x - 3)$ **5.** $(x - 2)(x - 1)$
7. $(x - 5)(x - 8)$ **9.** $(x - 9)(x + 9)$ **11.** $(x - 7)(x + 7)$
13. $(x + 3)^2$ **15.** $(x - 5)^2$ **17.** $(x + 9)^2$
19. $(x - 9)(x + 3)$ **21.** $(x - 9)(x + 5)$ **23.** $(x + 6)(x + 1)$

SECTION R-7

1. $(2x + 7)(x - 4)$ **3.** $(5x - 2)(x + 4)$
5. $(2x - 5)(3x + 1)$ **7.** $9(x - 2)(x + 2)$ **9.** $(2x + 5)^2$
11. $(5x - 7)^2$

SECTION R-8

1. $2x - 14$ **3.** $-x - 7$ **5.** x **7.** $\dfrac{x - 3}{x - 5}$ **9.** $\dfrac{x + 4}{x + 1}$

11. $\dfrac{x + 3}{x + 2}$ **13.** $\dfrac{1}{x}$ **15.** $\dfrac{x + 3}{x - 2}$ **17.** $\dfrac{x + 3}{x + 2}$

19. $\dfrac{x + 6}{2} = \dfrac{x}{2} + 3$ **21.** $\dfrac{9}{x}$ **23.** $\dfrac{-3(x + 16)}{x(x + 6)}$ or

$\dfrac{-3x - 48}{x(x + 6)}$ **25.** $\dfrac{9x - 49}{x^2 - 36}$ **27.** $\dfrac{7x - 5}{x(x - 9)}$ **29.** $x + \dfrac{7}{x}$

31. $3x - 36$ **33.** $4x^2 - 8x + 6$ **35.** $4x^2 + 8x - 12$

37. $5x^3 - 5x^2 + 30x - 10$ **39.** $x^3\left(1 - \dfrac{4}{x} + \dfrac{7}{x^2} + \dfrac{5}{x^3}\right)$

41. $x^2\left(1 + \dfrac{7}{x} + \dfrac{9}{x^2}\right)$ **43.** $\dfrac{1 - (1 + i)^{-20}}{i}$

45. $\dfrac{1 + i - (1 + i)^{-37}}{i}$

• EXTRA DIVIDENDS

1. 25% **3.** $72 **5.** $428.57 **7.** $14,800 **9.** $16,050
11. 123.3% **13.** 139.3% **15.** -1.6% **17.** $18,148.82
19. $22,321.43

• EXTRA DIVIDENDS

1. 175 **3.** $8,214,286 **5.** (a) 100% (b) 17.6% **7.** 1.18
9. 1.35 **11.** 1.1 **13.** 1.32 **15.** $321.44 **17.** $405.19

• CHAPTER 1

SECTION 1-1

1. (a) -2 (b) 10 **3.** (a) 7 (b) 5 (c) -3 (d) 13
5. (a) $\dfrac{5}{7}$ (b) $\dfrac{5}{8}$ (c) 5 (d) $\dfrac{1}{3}$

7.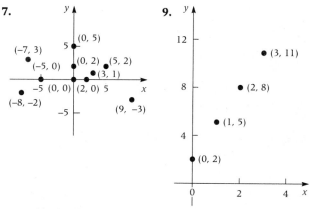

9.

11. All real x such that $x \ne 2$, $x \ne -7$ **13.** All real x such
that $x \ge 2$ **15.** All real x such that $x \ne 3$ **17.** a, c, d
19. *Not* a function: $(4, 3)$ and $(4, -3)$ satisfy equation
21. (a) $f(x + h) = x^2 + 2xh + h^2 - 4x - 4h + 5$
(b) $f(x + h) - f(x) = 2xh + h^2 - 4h$
(c) $\dfrac{f(x + h) - f(x)}{h} = 2x + h - 4$

23. $\dfrac{f(x + h) - f(x)}{h} = 10x + 5h - 2$

25. $\dfrac{g(x + h) - g(x)}{h} = 3x^2 + 3xh + h^2 - 8x - 4h + 5$

27.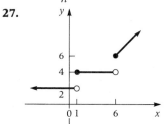

29. (a) $C(x) = \begin{cases} 5.00 & \text{if } 16 < x \le 40 \\ 2.00 & \text{if } 8 \le x \le 16 \\ 1.25 & \text{if } 0 < x < 8 \end{cases}$

(b)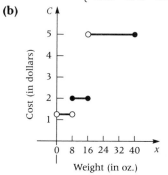

31. $P(x) = \begin{cases} 28 - x & \text{if } 0 \le x \le 35 \\ -7 & \text{if } x > 35 \end{cases}$

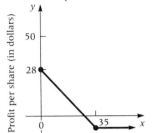

SECTION 1-2

1. (a) $\Delta y = 3$ **(b)** $\Delta x = 4$ **(c)** $\frac{3}{4}$ **(d)** For every 4 units of horizontal charge to the right there are 3 units of vertical change upward. **3.** $\frac{11}{3}$ **5.** $\frac{1}{4}$ **7.** 10 **9.** $\frac{-7}{5}$

11.

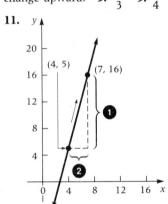

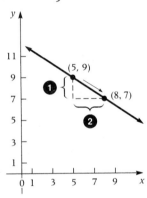

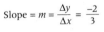

① $16 - 5 = 11$ units vertical change

② $7 - 4 = 3$ units horizontal change

Slope $= m = \frac{\Delta y}{\Delta x} = \frac{11}{3}$

① $7 - 9 = -2$ units vertical change

② $8 - 5 = 3$ units horizontal change

Slope $= m = \frac{\Delta y}{\Delta x} = \frac{-2}{3}$

continues

11. *Continued*

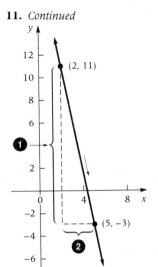

① $-3 - 11 = -14$ units vertical change

② $5 - 2 = 3$ units horizontal change

Slope $= m = \frac{\Delta y}{\Delta x} = \frac{-14}{3}$

15.

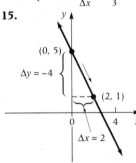

$m = \frac{-4}{2} = -2$

19.

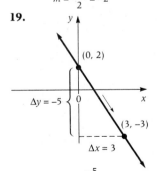

$m = \frac{-5}{3}$

13.

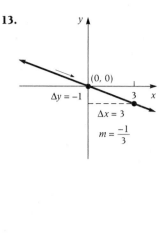

$m = \frac{-1}{3}$

17.

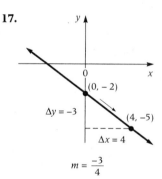

$m = \frac{-3}{4}$

21.

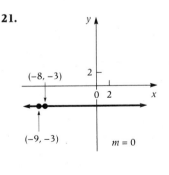

$m = 0$

23.

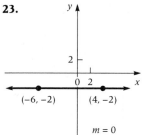

$m = 0$

25.

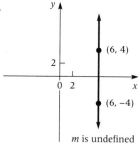

m is undefined

35.

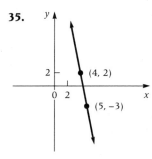

$y - 2 = -5(x - 4)$

$y = -5x + 22$

37.

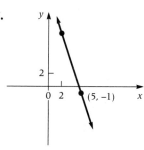

$y + 1 = -3(x - 5)$

$y = -3x + 14$

27.

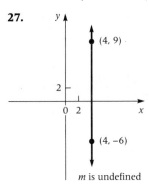

m is undefined

29.

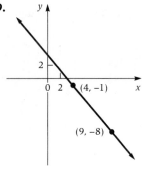

$y + 1 = \dfrac{-7}{5}(x - 4)$

$y = \dfrac{-7}{5}x + \dfrac{23}{5}$

39.

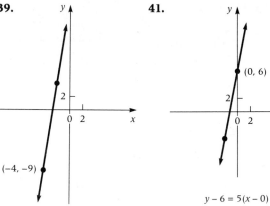

$y + 9 = 6(x + 4)$

$y = 6x + 15$

41.

$y - 6 = 5(x - 0)$

$y = 5x + 6$

31.

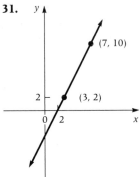

$y - 2 = 2(x - 3)$

$y = 2x - 4$

33.

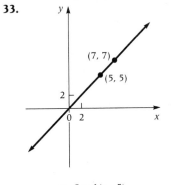

$y - 5 = 1(x - 5)$

$y = x$

43.

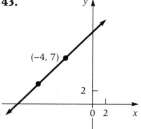

$y - 7 = 1(x + 4)$

$y = x + 11$

45. $(7, 1), (14, -1)$

47. $(1, 9), \left(\dfrac{-1}{2}, 0\right), (-1, -3)$ **49.** $(0, 0), (1, -3), (2, -6)$

51.

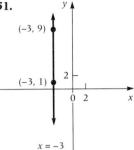

53.

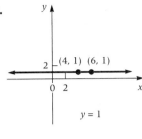

$y = 1$

55.

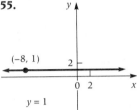

$y = 1$

57.

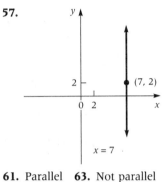

$x = 7$

59.

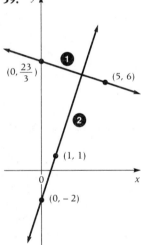

① $y = \dfrac{-x}{3} + \dfrac{23}{3}$

② $y = 3x - 2$

61. Parallel   **63.** Not parallel

65. Perpendicular   **67.** Perpendicular   **69.** $y = \dfrac{3}{5}x - \dfrac{11}{5}$

71. $y = \dfrac{3}{2}x$ **73.** Linear   **75.** Not linear   **77.** Linear

79. Not linear   **81. (a)** 132.825 **(b)** U.S. Overseas IOU's are increasing at the rate of 132.825 billion dollars per year during the indicated time interval.
(c) $y - 642 = 132.825(x - 1989)$
or
$y = 132.825x - 263{,}546.925$

(d) $y = 132.825(1992) - 263{,}546.925$
      $= 1040.475$ billion dollars
83. (a) -52.1 **(b)** Defects per 100 vehicles decreased at the rate of 52.1 per year during the indicated time interval.
(c) $y - 149 = -52.1(x - 1989)$
          or
          $y = -52.1x + 103{,}775.9$
(d) $y = -52.1(1991) + 103{,}775.9$
      $= 44.8$
85. (a) 2500 **(b)** The value of the investment increased by $2500 per percentage point increase in inflation.
87. (a)

$$y = \begin{cases} 0.15x & \text{if } 0 < x \le 15{,}475 \\ 2321.25 + 0.28(x - 15{,}475) & \\ & \text{if } 15{,}475 < x \le 37{,}425 \\ 8467.25 + 0.33(x - 37{,}425) & \\ & \text{if } 37{,}425 < x \le 117{,}895 \end{cases}$$

(b)

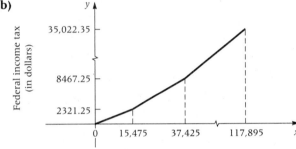

Taxable income (in dollars)

SECTION 1-3

1.

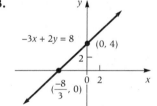

3.

5.

7.

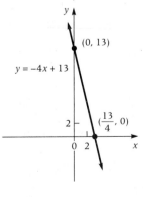

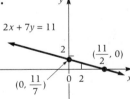

9.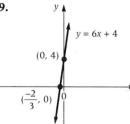

$y = 6x + 4$
$(0, 4)$
$\left(\dfrac{-2}{3}, 0\right)$

11.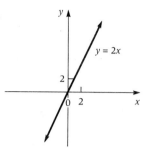

$y = 2x$

13.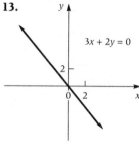

$3x + 2y = 0$

15.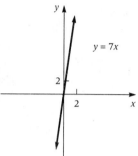

$y = 7x$

17.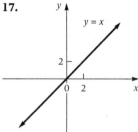

$y = x$

19.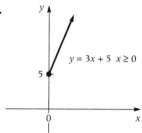

$y = 3x + 5 \quad x \geq 0$

21.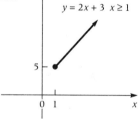

$y = 2x + 3 \quad x \geq 1$

(b) $C(x) = 50x + 700$ **(c)** $F = \$700$ **(d)** $\$3200$
5. $C(x) = 20x + 1000$ **7.** $C(x) = 15x + 8700$
$C(100) = \$3000$ $C(100) = \$10,200$
9. $C(x) = 40x + 900$
$R(x) = 70x$
$P(x) = 30x - 900$

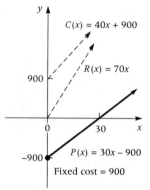

$C(x) = 40x + 900$
$R(x) = 70x$
900
30
-900
$P(x) = 30x - 900$
Fixed cost $= 900$

11. $C(x) = 100x + 8000$
$R(x) = 140x$
$P(x) = 40x - 8000$

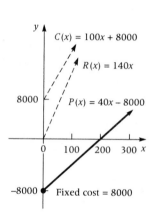

$C(x) = 100x + 8000$
$R(x) = 140x$
8000
$P(x) = 40x - 8000$
$100 \quad 200 \quad 300$
-8000 Fixed cost $= 8000$

13. $C(x) = 25x + 7500$
$R(x) = 40x$
$P(x) = 15x - 7500$

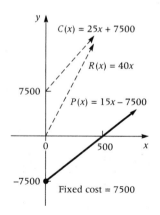

$C(x) = 25x + 7500$
$R(x) = 40x$
7500
$P(x) = 15x - 7500$
500
-7500 Fixed cost $= 7500$

SECTION 1-4

1. (a) $v = \$10$ **(b)** $C(x) = 10x + 800$ **(c)** $F = \$800$
(d)

Cost (in dollars)

$y = 10x + 800$
$(60, 1400)$
800
$(40, 1200)$
Fixed cost
$0 \quad 50 \quad 100$
Number of units

3. (a) $v = \$50$

15.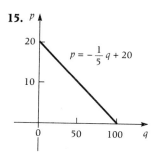
$p = -\frac{1}{5}q + 20$

17.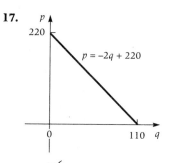
$p = -2q + 220$

(c)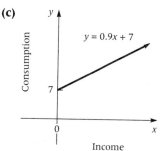
$y = 0.9x + 7$

19.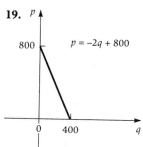
$p = -2q + 800$

21. $q = \frac{-6}{5}p + 6$

41. (a) MPC = 0.8 For each dollar increase in disposable income, consumption increases by \$0.80. **(b)** MPS = 0.2 For each dollar increase in disposable income, personal savings increases by \$0.20. **(c)** $y = 0.8x + 7$
(d) \$75 billion   **43.** $y = 90,000 - 20,000x$
45. $y = 45,000 - 15,000x$ **47. (a)** $y = 30,000 - 2900x$
(b)
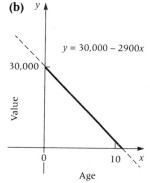
$y = 30,000 - 2900x$

(c) \$12,600

23. $q = -2p + 6$ **25.** $p = -3q + 6$ **27.** $p = \frac{-5}{8}q + 5$

29.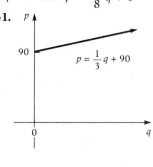
$p = 5q - 30$

31.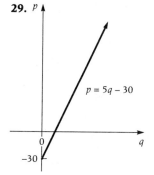
$p = \frac{1}{3}q + 90$

33. $q = \frac{4}{3}p - 4$ **35.** $p = \frac{5}{3}q + 10$ **37. (a)** MPC = 0.7
For each dollar increase in disposable income, consumption increases by \$0.70. **(b)** $y = 0.7x + 2$
(c)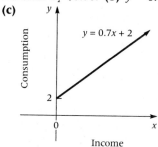
$y = 0.7x + 2$

39. (a) MPC = 0.9 For each dollar increase in disposable income, consumption increases by \$0.90. **(b)** $y = 0.9x + 7$

SECTION 1-5

1. $C(x) = 5x + 1000$
$R(x) = 9x$
$P(x) = 4x - 1000$
$x = 250$
3. $C(x) = 20x + 100,000$
$R(x) = 120x$
$P(x) = 100x - 100,000$
$x = 1000$
5. $C(x) = 25x + 80,000$
$R(x) = 65x$
$P(x) = 40x - 80,000$
$x = 2000$
7. (a) $C(x) = 5x + 2000$ **(b)** $R(x) = 15x$
(c) **(d)** 200
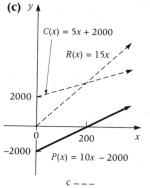
$C(x) = 5x + 2000$
$R(x) = 15x$
$P(x) = 10x - 2000$
c − − −
f ——

(e) $P(x) = 10x - 2000$ **(f)**

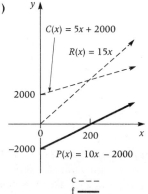

$C(x) = 5x + 2000$
$R(x) = 15x$
2000
0   200 x
-2000
$P(x) = 10x - 2000$

c - - -
f ———

(g) $1000 **(h)** -$1000 (a loss) **(i)** 4200   **9. (a)** $1300
(b) $C(x) = 1300x + 260,000$ **(c)** $R(x) = 1800x$
(d) $C(x) = 1300x + 260,000$ **(e)** 520

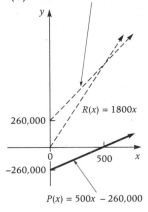

$R(x) = 1800x$
260,000
0   500 x
-260,000
$P(x) = 500x - 260,000$

d - - - -
g ———

(f) $P(x) = 500x - 260,000$
(g) $C(x) = 1300x + 260,000$ **(h)** $240,000 **(i)** 728

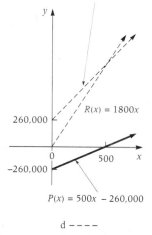

$R(x) = 1800x$
260,000
0   500 x
-260,000
$P(x) = 500x - 260,000$

d - - - -
g ———

11. (a) $R(x) = 100x$ **(b)** $C(x) = 50x + 2500$ **(c)** 50
(d) $P(x) = 50x - 2500$ **(e)** 130 **(f)** $P(125) = \$3750$
(g) $P(x) = 50x - 4200$
$x = 84$
13. (a) R = total sales revenue
$R = \$600,000$ for break-even
(b) $R = \$1,190,000$
15. $p = \$21.67, q = 4$ **17.** $q = 12, p = \$9$
19. (a) $p = \dfrac{-1}{10}q + 50$ **(b)** $p = \dfrac{1}{15}q + \dfrac{50}{3}$
(c) p **(d)** 200 **(e)** $30

$p = \dfrac{1}{15}q + \dfrac{50}{3}$
50
$p = -\dfrac{1}{10}q + 50$
0   500 q

• **EXTRA DIVIDENDS**

Cost Accounting

1. (a) $y = x + 1500$ **(b)** $1500 **(c)** $1   **3. (a)** $0.80 per
machine hour **(b)** $20,000 per month **(c)** $240,000

Model Fitting

1. (a) For $y = 2x + 1$, $S = 41$
For $y = 3x - 2$, $S = 55$ **(b)** $y = 2x + 1$ is the better fit.
3. (a) For $y = 4x - 3$, $S = 42$
For $y = 3x + 2$, $S = 64$ **(b)** $y = 4x - 3$ is the better fit.
5. (a) For $y = 13x + 130$, $S = 3481.0598$
For $y = 20x + 70$, $S = 15,051.2198$ **(b)** $y = 13x + 130$ is
the better fit.   **7. (a)** For $y = 3x + 120$, $S = 27$
For $y = 4x + 115$, $S = 121$ **(b)** $y = 3x + 120$ is the better
fit.   **9. (a)** For $y = 2x + 170$, $S = 5462$
For $y = 3x + 100$, $S = 11,786$ **(b)** $y = 2x + 170$ is the
better fit.

• **CHAPTER HIGHLIGHTS**

1. *Function, domain, range.* A **function** is a rule that
associates a unique output value with each element in a set
of possible input values. The set of input values is called
the **domain** of the function. The set of output values is
called the **range** of the function.
Dependent variable, independent variable. If a function is
defined by an equation such as $y = 5x^2 - 6$, then the value
of y depends upon the value of x. Therefore, y is called the

dependent variable and x is called the **independent** variable.

Ordered pair, x-*coordinate*, y-*coordinate*. Each point in the rectangular coordinate system is denoted by an **ordered pair** (x, y) where x is called the **x-coordinate** and y is called the **y-coordinate**. The x- and y-coordinates indicate the location of the point relative to the axes.

x-*axis*, y-*axis*, *origin*, *quadrant*. The **x-axis** is the horizontal axis of a rectangular coordinate system, and the **y-axis** is the vertical axis. The point where the axes intersect is called the **origin**. The x- and y-axes partition the plane into four regions called **quadrants**. **2.** Equation, relationship **3.** *Vertical line test*. If a vertical line intersects a graph at more than one point, then that graph does not represent a function. **4.**

5. Piecewise **6.** d.

7. y decreases by 5 units. **8. (a)**

(b)

(c)

(d)

9. Origin **10.** $y = c$ where c

is a constant **11.** $x = c$ where c is a constant **12.** y-intercept, positive, negative **13.** Tax rates **14.** x-*intercept*, y-*intercept*. The point where a straight line crosses the x-axis is called the **x-intercept**; the point

where a straight line crosses the y-axis is called the **y-intercept**. **15.** 0 **16.** 0 **17.** *Step 1:* Find the y-intercept by setting $x = 0$ and solving the resulting equation for y.

Step 2: Find the x-intercept by setting $y = 0$ and solving the resulting equation for x.

Step 3: Connect the intercepts with a straightedge.
18. Place a straightedge at the origin and set it so that the slope is m. **19.** Cost; number of units produced.
20. Sales revenue; number of units produced. **21.** Profit; number of units produced. **22.** Variable cost per unit
23. *Fixed cost:* The cost of producing 0 units. These are costs that must be paid regardless of how few or how many units are produced. **24.** Unit price, demand **25.** Unit price, supply **26.** Consumption, income **27.** The MPC is the slope of a consumption function. The MPC indicates the portion spent of an additional dollar earned.

28. $y = C - \left(\dfrac{C - S}{n}\right)x$ where C = total cost of an asset
S = salvage value of the asset
n = number of years of asset life

The y-intercept, C, denotes the total cost of the asset. The slope, $(C - S)/n$, is the annual depreciation.
29. *Break-even point:* The point where total sales revenue = total cost. **30.** Set $R(x) = C(x)$ and solve for x.
31. Break-even point **32.** Set $P(x) = 0$ and solve for x.
33. Intersection point, demand **34.** The first coordinate is called the **equilibrium quantity**; the second coordinate is called the **equilibrium price**. The equilibrium price is the unit price at which supply = demand for a given product; the corresponding supply or demand is the equilibrium quantity.

• REVIEW EXERCISES

1. $f(0) = -2$
$f(1) = 2$
$f(3) = 10$

3. $f(0) = -1$
$f(1) = 2$
$f(3) = 14$

5. 4 **7.** $2x + h - 4$ **9.** $x \geq 4$ **11.** All real x such that $x \neq 7, x \neq -5$ **13.** Not a function
15.

17. Let x = price per share of stock

$$P(x) = \begin{cases} -4 & \text{if } 0 \le x \le 20 \\ x - 24 & \text{if } x > 20 \end{cases}$$

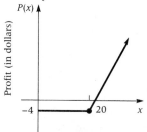

19. $m = 4$ **21.** $y = 5x - 17$ **23.** $(1, -3), (0, -5)$
25. Answers will vary.

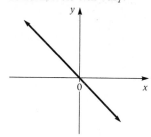   **27.**

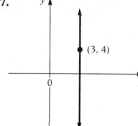

29. $x = 3$ **31.** Parallel   **33.**

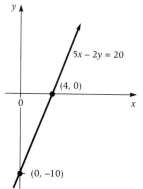

35.

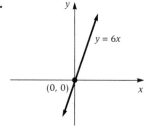

37. $C(x) = 30x + 1200$
$R(x) = 50x$
$P(x) = 20x - 1200$
$x = 60$, break-even point

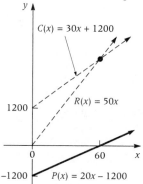

39. $P(x) = 0.4x - 2000$ **41.** $P(x) = 0.93x - 5600$
43. $P(x) = 4.4x - 7600$
$x = 1727$ units (nearest unit)
45. 1985 (nearest year)   **47. (a)** MPC = 0.9
For each dollar increase in disposable income, consumption increases by \$0.90. **(b)** MPS = 0.1
For each dollar increase in disposable income, savings increase by = 0.10. **(c)** $y = 0.9x + 40$

(d)

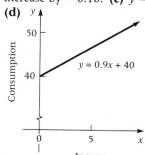

49. (a) $y = 80,000 - 15,000x$

(b)

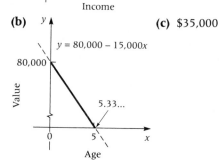

(c) \$35,000

• **CHAPTER 2**

SECTION 2-1

1.

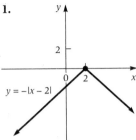

$y = -|x - 2|$

3.

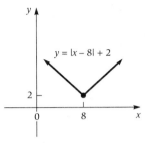

$y = |x - 8| + 2$

5.

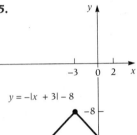

$y = -|x + 3| - 8$

7.

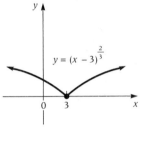

$y = (x - 3)^{\frac{2}{3}}$

9.

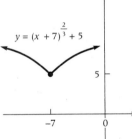

$y = (x + 7)^{\frac{2}{3}} + 5$

11.

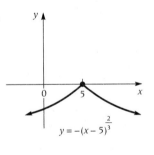

$y = -(x - 5)^{\frac{2}{3}}$

13.

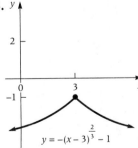

$y = -(x - 3)^{\frac{2}{3}} - 1$

15.

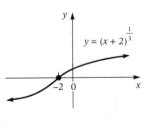

$y = (x + 2)^{\frac{1}{3}}$

17.

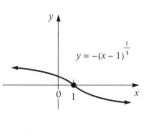

$y = (x - 2)^{\frac{1}{3}} + 9$

19.

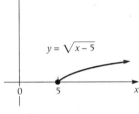

$y = -(x - 1)^{\frac{1}{3}}$

21.

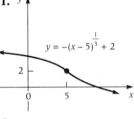

$y = -(x - 5)^{\frac{1}{3}} + 2$

23.

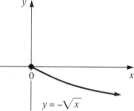

$y = \sqrt{x - 5}$

25.

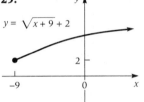

$y = \sqrt{x + 9} + 2$

27.

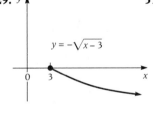

$y = -\sqrt{x}$

29.

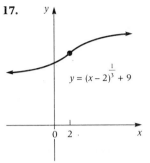

$y = -\sqrt{x - 3}$

31.

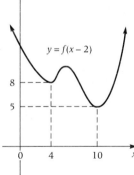

$y = f(x - 2)$

33

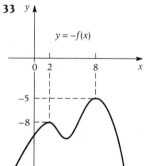

$y = -f(x)$

35.

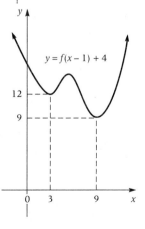

$y = f(x - 1) + 4$

37 $y = -f(x - 2) + 1$

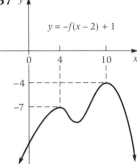

39. $y = -f(x) - 6$

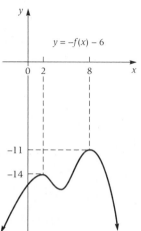

41. Odd   **43.** Odd   **45.** Odd

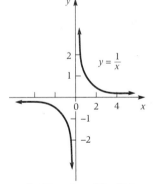

$y = x^3$

47. Odd

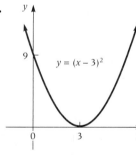

$y = \dfrac{1}{x}$

49. Shift upward 100 units   **51.** $10

SECTION 2-2

1.

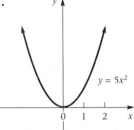

$y = 5x^2$

3.

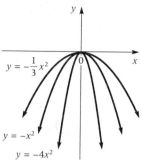

$y = -\dfrac{1}{3}x^2$

$y = -x^2$

$y = -4x^2$

5.

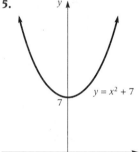

$y = x^2 + 7$

7.

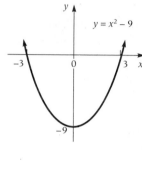

$y = x^2 - 9$

9.

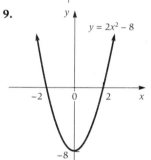

$y = 2x^2 - 8$

11.

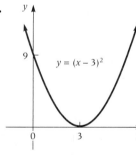

$y = (x - 3)^2$

13.

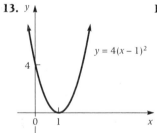

$y = 4(x - 1)^2$

15.

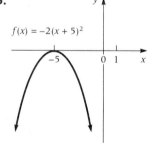

$f(x) = -2(x + 5)^2$

17.

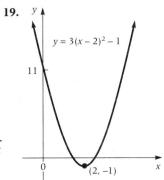

$y = 2(x-1)^2 + 3$

19.

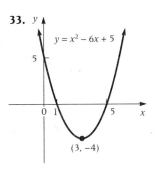

$y = 3(x-2)^2 - 1$

11

$(2, -1)$

33.

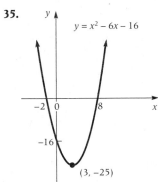

$y = x^2 - 6x + 5$

$(3, -4)$

35.

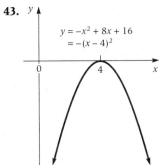

$y = x^2 - 6x - 16$

$(3, -25)$

21.

$y = -3(x+2)^2 - 5$

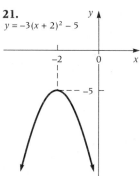

23.

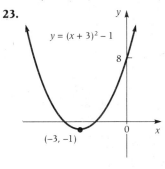

$y = (x+3)^2 - 1$

$(-3, -1)$

37.

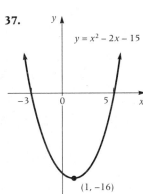

$y = x^2 - 2x - 15$

$(1, -16)$

39.

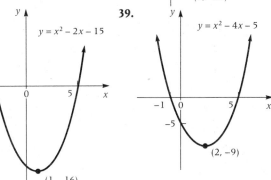

$y = x^2 - 4x - 5$

$(2, -9)$

25.

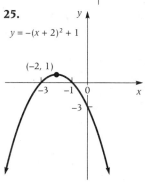

$y = -(x+2)^2 + 1$

$(-2, 1)$

27.

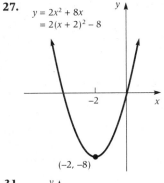

$y = 2x^2 + 8x$
$= 2(x+2)^2 - 8$

$(-2, -8)$

41.

$\left(\dfrac{3}{5}, \dfrac{9}{5}\right)$

$y = -5x^2 + 6x + 4$

43.

$y = -x^2 + 8x + 16$
$= -(x-4)^2$

29.

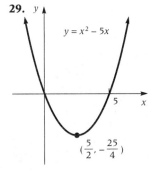

$y = x^2 - 5x$

$\left(\dfrac{5}{2}, -\dfrac{25}{4}\right)$

31.

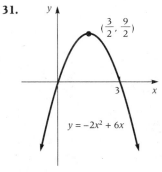

$\left(\dfrac{3}{2}, \dfrac{9}{2}\right)$

$y = -2x^2 + 6x$

45.

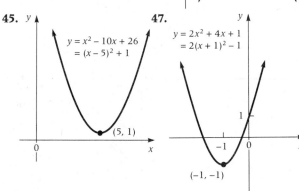

$y = x^2 - 10x + 26$
$= (x-5)^2 + 1$

$(5, 1)$

47.

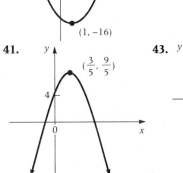

$y = 2x^2 + 4x + 1$
$= 2(x+1)^2 - 1$

$(-1, -1)$

49.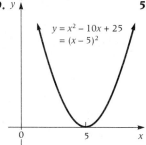

$y = x^2 - 10x + 25$
$= (x - 5)^2$

51.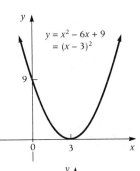

$y = x^2 - 6x + 9$
$= (x - 3)^2$

53.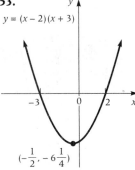

$y = (x - 2)(x + 3)$

$(-\frac{1}{2}, -6\frac{1}{4})$

55.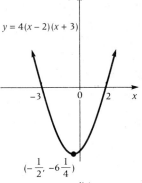

$y = 4(x - 2)(x + 3)$

$(-\frac{1}{2}, -6\frac{1}{4})$

57.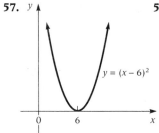

$y = (x - 6)^2$

59.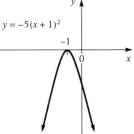

$y = -5(x + 1)^2$

61.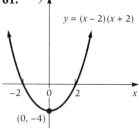

$y = (x - 2)(x + 2)$

$(0, -4)$

63.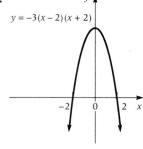

$y = -3(x - 2)(x + 2)$

SECTION 2-3

1. (a) $R(x) = -2x^2 + 100x$ **(b)**

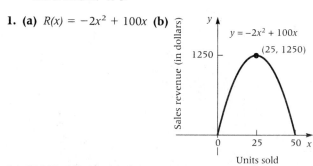

$y = -2x^2 + 100x$
$(25, 1250)$

(c) $1250 **(d)** 25 **(e)** $50

3. (a) $R(x) = -4x^2 + 320x$
(c) $6400 **(d)** 40 **(e)** $160
(b)

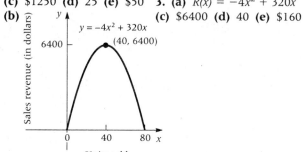

$y = -4x^2 + 320x$
$(40, 6400)$

5. (a) $R(x) = -6x^2 + 1800x$ **(b)**

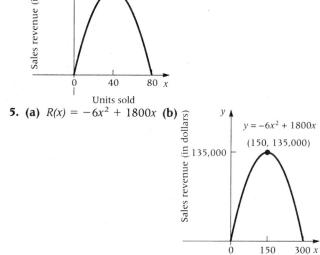

$y = -6x^2 + 1800x$
$(150, 135{,}000)$

(c) $135,000 **(d)** 150 **(e)** $900 **7. (a)** $R(x) = -x^2 + 1200x$

(b)

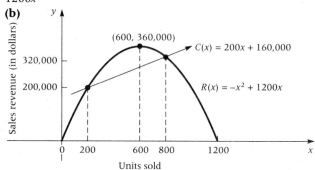

$(600, 360{,}000)$
$C(x) = 200x + 160{,}000$
$R(x) = -x^2 + 1200x$

(c) 200 and 800 **(d)** $200 \leq x \leq 800$ **(e)** $P(x) = -x^2 + 1000x - 160{,}000$

(f) 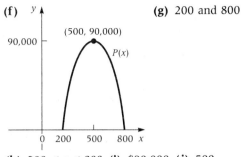   **(g)** 200 and 800

(h) $200 \le x \le 800$ **(i)** $90{,}000$ **(j)** 500

9. (a) $R(x) = -2x^2 + 2700x$

(b)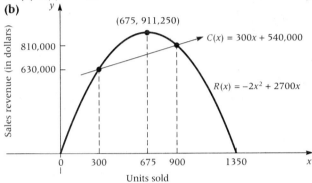

(c) 300 and 900 **(d)** $300 \le x \le 900$ **(e)** $P(x) = -2x^2 + 2400x - 540{,}000$ **(f)**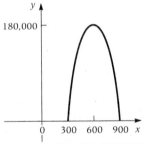

(g) 300 and 900 **(h)** $300 \le x \le 900$ **(i)** $180{,}000$ **(j)** 600

11. (a) 2 million units **(b)** $16

(c)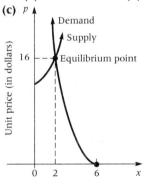

13. (a) 3 million units

(b) $25 **(c)**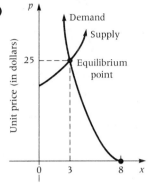

15. (a) $P(x) = 70x - \dfrac{x^2}{200}$ **(b)**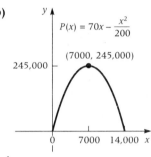

(c) $245{,}000 **(d)** 7000 barrels

17. (a) 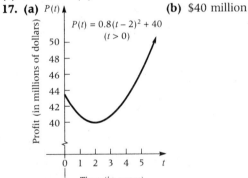   **(b)** $40 million

(c) $43.2 million **(d)** $47.2 million

19. (a) 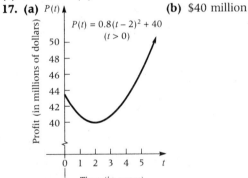   **(b)** 27.5 **(c)** 20

(d) $x = 15$, $y = 7.5$ **21. (a)**

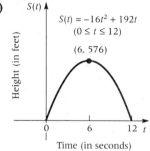

$S(t) = -16t^2 + 192t$
$(0 \leq t \leq 12)$
$(6, 576)$

Height (in feet)

Time (in seconds)

(b) 6 seconds, 576 ft **(c)** t = 0 sec and t = 12 sec
23. $(7, \frac{1}{2})$ **25.** $(1, 3\frac{1}{8})$ **27.** $(4, 7.5)$ **29.** $(0, 1)$
31. (a)

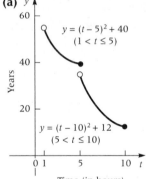

$y = (t - 5)^2 + 40$
$(1 < t \leq 5)$

Years

$y = (t - 10)^2 + 12$
$(5 < t \leq 10)$

Time (in hours)

(b) 44 **(c)** 41 **(d)** 28 **(e)** 16

SECTION 2-4

1. 1 **3.** 8 **5.** 3 **7.** 6
9. $f(x) = x^3$

x	-4	-3	-2	-1	0	1	2	3	4
$f(x)$	-64	-27	-8	-1	0	1	8	27	64

$f(-x) = -f(x)$
etc.

$f(x) = ax^n$
$f(-x) = a\,(-x)^n$ $n \geq 3$ and odd, $a > 0$
$\quad = -ax^n = -f(x)$
The graphs of an odd function $f(x) = ax^n$ resemble Figure 2-42.

11.

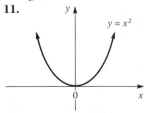

$y = x^2$

13.

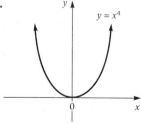

$y = x^4$

15.

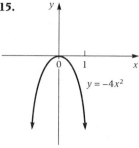

$y = -4x^2$

17.

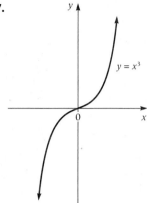

$y = x^3$

19.

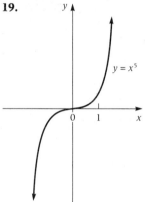

$y = x^5$

21.

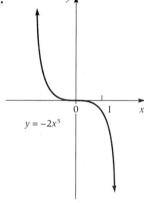

$y = -2x^5$

23. $f(x) = \dfrac{1}{x^3}$

x	-4	-3	-2	-1	0	1	2	3	4
$f(x)$	$-\dfrac{1}{64}$	$-\dfrac{1}{27}$	$-\dfrac{1}{8}$	-1	—	1	$\dfrac{1}{8}$	$\dfrac{1}{27}$	$\dfrac{1}{64}$

$f(-x) = -f(x)$
etc.

$f(x) = \dfrac{k}{x^n}$ n, odd positive; $k > 0$

$f(-x) = \dfrac{k}{(-x)^n}$

$\quad = -\dfrac{k}{x^n} = -f(x)$

The graphs of $f(x) = \dfrac{k}{x^n}$ (n, odd and positive) resemble Figure 2-47.

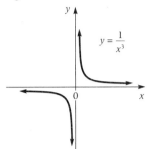
$y = \dfrac{1}{x^3}$

25.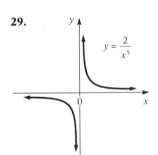
$y = \dfrac{3}{x^2}$

27.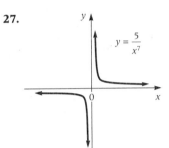
$y = \dfrac{5}{x^7}$

29.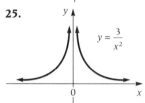
$y = \dfrac{2}{x^5}$

31.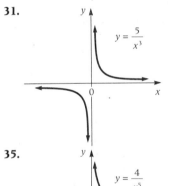
$y = \dfrac{5}{x^3}$

33.
$y = \dfrac{6}{x^8}$

35.
$y = \dfrac{4}{x^5}$

37.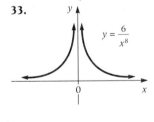
$y = -\dfrac{6}{x^8}$

39.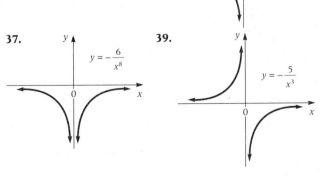
$y = -\dfrac{5}{x^3}$

41.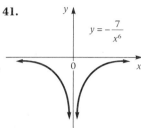
$y = -\dfrac{7}{x^6}$

43.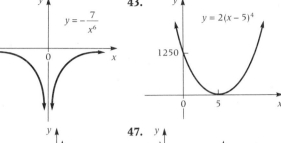
$y = 2(x-5)^4$
1250

45.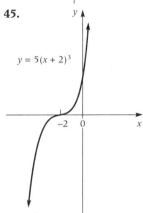
$y = 5(x+2)^3$

47.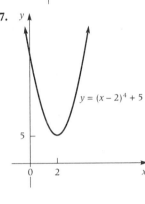
$y = (x-2)^4 + 5$
5

49.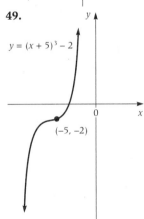
$y = (x+5)^3 - 2$
$(-5, -2)$

51.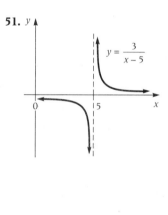
$y = \dfrac{3}{x-5}$

53.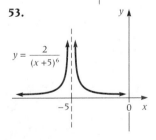
$y = \dfrac{2}{(x+5)^6}$

55.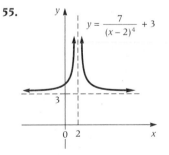
$y = \dfrac{7}{(x-2)^4} + 3$

57.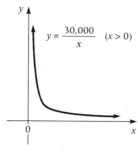
$y = \dfrac{2}{(x-3)^5} - 1$

59.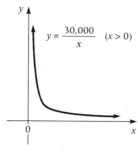
$y = \dfrac{30,000}{x}$ $(x > 0)$

(b)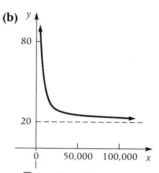

(b) 200 **(c)** 100 **(d)** 50

(c) $\overline{C}(1000) = 80$
$\overline{C}(10,000) = 26$
$\overline{C}(100,000) = 20.6$
Average cost decreases as production increases.
(d) 20

61. (a)

$y = \dfrac{200,000}{x}$
$(1000 \le x \le 5000)$

(b) 200 **(c)** 100 **(d)** 50

SECTION 2-5

1.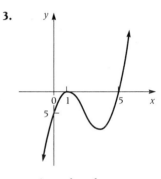
$f(x) = x^3 - 7x + 6$
$= (x - 1)(x + 3)(x - 2)$

3.
$f(x) = x^3 - 7x^2 + 11x - 5$
$= (x - 1)^2(x - 5)$

(e) 40 **63. (a)**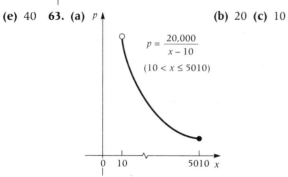

$p = \dfrac{20,000}{x - 10}$
$(10 < x \le 5010)$

(b) 20 **(c)** 10

5.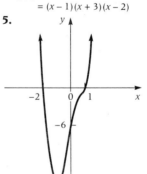
$y = 3x^4 - 3x^3 - 9x^2 + 15x - 6$
$= 3(x - 1)^3(x + 2)$

7.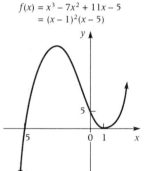
$f(x) = x^3 + 3x^2 - 9x + 5$
$= (x - 1)^2(x + 5)$

(d) 5 **(e)** 4 **65. (a)** $\overline{C}(x) = 50 + \dfrac{40,000}{x}$

(b)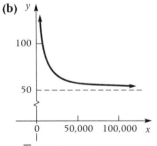

(c) $\overline{C}(1000) = 90$
$\overline{C}(10,000) = 54$
$\overline{C}(100,000) = 50.4$
Average cost decreases as production increases.

(d) 50 **67. (a)** $\overline{C}(x) = 20 + \dfrac{60,000}{x}$

9.

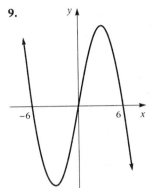

$f(x) = -x^3 + 36x$
$= -x(x^2 - 36)$

11.

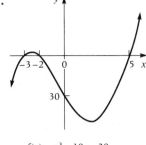

$f(x) = x^3 - 19x - 30$
$= (x + 2)(x - 5)(x + 3)$

21.

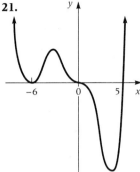

$f(x) = 2x^3(x - 5)(x + 6)^2$

23.

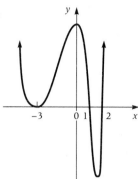

$y = (x - 2)(x + 3)^4(x - 1)$

13.

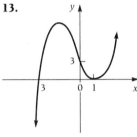

$f(x) = x^3 + x^2 - 5x + 3$
$= (x - 1)^2(x + 3)$

15.

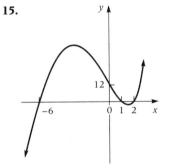

$y = x^3 + 3x^2 - 16x + 12$
$= (x - 1)(x + 6)(x - 2)$

25. (a)

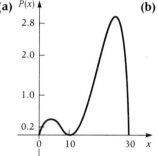

$P(x) = -0.0001x(x - 10)^2(x - 30)$

(b) 0, 10, and 20 **(c)** Yes

(d) Yes **(e)** \$2   **27. (a)** $V = x(10 - 2x)(20 - 2x)$

(b)

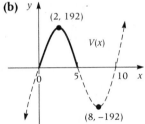

(c) $0 \le x \le 5$. Yes

(d) When $x \approx 2$.   **29. (a)**

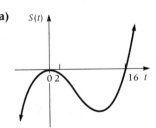

$S(t) = t^3 - 16t^2 = t^2(t - 16)$

(b) 275 units to the left **(c)** 1600 units to the right
(d) $t = 0$ and $t = 16$ sec

17.

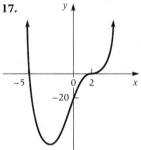

$f(x) = \dfrac{1}{2}(x - 2)^3(x + 5)$

19.

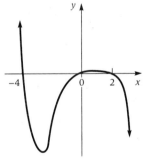

$f(x) = -3x^5(x - 2)^3(x + 4)$

SECTION 2-6

1.

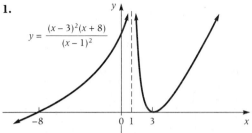

$$y = \frac{(x-3)^2(x+8)}{(x-1)^2}$$

3.

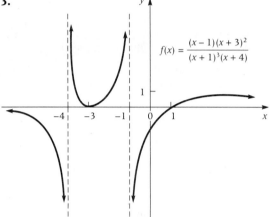

$$f(x) = \frac{(x-1)(x+3)^2}{(x+1)^3(x+4)}$$

5.

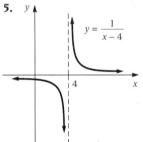

$$y = \frac{1}{x-4}$$

7.

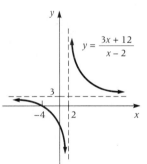

$$y = \frac{3x+12}{x-2}$$

9.

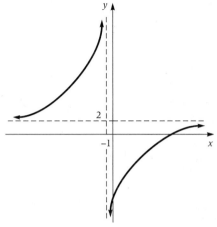

$$f(x) = \frac{2x-16}{x+1} = \frac{2(x-8)}{x+1}$$

11.

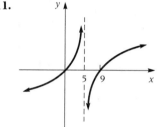

$$y = \frac{x^2-9x}{3x-15} = \frac{x(x-9)}{3(x-5)}$$

13. There are no vertical asymptotes since the denominator, $x^2 + 1$, is never zero.

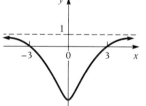

x	-2	-1	$-\frac{1}{2}$	0	$\frac{1}{2}$	1	2
$f(x)$	-1	-4	-7	-9	-7	-4	-1

15. (a)   **(b)** 400 **(c)** 200 **(d)** 390

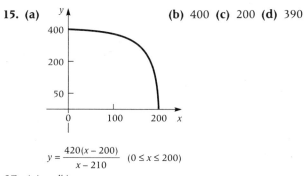

$$y = \frac{420(x-200)}{x-210} \quad (0 \le x \le 200)$$

17. (a)

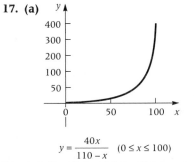

$$y = \frac{40x}{110-x} \quad (0 \le x \le 100)$$

(b) 4; 8.89; 33.3; 106.7; 400 (are in millions of dollars)

• EXTRA DIVIDENDS

1. For $y = 20x^2 + 10$, $S = 1600$
For $y = 100x - 90$, $S = 16,400$
$y = 20x^2 + 10$ is the better fit
3. $y = 48.4\,x + 768$

• CHAPTER HIGHLIGHTS

1. *Vertical shift*. Assume the graph of $y = f(x)$ is known. The graph of $y = f(x) + c$ is obtained by lifting the graph of $y = f(x)$ vertically by c units if $c > 0$ and lowering it by $|c|$ units if $c < 0$.   **2.** *Horizontal shift*. Assume that the graph of $y = f(x)$ is known. The graph of $y = f(x - c)$ is obtained by shifting the graph of $y = f(x)$ horizontally to the right by c units if $c > 0$ and horizontally to the left by $|c|$ units if $c < 0$.   **3.** *Reflection in the x-axis*. Assume the graph of $y = f(x)$ is known. The graph of $y = -f(x)$ is obtained by drawing the graph of $y = f(x)$ upside down.   **4.** The graph of a function $f(x)$ is symmetric with respect to the vertical axis if $f(-x) = f(x)$. This means that if (x, y) is on the graph of $f(x)$, then $(-x, y)$ is also on the graph. Such a function is called an **even function.**   **5.** If $f(-x) = -f(x)$, then $f(x)$ is an **odd function** and its graph is symmetric with respect to the origin.   **6.** $y = ax^2 + bx + c$ with $a \ne 0$; x-coordinate of the vertex is $-b/2a$; y-intercept $= (0, c)$.   **7.** If $a > 0$, the parabola opens up; if $a < 0$, the parabola opens down.   **8.** Set $y = 0$ and solve for x or use the quadratic formula $x = (-b \pm \sqrt{b^2 - 4ac})/2a$.   **9.** 2   **10.** Vertex

11. Sales revenue = (number of units sold)(unit price)
12. Profit = sales revenue − cost   **13.** Set $P(x) = 0$ and solve for x.   **14.** Set the supply equation equal to the demand equation and solve for x.   **15.** Time series
16. $f(x) = a_n x^n + a_{n-1}x^{n-1} + \ldots + a_1 x + a_0$
17. $n - 1, n$ **18.**

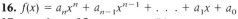
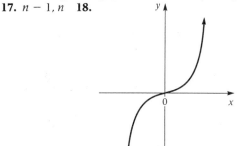

19.   **20.**

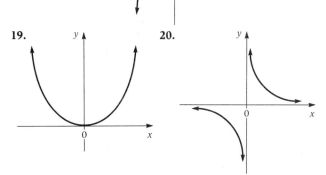

21.   **22.** Set the denominator = 0

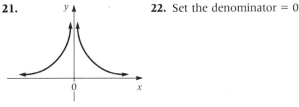

and solve for x. Verify that the numerator does not equal 0 at the solution values of x. If the numerator equals 0 at a solution value of x, then the graph of the rational function does not have a vertical asymptote at that solution value of x.   **23.** $\overline{C}(x) = C(x)/x$.   **24.** If the factor yielding the x-intercept has an odd exponent, then the graph of the function crosses the x-axis at that x-intercept. If the factor yielding the x-intercept has an even exponent, then the graph of the function is tangent to and does not cross the x-axis at that x-intercept.
25. *Step 1:* Find the y-intercept by setting $x = 0$ and solving for y. *Step 2:* Find any x-intercept(s) by setting $y = 0$ and solving for x. Apply the x-intercept rule to determine tangency or crossing. Draw a sign chart (optional). *Step 3:* Determine the behavior of the function as x gets more and more positive and, also, as x gets more and more negative. Use the highest powered term for this analysis.
26. *Step 1:* Find the y-intercept by setting $x = 0$ and solving

for *y. Step 2:* Find any *x*-intercept(s) by setting *y* = 0 and solving for *x*. This results in setting the numerator = 0 and solving for *x*. Apply the *x*-intercept rule to determine tangency or crossing. *Step 3:* Find any vertical asymptotes by setting the denominator = 0 and solving for *x*. Then, verify that the numerator ≠ 0 at the solution values of *x*. Apply the vertical asymptote rule. *Step 4:* Determine the behavior of the function as *x* gets more and more positive and, also, as *x* gets more and more negative. Use the quotient

$$\frac{\text{highest powered term of numerator}}{\text{highest powered term of denominator}}$$

for this analysis. **27.** If the exponent of the factor yielding the vertical asymptote is even, the graph approaches the same end of the vertical asymptote from both sides. If the exponent of the factor yielding the vertical asymptote is odd, the graph approaches different ends of the vertical asymptote from both sides.

• REVIEW EXERCISES

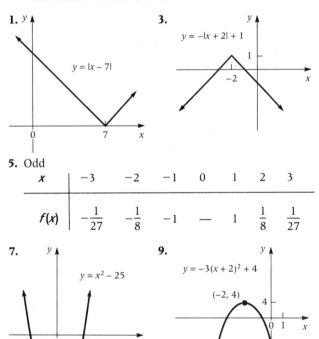

1. $y = |x - 7|$

3. $y = -|x + 2| + 1$

5. Odd

x	-3	-2	-1	0	1	2	3
$f(x)$	$-\frac{1}{27}$	$-\frac{1}{8}$	-1	—	1	$\frac{1}{8}$	$\frac{1}{27}$

7. $y = x^2 - 25$

9. $y = -3(x + 2)^2 + 4$, $(-2, 4)$

11. 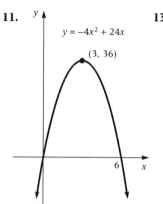 $y = -4x^2 + 24x$, $(3, 36)$

13. 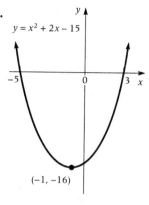 $y = x^2 + 2x - 15$, $(-1, -16)$

15. 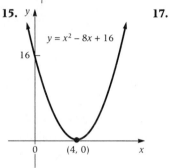 $y = x^2 - 8x + 16$, $(4, 0)$

17. 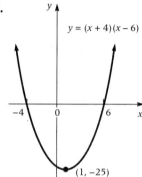 $y = (x + 4)(x - 6)$, $(1, -25)$

19. (a) $R(x) = -2x^2 + 140x$ **(b)**

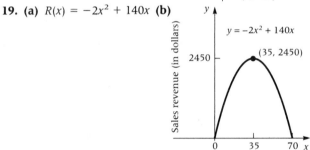

$y = -2x^2 + 140x$, $(35, 2450)$

(c) \$2450 **(d)** 35 units **(e)** \$70 **21. (a)** 1 million units **(b)** \$9 **(c)**

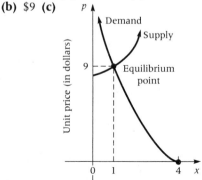

23.

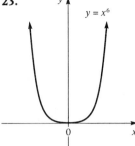

$y = x^6$

25.

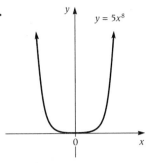

$y = 5x^8$

37.

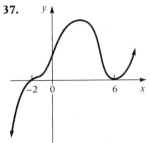

$f(x) = (x + 2)^3(x - 6)^2$

39.

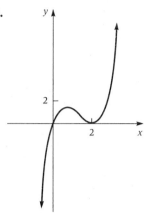

$f(x) = x^3 - 4x^2 + 4x$
$= x(x - 2)^2$

27.

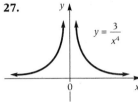

$y = \dfrac{3}{x^4}$

29.

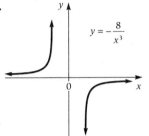

$y = -\dfrac{8}{x^3}$

41.

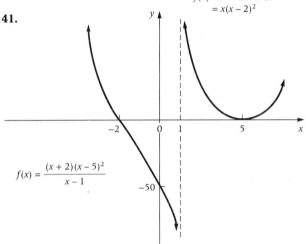

$f(x) = \dfrac{(x + 2)(x - 5)^2}{x - 1}$

31.

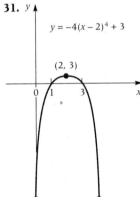

$y = -4(x - 2)^4 + 3$

$(2, 3)$

33.

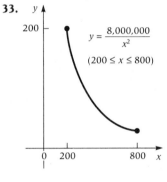

200

$y = \dfrac{8{,}000{,}000}{x^2}$

$(200 \le x \le 800)$

(b) 200 **(c)** 22.2 **(d)** 12.5

35. (a) $\overline{C}(x) = 800 + \dfrac{480{,}000}{x},\ x > 0$

(b)

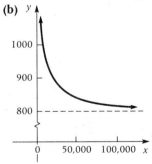

$\overline{C}(x) = 800 + \dfrac{480{,}000}{x} \quad (x > 0)$

(c) $1040; $848; $804.80 **(d)** $800

43.

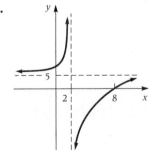

$f(x) = \dfrac{5x - 40}{x - 2} = \dfrac{5(x - 8)}{x - 2}$

45.

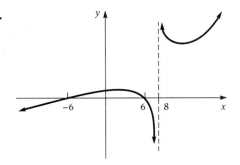

$$f(x) = \frac{x^2 - 36}{x - 8} = \frac{(x-6)(x+6)}{x-8}$$

• CHAPTER 3

SECTION 3-1

1. $(0,1)$; $y = 0$

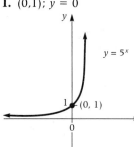

3. $(0,1)$; $y = 0$

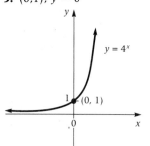

5. $(0,2)$; $y = 0$

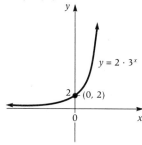

7. $(0,-4)$; $y = 0$

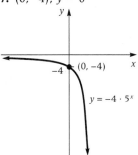

9. $(0,-3)$; $y = 0$

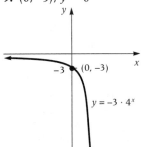

11. $(0,7)$; $y = 0$

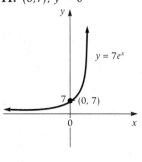

13. $(0,-3)$; $y = 0$

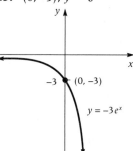

15. $(0,-10)$; $y = 0$

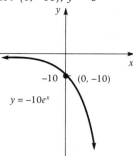

17. $(0,5)$; $y = 8$

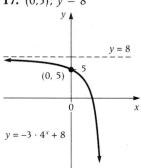

19. $(0,3)$; $y = -1$

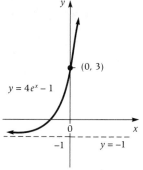

21. $(0,-7)$; $y = -5$

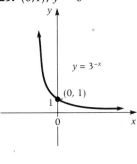

23. $(0,1)$; $y = 0$

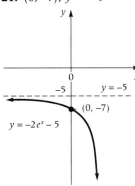

25. $(0,4)$; $y = 0$

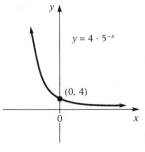

27. $(0,3)$; $y = 0$

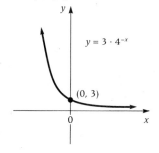

29. $(0,-2)$; $y = 0$

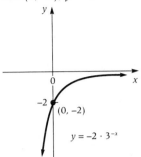

31. $(0,3)$; $y = 0$

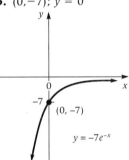

45. $(0,0)$; $y = 10$

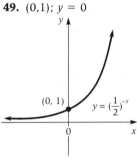

47. $(0,1)$; $y = 0$

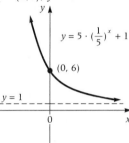

33. $(0,10)$; $y = 0$

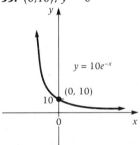

35. $(0,-7)$; $y = 0$

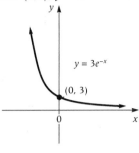

49. $(0,1)$; $y = 0$

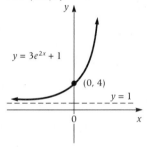

51. $(0,6)$; $y = 1$

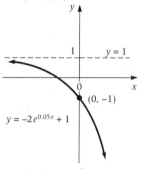

37. $(0,7)$ $y = 5$

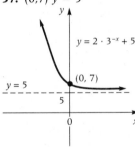

39. $(0,5)$; $y = 1$

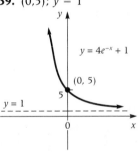

53. $(0,4)$; $y = 1$

55. $(0,-1)$; $y = 1$

41. $(0,28)$; $y = 30$

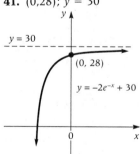

43. $(0,60)$; $y = 30$

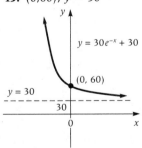

57. $(0,10)$; $y = 0$

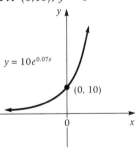

59. $(0,7)$; $y = 0$

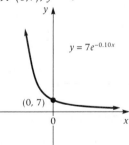

61. $(0,0)$; $y = 10$

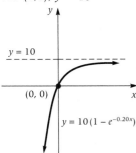

$y = 10$

$(0, 0)$

$y = 10(1 - e^{-0.20x})$

63. $(0,-8)$; $y = 0$

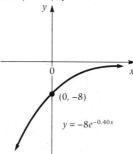

$(0, -8)$

$y = -8e^{-0.40x}$

65. (a) $y = 500,000(3^t)$ **(b)**

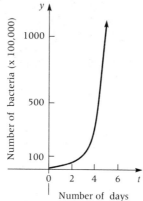

Number of bacteria (x 100,000)

1000

500

100

0   2   4   6 t

Number of days

(c) $500,000(3^4) = 40,500,000$ **(d)** $500,000(3^6) = 3.645 \times 10^8$ **67. (a)**

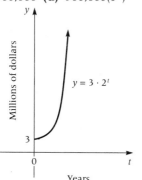

Millions of dollars

$y = 3 \cdot 2^t$

3

0   t

Years

(b) \$3 million; \$6 million; \$12 million

69. (a)

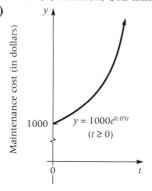

Maintenance cost (in dollars)

1000

$y = 1000e^{0.05t}$

$(t \geq 0)$

0   t

(b) \$1105.17

71. (a)

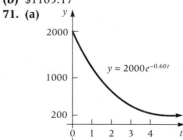

y

2000

$y = 2000e^{-0.60t}$

1000

200

0   1   2   3   4 t

(b) 2000 grams **(c)** 1481.6 grams **(d)** 330.6 grams

73. (a)

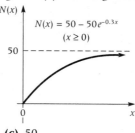

$N(x)$

$N(x) = 50 - 50e^{-0.3x}$

$(x \geq 0)$

50

0   x

(b) 38.8 **(c)** 50

75. (a)

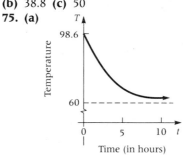

T

98.6

Temperature

60

0   5   10 t

Time (in hours)

(b) 60° **(c)** 94.9°

77. (a)

y

80

Percent of market penetration

60

40

20

0   5   10 x

Years

(b) 65.2% **(c)** 79.9% **(d)** 80%

SECTION 3-2

1. $\log_5 25 = 2$ **3.** $\log_2 64 = 6$ **5.** $\log_{10} 0.01 = -2$
7. $\log_t s = w$ **9.** $\log_b N = x + y$ **11.** 2 **13.** 0 **15.** 1
17. 1 **19.** 3 **21.** 5 **23.** 2 **25.** 5 **27.** 0 **29.** 0 **31.** 1

33. 3 **35.** 5 **37.** (1,0)

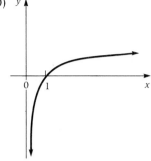

39. 0.5441 **41.** 1.6902 **43.** 1.7481 **45.** 0.1003
47. 0.5731 **49.** 0.9956 **51.** 2.5694 **53.** 4.5694
55. −0.4306 **57.** −2.4306 **59.** 1.791759
61. −0.405465 **63.** 2.079441 **65.** 0.549306
67. −0.287682 **69.** 0.9410 **71.** 3.6776 **73.** −0.0969
75. 2.3026 **77.** −1.8971 **79.** 4.3820 **81.** 8.0297126
83. 8029.7126 **85.** 256,980.4 **87.** 22.9615 **89.** 5.4997
91. $e^{1.22378}$ **93.** $e^{1.7047}$ **95.** $\log x + \log y - \log z$

97. $2 \log x + \log y$ **99.** $\frac{1}{2}(\log x + \log y)$

101. (a) $108,788.9 thousand
  $112,875.5 thousand
  $119,879.3 thousand
  $124,728.3 thousand
(b) $355.6 thousand; If the company increases its
advertising expenditures from 20 to 21 thousand dollars,
sales increase by $355.6 thousand. **(c)** $246.2 thousand
103. (a) $13.22 thousand; revenue from the sale of 1 unit.
  $16.13 thousand; revenue from the sale of 2
  units.
  $20.04 thousand; revenue from the sale of 5
  units.
  $23.03 thousand; revenue from the sale of 10
  units.
(b) $0.41 thousand; If the company increases its sales from
10 units to 11 units, revenue will increase by $0.41
thousand. **(c)** $0.21 thousand **105. (a)** 2000 **(b)** 5.49
days **(c)** 6.93 days **107. (a)** 13.9 years **(b)** 22.0 years

109. (a) $y = \dfrac{\ln p - 1}{0.3}$ **(b)** 4,341,950

SECTION 3-3

1. $a = 3.19$, $b = 1.37$ **3.** $a = 5.71$, $b = 1.52$ **5.** $a = 9.72$,
$b = 1.54$ **7. (a)** $y = 0.997(1.163)^x$ **(b)** 5.25
9. (a) $y = 2.965(1.157)^x$ **(b)** 9.52

• CHAPTER HIGHLIGHTS

1. 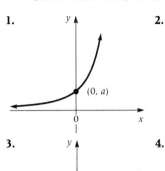 **2.**

3. 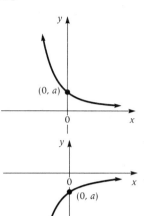 **4.**

5. *Step 1:* Begin with the graph of $y = ab^x$ or $y = ab^{-x}$.
Step 2: Vertical Shift. If $c > 0$, lift the graph of Step 1
vertically by c units. If $c < 0$, lower the graph of Step 1
vertically by $|c|$ units. **6.** $y = ae^{-kt} + c$ where y denotes the
temperature of the cooling object after t units of time and c
denotes the temperature of the medium surrounding the
cooling object. The letters a and k represent constants
associated with the cooling object.
7. *Modified exponential model:* $y = A - Be^{-mx}$

Logistic growth model: $y = \dfrac{A}{1 + Be^{-mx}}$

where y denotes the percentage of the market penetrated
by the product x years after it has been introduced; A and B
are constants. **8.** Exponent **9.** Natural (or Napierian)
10. Common **11.** $\ln b$ **12.** 1 **13.** Let x, y, and b be
positive real numbers with $b = 1$. Let p be any real
number.
Property 1: $\log_b xy = \log_b x + \log_b y$
The logarithm of a product of two numbers equals the sum
of their logarithms. Example: $\log(5 \cdot 8) = \log 5 + \log 8$
Property 2: $\log_b(x/y) = \log_b x - \log_b y$
The logarithm of a quotient of two numbers equals the
difference of their logarithms. *Example:* $\log(7/9) = \log 7 - \log 9$
Property 3: $\log_b x^p = p \cdot \log_b x$
The logarithm of the pth power of a number equals p times
the logarithm of the number. *Example:* $\log 5^3 = 3 \log 5$
Property 4: $\log_b b = 1$
The logarithm of its base equals 1. *Example:* $\log_5 5 = 1$
Property 5: $\log_b 1 = 0$.
The logarithm of 1 equals 0. *Example:* $\log_8 1 = 0$
14. $\log y = \log a + x \cdot \log b$ **15.** straight line

• **REVIEW EXERCISES**

1.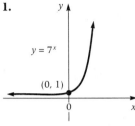

3.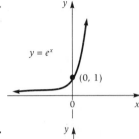

5.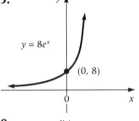

7.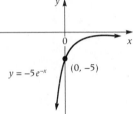

9.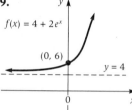

11.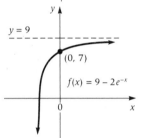

13.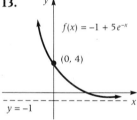

15.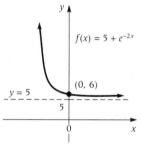

17. (a)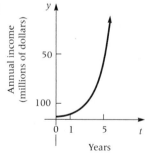

(b) $36.9 million
  $100.4 million
  $742.1 million

19. (a)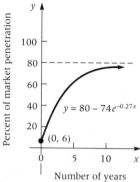

(b) 47% **(c)** 75% **(d)** 80% **21.** $\log 10{,}000 = 4$
23. $\ln y = x$ **25.** 2 **27.** 0 **29.** 1 **31.** -0.0131
33. 7.7179 **35.** 36,307.8 **37.** $e^{1.5260563}$
39. $\log s + \log t - \log r$ **41.** $5(\log u + \log v)$
43. $\log u + \log v$ **45.**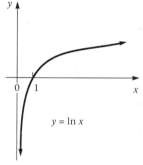

47. $a = 2.10$, $b = 1.95$
  $y = 2.10(1.95)^x$

• **CHAPTER 4**

SECTION 4-1

1. $210; $1210 **3.** $200; $5200 **5.** $60; $2060
7. (a) $S = 10{,}000 + 900t$ **(b)**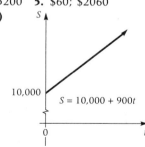

(c) $900 (the slope of the graph) **9.** $6779.66
11. $12,500 **13.** $19,607.84 **15.** $9700 **17.** $4850
19. $28,200 **21.** 9.27835% **23.** 6.18557%
25. 9.57447% **27.** $8510.64 **29.** $13,333.33
31. $9473.68 **33.** $10,494 **35.** $14,208.60
37. $32,007 **39.** $9433.96 **41.** $6666.67

43. (a) $2700 **(b)** $3300 **(c)** 16.3634%
45. (a) $5119.45 **(b)** 7.16736% **47.** $612
49. (a) $21,965 **(b)** $1035 **51.** $29,415

SECTION 4-2

1. $2208.04; $1208.04 **3.** $14,326.78; $6326.78
5. $6348.67; $1348.67 **7.** $4836.68; $1836.68
9. $5404.51 **11.** $2941.34 **13.** $1930.93 **15.** $5827.57
17. $4165.78 **19. (a)** $22,080.40 **(b)** $12,080.40
21. $1326.65 **23.** $24,405.82 **25.** $1879.82
27. $744.09 **29. (a)** $7013.80 **(b)** $8884.87
31. 6.09% **33.** 12.6825% **35.** 11.72 ≈ 12 years
37. 9.0065 ≈ 9 years **39.** 13.87 ≈ 14 years
41. 17.5 years **43.** 1.232926 ≈ 1.23
45. 1.489354 ≈ 1.49 **47.** 1.197031 ≈ 1.20
49. 1.309921 ≈ 1.31 **51.** 1.377079 ≈ 1.38
53. $14,917.59 **55.** $40,530.03 **57.** 8.08%
59. 5.92635% **61.** 8.5% compounded daily
63. 8.75% compounded monthly **65.** $7459.12
67. $8099.15 **69.** $4965.85 **71.** $3477.43
73. 7.25082% **75.** 9.41743%

SECTION 4-3

1. 312 **3.** 38,227 **5.** $75,401.26 **7.** 165,329.77
9. $45,632.79 **11.** $77,663.30 **13.** $173,596.26
15. $46,545.45 **17. (a)** $49,598.93 **(b)** $19,598.93
19. $6183.48 **21.** $6122.26 **23.** $16,770.91
25. 228.80304 **27.** 376.0953 **29.** $48,380.17
31. $48,783.34

SECTION 4-4

1. $56,741.78 **3.** $29,754.95 **5.** $109,161.26
7. $57,876.61 **9.** $30,647.60 **11.** $112,436.10
13. $24,924.42 **15.** 6540.57 **17.** $15,204.29
19. $19,327.03 **21.** $6671.38 **23.** 41.659417
25. 103.62462 **27.** $25,056.12 **29.** 25,202.28
31. $35,192.67

SECTION 4-5

1. $1440.49 **3.** $704.62 **5.** $3721.75 **7.** $699.78
9. $7712.77 **11.** $1836.62 **13.** $5886.54 **15.** $2201.25
17. $411.57 **19.** $352.31 **21.** $1956.11
23. (a) $12,928.25
(b) $8287

(c) Sinking fund schedule

Payment number	Payment	Interest	Total
1	$12,928.25	$0	$12,928.25
2	12,928.25	1292.83	27,149.33
3	12,928.25	2714.93	42,792.51
4	12,928.25	4279.25	60,000.01

25. (a) $23,138.32
(b) $25,691.60
(c) Amortization schedule

Payment number	Payment	Interest	Principal reduction	Balance
0				$90,000.00
1	$23,138.32	$8100.00	$15,038.32	74,961.68
2	23,138.32	6746.55	16,391.77	58,569.91
3	23,138.32	5271.29	17,867.03	40,702.88
4	23,138.32	3663.26	19,475.06	21,227.82
5	23,138.32	1910.50	21,227.82	0.00
		25,691.60		

(d) $58,569.91
27. (a) $804.62 **(b)** $96,857.75 **29. (a)** $1080.15
(b) $194,427.00; $104,427.90 **(c)** $48,558.19

31. For a loan of L dollars: $R_L = \dfrac{L}{a_{\overline{n}|i}}$

For a loan of $2L$ dollars: $R_{2L} = \dfrac{2L}{a_{\overline{n}|i}} = 2R_L$ $\Bigg\}$ $R_{2L} = 2R_L$

Let $A = R \cdot a_{\overline{n}|i}$, with fixed values of n and i. Then, $R = \dfrac{A}{a_{\overline{n}|i}} = cA$, where $c = \dfrac{1}{a_{\overline{n}|i}}$ is a constant. If $A = kL$, $R = c(kL) = k(cL)$. Hence, the periodic payment is proportional to the amount of the loan. **33.** For interest rate of 9.75% compounded monthly: $859.15; $209,294. For interest rate of 10.75% compounded monthly: $933.48; $236,052.80 **35.** $430,941.61 **37.** $1330.36 **39.** $3105.56

SECTION 4-6

1. $5127.98 **3.** $2191.05 **5.** $1914.80 **7.** $3656.26
9. $205.53 **11.** $2515.06 (years 1-2); $3772.59 (years 3-5) **13.** 7 quarters of deferment **15.** 17 monthly periods of deferment **17.** 21 quarterly periods of deferment **19.** $8797.85 **21.** $8417.48 **23.** $5120.61
25. $26,952.80; $14,836.16 **27.** $584,109.57; $287,343.90 **29.** $10,972.49 **31.** $17,274.71
33. $1109.41 **35.** $8142.58; $6427.83 **37.** $16,211.10; $6,847.74 **39.** $92.54 **41.** $1719.52

• EXTRA DIVIDENDS

1. $10,734.80 **3.** $36,663.67 **5.** $109,375 **7. (b)** Less than 10%, but more than 0% **9.** $80,640

• CHAPTER HIGHLIGHTS

1. $I = Prt$ where I is the amount of simple interest, P is the principal, r is the annual rate, and t is the time in years.
2. Total amount, S, is the sum of principal and interest and is given by the formula $S = P + I$ or by the equivalent formula $S = P(1 + rt)$. **3.** Present value (or principal) is the amount of money needed now that will result in a specified future value at a given interest rate. Present value (assuming simple interest) is determined by the formula $P = S/(1 + rt)$. **4.** Simple interest is based on the principal whereas simple discount is based on the maturity value.
5. $D = Sdt$ where D is the amount of simple discount, S is the maturity value, d is the discount rate, and t is the time in years. **6.** The amount of money received by a borrower using a discount note is called the **proceeds.** Proceeds, B, are determined by the formula $B = S - D$ or by the equivalent formula $B = S(1 - dt)$. **7.** Maturity value
8. $S = P(1 + i)^n$ where S is the compound amount, i is the interest rate per period, and n is the total number of conversion periods.

$$\underbrace{|\,1\,|\,2\,|\,3\,|\ldots\ldots|\,n\,|}_{}$$
$$P \longrightarrow\!| S = P(1 + i)^n$$

9. The **interest rate per conversion period** is the annual rate divided by the number of conversion periods per year. It is given by the formula $i = r/m$ where r is the annual rate and m is the number of conversion periods per year.
10. The **total number of conversion periods,** n, is the number of conversion periods (or compoundings) throughout the duration of the investment. The formula for n is $n = mt$ where m is the number of conversion periods (or compoundings) per year and t is the duration (time) of the investment in years. **11.** $P = S(1 + i)^{-n}$ where P is the present value, S is the future value, i is the interest rate per conversion period, and n is the total number of conversion periods.

$$\underbrace{|\,1\,|\,2\,|\,3\,|\ldots\ldots|\,n\,|}_{}$$
$$P = S(1 + i)^{-n}\,|\!\longleftarrow\!\longrightarrow S$$

12. If the compound amount of P dollars, invested for a given length of time at an annual rate r compounded m times a year equals the compound amount of P dollars invested for the same time period at an annual rate s compounded k times per year, then the rates are said to be *equivalent*. The following equation is used to find equivalent rates: $(1 + r/m)^m = (1 + s/k)^k$ where r, s, m, and k are defined in the preceding sentence. **13.** The **effective rate** is the rate s compounded annually that is equivalent to an annual rate r compounded m times per year. The effective rate is given by $s = (1 + r/m)^m - 1$. **14.** $S = Pe^{rt}$ where S is the future value, P is the present value (or principal), r is the annual rate compounded continuously, and t is the duration (time) of the investment in years.

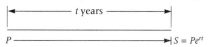

15. $P = Se^{-rt}$ where S is the future value, P is the present value (or principal), r is the annual rate compounded continuously, and t is the duration (time) of the investment in years.

16. $s = e^r - 1$ **17.** An **annuity** is a series of equal payments made at equal intervals of time. **18.** If each payment of an annuity is made at the end of a payment period, the annuity is called an **ordinary annuity.** If each payment of an annuity is made at the beginning of a payment period, the annuity is called an **annuity due.**
19. The **total amount** (or future value) or an ordinary annuity is the sum of the compound amounts of the individual payments and is determined by the formula

$$S = R\left[\frac{(1 + i)^n - 1}{i}\right]$$
$$= R \cdot s_{\overline{n}|i}$$

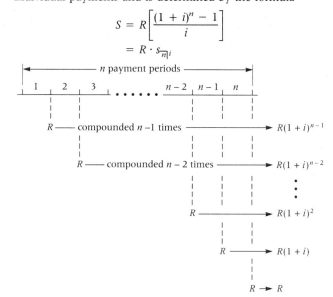

20.
$$S = R\left[\frac{(1 + i)^{n+1} - 1}{i} - 1\right]$$

Here, i is the interest rate per conversion period, n is the total number of conversion periods, and R is the periodic payment.

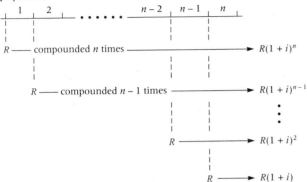

21. The **present value,** A, of an ordinary annuity is the sum of the present values of the individual payments and is determined by the formula

$$A = R\left[\frac{1 - (1 + i)^{-n}}{i}\right]$$
$$= R \cdot a_{\overline{n}|i}$$

22.
$$A = R\left[\frac{1 - (1 + i)^{-(n-1)}}{i} + 1\right]$$
$$= R[a_{\overline{n-1}|i} + 1]$$

Here, i is the interest rate per conversion period, n is the total number of conversion periods, and R is the periodic payment.

23. If a person desires to accumulate a sum of money by making periodic deposits into a fund so that, at the end of a specified time period, the deposits plus the interest earned equal the desired accumulated amount, the fund is called a **sinking fund.** The periodic payment is determined by the formula $R = S/s_{\overline{n}|i}$ where S is the desired accumulated amount, i is the interest rate per conversion period, n is the total number of conversion periods, and $s_{\overline{n}|i} = [(1 + i)^n - 1]/i$. **24.** The interest for a given period is the product of i and the total value of the fund at the beginning of the period. **25.** To repay a loan by an annuity is to **amortize** the loan. The formula for determining the periodic payment is $R = A/a_{\overline{n}|i}$ where A is the amount of the loan, i is the interest rate per conversion period, n is the total number of conversion periods, and $a_{\overline{n}|i} = [1 - (1 + i)^{-n}]/i$. **26. (a)** The **interest** for each period is determined by multiplying i times the previous period's balance. **(b)** The **balance** is the difference between the previous period's balance and the principal reduction for the given period. **27.** Find the present value of the remaining annuity. **28.** *Step 1:* Compute the simple interest on the original loan amount (the principal) for the term of the loan. *Step 2:* Add the interest to the original loan amount. *Step 3:* Divide the resulting sum by the number of payments. This method results in a larger periodic payment than that determined by using the annuity formula. This is because the add-on-interest method entails computation of interest on the original loan amount for the entire term of the loan despite the fact that payments are made throughout the term of the loan. **29.** $(1 + i)^n$ where i is the interest rate per period and n is the number of periods that the payment is to be brought forward. **30.** $(1 + i)^{-n}$ where i is the interest rate per period and n is the number of periods that the payment is to be brought back. **31.** $s_{\overline{n}|i}$ where i is the interest rate per period and n is the number of payments in the annuity. **32.** $a_{\overline{n}|i}$ where i is the interest rate per period and n is the number of payments in the annuity. **33.** A **variable annuity** is an annuity where, at some point, later payments differ from earlier payments. **34.** A **deferred annuity** is an annuity whose payments begin later than at the end of the first period. **35.** A **complex annuity** is an annuity where the payment period does not coincide with the conversion (or interest) period. A **simple annuity** is an annuity where the payment period does coincide with the conversion (or interest) period. **36.** Interest rate

• **REVIEW EXERCISES**

1. (a) $540 **(b)** $1540 **3. (a)** $8000 **(b)** $18,000
5. (a) $8333.33 **(b)** $8250; $250 **7.** $23,699.19
9. $5,536.76 **11.** $30,777.84 **13.** $9577.74
15. 9.3807% **17.** 8.2195% **19.** $19,486.24
21. $14,552.57 **23.** $5950.99 **25.** $143.33
27. $6831.90 **29.** $331.11 **31.** $39,927.10
33. $5525.20 **35.** $2526.17 **37.** $122.44 **39.** $8926.48
41. $8094.06 **43.** $7630.85 **45.** $7681.19
47. $3537.08; $2380.35 **49.** $60,852.60; $38,179.68
51. $2133.77

• CHAPTER 5

SECTION 5-1

1. $(-3, -4)$ **3.** $\left(\dfrac{1}{2}, 6\right)$ **5.** $(5, 2)$ **7.** $\left(\dfrac{10}{7}, \dfrac{45}{7}\right)$ **9.** $(6, 4)$
11. $(2, 3)$ **13.** $(3, 15)$ **15.** $(7, 48)$ **17.** $(-1, 2)$
19. $(-1, 1)$

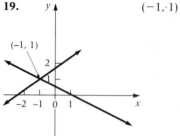

21. $\left(\dfrac{97}{28}, \dfrac{-19}{28}\right)$

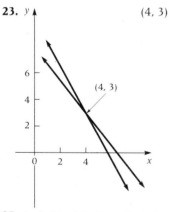

$\left(\dfrac{97}{28}, \dfrac{-19}{28}\right)$

23. $(4, 3)$

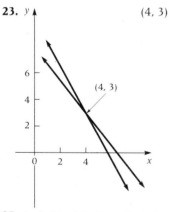

$(4, 3)$

25. $(-5, 2)$ **27.** $(1, -5)$ **29.** $(1, -3)$ **31.** $(-1, -2)$
33. Eq. (1) $5x - 7y = 70 \rightarrow 10x - 14y = 140$
Eq. (2) $-10x + 14y = 120$ $\underline{-10x + 14y = 120}$
$0 = 260$

Eq. (1) becomes $y = \dfrac{5}{7}x - 10$

Eq. (2) becomes $y = \dfrac{5}{7}x + \dfrac{60}{7}$

Lines of equal slope with different intercepts.

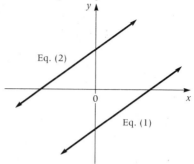

35. No solution   **37.** No solution   **39.** No solution
41. 2 lb meat, 1 lb spinach   **43.** 4000 wagons, 1000 cars
45. $(400, 10,000)$; When 400 units are sold, the company's
sale revenue and cost are equal at $10,000.   **47.** $25,000
in corporate bonds, $75,000 in U.S. Treasury bonds
49. 5 lb cashews, 15 lb peanuts   **51. (a)** 100,000 units
(b) Machine I; $600,000 **(c)** Machine II; $880,000

SECTION 5-2

1. $\begin{bmatrix} 2 & 7 & | & 9 \\ -1 & 4 & | & 15 \end{bmatrix}$ **3.** $\begin{bmatrix} 3 & 0 & | & -1 \\ 4 & 3 & | & 7 \end{bmatrix}$

5. $\begin{bmatrix} 1 & 2 & 5 & | & 6 \\ 2 & -3 & -8 & | & 4 \\ -1 & 4 & 5 & | & 9 \end{bmatrix}$

7. $\begin{bmatrix} 5 & -7 & 0 & | & 4 \\ 0 & 3 & 0 & | & 9 \\ 1 & 0 & 1 & | & 15 \end{bmatrix}$

9. $\begin{aligned} 4x_1 + 8x_2 &= 5 \\ -2x_1 + 6x_2 &= 0 \end{aligned}$ **11.** $\begin{aligned} -x_1 + x_2 + 2x_3 &= 3 \\ 4x_1 \qquad -x_3 &= 5 \\ 2x_1 + x_2 - x_3 &= 6 \end{aligned}$

13. $\begin{aligned} x_1 \quad + x_3 &= 2 \\ x_2 \qquad &= 3 \\ x_3 &= 5 \end{aligned}$ **15.** Not a final tableau
17. Final tableau; $x_1 = 8$, $x_2 = 3$ **19.** Final tableau; $x_1 = 2$,
$x_2 = -4$, $x_3 = 5$ **21.** Not a final tableau
23. Let $x_1 =$ no. of conservative sweaters
$x_2 =$ no. of sporty sweaters
$x_3 =$ no. of practical sweaters
$5x_1 + 2x_2 + 3x_3 = 660$ (cutting)
$3x_1 + 2x_2 + 4x_3 = 480$ (sewing)
$x_1 + 2x_2 + x_3 = 220$ (inspection)
25. $\begin{aligned} x_1 + x_2 \qquad\qquad &= 300 \\ x_3 + x_4 &= 200 \end{aligned}$ } production capacities
$\begin{aligned} x_1 \qquad + x_3 \qquad &= 150 \\ x_2 \qquad + x_4 &= 350 \end{aligned}$ } demands
27. Let $x_1 =$ investment in real estate
$x_2 =$ investment in stocks
$x_3 =$ investment in bonds

$$x_1 + x_2 + x_3 = 2{,}000{,}000 \text{ (funds)}$$
$$0.12x_1 + 0.09x_2 + 0.08x_3 = 0.11(2{,}000{,}000) \text{ (return)}$$
$$4x_1 + 6x_2 + 3x_3 = 5(2{,}000{,}000) \text{ (risk)}$$

SECTION 5-3

1. $\begin{bmatrix} 1 & 2 & | & 4 \\ 0 & 7 & | & 3 \end{bmatrix}$ **3.** $\begin{bmatrix} 1 & 2 & 8 & | & 5 \\ 0 & 1 & 8 & | & 9 \\ 3 & 1 & 2 & | & 4 \end{bmatrix}$

5. $\begin{bmatrix} 1 & 0 & 3 & | & 2 \\ 0 & -1 & -4 & | & 0 \\ 0 & 1 & 8 & | & 11 \end{bmatrix}$

7. $\begin{bmatrix} 1 & 0 & 0 & | & 8 \\ 0 & 1 & 0 & | & -14 \\ 0 & 0 & 1 & | & 3 \end{bmatrix}$ **9.** $(-3, -4)$ **11.** $(2, -4, 1)$

13. $\left(\dfrac{1}{2}, 1, 3\right)$ **15.** $(4, 3)$ **17.** $(-2, 1, 4)$ **19.** $(-1, 1, 3)$

21. $\left(\dfrac{-5}{2}, 1, \dfrac{19}{2}\right)$ **23.** $(-2, 3, -1)$ **25.** $(1, 2, 3, -1)$

27. No solution   **29.** Infinitely many solutions; $\left(\dfrac{5}{4} + \dfrac{1}{4}t, t\right)$

31. No solution   **33.** No solution   **35.** Infinitely many solutions; $\left(\dfrac{8}{3} - 3t, \dfrac{2}{3} + t, t\right)$ **37.** Infinitely many solutions; $\left(-11 + \dfrac{5}{2}t, 6 - \dfrac{3}{2}t, 3 + \dfrac{1}{2}t, t\right)$ **39.** No solution

41. Infinitely many solutions; $(9 + 7s + t, -2 - 3s, s, t)$

43. $(3, -2)$ **45.** Infinitely many solutions $(4 - 3t, t)$

47. $\left(\dfrac{1}{2}, 1, 3\right)$ **49.** $(40, 100, 80)$

51. $x = 100, y = 50, z = 20$, where
$x = $ no. of conservative sweaters
$y = $ no. of sporty sweaters
$z = $ no of practical sweaters

53. Infinitely many solutions; $x_1 = -50 + t, x_2 = 350 - t,$
$x_3 = 200 - t, x_4 = t$ Since $x_i \geq 0, 50 \leq t \leq 200$

55. $\left. \begin{aligned} x_1 + x_2 &= 500 \\ x_3 + x_4 &= 300 \end{aligned} \right\}$ production capacities
$\left. \begin{aligned} x_1 \quad + x_3 &= 600 \\ x_2 \quad + x_4 &= 200 \end{aligned} \right\}$ demands
Infinitely many solutions; $x_1 = 300 + t, x_2 = 200 - t,$
$x_3 = 300 - t, x_4 = t$
Since $x_i \geq 0, 0 \leq t \leq 200$

57. Let $x = $ gallons of A, $y = $ gallons of B, $z = $ gallons of C
$x + y + z = 100{,}000$ total gallons
$2x + 4y + 8z = 600{,}000$ cost
$-5.5x + z = 0 \qquad z = 5.5x$
10,000 gallons of A, 35,000 gallons of B, 55,000
gallons of C; solution is unique

59. 10 oz of food A, 20 oz of food B, 30 oz of food C

SECTION 5-4

1. 2×3 **3.** 3×3 **5.** 1×3 **7.** 4×1 **9.** Row matrix
11. Column matrix   **13.** Not square   **15.** Square matrix
17. True   **19.** False   **21.** $x = 4, y = -1$ **23.** $x = 1,$
$y = -4, z = 5, w = -7$ **25.** $\begin{bmatrix} 3 & -3 & 1 \\ -3 & 10 & -5 \end{bmatrix}$

27. $\begin{bmatrix} 7 & 4 & 2 \\ -3 & 10 & -3 \end{bmatrix}$ **29.** $\begin{bmatrix} 1 & 2 & -2 \\ -1 & 0 & 1 \end{bmatrix}$

31. $\begin{bmatrix} -4 & 1 & 1 \\ 4 & -10 & 4 \end{bmatrix}$ **33.** $\begin{bmatrix} 7 & 8 & 3 \\ -1 & 5 & 0 \end{bmatrix}$

35. $\begin{bmatrix} 7 & 0 & 1 \\ -5 & 15 & -6 \end{bmatrix}$ **37.** $\begin{bmatrix} 0 & 12 & 3 \\ 6 & -15 & 9 \end{bmatrix}$

39. $\begin{bmatrix} -9 & -3 & -6 \\ 3 & -15 & 6 \end{bmatrix}$ **41.** $\begin{bmatrix} -8 & -6 & 0 \\ 4 & -10 & 2 \end{bmatrix}$

43. $\begin{bmatrix} 3 & -11 & -1 \\ -7 & 20 & -11 \end{bmatrix}$ **45.** $\begin{bmatrix} -9 & 1 & -5 \\ 5 & -20 & 9 \end{bmatrix}$

47. $\begin{bmatrix} -5 & -1 & 3 \\ 5 & -10 & 3 \end{bmatrix}$ **49.** $\begin{bmatrix} 1 & -4 & 4 \end{bmatrix}$

51. $\begin{bmatrix} 9 & -12 & 3 \end{bmatrix}$ **53.** $\begin{bmatrix} -1 & -4 & 7 \end{bmatrix}$

55. $\begin{bmatrix} -7 & 12 & -6 \end{bmatrix}$ **57.** $\begin{bmatrix} 1 \\ 3 \end{bmatrix}$ **59.** $\begin{bmatrix} -15 \\ -1 \end{bmatrix}$

61. $\begin{bmatrix} 21 \\ -3 \end{bmatrix}$ **63.** $\begin{bmatrix} 33 \\ 11 \end{bmatrix}$ **65.** $\begin{bmatrix} -13 \\ 5 \end{bmatrix}$

67. $\begin{bmatrix} -1 & -5 \\ 5 & 9 \end{bmatrix}$ **69.** $\begin{bmatrix} -5 & 5 \\ 3 & -5 \\ 2 & -7 \end{bmatrix}$ **71.** $\begin{bmatrix} 1 & 8 \\ -7 & 22 \end{bmatrix}$

73. $\begin{bmatrix} 23 & 16 \\ 1 & -4 \end{bmatrix}$ **75.** $X = \begin{bmatrix} 3 \\ 4 \\ 6 \end{bmatrix}$

77. (a) $X = \begin{bmatrix} a & b \\ c & d \end{bmatrix}$, $X - X = \begin{bmatrix} a-a & b-b \\ c-c & d-d \end{bmatrix} = \begin{bmatrix} 0 & 0 \\ 0 & 0 \end{bmatrix} = Z$ **(b)** $X + Z = \begin{bmatrix} a & b \\ c & d \end{bmatrix} + \begin{bmatrix} 0 & 0 \\ 0 & 0 \end{bmatrix} = \begin{bmatrix} a & b \\ c & d \end{bmatrix} = X$

79. $J + A = \begin{bmatrix} 300 & 80 & 80 & 150 \\ 370 & 450 & 210 & 80 \end{bmatrix}$

81. $\begin{matrix} A & B & C \\ \begin{bmatrix} 30 & 40 & 60 \\ 25 & 40 & 50 \end{bmatrix} & & \begin{matrix} \text{scarves} \\ \text{mittens} \end{matrix} \end{matrix}$

83.

Person	Before	After
1	350	345
2	249	200
3	260	220
4	195	140
5	275	200
6	295	230

SECTION 5-5

1. 9 **3.** −2 **5.** 0.37 (rounded) **7.** 3 × 5 **9.** 4 × 4

11. Cannot be computed **13.** 2 × 2 **15.** 4 × 5

17. 2 × 2 **19.** $\begin{bmatrix} 11 & -2 \\ 3 & 0 \end{bmatrix}$ **21.** $[-6 \quad 9]$

23. $\begin{bmatrix} -17 \\ -28 \end{bmatrix}$ **25.** $\begin{bmatrix} 22 \\ -10 \\ 4 \end{bmatrix}$ **27.** $\begin{bmatrix} 11 & -13 \\ -8 & 17 \\ 13 & -9 \end{bmatrix}$

29. $\begin{bmatrix} 16 & 36 \\ 0 & 2 \\ 8 & 24 \end{bmatrix}$ **31.** $\begin{bmatrix} 2 & -7 & 9 \\ -8 & 2 & 7 \\ -1 & 5 & 6 \end{bmatrix}$

33. $\begin{bmatrix} -14 & 16 \\ -11 & 18 \end{bmatrix}$ **35.** No; $AB \neq BA$

37. BA cannot be computed **39.** CB cannot be computed

41. $\begin{bmatrix} 15 & 1 \\ -7 & 10 \end{bmatrix}$ **43.** AD cannot be computed

45. $\begin{bmatrix} -118 & 199 & 120 & -154 \\ -10 & 138 & 114 & 160 \\ 30 & 76 & 78 & 220 \end{bmatrix}$

47. $(AB)C = A(BC)$ by inspection **49.** $AB = \begin{bmatrix} 22 & 8 \\ 56 & -8 \end{bmatrix}$, $BA = \begin{bmatrix} 20 & 21 \\ 24 & -6 \end{bmatrix}$ $AB \neq BA$ **51. (a)** $A^3 = \begin{bmatrix} -16 & 75 \\ -25 & 34 \end{bmatrix}$

(b) $A^3 = \begin{bmatrix} -512 & 0 \\ 52 & 8 \end{bmatrix}$ **(c)** $A^3 = \begin{bmatrix} 17 & 22 & 17 \\ 44 & -9 & 8 \\ 34 & 8 & 18 \end{bmatrix}$

(d) $A^3 = \begin{bmatrix} -117 & 86 & 51 \\ 113 & -94 & -23 \\ 136 & -112 & -56 \end{bmatrix}$

53. $A^n = \underbrace{A \cdot A \cdot A \cdots A}_{n \text{ times}}$, n is a positive integer

(A must be a square matrix)

55. $\begin{bmatrix} 1 & 5 \\ 4 & 8 \end{bmatrix}\begin{bmatrix} x_1 \\ x_2 \end{bmatrix} = \begin{bmatrix} 6 \\ 11 \end{bmatrix}$ **57.** $\begin{bmatrix} 2 & 3 & 1 \\ 1 & 0 & 2 \\ 0 & 4 & 5 \end{bmatrix}\begin{bmatrix} x \\ y \\ z \end{bmatrix} = \begin{bmatrix} 11 \\ 9 \\ 17 \end{bmatrix}$

59. $\begin{bmatrix} 2 & -1 \\ 3 & 2 \end{bmatrix}\begin{bmatrix} x_1 \\ x_2 \end{bmatrix} = \begin{bmatrix} 6 \\ 9 \end{bmatrix}$

61. $\begin{bmatrix} -1 & 1 & -2 \\ 6 & 0 & 2 \\ 0 & 1 & -1 \end{bmatrix}\begin{bmatrix} x_1 \\ x_2 \\ x_3 \end{bmatrix} = \begin{bmatrix} 10 \\ 5 \\ 9 \end{bmatrix}$

63. $x_1 - 3x_2 = 3$ **65.** $4x_1 + x_2 - x_3 = -4$
$2x_1 + 4x_2 = -7$ $\qquad 5x_1 \qquad + 2x_3 = 1$
$\qquad\qquad\qquad\qquad -2x_1 + x_2 - 2x_3 = -1$

67. $x_1 + 4x_2 - x_3 = 2$
$2x_1 + x_2 \qquad = 1$
$4x_1 + x_2 - 5x_3 = 5$

69. $AI = \begin{bmatrix} 4 & 3 & 6 \\ 8 & 2 & 7 \\ -1 & 1 & 4 \end{bmatrix} = A$

$IA = \begin{bmatrix} 4 & 3 & 6 \\ 8 & 2 & 7 \\ -1 & 1 & 4 \end{bmatrix} = A$

71. $BI = \begin{bmatrix} 2 & 3 \\ 7 & 4 \\ 5 & 7 \end{bmatrix} = B$ **73.** $\begin{bmatrix} 31{,}000 \\ 46{,}000 \\ 79{,}000 \end{bmatrix}$ April May June

75. Votes

$\begin{bmatrix} 105{,}000 \\ 171{,}900 \\ 43{,}100 \end{bmatrix}$ Republican Democrat; Independent Democrat

SECTION 5-6

1. Yes **3.** Yes **5.** Yes **7.** No **9. (a)** $\begin{bmatrix} 11 & -5 \\ -2 & 1 \end{bmatrix}$

(b) $AA^{-1} = \begin{bmatrix} 1 & 0 \\ 0 & 1 \end{bmatrix} = A^{-1}A = I$

11. $\dfrac{1}{32}\begin{bmatrix} 7 & 1 \\ 3 & 5 \end{bmatrix} = \begin{bmatrix} 7/32 & 1/32 \\ 3/32 & 5/32 \end{bmatrix}$ **13.** $\begin{bmatrix} -1 & 1 \\ 1 & 0 \end{bmatrix}$

15. $\dfrac{1}{57}\begin{bmatrix} 1 & 10 & 7 \\ 16 & -11 & -2 \\ 22 & -8 & -17 \end{bmatrix} =$

$\begin{bmatrix} 1/57 & 10/57 & 7/57 \\ 16/57 & -11/57 & -2/57 \\ 22/57 & -8/57 & -17/57 \end{bmatrix}$

17. $\dfrac{1}{29}\begin{bmatrix} 7 & 4 \\ 2 & -3 \end{bmatrix} = \begin{bmatrix} 7/29 & 4/29 \\ 2/29 & -3/29 \end{bmatrix}$

19. $\dfrac{1}{14}\begin{bmatrix} 1 & 3 \\ 4 & -2 \end{bmatrix} = \begin{bmatrix} 1/14 & 3/14 \\ 2/7 & -1/7 \end{bmatrix}$

21. $\dfrac{1}{7}\begin{bmatrix} -1 & 2 & 1 \\ 4 & -1 & -4 \\ 0 & 0 & 7 \end{bmatrix} = \begin{bmatrix} -1/7 & 2/7 & 1/7 \\ 4/7 & -1/7 & -4/7 \\ 0 & 0 & 1 \end{bmatrix}$

23. K^{-1} does not exist

25. $\dfrac{1}{6}\begin{bmatrix} -2 & 0 & 0 & 1 \\ 2 & 0 & 2 & -1 \\ 2 & 0 & -2 & 2 \\ 0 & 3 & 0 & 0 \end{bmatrix} =$

$\begin{bmatrix} -1/3 & 0 & 0 & 1/6 \\ 1/3 & 0 & 1/3 & -1/6 \\ 1/3 & 0 & -1/3 & 1/3 \\ 0 & 1/2 & 0 & 0 \end{bmatrix}$

SECTION 5-7

1. $x_1 = 12, x_2 = 1$ **3.** $x_1 = 18, x_2 = 1$

5. $\begin{bmatrix} 1 & 2 \\ -1 & 3 \end{bmatrix}\begin{bmatrix} x_1 \\ x_2 \end{bmatrix} = \begin{bmatrix} 9 \\ 1 \end{bmatrix}; A^{-1} = \dfrac{1}{5}\begin{bmatrix} 3 & -2 \\ 1 & 1 \end{bmatrix}; \begin{bmatrix} x_1 \\ x_2 \end{bmatrix} = \begin{bmatrix} 5 \\ 2 \end{bmatrix}$

7. $\begin{bmatrix} 1 & 0 & 1 \\ 0 & 1 & 4 \\ 2 & 3 & 1 \end{bmatrix}\begin{bmatrix} x_1 \\ x_2 \\ x_3 \end{bmatrix} = \begin{bmatrix} 11 \\ 39 \\ 22 \end{bmatrix};$

$A^{-1} = \dfrac{1}{13}\begin{bmatrix} 11 & -3 & 1 \\ -8 & 1 & 4 \\ 2 & 3 & -1 \end{bmatrix}; \begin{bmatrix} x_1 \\ x_2 \\ x_3 \end{bmatrix} = \begin{bmatrix} 2 \\ 3 \\ 9 \end{bmatrix}$

9. $\begin{bmatrix} 1 & 1 & 1 \\ 1 & 2 & 3 \\ 0 & 1 & 4 \end{bmatrix}\begin{bmatrix} x_1 \\ x_2 \\ x_3 \end{bmatrix} = \begin{bmatrix} 3 \\ 10 \\ 17 \end{bmatrix};$

$A^{-1} = \dfrac{1}{2}\begin{bmatrix} 5 & -3 & 1 \\ -4 & 4 & -2 \\ 1 & -1 & 1 \end{bmatrix}; \begin{bmatrix} x_1 \\ x_2 \\ x_3 \end{bmatrix} = \begin{bmatrix} 1 \\ -3 \\ 5 \end{bmatrix}$

11. $\begin{bmatrix} 1 & 1 & 0 \\ 0 & 1 & 3 \\ 4 & 6 & 7 \end{bmatrix}\begin{bmatrix} x_1 \\ x_2 \\ x_3 \end{bmatrix} = \begin{bmatrix} 3 \\ -7 \\ -5 \end{bmatrix};$

$A^{-1} = \begin{bmatrix} -11 & -7 & 3 \\ 12 & 7 & -3 \\ -4 & -2 & 1 \end{bmatrix}; \begin{bmatrix} x_1 \\ x_2 \\ x_3 \end{bmatrix} = \begin{bmatrix} 1 \\ 2 \\ -3 \end{bmatrix}$

13. $\begin{bmatrix} 2 & -3 \\ 1 & -7 \end{bmatrix}\begin{bmatrix} x \\ y \end{bmatrix} = \begin{bmatrix} 6 \\ 25 \end{bmatrix}; A^{-1} = \dfrac{-1}{11}\begin{bmatrix} -7 & 3 \\ -1 & 2 \end{bmatrix};$

$\begin{bmatrix} x \\ y \end{bmatrix} = \begin{bmatrix} -3 \\ -4 \end{bmatrix}$

15. $\begin{bmatrix} 2 & 3 & -5 \\ 1 & 2 & 3 \\ 3 & -4 & -7 \end{bmatrix}\begin{bmatrix} x \\ y \\ z \end{bmatrix} = \begin{bmatrix} -13 \\ -7 \\ 15 \end{bmatrix};$

$A^{-1} = \dfrac{1}{94}\begin{bmatrix} -2 & 41 & 19 \\ 16 & 1 & -11 \\ -10 & 17 & 1 \end{bmatrix}; \begin{bmatrix} x \\ y \\ z \end{bmatrix} = \begin{bmatrix} 12/47 \\ -190/47 \\ 13/47 \end{bmatrix}$

17. $\begin{bmatrix} 5 & 7 & 1 \\ 3 & 2 & 3 \\ 2 & 3 & 5 \end{bmatrix}\begin{bmatrix} x_1 \\ x_2 \\ x_3 \end{bmatrix} = \begin{bmatrix} 1 \\ 8 \\ 19 \end{bmatrix};$

$A^{-1} = \dfrac{1}{53}\begin{bmatrix} -1 & 32 & -19 \\ 9 & -23 & 12 \\ -5 & 1 & 11 \end{bmatrix}; \begin{bmatrix} x_1 \\ x_2 \\ x_3 \end{bmatrix} = \begin{bmatrix} -2 \\ 1 \\ 4 \end{bmatrix}$

19. $\begin{bmatrix} 4 & 1 \\ 6 & -2 \end{bmatrix}\begin{bmatrix} x_1 \\ x_2 \end{bmatrix} = \begin{bmatrix} 8 \\ -9 \end{bmatrix}; A^{-1} = \dfrac{1}{14}\begin{bmatrix} 2 & 1 \\ 6 & -4 \end{bmatrix};$

$\begin{bmatrix} x_1 \\ x_2 \end{bmatrix} = \begin{bmatrix} 1/2 \\ 6 \end{bmatrix}$

21. $\begin{bmatrix} 2 & 1 & 3 \\ 4 & 3 & -2 \\ 6 & 5 & -4 \end{bmatrix}\begin{bmatrix} x \\ y \\ z \end{bmatrix} = \begin{bmatrix} 11 \\ -1 \\ -4 \end{bmatrix};$

$A^{-1} = \dfrac{1}{6}\begin{bmatrix} -2 & 19 & -11 \\ 4 & -26 & 16 \\ 2 & -4 & 2 \end{bmatrix}; \begin{bmatrix} x \\ y \\ z \end{bmatrix} = \begin{bmatrix} 1/2 \\ 1 \\ 3 \end{bmatrix}$

23. $\begin{bmatrix} 1 & 0 & 1 & -1 \\ 0 & 1 & -1 & 2 \\ 4 & 0 & 5 & -3 \\ 0 & 0 & 2 & 3 \end{bmatrix}\begin{bmatrix} x_1 \\ x_2 \\ x_3 \\ x_4 \end{bmatrix} = \begin{bmatrix} -2 \\ 12 \\ 2 \\ 27 \end{bmatrix};$

$A^{-1} = \begin{bmatrix} 21 & 0 & -5 & 2 \\ -28 & 1 & 7 & -3 \\ -12 & 0 & 3 & -1 \\ 8 & 0 & -2 & 1 \end{bmatrix}; \begin{bmatrix} x_1 \\ x_2 \\ x_3 \\ x_4 \end{bmatrix} = \begin{bmatrix} 2 \\ 1 \\ 3 \\ 7 \end{bmatrix}$

25. (a)

$A = \begin{matrix} \text{Meat} & \text{Spinach} \\ \begin{bmatrix} 500 & 200 \\ 100 & 800 \end{bmatrix} & \begin{matrix} \text{protein} \\ \text{iron} \end{matrix}\end{matrix}$

(b) $B = \begin{bmatrix} 1200 \\ 1000 \end{bmatrix} \begin{matrix} \text{protein} \\ \text{iron} \end{matrix}$

(c) $\begin{bmatrix} 500 & 200 \\ 100 & 800 \end{bmatrix}\begin{bmatrix} x \\ y \end{bmatrix} = \begin{bmatrix} 1200 \\ 1000 \end{bmatrix}$

(d) $\begin{bmatrix} x \\ y \end{bmatrix} = \begin{bmatrix} 2 \\ 1 \end{bmatrix};$ Hence $x = 2$ lb meat, $y = 1$ lb spinach

(e) $\begin{bmatrix} x \\ y \end{bmatrix} = \begin{bmatrix} 3 \\ 4 \end{bmatrix}$

27. Let $x = $ # units of XB17, $y = $ # units of XB18

(a) $0.01x + 0.03y = 220$
$0.02x + 0.005y = 330$

(b) $\begin{bmatrix} 0.01 & 0.03 \\ 0.02 & 0.005 \end{bmatrix}\begin{bmatrix} x \\ y \end{bmatrix} = \begin{bmatrix} 220 \\ 330 \end{bmatrix}$

(c) $A^{-1} = \begin{bmatrix} -100/11 & 600/11 \\ 400/11 & -200/11 \end{bmatrix}$

(d) $\begin{bmatrix} x \\ y \end{bmatrix} = \begin{bmatrix} -100/11 & 600/11 \\ 400/11 & -200/11 \end{bmatrix}\begin{bmatrix} 220 \\ 330 \end{bmatrix} = \begin{bmatrix} 16,000 \\ 2000 \end{bmatrix}$

(e) $\begin{bmatrix} x \\ y \end{bmatrix} = \begin{bmatrix} -100/11 & 600/11 \\ 400/11 & -200/11 \end{bmatrix} \begin{bmatrix} 440 \\ 110 \end{bmatrix} = \begin{bmatrix} 2000 \\ 14{,}000 \end{bmatrix}$

29. (a) $x + y = 100{,}000$ available funds
$0.07x + 0.09y = 8500$ yield

(b) $\begin{bmatrix} 1 & 1 \\ 0.07 & 0.09 \end{bmatrix} \begin{bmatrix} x \\ y \end{bmatrix} = \begin{bmatrix} 100{,}000 \\ 8500 \end{bmatrix}$

(c) $A^{-1} = \begin{bmatrix} 4.5 & -50 \\ -3.5 & 50 \end{bmatrix}$

(d) $x = \$25{,}000$ invested at 7%
$y = \$75{,}000$ invested at 9%

(e) $x = \$150{,}000$; $y = \$50{,}000$

SECTION 5-8

1. (a) $A = \begin{bmatrix} 0 & 1/4 \\ 1/2 & 0 \end{bmatrix} \begin{matrix} \text{oil} \\ \text{coal} \end{matrix}$

(b) $\begin{bmatrix} 380 \\ 680 \end{bmatrix}$

3. $\begin{bmatrix} 41\frac{1}{3} \\ 36 \end{bmatrix}$ **5.** $\begin{bmatrix} 120.8 \\ 75.2 \\ 135.2 \end{bmatrix}$ **7.** $\Delta x = \begin{bmatrix} 2 \\ 3.2 \end{bmatrix}$ **9.** $\Delta x = \begin{bmatrix} 7.7 \\ 2.4 \end{bmatrix}$

• EXTRA DIVIDENDS

1.

	Well in Saudi Arabia	Well in Kuwait	Well in Egypt	Demand
Regular	0.2	0.3	0.4	19
Unleaded	0.1	0.2	0.1	10
Kerosene	0.3	0.1	0.4	20

3. $\begin{bmatrix} 0.2 & 0.3 & 0.4 \\ 0.1 & 0.2 & 0.1 \\ 0.3 & 0.1 & 0.4 \end{bmatrix} \begin{bmatrix} x \\ y \\ z \end{bmatrix} = \begin{bmatrix} 19 \\ 10 \\ 20 \end{bmatrix}$

5. $\begin{bmatrix} x \\ y \\ z \end{bmatrix} = \begin{bmatrix} 50/3 \\ 100/3 \\ 50/3 \end{bmatrix} \begin{matrix} \text{Saudi Arabia} \\ \text{Kuwait} \\ \text{Egypt} \end{matrix}$

• CHAPTER HIGHLIGHTS

1. Straight line   **2.** Intersection point   **3.** Parallel
4. Coincide   **5.** Method of elimination; method of substitution
6. *Step 1:* Identify the unknowns *Step 2:* Organize the information and write the linear system *Step 3:* Solve the linear system

7. (a) $\begin{bmatrix} 1 & 0 & | & c_1 \\ 0 & 1 & | & c_2 \end{bmatrix}$ **(b)** $\begin{bmatrix} 1 & 0 & 0 & | & c_1 \\ 0 & 1 & 0 & | & c_2 \\ 0 & 0 & 1 & | & c_3 \end{bmatrix}$

8. (a) $a_1 x_1 + a_2 x_2 = b$ **(b)** $a_1 x_1 + a_2 x_2 + a_3 x_3 = b$
(c) $a_1 x_1 + a_2 x_2 + \ldots + a_n x_n = b$

10. $\begin{bmatrix} 1 & 0 & 0 & 0 & | & c_1 \\ 0 & 1 & 0 & 0 & | & c_2 \\ & & \vdots & & | & \vdots \\ 0 & 0 & 0 & 1 & | & c_n \end{bmatrix}$

no solutions or infinitely many solutions

11. $\begin{bmatrix} 1 & 4 & | & 7 \\ 0 & 0 & | & 5 \end{bmatrix}$

12. Variables than equations; basic variables in terms of the nonbasic variables   **13.** Rectangular   **14.** Same dimension and corresponding entries must be equal   **15.** Same dimension   **16.** Multiply each matrix entry by the number.
17. $m \times r$ **18.** The number of columns of the left matrix must equal the number of rows of the right matrix.

19. $\begin{bmatrix} 1 & 0 & 0 \\ 0 & 1 & 0 \\ 0 & 0 & 1 \end{bmatrix}$ $\begin{bmatrix} 1 & 0 & 0 & 0 \\ 0 & 1 & 0 & 0 \\ 0 & 0 & 1 & 0 \\ 0 & 0 & 0 & 1 \end{bmatrix}$

$\begin{bmatrix} 1 & 0 & 0 & 0 & 0 \\ 0 & 1 & 0 & 0 & 0 \\ 0 & 0 & 1 & 0 & 0 \\ 0 & 0 & 0 & 1 & 0 \\ 0 & 0 & 0 & 0 & 1 \end{bmatrix}$

20. Given a square matrix A, its inverse (if it exists) is that square matrix A^{-1} that satisfies both conditions $AA^{-1} = I$ and $A^{-1}A = I$.   **21.** No   **22.** Yes   **23.** Multiplicative inverse; A^{-1} **24.** $A^{-1}B$; A^{-1} **25.** Internal demand; final (or external) demand   **26. (a)** Production or total output matrix **(b)** Internal demand matrix **(c)** Final or external demand matrix   **27.** X; $X = (I - A)^{-1}D$; $(I - A)^{-1}$

• REVIEW EXERCISES

1. $(4, -1)$ **3.** No solution   **5.** $(4, 15)$ **7.** $(6, 30)$
9. (a) (1) $15x - 6y = 60$
     (2) $\underline{-15x + 6y = -60}$
                   $0 = 0 \Rightarrow$ infinitely many solutions

Let $x = t$, $y = \frac{5}{2}t - 10$

(b) Eq. (1) becomes $y = \frac{5}{2}x - 10$

Eq. (2) becomes $y = \frac{5}{2}x - 10$

Equations are the same.

(c) Let $t = 0, 1, 2$.

Solutions are $(0, -10)$, $\left(1, \dfrac{-15}{2}\right)$, $(2, -5)$

11.

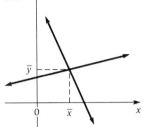

$(\bar{x}, \bar{y})$ is the solution.

13. Two lines coincide.

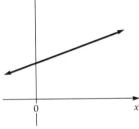

15. $(3, -4, 5)$ **17.** No solution   **19.** No solution

21. $\left(\dfrac{-11}{7}, \dfrac{-12}{7}, \dfrac{17}{7}\right)$ **23.** No solution   **25.** No solution

27. Infinitely many solutions $(9, -3, t)$ **29.** $\begin{bmatrix} 5 & 1 \\ 0 & -1 \\ -1 & -1 \end{bmatrix}$

31. $\begin{bmatrix} 9 & -5 \\ -2 & 1 \\ -3 & -5 \end{bmatrix}$ **33.** $\begin{bmatrix} 5 & 1 \\ 7 & 6 \end{bmatrix}$ **35.** $\begin{bmatrix} 11 & 16 \\ -2 & -5 \\ 19 & 13 \end{bmatrix}$

37. (a) $\begin{bmatrix} -1/5 & 2/5 & -12/5 \\ 0 & 0 & 1 \\ 3/5 & -1/5 & 1/5 \end{bmatrix}$

(b) $AA^{-1} = A^{-1}A = I$

39. $(3, 4)$ **41.** $(3, -4, 5)$ **43.** 20 lb alloy containing 30% silver, 80 lb alloy containing 80% silver   **45.** Infinitely many solutions; $x_1 = 200 + t$, $x_2 = 600 - t$, $x_3 = 500 - t$, $x_4 = t$; since each $x_i \geq 0$, $0 \leq t \leq 500$

47. (a) $A = \begin{bmatrix} 0.4 & 0.2 & 0.3 \\ 0.2 & 0.4 & 0.3 \\ 0.3 & 0.3 & 0.4 \end{bmatrix}$

a_{ij} = amount of item i consumed in making one unit of item j

(b) $D = \begin{bmatrix} 200 \\ 500 \\ 400 \end{bmatrix}$

d_i = units of item i for external demand

(c) $X = \begin{bmatrix} 5312\frac{1}{2} \\ 5687\frac{1}{2} \\ 6166\frac{2}{3} \end{bmatrix}$

x_i = total output of item i

• CHAPTER 6

SECTION 6-1

The solutions to problems 1–24 are graphs, shown in the accompanying figures. Shaded areas include points that do *not* satisfy the given inequalities.

1.

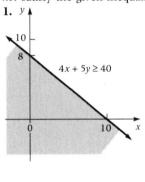

$4x + 5y \geq 40$

3.

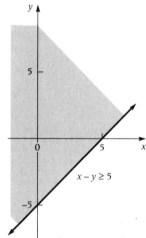

$x - y \geq 5$

5.

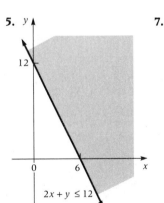

$2x + y \leq 12$

7.

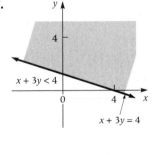

$x + 3y < 4$

$x + 3y = 4$

9.

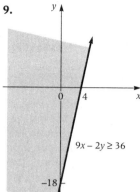

$9x - 2y \geq 36$

11.

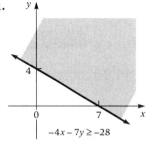

$-4x - 7y \geq -28$

21.

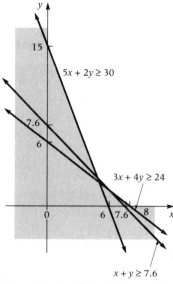

$5x + 2y \geq 30$

$3x + 4y \geq 24$

$x + y \geq 7.6$

13.

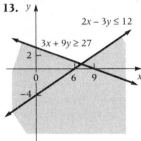

$2x - 3y \leq 12$

$3x + 9y \geq 27$

15.

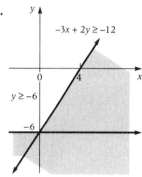

$-3x + 2y \geq -12$

$y \geq -6$

23. No points satisfy both inequalities.

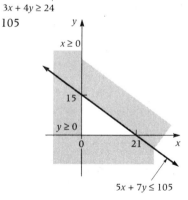

$3x + 4y \leq 12$

$3x + 4y \geq 24$

25. $5x + 7y \leq 105$

17.

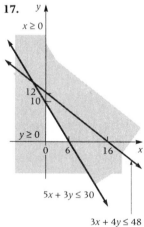

$x \geq 0$

$y \geq 0$

$5x + 3y \leq 30$

$3x + 4y \leq 48$

19.

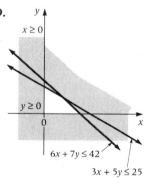

$x \geq 0$

$y \geq 0$

$6x + 7y \leq 42$

$3x + 5y \leq 25$

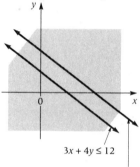

$x \geq 0$

$y \geq 0$

$5x + 7y \leq 105$

27. Let g and w represent the gadgets and widgets, respectively. $4g + 5w \leq 80$

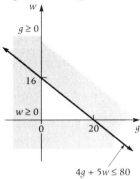

29. (a) $2A + 5B \leq 250$ (Department 1)
$A + 2B \leq 120$ (Department 2)

(b)

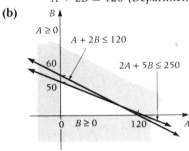

(c) Vertex points are $(0, 0)$, $(0, 50)$, $(100, 10)$ and $(120, 0)$

31. Let x = number of families in city 1
y = number of families in city 2

(a) $30x + 40y \leq 12{,}000$ (cost)
$x \geq 100$
$y \geq 120$

(b)

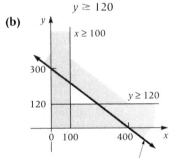

(c) $(100, 120)$, $(100, 225)$, $(240, 120)$

33. (a) Let x = acres to be zoned A-2,
y = acres to be zoned A-3
$x + y \leq 1{,}000{,}000$ (acres)
$\dfrac{x}{2} + \dfrac{y}{3} \geq 480{,}000$ (lots)
$x \geq 200{,}000$
$y \geq 60{,}000$

(b)

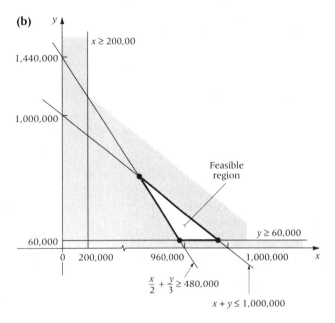

(c) $(880{,}000, 120{,}000)$, $(920{,}000, 60{,}000)$,
$(940{,}000, 60{,}000)$

SECTION 6-2

1. Maximum $Z = 73$ at $(6, 7)$ **3.** Minimum $Z = 4.6$ at
$(2, 8)$ **5.** Maximum $Z = 12.8$ at $(10, 16)$ **7.** Maximum
$P = 36.8$ at $(6.4, 1.2)$ **9.** Minimum $C = 48$ at $(12, 0)$
11. Maximum $Z = 165$ at $(0, 5.5)$ **13.** Minimum $Z = 240$
at $(12, 0)$ **15.** Maximum $Z = 122$ at $(4, 22)$
17. Maximum $Z = 344\dfrac{4}{9}$ at $\left(\dfrac{140}{9}, \dfrac{10}{9}\right)$
19. (a) x = number of casual jackets
y = number of formal jackets
Maximize $P = 30x + 50y$

	Casual	Formal	
Unit profits	30	50	At most
Cutting dept.	2 person-hrs/ jacket	3 person-hrs/ jacket	960 hrs
Sewing	1 person-hrs/ jacket	1 person-hrs/ jacket	400 hrs

At least 150 casual jackets must be produced.
At least 50 formal jackets must be produced.
Constraints:
Cutting dept.: $2x + 3y \leq 960$
Sewing dept.: $x + y \leq 400$
Demand $x \geq 150$
                     $y \geq 50$

Maximum P = \$15,500 at (150, 220).
Cutting dept.: slack = 0
Sewing dept.: slack = 3.
Constraint: $x \geq 150$, surplus = 0
  $y \geq 50$, surplus = 170
(b) 960 **(c)** 370
21. Maximize $R = 0.18x + 0.22y$
  Maximum R = 3760 at (16,000, 4000)
  Constraint 1: Total amount invested = 20,000
    slack = 0
  Constraint 2: Average risk level for the optimal
    solution = 3
    slack = 0
23. (a) 1500 radio ads and no TV ads **(b)** \$1,800,000
(c) *Constraint 1:* surplus = 300 ads
  Constraint 2: surplus = 0 families
(d) 1,500,000 families **(e)** 1500 ads
25. Minimum cost of \$7.50 at 2 lb meat and 1 lb spinach.
Constraint 1: surplus = 0
Constraint 2: surplus = 0
27. (a) 70 acres of A and 30 acres of B **(b)** \$43,000
(c) *Constraint 1:* slack = 0 acres
  Constraint 2: slack = 0 person-hours
(d) 100 **(e)** 6600 **29. (a)** 1960 gallons of F10,
1840 gallons of F20 **(b)** \$4964
(c) *Constraint 1:* surplus = 0
  Constraint 2: surplus = 11.2 lbs ash
  Constraint 3: 0
(d) 3800 **(e)** 131.2 **(f)** 136 **31. (a)** All points on the
line connecting (170, 80) and (185, 50) are equally
profitable. **(b)** \$840 **(c)** At (170, 80), *Constraint 1:*
slack = 0; *Constraint 2:* slack = 0; *Constraint 3:* slack = 20;
Constraint 4: surplus = 120; *Constraint 5:* surplus = 30
(d) 420 **(e)** 500 **(f)** 580 **33. (a)** 2400 units to
wholesale outlets, 3200 units to retail outlets **(b)** \$600,000
(c) *Constraint 1:* slack = 0, *Constraint 2:* slack = 0 **(d)** 5600
(e) 17,280 **35. (a)** 4480 units to wholesale outlets, 1120
units to retail outlets **(b)** \$537,600 **(c)** *Constraint 1:*
slack = 2496 hrs, *Constraint 2:* slack = 0, *Constraint 3:*
slack = 0 **(d)** 5600 **(e)** 14,784

SECTION 6-3

1. (2, 9) **3.** (9, 0) **5.** Along the boundary from (0, 8)
to (7, 5) **7.** (2, 4) **9.** (9, 4) **11.** (9, 4) **13.** (1, 2.5)
15. No feasible region since $x + y$ cannot be both ≤ 5
and ≥ 7. **17.** Minimum z = 48 at (4, 0)
19. Unbounded solution: an optimal solution does not
exist because there is always a better solution.

• CHAPTER HIGHLIGHTS

1. $ax + by \leq c$ or $ax + by \geq c$ **2.** First graph the
corresponding straight line and then determine whether the
points (x, y) satisfying the inequality lie above or below the
straight line. **3.** Graph each inequality on the same set of
axes. For each inequality, shade the region to be discarded.
The remaining region, the unshaded (white) region, if it
exists, constitutes the region associated with the system.
4. *Step 1:* Identify the quantity to be either maximized or
minimized and the related unknowns. *Step 2:* Organize the
given information and write the inequalities that express
any relationships existing among the unknowns.
Step 3: Determine the values of x and y that satisfy the
constraints and, also, optimize the value of the objective
function. *Step 4:* Investigate the implications of the optimal
solution. **5.** *Step 1:* Graph the feasible region (if it exists).
Step 2: Identify the vertex points. *Step 3:* Substitute the
coordinates of each vertex point into the objective function
to determine the optimal solution (if it exists).
6. For a ($\leq$) constraint, Slack = RHS − LHS. Slack
represents any unused capacity for a ($\leq$) constraint.
7. ($\leq$) **8.** *Binding constraint:* This means that all of the
available capacity or resource of the constraint is being
utilized by the optimal solution. **9.** For a ($\geq$) constraint,
Surplus = LHS − RHS. Surplus represents the amount by
which the minimal constraint requirement is exceeded.
10. ($\geq$) **11.** *Binding constraint:* This means that the
minimal requirement of the constraint is being met exactly.
12. An optimal solution, if one exists, to a linear
programming problem will occur at one or more of the
vertex points or on the boundary of the feasible region.
13. Yes **14.** There may or may not be an optimal solution.
15. There is more than one optimal solution.
16. An unbounded feasible region that results in there not
being an optimal solution because there is always a better
solution. **17.** There is no optimal solution.

• REVIEW EXERCISES

The solutions of Exercises 1−8 are graphs, shown in the
accompanying figures. *Shaded areas* include points that do
not satisfy the given inequalities.

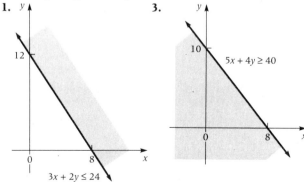

1. $3x + 2y \leq 24$

3. $5x + 4y \geq 40$

5.
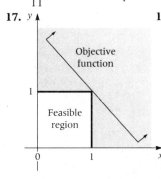

7.
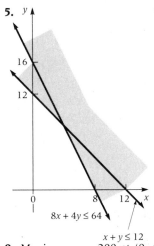

9. Maximum $z = 200$ at $(0, 40)$

11. Minimum $z = 40$ at $(0, 20)$

13. (a) Let x = number of type A branches,
y = number of type B branches
Maximize $P = 46{,}000x + 18{,}000y$
subject to $650{,}000x + 335{,}000y \leq 5{,}200{,}000$ costs
$10x + 5y \leq 100$ personnel
$x \geq 0$
$y \geq 0$
(b) Maximum $P = \$368{,}000$ at $(8, 0)$
(c) *Constraint 1:* slack = 0
Constraint 2: slack = 20 people

15. $\dfrac{500}{11} \approx 45$ units of product A,

$\dfrac{450}{11} \approx 41$ units of product B

17.
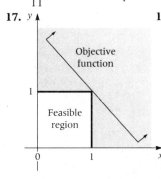

19.
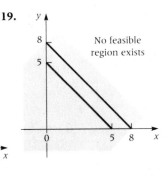

• **CHAPTER 7**

SECTION 7-1

1. (a)
$$\begin{aligned}
2x_1 + 3x_2 + s_1 \qquad\qquad &= 90 \\
5x_1 + x_2 \qquad + s_2 \qquad &= 160 \\
-120x_1 - 60x_2 \qquad\qquad + z &= 0
\end{aligned}$$

(b)

x_1	x_2	s_1	s_2	z	
2	3	1	0	0	90
5	1	0	1	0	160
−120	−60	0	0	1	0

(c) $x_1 = 0$, $x_2 = 0$, $s_1 = 90$, $s_2 = 160$; $z = 0$

3. (a)
$$\begin{aligned}
x_1 + x_2 + s_1 \qquad\qquad &= 100 \\
60x_1 + 80x_2 \qquad + s_2 \qquad &= 6600 \\
-400x_1 - 500x_2 \qquad\qquad + z &= 0 \\
x_1, x_2 &\geq 0
\end{aligned}$$

(b)

x_1	x_2	s_1	s_2	z	
1	1	1	0	0	100
60	80	0	1	0	6600
−400	−500	0	0	1	0

(c) $x_1 = 0$, $x_2 = 0$, $s_1 = 100$, $s_2 = 6600$; $z = 0$

5. (a)
$$\begin{aligned}
2x_1 + 3x_2 + x_3 + s_1 \qquad\qquad &= 6 \\
4x_1 + 2x_2 + 3x_3 \qquad + s_2 \qquad &= 12 \\
4x_1 + 2x_2 + x_3 \qquad\qquad + s_3 \quad &= 8 \\
-20x_1 - 42x_2 - 56x_3 \qquad\qquad + z &= 0 \\
x_1, x_2, x_3 &\geq 0
\end{aligned}$$

(b)

x_1	x_2	x_3	s_1	s_2	s_3	z	
2	3	1	1	0	0	0	6
4	2	3	0	1	0	0	12
4	2	1	0	0	1	0	8
−20	−42	−56	0	0	0	1	0

(c) $x_1 = 0$, $x_2 = 0$, $x_3 = 0$, $s_1 = 6$, $s_2 = 12$, $s_3 = 8$; $z = 0$

7. $x_1 = 3$, $x_2 = 0$, $x_3 = 6$, $s_1 = 0$, $s_2 = 5$, $s_3 = 0$; $z = 5670$

9. $x_1 = 75$, $x_2 = 0$, $x_3 = 60$, $x_4 = 0$, $s_1 = 0$, $s_2 = 0$; $z = 50$

SECTION 7-2

1.

Quotient value	s_1	s_2	s_3
425	0	150	−225
500	−150	0	−900
400	50	200	0

3. (a) x_1 can increase 120 units before s_1 becomes negative and x_1 can increase 100 units before s_3 becomes negative. x_2 can increase indefinitely. **(b)** An increase of 100 units in x_1 is the maximum that retains nonnegative values of s_1, s_2, and s_3. **5.** $x_1 = 0$, $x_2 = 10$, $s_1 = 0$, $s_2 = 20$, $z = 300$
7. $x_1 = 0$, $x_2 = 7$, $x_3 = 0$, $s_1 = 9$, $s_2 = 0$, $s_3 = 3$, $z = 42$
9. $x_1 = 40$, $x_2 = 0$, $x_3 = 0$, $x_4 = 0$, $s_1 = 0$, $s_2 = 10$, $z = 3200$
11. $x_1 = 0$, $x_2 = 30$, $x_3 = 0$, $s_1 = 0$, $s_2 = 60$, $s_3 = 30$, $z = 240$
13. $x_1 = 20$, $x_2 = 15$, $x_3 = 0$, $s_1 = 0$, $s_2 = 20$, $s_3 = 0$, $z = 235$
15. $x_1 = 30$, $x_2 = 40$, $x_3 = 60$, $s_1 = 20$, $s_2 = 0$, $s_3 = 0$,
$s_4 = 0$, $z = 330$ **17. (a)** $x_1 = 0$, $x_2 = 22.5$, $x_3 = 5$,
$s_1 = 72.5$, $s_2 = 0$, $s_3 = 0$, $z = 115$ **(b)** x_1 **(c)** $x_1 = 36$,·
$x_3 = 1.4$, $s_1 = 62.6$, $x_2 = 0$, $s_2 = 0$, $s_3 = 0$, $z = 115$
(d) Note that for the solution to part c, x_1 is nonzero and $x_2 = 0$ whereas for the solution to part a, the opposite is true. Also note the change in the value of s_1 when comparing both solutions.

19.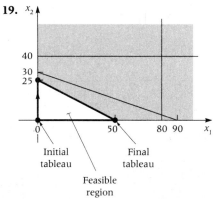

Initial
tableau

Final
tableau

Feasible
region

Simplex method: $x_1 = 50, x_2 = 0, s_1 = 0, s_2 = 40, s_3 = 30,$
$s_4 = 40, z = 500$

21. Let x_1 = number of units of product A
x_2 = number of units of product B
x_3 = number of units of product C
$x_1 = 0, x_2 = 0, x_3 = 750, s_1 = 0, s_2 = 450, P = 45,000$

23. Let x_1 = dollars invested in stocks
x_2 = dollars invested in bonds
x_3 = dollars invested in money market funds
$x_1 = 1,000,000, x_2 = 0, x_3 = 1,000,000,$
$s_1 = 0, s_2 = 200,000, s_3 = 0, R = 160,000$

25. $x_1 = 800, x_2 = 200, x_3 = 0, x_4 = 1800, s_1 = 0, s_2 = 0,$
$s_3 = 400, s_4 = 0, P = 16,400$
There are alternate solutions, since x_3 can be brought into
the basis.

27. Let x_1 = acres for crop A
x_2 = acres for crop B
x_3 = acres for crop C
$x_1 = 500, x_2 = 200, x_3 = 300, s_1 = 0, s_2 = 2300, s_3 = 0,$
$s_4 = 0, P = 510,000$

29. Let x_1 = units marketed through retail outlet 1
x_2 = units marketed through retail outlet 2
x_3 = units marketed through the wholesale outlet
$x_1 = 3000, x_2 = 0, x_3 = 7000, s_1 = 0, s_2 = 0, P = 3,300,000$

31. Let x_1 = number of professional pollsters at location 1
x_2 = number of semiprofessional pollsters at
location 1
x_3 = number of professional pollsters at location 2
x_4 = number of semiprofessional pollsters at
location 2
$x_1 = 0, x_2 = 15, x_3 = 0, x_4 = 25, s_1 = 0, s_2 = 0, V = 2400$
Note: No professional pollsters are used in the optimal
solution.

SECTION 7-3

1. (a) *Dual:* Maximize $z = 6y_1 + 8y_2$
Subject to $2y_1 + 4y_2 \le 40$
$y_1 + 6y_2 \le 60$
$y_1, y_2 \ge 0$

(b) $y_1 = 20, y_2 = 0, s_1 = 0, s_2 = 40, z = 120$
(c) $x_1 = 3, x_2 = 0, z = 120$
(d) Surplus in $2x_1 + x_2 \ge 6$ is 0; Surplus in $4x_1 + 6x_2 \ge$
8 is 4
(e) *Shadow prices:* $y_1 = 20, y_2 = 0; y_1 = 20$ is the change
that will occur in the optimal value of the objective
function if the right-hand side of the first constraint in the
primal is increased by 1 unit, that is, to
$2x_1 + x_2 \ge 7. y_2 = 0$ is the change that will occur in the
optimal value of the objective function if the right-hand
side of the second constraint in the primal is increased by
1 unit, that is to $4x_1 + 6x_2 \ge 9$. *Note:* Each shadow price is
valid only for a specific interval within which its
corresponding right-hand-side value can vary.
3. (a) *Dual:* Maximize $z = 120y_1 + 100y_2$
subject to $4y_1 + y_2 \le 300$
$2y_1 + 8y_2 \le 150$
$y_1, y_2 \ge 0$
(b) $y_1 = 75, y_2 = 0, s_1 = 0, s_2 = 0, z = 9000$
(c) $x_1 = 0, x_2 = 60, z = 9000$ **(d)** 0 and 380
(e) *Shadow prices:* $y_1 = 75, y_2 = 0$; An increase of 1 unit in
the right-hand side of the first primal constraint will
increase the optimal value of the objective function by 75
units. *Note:* The solution for (x_1, x_2) is not unique. Any
point between $(0, 60)$ and $(76/3, 28/3)$ will satisfy the
constraints and yield the same minimum.
5. (a) *Dual:* Maximize $z = 6y_1 + 8y_2 + 4y_3$
subject to $y_1 + y_2 + y_3 \le 200$
$2y_1 + 6y_2 + 4y_3 \le 240$
$y_1, y_2 \ge 0$
(b) $y_1 = 120, y_2 = 0, y_3 = 0, s_1 = 80, s_2 = 0, z = 720$
(c) $x_1 = 0, x_2 = 3, z = 720$ **(d)** 0, 10, 8
(e) $y_1 = 120, y_2 = 0, y_3 = 0$; An increase of 1 unit in the
right-hand side of the first primal constraint will increase
the optimal value of the objective function by 120 units;
changes in the right-hand side values of the remaining
constraints will not result in changes in the value of the
objective function because the shadow prices are 0.
7. (a) *Dual:* Maximize $z = 6y_1 + 9y_2 + 5y_3$
subject to $2y_1 + 4y_2 \le 80$
$y_1 + 2y_2 + 2y_3 \le 100$
$y_1 \le 10$
$y_1, y_2, y_3 \ge 0$
(b) $y_1 = 10, y_2 = 15, y_3 = 30, s_1 = 0, s_2 = 0, s_3 = 0, z = 345$
(c) $x_1 = 1, x_2 = 5/2, x_3 = 3/2, z = 345$ **(d)** All 0.
(e) $y_1 = 10, y_2 = 15, y_3 = 30$; An increase of one unit in
the right-hand side of the ith primal constraint $(i = 1, 2, 3)$
will increase the optimal value of the objective function by
y_i units.

9. (a) *Dual:* Maximize $z = 40y_1 + 60y_2 + 50y_3$

subject to
$$2y_1 + y_2 + 2y_3 \le 600$$
$$y_1 + 2y_2 + 2y_3 \le 460$$
$$y_1 + y_2 \le 600$$
$$y_2 + y_3 \le 800$$
$$y_1, y_2, y_3 \ge 0$$

(b) $y_1 = 740/3$, $y_2 = 320/3$, $y_3 = 0$, $s_1 = 0$, $s_2 = 0$, $s_3 = 740/3$, $s_4 = 2080/3$, $z = 48{,}800/3$

(c) $x_1 = 20/3$, $x_2 = 80/3$, $x_3 = 0$, $x_4 = 0$, $z = 48{,}800/3$

(d) $s_1 = 0$, $s_2 = 0$, $s_3 = 50/3$

(e) $y_1 = 740/3$, $y_2 = 320/3$, $y_3 = 0$; An increase of 1 unit in the right-hand side of the *i*th primal constraint ($i = 1, 2, 3$) will increase the optimum value of the objective function by y_i units.

11. (a) *Dual:* Maximize $z = 7y_1 + 8y_2 + 9y_3 + 10y_4$

subject to
$$y_1 + y_2 \le 90$$
$$y_3 + y_4 \le 100$$
$$y_1 + y_4 \le 60$$
$$y_2 + y_3 \le 80$$

(b) $y_1 = 0$, $y_2 = 40$, $y_3 = 40$, $y_4 = 60$, $s_1 = 50$, $s_2 = 0$, $s_3 = 0$, $s_4 = 0$, $z = 1280$

(c) $x_1 = 0$, $x_2 = 1$, $x_3 = 9$, $x_4 = 8$, $z = 1280$ **(d)** 2, 0, 0, 0

(e) $y_1 = 0$, $y_2 = 40$, $y_3 = 40$, $y_4 = 60$; An increase of 1 unit in the right-hand side of the *i*th primal constraint ($i = 1, 2, 3, 4$,) will increase the optimum value of the objective function by y_i units.

13. (a) Minimize $C = 6x_1 + 8x_2 + 10x_3 + 9x_4$

subject to
$$\left.\begin{array}{l} x_1 + x_2 \le 500 \\ x_3 + x_4 \le 600 \end{array}\right\} \text{capacity}$$
$$\left.\begin{array}{l} x_1 + x_3 \ge 400 \\ x_2 + x_4 \ge 650 \end{array}\right\} \text{demand}$$

(b) *Dual:*

Maximize $C = -500y_1 - 600y_2 + 400y_3 + 650y_4$
$$-y_1 + y_3 \le 6$$
$$-y_1 + y_4 \le 8$$
$$-y_2 + y_3 \le 10$$
$$-y_2 + y_4 \le 9$$
$$y_1, y_2, y_3, y_4 \ge 0$$

(c) $y_1 = 1$, $y_2 = 0$, $y_3 = 7$, $y_4 = 9$, $s_1 = 0$, $s_2 = 0$, $s_3 = 3$, $s_4 = 0$, $C = 8150$ **(d)** $x_1 = 400$, $x_2 = 100$, $x_3 = 0$, $x_4 = 550$, $C = 8150$ **(e)** 0, 50 (slack), 0, and 0

(f) $y_1 = 0$, $y_2 = 0$, $y_3 = 7$, $y_4 = 9$; An increase of 1 unit in the right-hand side of the *i*th primal constraint ($i = 1, 2, 3, 4$) will increase the optimum value of the objective function by y_i units.

15. (a) Minimize $C = 8x_1 + 10x_2 + 15x_3 + 9x_4$

subject to
$$\left.\begin{array}{l} x_1 + x_2 \le 450 \\ x_3 + x_4 \le 600 \end{array}\right\} \text{capacities}$$
$$\left.\begin{array}{l} x_1 + x_3 \ge 400 \\ x_2 + x_4 \ge 500 \end{array}\right\} \text{demands}$$

(b) *Dual:*

Maximize $C = -450y_1 - 600y_2 + 400y_3 + 500y_4$
$$-y_1 + y_3 \le 8$$
$$-y_1 + y_4 \le 10$$
$$-y_2 + y_3 \le 15$$
$$-y_2 + y_4 \le 9$$
$$y_1, y_2, y_3, y_4 \ge 0$$

(c) $y_1 = 0$, $y_2 = 0$, $y_3 = 8$, $y_4 = 9$, $s_1 = 0$, $s_2 = 1$, $s_3 = 7$, $s_4 = 0$, $C = 7700$ **(d)** $x_1 = 400$, $x_2 = 0$, $x_3 = 0$, $x_4 = 500$, $C = 7700$ **(e)** 50 (slack), 100 (slack), 0, and 0

(f) $y_1 = 0$, $y_2 = 0$, $y_3 = 8$, $y_4 = 9$

An increase of 1 unit in the right-hand side of the *i*th primal constraint ($i = 1, 2, 3, 4$) will increase the optimum value of the objective function by y_i units.

17. (a) Let $x_1 =$ units of food *A*

$x_2 =$ units of food *B*

$x_3 =$ units of food *C*

Minimize $C = 800x_1 + 500x_2 + 600x_3$ calories

subject to
$$5x_1 + 4x_2 + 2x_3 \ge 25 \text{ protein}$$
$$10x_1 + 5x_2 + 8x_3 \ge 60 \text{ calcium}$$
$$2x_1 + x_2 + 3x_3 \ge 10 \text{ iron}$$
$$x_1, x_2, x_3 \ge 0$$

(b) *Dual:* Maximize $C = 25y_1 + 60y_2 + 10y_3$

subject to
$$5y_1 + 10y_2 + 2y_3 \le 800$$
$$4y_1 + 5y_2 + y_3 \le 500$$
$$2y_1 + 8y_2 + 3y_3 \le 600$$
$$y_1, y_2, y_3 \ge 0$$

(c) $y_1 = 20$, $y_2 = 70$, $y_3 = 0$, $s_1 = 0$, $s_2 = 70$, $s_3 = 0$, $C = 4700$ **(d)** $x_1 = 4$, $x_2 = 0$, $x_3 = 5/2$, $C = 4700$

(e) 0, 0, 11/2 **(f)** $y_1 = 20$, $y_2 = 70$, $y_3 = 0$; An increase of 1 unit in the right-hand side of the *i*th primal constraint ($i = 1, 2, 3$) will increase the optimum value of the objective function by y_i units.

19. (a) Let $x_1 =$ number of professional pollsters at location 1

$x_2 =$ number of semiprofessional pollsters at location 1

$x_3 =$ number of professional pollsters at location 2

$x_4 =$ number of semiprofessional pollsters at location 2

Minimize $C = 400x_1 + 300x_2 + 400x_3 + 300x_4$

subject to
$$80x_1 + 50x_2 \ge 440$$
$$80x_3 + 50x_4 \ge 800$$
$$50x_2 + 50x_4 \ge 200$$
$$x_1, x_2, x_3, x_4 \ge 0$$

(b) Dual: Maximize $C = 440y_1 + 800y_2 + 200y_3$

subject to
$$80y_1 \le 400$$
$$50y_1 + 50y_3 \le 300$$
$$80y_2 \le 400$$
$$50y_2 + 50y_3 \le 300$$
$$y_1, y_2, y_3, y_4 \ge 0$$

(c) $y_1 = 5, y_2 = 5, y_3 = 1, s_1 = 0, s_2 = 0, s_3 = 0, s_4 = 0,$ $C = 6400$ **(d)** $x_1 = 3, x_2 = 4, x_3 = 10, x_4 = 0, C = 6400$ **(e)** Surplus $= 0$ for all constraints. **(f)** $y_1 = 5, y_2 = 5,$ $y_3 = 1$; An increase of 1 unit in the right-hand side of the ith primal constraint ($i = 1, 2, 3$) will increase the optimum value of the objective function by y_i units.

SECTION 7-4

1. (a) Maximize
$$z = 5x_1 + 8x_2 + 6x_3 + 0s_1 + 0s_2 - Ma_1 - Ma_2$$
subject to $2x_1 + x_2 + 4x_3 + s_1 \qquad = 190$
$\qquad\qquad x_1 + 2x_2 + 4x_3 \qquad - s_2 + a_1 \qquad = 20$
$\qquad\qquad x_1 + x_2 + x_3 \qquad\qquad + a_2 = 160$
$$x_1, x_2, x_3, s_1, s_2, a_1, a_2, \geq 0$$
(b) $x_1 = 0, x_3 = 0; x_2 = 160, s_1 = 30, s_2 = 300; z = 1280$
3. (a) $x_2 = 0, x_3 = 0, s_1 = 0; x_1 = 33.333, s_2 = 83.333,$ $s_3 = 126.667; z = 333.333$
(b) Only the first constraint is binding. **(c)** 3.333, 0, and 0; An increase of 1 unit in the right-hand side of the first constraint increases the optimal value of the objective function by 3.333 units. The other constraints have no effect.
5. (a) $x_1 = 0, s_1 = 0, s_2 = 0; x_2 = 2.778, x_3 = 39.444;$ $z = 290$ **(b)** Both constraints are binding. **(c)** 0.5 and 1; An increase of 1 unit in the right-hand side of the first constraint will increase the optimum value of the objective function by 0.5 unit. For the second constraint an increase of 1 unit will increase the value of the objective function by 1 unit.
7. (a) $x_3 = 0, s_1 = 0, s_3 = 0; x_1 = 146.67, x_2 = 53.33,$ $s_2 = 606.67; z = 15,066.67$ **(b)** The first and third constraints are binding. **(c)** 6.67, 0, and 56.67; An increase of 1 unit in the right-hand side of the first constraint will increase the optimum value of the objective function by 6.67 units (the first dual price). For the third constraint an increase of 1 unit increases the value of the objective function by 56.67 units.
9. (a) $x_3 = 0, s_1 = 0, s_3 = 0; x_1 = 90, x_2 = 10, s_2 = 60,$ $z = 1100$ **(b)** The first and third constraints are binding. **(c)** -5, 0, and -5; An increase of 1 unit in the right-hand side of the first or third constraint will not lead to an improvement in the value of the objective function but will increase that value by 5 units.
11. (a) $x_2 = 0, s_2 = 0, s_3 = 0, x_1 = 24, x_3 = 14.5,$ $s_1 = 108, z = 216.5$ **(b)** The surplus in the first constraint is 108; the remaining constraints are binding. **(c)** 0, 0.45, and -2.15; An increase of 1 unit in the right-hand side of the second constraint will improve the value of the objective function by 0.45 (z will decrease). For the third constraint an increase in the right-hand side will not improve the value of the objective function (z will increase by 2.15)

13. (a) Let $x_1 =$ number of chairs, $x_2 =$ number of desks, $x_3 =$ number of tables
Maximize $P = 30x_1 + 100x_2 + 160x_3$ profit function
subject to $30x_1 + 20x_2 + 10x_3 \leq 46,000$ cutting
$\qquad\qquad 20x_1 + 60x_2 + 20x_3 \leq 32,000$ assembly
$\qquad\qquad 10x_1 + 40x_2 + 90x_3 \leq 26,000$ finishing
$$x_1, x_2, x_3 \geq 0$$
(b) $x_2 = 0, s_2 = 0, s_3 = 0; x_1 = 1475, x_3 = 125, s_1 = 500,$ $z = 64,250$ **(c)** The second and third constraints are binding. The slack in the first constraint is 500 hours. **(d)** Since there is already slack time in the cutting department, additional hours are worth no money. **(e)** \$0.69 (one additional hr will increase profit by 0.6875) **(f)** \$1.625 (one additional hr will increase profit by 1.625)
15. (a) Let $x_1 =$ dollars invested in treasury bills
$\qquad\qquad x_2 =$ dollars invested in municipal bonds
$\qquad\qquad x_3 =$ dollars invested in real estate
$\qquad\qquad x_4 =$ dollars invested in mutual funds
$\qquad\qquad x_5 =$ dollars invested in energy stocks
Maximize
$$z = 0.083x_1 + 0.098x_2 + 0.159x_3 + 0.163x_4 + 0.184x_5$$
subject to $x_1 + x_2 + x_3 + x_4 + x_5 = 800,000$
$\qquad\qquad 0x_1 + 1x_2 + 3x_3 + 4x_4 + 6x_5 \leq 5.7(800,000)$
$$\text{or } 4,560,000$$
$$x_5 \leq 200,000$$
$$x_1, x_2, x_3, x_4, x_5 \geq 0$$
(b) $x_1 = 0, x_2 = 0, x_3 = 0, s_1 = 0, s_3 = 0; x_4 = 600,000,$ $x_5 = 200,000, s_2 = 960,000; z = 134,600$
(c) Constraints 1 and 3 are binding. **(d)** If the amount invested is increased by \$1, the annual return is increased by \$0.163. **(e)** An additional dollar invested in such stocks will increase the annual return by \$0.021.
17. (a) Let $x_1 =$ truckloads from plant 1 shipped to distribution center 1
$\qquad\qquad x_2 =$ truckloads from plant 1 shipped to distribution center 2
$\qquad\qquad x_3 =$ truckloads from plant 1 shipped to distribution center 3
$\qquad\qquad x_4 =$ truckloads from plant 2 shipped to distribution center 1
$\qquad\qquad x_5 =$ truckloads from plant 2 shipped to distribution center 2
$\qquad\qquad x_6 =$ truckloads from plant 2 shipped to distribution center 3
Minimize
$$z = 400x_1 + 800x_2 + 600x_3 + 500x_4 + 700x_5 + 900x_6$$
subject to $x_1 + x_2 + x_3 \leq 50$ plant 1 capacity
$\qquad\qquad x_4 + x_5 + x_6 \leq 40$ plant 2 capacity
$\qquad\qquad x_1 + x_4 \geq 20$ center 1 demand
$\qquad\qquad x_2 + x_5 \geq 50$ center 2 demand
$\qquad\qquad x_3 + x_6 \geq 15$ center 3 demand
$$x_1, x_2, x_3, x_4, x_5, x_6 \geq 0$$

(b) $x_4 = 0$, $x_6 = 0$, $s_2 = 0$, $s_3 = 0$, $s_4 = 0$, $s_5 = 0$; $x_1 = 20$, $x_2 = 10$, $x_3 = 15$, $x_5 = 40$, $s_1 = 5$; $z = 53,000$
(c) Constraints 2, 3, 4, and 5 are binding.
(d) No; the slack variable is not zero for constraint 1.
(e) Yes; constraint 2 is binding and the shadow price is positive. An increase of 1 truckload in the capacity will improve the optimal value of the objective function by 100 units. **(f)** The total transportation cost will not improve (shadow price = -400) but will increase by 400.
(g) The total transportation cost will not improve (shadow price = -800) but will increase by 800.
(h) The total transportation cost will not improve (shadow price = -600) but will increase by 600. **(i)** Distribution center 2
19. (a) Minimize
$$z = x_1 + x_2 + x_3 + x_4 + x_5 + x_6 \quad \text{total manpower}$$
$$\text{subject to} \quad x_1 + x_6 \geq 3 \quad \text{midnight to 4 AM}$$
$$x_1 + x_2 \geq 5 \quad \text{4 AM to 8 AM}$$
$$x_2 + x_3 \geq 14 \quad \text{8 AM to noon}$$
$$x_3 + x_4 \geq 16 \quad \text{noon to 4 PM}$$
$$x_4 + x_5 \geq 14 \quad \text{4 PM to 8 PM}$$
$$x_5 + x_6 \geq 10 \quad \text{8 PM to midnight}$$
$$x_1, x_2, x_3, x_4, x_5, x_6 \geq 0$$
(b) $x_6 = 0$, $s_1 = 0$, $s_2 = 0$, $s_3 = 0$, $s_4 = 0$, $s_5 = 0$, $s_6 = 0$; $x_1 = 3$, $x_2 = 2$, $x_3 = 12$, $x_4 = 4$, $x_5 = 10$; $z = 31$ **(c)** 31
(d) All constraints are binding. There are no surplus amounts. **(e)** The total number of officers needed to satisfy minimal personnel requirements will be increased by 1 (shadow price = -1). **(f)** No additional officers will be needed, provided the right-hand side can vary in this way. In fact, it cannot do so without violating other constraints. Several solutions to the new problem, with $x_2 + x_3 \geq 15$, are possible but the total number of officers is at least 32. Two solutions are
$x_1 = 3$, $x_2 = 3$, $x_3 = 12$, $x_4 = 4$, $x_5 = 10$, $x_6 = 0$ and
$x_1 = 3$, $x_2 = 2$, $x_3 = 13$, $x_4 = 4$, $x_5 = 10$, $x_6 = 0$

SECTION 7-5

1. (a) $x_2 = 0$, $s_1 = 0$, $s_3 = 0$; $x_1 = 28.2609$, $x_3 = 8.6957$, $s_2 = 30$; $z = 182.6087$ **(b)** The slack for constraint 2 is 30 units. Constraints 1 and 3 are binding. **(c)** The dual prices corresponding to constraints 1 and 3 are 1.56522 and 0.1739. An increase of 1 unit in the right-hand side of constraint 1 or 3 will increase the value of the optimal solution by 1.56522 or 0.1739, respectively. **(d)** The coefficient of x_1 can vary from 3.2 to 5.5 without changing the optimum values of x_1, x_3 or s_2. The coefficient of x_2 has a maximum value of 8.3478 and no lower limit. The coefficient of x_3 has a range of 6.7143 to 10, within which the optimum values of the basic variables (x_1, x_3, and s_2) will not change. **(e)** The range for the right-hand side of constraint 1 is 60$-$750, for constraint 2 is 150 up to no

upper limit, and for constraint 3 is 20$-$180. Within each range, taken individually, the optimal basis still contains x_1, x_3 and s_2, and the interpretation of the dual prices remains valid. The values of the basic variables may change.
3. (a) $x_2 = 0$, $s_2 = 0$, $s_3 = 0$; $x_1 = 8.6557$, $x_3 = 7.82609$, $s_1 = 36.52174$; $z = 140$ **(b)** Constraints 2 and 3 are binding. The surplus in constraint 1 is 36.52174.
(c) The dual prices for constraints 2 and 3 are -1 and -2, indicating that an increase of 1 unit in the right-hand side of either constraint will not improve the optimal value of z but will lead to increases of 1 and 2 units, respectively.
(d) The coefficients of x_1, x_2, and x_3 can vary from 2.25$-$14.3889, 0 to no upper limit, and 1.8125$-$32, respectively. Within these individual ranges the optimal values of the basic variables will not change.
(e) The ranges for the right-hand side of constraints 1, 2, and 3 are no lower limit to 56.52174, 10$-$240, and 10$-$240, respectively. Within each range, taken individually, the optimal basis still contains x_1, x_3, and s_1, and the interpretation of the dual prices remains valid. The values of the basic variables may change.
5. (a) $s_1 = 0$, $s_2 = 0$, $s_3 = 0$; $x_1 = 10.7143$, $x_2 = 16.0714$, $x_3 = 5$; $z = 255$ **(b)** All constraints are binding.
(c) The dual prices for constraints 1 and 2 are positive, indicating that an increase of 1 unit in the right-hand side of either constraint will improve (increase) the optimum value of z by 1 unit (the dual price). The dual price for constraint 3 is negative, indicating that an increase of 1 unit in the right-hand side will not improve the optimum value of z but will lead to a decrease of 1 unit in z.
(d) The coefficients of x_1, x_2, and x_3 can vary from 6.6667$-$9.6364, 7.6216$-$10.8, and no lower limit to 7, respectively. Within each range, taken individually, the optimal values of the basic variables will not change.
(e) The ranges for the right-hand sides of the constraints are 45$-$115, 133.75$-$265, and 0$-$11.0811, respectively. Within each range, taken individually, the optimal basis still contains x_1, x_2; and x_3, and the interpretation of the dual prices remains valid. The values of the basic variables may change.
7. (a) Let $x_1 = $ units of product A,
$x_2 = $ units of product B
$x_3 = $ units of product C
Maximize $z = 50x_1 + 40x_2 + 60x_3$ profit function
subject to $2x_1 + 3x_2 + x_3 \leq 760$ capacity, department 1
$x_1 + 2x_2 + 4x_3 \leq 600$ capacity, department 2
$2x_1 + x_2 + 2x_3 \leq 660$ capacity, department 3
(b) $s_1 = 0$, $s_2 = 0$, $s_3 = 0$, $x_1 = 240$, $x_2 = 76$, $x_3 = 52$, $z = 18,160$ **(c)** All constraints are binding. **(d)** \$4
(e) 570$-$1020. Since the current value is 760, up to 260 hours can be added within this range. **(f)** Department 3; \$18.67 in profit (dual price 3); 822.857 person-hours.
(g) 30 to 80

9. (a) Let x_1 = units of food A
x_2 = units of food B
x_3 = units of food C
Minimize $z = 30x_1 + 20x_2 + 35x_3$ cost function
subject to $3x_1 + 5x_2 + 6x_3 \geq 30$ protein
$6x_1 + 12x_2 + 5x_3 \geq 72$ calcium
$4x_1 + 2x_2 + x_3 \geq 15$ iron
$x_1, x_2, x_3 \geq 0$
(b) $x_3 = 0$, $s_2 = 0$, $s_3 = 0$, $x_1 = 1$, $x_2 = 5.5$, $s_1 = 0.5$, $z = 140$ **(c)** Constraints 2 and 3 are binding. The surplus for constraint 1 is 0.5 milligrams of protein. **(d)** There will be no effect on the optimal diet cost, since constraint 1 is not binding. **(e)** iron; a decrease of 6.67 cost units; 12 milligrams **(f)** 15 to 60 **(g)** 9.44 to no upper limit.
11. (a) Let x_1 = units of product A produced at plant 1
x_2 = units of product B produced at plant 1
x_3 = units of product C produced at plant 1
x_4 = units of product A produced at plant 2
x_5 = units of product B produced at plant 2
x_6 = units of product C produced at plant 2
Minimize $z = 80x_1 + 100x_2 + 150x_3 + 90x_4 + 70x_5 + 60x_6$

cost function
subject to $x_1 + x_2 + x_3 \leq 900$ ⎫ capacities
$x_4 + x_5 + x_6 \leq 1000$ ⎭
$x_1 + x_4 \geq 800$ ⎫
$x_2 + x_5 \geq 600$ ⎬ demands
$x_3 + x_6 \geq 400$ ⎭
$x_1, x_2, x_3, x_4, x_5, x_6 \geq 0$
(b) $x_2 = 0$, $x_3 = 0$, $x_4 = 0$, $s_2 = 0$, $s_3 = 0$, $s_4 = 0$, $s_5 = 0$, $x_1 = 800$, $x_5 = 600$, $x_6 = 400$, $s_1 = 100$, $z = 130{,}000$
(c) Constraints 2, 3, 4, and 5 are binding. The slack in constraint 1 is 100 units. **(d)** The dual price for constraint 2 is zero, indicating that there is no advantage in increasing the capacity of plant 2. Plant 1 already has excess capacity. **(e)** An increase in the demand will not improve the optimal cost but will cause it to increase by $60. **(f)** Optimal cost will improve (decrease) by $70. **(g)** Product A. Decrease of $80. Lower limit is 0. **(h)** $80 to no upper limit **(i)** $0 to $150
13. (a) Minimize
$z = 50x_1 + 70x_2 + 60x_3 + 90x_4$ cost function
subject to $x_1 + x_2 \geq 150$ ⎫ minimum number to be
$x_3 + x_4 \geq 120$ ⎭ interviewed by type
$x_1 + x_3 \leq 200$ ⎫ maximum number to be
$x_2 + x_4 \leq 250$ ⎭ interviewed by city
$x_4 \geq 20$ minimum number of
specialists in city 2
$x_1, x_2, x_3, x_4 \geq 0$
(b) $s_1 = 0$, $s_2 = 0$, $s_3 = 0$, $s_5 = 0$, $x_1 = 100$, $x_2 = 50$, $x_3 = 100$, $x_4 = 20$, $s_4 = 180$, $z = \$16{,}300$ **(c)** Constraints 1, 2, 3, and 5 are binding. The slack in constraint 4 is 180 interviewers. **(d)** The total interview cost will be improved

(decreased) by $20; valid for right-hand side between 100 and 250. **(e)** The total interview cost will be increased by $80; valid for the right-hand side between 70 and 220. **(f)** $50 to $80
15. (a) Let x_1 = number of dollars invested in money market funds.
x_2 = number of dollars invested in mutual funds
x_3 = number of dollars invested in growth and income stocks
x_4 = number of dollars invested in aggressive growth stocks
Maximize
$z = 0.07x_1 + 0.15x_2 + 0.18x_3 + 0.25x_4$ total return
subject to $x_1 + x_2 + x_3 + x_4 = 5{,}000{,}000$ total funds
$0x_1 + 3x_2 + 5x_3 + 9x_4 \leq 4.7(5{,}000{,}000)$
or $23{,}500{,}000$
$x_1, x_2, x_3, x_4 \geq 0$
(b) $x_1 = 0$, $x_3 = 0$, $s_1 = 0$, $s_2 = 0$, $x_2 = 3{,}583{,}333.80$, $x_4 = 1{,}416{,}666.50$, $z = \$891{,}666.69$ **(c)** Both constraints are binding. **(d)** The optimum projected annual return will increase by $0.10 (dual price for constraint 1); valid between $2,611,111 and $7,833,333 **(e)** 0.24 to 0.31
17. (a) Let x_1 = number of units of product 1
x_2 = number of units of product 2
x_3 = number of units of product 3
Minimize $z = 30x_1 + 50x_2 + 50x_3$ total variable cost
subject to $50x_1 + 70x_2 + 40x_3 = 63{,}000$ break-even point
$x_1 \geq 200$ demand
$x_2 \leq 300$ production limit
$x_3 \geq 400$ demand
$x_1, x_2, x_3 \geq 0$
(b) $x_2 = 0$, $s_1 = 0$, $s_4 = 0$, $x_1 = 940$, $x_3 = 400$, $s_2 = 740$, $s_3 = 300$, $z = \$48{,}200$ **(c)** Constraints 1 and 4 are binding. The surplus in constraint 2 is 740 units. The slack in constraint 3 is 300 units. **(d)** The optimum total variable cost will be increased by $0.60 (dual cost for constraint 1). **(e)** There will be a decrease of $26.00 in the optimal total variable cost; valid within the range of 0 to 1325 for the right-hand side. **(f)** No lower limit to $35.71. **(g)** $24 to no upper limit.
19. (a) Let x_1 = number of units of product A
x_2 = number of units of product B
x_3 = number of units of product C
Maximize $z = 90x_1 + 60x_2 + 70x_3$ profit function
subject to $3x_1 + 2x_2 + 5x_3 \leq 30{,}000$ raw material 1
$2x_1 + 4x_2 + 6x_3 \leq 33{,}000$ raw material 2
$4x_1 + 2x_2 + 7x_3 \leq 37{,}000$ raw material 3
$x_1 \geq 800$ ⎫
$x_2 \geq 400$ ⎬ demands
$x_3 \geq 500$ ⎭
$x_1, x_2, x_3 \geq 0$

(b) On your computer. **(c)** $s_2 = 0, s_3 = 0, s_6 = 0$; $x_1 = 6166.67, x_2 = 4416.67, x_3 = 500$ $s_1 = 166.67$, $s_4 = 5366.67, s_5 = 4016.67, z = \$855,000$ **(d)** Constraints 2, 3, and 6 are binding. The slack in constraint 1 is 166.67 units. The surplus amounts in constraints 4 and 5 are 5366.67 and 4016.67, respectively. **(e)** The maximum amount to be paid per pound is 0, since there is already a surplus. **(f)** The maximum amount to be paid per pound is $5, the dual price for constraint 2; valid for up to 1000 additional pounds. **(g)** Raw material 3; $20 per additional pound. The limit is 250 additional pounds. **(h)** $45 to $180.

• CHAPTER HIGHLIGHTS

1. A **slack variable** is a variable that represents the amount of slack in a particular constraint. A **feasible solution** consists of values of variables that satisfy all constraints of a linear programming problem. A **basic feasible solution** is a feasible solution that contains exactly as many nonzero variables as the number of constraint equations; the remaining variables must equal 0. The nonzero variables of a basic feasible solution are called **basic variables.** The zero variables of a basic feasible solution are called **nonbasic variables.** A linear programming problem is in **standard maximization form** if:
1) The objective function is to be maximized and is of the linear form, $z = c_1x_1 + c_2x_2 + \ldots + c_nx_n$
2) All variables are nonnegative (i.e., $x_i \geq 0$)
3) All constraints are linear inequalities of the form $a_1x_1 + a_2x_2 + \ldots + a_nx_n \leq b$ where $b \geq 0$.
A **simplex tableau** is obtained by including slack variables for all ($\leq$) constraints, writing the objective function below the constraints and then writing the matrix (or tableau) to the resulting linear system. **2.** It is a binding constraint. **3.** The column corresponding to the variable to be increased is called a **pivot column.** A **pivot row** is the row that corresponds to the minimum quotient resulting from dividing right-hand side values by corresponding positive pivot column coefficients. The entry that lies at the intersection of a pivot column and a pivot row is called the **pivot element.** The coefficients of the last row of a simplex tableau are called **indicators.** Each indicator corresponds to a variable. An indicator gives the effect on the value of the objective function of a unit increase in the value of its corresponding variable. A **degeneracy** occurs when, for some tableau, one or more of the basic variables is zero. Such a solution is called a **degenerate solution.** **4.** Increase the value of the variable with the most negative indicator. **5.** For each positive pivot column coefficient, divide the corresponding right-hand side value by the pivot column coefficient.

Determine the *minimum such quotient.* (In the event of ties, arbitrarily choose either of the tied coefficients.) The row corresponding to the minimum quotient is called the **pivot row.** The pivot-row coefficient located in the pivot column is called the pivot element. The pivot element must be changed to 1 by a row operation. **6.** Multiply a row by a nonzero constant. Add a multiple of a row to another row. **7.** A simplex tableau yields an optimal solution if there are no negative indicators. **8.** Alternate optimal solutions exist if a nonbasic variable indicator has a value of 0. **9.** A linear programming problem is in **standard minimization form** if:
1) The objective function is to be minimized and is of the linear form $z = c_1x_1 + c_2x_2 + \ldots + c_nx_n$
2) All variables are nonnegative (i.e., $x_i \geq 0$)
3) All constraints are linear inequalities of the form $a_1x_1 + a_2x_2 + \ldots + a_nx_n \geq b$ where $b \geq 0$.
This is also called a **primal problem.** The optimal solution to a minimization problem is determined by solving a companion problem called the **dual.** **10.** The dual of a primal problem is determined as follows:
1) Place the objective function below the constraints and write the corresponding matrix.
2) Assign a dual variable to each primal constraint and read the matrix vertically so that column 1 of the primal becomes row 1 of the dual, column 2 of the primal becomes row 2 of the dual, and so on until the right-hand side values of the primal become the objective function coefficients.
3) For the dual, the objective function is to be maximized and all constraints are of the ($\leq$) type. *Note:* The dual of a maximization problem with ($\leq$) constraints is a minimization problem with ($\geq$) constraints. Also, the dual of a dual equals the primal.
11. The **fundamental theorem of duality** is as follows:
1) If either the primal or dual problem has an optimal solution, then they both have optimal solutions. If an optimal solution exists, both primal and dual objective functions have the same optimal value.
2) The optimal values of the primal variables $x_1, x_2, \ldots$, etc. are given by the indicators corresponding to the slack variables in the dual optimal tableau.
12. *Shadow prices.* A **shadow price** represents the amount of change in the optimal value of an objective function resulting from a change in the right-hand side value of a primal constraint. A shadow price is valid only for a specific interval within which a right-hand side value can vary. **13.** *Binding constraint.* This means that the minimal requirement of the constraint is being met exactly by the optimal solution. **14.** If a linear programming problem contains any combination of ($\leq$), ($\geq$), and ($=$) constraints, it is said to have mixed constraints. **15.** An artificial variable is a nonnegative variable added to the left-hand side

of either a ($\geq$) constraint or an ($=$) constraint to ensure a positive solution value. Artificial variables have no meaning and are driven to zero by the time the simplex process yields an optimal solution. **16. (a)** ($\leq$) **(b)** ($\geq$) **(c)** ($\geq$) and ($=$) **17.** Assign $-M$ if the objective function is to be maximized and M if the objective function is to be minimized. **18.** 0 **19.** Shadow prices are given among the indicators corresponding to slack and or surplus variables.

20. 1) The dual price for a constraint gives the improvement in the optimal value of the objective function resulting from a one-unit increase in the right-hand-side value of the constraint.

2) The meaning of the word improvement depends upon whether the objective function is to be maximized or minimized. Specifically, if the objective function is to be maximized, improvement means an increase in its value; minimized, improvement means a decrease in its value.

3) Also,
   - a positive dual price means that the optimal value of an objective function will improve,
   - a negative dual price means that the optimal value of an objective function will not improve as a result of an increase in the right-hand side value of the associated constraint.

21. Sensitivity analysis entails a study of the effects of changes to an original problem after an optimal solution has been found. The **objective coefficient range** gives the amount by which an objective function coefficient can vary in order that the optimal basis (in other words, vertex point) remains optimal. The **right-hand side range** gives the amount by which the right-hand side value of a constraint can change in order that the optimal basis remains feasible, and, thus, the respective shadow price (or dual price) interpretation remains applicable.

• REVIEW EXERCISES

1. (a) $x_2 = 4$, $x_3 = 7$, $s_3 = 9$; $z = 856$ **(b)** Not optimal, since there is a negative value in the indicator row.

3. $x_2 = 30$, $s_2 = 10$; $x_1 = 0$, $x_3 = 0$, $s_1 = 0$, $z = 240$

5. $x_1 = 8$, $x_2 = 8$, $s_2 = 6$, $x_3 = 0$, $s_1 = 0$, $s_3 = 0$, $z = 112$

7. (a) $x_1 = 11$, $s_2 = 84$; $x_2 = 0$, $s_1 = 0$; $z = 88$

(b) x_2 has a zero indicator in the tableau.

(c) $x_1 = 5$, $x_2 = 12$; $s_1 = 0$, $s_2 = 0$; $z = 88$

(d) Note that for the solution in part a, constraint 2 has 84 units of slack whereas for the solution in part c, constraint 2 has no slack. Thus, one optimal solution uses up all resource capacities and another does not.

9. (a) $s_1 = 0$, $s_3 = 0$; $x_2 = 0$, $x_1 = 30$, $s_2 = 200$; $z = 180$
Two quotients tie for a pivot row choice (R1, & R3)

(b)

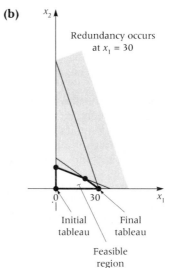

11. (a) Dual: Maximize $z = 10y_1 + 12y_2 + 8y_3$
subject to $y_1 + 4y_2 + y_3 \leq 4$
$y_1 + y_2 + 2y_3 \leq 8$
$y_1 + 2y_2 + 2y_3 \leq 2$
$y_1, y_2, y_3 \geq 0$

(b) $y_1 = 2$, $s_1 = 2$, $s_2 = 6$, $y_2 = 0$, $y_3 = 0$, $s_3 = 0$, $z = 20$
(c) $x_1 = 0$, $x_2 = 0$, $x_3 = 10$; $z = 20$
(d) $s_1 = 0$, $s_2 = 8$, $s_3 = 12$
(e) y values: 2, 0, and 0
An increase of 1 unit in the right-hand side of the ith primal constraint ($i = 1, 2, 3$) will increase the optimum value of the objective function by y_i units.

13. (a) Dual: Maximize $z = 5y_1 + 7y_2 + 6y_3$
subject to $2y_1 + 6y_2 + 4y_3 \leq 96$
$y_1 + 4y_2 + 2y_3 \leq 64$
$2y_1 + y_2 + y_3 \leq 48$
$y_1, y_2, y_3 \geq 0$

(b) $y_1 = 16$, $y_3 = 16$, $s_2 = 16$, $y_2 = 0$, $s_1 = 0$, $s_3 = 0$, $z = 176$ **(c)** $x_1 = 7/6$, $x_2 = 0$, $x_3 = 4/3$; $z = 176$
(d) $s_1 = 0$, $s_2 = 4/3$, $s_3 = 0$
(e) 16, 0 and 16
If the right-hand side of either constraints 1 or 3 is increased by 1 unit, then the optimal value of the objective function will be increased by 16 units. For the second constraint, there is no effect

15. (a) $x_1 = 0$, $x_2 = 1$, $x_3 = 3$, $z = 51$ **(b)** 0, 0, and 4, respectively. **(c)** The shadow prices are the y values: 3, 6, and 0. If the right-hand side of the first primal constraint is increased by 1 unit, the optimal value of the objective function will be increased by 3 units. For the second constraint a change of 1 unit will lead to a change of 6 units in the value of the objective function. For the third constraint there is no effect. **17. (a)** $x_1 = 3$, $x_2 = 6$, $x_3 = 0$, $z = 48$ **(b)** The values of the slack variables are

$s_1 = 1, s_2 = 0, s_3 = 0$. The second and third constraints are binding. **(c)** The shadow prices are given in the indicator row under s_1, s_2, and s_3. They are 0, 1.333, and 2.333. An increase of 1 unit in the right-hand side of the second constraint, for example, will lead to an increase of 1.333 units in the optimal value of the objective function.

19. (a) $x_1 = 16.364, x_2 = 14.545, x_3 = 0, z = 1072.72$
(b) The values of the slack variables are $s_1 = 22.727$, $s_2 = 0$, and $s_3 = 0$. The second and third constraints are binding. **(c)** The shadow prices are given in the indicator row under s_1, s_2, and s_3. They are 0, 11.818, and 4.545. An increase of 1 unit in the right-hand side of the second constraint, for example, will lead to an increase of 11.818 units in the optimal value of the objective function.

21. Maximize
$$z = 19x_1 + 17x_2 + 15x_3 + 0s_1 + 0s_2 - Ma_1 - Ma_2$$
subject to
$$5x_1 + x_2 + 5x_3 - s_1 + a_1 \quad\quad = 15$$
$$3x_1 + 6x_2 + 8x_3 \quad\quad + s_2 \quad\quad = 90$$
$$2x_1 + 5x_2 + 8x_3 \quad\quad\quad\quad + a_2 = 180$$
$$x_1, x_2, x_3, s_1, s_2, a_1, a_2 \geq 0$$

23. Minimize
$$z = 5x_1 + 9x_2 + 8x_3 + 0s_1 + 0s_2 + Ma_1 + Ma$$
subject to
$$x_1 + 5x_2 + 8x_3 + s_1 \quad\quad\quad\quad = 100$$
$$x_1 + 15x_2 + 8x_3 \quad\quad + a_1 \quad\quad = 160$$
$$2x_1 + 3x_2 + 9x_3 \quad\quad - s_2 + a_2 = 50$$
$$x_1, x_2, x_3, s_1, s_2, a_1, a_2 \geq 0$$

25. (a) $x_1 = 0, x_2 = 17.333, x_3 = 0.667, z = 73.333$
(b) The surplus amount for constraint 1 is 0. The constraint is binding. The slack for constraint 3 is 137.333 units.
(c) The dual prices are -1.333, -0.667, and 0. An increase of 1 unit on the right-hand side of either constraint 1 or constraint 2 will not improve the optimal value of the objective function but will lead to an increase of 1.333 units or 0.667 units, respectively. Constraint 3 is not binding. **27. (a)** $x_1 = 4, x_2 = 0, x_3 = 14, z = 154$ Surplus / slack variables: $s_1 = 0, s_2 = 20, s_3 = 0$
(b) Constraints 1 and 3 are binding. **(c)** The dual prices are .543, 0, and 2.11. An increase of 1 unit in the right-hand side of constraint 1 or 3 will increase the optimal value of the objective function by .543 or 2.11, respectively.

29. (a) x_1: 4.66667−no upper limit
$\quad\quad x_2$: no lower limit−24
$\quad\quad x_3$: 1−10.54545
Within these ranges, taken individually, the basis for the optimal solution will not change. The value of the objective function may change.
(b) Constraint 1: 17.5−86.45161
$\quad\quad$ Constraint 2: 5−80
$\quad\quad$ Constraint 3: 22.66667−no upper limit
Within these ranges, taken individually, an increase of 1 unit in the right-hand side will improve the values of the objective function by the amount of the corresponding

shadow price if the shadow price is positive. If the shadow price is negative, the value of the objective function will not be improved. Within these ranges, the optimal basis remains feasible and the interpretation of the dual prices remains valid.

31. (a) Let x_1 = number of units of model MCW01
$\quad\quad\quad x_2$ = number of units of model MCW02
$\quad\quad\quad x_3$ = number of units of model MCW03
Maximize $z = 100x_1 + 150x_2 + 200x_3$ profit function
subject to $\quad x_1 + x_2 + x_3 \leq 500$ production limit
$\quad\quad\quad 2x_1 + x_2 + 3x_3 \leq 400$ component A
$\quad\quad\quad x_1 + 2x_2 + 2x_3 \leq 600$ component B
$\quad\quad x_3 \geq 2x_2$ or $2x_2 - x_3 \leq 0$
$\quad\quad\quad\quad x_1, x_2, x_3 \geq 0$
(b) $x_1 = 0, x_2 = 57.14, x_3 = 114.29, z = \$31,428.57$
Since integral values of x_1, x_2, and x_3 are appropriate, we would produce 57 model MCW02's and 114 MCW03's.
(c) Slack variables: $s_1 = 328.57, s_2 = 0, s_3 = 257.14, s_4 = 0$. Constraints 2 and 4 are binding. **(d)** The dual prices are 0, 78.57, 0, and 35.71. An increase of 1 unit in the number of component A units available will increase the optimal profit by \$78.57. **(e)** The coefficients of x_1, x_2 and x_3 can vary from no lower limit to 157.14, 66.67 to no upper limit and 100 to 450, respectively. Within these individual ranges, the optimal values of the basic variables will not change. **(f)** The ranges for the right-hand side of constraints 1, 2, 3, and 4 are 171.43 to no upper limit, 0 to 700, 342.86 to no upper limit, and −133.33 to 450 respectively. Within each range, taken individually, the optimal basis still contains x_1, x_2, x_3, and s_3 and the interpretation of the dual prices remains valid. The values of the basic variables may change.

33. (a) Let x_1 = number of gallons of crude 1 used in regular gasoline
$\quad\quad\quad x_2$ = number of gallons of crude 1 used in premium gasoline
$\quad\quad\quad x_3$ = number of gallons of crude 2 used in regular gasoline
$\quad\quad\quad x_4$ = number of gallons of crude 2 used in premium gasoline
Minimize
$$z = 0.20x_1 + 0.20x_2 + 0.25x_3 + 0.25x_4 \quad \text{cost function}$$
subject to $\quad 0.15x_1 + 0.45x_3 \geq 0.30 (x_1 + x_3)$ component A
$\quad\quad\quad 0.5x_2 + 0.4x_4 \leq 0.45 (x_2 + x_4)$ component B
$\quad\quad\quad x_1 + x_3 \geq 900,000$ $\left.\right\}$ demands
$\quad\quad\quad x_2 + x_4 \geq 1,200,000$
(b) $x_1 = 450,000, x_2 = 600,000, x_3 = 450,000$, $x_4 = 600,000, z = \$472,500$ **(c)** The values of the surplus quantities are all zero, indicating that all constraints are binding. **(d)** The dual prices are $-1/6$, $1/2$, -0.225, and -0.225. An increase of 1 unit in the right-hand side of constraints 1, 3, and 4 will not improve the optimal solution but will increase it by the amount of the dual price.

(e) The coefficients of x_1, x_2, x_3, and x_4 can vary from -0.25 to 0.25, -0.25 to 0.25, 0.20 to no upper limit and, 0.20 to no upper limit, respectively. Within these individual ranges, the optimal values of the basic variables will not change. **(f)** The ranges for the right-hand side of constraints 1, 2, 3, and 4 are $-135,000$ to $135,000$, $-60,000$ to $60,000$, 0 to no upper limit, and 0 to no upper limit, respectively. Within each range, taken individually, the optimal basis still contains x_1, x_2, x_3, and x_4 and the interpretation of the dual prices remains valid. The values of the basic variables may change.

• CHAPTER 8

SECTION 8-1

1. (a) True **(b)** True **(c)** True **(d)** True **(e)** True **(f)** False **(g)** False **(h)** False   **3. (a)** Yes **(b)** Yes **(c)** Yes
5. $\{4, 5\}$ **7.** 4   **9.** $\{2, 3\}$ **11.** $\{1, 2, 3, 6, 7, 8, 9\}$
13. $\{1, 2, 3, 6, 7, 8, 9\}$ **15.** 5   **17.**

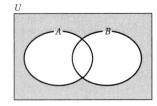

19.   **21.**

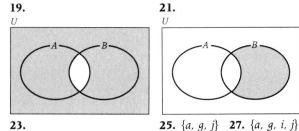

23.

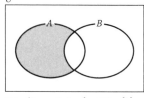

25. $\{a, g, j\}$ **27.** $\{a, g, i, j\}$

29. $\{b, e, f, h, i\}$ **31.** $\{b\}$ **33.** $\{a, b, c, d, e, g, h, j\}$
35. $\{a, b, c, d, f, g, i, j\}$ **37.** $\{a, c, d, g, j\}$
39. $\{a, c, d, f, g, j\}$ **41.** $\{a, g, i, j\}$

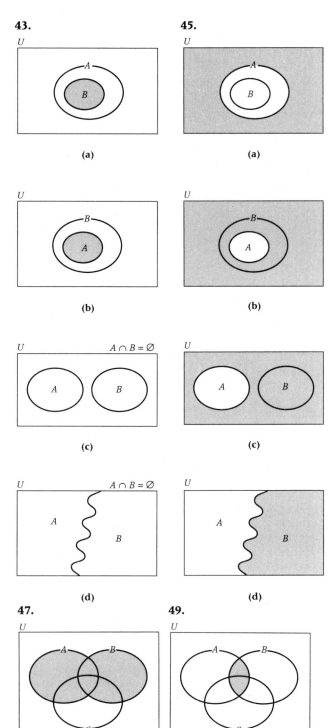

43.

(a)

(b)

$A \cap B = \varnothing$

(c)

$A \cap B = \varnothing$

(d)

45.

(a)

(b)

(c)

(d)

47.

49.

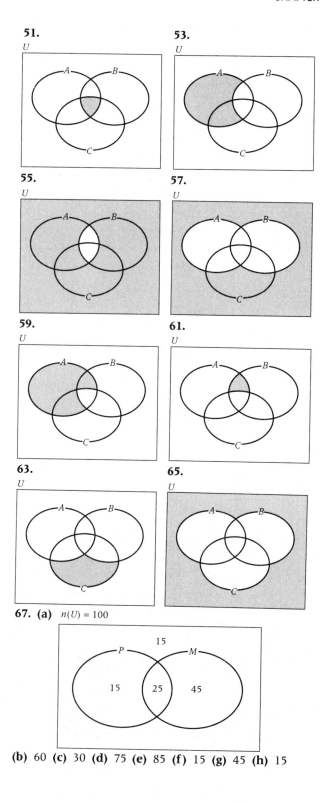

51.

53.

55.

57.

59.

61.

63.

65.

67. (a) $n(U) = 100$

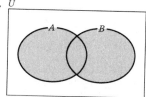

(b) 60 **(c)** 30 **(d)** 75 **(e)** 85 **(f)** 15 **(g)** 45 **(h)** 15

69. (a) $n(U) = 200$

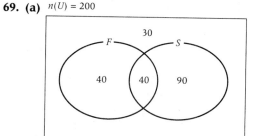

(b) 170 **(c)** 30 **(d)** 40 **(e)** 90 **(f)** 70
(g) 30.77% **(h)** 50%

71. (a) $n(U) = 500$

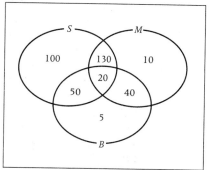

(b) 145 **(c)** 50 **(d)** 130 **(e)** 100 **(f)** 10 **(g)** 350
73. (a) 210 **(b)** 90 **(c)** 150 **(d)** 250 **(e)** 310 **(f)** 150
(g) 0 **(h)** 190 **(i)** 0 **(j)** 40% **(k)** 40% **(l)** 47.4%
75. (a) 24 **(b)** 10 **(c)** 16 **(d)** 6 **(e)** 18 **(f)** 3 **(g)** 28
(h) 41 **(i)** 17 **(j)** 34 **(k)** 40 **(l)** 4 **(m)** 60% **(n)** 25%
(o) 70% **(p)** 17.5%
77. U

$A \cup B$ is the set that is shaded above. The overlapping
region includes those elements that are common to sets A
and B. The sample count of $n(A) + n(B)$ counts such
elements twice. To correct the count, subtract the number
of elements in common, i.e., $n(A \cap B)$. Hence,
$n(A \cup B) = n(A) + n(B) - n(A \cap B)$.
79. 43 **81.** 67 **83. (a)** 37 **(b)** 33 **85. (a)** 90 **(b)** 130
(c) 110 **(d)** 0 **87. (a)** 80 **(b)** 60 **(c)** 110

SECTION 8-2

1. 24 **3.** 1 **5.** 720 **7.** 24 **9.** 120 **11.** 210 **13.** 1
15. 190 **17.** 24 **19.** $5^{10} = 9,765,625$ **21.** $6^4 = 1296$
23. (a) 676,000 **(b)** 650,000 **(c)** 486,720 **25.** 360
27. 60 **29.** 5040 **31.** 360 **33.** 10 **35.** 84 **37.** 28
39. 1 **41.** 1 **43.** 20 **45.** 1 **47.** 36 **49.** 30 **51.** 360

53. 44,100 **55.** 113,256 **57.** 120 ways **59.** 60 ways
61. 10 ways **63.** 10 lines **65.** 60,480 possibilities
67. 635,013,559,600 hands **69.** 35 teams
71. 5040 possibilities **73.** 2,598,960 hands
75. 4320 ways **77. (a)** 9,000,000 numbers
(b) 544,320 numbers **79. (a)** $10^5 = 100,000$ **(b)** 30,240
81. $C(4, 2) \cdot C(48, 11) + C(4, 8) \cdot C(48, 10) +$
$C(4, 4) \cdot C(48, 9) = 163,411,172,432$
83. (a) 5,852,925 samples **(b)** 5,262,400 **(c)** 1,381,380
(d) 6,921,850 samples **(e)** 8,206,055 samples
85. $\approx 1.050421 \times 10^{15}$ committees

SECTION 8-3

1. (a) $S = \{$mo, mn, me, my, om, on, oe, oy, nm, no, ne,
ny, em, eo, en, ey, ym, yo, yn, ye$\}$ **(b)** $\frac{1}{5}$, or 20%.

(c) $\frac{1}{5}$, or 20% **(d)** 0 **3. (a)** {pn, pd, pq, np, nd, nq, dp,
dn, dq, qp, qn, qd} **(b)** $\frac{1}{6}$, or 16.7% **(c)** 0
5. (a) {hhhh, hhht, hhth, hhtt, hthh, htht, htth, httt, thhh,
thht, thth, thtt, tthh, ttht, ttth, tttt} **(b)** $\frac{1}{4}$, or 25%

(c) $\frac{15}{16}$, or 93.75% **(d)** $\frac{5}{16}$, or 31.25% **(e)** $\frac{1}{8}$, or 12.5%

7. $\frac{35}{100}$, or 35% **9.** $\frac{85}{100}$, or 85% **11.** $\frac{10}{100}$, or 10%

13. $\frac{1}{6}$, or 16.7% **15.** $\frac{1}{4}$, or 25% **17.** 0

19. 0.833, or 83.3% **21.** $\frac{1}{13}$, or 7.69%. **23.** $\frac{1}{2}$, or 50%

25. $\frac{12}{13}$, or 92.31% **27.** $\frac{1}{52}$, or 1.92% **29.** $\frac{2}{13}$, or 15.38%

31. $\frac{5}{8}$, or 62.5% **33.** $\frac{3}{11}$, or 27.3% **35.** $\frac{2}{7}$, or 28.6%

37. 4 to 1 **39.** 5 to 4 **41.** 6 to 1 **43.** $\frac{2}{7}$, or 28.6%

45. 7 to 3 **47.** 1 to 9 **49.** In error, since $e_2 = -0.2$,
a negative probability, is not possible. **51.** In error, since
the sum of the probabilities is > 1.0. **53.** In error, since
the sum of the probabilities is > 1.0. **55. (a)** .35 **(b)** .60

57. (a)

Opinion	Probability
strongly in favor	.20
somewhat in favor	.50
neutral	.05
somewhat opposed	.10
strongly opposed	.15

(b) .20 **(c)** .25 **(d)** .70 **59. (a)** $S = \{(1, 1), (1, 2), (1, 3),$
$(1, 4), (1, 5), (1, 6), (2, 1), (2, 2), (2, 3), (2, 4), (2, 5),$
$(2, 6), (3, 1), (3, 2), (3, 3), (3, 4), (3, 5), (3, 6), (4, 1),$
$(4, 2), (4, 3), (4, 4), (4, 5), (4, 6), (5, 1), (5, 2), (5, 3),$
$(5, 4), (5, 5), (5, 6), (6, 1), (6, 2), (6, 3), (6, 4), (6, 5), (6, 6)\}$
(b) $S_1 = \{(1, 1), (1, 2), (1, 3), (1, 4), (2, 1), (2, 2), (2, 3),$
$(3, 1), (3, 2), (4, 1)\}$ $P(A) = \frac{10}{36}$, or 27.8% **(c)** $S_2 = \{(1, 1),$
$(2, 2), (3, 3), (4, 4), (5, 5), (6, 6)\}$ $P(B) = \frac{1}{6}$, or 16.7%.
(d) No; $(1, 1)$ and $(2, 2)$ occur in both S_1 and S_2
(e) $\frac{14}{36}$, or 38.9% **(f)** $S_3 = \{(1, 5), (2, 4), (3, 3), (4, 2),$
$(5, 1)\}$ $P(C) = \frac{1}{6}$, or 16.7% **(g)** $S_4 = \{(3, 6), (4, 5), (5, 4),$
$(6, 3)\}$ $P(D) = \frac{1}{9}$, or 11.1% **(h)** Yes; S_3 and S_4 are disjoint
(i) $\frac{10}{36}$, or 27.8% **61. (a)** $\frac{1}{5}$, or 20% **(b)** $\frac{1}{10}$, or 10%
(c) $\frac{3}{10}$, or 30%; Yes these events are mutually exclusive.
(d) $\frac{7}{10}$, or 70%; Yes, these events are mutually exclusive.
63. .70 **65. (a)** $\frac{2}{3}$, or .667, or 66.7% **(b)** $\frac{1}{2}$, or .50, or 50%
(c) $\frac{1}{3}$, or .333, or 33.3% **(d)** $\frac{5}{6}$ or .833, or 83.3%
(e) $\frac{1}{2}$, or .50, or 50% **(f)** $\frac{1}{6}$, or .167, or 16.7%.
67. (a) $\frac{1}{5}$, or 20% **(b)** $\frac{7}{20}$, or 35% **(c)** $\frac{36}{100}$, or 36%
(d) $\frac{24}{100}$, or 24% **(e)** $\frac{15}{100}$, or 15% **(f)** $\frac{30}{100}$, or 30%
(g) $\frac{25}{100}$, or 25% **(h)** 0 **(i)** $\frac{29}{100}$, or 29% **(j)** $\frac{51}{100}$, or 51%
(k) $\frac{1}{2}$, or 50% **(l)** $\frac{65}{100}$, or 65% **(m)** $\frac{60}{100}$, or 60%
(n) $\frac{1}{2}$, or 50% **(o)** $\frac{59}{100}$, or 59% **(p)** .25, or 25%
(q) .35, or 35% **69. (a)** .4, or 40% **(b)** .21, or 21%
(c) .53, or 53% **(d)** .83, or 83%
71. (a) $\frac{1}{270,725} \approx 3.694 \times 10^{-6}$ **(b)** $\frac{46}{833} \approx .05522$, or
5.522% **73. (a)** ≈ 0.2135, or 21.35%
(b) $\frac{11}{4165} \approx .002641 = 0.2641\%$ **(c)** $\frac{5359}{20,825} \approx .2573$, or
25.73% **75. (a)** .1, or 10% **(b)** $\frac{1}{10} = .10$, or 10%
77. (a) $\frac{1}{42} \approx .02381$, or 2.381% **(b)** $\frac{5}{21} \approx .2381$, or
23.81% **(c)** $\frac{11}{42} \approx .2619$, or 26.19% **(d)** 0.7381, or

73.81% **79. (a)** 5,852,925 **(b)** $\frac{209}{783} \approx$ .2669, or 26.69%

(c) $\frac{352}{783} \approx$ .4496, or 44.96% **(d)** $\frac{308}{1305} \approx$ .2360, or 23.60%

(e) .9525, or 95.25% **(f)** .0475, or 4.75% **81. (a)** 365^5

(b) $365 \cdot 364 \cdot 363 \cdot 362 \cdot 361 \approx 6.302555 \times 10^{12}$ ways

(c) .02714

SECTION 8-4

1. $\frac{1}{6} \approx 0.167$, or 16.7% **3.** $\frac{1}{10}$, or .1, or 10%

5. .375, or 37.5% **7.** $\frac{1}{6} \approx$ .167, or 16.7% **9.** .10, or 10%

11. $\frac{5}{6} \approx$ .833, or 83.3% **13.** .50, or 50% **15.** .15

17. .52 **19.** .87 **21.** .192 **23.** .48 **25.** .90

27. (a) .50, or 50% **(b)** $\frac{2}{3} \approx$ .667, or 66.7% **29. (a)** .40

(b) $\approx$.3939 **(c)** $\approx$.6061 **31. (a)** .10 **(b)** $\approx$.0955

(c) $\approx$.0909 **(d)** $\approx$.1010 **33. (a)** .50, or 50%

(b) $\approx$.490, or 49.0% **(c)** .48, or 48% **(d)** .52, or 52%

35. (a) .05, or 5% **(b)** .75, or 75% **37. (a)** .04, or 4.0%

(b) .0625, or 6.25% **(c)** .11, or 11.0% **(d)** .11, or 11.0%

(e) .22, or 22.0% **39. (a)** .08, or 8% **(b)** .22, or 22%

(c) .40, or 40% **41. (a)** .30 **(b)** .45 **(c)** .15 **(d)** .55

43. (a) .18 **(b)** .72 **(c)** .30 **(d)** .60 **45. (a)** $\approx$.4033

(b) $\approx$.005815 **(c)** $\approx$.1048 **(d)** $\approx$.02552

47. (a) $\approx$.000133 **(b)** $\approx$.00133 **(c)** $\approx$.00133 **(d)** $\approx$.5797

49. (a) $\approx$.000258 **(b)** $\approx$.0157 **(c)** $\approx$.0961 **(d)** $\approx$.512

SECTION 8-5

1. $\frac{53}{80} \approx$ .6625 **3.** $\frac{1}{20} =$ .05 **5.** $\frac{15}{23} \approx$ .6522

7. $\frac{8}{23} \approx$ .3478 **9.** $\approx$.4211 **11.** $\approx$.3947 **13.** .3635

15. $\approx$.216 **17.** .7955 **19.** .081 **21.** .812 **23.** $\approx$.00366

• EXTRA DIVIDENDS

1. $\approx$.876 **3.** $\approx$.955

5. $P(S) = P[(A \cap B) \cup C]$

$= 1 - [1 - P(A)P(B)] \, P(C')$

$= 1 - [1 - P(A) \, P(B)] \, [(1 - P(C))]$

• CHAPTER HIGHLIGHTS

1. A **set** is a collection of things. The **empty set,** or **null set,** is the set containing no elements. Two sets are equal if they contain exactly the same elements. Set A is as **subset** of a set B if each element of A is also an element of B. A **universal set** contains all elements of all sets of a given

problem. The **intersection** of two sets is the set of elements belonging to both sets. It is the set of elements common to both sets. The **union** of two sets is the set of elements belonging either to one set or the other set or both. Two sets are **disjoint** if their intersection is empty. In other words, they have no elements in common. The **complement** of set A is the set of elements of the universal set that are not in set A.

De Morgan's laws are:

1) $(A \cup B)' = A' \cap B'$. In other words, the complement of a union equals the intersection of the complements.

2) $(A \cap B)' = A' \cup B'$. In other words, the complement of an intersection equals the union of the complements.

A **cross-classification table** exhibits a classification of individuals or things with respect to various attributes or groups. A **Venn diagram** is a pictorial way of illustrating sets.

2. The **multiplication rule of counting** states that if a task consists of m operations $O_1, O_2, \ldots, O_m$ to be performed in sequence and if there are n_1 possible outcomes for O_1, n_2 possible outcomes for $O_2, \ldots, n_m$ possible outcomes for O_m, then there are $n_1 \cdot n_2 \cdot \ldots \cdot n_m$ possible ways of first performing O_1, then $O_2, \ldots$, and lastly O_m. The product of all consecutive integers from 1 to n is called n **factorial** and is denoted by the symbol $n!$.

3. The number of **permutations** of n elements taken r at a time $(r \le n)$ is the number of all possible ways of selecting r elements from a set of n elements where order of selection is important and replacement between selections is not allowed. The number of **combinations** of n elements taken r at a time $(r \le n)$ is the number of all possible ways of selecting r elements from a set of n elements where order of selection makes no difference and replacement between selections is not allowed.

4. The **MRCC model** states that if we begin with an n-element set that is divided into two subsets, the first containing n_1 elements and the second containing n_2 elements so that $n_1 + n_2 = n$, then we select a sample of r elements from the n-element set so that the sample contains r_1 elements from the n_1-element subset and r_2 elements from the n_2-element subset where $r_1 + r_2 = r$, there are $C(n_1, r_1) \cdot C(n_2, r_2)$ ways of selecting such an r-element subset. **5.** A **chance experiment** is a happening with an uncertain outcome. A **sample space** is the set of all possible outcomes of a chance experiment. An **event** is a subset of a sample space. A **probability** is a ratio indicating the likelihood of occurrence of a chance event. The **law of large numbers** implies that if the probability of some event occurring is 70%, then as the number of trials gets larger and larger, the ratio of the cumulative number of times the event occurs to the cumulative number of trials approaches 70%. An **empirical probability** is a probability derived from actual experience. For example, if an event occurs m times out of n trials, then the probability of the event is approximated by the ratio m/n where the approximation gets better as n gets larger and larger. A **subjective probability** is one that is assigned subjectively. If $S = \{e_1, e_2, \ldots, e_n\}$ where the outcomes of S are assigned probabilities as given in the table below,

Outcomes	Probabilities	
e_1	p_1	$0 \le p_1 \le 1$
e_2	p_2	$0 \le p_2 \le 1$
$\vdots$	$\vdots$	$\vdots$
e_n	p_n	$0 \le p_n \le 1$

where $p_1 + p_2 + \ldots + p_n = 1$, then such a table is called a **probability distribution** for the sample space S.
6. The **basic probability formula** states that the probability of event E is given by $P(E) = n(E)/n(S)$ where $n(S)$ is the number of elements of a finite sample space whose outcomes are equally likely to occur and $n(E)$ is the number of elements of an event set E.
7. Addition rule. If A and B are events, then $P(A \cup B) = P(A) + P(B) - P(A \cap B)$. The key word is *or*.
8. If A and B are mutually exclusive events, then $P(A \cup B) = P(A) + P(B)$. **9.** Not **10.** The likelihood of an event occurring can be expressed in terms of **odds.** For example, the odds of snow tomorrow are 1 to 9 indicates the likelihood of snow tomorrow. **11.** If the odds in favor of an event are a to b, then the probability of the event is given by $a/(a + b)$. **12.** If the probability of an event E is $P(E)$, then the odds in favor of E are given by $P(E)/P(E')$ provided that $P(E) \ne 1$. **13.** If A and B are events in a sample space S, then the probability of A occurring given that B has occurred is called the **conditional probability** of A given that B has occurred and is denoted by $P(A|B)$. Two formulas for $P(A|B)$ are $P(A|B) = n(A \cap B)/n(B)$ and $P(A|B) = P(A \cap B)/P(B)$. **14. Product rules.** If A and B are events with nonzero probabilities, then $P(A \cap B) = P(A)P(B|A)$ or $P(A \cap B) = P(B)P(A|B)$. The product rules are usually used to determine $P(A$ and $B)$ for chance experiments consisting of multiple trials. The key word is *and*. **15.** Two events are **independent** if the occurrence of one does not change the probability of the occurrence (or nonoccurrence) of the other. Equivalently, the two events A and B are independent if $P(A|B) = P(A)$. The **special case product rule** states that if A and B are independent events, then $P(A \cap B) = P(A)P(B)$. This rule applies only to independent events. **16.** Bayes' formula states that if $B_1, B_2, \ldots, B_k$ are mutually exclusive events such that $P(B_1) + P(B_2) + \ldots + P(B_k) = 1$, then for an event A such that $P(A) \ne 0$,

$$P(B_i|A) =$$
$$\frac{P(B_i)P(A|B_i)}{P(B_1)P(A|B_1) + P(B_2)P(A|B_2) + \ldots + P(B_k)P(A|B_k)}$$

• REVIEW EXERCISES

1. (a)

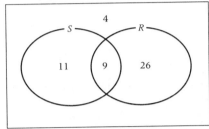

(b) 30 **(c)** 46 **(d)** 4 **(e)** 25.7% **(f)** 45.0% **(g)** 11

3. (a) Column percent table

	Good	Average	Poor	Totals
Male	66.7	40.0	47.6	56.0
Female	33.3	60.0	52.4	44.0
Total	100.0	100.0	100.0	100.0

Column 1 lists the distribution of good sentiments among male and female employer. Similarly, columns 2 and 3 list the distributions of average and poor sentiments.

(b) Row percent table

	Good	Average	Poor	Totals
Male	57.14	7.14	35.72	100.0
Female	36.36	13.64	50.00	100.0
Totals	48.0	10.0	42.0	100.0

Row 1 lists the distribution of good, average, and poor sentiments among male employees. Row 2 lists the distribution among female employees.
(c) .22 or 22% **(d)** .62, or 62% **(e)** .52, or 52%
(f) .58, or 58% **5.** 1 **7.** 24 **9.** 42 **11.** 56
13. (a) 840 ways **(b)** 35 ways **15. (a)** 142,506 samples
(b) 30,360 samples **(c)** 42,504 samples **(d)** 366 samples
17. (a) .90 **(b)** .60 **(c)** .50 **(d)** 1.0 **(e)** .50 **(f)** 0
19. (a) $\approx$.2361 **(b)** $\approx$.07236 **(c)** .9905 **(d)** .000474
21. $\frac{1}{6} \approx .1667$ **23.** $\frac{3}{10} = .30$ **25.** 4 to 1 **27.** 3 to 7
29. $\frac{5}{7} \approx .7143$ **31.** 3 to 2 **33. (a)** $\frac{1}{6} \approx .1667$
(b) $\frac{1}{3} \approx .3333$ **(c)** .80, or 80% **35. (a)** .08 **(b)** $\approx$.0802
(c) $\approx$.000477 **37. (a)** .081 **(b)** $\approx$.296

• CHAPTER 9

SECTION 9-1

1. 6　**3.** 8　**5.** 2　**7.** 9　**9.** 0　**11.** Does not exist　**13.** 0
15. Does not exist　**17.** 15　**19.** Does not exist　**21.** -5
23. 5　**25.** 0　**27.** 0　**29.** 3　**31.** Does not exist　**33.** 7
35. 5　**37.** 0　**39.** 0
41.

x	-2	-1.5	-1	-0.5	-0.0001	0.0001	0.5	1	1.5	2
$f(x) = \dfrac{\lvert x \rvert}{x}$	-1	-1	-1	-1	-1	1	1	1	1	1

$\lim\limits_{x \to 0} f(x)$ does not exist

43.

x	3	3.5	3.75	3.95	4.05	4.25	4.5
$f(x) = \dfrac{\sqrt{x} - 2}{x - 4}$	0.268	0.258	0.254	0.250	0.249	0.246	0.243

$\lim\limits_{x \to 4} f(x) = 0.250$

Note: The limit can also be found algebraically:
$$\lim_{x \to 4} \frac{\sqrt{x} - 2}{x - 4} = \lim_{x \to 4} \frac{1}{\sqrt{x} + 2} = \frac{1}{4}$$

45.

x	1,000	10,000	100,000	1,000,000	10,000,000
$f(x) = \left(1 + \dfrac{1}{x}\right)^x$	2.717	2.7181	2.7183	2.71828	2.718281828

$\lim\limits_{x \to \infty} f(x) = e$

47.

x	100	1,000	10,000	100,000	1,000,000
$f(x) = \dfrac{1}{x^2}$	10^{-4}	10^{-6}	10^{-8}	10^{-10}	10^{-12}

$\lim\limits_{x \to \infty} f(x) = 0$

49. (a)

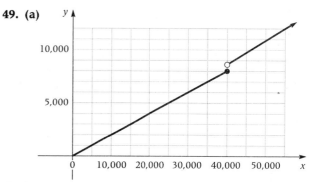

(b) $\lim\limits_{x \to 40,000} T(x)$ does not exist
51. 12　**53.** 1　**55.** 1.6

SECTION 9-2

1. Continuous　**3.** Continuous　**5.** Not continuous
7. Continuous　**9.** Continuous　**11.** Not continuous
13. The function is discontinuous at $x = 0$.

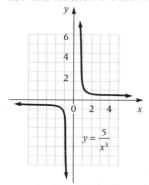

$y = \dfrac{5}{x^3}$

15. The function is discontinuous at $x = 2$.

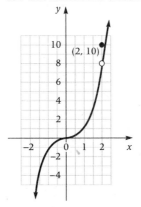

$(2, 10)$

17. The function is discontinuous at $x = 5$.

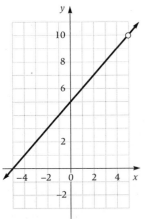

19. (a) $P_0 = \$100,000$; $P_1 = \$103,000$; $P_2 = \$106,090$; $P_3 = \$109,272.70$; $P_4 = \$112,550.88$

(b)

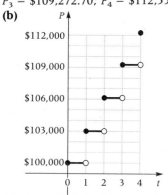

(c) At $t = 1, 2, 3, 4$ (quarters)

21. (a) $C(x) = \begin{cases} 40,000 + 30x & \text{if } 0 \le x \le 50,000 \\ 50,000 + 30x & \text{if } 50,000 < x \end{cases}$

$x =$ number of units produced

(b)

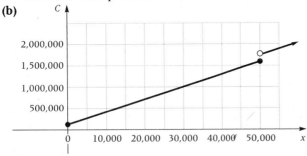

(c) At $x = 50,000$

23. (a) At $x = 29,300$ **(b)** $0 \le x < 29,300$ and $x > 29,300$

25. (a)

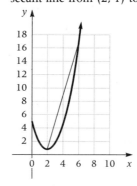

(b) at $x = 120$

SECTION 9-3

1. (a) 0.5 **(b)** 0.59375 **3.** 17.64 points / week
5. (a) 0.09375% / year to maturity **(b)** 0.07983% / year to maturity **7. (a)** 3.7% / year **(b)** 6.5% / year
(c) 5.25% / year **9. (a)** 20.5 thousands / year
(b) 23 thousands / year **(c)** 12.8 thousands / year
11. 3 **13.** -2 **15.** $8x + 4\Delta x$ **17.** $2x - 5 + \Delta x$
19. $-10x - 5\Delta x$ **21.** $2x - 2 + \Delta x$ **23.** $4x - 1 + 2\Delta x$
25. $3x^2 + 3x\Delta x + (\Delta x)^2$
27. $4x^3 + 6x^2\Delta x + 4x(\Delta x)^2 + (\Delta x)^3$
29. $4x^3 + 2x + 4 + (6x^2 + 1)\Delta x + 4x(\Delta x)^2 + (\Delta x)^3$

31. $\dfrac{\Delta y}{\Delta x} = 2x - 4 + \Delta x$; 4 graphically, $\dfrac{\Delta y}{\Delta x}$ is the slope of secant line from $(2, 1)$ to $(6, 17)$.

33. 4;4 graphically, $\dfrac{\Delta y}{\Delta x}$ is the slope of the secant line from

(2, 15) to (3, 19)

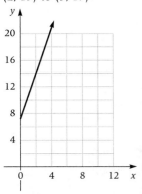

35. $-6x - 2 - 3\Delta x$; -23 graphically, $\dfrac{\Delta y}{\Delta x}$ is the slope of the

secant line from (2, −15) to (5, −84).

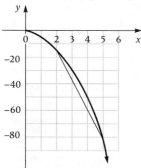

37. 4; graphically, $\dfrac{\Delta R}{\Delta x}$ is the slope of the secant line from

(4, 1) to (6, 9)

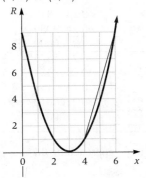

39. 210; The slope of the secant line from 200 to 220 is 210.

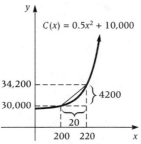

41. 1.3 million dollars/1000 units, this is the slope of the secant line from 12 to 15.

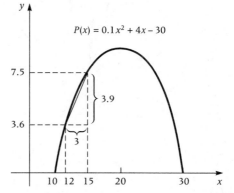

43.

x	Δx	$\dfrac{f(x + \Delta x) - f(x)}{\Delta x}$
4	0.75	.239266
4	0.50	.242641
4	0.25	.246211

45.

x	Δx	$\dfrac{f(x + \Delta x) - f(x)}{\Delta x}$
1	0.60	−1.015625
1	0.40	−1.224490
1	0.20	−1.527777

SECTION 9-4

1. $2x$ **3.** $18x^2$ **5.** $4x^3$ **7.** 3 **9.** $2x - 5$ **11.** $-6x + 4$
13. $10x$ **15.** $3x^2 - 2x + 5$ **17.** −2; 0; −8 **19.** 8; 10; 2
21. −6; −12; 12 **23.** −3; −1; −9 **25.** −7; −8; 32
27. 0; 12; 36

29. $y' = 2x - 10$; $y'(2) = -6$; $y'(3) = -4$

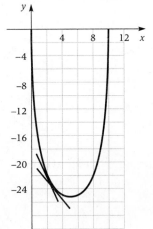

31. $y' = 5$; $y'(4) = 5$; $y'(5) = 5$

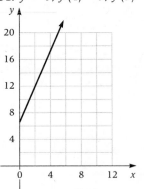

33. $6x$ **35.** $10x - 3$ **37.** $2x - 3$

39. $f'(x) = 2x - 4$; $f'(2) = 0$; Tangent line: $y = 1$

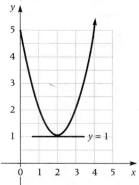

41. $f'(x) = 4$; $f'(2) = 4$; Tangent line: $y = 4x + 7$

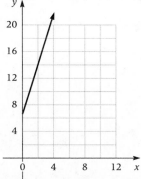

43. $f'(x) = 2x - 16$; $f'(1) = -14$; Tangent line: $y = -14x - 1$

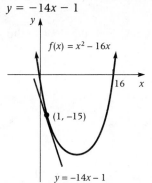

45. **(a)** $f'(x) = -6x + 60$ **(b)** $f'(3) = 42$ **(c)** $y = 42x + 27$

47.

x	Δx	$\dfrac{f(x + \Delta x) - f(x)}{\Delta x}$
4	0.1	0.2484567
4	0.01	0.2498439
4	0.001	0.2499843
4	0.0001	0.2499980
4	0.00001	0.2500000
4	−0.1	0.2515823
4	−0.01	0.2501564
4	−0.001	0.2500156
4	−0.0001	0.2500012
4	−0.00001	0.2500000

The difference quotient appears to be approaching 0.25.

49.

x	Δx	$\dfrac{f(x + \Delta x) - f(x)}{\Delta x}$
1	0.1	-1.7355372
1	0.01	-1.9703951
1	0.001	-1.9970040
1	0.0001	-1.9997001
1	0.00001	-1.9999710
1	-0.1	-2.3456790
1	-0.01	-2.0304051
1	-0.001	-2.0030040
1	-0.0001	-2.0003000
1	-0.00001	-2.0000300

The difference quotient appears to be approaching -2.
51. 7.0 **53.** 4.0 **55.** 0.76 **57.** 0.25 **59.** -0.006887

SECTION 9-5

1. a and d
3. (a) 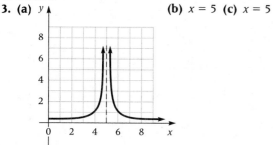 **(b)** $x = 5$ **(c)** $x = 5$

5. $x = 0$
7. (a) 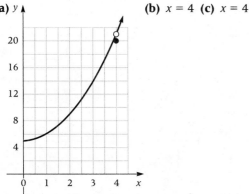 **(b)** $x = 4$ **(c)** $x = 4$

9. (a) 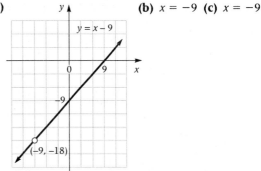 **(b)** $x = -9$ **(c)** $x = -9$

11. $x \le 5$ **13.** $x = 2$ **15.** $x = 1$ **17.** $x \le 3$ **19.** $x = 7$
21. $x = \dfrac{1}{4}$ **23.** $x < 6$

SECTION 9-6

1. $3x^2$ **3.** $20x^{19}$ **5.** 4 **7.** $\dfrac{-6}{x^7}$ **9.** $5x^4$ **11.** $\dfrac{-3}{x^4}$

13. $\dfrac{-1}{4}x^{-5/4}$ **15.** 0 **17.** $-8x^7$ **19.** $6x^{-3}$ **21.** $\dfrac{-15}{2x^{5/2}}$

23. 0 **25.** $\dfrac{-5}{16}$ **27.** 24 **29.** $\dfrac{3}{128}$ **31.** $2x - 8$ **33.** $16x$

35. $3x^2 + 4x$ **37.** $6x^5 - 5x^4 - \dfrac{8}{x^3}$ **39.** $-15x^2 - 12x + 8$
41. $5x^4 - 24x^3 + 24x^2$ **43.** $6x$ **45.** $-4x$ **47.** $-9x^2$
49. $3x^2 - 8x$ **51.** $\dfrac{-1}{2x^{3/2}} + \dfrac{2}{\sqrt{x}}$ **53.** $-6t + 8$ **55.** $3w^2 - 5$

57. -2 **59.** 3 **61.** -137 **63.** $\dfrac{1}{2}$ **65.** $-6x + 2$
67. $3x^2 + 12x + 8$ **69.** $5x^4 - 18x^2 + 6$ **71.** $50x^9$
73. $\dfrac{6}{x^3}$ **75.** $12x^2 - 12x + 4$
77.

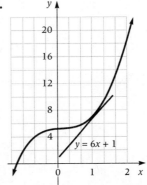

79. (a) 0.12 million dollars/year
(b) 0.18 million dollars/year
(c) $P(x) = 0.18x + 4.73$
$P(7) = 5.99$ million dollars

81. (a) $12x$ **(b)** $f'(2) = 24$; $f'(3) = 36$; The rate of change is not constant. **(c)** 126 million dollars

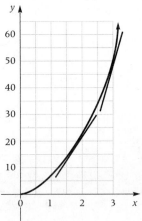

83. (a) $R'(x) = -4x + 60$
(b) $R'(10) = 20$; This is approximately the additional revenue obtained by selling one more unit beyond 10 units. It is the slope of the line tangent to the graph of $R(x)$ at $x = 10$.
(c)

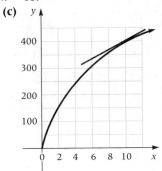

85. (a) 32 ft/sec **(b)** 0 ft/sec **(c)** -32 ft/sec
(d)

87. (a) Marginal profit = $P'(x) = 4 - \dfrac{3x^2}{1,000,000}$

(b) 3.97; This is the approximate additional profit gained from selling one more unit when at the level of $x = 100$.
(c) -6.83; The approximate change in profit in moving from a sales level of 1900 units to one additional unit is negative. **89. (a)** $y' = \dfrac{45}{\sqrt{x}}$ units/ hour **(b)** 22.5 units/hour

(c) 15 units/hour **91. (a)** $P'(t) = 8000t$ people/year
(b) 24,000 people/year **(c)** 48,000 people/year

SECTION 9-7

1. $5x^4 + 8x^3 - 9x^2 - 6x + 28$
3. $(x^3 - 2x + 6)(2x - 3) + (x^2 - 3x + 2)(3x^2 - 2)$
$= 5x^4 - 12x^3 - 6x^2 + 24x - 22$
5. $(x^3 - x^2 - 2)(2x - 1) + (x^2 - x - 1)(3x^2 - 2x)$
$= 5x^4 - 8x^3 - 2x + 2$
7. $(x^7 - 6x^2)(8x - 3) + (4x^2 - 3x + 4)(7x^6 - 12x)$
$= 36x^8 - 21x^7 + 28x^6 - 96x^3 + 54x^2 - 48x$
9. $(5x^2 - 3x + 1)(12x^2) + (3x^4 - 7)(10x - 3)$
$= 30x^5 + 51x^4 - 36x^3 + 12x^2 - 70x + 21$
11. $\dfrac{(x^3 - 3x + 9)(2x - 4) - (x^2 - 4x + 5)(3x^2 - 3)}{(x^3 - 3x + 9)^2}$
$= \dfrac{-x^4 + 8x^3 - 18x^2 + 18x - 21}{(x^3 - 3x + 9)^2}$
13. $\dfrac{2x^3 + 15x^2}{(x + 5)^2}$ **15.** $\dfrac{-x^3 - 28}{x^5}$ **17.** $\dfrac{6}{(x - 2)^2} + \dfrac{3}{(5x + 1)^2}$
19. $\dfrac{x^4 - 27x^2 - 18x}{(x^2 - 9)^2}$ **21.** $\dfrac{-2x + 3}{(x^2 - 3x)^2}$
23. $\dfrac{-2(6x^2 + 3x - 1)}{(3x^2 - 2x)^2}$ **25.** $\dfrac{14x^3 - \frac{8}{5}x - \frac{1}{5}}{x^{6/5}}$
27. $(5x^3 - 7x^2 + 3)(4x^3 - 24x^2 + 5) -$
$\dfrac{(x^4 - 8x^3 + 5x + 1)(15x^2 - 14x)}{(5x^3 - 7x^2 + 3)^2}$
$= \dfrac{5x^6 - 14x^5 + 56x^4 - 38x^3 - 22x^2 + 14x + 15}{(5x^3 - 7x^2 + 3)^2}$
29. $\dfrac{\left(x - \frac{1}{\sqrt{x}}\right)\left(\frac{1}{2\sqrt{x}} + 1\right) - (\sqrt{x} + x)\left(1 + \frac{1}{2x^{3/2}}\right)}{\left(x + \frac{1}{\sqrt{x}}\right)^2}$
$= \dfrac{-\frac{1}{2}\sqrt{x} - \frac{1}{x} - \frac{3}{2\sqrt{x}}}{\left(x + \frac{1}{\sqrt{x}}\right)^2} = \dfrac{-(x\sqrt{x} + 2 - 3\sqrt{x})}{2x\left(x + \frac{1}{\sqrt{x}}\right)^2}$
31. 2 **33.** $-41/2$
35. $(x^3 - 4x^2 + 5)(2x - 8) + (x^2 - 8x + 7)(3x^2 - 8x)$
$= 5x^4 - 48x^3 + 117x^2 - 46x - 40$

37. $[x^3 - 6x + 1][(x^3 - 4x + 7)(2x - 2) +$
$(x^2 - 2x)(3x^2 - 4)] -$
$$\frac{(x^3 - 4x + 7)(x^2 - 2x)(3x^2 - 6)}{(x^3 - 6x + 1)^2}$$

39. $(x^5 - 8x^2)(x^3 + 1)[(x^3 - 6x^2 + 5)(2x - 4) +$
$(x^2 - 4x)(3x^2 - 12x)] -$
$(x^3 - 6x^2 + 5)(x^2 - 4x)[(x^5 - 8x^2)(3x^2) +$
$$\frac{(5x^4 - 16x)(x^3 + 1)]}{[(x^5 - 8x^2)(x^3 + 1)]^2}$$

41. $(t^5 - 4)\left[\dfrac{(t^4 + 7)(3t^2) - (t^3 + 6)(4t^3)}{(t^4 + 7)^2}\right] + \left(\dfrac{t^3 + 6}{t^4 + 7}\right)(5t^4)$
$$\frac{-t^6 - 24t^3 + 21t^2}{x^4 + 23x^2 - 30}$$

43. $(x^2 - 4x + 1)\left[\dfrac{(x^2 + 6)(3x^2 - 5) - (x^3 - 5x)(2x)}{(x^2 + 6)^2}\right] +$
$\left(\dfrac{x^3 - 5x}{x^2 + 6}\right)(2x - 4)$

45. (a) $9x^8 - 40x^4 = x^4(9x^4 - 40)$ **(b)** $9x^8 - 40x^4$

47. 11 **49.** $y = 4x - 52$

51. $y = \dfrac{-2}{343}x + \dfrac{3}{49}$

53. $y = \dfrac{47}{128}x + \dfrac{233}{128}$, or $128y - 47x = 233$

55. (a) $R(t) = (10 + 2t)(20 + 0.2t^2)$
$= 200 + 40t + 2t^2 + 0.4t^3$

(b) $(10 + 2t)(0.4t) + (20 + 0.2t^2)2 = 40 + 4t + 1.2t^2$

(c) \$52.80/unit **57. (a)** $\overline{C}(x) = 10 + \dfrac{500}{x}$ **(b)** $\dfrac{-500}{x^2}$

(c) $\overline{C}'(4) = -31.25$ ⎱ In each case $\overline{C}'(x_0)$ represents the
$\overline{C}'(5) = -20$ ⎬ rate of change of the average cost at
$\overline{C}'(6) = -13.89$ ⎰ $x = x_0$.
At $x = 5$, the average cost per unit in going to $x = 6$
decreases by approximately \$20.

59. (a) $\overline{C}(x) = -x + 30$ **(b)** -1
(c) $\overline{C}'(4) = \overline{C}'(5) = \overline{C}'(6) = -1$
The average cost per unit decreases by \$1 when the
production is increased by one unit.

61. (a) $\dfrac{30}{(110 - x)^2}$ **(b)** $\dfrac{dy}{dx}\Big|_{x = 60} = 0.012;$

$\dfrac{dy}{dx}\Big|_{x = 80} = 0.0333; \dfrac{dy}{dx}\Big|_{x = 90} = 0.075;$

In each case $\dfrac{dy}{dx}\Big|_{x = x_0}$ represents the rate of change in the
cost y as x is increased. The cost rises more rapidly as x_0
approaches 110.

SECTION 9-8

1. $5t^4 - 12t^2 + 7$ **3.** $5u^4$ **5.** $18u^5 - 40u^4 + 4$
7. $-21u^2 - 16u$ **9.** $33x^2(x^3 + 5)^{10}$

11. $\dfrac{-4(3x^2 - 6)}{(x^3 - 6x)^5} = \dfrac{-12(x^2 - 2)}{(x^3 - 6x)^5}$ **13.** $60x^3(x^4 - 9)^{14}$

15. $\dfrac{-2(6x^5 - 8)}{3(x^6 - 8x)^{5/3}}$ **17.** $20(3x^2 - 8x)(x^3 - 4x^2 + 5)^{19}$

19. $10(x^3 - 4x)^9(3x^2 - 4)(x^2 + 5) + (x^3 - 4x)^{10}(2x)$

21. $7\left(\dfrac{5x - 3}{8 - x^4}\right)^6\left(\dfrac{15x^4 - 12x^3 + 40}{(8 - x^4)^2}\right)$

23. $7\left(\dfrac{5x - 3}{8 - x^4}\right)^6\left(\dfrac{15x^4 - 12x^3 + 40}{(8 - x^4)^2}\right)$

25. $10[(5x - 3)(x^2 - 1)]^9[15x^2 - 6x - 5]$

27. $10[(5x - 3)(x^2 - 1)]^9[15x^2 - 6x - 5]$

29. $6x(x^3 - 4x^2)^5(x^2 - 1)^2 +$
$5(x^3 - 4x^2)^4(3x^2 - 8x)(x^2 - 1)^3$

31. $15x^2(x^3 + 1)^4 + 14x(x^2 - 2)^6$ **33.** $\dfrac{5}{2\sqrt{x}}(\sqrt{x} + 9)^4$

35. $\dfrac{5x^3 + 2}{2\sqrt{x^3 + 1}}$ **37.** $\dfrac{5x^3 + 6x^2}{2(x + 1)^{3/2}}$ **39.** $-\dfrac{3}{25}$ **41.** $\dfrac{17}{20\sqrt{10}}$ or

$\dfrac{17\sqrt{10}}{200}$ **43.** $y = 1280x - 4864$ **45. (a)** $\dfrac{dC}{dt} = 15(5t + 4)^2$
(b) 17,340; The instantaneous rate of change with respect
to t at $t = 6$. **47.** 60,000 millions of dollars/month =
60 billion dollars/month **49. (a)** $\dfrac{dS}{dr} = 700\left(1 + \dfrac{r}{400}\right)^{27}$

(b) 1194.82 **(c)** 1363.46; $\dfrac{dS}{dr}$ represents the instantaneous
rate of change of S with respect to r. At $r = 10$, for
example, the rate of change is \$1363.46/unit change in r.

51. (a) $\dfrac{dS}{dr} = \left(\dfrac{48,000}{r}\right)\left(1 + \dfrac{r}{100}\right)^7 -$
$\left(\dfrac{600,000}{r^2}\right)\left[\left(1 + \dfrac{r}{100}\right)^8 - 1\right]$

(b) 2305.48; An increase of 1% in the interest rate will
increase the value of S by approximately \$2305.48
(c) 2492.31; An increase of 1% in the interest rate will
increase the value of S by approximately \$2492.31.

• CHAPTER HIGHLIGHTS

1. If the y-values of a function get closer and closer to a
single number L as the x-values get closer and closer to a
number a, then L is the limit of the function as x
approaches a. **2.** Right-hand limit. **3.** Yes.

4. *Property 1:* $\lim_{x \to a} c = c$. This property states that the limit of a constant function is the constant value.

Property 2: $\lim_{x \to a} [f(x) \pm g(x)] = \lim_{x \to a} f(x) \pm \lim_{x \to a} g(x)$. This property states that the limit of a sum (or difference) is the sum (or difference) of the individual limits provided that these limits exist.

Property 3: $\lim_{x \to a} kf(x) = k \lim_{x \to a} f(x)$. This property states that the limit of a constant times a function is the constant times the limit of the function provided that the limit exists.

Property 4: $\lim_{x \to a} [f(x)]^r = [\lim_{x \to a} f(x]^r$. This property states that the limit of a function raised to a power is the power of the limit provided that the limit exists.

Property 5: $\lim_{x \to a} [f(x)g(x)] = [\lim_{x \to a} f(x)][\lim_{x \to a} g(x)]$. This property states that the limit of a product is the product of the limits provided that the limits exist.

Property 6: $\lim_{x \to a} [f(x)/g(x)] = [\lim_{x \to a} f(x)]/[\lim_{x \to a} g(x)]$ provided that $\lim_{x \to a} g(x) \neq 0$. This property states that the limit of a quotient is the quotient of the limits provided that the limits exist and the limit of the denominator is not 0. **5.** 0 **6.** Horizontal asymptote. **7.** A function is continuous at a point if its graph has no break at that point. **8.** A function f is continuous at $x = a$ if $f(a)$ exists, $\lim_{x \to a} f(x)$ exists, and $\lim_{x \to a} f(x) = f(a)$. **9.** A function is continuous over an interval if it is continuous at each point in the interval. **10.** *Property 1: Constant function.* If $f(x) = k$ where k is a constant, then $f(x)$ is continuous for all x. This means that a constant function is continuous for all values of x.

Property 2: Power functions. Functions of the form $f(x) = x^n$ and $g(x) = \sqrt[n]{x}$, where n is a positive integer, are continuous for all values of x in their respective domains.

Property 3: Sum, difference, and product. If $f(x)$ and $g(x)$ are continuous at a point, then $f(x) + g(x)$, $f(x) - g(x)$, and $f(x) \cdot g(x)$ are continuous at that point.

Property 4: Quotient. If $f(x)$ and $g(x)$ are continuous at a point, then $f(x)/g(x)$ is continuous at that point provided that $g(x) \neq 0$ at the point. **11.** Polynomial functions are continuous at all values of x. **12.** A rational function is continuous at all values of x where its denominator does not equal 0. **13.** $[f(x + \Delta x) - f(x)]/\Delta x$; difference quotient **14.** Secant line **15.** $\lim_{\Delta x \to 0} [(f(x + \Delta x) - f(x))/\Delta x]$ **16.** Slope; tangent **17.** Derivative; point **18.** The function has a unique nonvertical tangent line at that point. **19.** No **20.** Yes **21.** Yes **22.** If $f(x) = k$ where k is a constant, then $f'(x) = 0$. In other words, the derivative of a constant is 0. **23.** If $f(x) = x^n$ where n is a real number, then $f'(x) = nx^{n-1}$. **24.** If $y = kf(x)$ where k is a constant and $f'(x)$ exists, then $dy/dx = kf'(x)$. In other words, the derivative of a constant times a function is the constant times the derivative of the function. **25.** If $y = f(x) \pm g(x)$ where $f(x)$ and $g(x)$ are differentiable functions of x, then $dy/dx = f'(x) \pm g'(x)$. In other words,

the derivative of a sum or difference of two functions is the sum or difference of the derivatives. **26.** Marginal cost is the cost of producing one more unit. Marginal revenue is the revenue gained from selling one more unit. **27.** If $y = f(x)s(x)$ where $f(x)$ and $s(x)$ are differentiable functions at x, then $dy/dx = f \cdot s' + s \cdot f'$. In other words, the derivative of a product of two functions is the first times the derivative of the second plus the second times derivative of the first. **28.** If $y = n(x)/d(x)$ where $n(x)$ and $d(x)$ are differentiable functions at x and $d(x) \neq 0$, then $dy/dx = [d \cdot n' - n \cdot d']/d^2$. In other words, the derivative of a quotient of two functions is the denominator times the derivative of the numerator minus the numerator times the derivative of the denominator all divided by the square of the denominator. **29.** If $y = f(u)$ is a differentiable function of u and $u = g(x)$ is a differentiable function of x, then $dy/dx = [dy/du][du/dx]$. **30.** If $y = u^n$ where u is a differentiable function of x, then $dy/dx = [nu^{n-1}][du/dx]$.

• **REVIEW EXERCISES**

1. Does not exist **3.** Exists; 16 **5.** Exists; $\dfrac{1}{2\sqrt{2}}$

7. Discontinuous at $x = 2$ **9.** Continuous everywhere **11.** Discontinuous at $x = 2$

13. (a) $P_0 = \$1000$
$P_1 = \$1040$
$P_2 = \$1081.60$
$P_3 = \$1124.86$
$P_4 = \$1169.86$

(b)

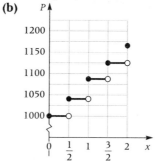

(c) at $t = \dfrac{1}{2}, 1, \dfrac{3}{4}, 2$ **15.** $2x + \Delta x - 3$ **17.** 1

19. (a) 4000 **(b)** 5000 **(c)** The value calculated is the slope of the secant line from $(1000, 7,000,000)$ to $(3000, 15,000,000)$. **(d)** The value calculated is the slope of the secant line from $(1000, 7,000,000)$ to $(3000, 12,000,000)$.

(e) & **(f)**

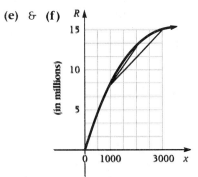

21. (a) $-10x + 2$ **(b)** -8 **(c)** 22 **23. (a)** $8x^7 - 8$ **(b)** 0
(c) -1032 **25. (a)** $10,000t$ people/year **(b)** $40,000$
(c) $60,000$ **(d)** $90,000$

27. $(x^2 + 4x + 7)(3x^2 + 6x) + (x^3 + 3x^2 + 8)(2x + 4)$
$= 5x^4 + 28x^3 + 57x^2 + 58x + 32$

29. $6(x^4 - 6x + 1)^5(4x^3 - 6)$ **31.** $\dfrac{-18(x + 4)}{(x^2 + 8x + 2)^{10}}$

33. $2(x^3 + x^2 + 4)^5(x + 2) +$
$5(x^3 + x^2 + 4)^4(3x^2 + 2x)(x^2 + 4x + 5)$

35. $\dfrac{(x^3 - 6x + 8)(4x^3 + 10x) - (x^4 + 5x^2 + 7)(3x^2 - 6)}{(x^3 - 6x + 8)^2}$
$= \dfrac{-8x^6 - 23x^4 + 32x^3 - 51x^2 + 80x + 42}{(x^3 - 6x + 8)^2}$

37. $9(x^3 - 4x + 2)(x^4 + 4x + 7)^8(4x^3 + 4) -$
$\dfrac{(x^4 + 4x + 7)^9(3x^2 - 4)}{(x^3 - 4x + 2)^2}$

39. $6(x^8 + 9)\left(\dfrac{x^2 - 9}{x^4 + 7}\right)^5\left[\dfrac{(x^4 + 7)(2x) - (x^2 - 9)(4x^3)}{(x^4 + 7)^2}\right] +$
$8x^7\left(\dfrac{x^2 - 9}{x^4 + 7}\right)^6$

41. $\dfrac{-88 (x + 6)^7}{(x - 5)^9}$ **43. (a)** $\overline{C}(x) = 8 + \dfrac{240}{x}$ **(b)** $\dfrac{-240}{x^2}$
(c) $\overline{C}'(5) = -9.6$
$\overline{C}'(20) = -0.6$
$\overline{C}'(50) = -0.096$
A value of $\overline{C}'(x_0)$ represents the instantaneous rate of change of the average cost per unit at a production level of x_0.

45. (a) $\dfrac{dS}{dr} = -\dfrac{900,000}{r^2}\left[\left(1 + \dfrac{r}{100}\right)^6 - 1\right] +$
$\dfrac{6(900,000)}{r}\left(1 + \dfrac{r}{100}\right)^5\left(\dfrac{1}{100}\right)$
(b) 1665.04; At $r = 8$, a change of 1 unit in r will result in a change of approximately \$1665.04 in S **(c)** 1752.71; At $r = 10$, a change of 1 unit in r will result in an approximate change of \$1752.71 in S. **47. (a)** $x < 5$ because $f(x)$ does not exist for $x < 5$. **(b)** $x \le 5$ **49.** $x = 0$

• CHAPTER 10

SECTION 10-1

1. $f'(x) = 3x^2 - 8x + 7$
$f''(x) = 6x - 8$
3. $f'(x) = 5x^4 - 24x^2 + 4x + 4$
$f''(x) = 20x^3 - 48x + 4$
5. $f'(x) = 5x^4 - 4x^3 + 12x^2 + 2x - 1$
$f''(x) = 20x^3 - 12x^2 + 24x + 2$
7. $f'(x) = (x + 1)^4 + 4(x + 1)^3(x - 2) = (x + 1)^3(5x - 7)$
$f''(x) = 8(x+1)^3 + 12(x + 1)^2(x - 2) = 4(x + 1)^2(5x - 4)$

9. $\dfrac{dy}{dx} = 3x^2 - 4x + 8$
$\dfrac{d^2y}{dx^2} = 6x - 4$

11. $\dfrac{dy}{dx} = \dfrac{x^6 - 28x^3 - 18x^2}{(x^3 - 7)^2}$
$\dfrac{d^2y}{dx^2} = \dfrac{(x^3 - 7)(6x^5 - 84x^2 - 36x) - 6x^2(x^6 - 28x^3 - 18x^2)}{(x^3 - 7)^3}$

13. $\dfrac{dy}{dx} = (x - 4)^3 + 3(x - 4)^2(x - 7) = (x - 4)^2(4x - 25)$
$\dfrac{d^2y}{dx} = 6(x - 4)(2x - 11)$

15. $g'(x) = \dfrac{x^2 - 10x + 1}{(x - 5)^2}$
$g''(x) = \dfrac{2(x - 5)^2 - 2(x^2 - 10x + 1)}{(x - 5)^3} = \dfrac{48}{(x - 5)^3}$
$g''(2) = -\dfrac{16}{9} \approx -1.778$

17. $\dfrac{dy}{dx} = 4x^3 - 15x^2 + 12x + 3$
$\left.\dfrac{dy}{dx}\right|_{x = 1} = 4$
$\dfrac{d^2y}{dx^2} = 12x^2 - 30x + 12$
$\left.\dfrac{d^2y}{dx^2}\right|_{x = 1} = -6$

19. $f'(x) = 4x^3 - 18x^2 + 16x - 4$
$f'(1) = -2$
$f''(x) = 12x^2 - 36x + 16$
$f''(3) = 16$

21. $f'(x) = 6x^5 - 40x^4 + 24x^3 - 6x^2 + 1$
$f''(x) = 30x^4 - 160x^3 + 72x^2 - 12x$
$f'''(x) = 120x^3 - 480x^2 + 144x - 12$
$f^{(4)}(x) = 360x^2 - 960x + 144$
$f^{(4)}(3) = 504$

23. $f'(x) = 4x^3 - 18x^2 + 8x - 8$
$f''(x) = 12x^2 - 36x + 8$
$f'''(x) = 24x - 36$

$f^{(4)}(x) = 24$
$f^{(5)}(x) = 0$
$f^{(6)}(x) = 0$

25. (a) $\dfrac{dS}{dt}\Big|_{t\,=\,2} = 128$ ft/sec; $\dfrac{dS}{dt}\Big|_{t\,=\,3} = 96$ ft/sec;

$\dfrac{dS}{dt}\Big|_{t\,=\,8} = -64$ ft/sec (downward) **(b)** $\dfrac{d^2S}{dt^2} = -32$ ft/sec²
at $t = 2$, 3, and 8

SECTION 10-2

1. (a) $x_1 < x < x_2$ and $x_3 < x < x_4$ **(b)** $x_2 < x < x_3$ and
$x_4 < x < x_5$ **(c)** relative maxima: $f(x_2)$ and $f(x_4)$;
relative minimum: $f(x_3)$ **(d)** absolute maximum: $f(x_4)$;
absolute minimum: $f(x_1)$ **3. (a)** $-2 < x < 2$
(b) $-\infty < x < -2$ and $2 < x < \infty$. **(c)** relative minimum at
$x = -2$; relative maximum at $x = 2$ **5. (a)** $-\infty < x < -4$
and $-4 < x < 5$ **(b)** $5 < x < \infty$ **(c)** relative maximum at
$x = 5$; no relative minima **7. (a)** $-3 < x < -1$,
$-1 < x < 2$, and $4 < x < \infty$ **(b)** $-\infty < x < -3$ and
$2 < x < 4$ **(c)** relative minima at $x = -3$ and $x = 4$;
relative maxima at $x = 2$ **9. (a)** $-\infty < x < -1$ and
$5 < x < \infty$ **(b)** $-1 < x < 5$ **(c)** relative minimum at $x = 5$;
relative maximum at $x = -1$ **11. (a)** $0 < x < 3000$ and
$7000 < x < 10{,}000$ **(b)** $3000 < x < 7000$ **(c)** 45,000 is a
relative maximum; 35,000 is a relative minimum
(d) 10,000 units **(e)** \$83,000; not a relative maximum;
It is an absolute maximum. **13. (a)** 3000 units
(b) \$2; This is both a relative and an absolute minimum.
15. (a) $-\infty < x < \infty$ **(b)** nowhere **(c)** no relative maxima
or minima **17. (a)** $-\infty < x < 4$ **(b)** $4 < x < \infty$
(c) $f(4) = 16$ is a relative maximum **19. (a)** $1 < x < \infty$
(b) $-\infty < x < 0$ and $0 < x < 1$ **(c)** $f(1) = 9$ is a relative
minimum **21. (a)** $0 < x < \infty$ **(b)** $-\infty < x < 0$
(c) $f(0) = 2$ is a relative minimum **23. (a)** $-\infty < x < 5$
and $5 < x < \infty$ **(b)** Nowhere **(c)** No relative maxima or
minima **25. (a)** Nowhere **(b)** $-\infty < x < -1$ and
$-1 < x < \infty$ **(c)** No relative maxima or minima
27. (a) $-\infty < x < 4$ **(b)** $4 < x < \infty$ **(c)** relative maximum
at $f(4) = 25$ **(d)**

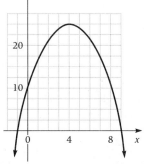

29. (a) $-\infty < x < 0$ and $4 < x < \infty$ **(b)** $0 < x < 4$
(c) relative maximum at $f(0) = 0$; relative minimum at
$f(4) = -32$ **(d)**

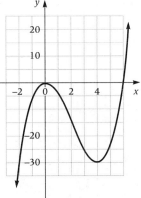

31. (a) $-2 < x < 0$ and $2 < x < \infty$ **(b)** $-\infty < x < -2$ and
$0 < x < 2$ **(c)** relative minima at $f(-2) = -16$ and
$f(2) = -16$; relative maximum at $f(0) = 0$
(d)   **33. (a)** $0 < x < \infty$

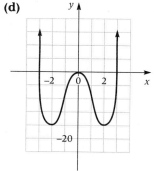

(b) $-\infty < x < 0$ **(c)** relative minimum at $f(0) = 5$
(d)   **35.** relative maximum at

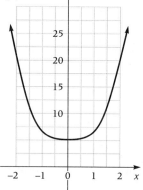

$f(-5) = 101$; relative minimum at $f(1) = -7$; absolute minimum at $f(-10) = -249$; absolute maximum at $f(11) = 1893$

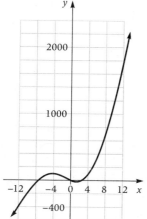

37. $f(x) = ax^2 + bx + c$

$f'(x) = 2ax + b$; $f'(x) = 0 \Rightarrow x = -\dfrac{b}{2a}$

For $x < -\dfrac{b}{2a}$, $f'(x) < 0$; for $x > -\dfrac{b}{2a}$, $f'(x) > 0$.

$\therefore f\left(-\dfrac{b}{2a}\right)$ is a relative minimum of f

39. (a) $x_1 < x < x_4$ **(b)** Increasing at an increasing rate
41. (a) $0 < x < 20$ **(b)** $20 < x < 40$ **(c)** relative maximum at $R(20) = 400$ **(d)**

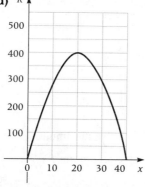

(e) $x = 20$; $R(20)$ is both a relative and an absolute maximum. **(f)** 144 **43. (a)** $100 < x < \infty$
(b) $90 \le x < 100$

(c)

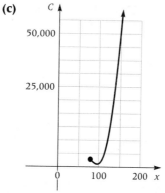

(d) 100; $C(100) = 1000$ is both a relative and an absolute minimum. **(e)** $C(100) = 1000$

SECTION 10-3

1. (a) $x_3 < x < x_5$ and $x_5 < x < x_7$ **(b)** $x_1 < x < x_3$ and $x_7 < x < x_8$ **(c)** $x = x_3$ and $x = x_7$ **(d)** relative maxima occur at $x = x_2$ and $x = x_5$; relative minima occur at $x = x_4$ and $x = x_6$ **3. (a)** $-\infty < x < -2$ and $4 < x < \infty$
(b) $-2 < x < 4$ **(c)** $x = -2$ and $x = 4$
5. (a) $-\infty < x < -3$ and $3 < x < \infty$ **(b)** $-3 < x < 3$
(c) $x = -3$ and $x = 3$ **7. (a)** $-\infty < x < -1$ and $2 < x < \infty$ **(b)** $-1 < x < 2$ **(c)** $x = -1$ and $x = 2$
9.

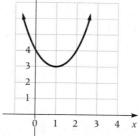

relative minimum: $f(1) = 3$; concave up everywhere; no asymptotes. y-intercept: $(0, 4)$
11. relative maximum: $f(-1) = 13$; relative minimum: $f(9) = -487$; inflection point at $x = 4$; no asymptotes. y-intercept: $(0, -1)$

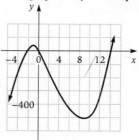

13. relative minimum: $f(3) = -128$; inflection points at $x = 0$ and $x = 2$; no asymptotes. y-intercept: $(0, 7)$

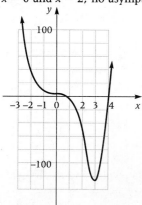

15. relative maximum: $f(-1) = 4$; relative minimum: $f(1) = 0$; inflection point at $x = 0$; no asymptotes. y-intercept: $(0, 2)$

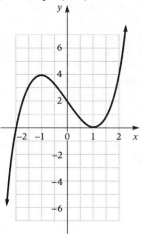

17. no relative extrema. inflection point at $x = 5$; no asymptotes. y-intercept: $(0, -125)$

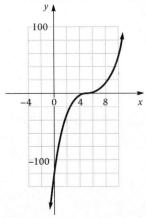

19. relative minimum: $f(-3) = 2$; no inflection points; no asymptotes. y-intercept: $(0, 59,051)$

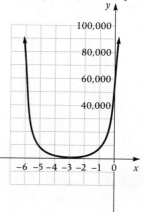

21. relative maximum: $f\left(-\dfrac{3}{5}\right) = 1382.8$;

relative minimum: $f(5) = 6$; inflection point at $x = \dfrac{4}{5}$; no asymptotes. y-intercept: $(0, 1256)$

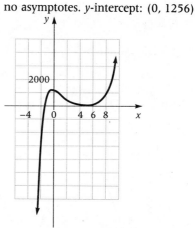

23. relative maximum: $f(-2) = 0$;

relative minimum: $f\left(\dfrac{2}{5}\right) \approx -268.74$;

inflection points at $x = \dfrac{2 - 3\sqrt{6}}{5}$, $x = \dfrac{2 + 3\sqrt{6}}{5}$, and $x = 4$;

no asymptotes. y-intercept: $(0, -256)$

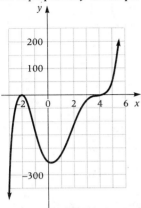

25. no relative extrema; inflection point at $x = 0$; no asymptotes. y-intercept: $(0, 0)$

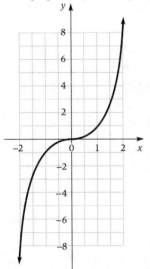

27. relative minimum: $f(0) = 0$; no inflection points; no asymptotes. y-intercept: $(0, 0)$

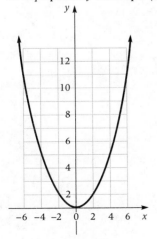

29. relative minimum: $f(0) = -3$; inflection points at $x = -\sqrt{\dfrac{2}{3}}$ and $x = \sqrt{\dfrac{2}{3}}$; horizontal asymptote: $y = 0$; y-intercept: $(0, -3)$

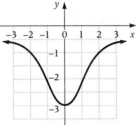

31. relative minimum: $f(-1) = \dfrac{-1}{2}$; relative maximum: $f(1) = \dfrac{1}{2}$; inflection points at $x = -\sqrt{3}$, $x = 0$, and $x = \sqrt{3}$; horizontal asymptote: $y = 0$; y-intercept: $(0, 0)$

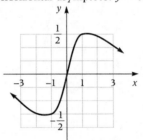

33. relative maximum: $f(-20) = -80$; relative minimum: $f(20) = 80$; no inflection points; vertical asymptote: $x = 0$

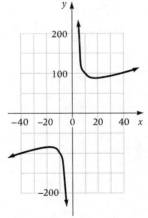

35. relative maximum: $f(-5) = -16$;
relative minimum: $f(3) = 0$; no inflection points;
vertical asymptote: $x = -1$

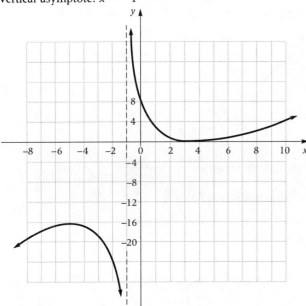

37. relative minimum: $f(0) = 0$;
relative maximum: $f(4) \approx 1.185$;
inflection points at $x = \dfrac{5 - \sqrt{33}}{2} \approx -0.37$ and
$x = \dfrac{5 + \sqrt{33}}{2} \approx 5.37$; vertical asymptote: $x = 1$;
horizontal asymptote: $y = 1$

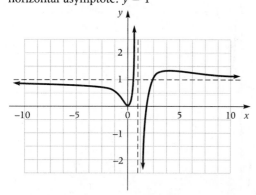

39. relative maximum: $f(-2\sqrt{5}) = 9 - 4\sqrt{5} \approx 0.06$;
relative minimum: $f(2\sqrt{5}) = 9 + 4\sqrt{5} \approx 17.9$;
no inflection points; vertical asymptote: $x = 0$;
oblique asymptote: $y = x + 9$

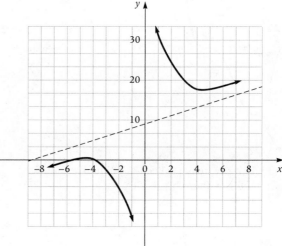

41. relative maximum: $f(0) = 0$; inflection point at $x = \dfrac{16}{3}$; no asymptotes. y-intecept: $(0, 0)$

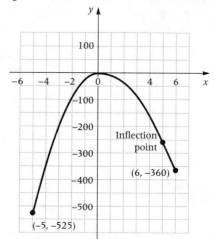

43. relative maximum: $f(1) = 0$;
relative minimum: $f\left(\dfrac{7}{3}\right) = -\dfrac{32}{27} \approx -1.18519$;

inflection point at $x = \dfrac{5}{3}$; no asymptotes.

y-intercept: $(0, -3)$

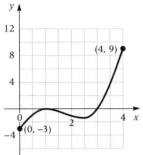

45. (a) $-\infty < x < 0$ **(b)** $0 < x < \infty$ **(c)** $x = 0$; $f''(x)$ is not defined at $x = 0$ **(d)**

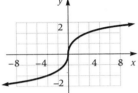

47. (a) relative minimum: $f(2) = 0.75$;
inflection point at $x = 2\sqrt{3}$;
horizontal asymptote: $y = 1$; y-intercept: $(0, 1)$

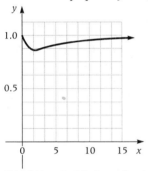

(b) $f(0) = 1$ **(c)** 2 weeks **(d)** After 2 weeks
(e) 0.75; occurring at $x = 2$ **(f)** 1.0; occurring at $x = 0$
and $x = +\infty$ **(g)** The level of oxygen reaches its initial level asymptotically.

49. (a)

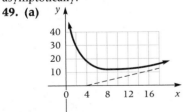

(b) $\overline{C}(8) = 12$ is a relative minimum **(c)** $x = 8$
(d) $\overline{C}(8) = 12$

51. (a)

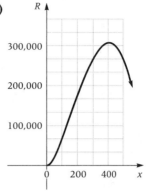

(b) $R(400) = 320,000$ is both a relative and an absolute maximum. $R(0) = 0$ is the absolute minimum.
(c) at $x = 200$ **(d)**

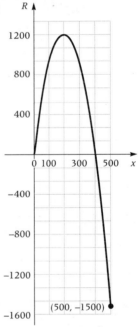

(e) relative and absolute maximum of 1200 at $x = 200$;
absolute minimum of -1500 at $x = 500$ **(f)** $x = 200$

SECTION 10-4

1. relative minimum: $f(4) = -7$
3. relative maximum: $f(0) = 7$;
relative minimum: $f(4) = -25$
5. relative maximum: $f(-1) = 7$;
relative minimum: $f(1) = 3$
7. relative maximum: $f(-2) = 21$;
relative minimum: $f(1) = -6$
9. relative maximum: $f(-3) = 90$;
relative minimum: $f(5) = -166$
11. relative maximum: $f(0) = 6$;
relative minimum: $f(-2) = -10$;
relative minimum: $f(2) = -10$

13. relative maximum: $y(-5) = -10$;
relative minimum: $y(5) = 10$
15. relative maximum: $f(-3) = -4$;
relative minimum: $f(3) = 4$
17. absolute minimum: $f(8) = -55$; no absolute maximum
19. absolute maximum: $f(4) = 19$; no absolute minimum
21. absolute maximum: $f(4) = 4$; no absolute minimum
23. absolute maximum: $f(-3) = 58$;
absolute minimum: $f(3) = -50$
25. absolute minimum: $f(5) = 59$; no absolute maximum
27. absolute minimum: $f(3) = 8$; no absolute maximum
29. absolute minimum: $f(0) = -40$;
absolute maximum: $f(4) = 40$
31. absolute maximum: $f(6) = 20$;
absolute minimum: $f(0) = -16$
33. 12 and 12 **35.** 300 and 300 **37.** 60
39. (a) 5 inches **(b)** $1,093,750
41. $x = 100$ ft, $y = 200$ ft **43.** $x = 100$ ft, $y = 200$ ft
45. $A = xy$; $2x + 2y = P$, a fixed number

$$A(x) = x\left(\frac{P - 2x}{2}\right) = \frac{P}{2}x - x^2$$

$$A'(x) = \frac{P}{2} - 2x$$

$$A'(x) = 0 \Rightarrow x = \frac{P}{4}; \; y = \frac{P}{4}$$

$A''(x) = -2 \Rightarrow$ a concave down. Thus, $A\left(\frac{P}{4}\right)$ is the
absolute maximum area. Since $x = y$, the rectangle is a square.
47. $x = 500$ ft, $y = 450$ ft; Area $= 405{,}000$ sq. ft
49. (a) $P(x) = -4x^2 + 3000x - 10{,}000$ **(b)** $x = 375$
(c) $P(375) = \$552{,}500$
51. (a) $P(x) = -0.01x^2 + 19.8x - 40$ **(b)** $x = 990$
(c) $P(990) = \$9761$ **53. (a)** $R(x) = -5x^2 + 3000x$
(b) $P(x) = -5x^2 + 2950x - 6000$ **(c)** $x = 295$ **(d)** $1525
(e) $429{,}125$ **55. (a)** $R(x) = -2x^2 + 2000x$
(b) $P(x) = -2x^2 + 1970x - 4000$ **(c)** $x = 492.5$
(d) $1016 **(e)** $481{,}112$ **57. (a)** $x = 293$ **(b)** $1535
(c) increased by $10 **(d)** 50%
59. (a) $x = 25$ hundred units **(b)** 16 thousand dollars
(c) 15 million dollars **61.** 2 weeks; $58.80 / tree
63. (a) $R(x) = (40 + 5x)(1000 - 50x)$ **(b)** $x = 6$
(c) $49{,}000 **65.** 3 in x 3 in **67.** $x = 8$ ft; $y = 4$ ft
69. $P = 150$; $H(150) = 225$ **71.** $P = 900$; $H(900) = 900$
73. No maximum sustainable harvest

75. $\dfrac{27}{\sqrt{7}} \approx 10.205$ miles

SECTION 10-5

1. (a) $C(Q) = \dfrac{2{,}500{,}000}{Q} + 10Q$ **(b)** $Q = 500$

3. (a) $C(Q) = \dfrac{18{,}000{,}000}{Q} + 12.5Q$ **(b)** $Q = 1200$ units
(c) $30{,}000/year **(d)** 250 orders/year **5. (a)** $16/unit
(b) $C(Q) = \dfrac{50{,}000{,}000}{Q} + 8Q$ **(c)** $Q = 2500$ units
(d) $40{,}000/year **(e)** 200 orders/year

7. $C''(Q) = \dfrac{2KD}{Q^3} > 0 \Rightarrow C$ concave up. Thus, the relative
extremum found in Exercise 6 is a relative minimum. Since the graph of C vs Q is concave up, the relative minimum is also the absolute minimum.

• EXTRA DIVIDENDS

1. $C(Q) = \dfrac{1.28 \times 10^8}{Q} + 2Q$ **3.** $32{,}000 **5.** $16{,}000

7. $C'(Q) = -\dfrac{KD}{Q^2} + \dfrac{H}{2}\left(\dfrac{P - D}{P}\right)$

$C''(Q) = \dfrac{2KD}{Q^3} > 0 \Rightarrow C$ concave up. Thus, the relative
extremum found in Exercise 6 is a relative minimum. The relative minimum is also the absolute minimum since C is concave up.

• CHAPTER HIGHLIGHTS

1. Take the derivative of the first derivative. **2.** Take the derivative of the second derivative. **3. (a)** Velocity is the rate of change of distance with respect to time and is given by the derivative dS/dt. **(b)** Acceleration is the rate of change of velocity with respect to time and is given by d^2S/dt^2.
4. (a)

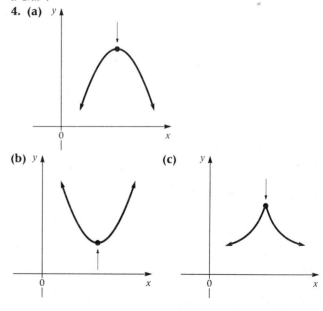

(d)

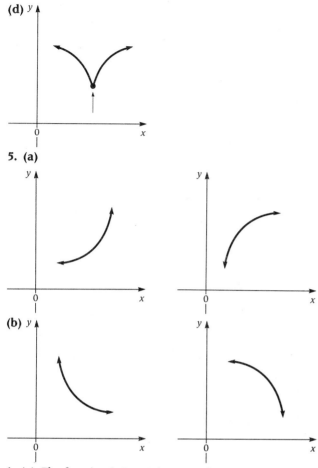

5. (a)

(b)

6. (a) The function is increasing over the interval.
(b) The function is decreasing over the interval.
7. (a) Critical values are values of x at which the derivative of a function is either 0 or undefined. The function must be defined at a critical value.
(b) Not necessarily **(c)** We look for a sign change in the first derivative at the critical value. **(d)** No.
8. (a) If the sign of the first derivative changes from positive to negative as we move from left to right across the critical value, then a relative maximum occurs at the critical value. **(b)** If the sign of the first derivative changes from negative to positive as we move from left to right across the critical value, then a relative minimum occurs at the critical value. **9. (a)** A relative maximum is higher than any of its neighboring points on the graph of the function whereas an absolute maximum is the highest or among the highest points on the graph of the function. An analogous statement can be made for minimum points.

(b) Yes. The figures below show relative maxima that are also absolute maxima. Analogous graphs can be drawn for minima.

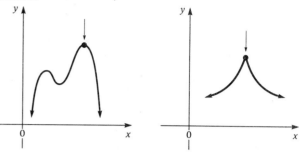

(c) No. The leftmost figure below shows an absolute maximum that is not a relative maximum. The rightmost figure below shows an absolute minimum that is not a relative minimum.

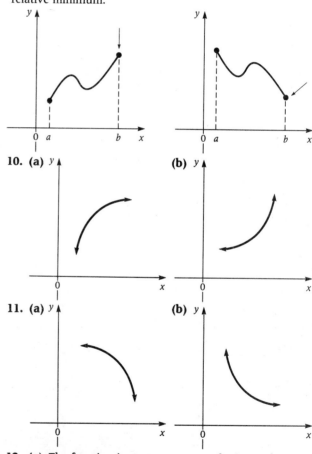

12. (a) The function is concave up over the interval.
(b) The function is concave down over the interval.
13. (a) An inflection point is a point where the graph of a function changes in concavity. **(b)** We look for a sign change in the second derivative. **14.** Vertical asymptotes

occur at values of x where the denominator of a rational function equals 0 but the numerator does not equal 0. **15.** No. **16.** A function $f(x)$ has a horizontal asymptote if and only if either $\lim\limits_{x \to \infty} f(x) = L$ of $\lim\limits_{x \to -\infty} f(x) = M$ where L and M are constants. It might be the case that $L = M$. In any case L would be a horizontal asymptote as x approaches positive infinity and M would be a horizontal asymptote as x approaches negative infinity. **17. (a)** No, it applies to only those critical values at which the first derivative is 0. **(b)** Yes. **(c)** No. **18. (a)** A relative minimum occurs at x_0. **(b)** A relative maximum occurs at x_0. **(c)** The test fails and gives no information regarding the existence of a relative extremum at x_0. **19.** Look for a sign change in the first derivative. **20.** No **21.** Yes **22.** No **23.** If a function that is continuous over some interval has only one critical value in the interval and the first derivative is 0 at that critical value, then: If the second derivative is negative at the critical value, an absolute maximum occurs at the critical value; if the second derivative is positive at the critical value, an absolute minimum occurs at the critical value; if the second derivative is 0 at the critical value, the test fails. **24.** *Step 1:* Find all the critical values on the closed interval. *Step 2:* Evaluate the function at the critical values and at the endpoints of the interval. *Step 3.* Write the largest value found in step 2; this is the absolute maximum value of the function over the interval. Step 4: Write the smallest value found in step 2; this is the absolute minimum value of the function over the interval. **25.** The annual ordering cost and annual carrying cost. The total annual inventory cost is given by $C(Q) = K(D/Q) + H(Q/2)$ where D is the annual demand for the product, K is the cost of placing an order, H is the cost of carrying (or holding) one unit in inventory for a year, Q is the order size, D/Q is the number of orders placed in a year, $K(D/Q)$ is the annual ordering cost, $Q/2$ is the average number of units in inventory, and $H(Q/2)$ is the annual carrying cost.

• REVIEW EXERCISES

1. (a) $2x - 6$ **(b)** 2 **(c)** -4 **(d)** 2 **3. (a)** $6x^5 - 32x^3$ **(b)** $30x^4 - 96x^2$ **(c)** -26 **(d)** -66 **5. (a)** 60 ft/sec; 40 ft/sec **(b)** -4 ft/sec² for both **7. (a)** $x = \dfrac{-1}{2} + \dfrac{\sqrt{41}}{2}$ and $x = \dfrac{-1}{2} - \dfrac{\sqrt{41}}{2}$ **(b)** $-\infty < x < \dfrac{-1}{2} - \dfrac{\sqrt{41}}{2}$ and $\dfrac{-1}{2} + \dfrac{\sqrt{41}}{2} < x < \infty$ **(c)** $\dfrac{-1}{2} - \dfrac{\sqrt{41}}{2} < x < \dfrac{-1}{2} + \dfrac{\sqrt{41}}{2}$

(d) relative maximum: $f\left(\dfrac{-1}{2} - \dfrac{\sqrt{41}}{2}\right) \approx 169.764$

relative minimum: $f\left(\dfrac{-1}{2} + \dfrac{\sqrt{41}}{2}\right) \approx -92.764$

(e)

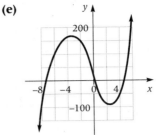

9. (a) $x = 0$ and $x = 16$ **(b)** $-\infty < x < 0$ and $16 < x < \infty$ **(c)** $0 < x < 16$ **(d)** relative maximum: $f(0) = 6$; relative minimum: $f(16) = -2042$

(e)

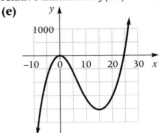

11.

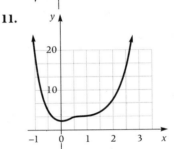

relative and absolute minimum: $f(0) = 2$; inflection points at $x = \dfrac{1}{3}$ and $x = 1$

13.

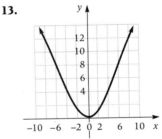

relative and absolute minimum: $f(0) = 0$; no inflection points

15.

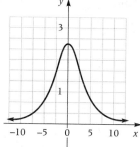

relative and absolute maximum: $f(0) = 2.5$;

inflection points at $x = \dfrac{-2}{\sqrt{3}}$ and $x = \dfrac{2}{\sqrt{3}}$

17. (a) $\overline{C}(x) = x - 8 + \dfrac{100}{x}$

(b)

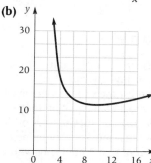

$\overline{C}(10)$ is both a relative and an absolute minimum; $y = x - 8$ is an oblique asymptote; $x = 0$ is a vertical asymptote **(c)** $\overline{C}(10) = 12$ is both a relative and an absolute minimum. **(d)** $x = 10$ **(e)** $\overline{C}(10) = 12$
19. relative maximum: $f(2) = 48$; relative minimum: $f(8) = -60$ **21.** relative maximum: $f(-10) = -20$; relative minimum: $f(10) = 20$

23. absolute maximum: $f\left(\dfrac{9}{4}\right) = \dfrac{9}{4}$; no absolute minimum

25. absolute minimum: $f(4) = 31$; no absolute maximum
27. absolute minimum: $f(2\sqrt[4]{12}) \approx 17.9264$;
no absolute maximum **29.** 200 ft × 200 ft **31. (a)** $16

(b) $105,600 **(c)** 6600 subscribers **33.** $20\sqrt{3}$ ft × $\dfrac{40}{\sqrt{3}}$ ft

or ≈ 34.64 ft × 23.09 ft

• CHAPTER 11

SECTION 11-1

1. $-\dfrac{4x^3 + y^3}{1 + 3xy^2}$ **3.** $-\dfrac{3x^2 + y^5}{y^3(5xy + 4)}$ **5.** $\dfrac{8y - 3x^2}{6y^5 - 8x}$

7. $\dfrac{3x^2 - 2xy + y^2}{x^2 - 2xy + 3y^2}$ **9.** $\dfrac{x - 2(x + y)^3}{2(x + y)^3 - y}$ **11.** $\dfrac{-7}{36}$ **13.** $\dfrac{7}{16}$

15. $\dfrac{4}{7}$ **17. (a)** $\dfrac{-x}{y}$ **(b)** $\dfrac{-1}{\sqrt{3}}$ **(c)** $y = \dfrac{-1}{\sqrt{3}}x + \dfrac{16}{\sqrt{3}}$

(d)   **19.** $\dfrac{1}{6}$ **21.** $\dfrac{1}{8x - 3}$; $x \neq \dfrac{3}{8}$

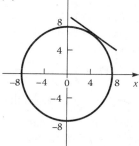

23. (a) $\dfrac{1}{2x - 4}$; $x \neq 2$ **(b)** $\dfrac{1}{2}$ **(c)** $\dfrac{dx}{dy} = \dfrac{1}{2}$ is the rate of change of x with respect to y at $x = 3$

25. (a) $\dfrac{1}{2p - 20}$; $p \neq 10$ **(b)** $\dfrac{-1}{6}$ **(c)** $\dfrac{dp}{dq} = \dfrac{-1}{6}$ is the rate of change of p with respect to q at $p = 7$.

27. $\dfrac{dS}{dt} = \dfrac{2(S - 6t^2 + 1)}{3S^2 - 2t}$ **29.** $\dfrac{dS}{dt} = \dfrac{3t(2S + t)}{4S^3 - 3t^2}$

SECTION 11-2

1. -16 **3.** $\dfrac{1}{4}$ **5.** $\dfrac{-9}{4}$ **7.** 2 **9.** $\dfrac{-1}{7}$ **11.** 1 **13.** -1

15. $-\dfrac{16}{3}$ ft/second **17. (a)** 40,000 **(b)** 4000 **(c)** 36,000

19. 76π or approximately 238.8 cm²/minute

21. $\dfrac{1}{4}$ foot/day **23. (a)** $\dfrac{100\sqrt{6}}{3}$ ft/sec ≈ 81.65 ft/sec

(b) ≈55.67 mi/hr **25.** 3200π ≈ 10,053 cm³/min

27. $\dfrac{-5}{2\pi}$ ≈ -0.796 foot/hr **29.** 1.0 ohm/sec

31. $\dfrac{1}{1800\pi}$ ≈ 1.768×10^{-4} foot/min

SECTION 11-3

1. $E = \dfrac{-p}{30 - p}$ **3.** $E = \dfrac{-p}{40 - p}$ **5.** $E = \dfrac{2p}{p - 4}$

7. $E = \dfrac{\sqrt{p}}{2\sqrt{p} - 8}$ **9.** $E = \dfrac{-p}{2(200 - p)}$ **11.** $E = \dfrac{-10}{p - 10}$

13. (a) $E = -1.5$ at $p = 10$

Since $E = \dfrac{\text{\% change in quantity demanded}}{\text{\% change in price}}$, the value of $E - 1.5$ means that if the price increases by 1% when $p = 10$, the quantity demanded will decrease by approximately 1.5%. If the price decreases by 1% when $p = 10$, the quantity demanded will increase by approximately 1.5% **(b)** elastic

15. (a) $E = -0.80$ at $p = 20$

Since $E = \dfrac{\% \text{ change in quantity demanded}}{\% \text{ change in price}}$, the value of

$E = -0.80$ means that if the price increases by 1% when $p = 20$, the quantity demanded will decrease by approximately 0.80%. If the price decreases by 1% when $p = 20$, the quantity demanded will increase by approximately 0.80%. **(b)** inelastic   **17. (a)** $E = \dfrac{-p}{65 - p}$

(b) $\dfrac{-10}{3} \approx -3.33$ **(c)** The value of $E = -3.33$ means that if the price increases by 1% when $p = 50$, the quantity demanded will decrease by approximately 3.33%. Also, if the price decreases by 1% when $p = 50$, the quantity demanded will increase by approximately 3.33%.

19. (a) $E = \dfrac{-8}{p - 8}$ **(b)** -4 **(c)** The value of $E = -4$ means that if the price increases by 1% when $p = 10$, the quantity demanded will decrease by approximately 4%. Also, if the price decreases by 1% when $p = 10$, the quantity demanded will increase by approximately 4%.

21. (a) $E = \dfrac{2p}{p - 10}$ **(b)** $\dfrac{-4}{3} \approx -1.33$ **(c)** The value of $E = -1.33$ means that if the price increased by 1% when $p = 4$, the quantity demanded will decrease by approximately 1.33%. Also, if the price decreases by 1% when $p = 4$, the quantity demanded will increase by approximately 1.33%.   **23. (a)** $E = -1$ **(b)** $E = -1$ means that an increase of 1% in the price will lead to a decrease of approximately 1% in the quantity demanded; a decrease of 1% in the price will lead to an increase of approximately 1% in the quantity demanded. **(c)** The demand has unit elasticity for all values of p. **(d)** The demand has unit elasticity for all values of p.   **25. (a)** $E = \dfrac{-p}{2(100 - p)}$

(b) $\dfrac{200}{3} < p < 100$ **(c)** $0 \le p < \dfrac{200}{3}$ **(d)** $p = \dfrac{200}{3}$

SECTION 11-4

1. $3x^2\ dx$ **3.** $32x^3\ dx$ **5.** $\dfrac{9}{2}\sqrt{x}\ dx$ **7.** $\dfrac{-32}{x^2}\ dx$

9. $\dfrac{1}{3\sqrt[3]{x^2}}\ dx$ **11.** 6 **13.** ≈ 0.000926 **15.** 16 **17.** 9.03

19. 8.063 **21.** 1.9938 **23.** 0.3975 million dollars

25. $-\$0.024$

27. $dC = 60$ million dollars
$\Delta C = 60.15$ million dollars

Graphically, the slope of the tangent line at $x = 200$ is 60, and 60 dx approximates Δy.

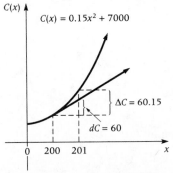

29. (a) $\overline{C}(x) = 100 + \dfrac{50,000}{x}$ **(b)** -1.25 **31.** 0.238%

33. (a) 20% **(b)** 10%

• CHAPTER HIGHLIGHTS

1. If y is not written completely in terms of x and constants, then y is defined implicitly in terms of x.
2. time. **3.** *Step 1:* Identify and list the variables involved. Draw a sketch if possible. *Step 2:* Find an equation that relates the variables. *Step 3:* Identify and list the rates of change that are given and those that must be determined. *Step 4:* Differentiate the equation of step 2 implicitly with respect to time, t. Solve for the derivative that gives the desired rate of change. *Step 5:* Substitute in all given values.
4. % change in quantity demanded; % change in price.
5. $E = (p/q)(dq/dp)$; negative. **6.** *Case 1:* If $|E| = 1$, then the percent change in demand equals the percent change in price. In this case, demand is said to have **unit elasticity.** *Case 2:* If $|E| > 1$, then the percent change in demand is greater than the percent change in price. In this case, demand is said to be **elastic.** *Case 3:* If $|E| < 1$, then the percent change in demand is less than the percent change in price. In this case, demand is said to be **inelastic.**
7. Positive **8.** Negative **9.** $dy = f'(x)\ dx$ **10.** dy is an approximation to y, the change in y, as shown below.

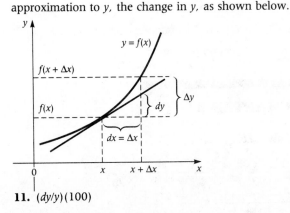

11. $(dy/y)(100)$

• REVIEW EXERCISES

1. $-\dfrac{3x^2 + y^4}{4xy^3 + 1}$ **3.** $\dfrac{2x - y + y^3}{x - 3xy^2 + 4y^3}$ **5.** $\dfrac{-x}{y}$ **7.** $\dfrac{1}{2(8x + 3)}$

9. -1.8 units/sec **11.** 1944π cm³/min ≈ 6107 cm³/min

13. $E = \dfrac{2p}{p - 7}$ **15.** $E = \dfrac{-30}{p - 30}$ **17.** $E = -1.4$ at $p = 20$

(a) The value of $E = -1.4$ means that an increase of 1% in the price when $p = 20$ leads to an approximate decrease of 1.4% in the quantity demanded. Also, a decrease of 1% in the price when $p = 20$ leads to an approximate increase of 1.4% in the quantity demanded. **(b)** Elastic

19. $(3x^2 - 8x)dx$ **21.** $dy = 10x^{3/2}\, dx$

23. $dy = 2(x + 1)dx$; 0.5 **25. (a)** 10 million dollars
(b) 3.33%

• CHAPTER 12

SECTION 12-1

1. $4e^{4x}$ **3.** $-8e^{-2x}$ **5.** $0.2e^{-0.1x}$ **7.** $(5x^4 - 7)e^{x^5 - 7x}$

9. $2e^{2x-5}$ **11.** $(2x - 3)(\ln 4)\, 4^{x^2 - 3x}$

13. $-0.02(\ln 4)4^{-0.02x}$

15. $[x^2(x^3 - 4)(4x^3 - 7) + x(5x^3 - 8)]e^{x^4 - 7x}$
$= (4x^8 - 23x^5 + 5x^4 + 28x^2 - 8x)e^{x^4 - 7x}$

17. $x(x^3 + 8)(3x^2 + 5) + 4x^3 + 8]e^{x^3 + 5x}$
$= (3x^6 + 5x^4 + 28x^3 + 40x + 8)e^{x^3 + 5x}$

19. $\dfrac{x(e^x - e^{-x}) - (e^x + e^{-x})}{x^2} = \dfrac{e^x(x - 1) - e^{-x}(x + 1)}{x^2}$

21. $\dfrac{x(e^x + e^{-x}) - (e^x - e^{-x})}{x^2} = \dfrac{e^x(x-1) + e^{-x}(x + 1)}{x^2}$

23. $\dfrac{[(x^2 - 3x)(3x^2 - 4) - 2x + 3]e^{x^3 - 4x}}{(x^2 - 3x)^2}$
$= \dfrac{(3x^4 - 9x^3 - 4x^2 + 10x + 3)e^{x^3 - 4x}}{(x^2 - 3x)^2}$

25. $\dfrac{-x}{\sqrt{25 - x^2}}e^{\sqrt{25 - x^2}}$ **27.** $\dfrac{1}{2\sqrt{x}}e^{\sqrt{x}}$ **29.** $\dfrac{96{,}000e^{-3x}}{(1 + 40e^{-3x})^2}$

31. $\dfrac{-160{,}000e^{-2x}}{(5 - 80e^{-2x})^2}$ **33.** $2(4x + e^{-x})(4 - e^{-x})$

35. $\dfrac{1 - e^{-x}}{2\sqrt{x + e^{-x}}}$ **37.** $\dfrac{x(1 - e^{-x^2})}{\sqrt{x^2 + e^{-x^2}}}$

39. $y = x + 1$

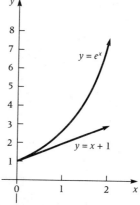

41. (a) $1000e^{0.10x}$ **(b)** 1349.86; $S'(3)$ is the instantaneous rate of change of S with respect to x at $x = 3$.
(c) 1491.82; $S'(4)$ is the instantaneous rate of change of S with respect to x at $x = 4$. **(d)** 1648.72 **(e)** \$23,082.09; \$24,596.03 **(f)**

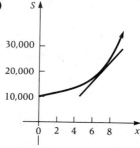

43. (a) 81; increasing **(b)** 109; increasing **(c)** 2149
(d)

45. increasing; 3.35 items/day **47. (a)** $24.6e^{-0.30x}$
(b) 18.22; This is the instantaneous rate of change of y with respect to x at $x = 1$. **(c)** 4.066; This is the instantaneous rate of change of y with respect to x at $x = 6$. **(d)** 0.0136; This is the instantaneous rate of change of y with respect to x at $x = 25$. **(e)** The slope of the tangent

line decreases rapidly as x increases. The graph of y vs. x is asymptotic to $y = 90$.

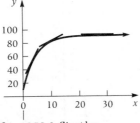

49. (a) 824.36 flies/day **(b)** 1359.1 flies/day

SECTION 12-2

1. $\dfrac{6}{x}$ **3.** $\dfrac{1}{x}$ **5.** $\dfrac{2x-4}{x^2-4x}$ **7.** $\dfrac{2x-4}{x^2-4x+1}$ **9.** $4x^3 + \dfrac{3}{x}$

11. $-\dfrac{3+7x^3}{x^4}$ **13.** $\dfrac{5}{2\sqrt{x}} - \dfrac{3}{x}$

15. $\dfrac{2x^4}{x^2+5} + 3x^2 \ln(x^2+5)$ **17.** $\dfrac{7(1-9\ln x)}{x^{10}}$

19. $\dfrac{2x(x^2+1)}{x^2+5} + 2x \ln(x^2+5)$

21. $\dfrac{2x(x^2+1)\ln(x^2+1) - 2x(x^2+6)}{[x^2+1][\ln(x^2+1)]^2}$

23. $60[\ln(x^6 - 8x^3)]^9\left(\dfrac{x^3-4}{x^4-8x}\right)$

25. $\dfrac{3x^2}{2(x^3+7)\sqrt{\ln(x^3+7)}}$ **27.** $\dfrac{3x^2}{2(x^3+7)}$

29. $\dfrac{e^x(x \ln x - 1)}{x(\ln x)^2}$ **31.** $\dfrac{x^2 e^x(x \ln x + 3 \ln x - 1)}{(\ln x)^2}$

33. $4x^3[\ln(x^3-2x)]e^{x^4-8} + \left(\dfrac{3x^2-2}{x^3-2x}\right)e^{x^4-8}$

35. 0   **37.** $\dfrac{1}{x \ln 10}$ **39.** $\dfrac{3x^2+8}{(x^3+8x)\ln 6}$ **41.** $\dfrac{3x^2-4}{(x^3-4x)\ln 2}$

43. $\dfrac{7(x^3+10)}{2x(x^3+7)}$ **45.** $\dfrac{15x^2}{x^3+7} + \dfrac{5}{2(4-5x)}$

47. $\dfrac{8x}{x^2+7} + \dfrac{18x^5}{x^6-5}$ **49. (a)** $N'(x) = \dfrac{1000}{x}$ items/day

(b) 250; Thus, at $x = 4$, the number of items produced by the worker is increasing at a rate of 250 per day.
(c) 125; Thus, at $x = 8$, the number of items produced by the worker is increasing at a rate of 125 per day.

51. (a) $C'(x) = \dfrac{10}{x+1}$ **(b)** $\dfrac{10}{11} \approx 0.909$; Thus, at $x = 10$, total cost is increasing at the rate of 0.909 per unit.

(c) $\dfrac{10}{21} \approx 0.476$; Thus, at $x = 20$, total cost is increasing at the rate of 0.476 per unit.   **53. (a)** $\dfrac{-\ln 3}{r^2}$

(b) -171.66; A small change in r, Δr, when $r = 0.08$, produces a change in t of approximately $-171.66 \, \Delta r$. Thus, a one percentage point increase in r (i.e., $\Delta r = 0.01$)

reduces the tripling time by approximately $171.66(0.01) \approx$ 1.72 years. **(c)** -109.86; A small change in r, Δr, when $r = 0.10$, produces a change in t of approximately $-109.86\Delta r$. Thus, a one percentage point increase in r (i.e., $\Delta r = 0.01$) reduces the tripling time by approximately $109.86(0.01) \approx 1.10$ years. **(d)** -27.47; when $r = 0.20$, a one percentage point increase in r reduces the tripling time by approximately $27.47(0.01) \approx 0.27$ years. **(e)** -12.21; when $r = 0.30$, a one percentage point increase in r reduces the tripling time by approximately $12.21(0.01) \approx 0.12$ years.

• CHAPTER HIGHLIGHTS

1. If $y = e^x$, then $dy/dx = e^x$.   **2.** If $y = e^u$ where u is a differentiable function of x, then $dy/dx = e^u(du/dx)$.
3. If $y = b^u$ where u is a differentiable function of x and $b > 0$, then $dy/dx = b^u(du/dx)\ln b$.   **4.** If $y = \ln x$, then $dy/dx = 1/x$.   **5.** If $y = \ln u$ where u is a differentiable function of x, then $dy/dx = (1/u)(du/dx)$.   **6.** If $y = \log_b u$ where u is a differentiable function of x, $b > 0$, and $b \neq 1$, then $dy/dx = (1/u \ln b)(du/dx)$.

• REVIEW EXERCISES

1. $5e^{5x}$ **3.** $8e^{8x+5}$ **5.** $(5x^2 + 42x + 8)e^{5x+9}$

7. $\dfrac{x(4e^x + e^{-x}) - (4e^x - e^{-x})}{x^2} = \dfrac{4e^x(x-1) + e^{-x}(x+1)}{x^2}$

9. $(2x+1)(3x^2 e^{6x})$ **11.** $\dfrac{-60,000e^{5x}}{(1+20e^{5x})^2}$

13. $2(8x + e^x)(8 + e^x)$ **15. (a)** $3200e^{0.08x}$
(b) 4068; A small change in x, Δx, when $x = 3$, results in a change in S of approximately $4068\Delta x$.
(c) 5171.4; A small change in x, Δx, when $x = 6$, results in a change in S of approximately $5171.4\Delta x$.
17. (a) $30e^{-0.60x}$ **(b)** 4.96; A small change in x, Δx, when $x = 3$, results in a change in f of approximately $4.96\Delta x$.
(c) 0.247; A small change in x, Δx, when $x = 8$, results in a change in f of approximately $0.247\Delta x$.   **19.** $\dfrac{-7}{x}$

21. $\dfrac{3(x-4)}{x(x-6)}$ **23.** $\dfrac{x^2(3x^2+7)}{x^3+7x} + 2x \ln(x^3+7x)$

25. $8[\ln(x^5+6x^2)]^7\left[\dfrac{5x^3+12}{x^4+6x}\right]$ **27.** $\left(\dfrac{1}{x} + 3 \ln x\right)e^{3x+5}$

29. $\left\{8[\ln(x^5-6x^2)] + \left(\dfrac{5x^3-12}{x^4-6x}\right)\right\}e^{8x}$ **31. (a)** $\dfrac{40}{x+3}$

(b) 2; A small change in x, Δx, when $x = 17$, will result in a change in C of approximately $2\Delta x$. **(c)** 1.6; A small change in x, Δx, when $x = 22$ will result in a change in C of approximately $1.6\Delta x$.

• CHAPTER 13

SECTION 13-1

1. $F'(x) = 7x^6 = f(x)$ **3.** $F'(x) = x^2 - 8x + 5 = f(x)$

5. $F'(x) = e^{2x} = f(x)$ **7.** $F'(x) = \dfrac{1}{x} = f(x)$ **9.** $\dfrac{1}{13}x^{13} + C$

11. $20\sqrt{x} + C$ **13.** $\dfrac{4}{5}x^{5/4} + C$ **15.** $-\dfrac{1}{8x^8} + C$

17. $\dfrac{3}{5}x^{5/3} + C$ **19.** $\dfrac{-28}{5}x^{5/7} + C$ **21.** $-6\sqrt{x} + C$

23. $\dfrac{5}{3}x^{3/5} + C$ **25.** $\dfrac{1}{5}e^{5x} + C$ **27.** $-\dfrac{1}{4}e^{-4x} + C$

29. $4e^{2x} + C$ **31.** $-4\ln|x| + C$ **33.** $300\ln|x| + C$

35. $\dfrac{1}{5}\ln|x| + C$ **37.** $\dfrac{-1}{5x^5} + C$ **39.** $\dfrac{-4}{3x^6} + C$

41. $x^4 - 16x + C$ **43.** $\dfrac{x^6}{6} - \dfrac{7}{2}x^2 + C$

45. $\dfrac{x^4}{4} + \dfrac{4}{x} + 6x + C$ **47.** $\dfrac{t^4}{4} - \dfrac{2}{3}t^3 + C$

49. $\dfrac{y^7}{7} - y^5 + y + C$ **51.** $u^4 - 16\sqrt{u} - \dfrac{5}{u} + C$

53. $7\ln|x| + \dfrac{1}{4}e^{4x} + C$ **55.** $9\ln|x| - e^{-x} + C$

57. $4\ln|x| + \dfrac{1}{5}e^{-5x} + C$ **59.** $\dfrac{-2}{x^2} + 2\ln|x| + C$

61. $\dfrac{-2}{x^3} - \dfrac{1}{4}e^{4x} + C$ **63.** $\dfrac{-1}{x} - e^{-x} + C$

65. $\ln|x| + \dfrac{1}{x} - e^x + C$ **67.** $\dfrac{x^4}{4} + \dfrac{4}{x} + C$

69. $\dfrac{x^3}{3} - x^2 + x + C$ **71.** $\ln|x| + e^{-x} + C$

73. $\dfrac{x^3}{3} - 4x + C$ **75.** $\dfrac{x^3}{3} - \dfrac{x^2}{2} - 6x + C$

77. $\dfrac{x^2}{2} - 2x + C$ **79.** $C(x) = 2x^3 + 2x^2 - 5x + 800$

81. **(a)** $V(t) = 8000t^3 + 1{,}000{,}000$ **(b)** $\$2{,}000{,}000$
83. $S(t) = 2(t^3 + 1)$ **85.** $S(t) = t^3 + 6$

87. $V(t) = 2t^2 + 30$ **89.** **(a)** $A(t) = \dfrac{20}{t^2} - 0.5$ **(b)** $0.3\ \text{cm}^2$

SECTION 13-2

1. 80   **3.** 3   **5.** $\dfrac{15}{8} = 1.875$ **7.** $10\ln 5 \approx 16.09$

9. $e^3 - 1 \approx 19.086$ **11.** $\dfrac{1}{2}(1 - e^{-4}) \approx 0.4908$

13. Lower approximation = 3.53125;
Upper approximation = 3.78125
15. Lower approximation = 4.08;

Upper approximation = 5.28   **17.** $\dfrac{1}{2}$ **19.** **(a)** 1 **(b)** 1

21. $\dfrac{14}{3} \approx 4.667$ **23.** 64

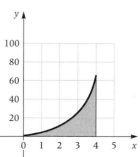

25. $\dfrac{2}{3}$

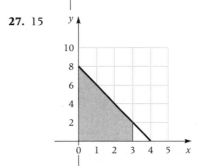

27. 15

29. 8

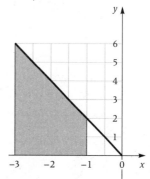

31. $\dfrac{250}{3} \approx 83.33$

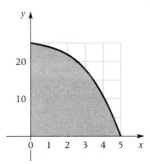

33. $\dfrac{160}{3} \approx 53.33$

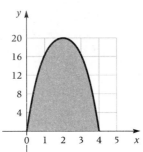

35. $\dfrac{64}{3} \approx 21.33$

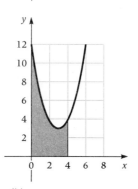

37. 66

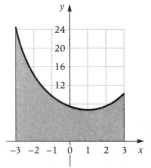

39. $e^3 - 1 \approx 19.086$

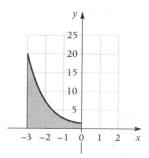

41. $e - \dfrac{1}{e} \approx 2.350$

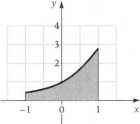

43. $\ln 5 \approx 1.609$

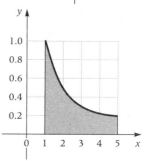

45. $\dfrac{21}{64} \approx 0.3281$

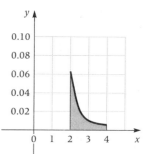

47. $\dfrac{1}{6} \approx 0.1667$

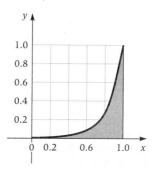

49. $\dfrac{23}{3} = 7\dfrac{2}{3}$

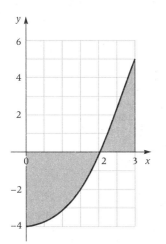

51. 16

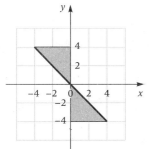

53. $\dfrac{23}{3} = 7\dfrac{2}{3}$

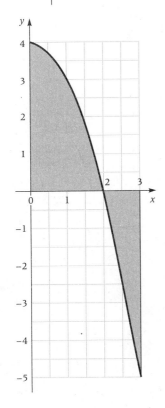

55. 18

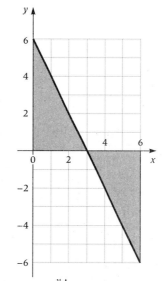

57. 68

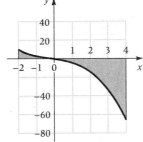

59. $\dfrac{31}{6} = 5\dfrac{1}{6}$

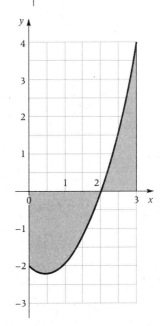

61. $-1 + 4 \ln \frac{8}{3} \approx 2.9233$

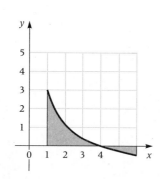

63. $5\frac{1}{2}$

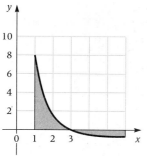

65. 176

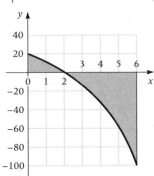

67. 4000 **69.** 1200 **71.** 7700 **73.** 522 ft **75.** 1 foot
77. (a) 225 cu. ft **(b)** 700 cu. ft **(c)** 65 cu. ft

(d) 75 cu. ft **79. (a)** $\dfrac{500}{e} \approx 183.94$

(b) $500(1 + e^{-2}) \approx 567.67$ **81. (a)** 190 jobs
(b) 279 jobs **(c)** 442 jobs **(d)** 787 jobs **83.** $2760
85. $5988.50 **87.** $11,843.50 **89.** $21,743.50

SECTION 13-3

1. $\dfrac{88}{3} = 29\dfrac{1}{3}$

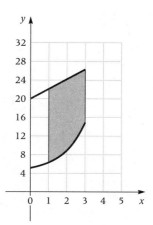

3. $\dfrac{1}{12}$

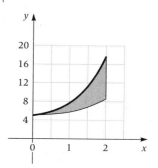

5. $\dfrac{16}{3} = 5\dfrac{1}{3}$

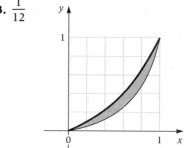

7. $\dfrac{1}{3}$

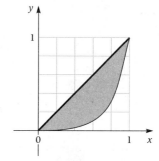

9. 21

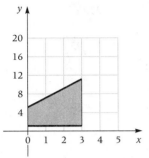

11. $4 - 3 \ln 3 \approx 0.7042$

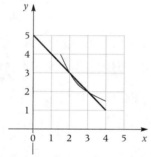

13. $\dfrac{5}{2} - 6 \ln \dfrac{3}{2} \approx 0.0672$

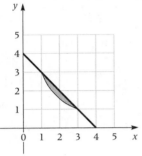

15. $e^2 - 3 \approx 4.389$

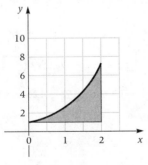

17. 4

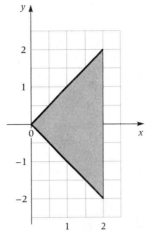

19. $\dfrac{1}{20}$

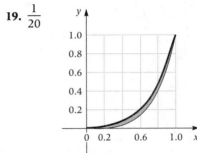

21. $e + e^{-1} - 2 \approx 1.0862$

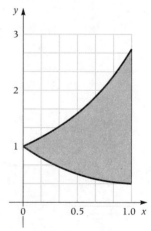

23. $\dfrac{125}{6} \approx 20.833$

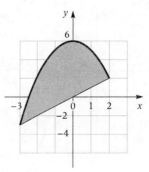

25. 5

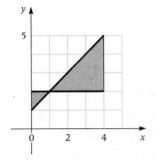

27. $\dfrac{29}{6} \approx 4.833$

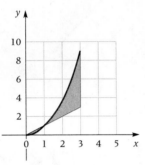

29. $\dfrac{227}{4} = 56.75$

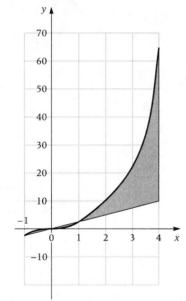

31. 64

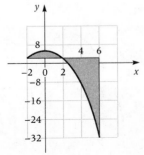

33. $e^3 + e^2 + e^{-2} + e^{-3} - 4 \approx 23.66$

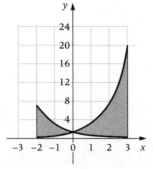

35. $4 + 8 \ln \dfrac{3}{4} \approx 1.699$

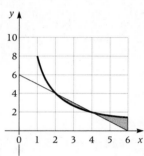

37. $CS = \$16$; $PS = \$32$ **39.** $CS = \$2333\dfrac{1}{3}$; $PS = \$666\dfrac{2}{3}$

41. $CS = \$4608$; $PS = \$1152$ **43.** \$268 **45.** \$2,987,862

SECTION 13-4

1. $\dfrac{1}{11}(x^3 - 7)^{11} + C$ **3.** $\dfrac{1}{6}(x^3 - 4x)^6 + C$

5. $\dfrac{1}{40}(x^4 - 8)^{10} + C$ **7.** $\dfrac{1}{10}(x - 3)^{10} + C$

9. $\dfrac{5}{24}(x^4 + 6)^6 + C$ **11.** $\dfrac{1}{33}(x^6 + 9)^{11} + C$

13. $-\dfrac{1}{27(x^3 - 5)^9} + C$ **15.** $\dfrac{1}{2}\sqrt{x^4 - 6} + C$

17. $-\dfrac{1}{9(3x - 5)^3} + C$ **19.** $\dfrac{1}{3}(125 - 13^{3/2}) \approx 26.043$

21. $\dfrac{1}{10}$

23. 4

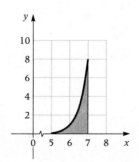

25. $\dfrac{5}{6}$

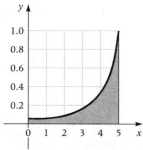

27. The substitution $u = x^3 - 5$, $du = 3x^2 dx$ does not work because we need to multiply $x\,dx$ by $3x$ in order to obtain $du = 3x^2\,dx$. However, we cannot do this because $3x$ is not a constant. **29.** 232,800 barrels

31. $P(x) = 250,000x^2 + 100,000x - 200,000$

SECTION 13-5

1. $e^x + C$ **3.** $\dfrac{1}{4}e^{4x} + C$ **5.** $2e^{x/2} + C$ **7.** $\dfrac{1}{3}e^{x^3-5} + C$

9. $\dfrac{1}{4}e^{x^4+6} + C$ **11.** $\dfrac{1}{2}e^{x^2+2x} + C$ **13.** $5\ln|x| + C$

15. $\ln\sqrt{x^2+1} + C$ **17.** $\ln(x^3+4)^2 + C$

19. $\dfrac{-1}{10}\ln|5x^2-6| + C$ **21.** $e^4 - 1 \approx 53.598$

23. $\dfrac{1}{2}(1 - e^{-1}) \approx 0.3161$ **25.** $\ln 4 \approx 1.3863$

27. $-6\ln 6 \approx -10.7506$ **29.** $\dfrac{1}{3}(\ln x)^3 + C$

31. $\dfrac{1}{5}(\ln 3x)^5 + C$ **33.** $\dfrac{1}{2}\ln|x^2 - 4x + 1| + C$

35. $\ln|\ln x| + C$ **37.** $\dfrac{1}{2}\ln|\ln x^2| + C$

39. $\dfrac{1}{2}(1 - e^{-2}) \approx 0.4323$

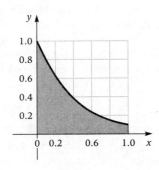

41. $\left|\ln\dfrac{5}{8}\right| \approx 0.470$

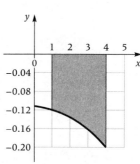

43. $4953.68 **45.** $B(x) = 2000\ln(5x+1) + 4204.21$

SECTION 13-6

1. $\dfrac{1}{3}xe^{3x} - \dfrac{1}{9}e^{3x} + C$ **3.** $2x\sqrt{x-3} - \dfrac{4}{3}(x-3)^{3/2} + C$

5. $-e^{-x}(x+1) + C$ **7.** $-\dfrac{x}{2(x-4)^2} - \dfrac{1}{2(x-4)} + C$

9. $-\dfrac{1}{4}e^{-4x}\left(x + \dfrac{1}{4}\right) + C$ **11.** $\dfrac{1}{4}x^4\left(\ln x - \dfrac{1}{4}\right) + C$

13. $\dfrac{x(x-9)^6}{6} - \dfrac{1}{42}(x-9)^7 + C$

15. $-\dfrac{x}{5(6+5x)} + \dfrac{1}{25}\ln|6+5x| + C$

17. $\dfrac{2}{3}x\sqrt{5+3x} - \dfrac{4}{27}(5+3x)^{3/2} + C$

19. $\dfrac{2}{3}x(3x+7)^{3/2} - \dfrac{4}{45}(3x+7)^{5/2} + C$

21. $\dfrac{x^2}{2}\ln 9x - \dfrac{1}{4}x^2 + C$ **23.** $e^x(x^3 - 3x^2 + 6x - 6) + C$

25. Let $u = x^n$ and $dv = e^x\,dx$; $du = nx^{n-1}\,dx$, $v = e^x$; $\int x^n e^x\,dx = x^n e^x - n\int x^{n-1}e^x\,dx$

27. $x(\ln x)^2 - 2x\ln x + 2x + C$ **29.** Let $u = (\ln x)^n$ and $dv = dx$, $n = $ integer > 0; $du = n(\ln x)^{n-1}\dfrac{dx}{x}$, $v = x$; $\int u\,dv = x(\ln x)^n - n\int(\ln x)^{n-1}\,dx$ **31.** $e^2 + 1 \approx 8.3891$

33. $\dfrac{1}{2}$ **35.** $e^x(x^2 - 2x + 2) + C$ **37.** $\ln|x + 6| + C$

39. $\dfrac{1}{2}\left[x - \dfrac{9}{2}\ln|2x+9|\right] + C$ **41.** $83,201.17$

43. 5940 decrease in cells

45. $R(x) = \dfrac{x^4}{4}\left(\ln x - \dfrac{1}{4}\right) + \dfrac{1281}{16}$

SECTION 13-7

1. $\ln(x + \sqrt{81 + x^2}) + C$ **3.** $\ln 3 \approx 1.0986$

5. $\dfrac{7}{18}\ln\left|\dfrac{9-x}{9+x}\right| + C$ **7.** $3\left(\dfrac{-1}{4x} - \dfrac{7}{16}\ln\left|\dfrac{4-7x}{x}\right|\right) + C$

9. $6 - 2e \approx 0.5634$ **11.** $x\ln|5x| - x + C$

13. $\frac{1}{\sqrt{5}} \ln \left| \dfrac{\sqrt{5-2x}-\sqrt{5}}{\sqrt{5-2x}+\sqrt{5}} \right| + C$

15. $\ln |x + \sqrt{x^2 - 100}| + C$

17. $\dfrac{-1}{5} \ln \left| \dfrac{5 + \sqrt{25 - x^2}}{x} \right| + C$ **19.** $\dfrac{x}{36(\sqrt{36 - x^2})} + C$

21. $x(\ln |x|)^2 - 2x \ln |x| + 2x + C$ **23.** $\dfrac{x^3}{3}\left(\ln |x| - \dfrac{1}{3}\right) + C$

25. $\dfrac{1}{25}\left(\dfrac{x}{\sqrt{x^2 + 25}}\right) + C$

27. $\dfrac{(x+1)^2}{2} \ln |x + 1| - \dfrac{(x+1)^2}{4} + C$

29. $\dfrac{4}{3} \ln \left| \dfrac{x}{3 + 7x} \right| + C$ **31.** $\dfrac{1}{16} \ln 7 \approx 0.1216$ foot

33. 599.64 gallons

• CHAPTER HIGHLIGHTS

1. $f(x)$ **2.** Constant **3.** (a) *Power Rule:* $\int x^n \, dx = \dfrac{1}{n+1} x^{n+1} + c$ for $n \neq -1$. The power rule states that the integral of x raised to a power other than -1 is x raised to the $n + 1$st power divided by $n + 1$ plus an arbitrary constant. (b) *Constant Multiplier Rule:* $\int k \cdot f(x) \, dx = k \int f(x) \, dx$. The constant multiplier rule states that the integral of a constant times a function is the constant times the integral of the function. (c) *Sum or Difference Rule:* $\int [f(x) \pm g(x] \, dx = \int f(x) \, dx \pm \int g(x) \, dx$. The sum or difference rule states that the integral of a sum or difference of two functions is the sum or difference of their individual integrals. **4.** $kx + c$ **5.** $e^x + c$ **6.** $(1/k)e^{kx} + c, k \neq 0$ **7.** $\ln |x| + c$ **8.** The marginal tax rate is the tax on an additional dollar of taxable income. **9.** A definite integral of a function $f(x)$ is evaluated over an interval of x-values; the endpoints of such an interval are called limits of integration. A definite integral of a function $f(x)$ evaluated over an interval $a \leq x \leq b$ is determined by finding the antiderivative $F(x)$ of the function $f(x)$ and evaluating $F(b) - F(a)$. A Riemann sum approximates the area under a curve over some interval using the sum of areas of rectangles so that the limit of the sum equals the actual area as the number of rectangles becomes infinite. **10.** The Fundamental Theorem of Calculus states that for a function $f(x)$ defined and continuous over some interval $a \leq x \leq b$, if $F(x)$ is an antiderivative of $f(x)$, then the limit of every possible Riemann sum over this interval equals $\int_a^b f(x) \, dx = F(b) - F(a)$. The Fundamental Theorem allows us to compute the area under a curve. If $f(x) \geq 0$ over the interval $a \leq x \leq b$, the area between the graph of $f(x)$ and the x-axis over the indicated interval is given by the definite integral $\int_a^b f(x) \, dx = F(b) - F(a)$. If $f(x) < 0$ over some interval, then the corresponding definite integral is negative

and, therefore, its absolute value equals the respective area between the curve and the x-axis over the interval.
11. To find areas: *Step 1.* Graph the function. *Step 2.* Find any x-intercepts. *Step 3.* Shade the area to be found. *Step 4.* Note whether the shaded area contains any regions that lie below the x-axis as well as above the x-axis. *Step 5.* Evaluate the appropriate definite integrals.
12. Find each area separately and take the sum. The definite integral corresponding to the area above the x-axis will be positive whereas the definite integral corresponding to the area below the x-axis will be negative and, therefore, its absolute value equals its respective area.
13. The area between the graphs of two continuous functions $f(x)$ and $g(x)$ over an interval $a \leq x \leq b$ where $f(x) \geq g(x)$ (as illustrated below) is given by the definite integral $\int_a^b [f(x) - g(x)] \, dx$

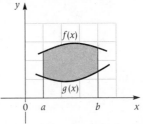

14. Consumers' surplus is the total amount of money saved by consumers as a result of the market being at equilibrium. It is represented by the area between the demand curve and the horizontal line $p = p_E$ over the interval $0 \leq q \leq q_E$ where p_E is the equilibrium price and q_E is the equilibrium quantity. Consumers' surplus is determined by the definite integral $\int_0^{q_E} [D(q) - p_E] dq$ where $D(q)$ denotes the demand curve. **15.** Producers' surplus is the additional revenue gained by producers as a result of the market being at equilibrium. It is represented by the area between the supply curve and the horizontal line $p = p_E$ over the interval $0 \leq q \leq q_E$ where p_E is the equilibrium price and q_E is the equilibrium quantity. Producers' surplus is determined by the definite integral $\int_0^{q_E} [p_E - S(q)] dq$ where $S(q)$ denotes the supply curve.

16. $\int u^n \, du = \dfrac{1}{n + 1} u^{n+1} + c$ where u is a differentiable function of x and du is the derivative of u times dx.
17. $\int e^u \, du = e^u + c$ where u is a differentiable function of x and du is the derivative of u times dx.
18. $\int du/u = \ln |u| + c$ where u is a differentiable function of x and du is the derivative of u times dx.
19. $\int u \, dv = uv - \int v \, du$ **20.** A table of integrals provides antiderivatives for many integral forms. Such a table allows one to integrate a greater variety of functions.

• REVIEW EXERCISES

1. $\dfrac{x^5}{5} + c$ **3.** $20 \ln |x| + c$ **5.** $-e^{-x} + c$ **7.** $7x + c$

9. $x^5 + 2x^3 - 4x^2 + 4x + c$ **11.** $4 \ln |x| + \dfrac{1}{6} e^{6x} + c$

13. $-\dfrac{4}{x} - \dfrac{x^5}{5} + c$ **15.** $\dfrac{x^3}{3} - 25x + c$

17. $C(x) = 3x^3 + 2x^2 - x + 5000$ **19.** 66

21. $20 \ln \dfrac{5}{2} \approx 18.3$ **23.** 80

25. 144

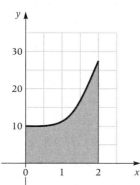

27. $\dfrac{132}{5} = 26.4$

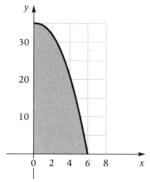

29. 16

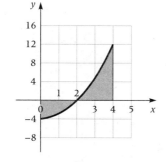

31. $\dfrac{512}{3} = 170\dfrac{2}{3}$

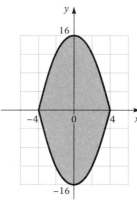

33. $CS = 128;\ PS = 64$ **35.** $\dfrac{1}{6}(x^4 + 6x)^6 + c$

37. $\dfrac{1}{2} e^{x^2+6} + c$ **39.** $\dfrac{1}{2} \ln(x^2 + 4) + c$ **41.** $\dfrac{(\ln 5x)^4}{4} + c$

43. $\dfrac{1}{14}(x^2 + 10x - 7)^7 + c$

45. $\dfrac{2}{3} x(x - 8)^{3/2} - \dfrac{4}{15}(x - 8)^{5/2} + c$

47. $\dfrac{x}{5} - \dfrac{8}{25} \ln |5x + 8| + c$ **49.** $-\ln |7 - x| + c$

51. $\dfrac{1}{\sqrt{7}} \ln \left| \dfrac{\sqrt{7 - 2x} - \sqrt{7}}{\sqrt{7 - 2x} + \sqrt{7}} \right| + c$ **53.** $\dfrac{1}{16}\left(\dfrac{x}{\sqrt{x^2 + 16}} \right) + c$

55. $\dfrac{e^{8x}}{8}\left(x^2 - \dfrac{1}{4}x + \dfrac{1}{32} \right) + c$ **57.** 5217 people, change in population

• CHAPTER 14

SECTION 14-1

1. (a) $10,000 **(b)** $8052.71 **(c)** $12,629.16
3. (a) $300,000 **(b)** $241,581.23 **(c)** $378,874.79
5. (a) $75,000 **(b)** $55,880.87 **(c)** $87,638.66
7. (a) $10 **(b)** $7.45 **(c)** $11.69   **9. (a)** $17,041.53
(b) $13,595.19 **(c)** $21,321.51   **11. (a)** $181,269.25
(b) $147,062.84 **(c)** $230,640.44   **13. (a)** $5002.50
(b) $4028.22 **(c)** $6317.50   **15. (a)** $9375 **(b)** $7737.51
(c) $12,134.83   **17. (a)** $70,000 **(b)** $50,341.47
(c) $101,375.27   **19. (a)** $80,000,000 **(b)** $58,472,625
(c) $94,496,112

SECTION 14-2

1. 1   **3.** Diverges   **5.** Diverges   **7.** $\dfrac{1}{2}$ **9.** 1   **11.** $\dfrac{1}{2}$

13. Diverges   **15.** $\dfrac{1}{3}$ **17.** $\dfrac{1}{2}$ **19.** 0   **21.** Diverges

23. Diverges   **25.** 1

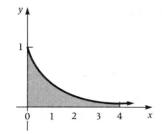

27. 1

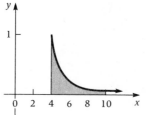

29. $\frac{1}{8}$

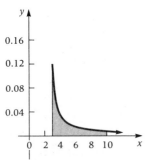

31. \$444,444.44   **33.** \$200,000   **35.** 200,000 units
37. 300 gallons

SECTION 14-3

1. (a) 0.40 **(b)** 0.25 **(c)** 0.25
3. (a) $f(x) = \begin{cases} 0.20 & \text{if } 2 \le x \le 7 \\ 0 & \text{otherwise} \end{cases}$ **(b)** 0.20 **(c)** 0.40
5. (a) 0.3935 **(b)** 0.3181 **(c)** 0.1353   **7. (a)** 0.2325
(b) 0.9502 **(c)** 0.00248   **9. (a)** $R(t) = e^{-0.5t}$
(b) 0.6065; $R(1)$ is the probability that the circuitry will
have a lifetime of at least 1 year. **(c)** 0.1353; $R(4)$ is the
probability that the circuitry will have a lifetime of at least
4 years.

SECTION 14-4

1. 7.5   **3.** $\frac{14}{9} \approx 1.556$ **5.** 5

7. 5

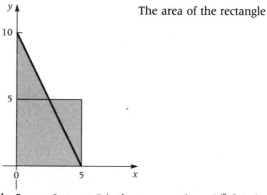

The area of the rectangle

of height 5 over $0 \le x \le 5$ is the same as that of $\int_0^5 f(x)\ dx$.
9. $\frac{100}{3} = 33\frac{1}{3}$ The area of the

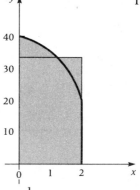

rectangle of height $33\frac{1}{3}$ over $0 \le x \le 2$ equals $\int_0^2 f(x)\ dx$.

11. 142.74° F   **13.** \$12,295.62

15. $y = f(x) = mx + b,\ 0 \le x \le -\frac{b}{m}$

Average value of $f = \dfrac{1}{\dfrac{-b}{m} - 0} \displaystyle\int_0^{-\frac{b}{m}} (mx + b)\ dx$

$= \dfrac{-m}{b}\left(\dfrac{mx^2}{2} + bx\right)\Big|_0^{-\frac{b}{m}}$

$= \dfrac{-m}{b}\left(\dfrac{b^2}{2m} - \dfrac{b^2}{m}\right) = \dfrac{b}{2}$

17. $\dfrac{128\pi}{3} \approx 134.0$

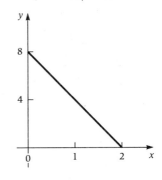

19. $\frac{96\pi}{5} \approx 60.32$

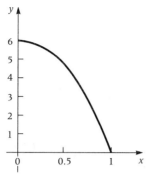

21. $\frac{\pi}{2}(1 - e^{-2}) \approx 1.358$

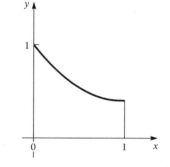

23. $\frac{15\pi}{2} \approx 23.56$

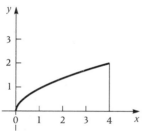

25. $\frac{32\pi}{3} \approx 33.51$

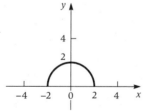

27. $\frac{256\pi}{3} \approx 268.08$

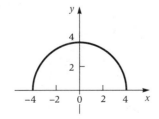

• **CHAPTER HIGHLIGHTS**

1. If money flows into a fund at a rate $f(x)$ during some time interval $0 \le x \le t$, then the total amount of money accumulated is given by $\int_0^t f(x) \, dx$. This formula assumes that the money earns no interest. **2.** If money flows into a fund at a rate of $f(x)$ dollars per year (where x denotes time in years) and is compounded continuously at an annual interest rate r during the tme interval $0 \le x \le t$, then the present value of the money flow is given by $\int_0^t f(x)e^{-rx} \, dx$ and the future value is given by either of the following: $e^{rt}\int_0^t f(x)e^{-rx} \, dx$ or e^{rt}(Present value). **3.** If a function $f(x)$ is continuous over the indicated intervals and if the indicated limits exist, then: (1) $\int_a^{\infty} f(x) \, dx = \lim\limits_{b \to \infty}\int_a^b f(x) \, dx$ (2) $\int_{-\infty}^b f(x) \, dx = \lim\limits_{a \to -\infty}\int_a^b f(x) \, dx$ (3) $\int_{-\infty}^{\infty} f(x) \, dx = \int_{-\infty}^c f(x) \, dx + \int_c^{\infty} f(x) \, dx$ where a, b, and c are real numbers. If the right-hand side expressions exist, then the improper integrals are said to be **convergent.** If the right-hand side expressions do not exist, then the improper integrals are said to be **divergent.** **4.** If a continuous stream of money flows perpetually into a fund at a rate of $f(x)$ dollars per year (x = time in years) during the time interval $0 \le x < \infty$, and if this money flow is compounded continuously at an annual rate r, then its present value at $t = 0$ is given by the improper integral $\int_0^{\infty} f(x)e^{-rx} \, dx$. **5.** A **random variable** is a letter that represents numerical chance outcomes. If a graph of values of a random variable on a number line results in disconnected points, then the random variable is termed **discrete.** If a graph of values of a random variable on a number line results in a interval, then the random variable is termed **continuous.** **6.** If a random variable x is **uniformly distributed** over the interval $a \le x \le b$, its density function is given by

$$f(x) = \begin{cases} 1/(b - a) & \text{for } a \le x \le b \\ 0 & \text{otherwise} \end{cases}$$

7. Let x be a continuous random variable. A function $f(x)$ is a **probability density function** over some interval $a \le x \le b$ if: (A) $f(x) \ge 0$ for $a \le x \le b$ (B) $\int_a^b f(x) \, dx = 1$. In other words, the area under the graph of the density function over the interval $[a, b]$ equals 1. (C) If $[c, d]$ is a subinterval of $[a, b]$, then $P(c \le x \le d) = \int_c^d f(x) \, dx$.

8. If a random variable x is **exponentially distributed,** then its density function is given by

$$f(x) = \begin{cases} ke^{-kx} & \text{if } x \geq 0 \\ 0 & \text{otherwise} \end{cases}$$

where $k > 0$.

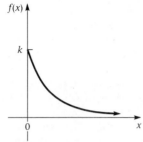

9. The **average value** of a continuous function $f(x)$ over the interval $[a, b]$ is given by $[1/(b - a)]\int_a^b f(x)\,dx$. Graphically, the average value of a continuous function over some interval gives the height H of a rectangle having the same area as that shaded under the continuous function as illustrated in the following graphs.

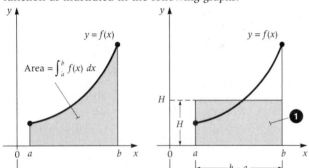

① Area = $H(b - a)$

10. The volume, V, of a solid of revolution formed by rotating about the x-axis the region between the graph of $y = f(x)$ and the x-axis from $x = a$ to $x = b$ (see the accompanying figure) is given by $V = \int_a^b \pi[f(x)]^2\,dx$.

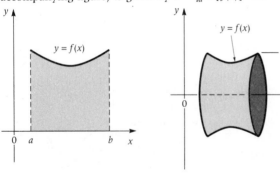

• REVIEW EXERCISES

1. (a) $20,000 **(b)** $17,115.69 **(c)** $23,570.49
3. (a) $9836.49 **(b)** $8328.71 **(c)** $11,469.70

5. Diverges **7.** 1 **9.** $\dfrac{1}{5}$ **11.** $1,250,000 **13. (a)** 0.25 **(b)**

(b) 0.60 **(c)** 0.60 **(d)** 0.45 **15. (a)** 0.3935 **(b)** 0.6988
(c) 0.4493 **(d)** $e^{-1} \approx 0.3679$ **17.** 10 **19.** $1600

21. $\dfrac{36,864\pi}{5} \approx 23,162.33$

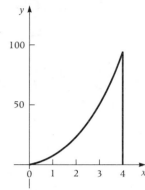

23. $\dfrac{256\pi}{15} \approx 53.617$

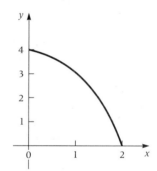

• CHAPTER 15

SECTION 15-1

1. (a) 2 **(b)** 82 **(c)** 8 **3.** $7\dfrac{3}{4}$ **5. (a)** 3 **(b)** 34 **(c)** 48

7. (a) 4 **(b)** -104 **(c)** 582 **9.** The domain of g is the set of all ordered pairs (x, y) for which the function is defined, namely, all ordered pairs (x, y) such that $x \neq 2$ and $y \neq 0$.
11. The domain of f is the set of all ordered pairs (x, y) for which the function is defined, namely, all ordered pairs (x, y) such that $x > 3$. **13.** The domain of f is the set of all ordered pairs (x, y) for which the function is defined, namely, all ordered pairs (x, y) such that x and y have the same sign, $x \neq 0$, and $y \neq 0$.

15.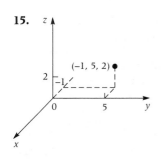

17.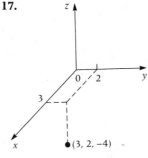

19.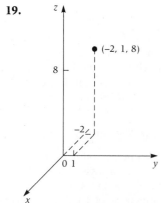

21. (a) $R(x_1, x_2) = 90x_1 - 4x_1^2 - 5x_1x_2 + 60x_2 - 5x_2^2$
(b) 334 **23.** $C(3, 5) = 136$; $136,000. **25. (a)** 5.9033
(b) 5.7217

SECTION 15-2

1. (a) $6x + 6y - 2xy^3$ **(b)** $12y^2 + 6x - 3x^2y^2$
(c) 2 **(d)** 12 **3. (a)** $3x^2 - 8y + 6x^2y^2$
(b) $5y^4 - 8x + 4x^3y$ **5. (a)** $24x^2 - 35x^4y^8 + 8y^2$
(b) $-4y - 56x^5y^7 + 16xy + 1$ **(c)** -8904 **(d)** -7143
7. (a) $24x^5 - 24x^2 - 7 + 6y + 3x^2y^5$ **(b)** $6x + 8 + 5x^3y^4$
(c) $120x^4 - 48x + 6xy^5$ **(d)** $20x^3y^3$ **(e)** $6 + 15x^2y^4$
(f) $6 + 15x^2y^4$ **9. (a)** $-3x^2 + 12x^2y^6$
(b) $-2y + 24x^3y^5 + 8$ **(c)** $-6x + 24xy^6$ **(d)** $-2 + 120x^3y^4$
(e) $72x^2y^5$ **(f)** $72x^2y^5$ **(g)** 36 **(h)** 9718
11. (a) $x^2e^{x^2+y^2}(3 + 2x^2)$ **(b)** $2x^3ye^{x^3+y^2}$
13. (a) $e^{2x+3y+5}(3x^2+2x^3 + 2y^2)$
(b) $e^{2x+3y+5}(3x^3 + 2y + 3y^2)$ **(c)** $2e^8$ **15. (a)** $940
(b) $700 **17. (a)** $18,002 \approx$ the increase in $P(x, y)$ if x is
increased by 1 **(b)** $8005 \approx$ the increase in $P(x, y)$ if y is
increased by 1

SECTION 15-3

1. $(5, -8)$ **3.** $\left(\dfrac{16}{3}, \dfrac{20}{3}\right)$ **5.** $(-4, 9)$ **7.** $\left(\dfrac{360}{11}, \dfrac{130}{11}\right)$
9. $\left(6, \dfrac{-221}{12}\right), \left(-6, \dfrac{221}{12}\right)$ **11.** $(4, -2), (4, 2)$
13. Relative minimum: $f(4, 5) = -48$

15. Relative minimum: $f\left(-\dfrac{9}{2}, 5\right) = \dfrac{-181}{4}$
17. Relative maximum: $f(20, 50) = 4300$
19. Relative minimum: $f(4, 3) = -58$
21. Relative maximum: $f(10, 4) = 416$
23. $(5, -15.8)$ and $(-5, 15.8)$ are saddle points.
25. Relative maximum: $f(5, -2\sqrt{2}) \approx 165.25$;
saddle point at $(5, 2\sqrt{2})$
27. $\dfrac{\partial f}{\partial x} = 2x - 18$; $\dfrac{\partial f}{\partial x} = 0$, $x = 9$

$\dfrac{\partial f}{\partial y} = -4y + 16$; $\dfrac{\partial f}{\partial y} = 0$, $y = 4$
$A = f_{xx}(9, 4) = 2$; $B = f_{yy}(9, 4) = -4$; $C = f_{xy}(9, 4) = 0$
$AB - C^2 = -8$; Since $AB - C^2 < 0$, $(9, 4)$ is a saddle point.
There are no relative maxima or minima. **29. (a)** $200;
$500 **(b)** $1,660,000 **31. (a)** 200; 500 **(b)** 500,000
33. (a) $R(p_1, p_2) = 200p_1 - 20p_1^2 + 3p_1p_2 + 300p_2 - 15p_2^2$
(b) $\dfrac{2300}{397}$; $\dfrac{4200}{397}$ or $\approx$$5.79; $10.58 **(c)** $2166.25
(d) $x_1 \approx 94.71$ cases; $x_2 \approx 152.90$ cases
35. $h = \sqrt[3]{200}$ in.; $w = \sqrt[3]{200}$ in.; $l = \sqrt[3]{200}$ in.;
≈ 5.85 in.; ≈ 5.85 in.; ≈ 5.85 in.
37. $h = 25$ ft; $w = 20$ ft; $l = 20$ ft

SECTION 15-4

1. (a) $y = 2.5 + 2.5x$ **(b)**

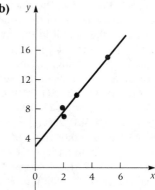

(c) $-0.5; 0; 0.5; 0$ **(d)** 0.5 **3. (a)** $y = 2 + 1.4x$
(b) **(c)** 0.4; 0.2; 0.8, -1.4

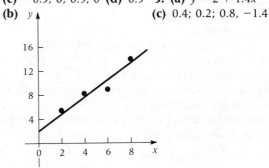

(d) 2.8   **5. (a)** $y = 1.4 + 2.2x$
(b)   **(c)** 0.4; 0.2; −1.0; −0.2; 0.6

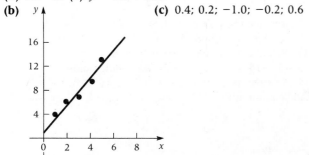

(d) 1.6   **7. (a)** $y = 7 + 2.6x$ **(b)**

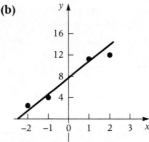

(c) 0.2; −0.4; 0; 0.4; −0.2 **(d)** 0.4 **9. (a)** 8.76
(b) 28.5058 **11. (a)** 10.59 **(b)** 37.6043
13. (a) Quadratic **(b)** $y = 6.619(1.809)^x$ or
$y = 6.619e^{0.593x}$ **(c)** 95.43 **(d)** 107.85 **15. (a)** $2211
(b) $0.841 **17.** 0.655; The change of 1 unit in the S & P
500 results in a change, in the same direction, of
approximately 0.655 unit in the mutual share.
19. 1.29; The change of 1 unit in the S & P 500 is
accompanied by a change, in the same direction, of
approximately 1.29 units in the Neuberger Manhattan
fund. **21. (a)** $y = 320.5(1.082)^x$ or $y = 320.5e^{0.0785x}$
(b) 8.17% **(c)** 4274; 4623; 5001 **23. (a)** Quadratic
(b) 439.6; 460.4; 481.2 **(c)** Decreasing **(d)** 345.9; 319.9;
286.7 **25. (a)** $y = 0.06 + 6.41x$ **(b)** An increase of 1 unit
in the GPA results in an increase of $6410 in the annual
starting salary. **27. (a)** Decrease by ≈ 7.8 million bushels
(b) Increase by ≈ 4.3 million bushels.

SECTION 15-5

1. $f(8, 10) = 44$, relative minimum
3. $f(10, -22) = -252$, relative minimum **5.** No solution
(no relative maximum or minimum) **7.** $f(5, 5) = -50$,
relative minimum **9.** In Exercise 2, $\lambda_0 = 2x + 6y$
$= 40$ evaluated at (5, 5). λ_0 measures the sensitivity of the
optional value of f to a change in c, where $g(x, y) = c = 10$
in this case. An increase of 1 unit in c increases the optimal
value of f by approximately 40 units. **11.** In Exercise 4,
$\lambda_0 = 4x + 1 = \dfrac{97}{3} \approx 32.33$, evaluated at $x_0 = \dfrac{47}{6}$.
λ_0 measures the sensitivity of the optimal value of f to
a change in c where $g(x, y) = c = 12$ in this case. An

increase of 1 unit in c increases the optimal value of f
by approximately 32.33 units. **13.** In Exercise 7,
$\lambda_0 = -5x + 4y = -5$, evaluated at (5, 5). λ_0 measures the
sensitivity of the optimal value of f to a change in c where
$g(x, y) = c = 20$ in this case. An increase of 1 unit in c
decreases the optimal value of f by approximately 5 units.
15. $x = 26$ units, $y = 14$ units
17. $u = \dfrac{\sqrt{34} - 3\sqrt{2}}{8} \approx 0.1985$, $v = \dfrac{1}{4}\sqrt{7 - \sqrt{17}} \approx 0.4240$
19. $x = 2$ feet, $y = 6$ feet; maximum volume = 24 cubic feet.
21. $x = \dfrac{96}{25} = 3.84$ mi, $y = \dfrac{72}{25} = 2.88$ mi; maximum
distance ≈ 4.8 miles **23.** $x = 6000$ units, $y = 3000$ units
25. In Exercise 15, $\lambda_0 = 2x - 5y = -18$, evaluated at
(26, 14). λ_0 measures the sensitivity of the optimal value
of C to a change in c, where $g(x, y) = c = 40$ in this case.
An increase of 1 unit in c decreases the optimal value of c
by approximately 18 units. **27.** In Exercise 17,
$\lambda_0 = \dfrac{4u}{v} \approx 1.8726$, evaluated at (0.1985, 0.4240).
λ_0 measures the sensitivity of the optimal value of A to a
change in c where $g(u, v) = c = 1$ in this case. An increase
of 1 unit in c increases the optimal value of A by
approximately 1.8726 unit. (an increase of 1 unit in c is
large, relative to c and the approximation is, consequently,
not good. It would be more reasonable to increase c by
0.01. Such an increase would increase the optimal value of
A by approximately 0.0187 unit.) **29.** In Exercise 19,
$\lambda_0 = (2xy - 6x)/(4y) = 1/2$ evaluated at (2, 6). λ_0 measures
the sensitivity of the optimal value of f to a change in c
where $g(x, y) = c = 60$ in this case. An increase of 1 unit in
c increases the optimal value of f by approximately $\dfrac{1}{2}$ unit.
31. In Exercise 21, $\lambda_0 = 0.2$. λ_0 measures the sensitivity of
the optimal value of f to a change in c, where
$g(x, y) = c = 24$ in this case. An increase of 1 unit in c
increases the optimal value of f by approximately 1.92 unit.
33. In Exercise 23, $\lambda_0 = \dfrac{x_0}{4} = 1500$. λ_0 measures the
sensitivity of the optimal value of C to a change in c, where
$g(x, y) = c = 9000$ in this case. An increase of 1 unit in c
increases the optimal value of C by approximately 1500
units.

• EXTRA DIVIDENDS

Back-Order Inventory Model

1. $C(Q, S) = 5\left(\dfrac{1200}{Q}\right) + 1.15\dfrac{(Q - S)^2}{2Q} + 2.40\left(\dfrac{S^2}{2Q}\right)$
3. $C(124, 40) = \$96.59$ **5.** $Q = 124$ are ordered;
$Q - S = 124 - 40 = 84$ are available for sale.

• EXTRA DIVIDENDS

Response Surface

1. A relative maximum occurs at the critical point $x_1 = 0.18$, $x_2 = -0.26$ **3.** $111.8°$ Celsius and 53.7 minutes

• CHAPTER HIGHLIGHTS

1. If a function has two independent variables, it is called a **function of two variables.** If a function has three independent variables, it is called a **function of three variables.** Functions of more than one variable are called **multivariate functions.**   **2.** The ordered triple $(2, 4, -1)$ is plotted by starting at the origin, then moving 2 units in the positive direction along the x-axis, then moving 4 units in the positive direction parallel to the y-axis, then moving 1 unit in the negative direction parallel to the z-axis.

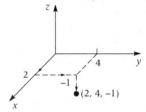

3. The partial derivative of z with respect to x gives the instantaneous rate of change of z with respect to x. It is determined by treating y as a constant and using the derivative rules (i.e., power rule, product rule, quotient rule, etc.). The partial derivative of z with respect to y gives the instantaneous rate of change of z with respect to y. It is determined by treating x as a constant and using the derivative rules (i.e., power rule, product rule, quotient rule, etc.).   **4.** The partial derivative of a partial derivative is called a **second partial derivative,** or simply a **second partial.**   **5.** Given a function $z = f(x, y)$, there are four types of second partials. They are $f_{xx}, f_{yy}, f_{xy}, f_{yx}$ **6.** A point (x_0, y_0) is called a **critical point** of $z = f(x, y)$ if $f_x(x_0, y_0) = 0$ and $f_y(x_0, y_0) = 0$.   **7.** Yes   **8.** No. Critical points yield candidates for relative maxima/minima. **9.** Let (x_0, y_0) be a critical point of $z = f(x, y)$ such that f_x, f_y, f_{xx}, f_{yy}, and f_{xy} are continuous at (x_0, y_0). Also let $A = f_{xx}(x_0, y_0)$, $B = f_{yy}(x_0, y_0)$, and $C = f_{xy}(x_0, y_0)$. Then: **(a)** $f(x_0, y_0)$ is a relative maximum if $AB - C^2 > 0$ and $A < 0$. **(b)** $f(x_0, y_0)$ is a relative minimum if $AB - C^2 > 0$ and $A > 0$. **(c)** $f(x_0, y_0)$ is a saddle point if $AB - C^2 < 0$. **(d)** The test fails and no information is given about the point (x_0, y_0) if $AB - C^2 = 0$.   **10. Step 1: Search for critical points.** Find f_x and f_y, set them equal to zero and solve for x and y. Determine all possible ordered pairs (x, y) that satisfy both equations $f_x(x, y) = 0$ and $f_y(x, y) = 0$. These are critical points. **Step 2: Apply the second-derivative test for functions of two variables.**

Compute $f_{xx}, f_{yy},$ and f_{xy} and evaluate each at each critical point. Apply the second-derivative test to each critical point.   **11.** The method of least squares provides a procedure for determining the best-fitting straight line to a set of data points. Here, the best-fitting straight line is the one that minimizes the sum of squares error.   **12.** Given data points (x_1, y_1), (x_2, y_2), . . . (x_n, y_n), the slope m and y-intercept b of the regression line are given by the formulas

$$m = \frac{\sum_{i=1}^{n} x_i y_i - n\bar{x}\bar{y}}{\sum_{i=1}^{n} x_i^2 - n\bar{x}^2} \qquad b = \bar{y} - m\bar{x}$$

where $\bar{x} = \sum_{i=1}^{n} x_i/n$, the average of the x-values, and

$\bar{y} = \sum_{i=1}^{n} y_i/n$, the average of the y-values. Also,

$$\sum_{i=1}^{n} x_i y_i = x_1 y_1 + x_2 y_2 + \ldots + x_n y_n$$

$$\sum_{i=1}^{n} x_i^2 = x_1^2 + x_2^2 + \ldots + x_n^2.$$

13. Beta denotes the risk of a mutual fund or stock relative to the market.   **14.** Fit a linear model to data points $(x, \ln y)$.   **15.** a, the coefficient of x^2; b, the coefficient of x; c, the y-intercept.   **16.** A multiple linear regression model relates y-values to more than one independent variable.   **17.** Maximize (or minimize) $z = f(x, y)$ subject to $g(x, y) = c$ where c is a constant. **18. Step 1: Determine the lagrangian function** $F(x, y, \lambda) = f(x, y) + \lambda(c - g(x, y))$ where λ is the lagrangian multiplier. **Step 2: Search for critical values.** Find F_x, F_y and F_λ, set them equal to zero and solve for x, y, and λ. Determine all possible triples (x, y, λ) that satisfy all three equations $F_x(x, y, \lambda) = 0$ $F_y(x, y, \lambda) = 0$ $F_\lambda(x, y, \lambda) = 0$. These are the critical points of F. **Step 3: Apply second-order conditions.** Compute g_x, g_y, f_{xx}, f_{yy}, f_{xy}, and f_{yx} and evaluate each at each critical point. Form the bordered Hessian matrix, H, for each critical point. Evaluate the determinant of each bordered Hessian matrix and apply the second-order condition to each such H as follows: If $|H| > 0$, a relative maximum exists. If $|H| < 0$, a relative minimum exists.   **19.** The lagrange multiplier, λ, gives the rate of change of z with respect to c or, in other words, dz/dc.

• REVIEW EXERCISES

1. (a) -2 **(b)** 11 **(c)** 25 **(d)** -87 **3.** All ordered pairs (x, y) of real numbers such that $x \neq 4$.

5.

7. (a) $4x + 6y + 5$

(b) $6x - 32y^3$ **(c)** 9 **(d)** -262 **9. (a)** $x^4e^{x+y}(5 + x)$
(b) x^5e^{x+y} **(c)** $6e$ **(d)** e^3 **11. (a)** 1680 **(b)** 1250
13. (a) $x^3e^{x+y}(4 + x)$ **(b)** $x^2e^{x+y}(12 + 8x + x^2)$ **(c)** x^4e^{x+y}
(d) x^4e^{x+y} **(e)** $x^3e^{x+y}(4 + x)$ **(f)** $x^3e^{x+y}(4 + x)$ **(g)** $5e^2$
(h) e^{-1} **(i)** $5e$ **15. (a)** $12x^2(x^3 + y^5)^3$
(b) $24x(x^3 + y^5)^3 + 108x^4(x^3 + y^5)^2$ **(c)** $20y^4(x^3 + y^5)^3$
(d) $300y^3(x^3 + y^5)^2 + 80y^3(x^3 + y^5)^3$ **(e)** $180x^2y^4(x^3 + y^5)^2$
(f) $180x^2y^4(x^3 + y^5)^2$ **(g)** $-3.338148 \times 10^8 \approx -3.34 \times 10^8$
(h) 92,871,040 **(i)** 0 **17.** Saddle point: $(-4, -5)$
19. Relative maximum; $f(6, 9) = 228$ **21.** Relative
maximum: $R(2.4, 1.125) = 77.85$
23. (a) $R(p_1, p_2) = 400p_1 - 12p_1^2 + 20p_1p_2 + 600p_2 - 15p_2^2$
(b) $p_1 = 75, p_2 = 70$ **(c)** \$36,000 **(d)** $x_1 = 480$ and
$x_2 = 0$. **25. (a)** $y = -0.4615 + 2.5769x$
(b)

(c) $-0.8461, -0.1537,$

0.7308, 0.2694 **(d)** 1.346 **(e)** 12.42 **27.** The slope of the
line is the beta value of the *xyz* Mutual Fund. A change of
1 unit in the *S & P* 500 is accompanied by a change, in the
same direction, of approximately 1.90 units in the *xyz* fund.
29. $\ln y = 6.6993 - 1.7405x; y = 811.8e^{1.7405}$; 59.65
31. $x = 42, y = 12$ **33.** In Exercise 30, $\lambda_0 = 2x_0 - 10y_0 = -184$. λ_0 measures the sensitivity of the optimal value of f
to a change in c, where $g(x, y) = c = 52$ in this case. An
increase of 1 unit in c decreases the optimal value of f by
approximately 184 units. **35.** In Exercise 32,
$\lambda_0 = 2x_0 + 6y_0 = 88$. λ_0 measures the sensitivity of the
optimal value of f to a change in c, where $g(x, y) = c = 24$
in this case. An increase of 1 unit in c increases the optimal
value of f by approximately 88 units. **37.** $x = 4$ ft,
$y = 2$ ft. Since $|H| > 0$, $f(4, 2)$ is a relative maximum.

$\lambda_0 = \dfrac{x_0}{40} = 0.10$. λ_0 measures the sensitivity of the optimal

value of V to a change in C, where $g(x, y) = c = 480$, in
this case. An increase of 1 unit in c increases the optimal
value of V by approximately 0.10 units.

Index

Continued

- Draw a sign chart for $f'(x)$ This will indicate where $f(x)$ is increasing or decreasing and any relative extrema.
- Find the y-coordinates of any relative extrema.

2. *Second-derivative analysis.* Find $f''(x)$.

- Draw a sign chart for $f''(x)$. This will indicate where $f(x)$ is concave up or down and any inflection points.
- Find the y-coordinates of any inflection points.

3. *Graph of $f(x)$.*

- Summarize the results of steps 1 and 2 on a graph.
- Plot the relative extrema and inflection points.
- Plot the points of any x- and y-intercepts that are easily determined.
- Sketch the graph of $f(x)$.

- **SECOND-DERIVATIVE TEST FOR RELATIVE EXTREMA**

If $f(x)$ is a function and x_0 is a number such that $f'(x_0) = 0$, then

1. If $f''(x_0) < 0$, $f(x)$ has a relative maximum at $x = x_0$.
2. If $f''(x_0) > 0$, $f(x)$ has a relative minimum at $x = x_0$.
3. If $f''(x_0) = 0$, the test fails. In other words, the test gives no information regarding a relative maximum or relative minimum at $x = x_0$.

Notes:

1. This test applies only to critical values for which $f'(x) = 0$. It does not apply to critical values for which $f'(x)$ is undefined.
2. This test can fail. In other words, it can give no information regarding the nature of the relative extrema at x_0.
3. If either of the above occurs, use the first-derivative test.

- **SECOND-DERIVATIVE TEST FOR ABSOLUTE EXTREMA**

When a Function Is Continuous Over Some Interval and *Only one Critical Value* Exists In the Interval Given that a function $f(x)$ is continuous over some interval, and x_0 is the only critical value interior to the interval, and $f'(x_0) = 0$, then

1. If $f''(x_0) < 0$, $f(x_0)$ is the **absolute maximum** value of $f(x)$ over the interval.
2. If $f''(x_0) > 0$, $f(x_0)$ is the **absolute minimum** value of $f(x)$ over the interval.
3. If $f''(x_0) = 0$, the test fails.

- **TO FIND ABSOLUTE EXTREMA**

For Continuous Functions Defined on Closed Intervals To find the absolute extrema of a continuous function $f(x)$ on the closed interval $[a, b]$:

1. Find all critical values of $f(x)$ in $[a, b]$.
2. Evaluate $f(x)$ at the endpoints a and b and at the critical values found in step 1.
3. Write the largest value found in step 2. This is the *absolute maximum* value of $f(x)$ on the interval $[a, b]$.
4. Write the smallest value found in step 2. This is the *absolute minimum* value of $f(x)$ on the interval $[a, b]$.

- **DERIVATIVE RULE FOR EXPONENTIAL FUNCTIONS**

If $y = e^u$, where u is a differentiable function of x, then

$$\frac{dy}{dx} = e^u \frac{du}{dx}$$

- **DERIVATIVE RULE FOR LOGARITHMIC FUNCTIONS**

If $y = \ln u$, where u is differentiable function of x, then

$$\frac{dy}{dx} = \frac{1}{u} \cdot \frac{du}{dx}$$

- **INDEFINITE INTEGRAL FORMULAS**

If k and c are constants:

1. $\int x^n \, dx = \dfrac{x^{n+1}}{n+1} + c \qquad (n \neq -1)$
2. $\int kf(x) \, dx = k \int f(x) \, dx$

continues

Continued

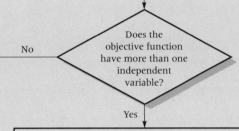

TO SOLVE OPTIMIZATION PROBLEMS

Objective function

Identify the quantity to be either maximized or minimized and the related variables. Write an equation for the quantity to be maximized or minimized. This equation is called the *objective function*.

Does the objective function have more than one independent variable?

No

Yes

Constraint equation

Reread the problem and search for an existing relationship between the independent variables. Write the equation that expresses such a relationship. This equation is called a *constraint equation*.

Solve and substitute

Solve the constraint equation for one independent variable in terms of the other. Substitute this result into the objective function. The objective function should now have only one independent variable.

Critical values

Find the critical values of the objective function.

Test for absolute extrema

1. If there is **only one critical value** in some interval, use the second-derivitive test for absolute extrema to test whether an absolute maximum or minimum occurs at the critical value.

2. If there is **more than one critical value** in some closed interval, evaluate the function at each critical value and at the endpoints to determine the absolute extrema.

3. If neither 1 nor 2 applies, then use both first and second derivatives to graph the function.

---

3. $\int k \, dx = kx + c$

4. $\int [f(x) \pm g(x)] \, dx = \int f(x) \, dx \pm \int g(x) \, dx$

5. $\int e^x \, dx = e^x + c$

6. $\int e^{kx} \, dx = \frac{1}{k} e^{kx} + c$

7. $\int x^{-1} \, dx = \int \frac{1}{x} \, dx = \ln |x| + c$

- **AREA UNDER A CURVE**

If $f(x) \geq 0$ over the interval $a \leq x \leq b$, the area bounded by the graph of $f(x)$ and the x-axis over the interval $a \leq x \leq b$, as illustrated in the figure below, is given by

$$\int_a^b f(x) \, dx = F(b) - F(a)$$

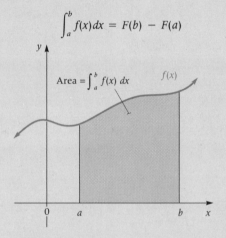

- **INTEGRATION BY SUBSTITUTION**

$$\int u^n \, du = \frac{1}{n+1} u^{n+1} + c \qquad (n \neq -1)$$

If $u = f(x)$ and $du = f'(x) \, dx$, then

$$\int e^u \, du = e^u + c$$

If $u = f(x)$ and $du = f'(x) \, dx$, then

$$\int \frac{du}{u} = \ln |u| + c$$

- **INTEGRATION BY PARTS**

If u and v are differentiable functions of x, then

$$\int u \, dv = uv - \int v \, du$$